BAILEY'S TEXTBOOK OF HISTOLOGY

SIXTEENTH EDITION

BAILEY'S TEXTBOOK OF HISTOLOGY

WILFRED M. COPENHAVER, PH.D.
PROFESSOR EMERITUS OF ANATOMY,
COLLEGE OF PHYSICIANS AND SURGEONS,
COLUMBIA UNIVERSITY

PROFESSOR OF BIOLOGICAL STRUCTURE,
UNIVERSITY OF MIAMI SCHOOL OF MEDICINE

And

RICHARD P. BUNGE, M.D.
PROFESSOR OF ANATOMY

MARY BARTLETT BUNGE, PH.D.
RESEARCH ASSISTANT PROFESSOR OF ANATOMY,
WASHINGTON UNIVERSITY SCHOOL OF MEDICINE

The Williams & Wilkins Company/Baltimore

Previous editions copyrighted in 1904, 1906, 1910, 1913, 1916, 1920, 1925, 1932, 1936, 1940, 1944, 1948, 1953, 1958, 1964

Spanish translations published in 1948; 1962

Indian Edition in 1967

Made in the United States of America

Library of Congress Catalogue Card No. 79-127303
SBN 683 02073 0

The scanning electron micrograph used on the cover was kindly furnished by Mr. Edward H. Finke and Dr. Charles Kuhn of the Department of Pathology, Washington University School of Medicine. For explanation of this illustration see Figure 18-8.

Composed and printed at the
WAVERLY PRESS, INC.
Mt. Royal and Guilford Avenues
Baltimore, Md. 21202, U. S. A.

PREFACE TO SIXTEENTH EDITION

In the interim since the previous edition of this textbook was published there have been marked advances in histology and related fields. The more recent information is particularly significant in that it provides a better understanding of structure in relation to function. In order to update the text, all chapters of this edition have been revised and many chapters have been largely rewritten.

Although this textbook has been rewritten a number of times since the first six editions were written by Professor Frederick R. Bailey in the 1904–1925 period, the present edition continues to adhere to Professor Bailey's philosophy of placing stress on fundamentals. At the same time, it holds to the view outlined in the XV edition preface that each topic should be discussed in sufficient detail to make the subject understandable. The objectives and contributions of the authors who succeeded Professor Bailey are outlined in the reprinted preface of the XV edition published in 1964.

It is a pleasure to report that Dr. Richard P. Bunge and Dr. Mary B. Bunge have joined in the authorship of this textbook. They have rewritten most of Chapters 1 and 2 and extensive sections of Chapters 9, 10, and 11, plus those parts of Chapter 22 which deal with the ear, olfactory organs, and sense of taste. They have also read my revisions of each of the other chapters and have contributed valuable suggestions.

I am indebted to Dr. Douglas E. Kelly for a critical review of a number of chapters, including the cell, epithelium, muscle, nervous tissue, and the section on the eye in Chapter 22. I am particularly indebted to Dr. Kelly for writing most of the section on the Pineal Body in Chapter 21. Dr. Richard L. Wood reviewed the preliminary revision of the Chapter on the Digestive System and offered a number of constructive suggestions for which I am most grateful. Comments offered by Dr. George W. Cooper were helpful in rewriting Chapter 2.

As in the previous XIV and XV editions, all new drawings for this edition were made by Mr. Robert Demarest, Medical Illustrator in the Department of Anatomy, College of Physicians and Surgeons, Columbia University. We are indebted to Mr. Demarest and we are grateful to Dr. Edward W. Dempsey for making it possible for Mr. Demarest to continue with this edition.

Many new electron micrographs have been added in this edition. They constitute a major asset in the new edition and we are grateful to colleagues of a number of different Universities for their generosity in contributing in this manner. Credits for each of the illustrations are cited in the respective figure elgends.

Finally, we wish to express appreciation to the publishers for their cooperation in all aspects of production of the book. Last, but not least, our thanks to the publishers for the chore of revising the index.

WILFRED M. COPENHAVER

PREFACE TO FIFTEENTH EDITION

There have been marked advances in microscopic anatomy and in its correlation with related subjects since the last edition of this textbook was published in 1958. Improved techniques for the preparation of thin sections for electron microscopy have given better resolution in electron micrographs; new methods have been devised for combining some histochemical and autoradiographic techniques with electron microscopy; and, new information has been gained by histochemical and autoradiographic techniques in light microscopy. Immunohistological techniques, x-ray diffraction studies, and polarization microscopy have also contributed new information. In addition, one must not overlook the fact that numerous contributions continue to come from conventional light microscopy used in conjunction with widely-planned experiments.

In the present edition, it has been necessary to revise all chapters and to rewrite large sections of some chapters in order to replace out-of-date interpretations with current information.

In microscopic anatomy, as in other fields, new research not only answers questions but raises new ones. In presenting the subject to students, it is important to acquaint them with current trends and with some of the unresolved problems. Likewise, it is essential to discuss each subject in sufficient detail to make it understandable. On the other hand, no textbook of microscopic anatomy can expect to be complete in itself. It should attempt to make the fundamentals stand out from the accompanying details and should stress the correlation of structure and function. As in previous editions, this textbook is presented primarily for students rather than as a source book for teachers and specialists.

A brief resume of the history of this textbook seems appropriate at this time. The first edition was written by Professor Frederick R. Bailey at the College of Physicians and Surgeons and was published by William Wood, and Company in 1904. Professor Bailey, with assistance from Professor Oliver Strong on the nervous system, continued the book through the sixth edition published in 1920. Although the text has been rewritten by a number of authors since the time of Professor Bailey it has adhered to his objective of emphasizing fundamentals.

Professors Oliver S. Strong and Adolph Elwyn revised the VII edition (1925) and a part of the VIII edition (1932). Professors R. L. Carpenter, C. M. Goss, and A. E. Severinghaus participated with Professor Philip E. Smith and myself in completing the VIII edition (1932) and in the subsequent revisions of the IX and X editions. The text retains valuable contributions made by them.

Professor Philip E. Smith served as editor of the IX and X revisions and as co-author of the XI, XII, and XIII editions. His contributions of material plus his sound editorial judgment had an important role in whatever success the textbook achieved during editions VIII to XIII inclusive. Professor Dorothy D. Johnson assisted with the XIII edition and became coauthor in the XIV edition. She made particularly valuable contributions to the Chapters on the Digestive System,

Respiratory System and Endocrine Glands. It is regretted that unavoidable circumstances prevented Professor Johnson from participating in this edition.

I am indebted to Mr. Robert Demarest for all new drawings for this edition and
for those which were added in the previous edition. I am also indebted to Mr. Carl
Kellner (now retired) for the drawings which appeared first in editions IX to XIII
inclusive.

Many valuable suggestions have come from my colleagues at Columbia and from
those in other schools. I am indebted particularly to Professor Thomas E. Hunt for
a number of constructive suggestions.

Finally, I wish to express my appreciation to the publishers for their cooperation
and for their patience in waiting for a text long over-due.

WILFRED M. COPENHAVER

INTRODUCTION

All living organisms consist of minute elements which are called cells. These cells are the smallest structural units possessing those properties which we commonly associate with life. They are able to nourish themselves, to grow, to respond to stimuli, and to reproduce. Some organisms, the protozoa, consist of one cell only; the higher types, metazoa, may consist of infinite numbers of cells varying greatly in structural characteristics. Each of these multicellular organisms starts its existence as a single cell, the fertilized ovum, which by a process of proliferation gives rise to the adult body. At first the cells of the developing embryo are similar in shape and structure. As growth continues, differentiation takes place leading to the formation of groups of specialized cells, each group differing in structure from the others, each group adapted to subserve one or more specific functions. These specialized groups form the *tissues* of the adult body. At a very early period the cells of the embryo become separated from each other by the formation of intercellular substance, which may be the result of cellular secretion or may represent actual modifications of cellular substance. In some of the tissues this intercellular material assumes enormous proportions. Thus the adult body is composed of cells and intercellular material, all elements so interrelated as to form a normally functioning machine.

Histology in a restricted sense is the study of the tissues of the body, but since the tissues are composed of cells and their products, a knowledge of the structure and activities of the cell must necessarily form the basis of histology. The first two chapters of the book are therefore given to a discussion of the cell, the first of these dealing with the cell after fixation and the second with the living cell. Each of these chapters obviously supplements the other. Physiology is stressed in both. Succeeding these, the structure of the tissues is presented. This is followed by the microscopic anatomy of the various organs.

While histology is a structural science and serves to complete the anatomical knowledge gained from dissection, its intimate relation to biochemistry, physiology and pathology must be emphasized. The cell is not only a unit of structure but also of physiological activity. The formation of the specialized tissues is the structural expression of a physiological division of labor. The structures seen under the microscope assume a meaning only in the light of their functional significance. Thus the structure of muscles and glands can only be studied by constant reference to contraction and secretion. Normal physiological processes are associated with normal structure, abnormal processes are usually expressed in the altered structure and relationship of the cells and intercellular substance. A thorough knowledge of normal histology is essential for the understanding of the altered structure seen in the various conditions of disease.

CONTENTS

1

The Cell

The introduction states that the chief objective of anatomical studies is the accumulation of sufficient knowledge of structure to enable us to understand the functioning of living tissues. The dissections of gross anatomy and the microscopic analyses of histology have in turn made important contributions to this end. We have recently seen an enormous expansion of the youngest of the anatomical sciences, cell anatomy or cytology, utilizing the methods of histochemistry, electron microscopy and tissue culture. Cytological studies have most recently clarified much of the structure of subcellular elements. These revelations combined with new knowledge from biochemistry have led to a basic understanding of many of the ongoing processes of the living cell.

Neither the term "cell" nor the term "cell concept" will be new to readers of this text. The 19th century histologist Leydig defined a cell as "a mass of protoplasm containing a nucleus." This simple and useful description is still appropriate for animal cells today, for the minimal structural unit of protoplasm is that unit having available the genetic material (within the nucleus) which allows it to carry out, relatively independently, all of the vital functions necessary to sustain life. Although cells in higher organisms may develop some dependence on one another, each retains within its nucleus all of the information necessary to carry out all cell functions. Cells which lose

their nuclei may continue to function for some time because the nucleus had previously made provision for the manufacture of all of the substances needed during the remaining life of the cell.

Cytology now employs the term *protoplasm* to denote the entire living substance of the cell. This includes the cell body and its extensions and the nucleus which lies in it. The substance of the cell outside the nucleus is called *cytoplasm;* the substance of the nucleus is *karyoplasm* or *nucleoplasm*. The entire cell is circumscribed by a membrane termed the *plasma membrane*.

METHODS OF STUDY

Our present knowledge of cell structure has been gained from a variety of methods of study. These methods fall logically into two groups, (*1*) methods employed with the living cell and (*2*) methods employed with dead cells (fixed or preserved). Some of the special methods employed in studies on the living cell are treated in the second chapter, but it should be emphasized that no single method should be used to the exclusion of all others. Studies on the living cell and those on preserved material yield supplementary data and, by their different approaches, corroborate or question the other's findings.

Preparation of Material. Some types of cells can be satisfactorily studied by placing them directly on slides for staining and for microscopic observation (e.g., Wright's

1

stained blood smears). However, for most cytological work it is necessary to cut tissues into thin, translucent slices only a few microns thick. Sectioning is done on a mechanical instrument, the microtome, and is facilitated by freezing the tissue or by embedding it in a supporting medium such as paraffin or celloidin. A brief outline of some of the technical procedures is given to aid the student in the interpretation of slides prepared for his study. Those who wish more details on technique should refer to the books listed at the end of the chapter.

Most commonly, the first step in the preparation of histologic material is *fixation*. Numerous chemicals and their mixtures are used as fixatives (formalin, alcohol, Bouin's fluid, Zenker's fluid, etc.). Fixation preserves tissue, stops post-mortem change, begins a hardening which facilitates sectioning, and affects the affinity of certain tissue elements for particular dyes. In the process of fixation, proteins are precipitated and rendered insoluble; lipids and carbohydrates may or may not be preserved, depending on the nature of the fixative. For example, many fats are removed from tissues immersed in alcohols. Therefore, is is often necessary to use different technical procedures to study all of the various constituents of a cell.

For sectioning, the tissue is commonly infiltrated with paraffin. Since paraffin will not mix with water, the former will not penetrate into tissues until the latter is removed. *Dehydration* is accomplished by passing the tissues through a series of graded alcohols, up to 100%. Now, since paraffin is also insoluble in alcohol, the latter must be replaced by an agent miscible with both alcohol and paraffin, e.g., xylene or cedar wood oil. These agents render the tissue translucent and therefore this step in technique is known as *clearing*. From the clearing agent, the tissue is placed in melted paraffin in an oven to replace the clearing agent with paraffin. Next, the tissue is *embedded* in paraffin by allowing the latter to harden, and then the material is ready for sectioning on a ro-

tary microtome and for subsequent staining. Figure 1-1 shows photomicrographs of cells prepared by this method. Sections are usually 3 to 10 μ thick. Celloidin is an alternative embedding medium which is particularly useful for cutting large objects (e.g., brain) and for hard and brittle material (e.g., cartilage).

Even the brief outline given above must have made it obvious that structures seen in sections may be altered by chemical fixation, by dehydration and by the temperature of the paraffin oven. Again and again, the description of features in the fixed cell has brought forth the objection that they are not true features of the living cell, but *artifacts* of technique. The answer to such objections must always be the consistency of the findings obtained by different technical procedures.

The *freeze drying technique* seems in some instances to cause less alteration of the living tissue than do the standard methods. In this technique, fresh tissue is preserved by placing it in a liquid such as isopentane chilled to about $-170°C$ with liquid nitrogen. The frozen tissue is dehydrated in a vacuum and may thus be embedded without previous chemical fixation and dehydration in alcohols. This method is particularly useful for studying the localization of certain enzymes which are destroyed by the standard methods.

In the *frozen section technique* (not to be confused with the freeze drying method just outlined), a piece of tissue is placed directly on the stage of a special microtome equipped with an outlet for compressed carbon dioxide gas which cools the stage and freezes the tissue sufficiently for the cutting of sections. This method is widely used in clinical work for sectioning biopsy material when speed is important. In cytological work, the freezing method is particularly useful for studying the lipid content of cells because it avoids the use of fat-solvent dehydrating and clearing agents. The method may be used for either fresh or fixed material; in the former case, it

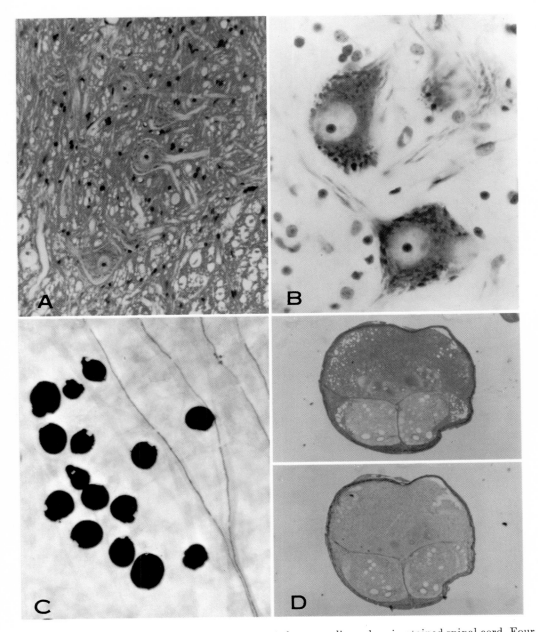

Fig. 1-1. Staining of various tissue components. *A*, hematoxylin and eosin-stained spinal cord. Four nerve cell bodies are stained blue to purple by hematoxylin because of their high content of basophilic nucleic acid. Much of the remaining tissue is stained magenta by eosin because of the preponderance of acidophilic protein components. ×225. *B*, staining of nucleic acid by cresyl echt violet. In these two nerve cell bodies from spinal cord, the ribonucleic acid in the cytoplasm and in the nucleolus is heavily stained. The deoxyribonucleic acid of the nerve cell nucleus remains largely unstained because it is in a dispersed state. Smaller nuclei in which the nucleic acid is more condensed do stain with this dye. ×440. *C*, the lipid stores of these 15 fat cells are revealed by staining with Sudan black. The small indentations in some of the black deposits are the unstained nuclei. The slender strands are myelin sheaths, which also stain because of their high lipid content. Nervous tissue in culture. ×175. *D* (*upper figure*), glycogen is stained pink by the periodic acid-Schiff reaction. If the tissue is first treated with amylase, which digests glycogen, the pink staining is not seen (*lower figure*). Non-glycogen components of the sheath surrounding this lobster nerve ganglion are stained purple with or without amylase treatment. ×20.

is useful for studying cell enzymes which are destroyed by chemical fixation.

The list of chemicals used for *staining* is even longer than that used for fixation. Most stains are classified as acids or bases. Actually they are neutral salts having both acidic and basic radicals. When the coloring property is in the acid radical of the neutral salt, the stain is spoken of as an acid dye, and the tissues which stain with the dye are called acidophilic. Eosin is an acid dye with such general usage that the terms eosinophilic and acidophilic are often used synonymously. In some cases, it is clear that basophilic substances which attract basic dyes are themselves acids, as in the staining of nucleic acids with methylene blue. It has long been realized that special methods and stains are frequently necessary to demonstrate different structures, but the nature of the reaction between tissue and dye is often poorly understood.

Histochemical methods for the study of chemically recognizable substances within tissues began many years ago with the iodine test for starch. Since that time, numerous techniques have been developed for the identification and localization of chemical substances at the cellular level. Methods of particular interest include Caspersson's use of spectrophotometry for nucleic acids, Brachet's method for RNA and Gomori's method for phosphatase. In applying spectrophotometry to cytology, ultraviolet light is useful because nucleic acids absorb light more strongly in the ultraviolet region than in other regions of the spectrum. Brachet's method uses an enzyme, ribonuclease, which selectively removes the RNA. When any material stains with a basic dye (such as pyronine or toluidine blue) in an ordinary section and then becomes unstainable after the section has been treated with pure ribonuclease, it may be concluded that the stained material was RNA. A similar principle is used in the histochemical study of glycogen. In this case, the control slides are treated with

saliva; the salivary enzyme amylase removes the glycogen.

The histochemical localization of the enzyme *acid phosphatase* is widely used to identify areas of lytic (digestive) activity in the cytoplasm (see below under "Lysosomes"). The section is placed in a fluid containing a phosphate compound and lead ions. The enzyme in the tissue frees the phosphate which combines with the lead to form an insoluble precipitate (which is visible in the electron microscope, Fig. 1-25, *C*). To make this visible in the light microscope, sulfide ions are added to form the coarser precipitate lead sulfide. Thus, the sites of dense reaction product reveal the location of the enzyme. Combining histochemical procedures such as this and the electron microscope enables more accurate localization.

Radioautography is a technique whereby a radioactive precursor is supplied to living tissue and, after incorporation, its intracellular location is detected by exposure to a photographic emulsion. The radioactivity lodged in the tissue activates the silver halide crystals in the emulsion, and with photographic development metallic silver grains are formed. They are visible in both the light (Fig. 1-2) and electron microscopes, depending upon the preparation. Again, more precise localization of activity results from the combined use of radioautography and electron microscopy. Electron microscopic radioautography has proved extremely useful in tracing the path of protein synthesis in the cell cytoplasm (see "Granular Endoplasmic Reticulum"). The use of radioactive thymidine, incorporated only into replicating DNA, has been helpful in identifying dividing cells and in tracing cell migration in developing tissues.

The *preparation of sectioned tissue for examination in the electron microscope* must be done with extreme care. Fixatives are chosen to preserve structure in as lifelike a form as possible; inferior preservation is far more apparent in the electron microscope than in the light microscope. Buffered

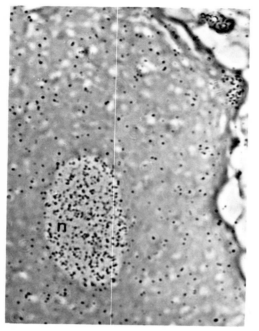

FIG. 1-2. Radioautogram photographed in the light microscope. The black dots overlying the tissue are silver grains which mark the sites of incorporation of radioactive uridine into newly formed ribonucleic acid. The silver grains are more concentrated over the nucleus (n) than the cytoplasm of this large lobster nerve cell. ×500.

osmium tetroxide, used alone or in conjunction with glutaraldehyde or formaldehyde, remains the fixative of choice. A very hard embedding medium (such as the epoxy resin, Araldite or Epon) is required in order to obtain the extremely thin sections (about 0.05 μ) that are examined in the electron microscope. Glass or diamond knives and especially designed microtomes are mandatory for thin sectioning. For thin sections, stains (such as uranyl acetate and lead citrate) are chosen for their ability to scatter electrons rather than to impart color. (The osmium tetroxide contributes to staining as well as acting as a preservative.) Because this technique yields preparations of superior quality, tissue prepared for electron microscopy is often sectioned at 1 or 2 μ, stained with a dye such as toluidine blue and utilized for light microscopic study. Figure 1-3 is a semi-thin section prepared in this way.

Other methods for studying cell structure include microincineration and ultracentrifugation. By means of microincineration, microscopic sections are reduced to ash on a quartz slide. The amounts and distribution

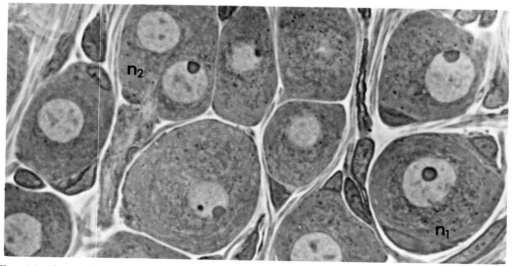

FIG. 1-3. Nerve cells fixed and embedded in plastic for electron microscopic study, and then sectioned at 1 μ and stained with toluidine blue for observation in the light microscope. This type of preparation is often termed a "semi-thin" section. At *lower right*, a typical neuron (n_1) is seen to contain a large, pale nucleus with a dense nucleolus. A binucleate neuron (n_2) is also shown. ×1100. (From Bunge, M. B., Bunge, R. P., Peterson, E. R., and Murray, M. R. 1967 J. Cell Biol., vol. 32, p. 439.)

TABLE 1-1
Measurements

Unit	Symbol and definition
Micron	$1\mu\ \ = 0.001$ mm. $= 10,000$ A $1\mu\ \ = 1 \times 10^{-3}$ mm.
Millimicron	$1\ m\mu = 0.001\ \mu = 10$ A $1\ m\mu = 1 \times 10^{-6}$ mm.
Angstrom	1 A $\ = 0.1\ m\mu = 0.0001\ \mu$ 1 A $\ = 1 \times 10^{-7}$ mm.

of inorganic components of the cell are demonstrated by this method. With the perfection of the ultracentrifuge, subcellular constituents could be separated. Combined with the use of solutions of varying density (density gradients), more and more precise separation could be obtained. Our present knowledge of subcellular elements was made possible by the parallel development of these separation methods and the introduction of the electron microscope for cytological analysis.

The Microscope. An understanding of the observations made with different types of microscopes requires familiarity with the units of measurement in common usage and an appreciation of the dimensions of some structures commonly studied by biologists (Tables 1-1 and 1-2).

The usefulness of any type of microscope is dependent not merely upon its ability to magnify but also upon its ability to resolve detail. Beyond certain limits of magnification, no new details are observable. The useful magnification of an ordinary light microscope is only about 1200×. The resolving power of a lens is its capacity to give clear images of points close together. It is measured as the least distance between two points which can be seen as two instead of one. The resolving power is governed by the numerical aperture (NA) or light gathering capacity of the objective lens and by the wavelength of light. With the ordinary light microscope, an oil immersion objective with a 1.40 numerical aperture has a resolving power of about

$0.2\ \mu$ (i.e., about 2000 Angstrom units). More exactly, the limit of resolution of an objective with a 1.40 numerical aperture is $0.185\ \mu$ when it is used with a violet light having a wavelength near 4000 A (the lowest value for the visible spectrum). In practice, a yellow-green light with a wavelength of about 5400 A is generally used because the eye is more sensitive to this part of the spectrum and with this light the limit of resolution of a 1.40 NA objective is only $0.24\ \mu$. With a 1.25 NA oil immersion objective used on most student microscopes, the limit of resolution with a yellow-green light is only $0.28\ \mu$. A resolution of $0.17\ \mu$ can be achieved by using an oil immersion objective of 1.50 NA, but the refractive index of most optical material makes it impossible to increase NA much further and it is evident that the way to increase resolving power is to use smaller wavelengths. However, glass lenses are not transparent to the lower wavelengths and it becomes necessary to use other refractive me-

TABLE 1-2
Dimensions of Some Elements Studied by Biologists

Structure	Dimension
Human ovum	100 μ 1,000,000 A
Skeletal muscle cells (cross section)	10–100 μ 100,000–1,000,000 A
Cardiac muscle cells (cross section)	9–20 μ 90,000–200,000 A
Lymphocytes	6–10 μ 60,000–100,000 A
Erythrocytes	7.7 μ 77,000 A
Bacteria	0.1–10 μ 1,000–100,000 A
Viruses	0.05–0.5 μ 500–5,000 A
RNP granules (ribosomes)	0.015 μ 150 A

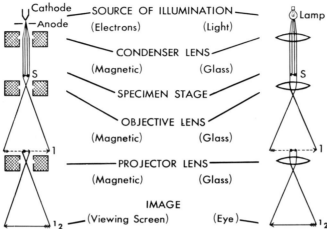

ELECTRON MICROSCOPE   **LIGHT MICROSCOPE**

Cathode — SOURCE OF ILLUMINATION — Lamp
— Anode   (Electrons)   (Light)

CONDENSER LENS
(Magnetic)   (Glass)

SPECIMEN STAGE

OBJECTIVE LENS
(Magnetic)   (Glass)

PROJECTOR LENS
(Magnetic)   (Glass)

IMAGE
(Viewing Screen)   (Eye)

FIG. 1-4. Diagrams of optical paths in the electron microscope (*left*) and the light microscope (*right*). The light microscope is shown in an inverted position to facilitate comparison. (Courtesy of RCA.)

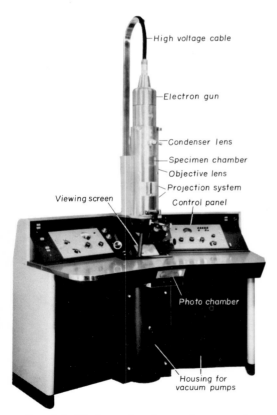

High voltage cable

Electron gun

Condenser lens

Specimen chamber

Objective lens

Projection system

Viewing screen

Control panel

Photo chamber

Housing for
vacuum pumps

FIG. 1-5. Photograph of an electron microscope. The column of the microscope houses the parts of the optical system at the levels shown by

dia. By using ultraviolet radiation having a wavelength of 2000 to 3000 A and quartz lenses, resolving power can be increased to about 0.1 μ (1000 A), but the main value of the ultraviolet microscope is for absorption spectrophotometry in histochemical studies.

The chief advance in increasing resolving power and magnification has been made with the *electron microscope* which uses electrons in place of light, and electromagnetic or electrostatic fields in place of lenses (Figs. 1-4, 1-5). The final image is visualized on a fluorescent screen and recorded on a photographic plate. The wavelength of a stream of high velocity electrons is so short that the resolving power of an electron microscope is about 20 A or even 5 A (0.0005 μ). With this amount of resolution, the electron microscope can be used profitably at very high magnifications. In common practice, the image is photographed at 5000 to 20,000$\times$ and the negative is enlarged about 6$\times$ when

the labels, and it also provides a vacuum enclosure for the electron beam as it passes through the optical system. The vacuum pumps are housed in the center and right sections of the cabinet. The width of the instrument shown is approximately 5 feet, its height is over 7 feet and its weight is about 1400 pounds.

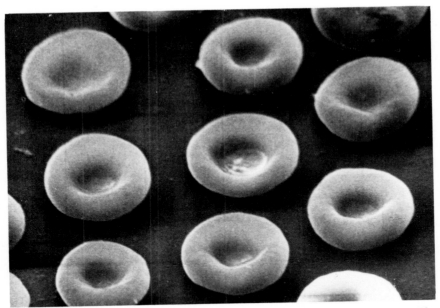

FIG. 1-6. Human red blood cells as they appear in the scanning electron microscope. The cells were first fixed in glutaraldehyde and then washed in water, air dried on coverslips and coated with a thin layer of gold. As illustrated here, this instrument allows unsectioned objects to be visualized in three dimensions. ×3700. (Courtesy of Dr. Sarah Luse.)

the photographic print is made, thus giving magnifications to about 120,000. With the best equipment and with careful attention to all technical procedures, it is possible to use even greater magnifications. One of the limitations in electron microscope work is the necessity of having extremely thin sections of 0.1 μ or less on account of the low penetration of the electrons. Another disadvantage stems from the fact that the tissues must be placed in a high vacuum in a dried state, thus prohibiting the study of living cells.

Other types of electron microscopes are gradually coming into use. The *scanning electron microscope* offers less resolution but its great depth of field allows the direct visualization of three-dimensional structures in unsectioned material (Fig. 1-6). As with the transmission electron microscope described above, the materials must be placed in a vacuum and therefore must be free of water when observed. For this reason the scanning electron microscope has been most useful in observing relatively anhydrous materials such as scales, hair or skin. The *high voltage electron microscope*, using 1,000,000 rather than 50,000 or 100,000 volts to accelerate the electron beam, permits a greater resolution than do other electron microscopes, and it also allows visualization of materials in quite thick sections. The instrument thus provides increased potential for preparing stereo pictures which aid in visualizing intracellular components in three dimensions at high resolution.

The desire to view cells and tissues without chemical fixation and without dehydration has recently led to an entirely new approach for preparing material for electron microscopy, called *freeze fracturing* or *freeze etching*. After freezing the tissue, a break is made directly through the frozen cells, and a metal cast is made of the fractured surface. This metal cast, called a replica, is then observed in the electron microscope. The technique is especially useful in the study of membranes, for the fracture frequently oc-

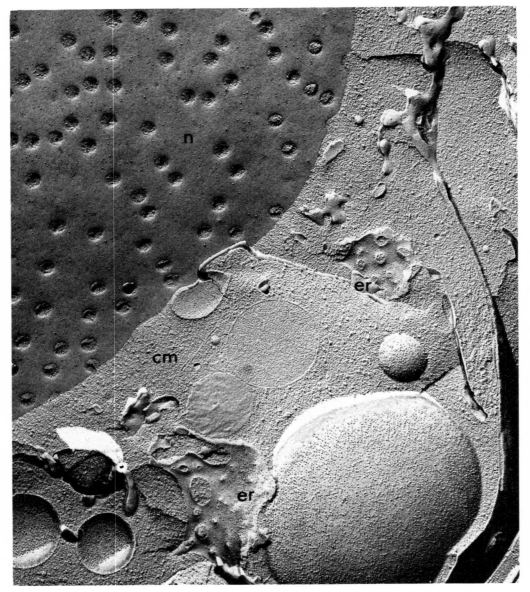

FIG. 1-7. Electron micrograph of a platinum replica of a cell which had been frozen without fixation and then fractured to enable visualization of the cell interior, especially membrane faces. After freeze fracturing pores in the otherwise smooth nuclear envelope (*n*), sheets of fenestrated endoplasmic reticulum (*er*), the cytoplasmic matrix (*cm*) and a variety of cytoplasmic vacuoles all are clearly visible. Onion root tip. ×36,000. (From Branton, D. 1966 Proc. Nat. Acad. Sci. U. S. A., vol. 55, p. 1048.)

curs along membrane surfaces. Figure 1-7 is an electron micrograph from a freeze fractured specimen.

The *phase microscope* is a modification of the light microscope particularly useful for the study of unstained cells, either living or fixed. Cellular components of unstained cells usually appear indistinct with the ordinary microscope because they are fairly transparent and produce very little change in the intensity of transmitted light. On the other hand, the different protoplasmic constituents produce phase changes because they vary in thickness and refractive index. The phase microscope converts phase variations into intensity variations and thereby enables the eye to detect more contrast between different structures.

The *interference microscope* utilizes the principles of the phase microscope more precisely. A light beam passing through the tissue is recombined with a separate light beam which has passed through the same optical apparatus without passing through the tissue. The manner in which these beams interfere with one another gives an index of the mass of the specimen, and it is thus possible to obtain precise information on the density of cellular regions, even in the living state. The recent development of differential interference (*Nomarski*) optics uses similar principles and provides remarkable three-dimensional images of living cells and cell components (Fig. 1-8).

The *fluorescence microscope* has recently come into common use. Selected wavelengths of light are used to illuminate the biological specimen. Specific molecules within the tissue absorb this light and emit light at other wavelengths. The exciting wavelength is absorbed with filters, and the emitted wavelength is viewed in the microscope objective. Because it is possible to label antibodies with molecules that fluoresce under these conditions (such as fluorescein), it becomes possible to localize antigen-antibody complexes within tissues. This can be a most precise method of localizing specific proteins within tissues.

CHEMICAL AND PHYSICAL PROPERTIES OF PROTOPLASM

The basic medium in which the protoplasmic constituents are dispersed is water. In combination with soluble organic molecules and salts, this "ground cytoplasm" forms a hydrosol or a hydrogel, with the physical properties of a colloidal mass. It is a semifluid or viscid substance, whose consistency varies in different cells or in the same cell under different conditions of physiological activity. It may change from a condition of greater fluidity, a state of sol, to a more viscous gel state. The nuclear protoplasm is ordinarily more viscous than the cytoplasm.

The chief ion of positive charge (cation) in solution in the cell cytoplasm is K^+. The chief cation outside the cell, in the general body fluids, is Na^+. Extracellular fluids contain about 120 meq/l of Na^+ but less than 5 meq/l of K^+; inside the cell a typical value would be 10 meq/l Na^+ and 140 meq/l K^+. The tendency for Na^+ to leak into the cell and for K^+ to diffuse out to regions of lower concentration is counteracted by special properties of the cell membrane. The chief extracellular ion of negative charge (anion) is Cl^-; intracellularly, the important negatively charged molecules are HCO_3^-, $HPO_4^=$, $SO_4^=$ and certain proteins. The cell membrane is quite impermeable to certain of these intracellular anions (which are osmotically active), and when membrane properties are altered and metabolic processes cease after death, the intracellular molecules tend to attract water and the cell may swell.

The difficulties in understanding the life processes occurring within the cell derive in large part from their profound complexity and their remarkable miniaturization. The nucleus of human cells which may be only a few microns in diameter contains information (according to one estimate) for the manufacture of approximately 30,000 different proteins. A single cell may utilize a thousand or more different enzymes in the course of its day to day activities.

Early chemical analyses of protoplasm were primarily concerned with the types and amounts of small molecules present. Such analyses showed that the cell contains a high percentage of water and a host of small molecules, both organic and inorganic. The most characteristic components of the living cell, however, are the macromolecules: nucleic acids, proteins, complex carbohydrates and

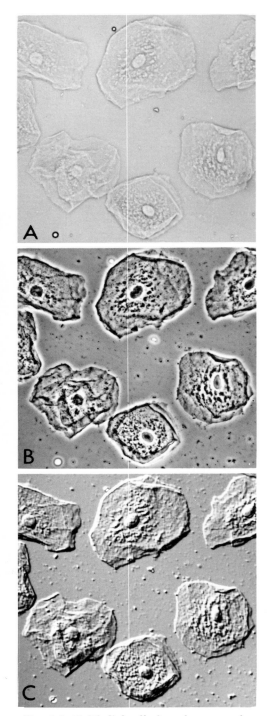

lipids. These macromolecules are, in fact, polymers of certain of the smaller molecules, as is discussed below.

More recently, the biochemist, by separating various cell components in a still viable state, has been able to study the dynamic relationships between various cell compounds. Such analyses indicate that many metabolic processes within the cell do not occur between constituents free in the ground cytoplasm. They occur instead within the framework of macromolecular aggregates called cell organelles. Many of these organelles are complex combinations of nucleic acids, proteins and lipids. The organelles compartmentalize the cytoplasm and provide regions where specific metabolic processes occur, as is discussed below. Protoplasm, in other words, is not a biological broth but a collection of highly organized components dispersed within the cell in a pattern suitable for their functional activities.

Despite the fact that many cell components are a combination of materials, it nevertheless is useful for the histologist to stain for specific components, for such staining can indicate regions of exceptional concentration. For example, a lipid stain will clearly delineate the nerve myelin sheath (Fig. 1-1, C). Myelin also contains protein and carbohydrate, but the exceptional concentration of lipids in myelin allows its differential staining. Thus, it is useful to discuss the major macromolecular components of cells in relation to methods for their histological demonstration. The student is referred to biochemical texts for details of the structure of macromolecules.

Nucleic Acids. Nucleic acids are considered the basis of life, containing the genetic information available within the cell. They provide the blueprint for the most important products of the cell, the proteins, and the kinds and proportions of

FIG. 1-8. Epithelial cells from human oral mucosa as they appear in A, the bright field light microscope, B, the phase contrast microscope, and C, the Nomarski optical system. ×250. (Courtesy of Carl Zeiss, Inc., New York.)

protein present give each cell its individuality.

Nucleic acids are complex compounds consisting of polymers of nucleotides. Each nucleotide contains a pentose sugar combined with phosphoric acid and with a nitrogen-containing base, either a purine (adenine, guanine) or a pyrimidine (thymine, uracil, cytosine). The phosphoric acid component gives the nucleic acids their marked affinity for basic dyes in stained preparations, and pyrimidines and purines absorb characteristic wavelengths of ultraviolet light. On the basis of the type of pentose sugar, the nucleic acids fall into two groups: (1) deoxyribonucleic acid (*DNA*, containing the sugar deoxyribose) and (2) ribonucleic acid (*RNA*, containing the sugar ribose). The nucleic acids combine with the basic proteins, protamine or histone, to form nucleoproteins. According to the Watson and Crick model (proposed in 1953), the DNA molecule is composed of two long polynucleotide chains coiled around each other in the form of a double helix. Certain forms of viral RNA are known to be double stranded, as is DNA; the conformation of native RNA molecules in animal cells is presently under active investigation.

The DNA is found chiefly in the nucleus, confined to chromosomes which contain the genetic units called genes. The DNA is the chief informational macromolecule of heredity. In the cytoplasm, small amounts of DNA are present within mitochondria (see below). The quantity of DNA in the nuclei of different cells of any given species is relatively constant with the exceptions of mature germ cells which have a reduced (haploid) number of chromosomes and certain other cells which may have a multiple (polyploid) number of chromosomes (some liver cells, for example). Naturally, there must be an increase in chromosomal DNA prior to chromosome division at mitosis; otherwise the DNA of the daughter cells would soon be depleted. Although the amount of DNA in the chromosomes of different cells is relatively constant, the amount of DNA-associated protein varies greatly. The latter is usually high in cells which have high metabolic activity in their cytoplasm (e.g., liver and kidney cells).

Ribonucleic acids are found both in the nucleus and in the cytoplasm, particularly in the latter. The RNA carries the information stored in the DNA of the gene to the sites of actual protein synthesis in the cell. The total amount of RNA per cell varies for different tissues and for the same cell type at different times. It is usually abundant in the nucleoli and in the cytoplasm of cells which are most active in synthesizing proteins. Thus, it is abundant in the cytoplasm of enzyme-secreting cells (chromophilic substance), in nerve cells (Nissl substance), in embryonic cells during the growth period and in regenerating cells of the adult organism (e.g., regenerating liver cells, myeloblasts of blood formation, etc.).

Recent studies have revealed the presence of different types of RNA in the cell, with differences in function. *Messenger* RNA is formed in the nucleus and then travels out into the cytoplasm where its linear sequence of bases provides the template for *transfer* RNA. The amino acids attached to transfer RNA are then combined in a specific sequence into a linear chain, the polypeptide chain, for the formation of proteins (Fig. 1-16). Messenger and transfer RNAs are relatively small molecules and probably contribute little to the staining of RNA in cells. Staining instead depends mostly on the presence of *ribosomal* RNA which, in combination with protein, constitutes ribosomes (see below). Thus, nucleic acid staining of cytoplasm depends primarily on the presence of ribosomal RNA (Fig. 1-1, *B*).

The Feulgen staining reaction is particularly useful for distinguishing DNA from RNA and from other basophilic substances. This reaction is specific for DNA because, following mild acid hydrolysis, only the aldehyde group of deoxyribose is available to change the colorless leuco fuchsin (Schiff reagent) to the characteristic magenta color. Reference has already been made to the fact that the identity of RNA can be confirmed by the use of a specific enzyme, ribonuclease. Although basophilia in itself is not a specific test for nucleic acids (other acids in the protoplasm will attract basic dyes), it is true that many basophilic structures contain nucleic acids. It may be pointed out again that the nucleic acids occur in combination with proteins as nucleoproteins. The nucleoprotein reaction seen in sections stained with both basic and acidic dyes will vary with the proportion of the different substances present. For example, the chromatin of the nucleus is very basophilic by reason of its high proportion of nucleic acid, whereas the nucleoprotein of the nucleolus is often acidophilic by reason of its proportion of certain basic proteins.

Amino Acids and Proteins. Proteins are indispensable for the metabolic processes of the cell, and they are also important in the structural organization of protoplasm. All enzymes, the vital catalysts of the chemical reactions in the cell, are proteins. Each type of protein is made up of a particular number and variety of amino acids joined in a precise sequence. Living systems contain about 20 different amino acids, each a single letter in the alphabet of protein structure. They have a characteristic capacity for combining with each other to form long chains. This property results from the presence of a carboxyl group (—COOH) and an amino group (—NH₂) in each molecule. Condensation occurs by the acid group of one amino acid molecule combining with the basic group of another with the loss of one molecule of water. This is known as a peptide linkage, or a *peptide bond*. Chains of amino acids connected by peptide bonds are known as polypeptides. The sequence of amino acids in the peptide chain is very important. For instance, the hemoglobin of patients with sickle cell anemia differs from normal hemoglobin only in the substitution of a molecule of glutamic acid in the place of a molecule of valine.

Protein molecules consist of one or more peptide chains, and they have molecular weights ranging from 10,000 to 1,000,000 or more. These large molecules are generally described as having three levels of organization. The *primary structure* is provided by the amino acid sequence. The primary structure of a substantial number of protein molecules is known. Insulin, for example, is known to be composed of two polypeptide chains (with a total of 51 amino acids) bound together at two points by disulfide bonds between sulfur-containing amino acids within the chain. The *secondary structure* of proteins is formed when peptide chains spontaneously coil as a result of secondary bonding (such as hydrogen bonding) between their constituent amino acids. This secondary coiling produces the helical arrangement of the protein molecules in hair and wool and in other fibrous proteins. Sometimes these helical arrangements involve a number of polypeptide chains coiled together, as in collagen (discussed in Chapter 5).

A *tertiary structure* of proteins may be formed when relatively straight sections of the polypeptide chain are sharply bent at a number of points to fold the molecule up into a globular configuration. The more biologically active proteins in the cell (such as enzymes and hormones) are globular in overall configuration, and are often soluble in the cell cytoplasm and in general body fluids. These globular proteins become partly unfolded in the presence of heat; this *denaturation* accounts for egg albumin turning white upon heating. Histological fixatives are often selected to stabilize the structural components of tissue while causing as little protein denaturation as possible.

Many proteins contain chemical entities in addition to amino acids; this forms the basis for another method of protein classification. The *simple proteins* yield only amino acids on hydrolysis. This group includes albumins, globulins, protamines and histones. *Conjugated proteins* consist of a simple protein combined with another organic substance called the prosthetic group. The conjugated proteins yield amino acids plus the prosthetic group on hydrolysis. The conjugated proteins include nucleoproteins (proteins combined with nucleic acid), glycoproteins or mucoproteins (proteins combined with a carbohydrate), lipoproteins (proteins with fatty acids) and chromoproteins (e.g., hemoglobin).

The amino acids which form proteins contain groupings which ionize to form acids, in some cases, and bases in others. Thus, proteins may be predominantly acidic or basic and take up dyes which bind either to acid groups (basic or cationic dyes, such as methylene blue) or to basic groups (acid or anionic dyes, such as eosin). Eosin colors acidophilic material (primarily basic proteins) pink or red (Fig. 1-1, *A*). A commonly used counterstain, hematoxylin, contains components which together stain basophilic material (nucleic acids and acid proteins) blue.

Lipids. Lipids form a diverse group of compounds (including fats, phospholipids, glycolipids and sterols) which are generally insoluble in water. Three examples of their functional role within the cell are as follows. First, they provide the most concentrated energy reserves of the cell. Fats, which contain fatty acids linked to glycerol, are generally stored within cells in droplets of varying size. These fats can be hydrolyzed to fatty acids and glycerol, and the fatty acids can then be oxidized for energy production. Further energy is derived as the 2-carbon fragments resulting from oxidation are used to fuel the citric acid cycle (see below). Second, certain lipids, particularly phospholipids and cholesterol, form important components of cell membranes. The phospholipids are key compounds, for they have the important property of having a hydrophobic end, which repels water, and a hydrophilic end, which attracts water; this property contributes to the ability of the membrane to partition cellular regions of differing function. It should be noted that the steroid hormones are structurally very similar to the membrane component cholesterol, and one of their important effects is to alter the permeability of the cell membrane.

Third, cell lipids, called glycolipids, are found in combination with sugar molecules, e.g., cerebrosides and gangliosides. These are also utilized in the construction of the cell membrane; it is believed that the lipid components form part of the membrane itself, with the carbohydrate component contributing to the extraneous coat of the membrane (see below under "Cell Membrane").

A substantial amount of lipid is extracted by the standard preparative techniques for histological sections. Lipids can be demonstrated either by the use of a special fixative such as osmium tetroxide, followed by a fat stain such as Sudan black, or by freezing the tissues for sectioning, thus avoiding the solvents used in the paraffin embedding procedure (Fig. 1-1, *C*).

Carbohydrates. Many of the cell macromolecular compounds which are composed primarily of polymers of sugars, or which are protein-carbohydrate complexes, are exported from the cell. Some become important constituents of the supportive and connective tissues of the organism. Others are components of body lubricants such as the mucus covering the surfaces of cells lining the gastrointestinal tract. Still others are stored within the cell, where they form the most readily available energy reserve in the body. Carbohydrate compounds have been classified in many different ways. It is convenient to divide them into four general categories: (1) polysaccharides, (2) polysaccharide-protein complexes, (3) glycoproteins and (4) glycolipids (discussed above).

Polysaccharides are polymers of sugars. The simplest polysaccharides are constructed from one repeating hexose unit. Their individuality is imparted by the types of chemical linkages within the polymer and the pattern of branching. The animal polysaccharide, glycogen, is a complexly branched polymer of glucose, as is also plant starch.

Both are stored within cells and are then readily available for use when needed (Fig. 1-1, *D*). Polysaccharides excreted by cells generally contain two or more monosaccharide components. Among these are hyaluronic acid (which is a copolymer of glucuronic acid and *N*-acetyl glucosamine) and chondroitin sulfate (which is a copolymer of glucuronic acid and *N*-acetyl hexosamine sulfate).

When these polysaccharide components are attached to a polypeptide component through "weak" chemical bonding, they are frequently termed *mucopolysaccharides*. Chondroitin sulfate-protein complexes occur widely in connective tissue (Chapter 5) and account for about 40 % of the dry weight of cartilage (Chapter 6). Hyaluronic acid-protein complexes are found in the vitreous and aqueous humors and cornea of the eye and in the fluids of joint cavities. The blood anticoagulant heparin is also a mucopolysaccharide.

Compounds containing substantial amounts of protein strongly (covalently) bound to smaller amounts of carbohydrate are usefully termed *glycoproteins* or mucoproteins. These compounds are frequently found on the surfaces of cells. Glycoproteins are especially important in immunological reactions in the body, comprising both the immunoglobulin produced by antibody-forming cells and the antigens responsible for the specificity of the ABO blood group system.

STRUCTURAL AND FUNCTIONAL ORGANIZATION OF THE CELL

Cells vary greatly in size, shape and structure, as shown in Figures 1-1, 1-3, 1-9, and 1-36. These variations are adaptations for the different functions which the cells perform in different tissues and organs, and they are considered in more detail in succeeding chapters. Regardless of specialization, most cells retain a number of features in common (see Fig. 1-10). These general characteristics form the subject for the present discussion.

THE NUCLEUS

The nucleus varies in shape and size in different types of cells. In rounded or cuboidal cells, it usually assumes a spherical form (Fig. 1-9, *D*). In tall columnar or spindle-shaped cells, the nucleus is usually elongated, with its long axis corresponding to that of the cell (Fig. 1-9, *C*). In cells whose cytoplasm becomes filled with inclusions, as in mucus-secreting and fat cells, the nucleus is generally flattened against the cell membrane (Fig. 1-1, *C*). It usually reverts to a rounded form after the cytoplasmic inclusions have been extruded.

In some cells, the nucleus becomes lobated, as in neutrophilic leukocytes and megakaryocytes. Cells with a lobed nucleus are often, although not always, in a highly differentiated stage and lack the ability to divide by mitosis (e.g., polymorphonuclear leukocytes). One must not conclude conversely from this that all highly differentiated cells lacking mitotic ability have lobed nuclei. In fact, many highly differentiated cells with little or no mitotic ability in vivo have either rounded or irregularly elongated, nonlobed nuclei (e.g., nerve and muscle cells).

Although a cell usually has only one nucleus, some types often have two or more. Parietal cells of the stomach, liver cells, and surface epithelial cells of the bladder are examples where two nuclei are found frequently. Osteoclasts of bone usually have a large number of nuclei, five or more.

Structure of the Nucleus. The interphase (nondividing) nucleus is bounded by a *nuclear envelope* and contains one or more *nucleoli* and particles or clumps of *chromatin* suspended in the nuclear ground substance.

With the advent of the electron microscope, it was found that the nuclear "membrane" seen by light microscopists was, in fact, a unit of two closely apposed membranes; this unit is called the *nuclear envelope*. At intervals the two membranes curve and join to form an opening, a *nuclear pore*

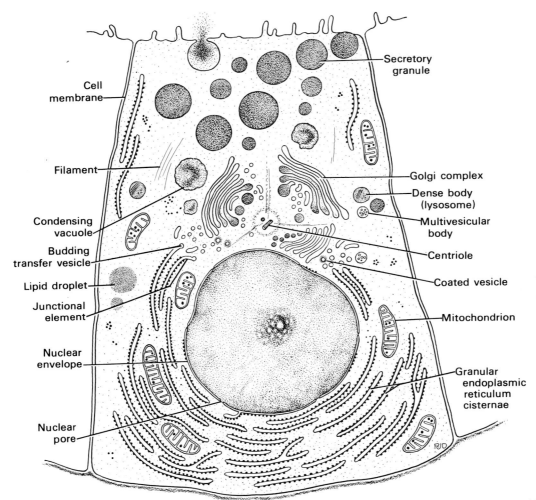

Fig. 1-10. Diagram of a cell as it would appear in a thin section viewed in the electron microscope. All of the organelles depicted here are described in the text. The cell components and their organization indicate that this is a secretory cell. The secretory product is synthesized near the base of the cell in the region of the granular endoplasmic reticulum and is transported to the Golgi region, where it is packaged for release from the upper (apical) surface of the cell.

(Fig. 1-23). A septum thinner than either membrane may span the pore. When the surface of the envelope is viewed, the opening is seen to be round. Pores are of interest because of their postulated role in the exchange of materials between the nucleus and cytoplasm. The nuclear envelope is related to the cytoplasmic endoplasmic reticulum because (1) ribosomes may be attached to the membrane facing the cytoplasm, (2) continuities between the envelope and the

sacs of endoplasmic reticulum have been seen, and (3) the envelope is reformed from endoplasmic reticulum elements near the end of each cell division.

The *nucleoli* are round and dense, well defined bodies, although they do not have a limiting membrane. In general, there may be from one to four per nucleus, although they vanish temporarily during part of the division cycle. They are composed of RNA (ribonucleic acid) and associated proteins.

FIG. 1-11. Electron micrograph, showing nuclear chromatin and a nucleolus. The nucleolus, indicated by *arrows*, contains granular and fibrillar elements which may be organized into a dense, meandering strand or network called the nucleolonema. Clumps of chromatin (*c*) abut on the nucleolus and the nuclear envelope. Acinar cell from bat pancreas. ×25,000. (From Fawcett, D. W. 1966 The Cell. Its Organelles and Inclusions. W. B. Saunders Company, Philadelphia.)

Nucleoli usually stain intensely but they exhibit a variable basophilia and acidophilia in different cells and at different times depending on the relative proportions of RNA and basic protein.

The constituents of the nucleolus as seen in the electron microscope are as follows. (1) A *fibrillogranular* ribonucleoprotein component consists of granules enmeshed in a matrix of filaments. These granules contain RNA which is destined for assembly in the cytoplasm into another kind of ribonucleoprotein particle, the ribosome. (2) Other portions of the nucleolus, often the center, consist of dense masses of ribonucleoprotein *filaments* 50 A thick. (3) Surrounding or extending into the nucleolus are clusters of *deoxy*ribonucleoprotein filaments known as *nucleolus-associated chromatin*. During re-

formation of the nucleolus after mitosis, the nucleolar components accumulate in association with particular regions of certain chromosomes known as *nucleolus organizers*. It is this organizer region of the chromosome which is seen in association with the mature nucleolus. Finally, it should be pointed out that the ribonucleoprotein components—both the fibrillogranular and filamentous elements—are often aggregated into a meandering thick thread or network called the *nucleolonema* (Fig. 1-11). The associated chromatin may occupy the interstices of the nucleolonema.

Dispersed throughout the nucleus is deoxyribonucleic acid (DNA), the carrier of hereditary characteristics. The DNA double helix (see "Protoplasm") is about 20 A in diameter; the proteins adhering to this

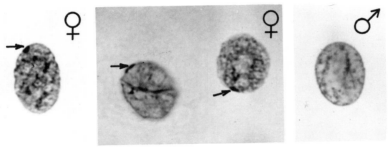

FIG. 1-12. Photomicrograph of four nuclei in a smear of oral mucosa cells from normal adult subjects. The three nuclei on the *left*, obtained from females, each contain a small dense body situated near the nuclear envelope. These "Barr bodies" are not found in nuclei from males, as shown on the *right*. Thionin staining. ×1800. (From Barr, M. L. 1963 *In* Intersexuality, edited by C. Overzier, p. 48, Academic Press, New York.)

strand increase the diameter to 40 to 50 A. Basic histone proteins and acid proteins play a role in the expression of activity of DNA, and they lend support to the helix as well. Deoxyribonucleoprotein (DNP) strands are coiled into units 200 to 250 A in diameter. This is the fundamental structural strand of genetic material, as first proposed by Ris. Masses of these extremely long threads intertwine throughout the nucleus; it has been reported that an individual strand may be as long as 22,000 μ in human lymphocyte nuclei. This thread is too thin to be resolved in the light microscope, thus explaining why many nuclei appear nearly empty in the light microscope (Fig. 1-1, *A* and *B*).

At certain intervals along the thread, however, the DNP is additionally coiled, forming clumps which can be seen in the light microscope after staining (Fig. 1-12). These scattered stained clumps and particles are called *chromatin* (Gr., *chroma*, color), a name derived from the fact that they stain brilliantly with basic coal tar dyes. Chromatin particles occur throughout the nucleus, are often clumped on the nuclear envelope and are associated with nucleoli, as mentioned above. These particles in the nondividing nucleus are also termed *heterochromatin* (or karyosomes); the DNP not stained, filling the empty appearing areas, is called *euchromatin*.

The heterochromatin is thought of as *condensed* chromatin which is inactive metabolically. The euchromatin, on the other hand, is the *dispersed* or extended form, the state in which chromatin is active. The light microscopist, then, can gain information about the relative activity of the cell by noting the appearance of the chromatin.

This generalization is illustrated by the following examples. In the development of the mammalian erythrocyte, the chromatin is initially dispersed but gradually becomes more condensed; as the cell reaches maturity (and hemoglobin synthesis nears completion), the nucleus is seen to be small, very darkly staining and homogeneously dense (Fig. 7-10). During maturation of sperm, a similar phenomenon is observed. The nucleus of the mature sperm is filled with "storage" DNP and is, as expected, extremely dense throughout. Once fertilization has occurred, the sperm nucleus inside the egg begins to swell and the chromatin begins to extend for initiation of gene activity.

During division, the chromatin threads become completely coiled or condensed into chromosomes (Fig. 1-13). One can imagine the confusion and entanglement of the genetic strands if this did not occur! Chromosomes are visible in the light microscope as stained rods of varying lengths. Division, then, is the only time when the entire length of each chromatin thread can be visualized. More is

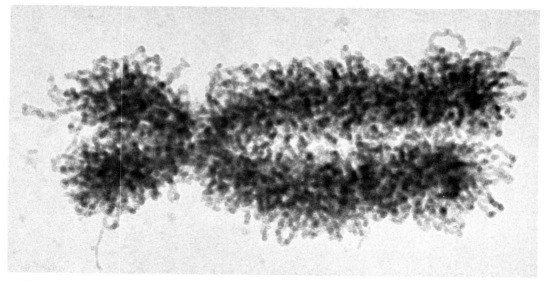

Fig. 1-13. Electron micrograph of an unsectioned human chromosome (# 12) obtained from a dividing cell. The chromosome is divided in half along its length (into two chromatids) except at the centromere. The chromosome is made up of a unit which varies from 100 to 500 A in diameter. This chromosome weighs 13.2×10^{-13} grams and contains about 4 cm. of DNA double helix per chromatid. Some of the looping and coiling which allows the packing of all this DNA into a chromosome 3 μ in length is visible. $\times 40,200$. (From DuPraw, E. J. 1970 DNA and Chromosomes. Holt, Rinehart and Winston, Inc., New York.)

said of chromosomes in Chapter 2, in which division is discussed. The configurations, as well as the number, of the mitotic (metaphase) chromosomes are constant, thus allowing their identification. This assumes importance in human disease and is also further considered in Chapter 2.

One of the sex chromosomes remains condensed in the interphase cell and is known as the *Barr body*. First described in 1949 by Barr and Bertram, it is the second X chromosome present normally only in female cells. Female cells contain two X sex chromosomes; male cells contain two sex chromosomes, one X and one Y. Apparently, one X chromosome (but not more than one) must exist in an extended state because it participates in a number of metabolic activities other than that of sex determination. Thus, in the normal situation, when two X chromosomes are present in female cells, one of them remains condensed. It appears as a small stained body (about 1 μ in diameter) beside

the nucleolus or adjacent to the nuclear envelope, depending upon the species (Fig. 1-12). The sex chromatin can be seen in sections or smears (from oral mucosa, blood, etc.). Identification of Barr bodies aids in the diagnosis of sex in intersexual states and also in studies of congenital diseases related to sex chromatin.

Considering the widely dispersed coiled threads of chromatin, it is not surprising that electron microscopic observations of nuclei in thin sections reveal only a wealth of granules and very short filaments (Fig. 1-11). If chromosomes of the dividing cell are processed for electron microscopy without sectioning, their overall configurations can be appreciated (Fig. 1-13). Visualization of active sites or genes on the chromatin threads is just now beginning to be realized, by careful selection of special systems for study.

For example, during development of an amphibian egg, the chromosomal nucleolus organizer is multiplied and produces about

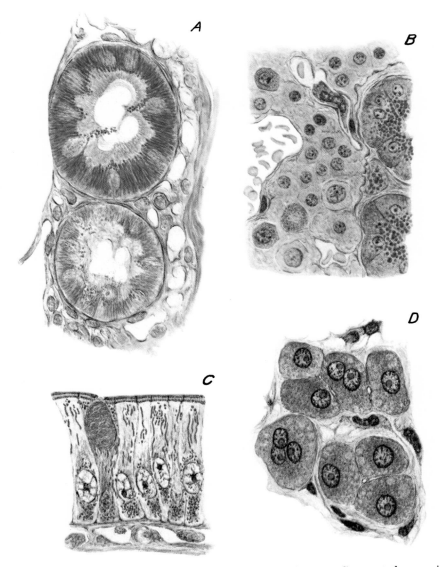

Fɪɢ. 1-9. Staining of tissues by various techniques. *A*, kidney of mouse. Contrast the prominence of parallel lined mitochondria in the proximal convoluted tubule *above* with the distal convoluted *below*. Regaud, Altmann acid fuchsin. *B*, island of Langerhans from human pancreas, bordered at *right* by acinar cells which show chromophilic substance and apical secretion granules. In the island tissue are many "B" cells (orange), three red granular "A" cells and two blue "D" cells. A polymorphonuclear leukocyte was caught in the upper sinusoid. Helly, modified Masson. *C*, intestinal epithelium of cat, showing one goblet cell among absorbing cells. Note polarized mitochondria and the striated cell border. Champy, modified Masson. *D*, liver cells from rhesus monkey filled with evenly distributed glycogen granules. One cell has two nuclei, another three, which is not uncommon. Biopsy, alcohol, Best's carmine. Camera lucida drawings. (Preparations by Dr. A. E. Severinghaus.)

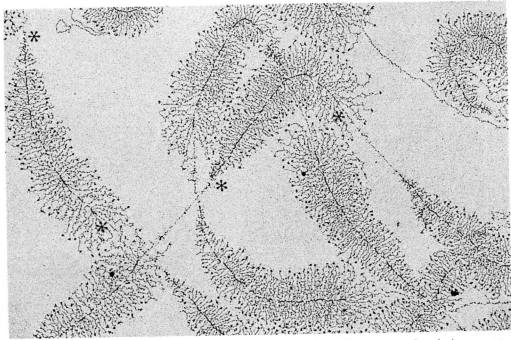

FIG. 1-14. During the development of amphibian oocytes, the DNA increases sharply in amount and is contained within the 1000 or so forming extrachromosomal nucleoli. When this DNA is maximally unwound, it is seen in the electron microscope to be an extremely slender strand with periodic adherent material arranged in a feather-like pattern. Each "feather" (as indicated between *asterisks* in two areas here) is about 2.5 μ long and results from the attachment to the DNA axis of 100 forming ribonucleoprotein molecules in progressive stages of completion. Thus it is shown that about 100 precursor molecules of ribosomal RNA are being formed simultaneously at each gene. $\times$25,000. (From Miller, Jr., O. L., and Beatty, B. R. 1969 Science, vol. 164, p. 955.)

1000 nucleoli. If these nucleoli are isolated, dispersed and then prepared for electron microscopy, thin strands of DNP (100 to 300 A in diameter) are found; on these fibers are repeating regions (2 to 5 μ long) containing about 100 thin fibrils connected by one end to the fiber and increasing in length from one end of that region to the other (Fig. 1-14). Each region on the DNA axis is one gene, and this gene has sites for the simultaneous production of 100 ribosomal RNA precursor molecules. It has been estimated that, in one of these oocyte nuclei, 3.6 meters of DNA double helix contain $2\frac{1}{3}$ million of these genes producing ribosomal RNA. This system allows the direct observation of the manufacture of RNA on the DNA molecule.

Functions. The standard histological section offers a few clues regarding nuclear activity. As has been discussed above, the degree of condensation of the chromatin is an inverse index of the amount of genetic material that is involved in synthetic activities. Cells with large, pale nuclei containing little condensed chromatin (such as neurons, Fig. 1-1, *A* and *B*) are metabolically very active cells. The size of the nucleolus also is related to cell activity. Nucleoli are small (or absent) in cells which are not actively forming proteins (e.g., mature leukocytes) and generally large in cells which are actively synthesizing proteins (e.g., nerve cells which must replenish their proteins during activity, cells of regenerating tissues and embryonic cells). These observations are consistent with the more recent knowledge that the nucleolus is the site of formation of ribosomal RNA, and that ribosomes are needed for protein synthesis.

A great deal of work in the field of nuclear cytoplasmic relationships has been done over the years. This is not the place to review or even to attempt to summarize it. One aspect of this work has involved bisecting unicellular organisms so that only one part retains a nucleus. The part without the nucleus will gradually die, whereas the nucleated portion will survive. With the removal of the nucleus, the DNA-RNA-protein production sequence is stopped, and the anucleate part will live only as long as survival time of its protein molecules will permit. The overall importance of the nucleus has been nicely stated by Allfrey: "The cell nucleus, central and commanding, is essential for the biosynthetic events that characterize cell type and cell function; it is a vault of genetic information encoding the past history and future prospects of the cell, an organelle submerged and deceptively serene in its sea of turbulent cytoplasm, a firm and purposeful guide, a barometer exquisitely sensitive to the changing demands of the organism and its environment."

THE CYTOPLASM

Cytoplasm contains a number of formed bodies embedded in a substance which appears translucent and homogeneous in the living cell. This substance has been given a variety of names such as ground cytoplasm, basic or fundamental cytoplasm or hyaloplasm. The formed bodies embedded in the cytoplasm are often divided into two groups: *organelles* when they are composed of living, differentiated cytoplasm and *inclusion bodies* when they are metabolic or ingested substances which are temporary constituents. The first group includes (1) ribosomes, (2) endoplasmic reticulum with and without ribosomes, (3) Golgi apparatus, (4) lysosomes, (5) central body and centrioles, (6) mitochondria, (7) filaments and (8) microtubules. The second group includes (1) yolk, (2) fat and carbohydrate (glycogen) deposits, (3) secretion granules and (4) pigment granules.

Ribosomes. Near the turn of the century, it was discovered that the cytoplasm of many cells contained material which stained with basic dyes just as the nuclear chromatin did. This basophilic material was called "chromophilic" substance. In certain gland cells, intensely basophilic areas were also given the name ergastoplasm (Gr., *ergaster*, a workman, + *plasma*, plasm) because they were thought to be involved in the work of producing secretory granules. This staining was later found to be due to the presence of RNA. Chromophilic regions absorbed a specific wavelength of ultraviolet light characteristic of nucleic acids. Staining for DNA by means of the Feulgen reaction proved negative. With the increased resolution of the electron microscope and the availability of new sectioning techniques, Palade discovered in the early 1950s that chromophilic regions in many cell types contained a wealth of small, dense granules (averaging 150 A in diameter). Though these granules frequently were aligned on flattened membranous sacs (endoplasmic reticulum), it was eventually concluded that the granules alone were responsible for the staining. Use of the enzyme ribonuclease abolished simultaneously the cytoplasmic chromophilia and the granules (but not the membranes). It also was observed that some chromophilic cells (e.g., lymphocytes) have numerous ribosomes but little or no membranous reticulum. The particles are now known to be composed of 60% RNA and 40% protein. Their composition is reflected in their present name, *ribosomes*.

Ribosomes have been found in all animal cells, with the exception of adult mammalian erythrocytes (which lose their organelles when they reach maturity). The ribosomes are most abundant in the cytoplasm of cells which show the most marked chromophilia in the light microscope. Highly chromophilic cells include those engaged in synthesizing secretory proteins, such as pancreatic and

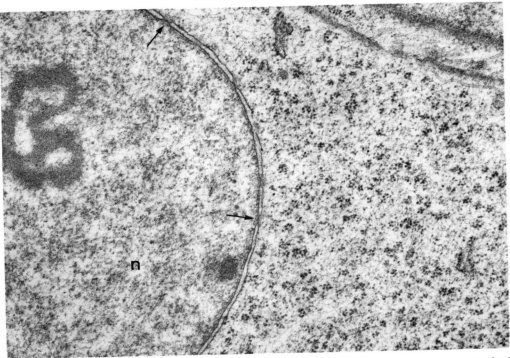

Fig. 1-15. The predominantly ribosomal (polysome) content of the cytoplasm of young developing cells is shown in this electron micrograph of a nerve cell from embryonic rabbit neural tube. The envelope around the nucleus (n) has a number of pores (arrows). ×32,000. (Courtesy of Dr. Virginia Tennyson.)

salivary acinar cells, and cells in active growth stages, such as lymphoblasts, myeloblasts and osteoblasts. In electron micrographs the ribosomal granules are seen to occur free in the cytoplasm or to be lined up on flattened sacs of endoplasmic reticulum membrane. Those ribosomes associated with endoplasmic reticulum are involved in the formation of proteins for export from the cell, such as the digestive enzymes secreted by the pancreatic acinar cell. When the ribosome is attached to endoplasmic reticulum, the exportable proteins produced are delivered into the reticulum cavities rather than into the cytoplasmic matrix. The free ribosomes, on the other hand, are involved in the formation of proteins, including the thousand or so enzymes necessary for normal cell activity. In rapidly growing and dividing cells, which are increasing in cytoplasmic volume, free ribosomes are the most prominent of the cytoplasmic organelles (Fig. 1-15).

Functions. Ribosomes have been studied extensively by many investigators because of their important role as the sites of protein synthesis. The collaborative efforts of cytologists and biochemists employing both in vivo and in vitro systems have led to a new understanding of protein manufacture and the involvement of various RNAs in this activity. This is an area of investigation which has been aided greatly by the techniques of differential centrifugation (in combination with radioactive tracers) and radioautography at the light and electron microscope levels. When homogenized cells are subjected to differential centrifugation, the nuclei sediment out first, the mitochondria next and submicroscopic components last. The submicroscopic material is named the *microsome*

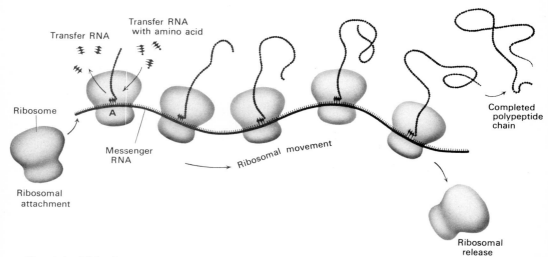

FIG. 1-16. This diagram depicts the role of ribosomes in protein synthesis. A ribosome becomes attached to one end of a strand of messenger RNA (*mRNA*). The ribosome is known to consist of two subunits of unequal size; it has been speculated that the mRNA strand fits into a groove formed at the junction of these two subunits. A molecule of transfer RNA (*tRNA*) becomes activated by linking with a specific amino acid; there are some 20 different tRNA molecules, one for each amino acid. The nature of the mRNA sites present in the receiving area of the ribosome (*A*) determines which tRNA and, thus, which amino acid is used. Thus, as the ribosome progresses along the mRNA strand, the code is translated by the tRNAs, which deposit in correct order the amino acids required for the production of a specific protein. The longer the mRNA strand, the farther the ribosome must travel and the greater is the number of amino acids assembled. Each ribosome makes a complete chain. That there are five ribosomes in a polysome at a given time, as drawn here, is determined by the mRNA molecule. When the ribosome reaches the end of the strand, it is released and is available for reuse with the same or a different species of mRNA, and the completed polypeptide chain is liberated. (Diagram based upon drawings and descriptions by A. Rich.)

fraction. Studies of this fraction under the electron microscope show that it is composed chiefly of fragments of endoplasmic reticulum and adhering ribosomes. The addition of a detergent, deoxycholate, solubilizes the membranes, resulting in, after additional centrifugation, a relatively pure preparation of ribosomes. Ribosomal fractions have the capacity to incorporate amino acids into protein molecules.

Ribosomes lying free in the cytoplasm or attached to membrane often occur in clusters called *polyribosomes* or *polysomes*. The cluster is held together by a single slender strand of RNA called *messenger RNA* (mRNA). In general, the number of ribosomes in a polysome and the length of polypeptide formed are proportional to the length of the mRNA strand. In the immature red blood cell which

is synthesizing hemoglobin, polysomes contain five ribosomes, and the polypeptide chains formed contain about 150 amino acids. In developing muscle cells which are producing myosin, 56 ribosomes constitute a polysome at a time when more than 1800 amino acids are assembled into a polypeptide chain. The longer mRNA strand has spaces for more ribosomes and requires each ribosome to travel farther, thus providing for the assembly of a greater number of amino acids (as explained in Fig. 1-16). This assembly process, not discovered until the 1960s, is very rapid: data from bacteria indicate that only 10 seconds are required for the assembly of a protein containing 500 to 1000 amino acids.

Granular Endoplasmic Reticulum. The *endoplasmic reticulum* was first seen in

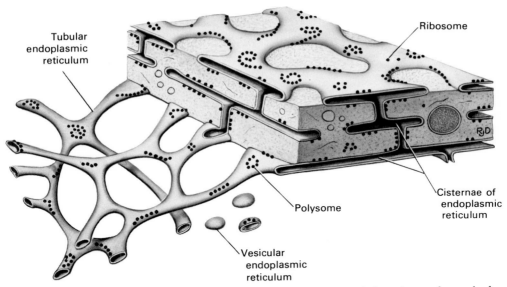

Tubular
endoplasmic
reticulum

Ribosome

Polysome

Cisternae of
endoplasmic
reticulum

Vesicular
endoplasmic
reticulum

FIG. 1-17. Diagram illustrating the interconnected cisternae and tubules of granular endoplasmic reticulum.

1945 by Porter, Claude and Fullam who were able to examine very thinly spread, cultured fibroblasts in the electron microscope. Because the preparation had not been sectioned, the arrangement of the newly found organelle in a network was quickly recognized. The presence of this lace-like network (or reticulum) in the inner or endoplasmic region of the cytoplasm (although it is not always so distributed) led to the name endoplasmic reticulum. Subsequent study of thin sections added more information. Endoplasmic reticulum exists in the form of vesicles, tubules and often broad but flattened sacs (cisternae) of membrane in reticular sheets interconnected by branchings and anastomoses (Fig. 1-17). Ribosomes cover much of the endoplasmic reticulum surface; this association of ribosomal granules and endoplasmic reticulum is termed *granular endoplasmic reticulum.* The term "rough" or "rough surfaced" endoplasmic reticulum also is used, referring to the uneven appearance of membrane encrusted with ribosomes.

Ribosomes attach to endoplasmic reticulum membrane and to the outer membrane of

the nuclear envelope, which is related to the reticulum, and to no other membranes of the cell. When the reticulum membrane is sectioned perpendicular to its surface, the ribosomes dot the surface at more or less regular intervals; when the membrane is sectioned such that patches of its cytoplasmic surface are visible, many of the ribosomes are seen to occur in circle, loop, spiral or rosette arrays which are the membrane-associated polysomes (Fig. 1-18). Occasionally the proteins synthesized on the ribosomes are visible as dense or filamentous material within the lumina of the reticulum elements.

The amount and configuration of the granular endoplasmic reticulum depend upon the cell type and the physiological state of the cell. Growing cells, full of free ribosomes and little endoplasmic reticulum, exhibit an intense, diffuse chromophilia. In differentiated cells, ribosomes are often less concentrated, and those present are in large part attached to endoplasmic reticulum; basophilia is correspondingly reduced and, in some cases, staining may occur only in certain areas of the cytoplasm. Examples of this transformation are provided by the rapidly dividing

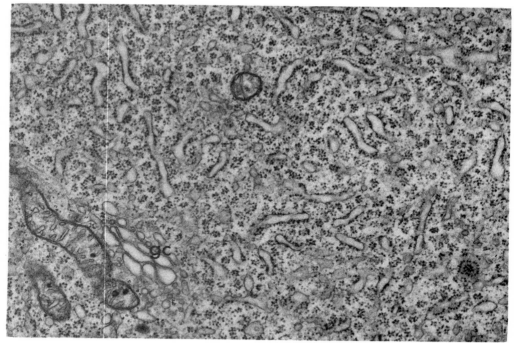

Fig. 1-18. This electron micrograph shows a region of granular endoplasmic reticulum in the cytoplasm of a mature neuron. Compare this with the immature nerve cell shown in Figure 1-15. Where the cisternae are cut *en face* (as at *lower right*), the coiled, looped or curved arrangement of ribosomes in the polysome is clearly seen. Part of a Golgi complex (*gc*) and mitochondria appear at *lower left*. ×29,000.

epithelial cells in the intestinal crypts and in the germinal layer of the epidermis.

Differentiated cells engaged in synthesis of protein (for export) as a rule appear intensely basophilic in certain cytoplasmic regions. For example, the pancreatic acinar cell, which secretes digestive enzymes (zymogen granules), is highly chromophilic in its basal region only. Such an area is filled with numerous granular endoplasmic reticulum cisternae which are closely and regularly packed in parallel rows (Fig. 1-10). Relatively few of the ribosomes lie free in the cytoplasmic matrix. It is this type of basally located, oriented granular endoplasmic reticulum that also may be referred to as *ergastoplasm*.

Functions. The pancreatic acinar cell has been popular among students of protein synthesis. It is a good system for tracing newly synthesized exportable proteins through the cell partly because different or-

ganelles involved at different times are concentrated in different regions of the cytoplasm. The ribosome-encrusted cisternae of endoplasmic reticulum are located chiefly in the basal portion of the cell along with the nucleus and mitochondria (an energy source). The apical region of the cell, nearer to the lumen into which the product will be emptied, contains numerous zymogen granules (Fig. 1-9, *B*), interspersed with a few granular reticulum elements. In between these two regions (above the nucleus) there is a well developed network of Golgi apparatus oriented around two centrioles (see diagram, Fig. 1-10). To investigate the synthesis, intracellular transport, storage and discharge of the digestive enzymes, Caro and Palade administered to guinea pigs the radioactive amino acid leucine and examined the pancreatic acini by means of light and electron microscopic radioautography. The path of the exportable protein through the cell was detected by looking for radioactive sites at various time intervals. Sites of radioactivity indicated the presence of the leucine which had been recently used in the synthesis of new exportable protein; unused radioactive leucine had been washed away during preparation. Five minutes after the guinea pigs had received the leucine, radioactivity was confined mainly to the granular reticulum in the basal region of the acinar cell. At 20 minutes, the Golgi zone contained most of the radioactivity. One to 4 hours after injection, the radioactivity was found chiefly in zymogen granules in the cell (and in the lumen as well). Thus it was concluded that the proteins were synthesized on the ribosomes attached to endoplasmic reticulum and were transported within the reticulum to the Golgi zone where they became concentrated and packaged into zymogen granules for temporary storage. In this manner the digestive enzymes remain isolated from the remainder of the cytoplasm.

The fact that continuities between the granular reticulum and the Golgi apparatus are seldom seen raises the question: how is the newly synthesized protein transported from reticulum cisternae to Golgi elements? In areas of granular endoplasmic reticulum bordering on the Golgi zone, some of the cisternae are partly devoid of ribosomes, i.e., a cisterna may be part rough and part smooth; these cisternae are called transitional or *junctional elements*. Interspersed among them are swarms of small vesicles (about 500 A in diameter) which occasionally appear to be continuous with, or budding from, the cisternae. It was concluded, therefore, that these vesicles, termed *transfer vesicles*, ferry the synthesized product to the Golgi elements. The newly synthesized proteins are later visualized in *condensing vacuoles*. These vacuoles, found in the Golgi zone, are the sites of progressive accumulation and concentration of protein; they will become the spherical, more dense zymogen granules. In experiments using radioactive tracers, condensing vacuoles become radioactive before the zymogen granules are so labeled.

Agranular Endoplasmic Reticulum. Endoplasmic reticulum devoid of ribosomes (*agranular endoplasmic reticulum;* smooth or smooth surfaced reticulum) is found in a variety of cell types, generally in those lacking a well developed granular reticulum. Unlike the granular reticulum, the smooth reticulum is primarily in the form of tubules which are often interconnected (or merely entangled), tortuous and very closely packed (Fig. 1-19). Although agranular reticulum elements may be continuous with or derived from rough reticulum, the constituent membrane may differ in that it appears thinner and is more difficult to preserve. The occurrence of agranular reticulum in cells was not recognized before the use of the electron microscope because it lacks staining properties which set it apart from the rest of the cytoplasm.

Functions. The agranular endoplasmic reticulum is known to perform a variety of functions depending upon the cell type in which it resides. In liver cells, this organelle is considered to function in lipid and cholesterol metabolism. (The liver cell is exceptional in that it contains numerous arrays of granular as well as agranular reticulum, undoubtedly reflecting the manifold activities known to occur in liver cells.) Agranular reticulum also aids in detoxification processes, e.g., by hydroxylation. When lipid-soluble drugs such as barbiturates or cancer-producing agents are given to animals, greatly enlarged arrays of smooth reticulum appear in the hepatic cells. There is a concomitant increase in drug-metabolizing enzymes in smooth membrane fractions isolated from these cells. Investigators speculate that the toxic agent is taken up in the lipid portion of the induced membrane and is thereby brought into contact with the detoxifying enzymes associated with the same membrane. Glycogen particles often are enmeshed within arrays of liver smooth reticulum, suggesting a functional relationship.

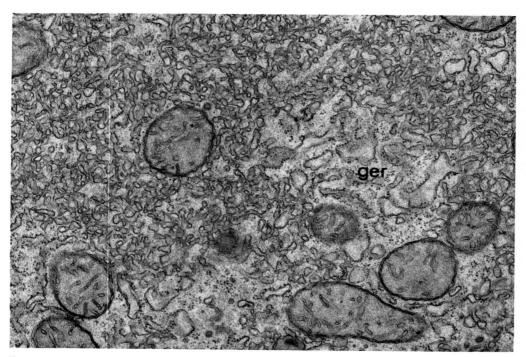

Fig. 1-19. Interspersed among the mitochondria and elements of granular endoplasmic reticulum (*ger*) of this liver cell are slender anastomosing tubules of agranular endoplasmic reticulum. The agranular reticulum is increased in response to the administration of phenobarbital (which is detoxified in these regions). ×26,000. (Courtesy of Dr. Don W. Fawcett.)

In the interstitial cells of the testis and in the cells of the ovarian corpus luteum and adrenal cortex, the very extensive agranular reticulum is considered to participate in the synthesis and storage of cholesterol and in the production of steroid hormones. The smooth reticulum contained within cells lining the intestine is involved in the synthesis of fats from components absorbed from the intestinal lumen and their packaging and transport within the cell. The prominent agranular endoplasmic reticulum in the gastric oxyntic cell is thought to participate in the secretion of chloride ions. Finally, the elaborate tubular network of smooth reticulum (sarcoplasmic reticulum) encasing each striated muscle myofibril functions in the excitation-contraction coupling mechanism (see Chapter 8 and Fig. 8-17).

The Golgi Apparatus. The *Golgi apparatus,* discovered by Golgi in 1898, is one of the organelles involved in secretory activity. It is arranged in a reticular network which is either distributed throughout the cytoplasm (Fig. 1-20) or confined to a zone near the nucleus, depending upon the cell type. In elongated cells which border on an enclosed space, the Golgi complex lies between the nucleus and the free surface border of the cell (Fig. 1-21). In the light microscope, the Golgi apparatus is visualized only after treatment with silver or osmium tetroxide which is reduced to a black deposit. In cells forming a carbohydrate product, the Golgi region is stained magenta by means of the periodic acid-Schiff technique. Variable results with these techniques stirred vigorous controversy about the reality of this cell organelle, and it was not until the era of the electron microscope that the Golgi apparatus was recognized as a ubiquitous cell structure of consistent form. In the electron mi-

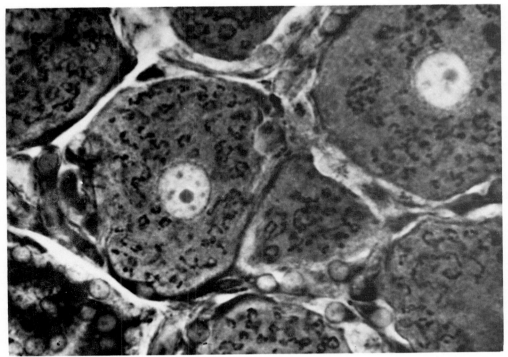

FIG. 1-20. Scattered throughout the cytoplasm of these large neurons are dense, ribbon-like deposits revealing the distribution of the Golgi apparatus. Light micrograph of 5 μ section; Nassonow-Kolatschew technique. ×914. (From Hild, W. 1959 Nervensystem. *In* Handb. mikr. Anat. Menschen., edited by v. Möllendorff, part 4, p. 116, Springer-Verlag, Vienna.)

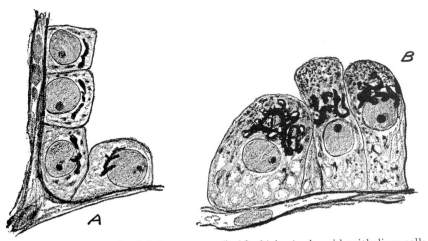

FIG. 1-21. Representation of the Golgi apparatus (in black) in *A*, thyroid epithelium cells from normal sheep, and *B*, cells from the thyroid after marked activation with hypophyseal hormone. The greatly hypertrophied Golgi apparatus remains apical in the heightened cells. Nassonow-Kolatschew preparations. Camera lucida. (Preparations by Dr. A. E. Severinghaus.)

croscope, the Golgi apparatus is seen as a number of stacks of closely packed agranular membrane cisternae with associated vacuoles and vesicles (Figs. 1-22 and 1-23). Each stack may be curved; those cisternae on the convex or "outer" face often are more flattened than those on the concave or "inner" face (Fig. 1-22).

Functions. More and more evidence is accumulating concerning the function of the Golgi apparatus. Light microscope studies early in this century had indicated that the apparatus was somehow involved in the elaboration of secretory substances in, for example, thyroid (Fig. 1-21), intestinal goblet, pancreatic acinar and sebaceous cells. In 1938 Kirkman and Severinghaus stated that, "A great deal of work strongly suggests that the Golgi apparatus neither synthesizes secretory substances nor is transformed directly into them; but it acts as a condensation membrane for the concentration, into droplets or granules, of products elaborated elsewhere and diffused into the cytoplasm. These elaborated products may be lipoids, yolk, bile constituents, enzymes, hormones, or almost any other formed substances."

The role of the Golgi apparatus in concentrating and packaging protein-rich materials has been firmly established with new techniques. The product formed on the ribosomes associated with endoplasmic reticulum becomes contained within the reticulum cisternae and then is transported to Golgi elements via small vesicles which pinch off the reticulum and merge with Golgi membrane. The product, now visible because of increased density, as a rule next appears in the inner Golgi cisternae and leaves the Golgi stack via vesicles or vacuoles which arise as terminal expansions of these cisternae. These vesicles may coalesce, their contents progressively increasing in density, until there is a population of large, very dense secretion droplets which move out of the Golgi zone. Because the product is thought to be delivered to the outer cisternae of the Golgi complex in some cells, this aspect is sometimes referred to as the "forming" face; the

inner surface is designated the "maturing" face for it is the region of the maturing secretion droplet. Thus, the protein-rich product is collected and concentrated in the Golgi region and is packaged in Golgi membrane, at all times remaining segregated from the remainder of the cell. In the pancreatic acinar cell, the newly synthesized product is first seen in the condensing vacuoles in the Golgi region rather than in the cisternae of the Golgi stack.

Almost all proteins secreted by the cell contain some sugar moieties, in contrast with those which remain inside. Recent work indicates that it is in the region of the Golgi apparatus that sugars are added to the protein on its way from the granular endoplasmic reticulum to the cell exterior. A suitable cell for such study is the intestinal goblet cell which manufactures mucus, a substance composed mainly of protein with a small amount of carbohydrate (glycoprotein). The exportable product enters the Golgi apparatus and collects in the uppermost cisternae. Portions of the cisternae bulge and bud off, becoming spherical, mucus-filled globules which move to the cell apex where they are discharged. Utilizing electron microscopic radioautography, Leblond and collaborators found that radioactive glucose administered to rats was added to protein in the Golgi region prior to the formation of mucus globules. Incorporated radioactivity was first seen, within 15 minutes, over Golgi stacks. At later intervals, sites of radioactivity were mainly in the mucus globules and, still later, near the apical cell surface. This work also demonstrates the turnover in Golgi membrane: in spite of successive budding to form globules at the maturing surface, the stack of Golgi cisternae is maintained. Other investigations have indicated that the Golgi region is also the site of assembly of polysaccharides for export to the cell exterior as a coating on the plasma membrane or as matrix material contributing to cartilage. Sulfate is also added to these substances in the Golgi region.

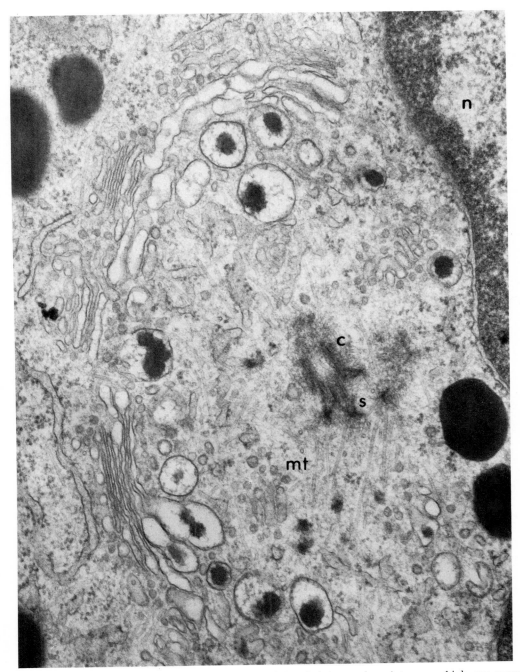

FIG. 1-22. This electron micrograph is dominated by Golgi complex cisternae which are curved around the centrioles (one of which is indicated at c) and toward the nucleus (n). Microtubules (mt) radiate from densities associated with the centrioles (pericentriolar satellites, s) and may be seen as circles (when sectioned transversely) or as double lines (when longitudinally sectioned). The largest dense inclusions here are azurophil granules, a typical component of this polymorphonuclear leukocyte. They arise from the inner (or concave) surface of the Golgi complex by budding off the cisternae. They first appear as dense-centered vacuoles and gradually change into large, dense granules. ×50,000. (From Bainton, D. F., and Farquhar, M. G.   1966   J. Cell Biol., vol. 28, p. 277.)

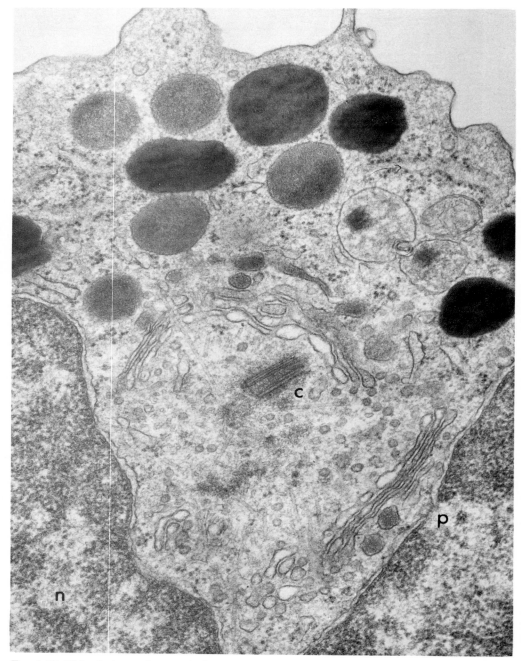

Fig. 1-23. This electron micrograph shows other polymorphonuclear leukocyte granules, the specific granules, in various stages of formation from the outer or convex face of the Golgi complex at a later stage of development than that represented in Figure 1-22. Beneath the Golgi complex, in the cell center, is a longitudinally sectioned centriole (*c*). Extending from this region are straight profiles of microtubules. In the envelope surrounding the nucleus (*n*) are several pores, one of which is designated *p*. ×50,000. (From Bainton, D. F., and Farquhar, M. G. 1966 J. Cell Biol., vol. 28, p. 277.)

It appears now that the Golgi complex is polarized; i.e., different cisternae perform different functions, sometimes at different maturational stages. Working with maturing polymorphonuclear leukocytes from rabbit bone marrow, Bainton and Farquhar have shown that two kinds of granules are formed in a manner similar to secretory granule production, i.e., by the accumulation, condensation and packaging of product in the Golgi apparatus. But one type of granule (azurophil) arises from the inner surface of the Golgi stack (Fig. 1-22) and the second variety of granule (specific) originates from the outer surface (Fig. 1-23). The granules are formed at different developmental stages, and they differ in enzymatic content. The polarity of the Golgi apparatus is suggested also by osmium impregnation and histochemical investigations. Only the outer cisternae become blackened after prolonged exposure to osmium tetroxide. Histochemists have found that some hydrolytic enzymes are associated with middle cisternae, whereas others are confined only to inner cisternae. Histochemical demonstration of hydrolytic enzymes introduces still another function of the Golgi apparatus, the production of lysosomes.

Lysosomes. By centrifuging the mitochondrial fraction in graded concentrations of sucrose, a class of particles different in enzymatic content from mitochondria was discovered by de Duve in 1955. Enzymatic activity was not fully evident until the membrane bounding the particle became more permeable or was broken, a characteristic of importance for the cell as discussed below. The dozen or more enzymes associated with these particles are hydrolases which break down proteins, carbohydrates, and nucleic acids at acid pH (e.g., cathepsins, glycosidases, sulfatases, phosphatases, ribonuclease, deoxyribonuclease). The lytic activity of these bodies prompted the name *lysosome*.

The search for lysosomes in intact cells led to the realization that they are present in nearly all animal cell types. Lysosomes are small (0.25 to 0.5 μ), usually round bodies (Fig. 1-24, A) filled with fine granular material contained within a single membrane (Fig. 1-25, A). Particles and stacks of dense laminae may be present as well. In fact, it was soon realized that the appearance of lysosomes varied considerably, depending upon their most recent lytic or digestive activity, necessitating criteria other than morphology for their positive identification. Detection of characteristic enzymes by histochemical means has been employed widely, at both the light and electron microscope levels. For example, a lysosome may be identified in tissue sections on the basis of its acid phosphatase content. Acid phosphatase activity is revealed by the presence of an opaque lead product resulting from the Gomori procedure; lysosomes so treated appear as darkly stained granules. Lysosomes also are identified by their ability to take up vital dyes (such as acridine orange) or drugs which can be traced intracellularly by fluorescence microscopy (Fig. 1-24, B). Lysosomes are most accurately referred to as *dense bodies* in conventional electron micrographs in which positive identification by histochemical or other means has not been made.

Functions. The lysosomes perform a variety of important roles for the cell. Intracellular digestion, summarized in Figure 1-26, is one of the most important. Lysis takes place within the confines of membrane-enclosed digestion vacuoles, with no visible damage to the cytoplasm outside because the lysosomal membrane prevents enzyme release. An example of intracellular digestion is provided by the polymorphonuclear leukocyte. Its numerous granules visible in the light microscope are in fact lysosomes. When a white cell engulfs bacteria, these granules cluster around the newly formed vacuole, fuse with its limiting membrane and discharge their content of destructive enzymes into the bacteria-laden vacuole.

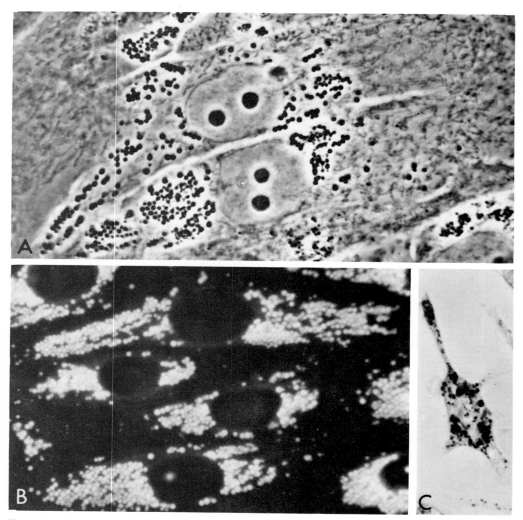

FIG. 1-24. Lysosomes. *A*, as they appear in the phase contrast microscope in living monkey kidney cells. The lysosomes are the small black granules near the nuclei and may be compared to the light gray filamentous mitochondria in the more peripheral cytoplasm. ×1200. *B*, as they appear in the fluorescence microscope. The brightly fluorescing granules are lysosomes which have taken up the fluorescent compound methylcholanthrene administered to similar cells in culture. Nuclei and mitochondria do not fluoresce. ×550. *C*, following the Gomori method, the lysosomes appear as blackened granules in the light microscope. They are "stained" black by the deposition of a reaction product, lead sulfide, which results from the presence of an enzyme (acid phosphatase) characteristic of lysosomes. Mouse macrophage. ×1130. (From Allison, A. 1967 Sci. Amer., vol. 217 (May), p. 62.)

During starvation the lysosomal system aids in cell survival by the sequestration of organelles for digestion (autophagy), thus providing essential nutrients for continued cell life. This mechanism also ensures turnover of organelles or removal of injured organelles. Substances in excess are digested by the lysosomal system; for example, droplets of hormone which are no longer needed are broken down by lysosomes of the same cell.

Injurious substances which may or may not be digestible are sequestered within the lysosomal system. Cells exposed to silica or

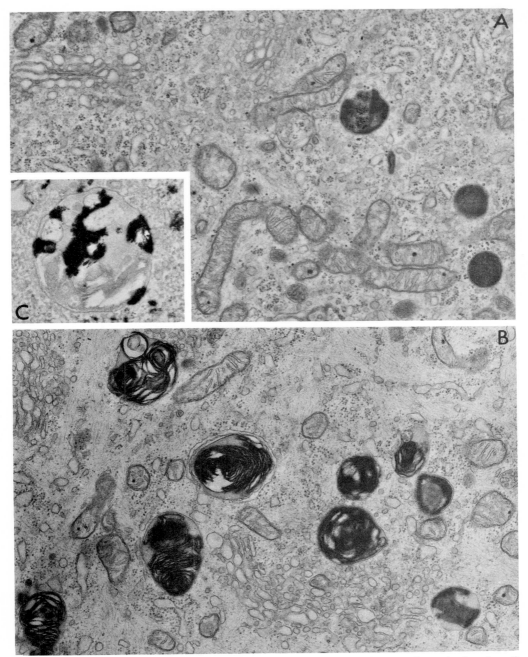

FIG. 1-25. Electron micrographs of lysosomes. *A*, scattered among the granular endoplasmic reticulum, mitochondria and Golgi complex are dense bodies. In normal tissue, dense bodies appear homogeneous or contain particles and stacked membrane-like structures. If the cultured nervous tissue illustrated here is given a tranquilizer, chlorpromazine, the dense bodies increase in number and size and take on a more heterogeneous appearance (*B*), as is typical for lysosomes following a variety of treatments. *C*, a chlorpromazine-induced dense body following the Gomori method as adapted for electron microscopy. The presence of dense patches of reaction product allow this body to be identified as a lysosome. *A* and *B*, ×24,000; *C*, ×34,500. (*B* and *C* from Brosnan, C. F., Bunge, M. B., and Murray, M. R. 1970 J. Neuropath. Exp. Neurol., vol. 29, p. 337.)

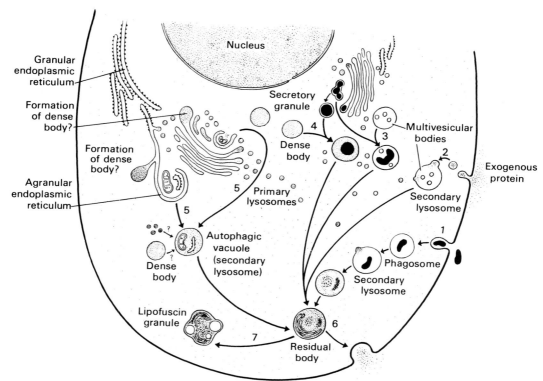

Fig. 1-26. Summary of pathways in the lysosomal or digestive system. A foreign body such as a bacterium is taken into the cell by invagination of the surface membrane, which then pinches off (endocytosis) (*1*). A *phagosome* thus formed acquires lytic enzymes by fusion with *primary lysosomes*, i.e., lysosomes which have not yet engaged in enzymatic activity. The resulting body is a *secondary lysosome*, i.e., a lysosome in which lytic activity is in progress or has occurred. Exogenous protein macromolecules may be taken up by the cell by means of small pinocytosis vesicles which form from surface membrane, break away and flow into the cytoplasm to merge with multivesicular bodies (*2*). Again, necessary enzymes for processing this material are brought to the multivesicular bodies by primary lysosomes. The digestion of endogenous protein (such as excess secretion granules) may occur in multivesicular bodies or dense bodies (*3, 4*). Bodies that contain identifiable organelles (such as mitochondria or granular endoplasmic reticulum) are known as *autophagic vacuoles* or cytolysomes; these bodies are thought to arise by engulfment of organelles by a cisterna of membrane (*5*). More work is needed to know whether the enzymes are furnished by the cisterna or by fusion with primary lysosomes. The structure resulting from the formation of all these *digestion vacuoles* is the *residual body*, which looks like a dense body filled with dense particles and whorls of membrane-like structures termed "myelin figures." In some cases, residual body contents may be released from the cell by fusion of the limiting membrane with the cell surface membrane (*6*). Or the residual body may be retained, participating over and over in digestive activity, growing larger and more heterogeneous in content and becoming in time a *lipofuscin granule* (*7*). It is believed that the lysosomal enzymes are produced on ribosomes, after which they are channeled into the granular endoplasmic reticulum and packaged in the Golgi region into primary lysosomes (the small vesicle or the larger dense body type). (Diagram based upon papers by Novikoff and co-workers and Farquhar and collaborators.)

asbestos particles, for instance, are seen in the electron microscope to have lysosomes filled with the dense spheres or rods characteristic of these substances. The list of compounds known to increase or decrease the permeability of the lysosomal membrane is growing; as examples, it is known that cortisone decreases the permeability, whereas vitamin A has the opposite effect. When a cell is deprived of oxygen or is damaged in some other way, the lysosomal membrane becomes more permeable or ruptures, thus allowing enzyme release with ensuing digestion of the cell (autolysis). This is the mechanism underlying the regression of the tadpole tail during metamorphosis, for example. Important questions under investigation today are whether mitosis is triggered by lysosomal digestion of a substance which normally represses division and whether certain types of cancer are due in part to chromosomal breakage by the lysosomal enzyme, deoxyribonuclease.

Related to the lysosomal population are *multivesicular bodies*, membrane-bound bodies containing small membrane-bound vesicles. Transitional forms between these organelles and dense bodies are often seen. Histochemical procedures have demonstrated that multivesicular bodies contain some acid hydrolases, notably acid phosphatase. Multivesicular bodies may receive exogenous or endogenous protein for breakdown (Fig. 1-26). Small primary lysosomes which bring enzymes to the multivesicular body may be covered with evenly spaced bristle-like structures. These vesicles are designated *coated vesicles*.

Lipofuscin pigment is now thought to be contained within residual bodies, the end points in the lysosomal digestive system, because of the discovery of associated hydrolytic enzymes. Not all of the cellular material taken up by lysosomes is digestible, and it is some of this residue that is transformed into pigment. In the electron microscope, the lipofuscin pigment granules are very heterogeneous in appearance (Fig. 1-27), often containing lipid droplets or vacuoles and matrix substance (which contains the lytic activity) as well as the dense pigment. In the light microscope, they are seen as light brown granules in unstained preparations, as darkened bodies after staining with fat-soluble dyes and as fluorescent particles in ultraviolet light. The pig-

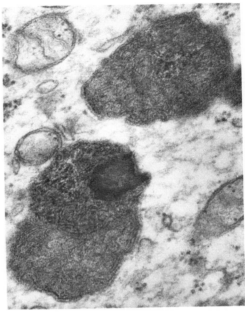

FIG. 1-27. Lipofuscin pigment bodies. In untreated but aging animals, dense bodies may become markedly enlarged, very irregular in contour and highly heterogeneous in appearance, at which point they are known as lipofuscin bodies or granules. They often contain a wealth of thin, curving, dense bands, as in this figure, and a large, light vacuole. Mature rabbit nerve cell. ×58,000. (Courtesy of Dr. Virginia Tennyson.)

ment granules increase with age, especially in brain and heart tissues.

Bodies which are fairly similar to lysosomes in appearance but different in enzymatic content have been found in mammalian liver and kidney cells. Termed *microbodies* by Rhodin in 1954, they resemble dense bodies which may contain a core, crystalloid or plate-like structure. Like lysosomes, they are limited by a single membrane and measure 0.3 to 0.6 μ in diameter. Microbodies contain enzymes which are necessary for the production and destruction of hydrogen peroxide. Investigators now prefer the name "peroxisomes" to better describe these bodies in terms of their enzymatic content.

Central Body, Centrioles. The *central body* or *centrosome* is a specialized zone of cytoplasm that contains the *centrioles*. The

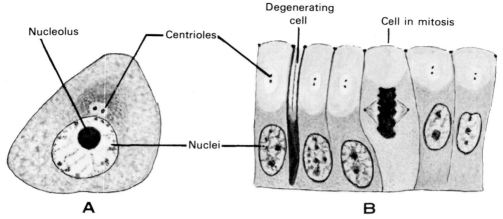

FIG. 1-28. *A*, central body in an interstitial cell of human testis. *B*, centrioles in columnar epithelial cells of human stomach. (*A*, redrawn after Petersen; *B*, redrawn after Zimmerman).

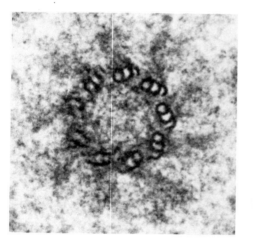

FIG. 1-29. Centriole sectioned perpendicular to its length. The "wall" of the centriole is seen here as a circle of nine units, each composed of three united tubule-like structures. Radiating from these units (resembling a pinwheel) are nine densities called pericentriolar satellites. Electron micrograph of rat ovarian follicle cell. ×140,000. (Courtesy of Dr. Daniel Szollosi.)

central body usually lies close to or indents the nucleus (Figs. 1-22 and 1-23), although its position varies somewhat in different cell types (Fig. 1-28). In glandular epithelial cells it is situated between the nucleus and the luminal surface. The central body is probably present in almost all mammalian cells but is often difficult to demonstrate. It has been observed in living cells, and it can be stained by iron hematoxylin in fixed preparations. Although it is most distinct during cell division, it can be demonstrated during the intermitotic stage. Its most constant feature is the presence of two sharply staining granules or centrioles, together called the *diplosome*. This organelle is self-replicating, as is discussed in Chapter 2. The cytoplasm surrounding the centrioles is more gelatinous and appears more homogeneous than that in other parts of the cell.

Scrutiny of the centrioles in the electron microscope has led to the following information. Each centriole is oriented perpendicular to its partner. It is a cylindrical organelle, 0.3 to 0.5 μ in length and about 0.15 μ in diameter, apparently closed at one end. The wall of the cylinder is composed of nine evenly spaced, longitudinally oriented, parallel units embedded in a dense material. Each unit consists of three tubular structures joined together. When the centriole is sectioned perpendicular to its long axis, the tubular units are seen as circles (Fig. 1-29). When sectioned parallel to its long axis, the tubules may be visualized as linear elements (Fig. 1-23). Microtubules radiate from the area around the centriole or from closely associated dense clumps of material, which are called *pericentriolar satellites* or *bodies* (Figs. 1-22 and 1-29).

Functions. As is indicated later, the central body has been clearly associated with the process of mitotic cell division, particularly in the organization of the spindle elements (microtubules). In the nondividing cell, it serves as a center about which other cytoplasmic organelles such as the Golgi apparatus are polarized and, as such, it is termed *cell center, centrosphere* or *cytocentrum* (Figs. 1-10, 1-22 and 1-23). In addition, a centriole may migrate near the cell surface where it becomes a *basal body* (kinetosome) which gives rise to a motile cilium or flagellum. The mechanisms by which the centrioles exert their important organizational capabilities are not understood.

Mitochondria. In the 1890s, Altmann and, subsequently, Benda devised improved histological techniques which preserved and stained a population of small cytoplasmic bodies which came to be known as mitochondria (Gr., *mitos*, a thread, + *chondros*, a grain). These bodies are visible as granules, rods or filaments in both living (by phase microscopy) and fixed (after special staining) protoplasm. Mitochondria may be identified in the living cell by applying supravital dyes, particularly Janus green B. An enzyme present only in mitochondria (cytochrome oxidase) is able to maintain the Janus green in its oxidized or colored form, while in the surrounding cytoplasm it is reduced to a colorless compound. The granules may measure 0.2 to 1 μ or more in diameter, whereas the filamentous mitochondria may be 2 to 4 μ long or, in some cases, up to 10 to 12 μ in length. Mitochondria are present in almost all cell types. Any given cell type as a rule contains a characteristic number of these organelles; a rat liver cell is purported to contain 800 to 1000 mitochondria. The number of mitochondria per cell may be as low as 20 (in sperm) and as high as 500,000 (in giant amebae).

The very plastic and sensitive nature of mitochondria has been realized from observations made on living cells grown in tissue culture. Here the mitochondria are seen to be in constant agitation—expanding and contracting, fusing, dividing and changing location. They often react more rapidly than any other cell organelle to temperature, metabolic, pH or osmotic changes. Studies of mitochondrial fractions indicate that mitochondria undergo swelling and contraction phases related to their physiological activity. Despite these known perturbations, mitochondria appear remarkably consistent in form and in position and orientation in some cell types in situ. In epithelial cells, mitochondria are often polarized such that their long axes are oriented in the direction of the secretory or transport process (see Fig. 1-9).

Electron microscopic studies (beginning with Sjöstrand and Palade) indicated that the mitochrondria are very uniquely constructed. Each mitochondrion is bounded by two membranes. The inner membrane lies closely apposed to the outer one and, in addition, is thrown into folds (*cristae*) which protrude inward (Figs. 1–10 and 1–30). Depending upon the cell type, and correlating with physiologic activity, the cristae vary in number and form (folds, as mentioned, or tubules or villi) and arrangement. They may or may not extend all of the way across the mitochondrion interior, and they are oriented either perpendicular (in most cases) or parallel to the long axis. Whereas these variations in cristae exist, the basic plan of the mitochondrion is nonetheless strikingly similar in all animal forms, ranging from protozoa to mammals. The cristae provide an increase in membrane surface area. An approximate calculation made for the liver cell suggests that the surface area of all of the mitochondrial membrane in that cell is 10 times greater than the surface area of the cell itself. In contrast with the outer membrane, the inner membrane on the matrix side is coated with *elementary particles* (or *inner membrane subunits*), about 90 A in diameter and connected to the membrane by means of a stalk 35 A wide and 40 A long (Fig. 1-31).

The interior not occupied by cristae is filled with *matrix* substance, a finely granular

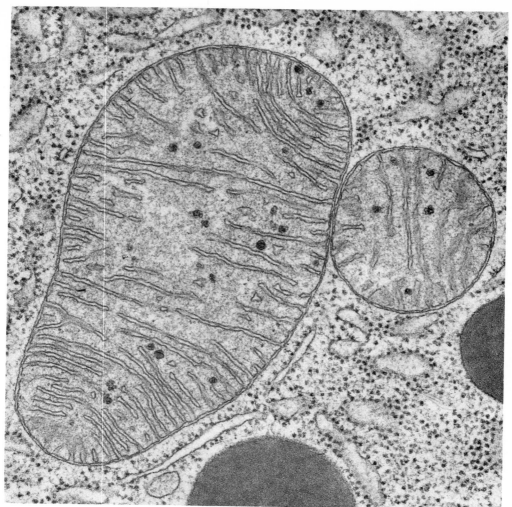

FIG. 1-30. This electron micrograph illustrates the morphological features of mitochondria. The inner membrane, unlike the outer one, is thrown into folds (cristae) which may span the interior. Within the mitochondrion matrix, which fills the area not occupied by cristae, are scattered dense granules. Bat pancreas. ×64,000. (From Porter, K. R., and Bonneville, M. A. 1968 Fine Structure of Cells and Tissues, 3rd ed. Lea & Febiger, Philadelphia.)

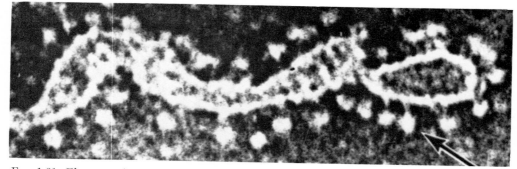

FIG. 1-31. Electron micrograph of a mitochondrial crista, negatively stained. The outer (or matrix) surface of each crista is covered by a regular array of "elementary" particles which are connected by means of slender stalks (arrow). Isolated beef heart mitochondria. ×500,000. (From Fernández-Morán, H., Oda, T., Blair, P. V., and Green, D. R. 1964 J. Cell Biol., vol. 22, p. 63.)

material. Highly dense matrix granules (300 to 500 A) may be found as well (Fig. 1-30). Their presence and size depends upon the metabolic state and type of cell. These are now known to be, in part, binding sites for ions, particularly cations such as Ca^{++}. Also in the matrix are delicate circular strands of DNA about 20 A in diameter, and RNA which is in part localized to granules slightly smaller than ribosomes. Cytologists, who had puzzled for years over the seemingly autonomous behavior of mitochondria, found in the discovery of mitochondrial DNA an explanation for their ability to divide as separate genetic units. The presence of nucleic acid and protein synthesis within mitochondria also explained their ability to replicate themselves by elongation and division. This self-replication provides for a constant number of mitochondria within the cell and within each daughter cell after division.

Functions. Like some of the other cytoplasmic organelles, mitochondria perform diversified functions. Most importantly, they are the chief source of energy in the cell. During cell respiration, enzymatic breakdown, mostly of carbohydrates but also of fats and amino acids, yields CO_2, water and energy as end products. The energy freed in this oxidation of foodstuffs is converted into phosphate bond energy. This energy, bound in adenosinetriphosphate (*ATP*), is required in many different processes, including transport of ions across the cell membrane, protein synthesis and muscle contraction.

The formation of ATP by the breakdown of glucose involves three different mitochondrial systems. The initial degradation of glucose occurs in the cytoplasm outside the mitochondria. The resulting product, a 3-carbon compound (pyruvate), enters the mitochondrion where it is processed by a sequence of enzymes known as the *Krebs citric acid cycle.* Liberated hydrogens are fed into a complex chain of flavoproteins and cytochromes called the *electron transport system* or *respiratory chain.* Eventually the

hydrogen combines with oxygen which is thereby reduced to water. At three points along this respiratory chain, sufficient energy becomes available from the transfer of electrons to form ATP by the addition of phosphate to adenosine*di*phosphate (*phosphorylation*). Because oxygen is the oxidizing agent at the terminus of the respiratory chain and the phosphorylation apparatus is intimately *coupled* to this chain, the process is termed *oxidative phosphorylation.*

The respiratory and phosphorylation systems are found in highly ordered recurring assemblies in or bound to the mitochondrial inner membrane. The elementary particles mentioned earlier are thought to contain phosphorylation factors. That the membranes hold these essential enzyme systems is reflected in the fact that, in cells requiring more energy, such as insect flight or mammalian cardiac muscle, the cristae are much more densely packed. In such cells, mitochondria also are more numerous and are situated close to the energy-requiring structures.

Contractile protein has been found recently in mitochondria, providing an explanation for the contraction observed earlier by light microscopists. Mitochondrial contraction, known to be related to respiratory activity, is thought to aid in mitochondrial movement and in the exchange of substances such as ATP and ions with the cytoplasm. Additional functions of mitochondria now include the accumulation of ions as well as the synthesis of nucleic acids and proteins. These synthetic pathways and the Krebs cycle reactions probably take place in the matrix, in contrast with the respiratory, phosphorylating, active transport and contractile processes, which occur in relation to the mitochondrial inner membrane.

Filaments. Slender threads or *filaments* occur in the cytoplasm of many cells. As a rule, they range from 30 to 100 A in diameter and are of indeterminate length. Whether the filaments are randomly scattered through-

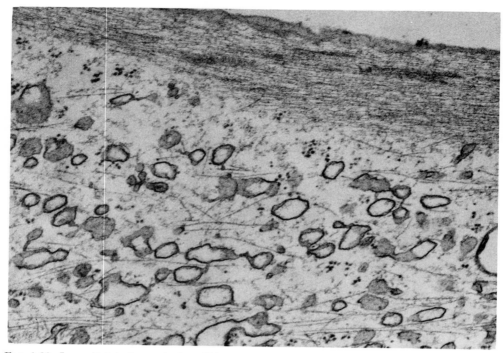

Fig. 1-32. Immediately beneath the cell border (which is shown at *upper right*) is a band of closely packed filaments. Filaments also are scattered throughout other areas of the cytoplasm of this cell grown in culture. ×42,500. (Courtesy of Drs. M. Bunge and D. Bray.)

out the cytoplasm, clustered into wisplike bundles, or aggregated into a meshwork depends upon the cell type. When the filaments occur in bundles, they are visible in the light microscope after staining as *fibrils*, but visualization of individual filaments depends upon the resolution of the electron microscope (Fig. 1-32).

Study of motile cells in the living state shows relatively clear pseudopods or a clear, thin, peripheral rim of cytoplasm. This is referred to as *ectoplasm*, which is more viscous or gelled than the rest of the cytoplasm. It is now known that these areas are full of filaments and that the apparent clarity is due to the exclusion of other organelles from these regions. Filaments in parallel array form the cores of the strikingly regular, slender microvilli of the intestinal epithelium. In nerve cells, filaments are a regular component (along with microtubules; see below) of the fiber where they lie parallel

to the long axis and in the larger cell bodies where they are loosely aggregated into gracile bundles. A narrow band of filaments just beneath the cell membrane is a feature of the cleavage furrow of dividing cells. Filaments of similar dimensions fill smooth muscle cells and, along with "thick" filaments of myosin, form the stout parallel arrays in striated muscle cells. Whereas the thin filaments of striated muscle are known to be composed of actin, it is not yet known if all filaments of similar thickness consist of this or a closely related protein. The variable diameter alone would suggest that the component protein differs. Recent investigations have revealed, however, the widespread occurrence of actomyosin-like proteins in a variety of sources, including the protozoa and also metazoan embryonic and cultured cells.

Functions. The thin filaments of muscle cells have been known for some time to participate in contraction. Evidence is accumulating that, in other cell types as well, the filaments form the structural basis for gelation or contraction of the protoplasm (as in the cleavage furrow). Various protoplasmic movements, including cytoplasmic streaming, probably also rely upon filaments. Filaments are considered to serve as a cytoskeleton; e.g., in supporting the microvilli, as mentioned above. Recent studies suggest that filaments are important also in the formation of microvilli by providing elongating cores around which they are molded. Thus, filaments function in contractile processes, in various types of protoplasmic movement, and in changes in cell shape as well as in the maintenance of cell form. More work is needed to understand the underlying mechanisms in nonmuscle cells: do the filaments themselves contract or do they act by sliding past one another or by interreacting with microtubules, as has been suggested?

Microtubules. One of the most exciting developments in very recent years has been the discovery of the widespread occurrence and importance in cells of long, slender, cylindrical structures, the *microtubules*. Their discovery depended not only upon the resolution of the electron microscope but also upon improved preservation by means of glutaraldehyde fixation. Microtubules vary somewhat in diameter from 180 to 300 A, but they usually measure about 240 A, and they have been followed for several microns in thin sections. They are straight or slightly curving, suggesting a rigid structure (see Figs. 1-22 and 1-23). When sectioned at right angles to its long axis, the microtubule appears as a circle composed of, on the average, 13 globular subunits, each about 40 to 50 A in diameter.

Microtubule proteins from diversified sources have been found to be quite similar in their sequences of amino acids and also to closely resemble the muscle protein, actin. Like actin, microtubule proteins have binding sites for nucleotides. The fact that these proteins also contain specific binding sites for colchicine explains the disruption of microtubules in the presence of this agent. This effect on microtubules accounts for the action of colchicine in blocking mitosis. Microtubules found in different locations, e.g., spindle, flagellum, vary in sensitivity to colchicine, pointing to at least subtle differences in the constituent proteins.

During cell division, microtubules increase greatly in number, to as many as 3000 per cell, to form the mitotic spindle (which is described in Chapter 2). In nondividing cells, microtubules are scattered throughout the cytoplasm. They may converge on the central body (Figs. 1-22 and 1-23) and are found in units of three (triplets) forming the framework of the basal body and the centriole (Fig. 1-29). Microtubules form the cores of cilia, flagella and sperm tails where they are often organized into 9 doublets encircling 2 centrally situated microtubules (see Fig. 4-8). During sperm maturation, hundreds of microtubules are clustered in a very orderly fashion around the nucleus at a time when the nucleus begins to elongate. During the development of chick lens epithelium, when cells may undergo a 4-fold increase in length, microtubules become prominent in the cortical cytoplasm, lying parallel to the axis of elongation. Microtubules are a regular component of the extensions of nerve cells. One of the most striking examples of microtubule arrays was discovered in a spherical protozoan, *Actinosphaerium*. Radiating from the cell body, which is about 100 μ in diameter, are numerous long, needle-like extensions or axopodia, often more than 400 μ long and only 5 to 10 μ in diameter. Each axopodium contains as many as 500 microtubules in a highly ordered arrangement. When these microtubules are disrupted, the axopodia collapse.

Functions. Findings like those just mentioned have led to the conclusion that microtubules play a role in maintaining cell shape. Their prominence and orientation during periods of changing cell shape have suggested that they are also active in changing cell form as well. If microtubules are experimentally disassembled during such a period, normal development may be arrested. For instance, disruption of microtubules in the sea urchin gastrula causes cells to round up and blocks the development of the primary mesenchyme. As components of the spindle, cilia and flagella, they not only provide a cytoskeletal framework but also may contribute to the mechanisms by which movement is accomplished. Structural and functional relationships between microtubules and filaments are being explored. Definitive proof of their participation in cytoplasmic streaming, positioning of cytoplasmic organelles and transport of materials throughout the cytoplasm awaits further study.

Cell Membrane. A membrane, the *plasma membrane* or *plasmalemma*, surrounds the cell, separating the cell contents from the external environment. In this important position it regulates the passage of materials into and out of the cell. This membrane, 70 to 110 A in thickness, is too thin to be resolved by the light microscope. But it may be visualized if in an histological section it slants (and is thereby obliquely sectioned) and thus occupies an area wider than its true thickness. Also, stain taken up by an exterior adherent coating on the membrane may enhance its visibility. Even when not directly visualized, the presence of a cell membrane can be inferred from observations on cells during micromanipulation, when cytoplasm spills out if the membrane is ruptured, and following alterations of the environmental tonicity. When red blood cells are placed in a hypotonic fluid or in water, they swell as a result of the action of osmotically active components of the cytoplasm. They may in fact burst, losing their contents (in this case, hemoglobin).

By treating red blood cells in the manner just described, it is possible to obtain a relatively pure preparation of plasma membrane for biochemical analysis. Such preparations contain about 35% lipid, including phospholipids and cholesterol, 60% protein and a small amount of carbohydrate. From these data and from estimates of the surface areas of red cells, it is possible to calculate that there are enough lipid molecules to cover each cell twice. This observation, as well as physical measurements of membrane thickness, birefringence, X-ray diffraction and surface tension, has lent support to a model of membrane structure proposed by Danielli and Davson in 1935. This model depicts the plasma membrane as a double layer or bimolecular leaflet of lipids sandwiched between two protein coats (Fig. 1-33). The phospholipid molecules of the membrane have both hydrophobic ends, where the fatty acids are located, and hydrophilic ends, where the phosphate groups are attached. It is assumed that the hydrophobic ends appose each other in the middle of the membrane, whereas the hydrophilic ends lie next to the enveloping protein layers. The presence of a continuous hydrophobic region could explain the low permeability of many membranes to water-soluble compounds and their high permeability to lipid-soluble materials.

When the cell membrane is sectioned at right angles to its surface and examined in the electron microscope at lower magnifications, it appears as a dense line. High magnifications and staining make it possible to demonstrate that this line is, in fact, a pair of thinner dense lines separated by a light inner zone, all roughly of similar thickness (Fig. 1-34). This tripartite or *trilaminar* structure (termed "unit membrane" by Robertson) seemed to fit the Danielli-Davson model very well; the dense laminae corresponded to the two protein layers and the light intermediate stratum represented the bimolecular leaflet of lipid (Fig. 1-33). The fact that many of the intracellular membranes also exhibited this trilaminar structure suggested that this was a basic design common to all membranes.

It seems clear, however, that a membrane with continuous lipid leaflets could not

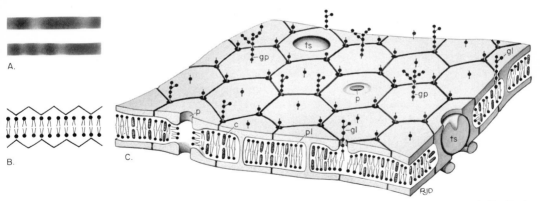

FIG. 1-33. The appearance of the cell membrane in electron micrographs is portrayed in *A*. In *B*, the Davson-Danielli model is presented. The middle of the bimolecular leaflet, in which the hydrophobic ends of the phospholipids are apposed, corresponds to the lighter regions in electron micrographs. Proteins coat both sides of the lipid bilayer. *C* depicts additional features of membrane structure. The bimolecular leaflet contains not only phospholipids (*pl*) but also cholesterol (*c*) and glycolipids (*gl*). Protein on the membrane outer surface is shown to be composed of hexagonal subunits some of which, by reason of their carbohydrate components, are glycoproteins (*gp*). Some of the carbohydrate moieties contain end groups which are negatively charged and provide the cell surface with specific properties. (At many sites, only the base of the carbohydrate is shown.) The membrane contains several special sites: pores (*p*) which may admit ions of certain size and transport sites (*ts*) which either (1) facilitate movement of metabolites across the membrane or (2) utilize energy in transporting ions against a concentration gradient.

provide for all of the diverse functions that membranes are known to perform. It is now generally believed that, within the basic membrane structure described above, there are scattered sites which provide for special membrane activities as, for example, the transport of sugars and amino acids across the membrane. At these sites, protein components may penetrate the lipid interface of the membrane (Fig. 1-33). An especially intriguing site is the protein-phospholipid complex, the *sodium pump*, which uses the energy of ATP to move K^+ into and Na^+ out of the cell: both ions are thus transported from regions of low concentration "uphill" into regions of high concentration. This energy-requiring process is termed *active transport*.

Membranes also are known to vary in protein content. In fact, the suggestion has been made that the protein content of membranes provides a rough index of their overall metabolic activity. Membranes such as myelin membrane with a low protein content (about

20%) have little associated enzymatic activity and function passively in influencing electrical properties of nerve fibers. Mitochondrial membranes, on the other hand, contain dozens of enzymes and are composed of about 65% protein.

Certain membranes within the cell, such as those in mitochondria, may have an organization fundamentally different from that of plasma membrane described above. Rather than being organized as a continuous bimolecular sheet of lipids surrounded by protein, these membranes may instead be constructed from globular subunits, each composed of protein and lipid, held together along their edges like pieces in a patchwork quilt. This more recently developed concept has been termed the subunit or globule hypothesis of membrane structure.

On the exterior of the cell, appended to the surface of the cell membrane, is a layer of material containing substantial amounts of carbohydrates which are usually associated with lipids (glycolipids) or proteins (glyco-

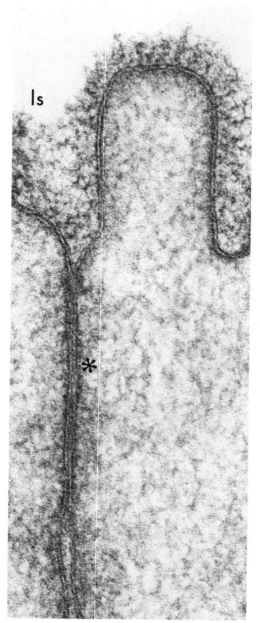

FIG. 1-34. In the digestive tract the luminal surface (*ls*) of the absorbing cells is covered with highly regular finger-like protuberances called microvilli, one of which is pictured here. This electron micrograph clearly illustrates the trilaminar nature of the bounding cell membrane and shows the largely amorphous, "fuzzy" material coating the luminal surface of the cell. Along the lateral cell surfaces the bounding membranes may be more closely apposed than usual (as at *). ×180,-

proteins). This coat or *glycocalyx* may be very thick, as over the microvilli of epithelial cells of the intestinal mucosa (Fig. 1-34), or extremely thin, as in the membranes of the myelin sheath, but nevertheless it appears to be quite universally present on cell surfaces. Ionized groups on the terminal units of the saccharide chains (e.g., sialic acid) give many cell surfaces a negative charge (Fig. 1-33). The presence of the glycocalyx and the negative charges undoubtedly contribute to the very consistent and regular spacing of at least 200 A which occurs between membranes of adjacent cells.

Functions. From the above discussion it will be apparent that there may well be as many different kinds of membrane as there are different kinds of cells and cell organelles. The importance of membrane within the cell is indicated by the fact that many of the cytoplasmic organelles (endoplasmic reticulum, Golgi apparatus, lysosomal bodies, mitochondria) and the nuclear envelope are constructed of or bound by membrane. The intracellular membranes serve vital functions in segregating the cytoplasm into compartments for the storage of formed products or the control of interactions of substances in their proper order and in increasing the surface area participating in metabolic processes.

At the cell surface, the plasma membrane provides for the selection of what enters and what leaves the cell. In addition, in nerve and muscle cells the plasma membrane contains mechanisms to allow for sudden changes in ion permeability in response to changes in its electrical potential or configuration. It also is able to alter its properties in response to hormones and neurotransmitters (discussed in Chapter 10). Its surface characteristics will determine how it relates to the surface on which it rests, and how it reacts (by adhesion, repulsion or fusion) with other cells. The content and the configura-

000. (From Porter, K. R., and Bonneville, M. A. 1968 Fine Structure of Cells and Tissues, 3rd ed. Lea & Febiger, Philadelphia.)

tion of the surface molecules are important factors in the immunological properties of the cell. The membrane may, in fact, be the most complex macromolecular aggregate in the cell, and the understanding of its structure and function may be expected to challenge biologists for many decades.

Cytoplasmic Inclusions. The cytoplasm of the cell may contain numerous inclusions of substances which are usually in the nature of raw food materials or the stored products of the cell's metabolic activity. Thus, deposits of proteins, fats and carbohydrates are characteristic features in certain cells. The storage of *glycogen* by cells of liver and muscle are the outstanding examples of carbohydrate storage (Fig. 1-9, *D*). Glycogen is a polymer formed from the carbohydrate glucose. It is stained magenta by the periodic acid-Schiff reaction or Best's carmine method. In the electron microscope, glycogen (after lead staining) appears as scattered or clustered small dense particles, 150 to 450 A (Fig. 1-35). Although fat cells are the chief sites of *lipid* storage, many other cell types store some lipid in the form of droplets of varying size. If frozen sections are stained with specific fat-soluble dyes or if the tissue is fixed in osmium tetroxide, the lipid droplets are retained and appear black (Fig. 1-1, *C*). In electron micrographs they appear as homogeneous spheres of varying density. Examples of the products of cell activity are *yolk granules* and *secretory granules*.

Another type of cytoplasmic inclusion is the *pigment granule*. Pigment granules possess color without staining. The occurrence of *lipofuscin* is considered above in the section describing lysosomes. Certain cells, melanocytes, contain dark brown or black granules which are composed of the pigment *melanin*. In the electron microscope, these granules appear as homogeneous dense bodies. In man they are present in the eye and in the skin (as described in Chapter 14).

GENERAL CONSIDERATIONS

Cell Form and Cell Size. The cells of the animal body show a wide variation in size

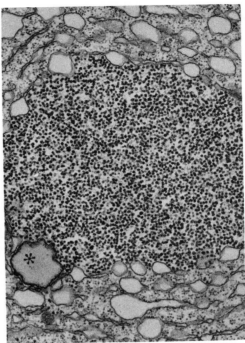

Fig. 1-35. An accumulation of glycogen particles in an X-irradiated neuron. These particles may be compared to the smaller ribosomes scattered among the swollen elements of endoplasmic reticulum. A lipid droplet is marked by an asterisk. Electron micrograph of rat nervous tissue in culture. ×25,000. (From Masurovsky, E. B., Bunge, M. B., and Bunge, R. P. 1967 J. Cell Biol., vol. 32, p. 467.)

and form, coincident with their adaptation to perform a diversity of specific functions (Fig. 1-36). The tissue cells which have acquired a fixed location in the body become polyhedral, columnar, flat (pavement), fusiform or spindle-shaped, and they may retain a smooth contour or send out numerous processes. The nerve cell with its processes sometimes several feet in length is perhaps the most aberrant type. The laws which control or limit cell size as well as body size are not well understood. Some groups of animals have larger cells than do others, but it does not follow that small animals have small cells and large animals large cells. The size of the individual is in general determined by the number of its cells, not by their size.

Cell Life and Cell Death. Biologists

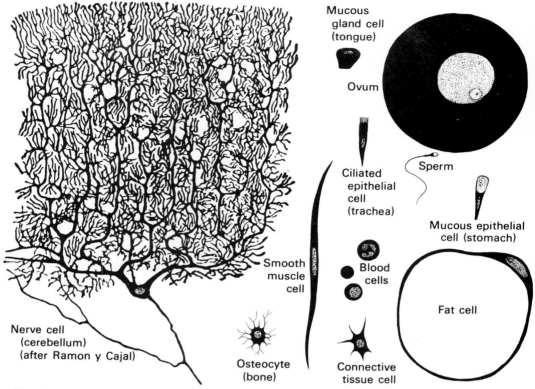

FIG. 1-36. Cells vary widely in size and shape and their nuclei occupy differing positions, as depicted diagrammatically here. All of the cells are drawn to scale (100 μ = nearly 1½ inches), with the measurements based on data from humans.

generally believe that living matter is constructed according to the same basic principles as is the physical world in which it exists. Considering the tenets of physics, particularly of thermodynamics, living systems might be expected to gradually decrease in complexity, for energy is always involved in the maintenance of high degrees of organization. Yet the trend in the evolution of living systems is toward more and more complexity.

The key to this riddle is, of course, the continual input into living systems of free energy from the sun. This energy was initially used in the synthesis of the simplest of organic substances and is now continuously used to maintain and extend the organization of living things. Many higher organisms do not, of course, use the energy of the sun directly but feed on lower forms that do.

The process of cell growth can occur with remarkable rapidity, for the chemical reactions within the cell are efficiently catalyzed by the cell *enzymes*. The process of the construction of macromolecules, which is the process of growth, is called *anabolism*. The cell also uses mechanisms of *catabolism* for the breakdown of its components. These catabolic mechanisms can release stored energy for use by the cell, as in the breakdown of fatty acids, and are a necessary part of the ongoing activities of the cell. Both anabolism and catabolism are important for maintaining the proper functional levels of materials within the cell. Several important diseases, called storage diseases, result not from the lack of anabolic activity within the cell but from the failure of the proper enzymatic degradation of cellular constituents. In these conditions, specific cell components accumulate within the cell in abnormal amounts and in time seriously interfere with cell function.

Cell death is an integral part of the growth of tissues and organs. During the development of some tissues, large numbers of cells may die. In these cases there is an initial overproduction of certain cell types, and only those required for the functional needs of the tissue will survive. Local cell death (*necrosis*) occurs normally in the body, or may be the result of influences which cause disease, such as trauma and inflammation. Morphologically, necrotic tissue can be recognized by the altered structure of the cells and intercellular substance. Coagulation of proteins takes place in the cytoplasm, the latter appearing flocculated or in the nature of a fibrous network. The cells appear fused by the obliteration of cellular boundaries. Or the cell may liquefy, swell and finally burst (cytolysis), the liquefaction being often preceded by the appearance of numerous fat granules. These proteolytic processes are in many cases due to intracellular enzymes liberated after the death of the cell (autolysis). The nucleus, likewise, shows various forms of structural disintegration. The chromatin may contract into a dense, deeply staining irregular mass (pyknosis), it may fragment into a number of small pieces with obliteration of nuclear boundary (karyorrhexis), or it may gradually disappear, as evidenced by the loss of its staining capacity (karyolysis).

REFERENCES

TECHNIQUES

ALLFREY, V. 1959 The isolation of subcellular components. *In* The Cell; Biochemistry, Physiology, Morphology (Brachet, J., and Mirsky, A. E., editors), vol. I, pp. 193–290. Academic Press, New York.

BAKER, J. R. 1966 Cytological Technique; The Principles Underlying Routine Methods, ed. 5. John Wiley & Sons, Inc., New York.

BARKA, T., AND ANDERSON, P. J. 1963 Histochemistry: Theory, Practice, and Bibliography. Hoeber Medical Division, Harper & Row, Publishers, New York.

COONS, A. H. 1956 Histochemistry with labeled antibody. Int. Rev. Cytol., vol. 5, pp. 1–23.

HAMA, K., AND PORTER, K. R. 1969 An application of high voltage electron microscopy to the study of biological materials. High voltage electron microscopy. J. Microscop., vol. 8, pp. 149–158.

LEBLOND, C. P., AND WARREN, K. B. (editors) 1965 The Use of Radioautography in Investigating Protein Synthesis. Academic Press, New York.

PEARSE, A. G. E. 1968 Histochemistry, Theoretical and Applied, ed. 3. J. & A. Churchill Ltd., London.

PEASE, D. C. 1964 Histological Techniques for Electron Microscopy, ed. 2. Academic Press, New York.

POLLISTER, A. W. (editor) 1966–1969 Physical Techniques in Biological Research, ed. 2, vol. 3, parts A, B, C. Topics such as phase contrast and interference microscopy, birefringence, microtomy, freeze drying, fluorescence microspectrophotometry and autoradiography are considered. Academic Press, New York.

ROGERS, A. W. 1967 Techniques of Autoradiography. American Elsevier Publishing Company, New York.

SIEGEL, B. M. (editor) 1964 Modern Developments in Electron Microscopy. Academic Press, New York. Included are chapters on the electron microscope (by Siegel), ultramicrotomy (by Porter), histology and cytology (by Fawcett), and macromolecules (by Hall).

SJÖSTRAND, F. S. 1967 Electron Microscopy of Cells and Tissues, vol. I: Instrumentation and Techniques. Academic Press, New York.

WIED, G. L. (editor) 1966 Introduction to Quantitative Cytochemistry. Academic Press, New York.

GENERAL TOPICS

BRACHET, J., AND MIRSKY, A. E. 1959–1964 The Cell; Biochemistry, Physiology, Morphology, 6 vols. Academic Press, New York.

CURTIS, H. 1968 Biology. Worth Publishers, Inc., New York.

DuPRAW, E. J. 1968 Cell and Molecular Biology. Academic Press, New York.

CASPERSSON, T. O. 1950 Cell Growth and Cell Function. W. W. Norton and Company, New York.

COWDRY, E. V. (editor) 1924 General Cytology. The University of Chicago Press, Chicago.

DARNELL, JR., J. E. 1968 Ribonucleic acids from animal cells. Bact. Rev., vol. 32, pp. 262–290.

DEROBERTIS, E. D. P., NOWINSKI, W. W., AND

Saez, F. A. 1970 Cell Biology, ed. 5. W. B. Saunders Company, Philadelphia.

Fawcett, D. W. 1966 An Atlas of Fine Structure: The Cell, Its Organelles and Inclusions. W. B. Saunders Company, Philadelphia.

Finean, J. B. 1967 Engström-Finean Biological Ultrastructure, ed. 2. Academic Press, New York.

Giese, A. C. 1968 Cell Physiology, ed. 3. W. B. Saunders Company, Philadelphia.

Ingram, V. M. 1965 The Biosynthesis of Macromolecules. W. A. Benjamin, Inc., New York.

Loewy, A. G., and Siekevitz, P. 1969 Cell Structure and Function, ed. 2. Holt, Rinehart and Winston, Inc., New York.

Porter, K. R., and Bonneville, M. A. 1968 Fine Structure of Cells and Tissues, ed. 3. Lea & Febiger, Philadelphia.

Rhodin, J. A. G. 1963 An Atlas of Ultrastructure. W. B. Saunders Company, Philadelphia.

Smellie, R. M. S. 1968 The biosynthesis and function of nucleic acids. In The Biological Basis of Medicine (Bittar, E. E., editor), vol. I, pp. 243–281. Academic Press, New York.

Swanson, C. P. 1969 The Cell, ed. 3. Prentice-Hall, Inc., New York.

Note: In order to reduce the number of references, many of the important earlier papers have not been listed because they are cited in the subsequent reports and reviews given below.

Nucleus

Envelope

Gall, J. G. 1967 Octagonal nuclear pores. J. Cell Biol., vol. 32, pp. 391–399.

Heilbrunn, L. V., and Weber, F. (editors) 1964 The nuclear membrane and nucleocytoplasmic interchanges (Protoplasmatologia), vol. 5, no. 2. Springer-Verlag, Vienna. This volume contains a preface by Mirsky, and reviews on the electron microscopy of the nuclear envelope (by Gall), permeability of the envelope (by Loewenstein and by Feldherr and Harding) and nuclear transplantation studies (by Goldstein).

Ito, S., and Loewenstein, W. R. 1965 Permeability of a nuclear membrane: changes during normal development and changes induced by growth hormone. Science, vol. 150, pp. 909–910.

Wiener, J., Spiro, D., and Loewenstein, W. R. 1965 Ultrastructure and permeability of nuclear membranes. J. Cell Biol., vol. 27, pp. 107–117.

Nucleolus

Bernhard, W., and Granboulan, N. 1968 Electron microscopy of the nucleolus in vertebrate cells. In The Nucleus (Dalton, A. J., and Haguenau, F., editors), pp. 81–149. Academic Press, New York.

Hay, E. D. 1968 Structure and function of the nucleolus in developing cells. In The Nucleus (Dalton, A. J., and Haguenau, F., editors), pp. 1–79. Academic Press, New York.

Perry, R. P. 1967 The nucleolus and the synthesis of ribosomes. Progr. Nucl. Acid Res., vol. 6, pp. 219–257.

Vincent, W. S., and Miller, Jr., O. L. (editors) 1966 International Symposium on the Nucleolus, Its Structure and Function. National Cancer Institute Monograph No. 23, United States Government Printing Office, Washington, D. C.

Genetic Material

Barr, M. L. 1966 The significance of the sex chromatin. Int. Rev. Cytol., vol. 19, pp. 35–95.

Harris, H. 1968 Nucleus and Cytoplasm. Clarendon Press, Oxford.

Hay, E. D., and Revel, J. P. 1963 The fine structure of the DNP component of the nucleus. An electron microscopic study utilizing autoradiography to localize DNA synthesis. J. Cell Biol., vol. 16, pp. 29–51.

Miller, Jr., O. L., and Beatty, B. R. 1969 Visualization of nucleolar genes. Science, vol. 164, pp. 955–957.

Mirsky, A. E., and Osawa, S. 1961 The interphase nucleus. In The Cell; Biochemistry, Physiology, Morphology (Brachet, J., and Mirsky, A. E., editors), vol. 2, pp. 677–770. Academic Press, New York.

Ris, H. 1961 Ultrastructure and molecular organization of genetic systems. Canad. J. Genet. Cytol., vol. 3, pp. 95–120.

Swift, H. 1965 Molecular morphology of the chromosome. In Vitro, vol. 1, pp. 26–49.

Watson, J. 1965 Molecular Biology of the Gene. W. A. Benjamin, Inc., New York.

Watson, J. D. 1968 The Double Helix; A Personal Account of the Discovery of the Structure of DNA. Atheneum Press, New York.

See also references at end of Chapter 2.

Function

Allfrey, V. 1968 Some chemical aspects of nuclear fine structure—a preface. In The

Nucleus (Dalton, A. J., and Haguenau, F., editors), pp. ix–xiii. Academic Press, New York.

BRACHET, J. 1961 Nucleocytoplasmic interactions in unicellular organisms. *In* The Cell; Biochemistry, Physiology, Morphology (Brachet, J., and Mirsky, A. E., editors), vol. 2, pp. 771–841. Academic Press, New York.

BRIGGS, R., AND KING, T. J. 1959 Nucleocytoplasmic interactions in eggs and embryos. *In* The Cell; Biochemistry, Physiology, Morphology (Brachet, J., and Mirsky, A. E., editors), vol. 1, pp. 537–617. Academic Press, New York.

GURDON, J. B. 1968 Transplanted nuclei and cell differentiation. Sci. Amer., vol. 219 (Dec.), pp. 24–35.

LOCKE, M. (editor) 1963 Cytodifferentiation and Macromolecular Synthesis (Society for the Study of Development and Growth, Symposium No. 21). Academic Press, New York. Included are chapters by Jacob and Monod (genetic repression, allosteric inhibition and cellular differentiation) and by Gall (chromosomes and cytodifferentiation).

SIRLIN, J. L. 1963 The intracellular transfer of genetic information. Int. Rev. Cytol., vol. 15, pp. 35–96.

Cytoplasm

Ribosomes, Endoplasmic Reticulum

CARO, L. G., AND PALADE, G. E. 1964 Protein synthesis, storage, and discharge in the pancreatic exocrine cell. An autoradiographic study. J. Cell Biol., vol. 20, pp. 473–495.

EMANS, J. B., AND JONES, A. L. 1968 Hypertrophy of liver cell smooth surfaced reticulum following progesterone administration. J. Histochem. Cytochem., vol. 16, pp. 561–570.

FAWCETT, D. W. 1965 Structural and functional variations in the membranes of the cytoplasm. *In* Intracellular Membranous Structure (Seno, S., and Cowdry, E. V., editors), pp. 15–36. Chugoku Press, Okayama.

HAGUENAU, F. 1958 The ergastoplasm: its history, ultrastructure and biochemistry. Int. Rev. Cytol., vol. 7, pp. 425–483.

JAMIESON, J. D., AND PALADE, G. E. 1967 Intracellular transport of secretory proteins in the pancreatic exocrine cell. I. Role of the peripheral elements of the Golgi complex. J. Cell Biol., vol. 34, pp. 577–596.

JAMIESON, J. D., AND PALADE, G. E. 1967 Intracellular transport of secretory proteins in the pancreatic exocrine cell. II. Transport to condensing vacuoles and zymogen granules. J. Cell Biol., vol. 34, pp. 597–615.

JONES, A. L., AND FAWCETT, D. W. 1966 Hypertrophy of the agranular endoplasmic reticulum in hamster liver induced by phenobarbital. J. Histochem. Cytochem., vol. 14, pp. 215–232.

PALADE, G. E. 1956 The endoplasmic reticulum. J. Biophys. Biochem. Cytol., vol. 2 (suppl.), pp. 85–98.

PALADE, G. E. 1958 A small particulate component of the cytoplasm. *In* Frontiers in Cytology (Palay, S. L., editor), pp. 283–304. Yale University Press, New Haven.

PALADE, G. E. 1966 Structure and function at the cellular level (Lasker Research Award lecture). J. A. M. A., vol. 198, pp. 815–825.

PALADE, G. E., AND PORTER, K. R. 1954 Studies on the endoplasmic reticulum. I. Its identification in cells *in situ*. J. Exp. Med., vol. 100, pp. 641–656.

PALADE, G. E., SIEKEVITZ, P., AND CARO, L. G. 1961 Structure, chemistry and function of the pancreatic exocrine cell. *In* Ciba Foundation Symposium on the Exocrine Pancreas (de Reuck, A. V. S., and Cameron, M. P., editors), pp. 23–49.

PORTER, K. R. 1961 The ground substance; observations from electron microscopy. *In* The Cell; Biochemistry, Physiology, Morphology (Brachet, J., and Mirsky, A. E., editors), vol. 2, pp. 621–675. Academic Press, New York.

PORTER, K. R., CLAUDE, A., AND FULLAM, E. F. 1945 A study of tissue culture cells by electron microscopy. J. Exp. Med., vol. 81, pp. 232–246.

RICH, A. 1963 Polyribosomes. Sci. Amer., vol. 209 (June), pp. 44–53.

RICH, A. 1968 On the assembly of amino acids into proteins. *In* Structural Chemistry and Molecular Biology (Rich, A., and Davidson, N., editors), pp. 223–237. W. H. Freeman and Company, San Francisco.

SPIRIN, A. S., AND GAVRILOVA, L. P. 1969 The Ribosome. Springer-Verlag, New York.

Golgi Apparatus

BAINTON, D. F., AND FARQUHAR, M. G. 1966 Origin of granules in polymorphonuclear leukocytes. Two types derived from opposite faces of the Golgi complex in developing granulocytes. J. Cell Biol., vol. 28, pp. 277–301.

BAINTON, D. F., AND FARQUHAR, M. G. 1968 Differences in enzyme content of azurophil and specific granules of polymorphonuclear leukocytes. II. Cytochemistry and electron microscopy of bone marrow cells. J. Cell Biol., vol. 39, pp. 299–317.

BEAMS, H. W., AND KESSEL, R. G. 1968 The

Golgi apparatus: structure and function. Int. Rev. Cytol., vol. 23, pp. 209–276.

BONNEVILLE, M. A., AND WEINSTOCK, M. 1970 Brush border development in the intestinal absorptive cells of *Xenopus* during metamorphosis. J. Cell Biol., vol. 44, pp. 151–171.

DALTON, A. J. 1961 Golgi apparatus and secretion granules. *In* The Cell; Biochemistry, Physiology, Morphology (Brachet, J., and Mirsky, A. E., editors), vol. 2, pp. 603–619. Academic Press, New York.

FRIEND, D. S., AND MURRAY, M. J. 1965 Osmium impregnation of the Golgi apparatus. Amer. J. Anat., vol. 117, pp. 135–149.

KIRKMAN, H., AND SEVERINGHAUS, A. E. 1938 A review of the Golgi apparatus. Anat. Rec., vol. 70, pp. 413–431 and 557–573; vol. 71, pp. 79–103.

LANE, N., CARO, L., OTERO-VILARDEBÓ, L. R., AND GODMAN, G. C. 1964 On the site of sulfation in colonic goblet cells. J. Cell Biol., vol. 21, pp. 339–351.

NEUTRA, M., AND LEBLOND, C. P. 1969 The Golgi apparatus. Sci. Amer., vol. 220 (Feb.), pp. 100–107.

PALAY, S. L. 1958 The morphology of secretion. *In* Frontiers in Cytology (Palay, S. L., editor), pp. 305–342. Yale University Press, New Haven.

RAMBOURG, A., HERNANDEZ, W., AND LEBLOND, C. P. 1969 Detection of complex carbohydrates in the Golgi apparatus of rat cells. J. Cell Biol., vol. 40, pp. 395–414.

REVEL, J. P., AND ITO, S. 1967 The surface components of cells. *In* The Specificity of Cell Surfaces (Davis, B. D., and Warren, L., editors), pp. 211–234. Prentice-Hall, Inc., New York.

WHALEY, W. G. 1968 The Golgi apparatus. *In* The Biological Basis of Medicine (Bittar, E. E., editor), vol. 1, pp. 179–208. Academic Press, New York.

Lysosomes, Microbodies

ALLISON, A. 1967 Lysosomes and disease. Sci. Amer., vol. 217 (May), pp. 62–72.

ALLISON, A. C. 1968 Lysosomes. *In* The Biological Basis of Medicine (Bittar, E. E., editor), vol. 1, pp. 209–242. Academic Press, New York.

DE DUVE, C. 1963 The lysosome. Sci. Amer., vol. 208 (May), pp. 64–72.

DE DUVE, C., AND BAUDHUIN, P. 1966 Peroxisomes (microbodies and related particles). Physiol. Rev., vol. 46, pp. 323–357.

DE DUVE, C., AND WATTIAUX, R. 1966 Functions of lysosomes. Ann. Rev. Physiol., vol. 28, pp. 435–492.

DE REUCK, A. V. S., AND CAMERON, M. P. (editors) 1963 Lysosomes. Ciba Foundation Symposium. Little, Brown and Company, Boston.

DINGLE, J. T., AND FELL, H. B. (editors) 1969 Lysosomes in Biology and Pathology. John Wiley & Sons, Inc., New York.

FRANK, A. L., AND CHRISTENSEN, A. K. 1968 Localization of acid phosphatase in lipofuscin granules and possible autophagic vacuoles in interstitial cells of the guinea pig testis. J. Cell Biol., vol. 36, pp. 1–13.

FRIEND, D. S., AND FARQUHAR, M. G. 1967 Functions of coated vesicles during protein absorption in the rat vas deferens. J. Cell Biol., vol. 35, pp. 357–376.

HIRSCH, J. G., AND COHN, Z. A. 1964 Digestive and autolytic functions of lysosomes in phagocytic cells. Fed. Proc., vol. 23, pp. 1023–1025.

HRUBAN, Z., AND RECHCIGL, JR., M. 1969 Microbodies and Related Particles; Morphology, Biochemistry and Physiology. Int. Rev. Cytol., Suppl. 1.

NOVIKOFF, A. B. 1961 Lysosomes and related particles. *In* The Cell; Biochemistry, Physiology, Morphology (Brachet, J., and Mirsky, A. E., editors), vol. 2, pp. 423–488. Academic Press, New York.

NOVIKOFF, A. B., AND SHIN, W.-Y. 1964 The endoplasmic reticulum in the Golgi zone and its relations to microbodies, Golgi apparatus and autophagic vacuoles in rat liver cells. J. Micr., vol. 3, pp. 187–206.

NOVIKOFF, A. B., ESSNER, E., AND QUINTANA, N. 1964 Golgi apparatus and lysosomes. Fed. Proc., vol. 23, pp. 1010–1022.

SMITH, R. E., AND FARQUHAR, M. G. 1966 Lysosome function in the regulation of the secretory process in cells of the anterior pituitary gland. J. Cell Biol., vol. 31, pp. 319–347.

SWIFT, H., AND HRUBAN, Z. 1964 Focal degradation as a biological process. Fed. Proc., vol. 23, pp. 1026–1037.

Central Body, Centrioles

DE HARVEN, E. 1968 The centriole and the mitotic spindle. *In* The Nucleus (Dalton, A. J., and Haguenau, F., editors), pp. 197–227. Academic Press, New York.

GALL, J. G. 1961 Centriole replication. A study of spermatogenesis in the snail *Viviparus*. J. Biophys. Biochem. Cytol., vol. 10, pp. 163–193.

RENAUD, F. L., AND SWIFT, H. 1964 The development of basal bodies and flagella in *Allomyces arbusculus*. J. Cell Biol., vol. 23, pp. 339–354.

SZOLLOSI, D. 1964 The structure and function

of centrioles and their satellites in the jelly-fish *Phialidium gregarium*. J. Cell Biol., vol. 21, pp. 465–479.

See also references at end of Chapter 2.

Mitochondria

ANDRÉ, J., AND MARINOZZI, V. 1965 Présence, dans les mitochondries, de particules ressemblant aux ribosomes. J. Microscop., vol. 4, pp. 615–626.

ATTARDI, G., AND ATTARDI, B. 1968 Mitochondrial origin of membrane-associated heterogeneous RNA in HeLa cells. Proc. Nat. Acad. Sci. U. S. A., vol. 61, pp. 261–268.

BENSLEY, R. R., AND HOERR, N. L. 1934 Studies on cell structure by the freezing-drying method. VI. The preparation and properties of mitochondria. Anat. Rec., vol. 60, pp. 449–455.

BORST, P., AND KROON, A. M. 1969 Mitochondrial DNA: physicochemical properties, replication, and genetic function. Int. Rev. Cytol., vol. 26, pp. 107–190.

HALL, D. O., AND PALMER, J. M. 1969 Mitochondrial research today. Nature, vol. 221, pp. 717–723.

HOGEBOOM, G. H., SCHNEIDER, W. C., AND PALADE, G. E. 1948 Cytochemical studies of mammalian tissues. I. Isolation of intact mitochondria from rat liver; some biochemical properties of mitochondria and submicroscopic particulate material. J. Biol. Chem., vol. 172, pp. 619–635.

LEHNINGER, A. L. 1964 The Mitochondrion; Molecular Basis of Structure and Function. W. A. Benjamin, Inc., New York.

LUCK, D. J. L. 1965 Formation of mitochondria in *Neurospora crassa*. Proc. Nat. Acad. Sci. U. S. A., vol. 52, pp. 931–938.

NOVIKOFF, A. B. 1961 Mitochondria (chondriosomes). *In* The Cell; Biochemistry, Physiology, Morphology (Brachet, J., and Mirsky, A. E., editors) vol. 2, pp. 299–421. Academic Press, New York.

PALADE, G. 1953 An electron microscope study of the mitochondrial structure. J. Histochem. Cytochem., vol. 1, pp. 188–211.

PARSONS, D. F. 1965 Recent advances in correlating structure and function in mitochondria. Int. Rev. Exp. Pathol., vol. 4, pp. 1–54.

PEACHEY, L. D. 1964 Electron microscope observations on the accumulation of divalent cations in intramitochondrial granules. J. Cell Biol., vol. 20, pp. 95–111.

RACKER, E. 1968 The membrane of the mitochondrion. Sci. Amer., vol. 218 (Feb.), pp. 32–39.

ROODYN, D. B. 1968 The mitochondrion. *In* The Biological Basis of Medicine (Bittar, E. E., editor), vol. 1, pp. 123–177. Academic Press, New York.

SWIFT, H. 1965 Nucleic acids of mitochondria and chloroplasts. Amer. Natur., vol. 99, pp. 201–227.

TANDLER, B., ERLANDSON, R. A., SMITH, A. L., AND WYNDER, E. L. 1969 Riboflavin and mouse hepatic cell structure and function. II. Division of mitochondria during recovery from simple deficiency. J. Cell Biol., vol. 41, pp. 477–493.

TAPLEY, D. F., KIMBERG, D. V., AND BUCHANAN, J. L. 1967 The mitochondrion. New Eng. J. Med., vol. 276, pp. 1124–1132, 1182–1191.

Filaments

BONNEVILLE, M. A., AND WEINSTOCK, M. 1970 Brush border development in the intestinal absorptive cells of *Xenopus* during metamorphosis. J. Cell Biol., vol. 44, pp. 151–171.

BRODY, I. 1960 The ultrastructure of the tonofibrils in the keratinization process of normal human epidermis. J. Ultrastruct. Res., vol. 4, pp. 264–297.

BUCKLEY, I. K., AND PORTER, K. R. 1967 Cytoplasmic fibrils in living cultured cells. A light and electron microscope study. Protoplasma, vol. 64, pp. 349–380.

CLONEY, R. A. 1966 Cytoplasmic filaments and cell movements: epidermal cells during Ascidian metamorphosis. J. Ultrastruct. Res., vol. 14, pp. 300–328.

FRANKS, L. M., RIDDLE, P. N., AND SEAL, P. 1969 Actin-like filaments and cell movement in human ascites tumour cells. An ultrastructural and cinemicrographic study. Exp. Cell Res., vol. 54, pp. 157–162.

JAHN, T. L., AND BOVEE, E. C. 1969 Protoplasmic movement within cells. Physiol. Rev., vol. 49, pp. 793–862.

NAGAI, R., AND REBHUN, L. I. 1966 Cytoplasmic microfilaments in streaming *Nitella* cells. J. Ultrastruct. Res., vol. 14, pp. 571–589.

SZOLLOSI, D. 1970 Cortical cytoplasmic filaments of cleaving eggs: a structural element corresponding to the contractile ring. J. Cell Biol., vol. 44, pp. 192–209.

TILNEY, L. G., AND GIBBINS, J. R. 1969 Microtubules and filaments in the filopodia of the secondary mesenchyme cells of *Arbacia punctulata* and *Echinarachnius parma*. J. Cell Sci., vol. 5, pp. 195–210.

WOHLMAN, A., AND ALLEN, R. D. 1968 Structural organization associated with pseudopod extension and contraction during cell locomotion in *Difflugia*. J. Cell Sci., vol. 3, pp. 105–114.

Microtubules

ADELMAN, M. R., BORISY, G. G., SHELANSKI, N. H., WEISENBERG, R. C., AND TAYLOR, E. W. 1968 Cytoplasmic filaments and tubules. Fed. Proc., vol. 27, pp. 1186–1193.

BEHNKE, O., AND FORER, A. 1967 Evidence for four classes of microtubules in individual cells. J. Cell Sci., vol. 2, pp. 169–192.

FAWCETT, D. 1961 Cilia and flagella. *In* The Cell; Biochemistry, Physiology, Morphology (Brachet, J., and Mirsky, A. E., editors), vol. 2, pp. 217–297. Academic Press, New York.

GIBBONS, I. R. 1967 The structure and composition of cilia. *In* Formation and Fate of Cell Organelles (Warren, K. B., ed.), pp. 99–113. Academic Press, New York.

MALAWISTA, S. E., SATO, H., AND BENSCH, K. G. 1968 Vinblastine and griseofulvin reversibly disrupt the living mitotic spindle. Science, vol. 160, pp. 770–772.

McINTOSH, J. R., AND PORTER, K. R. 1967 Microtubules in the spermatids of the domestic fowl. J. Cell Biol., vol. 35, pp. 153–173.

PORTER, K. R. 1966 Cytoplasmic microtubules and their functions. *In* Principles of Biomolecular Organization (Wolstenholme, G. E. W., and O'Connor, M., editors), Ciba Foundation Symposium, pp. 308–345. Little, Brown and Company, Boston.

SCHMITT, F. O., AND SAMSON, F. E., JR. 1968 Neuronal fibrous proteins. A review based on two NRP conferences. Neurosciences Research Program Bulletin, vol. 6 (2), pp. 113–219.

SLAUTTERBACK, D. B. 1963 Cytoplasmic microtubules. I. Hydra. J. Cell Biol., vol. 18, pp. 367–388.

TILNEY, L. G., AND PORTER, K. R. 1965 Studies on microtubules in heliozoa. I. The fine structure of *Actinosphaerium nucleofilum* (Barrett), with particular reference to the axial rod structure. Protoplasma, vol. 60, pp. 317–344.

TILNEY, L. G., AND PORTER, K. R. 1967 II. The effect of low temperature on these structures in the formation and maintenance of the axopodia. J. Cell Biol., vol. 34, pp. 327–343.

TILNEY, L. G., HIRAMOTO, Y., AND MARSLAND, D. 1966 III. A pressure analysis of the role of these structures in the formation and maintenance of the axopodia of *Actinosphaerium nucleofilum* (Barrett). J. Cell Biol., vol. 29, pp. 77–95.

TILNEY, L. G. 1968 IV. The effect of colchicine on the formation and maintenance of the axopodia and the redevelopment of pattern in *Actinosphaerium nucleofilum* (Barrett). J. Cell Sci., vol. 3, pp. 549–562.

TILNEY, L. G., AND GIBBINS, J. R. 1969 Microtubules in the formation and development of the primary mesenchyme in *Arbacia punctulata*. II. An experimental analysis of their role in development and maintenance of cell shape. J. Cell Biol., vol. 41, pp. 227–250.

Cell Membrane

BENNETT, H. S. 1963 Morphological aspects of extracellular polysaccharides. J. Histochem. Cytochem., vol. 11, pp. 14–23.

BRANDT, P. W. 1962 A consideration of the extraneous coats of the plasma membrane. *In* Symposium on the Plasma Membrane. Circulation, vol. 26, pp. 1075–1091.

CHAMBERS, R. 1940 The relation of extraneous coats to the organization and permeability of cellular membranes. Cold Spring Harbor Sympos. Quant. Biol., vol. 8, pp. 144–153.

DALTON, A. J., AND HAGUENAU, F. (editors) 1968 The Membranes. Academic Press, New York.

DANIELLI, J. F., AND DAVSON, H. 1934–1935 A contribution to the theory of permeability of thin films. J. Cell. Comp. Physiol., vol. 5, pp. 495–508.

KORN, E. D. 1968 Structure and function of the plasma membrane; a biochemical perspective. *In* Biological Interfaces: Flows and Exchanges. Proceedings of a symposium sponsored by the New York Heart Association, pp. 257–274. Little, Brown and Company, Boston.

REVEL, J.-P., AND ITO, S. 1967 The surface components of cells. *In* The Specificity of Cell Surfaces (Davis, B. D., and Warren, L., editors), pp. 211–234. Prentice-Hall, Inc., New York.

ROBERTSON, J. D. 1964 Unit membranes: A review with recent new studies of experimental alterations and a new subunit structure in synaptic membrane. *In* Cellular Membranes in Development (Locke, M., editor), pp. 1–81. Academic Press, New York.

SJÖSTRAND, F. S. 1963 A comparison of plasma membrane, cytomembranes, and mitochondrial membrane elements with respect to ultrastructural features. J. Ultrastruct. Res., vol. 9, pp. 561–580.

STEIN, W. D. 1967 The Movement of Molecules Across Cell Membranes. Academic Press, New York.

STOECKENIUS, W., AND ENGELMAN, D. M. 1969

Current models for the structure of biological membrane. J. Cell Biol., vol. 42, pp. 613–646.

Inclusions

BJÖRKERUD, S. 1963 The isolation of lipofuscin granules from bovine cardiac muscle, with observations on the properties of the isolated granules on the light and electron microscopic levels. J. Ultrastruct. Res., Suppl. 5, pp. 1–49.

DELLA PORTA, G., AND MÜHLBOCK, O. (editors) 1966 Structure and Control of the Melanocyte. Springer-Verlag, New York.

DROCHMANS, P. 1963 Melanin granules: their fine structure, formation, and degradation in normal and pathological tissues. Int. Rev. Exp. Path., vol. 2, pp. 357–422.

REVEL, J. P. 1964 Electron microscopy of glycogen. J. Histochem. Cytochem., vol. 12, pp. 104–114.

2

Studies of Living Cells

Cell Culture, Cell Differentiation, Cell Division

Fixed and stained preparations have the advantage of being more or less permanent and available for repeated microscopic examination. Unfortunately, fixatives, dehydrating agents and stains may significantly alter living tissues, and there is always a question of how much artifact the preparative procedures have introduced. It is therefore advantageous to study living cells and tissues whenever possible. In addition, there is the distinct advantage that living cells are observed in action, and functional changes can be observed directly. Studies of living cells also offer the opportunity to control directly the immediate environment of the cell during experimentation.

The living cell is delicate, however, and its study requires great care. The first extensive studies on living tissues were carried out on free living unicellular organisms and on the eggs and early embryos of lower forms of both plants and animals. Whereas much was learned about the physical properties of the living cell, the methods used could not be applied directly to cells from higher animals, particularly man.

The first human cells studied in detail in the living condition were blood cells. They were easy to obtain and could be brought under the highest powers of the microscope while still surrounded by their natural environment, the plasma. Because of the fluid nature of the blood, a thin film could be made between a cover glass and slide. If the coverslip edges were sealed to prevent evaporation and the stage of the microscope heated to body temperature, the conditions inside the body were approximated. With this preparation, the various types of white blood cells were recognized and their ameboid and phagocytic activity was observed. This method is still one of the best for the study of blood cells, as well as for an introduction to active living human cells.

This simple procedure cannot be used for the preparation of living cells from organized tissues. Attempts have been made to study solid tissues by teasing the tissue apart with fine instruments until it is spread thinly enough to be viewed with the light microscope. Subcutaneous connective tissue can be studied quite effectively by teasing very small pieces with needles until a thin spread has been drawn out on a slide. Muscle and nerve fibers also have been studied frequently in teased preparations. These preparations were short lived, however,

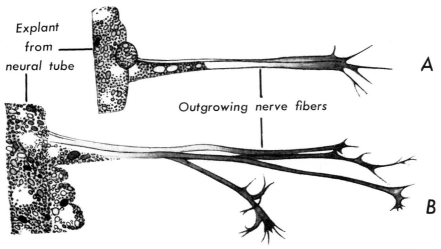

FIG. 2-1. Outgrowth of nerve fibers from pieces of embryonic frog neural tube (which contains the nerve cell bodies) grown in tissue culture. *A*, after 25 hours; *B*, after 34 hours. The expanded tips of the elongating nerve fibers, called growth cones, are regions of vigorous motility. (Redrawn from v. Möllendorff, editor, Handb. mikr. Anat. Menschen., Springer-Verlag, Vienna, after Harrison.)

and the search continued to find methods of maintaining living cells for extended periods for repeated direct microscopic examinations.

CELL, TISSUE AND ORGAN CULTURE

New biological methods often arise out of the need to solve a particular question, and the most dramatic early tissue culture experimentation was devised to solve a problem of nerve fiber growth. Early in this century, histologists were debating whether nerve fibers grew out from the nerve cell body or whether the nerve fiber formed from the fusion of longitudinally arrayed elements within the peripheral nerve. The resolving power of the microscopes available at that time did not allow a clear resolution of this controversy. Harrison attacked the problem directly by placing a part of the developing nervous system of a frog into a clot of sterile lymph and watching nerve fiber formation under the microscope. His experiments provided a clear demonstration that nerve fiber elongation occurs by direct extension and growth of the nerve cell (Fig. 2-1). Soon thereafter many of the tissues of

the body found themselves in oddly shaped glass containers surrounded by complex feeding solutions and clots of every sort. Tissue culture was to become, along with the electron microscope, one of the most powerful tools of the cytologist.

The maintenance of cells outside the body commonly known as tissue culture (or cultivation in vitro, which literally means "in glass"), is now generally divided into three categories. (1) *Cell culture* involves the growth of continuously dividing cells, which are transferred from vessel to vessel as their numbers continuously increase. (2) *Tissue culture* most often involves the explantation of an immature tissue fragment into culture. The cultured fragment, called the *explant*, generally undergoes some growth and reorganization. Cells growing out from the explant are termed the *outgrowth*. The outgrowth cells are often of the connective tissue variety, whereas the primary cells of the organ remain in the compact, and therefore hard to visualize, explant. To circumvent this difficulty, the tissue may be dissociated (as discussed below) prior to placing in culture. (3) *Organ culture* generally involves the explantation and maintenance

TABLE 2-1

EAGLE'S MINIMUM ESSENTIAL MEDIUM (FROM EAGLE, H. 1959 SCIENCE, VOL. 130, P. 432)

Components	mg./liter
Amino acids	
L-Arginine HCl	126.4
L-Cystine	24.0
L-Glutamine	292.0
L-Histidine HCl·H_2O	41.9
L-Isoleucine	52.5
L-Leucine	52.4
L-Lysine HCl	73.1
L-Methionine	14.9
L-Phenylalanine	33.0
L-Threonine	47.6
L-Tryptophan	10.2
L-Tyrosine	36.2
L-Valine	46.8
Vitamins	
D-Ca-pantothenate	1.0
Choline chloride	1.0
Folic acid	1.0
i-Inositol	2.0
Nicotinamide	1.0
Pyridoxal HCl	1.0
Riboflavin	0.1
Thiamine HCl	1.0
Inorganic salts and other components	
$CaCl_2·2H_2O$	265.0
KCl	400.0
$MgSO_4·7H_2O$	200.0
NaCl	6800.0
$NaHCO_3$	2200.0
$NaH_2PO_4·H_2O$	140.0
Dextrose	1000.0
Phenol red	10.0

of mature tissues or organ fragments. This technique is particularly useful for study of the direct effects of drugs or hormones on various tissues of the body.

Successful in vitro studies require that the tissue be obtained in a sterile state (or that it be treated with antibiotics to render it sterile), for the conditions favoring cell growth are similar to those for bacterial multiplication. At all times the tissues must be handled in a fluid environment with salt concentrations and a pH resembling that of the body fluids. Such salt solutions are called balanced salt solutions (BSS). The

tissue may be dissociated into individual cells, often by mild treatment with a digestive enzyme, such as trypsin, which loosens the adhesions between cells, or it may be put out as small fragments. After washing in BSS, the cells are provided with a nutrient *medium* and maintained either in suspension culture, where the cells are kept floating in the medium by constant agitation, or on a surface to which the cells attach. The surface provided for cell growth may be either glass or plastic, sometimes covered with a thin layer of collagen. Sometimes it is advantageous to attach the tissue to this surface (and provide a matrix for growth) by clotting blood plasma around it.

The medium may be completely *defined*, i.e., a mixture of known composition containing vitamins, amino acids and salts, or *natural*, i.e., a mixture containing one of the complex products of the body, such as blood serum. Certain continuously propagated cell lines can be maintained and will continue to grow on completely defined media. The content of one of the simplest of these is given in Table 2-1. For the propagation of other cells, this medium is often supplemented with 10 % serum.

To obtain the fullest possible expression of the organization and functions of certain tissues in culture, it is sometimes necessary to add additional organic ingredients to the medium. The most generally employed substance is embryo extract. In its preparation, embryos are crushed or chopped in an equal quantity of BSS. The solid embryo debris is separated by centrifugation, and a supernatant fluid containing a multitude of undefined cellular constituents is obtained. In addition, certain specific proteins, called growth factors, have been discovered; these enhance the growth of specific tissues in culture. A most dramatic example is the stimulation of the growth of certain types of nerve fibers by a factor present in the salivary gland of the mouse. This protein is termed *nerve growth factor* and this puzzling circumstance—a protein present in a diges-

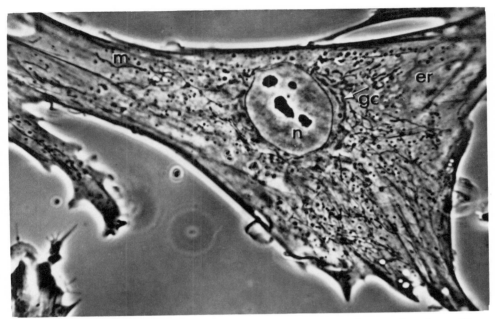

FIG. 2-2. Phase contrast photomicrograph of a living rat embryo cell grown in culture. Many cytoplasmic organelles are visible. The Golgi complex (*gc*) may be seen near the nucleus (*n*). Endoplasmic reticulum (*er*) is visible as a shadowy, branching structure. The long sinuous threads are mitochondria (*m*). ×1450. (From Buckley, I. K., and Porter, K. R. 1967 Protoplasma, vol. 64, p. 349.)

tive gland exerting a very specific effect on nervous tissue—has not yet been satisfactorily explained. Other instances of specific growth factors are known, but it is not yet clear how frequently they are used in the body as control mechanisms governing normal growth.

Morphology of the Living Cell. The greatest detail in living animal cells can generally be observed in thinly spread culture preparations. It is necessary to use a phase contrast or differential interference (Nomarski) optical system to enhance contrast because living cells, being composed chiefly of water, are quite transparent. Even under the best light microscopic conditions, however, only a fraction of the great internal complexity of the cell known from electron microscopic work can be seen (compare Figs. 1-10 and 2-2). The nucleus and its contained nucleoli are clearly visible. It is clear that the cell contents are contained within a very flexible and often very active covering. The cytoplasm is seen to contain varying numbers

of dense granules and somewhat less dense, threadlike elements. The dense, particulate granules are elements of the lysosomal system or lipid droplets; the less dense linear organelles are mitochondria. Occasionally the Golgi apparatus and endoplasmic reticulum can be visualized (Fig. 2-2).

When the cell contains substantial arrays of molecules in a patterned orientation, these will alter the path of transmitted light, and the manner in which the light is altered will give some clue regarding the basic molecular organization. Thus, with polarizing microscopy, areas containing linear arrays of filamentous material, such as the actin and myosin of muscle cells, can be detected. Similarly, a mass of microtubules such as is found in the mitotic spindle can be dramatically brought into view (see Fig. 2-17).

EXPERIMENTAL MANIPULATION OF LIVING CELLS

Simple observations on living cells have been usefully supplemented with a host of techniques which can be applied more or less directly to living cells.

Vital and Supravital Staining. In *vital staining,* dyes are injected into the living animal so that the activity of certain cells can be demonstrated by their selective absorption of the coloring matter. An outstanding example has been the identification of a macrophage or reticuloendothelial system. When trypan blue is injected into an experimental animal, accumulations of the dye are found in vacuoles in the macrophages of the loose connective tissue, the reticular cells of the spleen, lymph nodes and bone marrow, and in the stellate cells of Kupffer in the liver. This method groups together widely dispersed and morphologically different cells on the basis of their ability to phagocytize foreign particles.

Supravital staining consists of adding dyes to the medium of cells already removed from the organism. When trypan blue is placed on a tissue culture, the macrophages take it up in abundance. Small phagocytic cells have been marked in this way, and their subsequent development into epithelioid and giant cells has been followed. The use of supravital dyes such as neutral red to mark the lysosomal systems of cells is discussed in Chapter 1, as is the staining of mitochondria by Janus green.

The selective staining of organelles with a colored dye combined with the high intensities of light available from laser sources provides the opportunity for a new form of *cellular microsurgery.* Laser light, like other visible light, is not much absorbed by living tissue, unless the cells contain pigment granules. If the mitochondria are colored green, however, and laser light of a wavelength absorbed by the green dye is directed at the cell, the light absorption will lead to local heating, as well as other effects, and thus to more or less selective destruction of the mitochondria of the cell. If the cone of laser light is restricted to a part of the cell, only some of the mitochondria are damaged. Similarly, chromosomes which have been

supravitally stained with acridine orange can be irradiated during mitosis with a laser microbeam. Using this technique, lesions less than 1 μ can be placed on desired sites of individual chromosomes (Fig. 2-3).

Micromanipulation. Several new techniques have been made possible by the development of an instrument, called a micromanipulator, which moves fine glass needles or pipettes with such precision that single cells can be dissected under the highest powers of the microscope. In a procedure called *microdissection,* fine glass needles are made in a very small flame and may be drawn to points which are too small to be resolved by the light microscope. The material to be dissected is placed in a hanging drop on a cover glass which is placed over a moist chamber designed to prevent evaporation. Experiments with the microneedles have made our concept of the physical nature of cells much clearer. Protoplasm in general has been shown to be a viscous fluid, its viscosity varying in different cells. The granules, vacuoles and mitochondria have been moved about within the cell, showing that there is no fixed structure except in highly specialized cells. The nucleus is a bag of fluid which may be pushed about from one part of the cell to another and which can be indented by the pressure of the needle. Microdissection also provided some of the first direct evidence of the presence of a cell membrane enclosing the cell contents.

Microelectrodes, which are extremely fine pipettes (whose tips may be less than 1 μ in diameter) filled with concentrated salt solutions, may also be mounted in micromanipulators. If these are inserted into cells with great care, the cell membrane will seal up around them and allow measurements of the differences in electrical potential between the inside of the cell and the external environment (Fig. 2-4). This technique has been especially useful to the physiologist in the study of nerve and muscle tissues, which

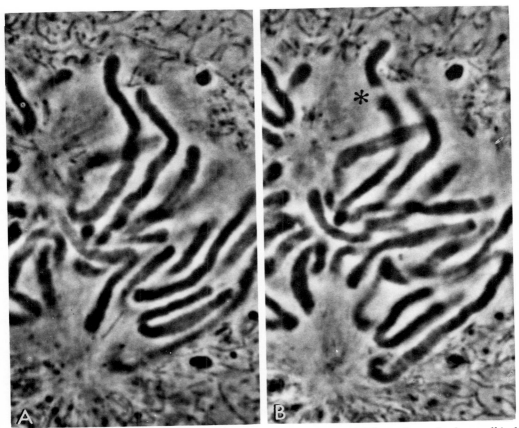

FIG. 2-3. Phase contrast photomicrographs of chromosomes in a dividing salamander lung cell before (A) and after (B) irradiation with laser microbeam. The cells had been previously treated with a nucleic acid stain, acridine orange, to enhance absorption of the microbeam by the chromosomal material. After irradiation, a discrete lesion is seen (at *) in one of the chromosomes. ×2500. (From Berns, M. W., Rounds, D. E., and Olson, R. S. 1969 Exp. Cell Res., vol. 56, p. 292.)

employ changes in membrane potentials as a method of signaling (see Chapter 10).

If a microelectrode is filled with a dye carrying a charge and if current of the appropriate polarity is passed into the cell via the electrode, then dye will pass into the cell with the current flow. There are charged dyes which can be made to fluoresce in the light microscope. When injected into cells, these diffuse widely through the cytoplasm. This technique, which may be termed micro-dye injection, is useful in delineating the contour of individual cells in complexly organized tissues such as the nervous system (Fig. 2-5). Radioactive materials can be

similarly employed, but the cell configuration must then be reconstructed from radio-autograms of serial sections through the cell.

Cinematography. Another technique which has been used with tissue culture cells is cinematography, motion pictures taken through the objectives of a microscope. It is useful not only to obtain permanent records of cell activity but also as an experimental aid in the analysis of movement too slow or too fast to be appreciated by the unaided eye. When the exposures are taken at intervals of several seconds and projected on the screen at the usual speed, the photographed processes are speeded up more than a hundred times. In such a film, the movements of the macrophages, which are scarcely appreciated by direct observation, become visible. In the division of the cell by mitosis, the shifting of the nucleus during the prophase, the rounded blebs or pseudopodia which are sent out and withdrawn from every part of the surface of the cell, and the violent agitation just before the chromosomes separate are all aspects which cannot be appreciated by any other means. Within the resting cell, the shifting of the granules and mitochondria is beautifully demonstrated by these speeded films.

In order to reverse the process and slow activities too quick for the eye, the exposures are taken three or four times as rapidly as they are to be shown on the screen. The movement of cilia has been studied by this method. The contraction of cardiac muscle differentiated in tissue cultures, slowed to one-fourth the actual speed, offers an op-portunity to study the mechanism of muscle contraction.

ACTIVITIES OF LIVING CELLS

Application of the techniques discussed above, as well as observations on single cell organisms, has led to the recognition of a variety of types of cellular movements. In the mature mammal, the flagellum of the sperm tail and the cilia of epithelia move, muscle cells contract and chromosomes move within dividing cells. In addition, certain cells such as leukocytes have the capability of locomotion by other means. All cell types exhibit various intracellular movements.

Intracellular Movements. When one looks inside the living cell, both nuclear motion and movement within the cytoplasm are observed. The simplest form of movement that is exhibited to some extent by all cells which have been studied adequately is a shifting about of the elements within the cytoplasm. This is often very slight and so slow that it is frequently overlooked unless cinematography is employed. There are local currents within the cytoplasm which cause the granules and mitochondria to move slowly for varying distances. In addition, one observes, rapid linear movements of cytoplasmic particles; this distinctive activity is termed *saltatory movement.* Saltatory activity must not be confused with the more random motions of Brownian movement, which is dampened in healthy cells but which becomes marked in cells after death. Cytoplasmic movement may sometimes involve the transport of materials from the perikaryon into cell processes and is especially important in cells with long processes such as neurons.

In certain cells, a surprising rotation of the entire nucleus within the relatively immobile cytoplasm has been observed. These periodic rolling motions can be seen when several nucleoli are present to mark the disposition of the nucleus, thus allowing accurate detection of its movements.

Cell Locomotion. Cell locomotion means

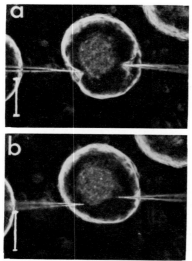

FIG. 2-4. Photomicrographs of frog oocytes being impaled with two extremely fine microelectrodes. The microelectrodes can be seen to first indent the plasma membrane (*a*) and then to penetrate the cell cytoplasm (*b*). This manipulation allows the measurement of intracellular electrical activity. The *bar* indicates 100 μ. (From Kanno, Y., and Loewenstein, W. R. 1963 Exp. Cell Res., vol. 31, p. 149.)

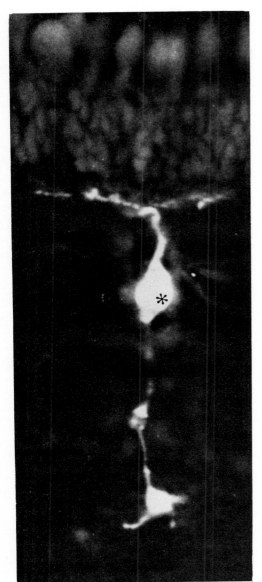

FIG. 2-5. The cell body (*) and cytoplasmic extensions of a neuron in the goldfish retina are here demonstrated after the injection of a fluorescent dye (Procion yellow) directly into the cell soma. After injection the tissue is fixed, embedded and sectioned for viewing in the fluorescence microscope. This technique is useful both in identifying cells penetrated by microelectrodes (which inject the dye as well as record electrical activity) and in delineating the extensions of cells in complex tissues. At the *top* of the figure are rod and cone cells, which fluoresce faintly without dye injection (autofluorescence). Scale:

the movement of the whole cell from one place to another. Studies utilizing the tissue culture and cinematography techniques discussed above have revealed at least two quite different mechanisms by which cells move. Amebae locomote by pseudopodial propagated movement. They dispatch long processes in the appropriate direction and then appear to flow into these processes. Among animal cells, leukocytes and histiocytes (i.e., macrophages) appear to move in a similar fashion, i.e., by *ameboid movement.*

Other types of animal cells (such as the mesodermally derived fibroblast and the endodermal- or ectodermal-derived epithelial cells) exhibit quite different movement patterns. These cells flatten and adhere to surfaces on which they are placed and then glide along this surface without true pseudopodium formation (or gross changes in their overall shape). The membrane along the flattened edges of these cells ruffles, and this ruffling is most active at the edge of the cell marking the direction of movement. The adhesiveness and other properties of the cell surface and of the substrate are important in determining the extent and speed of this locomotion, for movement can be influenced by the shape and properties of the terrain. Changes in the adhesive properties of the cell membrane are especially important during developmental stages of the organism because these properties will influence the migration of cells.

The agencies responsible for the actual movements at the cell border are not known. These movements may be based on mechanisms similar to those operative in muscle cells for active membranes are sometimes underlain by fine filamentous material. It is now known that actomyosin-like proteins occur widely in many cell types, suggesting that many cells contain a system that is in some ways similar to the muscle contraction system. The direction of movement of a

50 μ = 2 inches. (From Kaneko, A. 1970 J. Physiol., vol. 207, p. 623.)

cell can be influenced by a concentration gradient of some substance in solution. The cell is then said to be influenced by *chemotaxis*. Some white blood cells are chemotactically responsive to certain bacteria and move toward any such organism in their vicinity.

An interesting and important aspect of the control of cell movement is the phenomenon of *contact inhibition*. When a moving fibroblast contacts an adjacent fibroblast, its ruffling membrane becomes paralyzed and movement in this region of the cell stops; this is called contact inhibition. This phenomenon is common in certain cell types in culture and is thought to explain why these cells continue to proliferate and spread only until they form a continuous sheet and then stop. As the cell-free surfaces become covered and as the cells are contact-inhibited along their borders, cell movement and proliferation stop. The cytological significance of contact inhibition is under active investigation, for it has been observed that some cancer (sarcoma) cells, which like fibroblasts are derived from mesodermal tissue, are not contact-inhibited when they approach normal fibroblasts in culture. It is thus possible that the invasiveness of some types of cancer are related to a failure in this type of inhibition.

It is known that, in some cases where two cells come together and exhibit contact inhibition, the involved membranes form low resistance junctions, regions where cell membranes come into especially close apposition. These junctions are described later in the text where tissues containing them are discussed. This type of cell to cell junction is known to allow small molecules or ions to pass from one cell to another without diffusing into the extracellular spaces. They therefore provide special regions for cell to cell interaction. This type of junction is known to form, sometimes transiently, during various phases of development. Can you postulate how this type of contact may act to allow one cell to influence the embryological differentiation of another?

Phagocytosis and Pinocytosis. The term phagocytosis is generally used to describe the ingestion of solid material by the cell, whereas pinocytosis refers to the ingestion of fluids. Both mechanisms involve a reaction (or adsorption) of the material with the surface coat of the cell membrane, with subsequent invagination of the surface membrane and the sequestration of the ingested material within a vacuole in the cell cytoplasm.

The process of *phagocytosis* is used by certain single cell organisms for feeding (Gr., *phagein*, to eat), but in higher organisms phagocytosis is more commonly used as a defense mechanism for the ingestion of particles foreign to the organism. Actively ameboid cells usually have the power of phagocytosis. In the case of the more rapidly moving cells such as neutrophilic leukocytes, engulfment is facilitated by the passage of the cell over the particle to be ingested. This can be observed in a thin film preparation made by mixing a suspension of bacteria with a drop of blood. The bacteria settle to the glass surface and remain motionless until the leukocyte passes partway over them. Suddenly they begin to move in unison with the interior of the cell and soon appear in small vacuoles which are carried about with the granules in the currents of the cytoplasm. Cells with less rapid locomotion, such as the histiocytes, come in contact with the material to be engulfed by sending out pseudopodia, which adhere to the debris and surround it, either by drawing it toward the cell or by expanding the pseudopodium.

The ingestion of droplets of fluid by cells in tissue culture was described by Lewis in 1931 as *pinocytosis* (Gr., *pinein*, to drink). A similar process is known to occur in vivo, and the term pinocytosis is now generally used to describe the ingestion of fluids and their contained solutes, whether observed with the light (Fig. 2-6) or the electron microscope. Recent electron microscopic observations indicate that the ingestion of

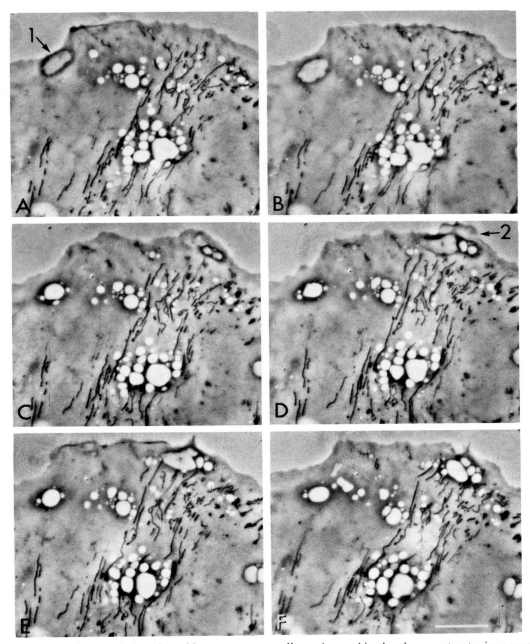

Fɪɢ. 2-6. Pinocytosis in cultured human sarcoma cells as observed in the phase contrast microscope. The figures shown here are but a few of those obtained every 2 seconds for a time-lapse film and were obtained over a 12 minute period. Pinocytosis occurs in regions of the cell body which are undulating vigorously. Recent intake of fluid appears as an irregular lake just inside the cell (as at *1, A* and *2, D*). Secondarily the collected fluid assumes the appearance of more refractile spheroidal droplets which start to migrate interiorly. The *bar* indicates 5 μ. (From Gropp, A. 1963 *In* Cinemicrography in Cell Biology, edited by G. G. Rose, p. 279. Academic Press, New York.)

tiny vacuoles below the resolution of the light microscope is a common phenomenon in many cell types. The presence of protein outside the cell generally acts as a stimulus to pinocytosis. Proteins thus ingested are broken down by the lysosomal system of the cell (as discussed in Chapter 1). Certain cell types apparently use the process of pinocytosis for the transcellular transport of large molecules (see "Capillaries," Chapter 12).

OBSERVATION OF CELLS OF LIVING ANIMALS

The descriptions up to this point have dealt with cells surviving after their removal from the body, but cells have been observed by various methods within the living organism. The earliest attempts were made on the vascular system, the blood cells circulating in the tadpole's tail fin, in the tongue, foot web and mesentery of the adult frog and the mesentery and omentum of mammals. The transparency of the tail fin of the tadpole makes the latter particularly advantageous for the observation of many kinds of cells. It has been used to study the outgrowth of nerve fibers and the formation of special sensory nerve endings. The growth of blood vessels and lymphatics and the activity of the endothelium, connective tissue cells and phagocytes have been extensively studied.

Mammalian material has been made available for similar observation, by the perfection of a technique for inserting a transparent window in the rabbit's ear. Through it, the growth of new blood vessels and lymphatics, the activity of capillaries, the opening and closing of vascular anastomoses, the behavior of the phagocytic cells of connective tissue and the growth and resorption of other tissues have been studied in detail.

CYTOLOGICAL ANALYSIS IN CELL CULTURE

Cell culture techniques permit certain types of cytological analysis that cannot be undertaken in whole tissues. Several of these are discussed below.

Determination of Karyotype. The chromosomal content of cells is best visualized when the chromosomes are fixed and stained while tightly coiled during mitosis. This is accomplished by placing cells with the capability of multiplication in a medium fostering cell division. An agent (colchicine) which prevents completion of the mitotic process is added, and the cells arrested during mitosis accumulate in the culture. These cells are made to swell by the addition of hypotonic medium and are then flattened with pressure. After staining, the chromosomes are counted and classified by size and shape. This analysis allows the determination of the *karyotype* of an organism. Normal human cells contain 46 chromosomes, 22 pairs not associated with sex determination (autosomes) and 2 chromosomes that determine sex (Fig. 2-7).

These techniques have made it possible to demonstrate that a variety of human congenital abnormalities results from an abnormal karyotype. For example, the basis for certain types of abnormal sexual development has been traced to abnormalities in sex chromosome number. Thus, if the normal XX sex chromosome pattern of female human cells is altered so that only one X chromosome is present (a condition called Turner's syndrome), or if the normal XY composition of the male is supplemented with a second X to give a XXY complement (a condition called Kleinfelter's syndrome), then sexual and other traits of the individual are abnormal. Mongolism is also a condition of abnormal chromosome content; in these cases there is an extra autosome, giving a total chromosome number of 47 instead of the normal 46.

Repeated analysis of cultured cell lines has led to the observation that cells carried for long periods in culture often develop abnormal karyotypes. When cells from normal tissues are set out in culture, they have

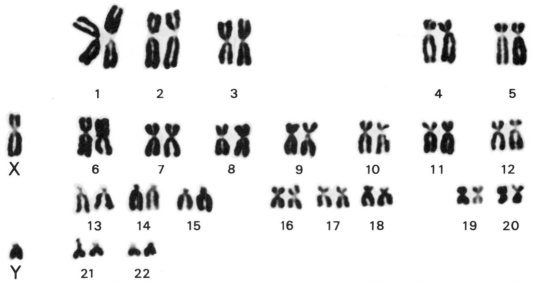

FIG 2-7. A normal karyotype prepared from a human leukocyte dividing in culture. The chromosomes were fixed in acetic alcohol and stained with acetic orcein. When this preparation is viewed in the light microscope the metaphase chromosomes appear in a cluster on the slide. A photograph of these chromosomes is obtained and is then cut up so that the chromosomes may be grouped as shown here. ×1500. (Courtesy of Dr. Orlando Miller.)

the number of chromosomes characteristic of the species. For human cells this would be 46, the *diploid* number of chromosomes. Cells are termed *euploid* if they contain this number of chromosomes or an exact multiple of it; cells with multiples of the diploid number also are referred to as *polyploid*. After long periods in culture, many cell types undergo a transformation and the number of chromosomes per cell changes. The cell line is then said to be *aneuploid* (or *heteroploid*) if the cells contain an odd number of chromosomes. The extensively studied HeLa cell lines, derived from a human cervical cancer in 1952 and whose progeny is still carried in many laboratories, may have from 50 to 350 chromosomes per cell.

Various interpretations have been offered for changes in chromosome number in cultured cells. Some investigators believe that it indicates damage to the replicating mechanism resulting from less than optimal culture conditions. Others have suggested that the change from euploid to aneuploid

is the mechanism of adaptation of cells to permanent growth in culture, and that if aneuploidy does not occur, cells will not adapt to permanent culture as cell lines. Hayflick has suggested that if cells remain euploid they have a limited life span in culture and undergo only a limited (preset) number of divisions before losing their capacity to survive in culture. This limited life span of euploid cultured cells has been related to an aging process, and the transformation to the aneuploid state has been related to the origin of malignancy, i.e., cancer. When reintroduced into animal hosts, many transformed cells will grow as tumors. It should be noted, however, that not all malignant cells are aneuploid.

Cloning. As the above discussion indicates, cells established in culture may be a diverse group, and it is often desirable to select a single cell and to establish it and its progeny as the only cells present in a cell culture line. This process is called *cloning* (Gr., twig). It involves isolation of a single cell, either by dissociating and greatly diluting cell populations prior to culture, or by isolating a single cell in a micropipette. These cells are placed in the most propitious culture environment, and as they multiply their progeny provide, at least for a time, maximally homogeneous cell populations.

Cellular Aggregation. Tissue culture techniques have provided an opportunity to study the reaggregation of cells which have been separated and suspended in a fluid medium. As used by Moscona, this technique allows the dissociation of embryonic organs into individual cells by loosening intercellular adhesions, either by treatment with a proteolytic enzyme such as trypsin and/or a reduction in Ca^{++} concentration of the medium. After dissociation, cells will tend to reaggregate, often in structures resembling the tissue of origin. Cells of different organs, for example kidney and cartilage, can be mixed together after dissociation. Under these conditions, kidney cells aggregate in one mass and cartilage cells in another, even if the organs have been obtained from different species. Cells of a certain organ thus have the ability to recognize cells of similar type and maintain preferential association with them. These observations apply primarily to embryonic organs, for as organs mature the constituent cells lose their capability for cellular reaggregation.

A tissue containing cells from two different sources, for example a mixture of chick and mouse cartilage cells, is called *chimeric*. It is also possible to produce chimeric animals, i.e., animals containing cells from more than one source. Mintz has been able to dissociate the cells of two different mouse embryos at the blastula stage and allow them to reaggregate as one blastula. This is then reintroduced into a pseudopregnant mother, and subsequently develops and is delivered normally. If dissociated blastula cells from a strain of black and a strain of white mice are mixed together to form a single blastula, certain of the newborn mice develop alternating black and white areas of hair pigmentation. It is believed that each stripe is derived from a single clone of pigment cells, some clones arising from the cells of the black strain and others from the white.

Heterokaryons. In addition to the possibility of deriving tissues composed of cells from a variety of sources, tissue culture provides the opportunity of producing cells with mixtures of genetic material. Human cells can be cultured together with cells of, for example, chick tissues. If certain types of inactivated virus particles are added to these cultures, the two types of cells fuse together to become one cell with two or more nuclei. It is thus possible to observe the reactions of an inactive nucleus when introduced into an active cell (Fig. 2-8). As heterokaryons divide, the nuclei sometimes enter mitosis together and are reconstituted as a single larger nucleus. Cells thus formed contain, within a single nucleus, chromosomes derived from different species. With subsequent divisions certain of these chromosomes may be lost. In man-mouse hybrids, for example, the human chromosomes are gradually reduced in number until in some cases only one remains. This circumstance has been used to determine the localization of certain genes to a specific human chromosome.

Other Uses of Cell Culture. The uses of tissue culture in studies of cellular differentiation are discussed below. In addition, tissue culture has been essential in research on viruses. Functioning cells are necessary for virus growth, and tissue cultures offer an opportunity to study virus growth outside the animal host and to prepare large quantities of virus for vaccines. They are also necessary to assay the types and amounts of virus present in any biological preparation.

Observations on Organized Tissue in Culture. With the increasing refinement of tissue culture techniques, it has become possible to establish many of the tissues of

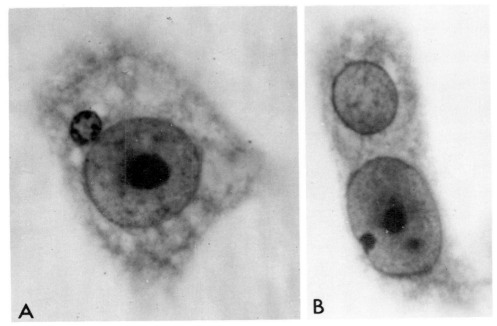

FIG. 2-8. Reactivation of a mature hen red blood cell (*RBC*) nucleus following introduction into an active HeLa cell. The heterokaryon in *A* contains the large, cultured HeLa cell nucleus (about 10 μ in diameter) and a typical small, dotted RBC nucleus. *B* shows the subsequent enlargement and disappearance of heterochromatin in the hen RBC nucleus. By applying radioautographic techniques to this type of preparation, it is possible to demonstrate that DNA and RNA synthesis (which normally does not occur in the mature RBC nucleus) is resumed in RBC nuclei residing in the cytoplasm of a continuously synthesizing HeLa cell. (From Harris, H. 1967 J. Cell Sci., vol. 2, p. 23.)

the body in culture, often with a high degree of organization and function. Three examples are given here to illustrate the degree of organization that can be achieved by cells maintained in vitro.

Skeletal muscle may be established in culture by taking cells from embryonic muscle before the muscle fibers are fully differentiated. A single cell is selected and, if culture conditions are very carefully controlled, it divides repeatedly, producing a prodigious progeny of like cells. After a substantial amount of cell division has occurred, some of these cells fuse together to form long multinucleated muscle fibers. Normally mitosis does not occur in the cells after they have fused. The muscle fibers thus formed develop cross striations, indicating that the muscle proteins actin and myosin are being formed and aligned within the fiber. The fibers are then capable of contraction. A single muscle cell has thus become a group of functioning muscle fibers (Fig. 2-9).

Nervous tissue in culture may similarly attain an impressive degree of histological organization. Young cells may be taken from the developing nervous system of embryos and placed in chambers where they can be kept for days, weeks or even months. Development of the tissue continues in vitro much as it would in vivo (Fig. 2-10). The nerve cells send out processes and these form contacts (synapses) with other neurons. The supporting cells of the neuron form a special ensheathment called myelin, just as they do in vivo. In addition, the nervous tissue in vitro demonstrates many of the electrical properties characteristic of its function in the body.

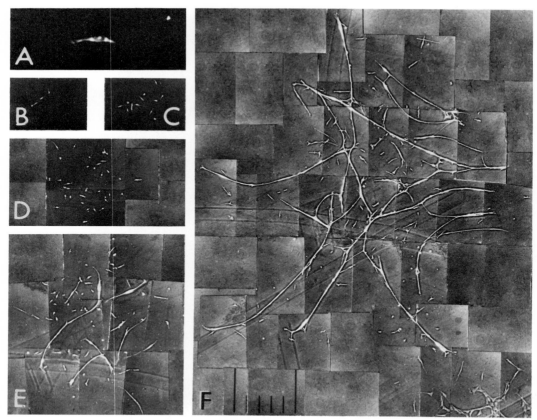

FIG. 2-9. This series of low power photomicrographs records the development of a muscle colony from a single bipolar cell. The colony produced by the single cell in *A* is shown after 1 day (*B*), 2 days (*C*), 3 days (*D*), 5 days (*E*) and 8 days (*F*) of development. After substantial cell division, the cells begin to fuse to form the straplike multinucleate muscle fibers seen in *E* and *F*. The entire muscle mass is a clone because it has arisen from a single cell. In *F*, each division of the scale represents 0.1 mm. (From Konigsberg, I. R. 1963 Science, vol. 140, p. 1273.)

Gland cells, such as those of the pancreas, can also express their activity in culture. Under proper conditions, this tissue forms zymogen, a complex of digestive enzymes, which is one of the characteristic products of the exocrine pancreas in the intact animal. Certain mechanisms involved in the development into functioning gland cells are discussed below.

The list of tissues capable of impressive in vitro performance continues to grow; skin keratinizes, hair and feathers grow, glands secrete, bone is deposited, heart cells beat, blood cells differentiate, collagen forms and cilia move. The usefulness of tissue culture techniques in the study of the cell is expanding.

CELL DIFFERENTIATION

The central problem in the study of development is the question of how a single cell, the fertilized egg, gives rise to the many cell types of the mature organism. The fertilized egg divides rapidly, forming first a ball of cells called a morula; later this mass of cells develops a cavity and is termed a blastula. In mammals this becomes embedded in the uterine wall and is subsequently nourished by the maternal tissues. With time, three classes of cells can

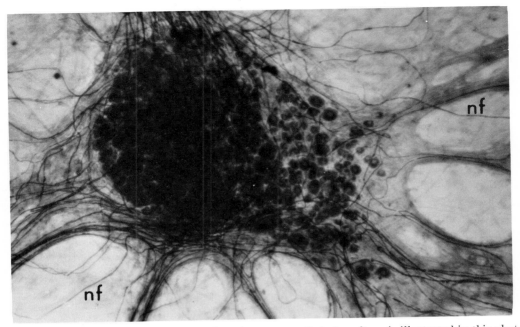

FIG. 2-10. The degree of organization that tissues may attain in culture is illustrated in this photomicrograph of a group of nerve cells which have matured in vitro. Clustered in the *center* are the nerve cell bodies (best seen at the *right*, where they are less concentrated). Radiating from these nerve cells are nerve fibers often gathered into fascicles. Some individual nerve fibers are visible because their fatty sheaths (the myelin sheaths) are stained with Sudan black; they are best seen when situated singly as at *nf*. This fat stain colors the neuron cytoplasm more intensely than the nucleus. Whole mount (unsectioned); dorsal root ganglion taken from a rat fetus and grown in culture for more than 6 months. ×100.

be distinguished in the embryonic germ disc of the blastula: the ectoderm or outside layer, the endoderm or inside lining, and the mesoderm, the cells between these surface layers. The organization and development of these three fundamental layers of embryonic tissue are discussed in the next chapter. From these layers and from their interaction, ultimately about a hundred kinds of cells will develop to form the adult mammal. The process of functional and structural specialization of these cells is called *differentiation*.

The whole of the problem of differentiation is as broad as the entire subject of embryology and is beyond the scope of the present discussion. But it does seem useful, in discussing the principles of cytology, to consider how differentiation might be ac-

complished by an individual cell. In order to differentiate during embryonic development, cells must make a series of small shifts in their potential, as, for example, when a cell of the blastocyst becomes a cell belonging to the endoderm. These will then proliferate to make more cells of their own kind. Then another shift is made, and members of this cell group may become either part of the gut wall or part of the lung. If the former occurs, then a third shift ensues, and the cell becomes either absorptive or secretory. Once the fate of the cell is set, the cell is said to be determined. It subsequently becomes structurally differentiated to perform specialized functions.

There can be little doubt that this orderly development rests ultimately on the activities of the genetic material in the cell nucleus, the genes. It is also generally agreed that the basic codes in the genetic material do not change with development but that different regions of the genome are "turned on" (and others "turned off") as cells develop. The genes are said to be differentially expressed as the cells are progressively determined.

It is also clear that alterations in the use of genetic material during development are not entirely preprogramed within the cell but are influenced by interactions with other cells. As soon as an organism becomes multicellular, the cells begin to react with one another; specific examples of this inter- action are given below. It should also be pointed out that the discussion of develop- ment must consider the properties of em- bryonic tissue because they may be different than those of adult tissue. The often dis- astrous effects of the German measles virus or the drug Thalidomide on the embryo, as compared with their mild effect on the older individual, are good examples.

The Operon. How do the sequential changes that occur in the cell during de- velopment take place? In 1961 the French molecular biologists Jacob and Monod sug- gested a mechanism by which the expression of genetic material in bacteria might be controlled. Their concept is based on the assumption, now generally accepted, that the genetic information of the organism, encoded in the nucleotide sequence of DNA, is transcribed into messenger RNA (mRNA), as has been discussed above. In union with ribosomes, the nucleotide sequences of mRNA are translated into the amino acid sequence of a specific polypeptide. Jacob and Monod suggest that the synthesis of mRNA on the gene is regulated by specific repressors which are products of other genes, called *regulator genes.* The *repressors* are thought to act by becoming engaged with the operator site of a group of genes. The *operator* plus the "structural" genes it con- trols is termed the *operon.* When the op- erator site is open, all of the genes of the

operon synthesize mRNA, and when it is closed by the repressor, none do. The affinity of the repressor for the operator site is influenced by the concentration of small molecular weight metabolites within the cell. This scheme is summarized in Fig. 2-11.

This concept explained how an enzyme could be *induced* in a cell at the level of the gene. Suppose a certain type of sugar mole- cule becomes available in the cell environ- ment and penetrates the cell nucleus. Within the nucleus it can react specifically with a repressor to open an operator site which initiates the synthesis of an enzyme used to break down this type of sugar. The cell is thus provided with a mechanism to use this sugar for its metabolic needs. The student should be able to extrapolate from this example a hypothesis suggesting how one cell could influence the genetic activities of another during development.

Unfortunately, the evidence for the operon mechanism of gene activity has come mostly from bacterial systems, and it is not yet clear to what extent this mechanism is involved in the complex differentiation of higher organisms. Harris has emphasized that a high degree of control of synthetic mechanisms occurs in the cell cytoplasm. Certain cells of lower forms can live, grow and in fact differentiate after their nucleus has been removed. This is considered pos- sible because the mRNA codes were made before the nucleus was removed and are stable for periods of several days or even weeks after the removal of the nucleus. Cytoplasmic control mechanisms determine when and to what extent the mRNA is to engage in protein synthesis. Thus it is clear that there are many levels of control of genetic expression, both in the nucleus and in the cytoplasm.

Recent work has led to the recognition that differentiation can be a remarkably reversible process in some cell types. One of the most dramatic examples has been pro- vided by the work of Gurdon utilizing tech- niques introduced in the pioneering studies

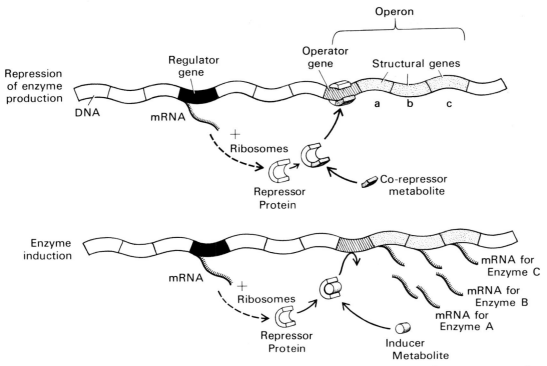

FIG. 2-11. Gene control: the operon concept. According to this concept a regulator gene occupying one site on the DNA strand controls the production of a repressor protein which, in combination with a corepressor substance, inhibits the activity of an operator gene on another site of the DNA strand. In the presence of an inducer compound, the repressor protein is unable to block the operator site. This operator gene controls the activity of adjacent structural genes on which there is assembly of messenger RNA (mRNA) molecules involved in enzyme manufacture.

of Briggs and King. It is possible to destroy the nucleus of an unfertilized frog egg with ultraviolet light and then, using an extremely fine pipette, to introduce a diploid nucleus into the egg to see whether it will be capable of directing the development of the egg (and subsequently the embryo) as the original nucleus would have done. Gurdon has demonstrated that nuclei from fully differentiated intestinal cells in tadpoles can be obtained in a viable state and injected into anucleate frog eggs. In a small number of cases, these eggs developed into normal frogs (Fig. 2-12).

Experiments relevant to this point have also been undertaken by Harris. He has demonstrated, for example, that the nucleus of the highly differentiated chicken red blood cell is dramatically altered upon in-

troduction into a cell already containing an active nucleus (Fig. 2-8). Normally the red cell nucleus does not synthesize measurable amounts of RNA, but in the heterokaryon it resumes RNA synthesis. Both of these experiments indicate that genes are not lost in the process of differentiation, nor are they permanently inactivated.

This should not be taken to imply that all differentiation is, in the normal animal, reversible. The neurons of the mammalian central nervous system do not reproduce themselves; many have very limited capacities of repair. When nerve cells are lost there is no mechanism for replacement, a point that should not be overlooked in an age which has witnessed an increasing reliance upon adjustment of the activities

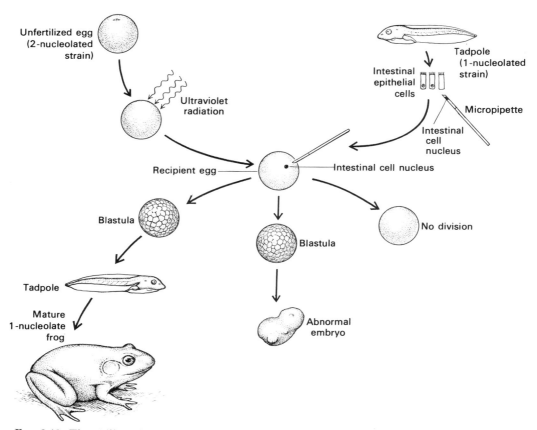

Fig. 2-12. The ability of a nucleus from a differentiated cell to perform all of the basic functions of the unspecialized embryonic nucleus may be demonstrated in the following way. After destruction of the frog egg nucleus by ultraviolet light, a nucleus isolated from an intestinal epithelial cell of a tadpole is substituted by microinjection. In a few cases, development of a normal frog occurs. Because the injected nucleus is the only functional nuclear material it must, in this case, be able to perform all of the functions of the egg nucleus. The use of two different frog strains (one with only one nucleolus in each nucleus and the other with two) allows confirmation of the presence of the intestinal cell nucleus. (After Gurdon, J. B. 1968 Sci. Amer., vol. 219 (Dec.), p. 24.)

of the nervous system with drugs of every nature and degree of purity.

Cell to Cell Interactions. It is known that there are critical periods during the development of certain cells when exposure to other cells, or to products of other cells such as hormones, is critical for differentiation. Embryonic *induction* involves the interaction between cells or tissues in which one tissue (sometimes termed the "organizer") induces a developmental change in another. A classic example is the formation of the lens of the eye. As the brain develops, that part destined to form the sensory portion of the eye bulges laterally and approaches the overlying ectoderm. As this portion of the nervous system comes in contact with the ectoderm, the ectoderm thickens, the cells elongate and form a lens placode, the precursor of the lens itself. If the nervous tissue is prevented from contacting the ectoderm, no lens is formed. The nervous tissue has induced the formation of the lens. Furthermore, if the nervous tissue destined to form the eye is transplanted under the ectoderm on the back of the animal instead of the head, it will induce lens formation in this region of the overlying ectoderm, a special form, one might say, of hindsight.

The development of the pancreas provides one of the best known examples of tissue to tissue interaction. Pancreatic cells first develop in an endoderm derivative, the lining of the primitive gut. Wessels and Rutter have discovered that, at a precise time and at a precise site in the gut wall, some of the lining cells begin to make small amounts of digestive enzymes that mark them unmistakably as pancreatic cells. At this point they bear little histological similarity to mature pancreatic cells. But in terms of gene control a critical change has taken place, for some new region of the DNA code is now being used to transcribe mRNA, and the production of the digestive enzymes is thus possible. Then a puzzling dependence develops. The endoderm from which the pancreas cells are forming requires the close proximity of mesodermal tissue to become fully differentiated into pancreatic tissue. Without mesoderm little further development takes place, but if mesoderm is present the presumptive pancreatic cells greatly multiply their numbers, form definitive gland tissues and increase their production of enzymes 50-fold—the tissue is now clearly pancreas. After this critical period the pancreatic cells are no longer dependent upon the mesoderm for normal development.

It is clear from this type of experiment that tissue type is determined before cell division ceases. Cell multiplication of the determined tissue type goes on until a certain volume of tissue is reached. In some tissues the process of cell division is then permanently halted, as with nerve cells or heart muscle cells. In other tissues, cell division may continue at a slower rate to replace tissue elements lost with time, as in the lining of the gut. In other adult tissues, the ongoing needs of rapid cell turnover are met by the division of multipotential "stem cells," cells which themselves do not differentiate but produce progeny that do. An

example is the bone marrow myeloblast, which gives rise to many different types of blood cells.

CELL DIVISION

". . . Life is an unbroken series of cell-divisions that extend backward from our own day throughout the entire past history of life. . . . It is a continuum, a never-ending stream of protoplasm in the form of cells, maintained by assimilation, growth and division. The individual is but a passing eddy in the flow which vanishes and leaves no trace, while the general stream of life goes forward."

E. B. Wilson, 1925

Cells arise by the division of preexisting cells. All of the cells of the adult human body, an estimated 10^{14} of them, are derived from just one cell, the fertilized egg. It is now realized that the structure and specificity of cells depend upon the population of proteins therein, and that these proteins are assembled under the direction of mRNA. The mRNA carries the code of the genetic material, the DNA, which is contained within the nucleus. Thus it should be apparent that newly formed cells must be endowed with exact replicas of the parent DNA complement. To accomplish this, the parent cell must duplicate exactly its DNA and then precisely divide it and distribute it to two daughter cells. The process by which the DNA molecules are duplicated is called *replication* and the mechanism by which the replicated DNA is divided to supply each daughter cell with its complete and exact complement of hereditary material is termed *mitosis*. The division of nuclear material is referred to as *karyokinesis*; the division of the cytoplasm is called *cytokinesis*. Mitosis as observed in living cells of certain species is one of the most spectacular sights in cell biology and should be viewed by every student.

DNA Replication. To achieve replication, the DNA double helix unwinds, and each strand becomes a template for the assembly of a new one, which then becomes incorporated into a new double helix. The end result,

TABLE 2-2

PERIODS OF THE CELL CYCLE, *I.E.*, FROM ONE CELL DIVISION TO THE NEXT

Period	Definition	Per Cent of Time from One Mitosis to the Next (Generation Time*)
	Interphase: Period of increasing mass with protein and RNA synthesis	
G_1	Gap$_1$: Period between previous mitosis and S	30–40% for regularly dividing cells. But time may vary considerably even lasting the lifetime of the organism
S	Synthesis: Period of DNA and histone synthesis	30–50% This interval usually constant depending upon cell type or state. May be 7 hr in some species
G_2	Gap$_2$: Period between S and beginning of mitosis	10–20% Interval fairly constant, lasting up to 2 hr
	Division	
M	Mitosis: Period when chromosomes shorten (and thus become visible), are aligned in the middle of the cell, and are divided equally	5–10% Usually lasts 1–2 hr but depends upon the cell type

* The generation time usually ranges from 10 to 30 hr; for certain human cultured cells it is 22 hours with the S period lasting about 6 hr.

therefore, is two double helices, each composed of one parent and one new strand. This mechanism of replication, termed "semi-conservative," is the usual one for mammalian somatic (body) cells. In this manner, the linear arrays of genes are copied exactly if conditions are normal. Utilization of radioactive thymidine, incorporated only into duplicating DNA molecules, has been helpful in studying the mechanism of DNA replication, as well as in discovering the time at which it occurs.

This replication is accomplished before the cell visibly enters mitosis. During the nondividing (*interphase* or "resting") period, three different phases have been defined: G_1, the gap between the previous mitosis and the start of DNA synthesis (*S*), and G_2, the gap between the end of S and the beginning of mitosis (*M*) (see Table 2-2). In general, the duplication of DNA may occur without cytokinesis, but cell division does not take place without the prefatory replication of DNA. It is known that mitosis is triggered by DNA synthesis, but the stimulus for DNA replication remains a mystery.

Mitosis. The nuclear DNA is contained within chromosomes which are not visible as such in the interphase nucleus and are therefore referred to as *chromatin.* Most of the chromosomal substance is in a dispersed form and takes little stain. After staining of the interphase nucleus, only scattered condensed areas of chromosomes are visible as particulate or clumped material, the *heterochromatin.* As the cells prepare for division, the entire chromosome becomes visible, as the term mitosis (Gr., *mitos,* thread) implies. Each chromosome becomes progressively thicker and shorter by a process of coiling. This extreme shortening of the chromosomes allows their disentanglement and precise alignment prior to their division and distribution into daughter cells.

Although mitosis is a continuous process, it is often divided into four stages: *prophase, metaphase, anaphase* and *telophase.* During a typical mitotic period, prophase may be the longest stage, perhaps 1.5 hours, whereas metaphase, anaphase and telophase take perhaps 20, 4 and 45 to 60 minutes, respectively. In cultured HeLa cells, mitosis is accomplished in about 80 minutes, the successive stages requiring about 18, 35, 13 and 14 minutes, respectively.

Prophase. The onset of prophase is recognizable as an increase in the number and density of stainable chromatin particles, which are gradually replaced by slender threads (Figs. 2-13 and 2-14). With continued coiling they become shorter and thickened in girth; the gyres of the threads (chromosomes) increase in diameter and decrease in number. The chromosomes may be studied in appropriately stained, preserved tissue or examined in the living state by means of phase optics or, better still, the Nomarski (differential interference contrast) system (Fig. 2-15).

As prophase progresses, the "double" nature of each chromosome becomes evident. Each chromosome contains twice the normal amount of DNA as a result of the replication before the onset of prophase. This doubling now becomes visible for the first time when the chromosome appears to be divided lengthwise into two parallel, closely apposing units called *chromatids*. As long as they remain attached (in one region only, the *centromere*), they are called chromatids (or "sister chromatids"; see Fig. 2-7); once they become separated (at a later interval) they are called "daughter chromosomes." The chromatids coil on themselves rather than around each other.

The organization of the DNA double helix and associated proteins within the chromatid is not yet known and remains one of the important questions in cell biology. The basic morphological unit is a 200 to 250 A diameter strand of DNA-protein, but it remains controversial whether this contains one or two strands of DNA double helix and associated protein. Furthermore, the number (probably multiple) of these 250 A units and the manner in which they are constructed into a larger chromatid remain to be clarified. Electron microscope examination of thin sections is not suited for elucidating the structure of these coiled, twisted, folded and tightly packed filaments and reveals a bewildering array of granules or short segments of filaments which vary only in packing throughout mitosis.

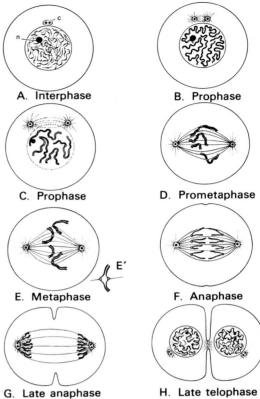

A. Interphase B. Prophase
C. Prophase D. Prometaphase
E′
E. Metaphase F. Anaphase
G. Late anaphase H. Late telophase

FIG. 2-13. Diagram illustrating the successive cellular events in mitosis, which is described in the text. *E′*, an enlargement of the two chromatids of one chromosome, showing completion of separation by detachment at the centromere region. *c*, centrosome; *n*, nucleolus.

Also during prophase, the nuclear envelope vanishes (thus allowing mixing of nuclear and cytoplasmic contents), the nucleolus disappears and centrioles start their migration to opposite poles of the cell. Prior to this, the two *centrioles* (a *diplosome*) have been clustered together, lying at right angles to one another. Between the centrioles a *mitotic spindle* of fine fibers begins to take form and enlarge. The centrioles thus act as organizing centers for the spindle and become the two poles of the spindle. The spindle fibers, now known to be microtubules, converge on, but are not continuous with, the centrioles. A small disc-like structure, the *kinetochore*, becomes visible (in

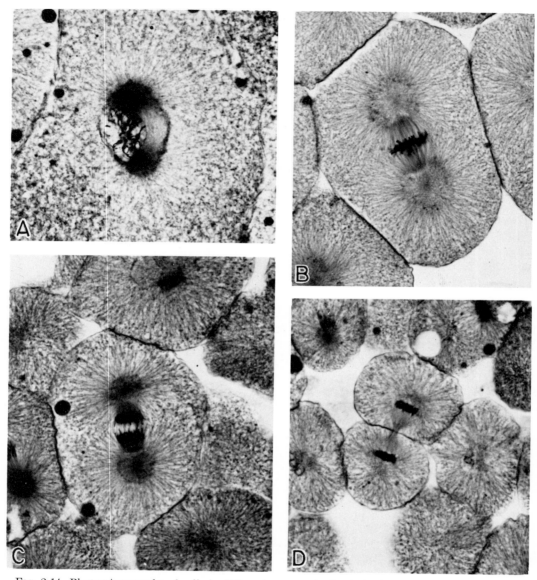

FIG. 2-14. Photomicrographs of cells in different stages of mitosis in the blastula of the white fish. *A*, late prophase, with chromosomes in coiled threads, nuclear membrane still present and the cell center divided into two new centers which have moved toward opposite poles of the nucleus; *B*, metaphase, in lateral view; *C*, early anaphase; *D*, telophase. Photographs at ×600, from slides purchased from the General Biological Supply House, Chicago.

electron micrographs) at the centromere region of each chromatid. It is in this region that some of the spindle tubules become attached to chromosomes (Fig. 2-16). The kinetochore is considered to participate in tubule assembly as well. The spindle struc-

ture provides the mechanism for subsequent chromosomal movement.

Metaphase. During *prometaphase* the spindle is fully developed and the chromosomes, all in a condensed state and thus visible in their entirety, move into it and become

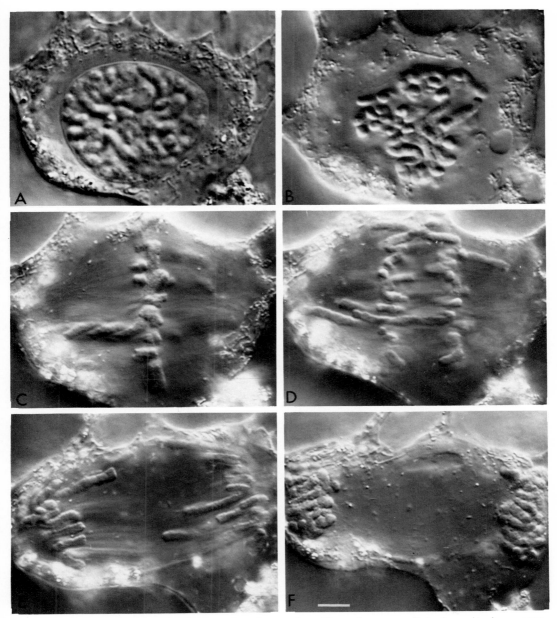

FIG. 2-15. Photomicrographs of successive changes in a lily endosperm cell during mitosis, as seen in the Nomarski optical system. This system has the advantage of revealing spindle fibers in living cells. Time after A: B, 14 min.; C, 1 hr. 4 min.; D, 1 hr. 14 min.; E, 1 hr. 33 min.; and F, 1 hr. 47 min. Compare with Figure 2-13. The *bar* indicates 10 μ. (From Bajer, A. 1968 Chromosoma, vol. 25, p. 249.)

situated midway in the spindle. During metaphase the chromatids continue to condense and shift slightly until they are oriented in a precise manner. Actually, it is the centromere portion of the chromatids which becomes aligned in the *equatorial* or *metaphase plate* of the cell (Fig. 2-13). The kinetochores of each chromatid pair are

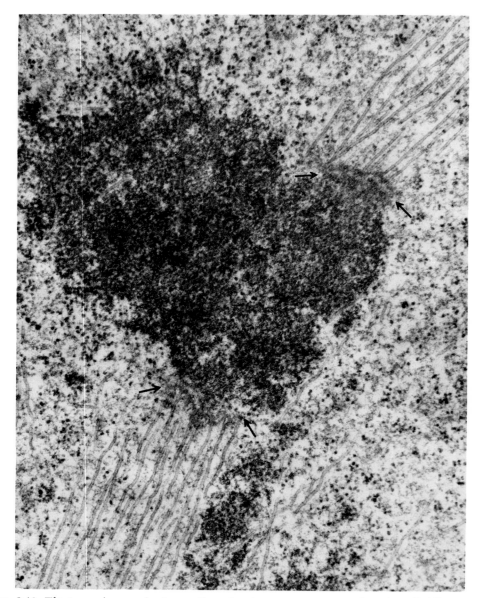

FIG. 2-16. Electron micrograph of a portion of a chromosome at metaphase in a dividing fibroblast in tissue culture. The sister chromatids are still joined in the centromere region shown here. On each chromatid, facing the pole to which it will be drawn, is the kinetochore (*arrows*). The chromosomal spindle fibers (in fact, microtubules as illustrated here) are attached to the chromatid in the kinetochore region. ×45,000. (From Brinkley, B. R. 1969. *In:* Advances in Cell Biology, edited by D. Prescott, vol. 1, p. 119. Appleton-Century-Crofts, New York.

oriented perpendicular to the spindle axis and face opposing poles, with the attached microtubules extending towards each pole (Fig. 2-16).

In living cells the spindle fibers are not visible in the phase microscope, although the spindle area is represented by a clear zone around which are clustered organelles, but they can be seen in the Nomarski system (Fig. 2-15) and appear as birefringent structures in the polarizing microscope (Fig. 2-17). The spindle may be demonstrated in fixed and stained preparations (Fig. 2-14). The spindle is resolved in the electron microscope (Fig. 2-18) as a large array of microtubules which may number in the hundreds or thousands, depending upon the species. A number of microtubules are attached to one kinetochore and may extend in bundles, which accounts for their visibility in the Nomarski system. There are two types of spindle fibers: *continuous fibers* which extend from pole to pole and *chromosomal fibers* which extend from the kinetochore to a pole. The spindle apparatus is highly labile, but it may be isolated from the cell for special study.

When colchicine or related compounds are administered to dividing cells, mitosis is arrested at the beginning of metaphase. Apparently colchicine blocks the migration of the centrioles, presumably because some continuous fibers cannot form to aid in their poleward movement. Because both kinetochores of a chromatid pair do not face opposing centrioles, one of the kinetochores lacks chromosomal fibers, with the result that the sister chromatids cannot be pulled apart. (If the colchicine is washed away, within minutes centriole migration is initiated, the spindle develops, the chromatids are aligned on the metaphase plate and anaphase movement is visible.)

During the paralysis of chromosome separation induced by colchicine, the chromatids nevertheless continue condensing and thus become shorter and thicker than normal, allowing their ready visualization and identification in the light microscope. At this point, each chromosome assumes a characteristic form, depending upon its length and the position of its centromere, or *primary constriction*. This array of chromosomes of varying form is distinctive for a given species and is known as the *karyotype*, explained earlier in the chapter.

Anaphase. Following chromosomal alignment in the metaphase plate, the chromatids are ready to be pulled apart. With division of the only point of attachment between each chromatid pair, the centromere, the two daughter chromosomes begin their journey to opposite poles. They are pulled at the kinetochore, with the remainder of the chromosome trailing behind. They are brought to the polar regions where they become maximally condensed and may appear to fuse with one another. At the same time the entire spindle elongates, and a furrow around the cell (in a plane midway in and perpendicular to the spindle axis) heralds the beginning of cytoplasmic cleavage.

The mechanism by which the separated daughter chromosomes are pulled to opposite poles is not yet clearly established, although it has been debated and there is no lack of hypothetical explanations. It is considered that the poleward pulling of chromosomes is at least partly explained by the shortening of fibers extending between the kinetochore and the centriole. This shortening occurs not by contraction but by depolymerization of the fibers (tubules) in the centriole region. Tubule subunits thus freed are then available for assembly into, and subsequent lengthening of, the continuous tubules, thereby providing the basis for the overall extension of the spindle. The recent discovery of bridges or arms 100 to 400 A long on the spindle tubules as seen in the electron microscope has prompted the suggestion that these structures contain an enzyme (ATPase) which is capable of releasing the chemical energy stored in ATP to do mechanical work such as pulling the tubules past one another. This mechanism is analogous to the sliding filament model of muscle. The interested reader is referred to discussions of chromosomal movement by Brinkley and coworkers, Inoué and Sato, and McIntosh and collaborators.

Centrioles usually are duplicated in anaphase or telophase to provide each daughter cell with its interphase complement. Centrioles are self-replicating, apparently not by

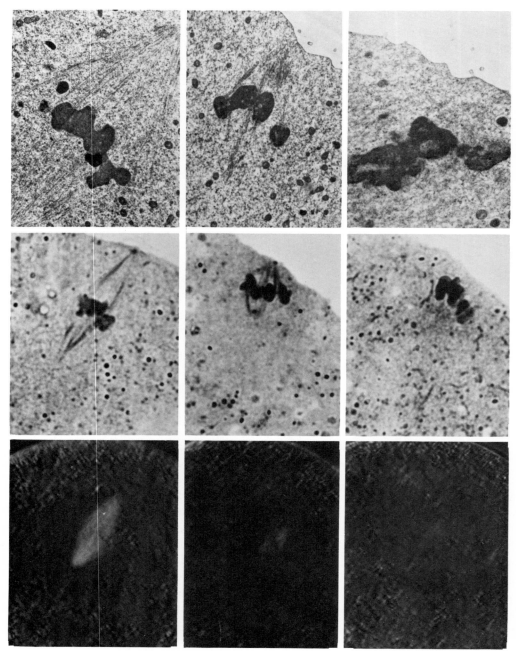

Fig. 2-17. Effect of administering an agent (vinblastine) known to arrest a dividing cell in metaphase. Division is interrupted because the spindle fibers disappear, as demonstrated in electron micrographs (*top row, left to right*), light micrographs (obtained by sectioning at 1 μ the tissue prepared for electron microscopy, staining with toluidine blue and viewing in the phase microscope; *middle row*) and photographs of living cells taken in the polarizing microscope (*bottom row*). This set of pictures also serves to demonstrate that spindle birefringence depends upon the presence of an array of spindle fibers. Living marine worm oocyte. (From Malawista, S. E., Sato, H., and Bensch, K. G. 1968 Science, vol. 160, p. 770.)

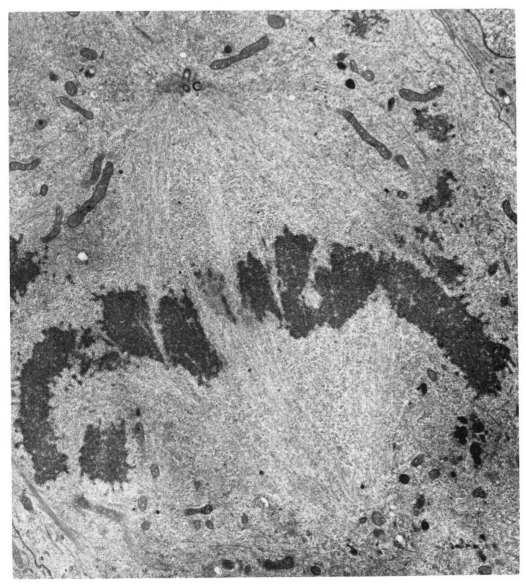

FIG. 2-18. Electron micrograph showing a mitotic spindle at metaphase. The dark objects in the *center* are the chromosomes, oriented in the metaphase plate. The chromosomes are suspended in myriads of linear elements which are barely visible at this low magnification; these elements are the chromosomal and the continuous spindle fibers. In this plane the centrioles (*c*) at one pole of the spindle can be seen; the daughter centriole is perpendicular to the parent centriole. Other cytoplasmic organelles such as mitochondria are confined to areas outside the spindle. Rat kangaroo fibroblast in tissue culture; ×10,000. (Courtesy of Dr. B. R. Brinkley.)

division but by one acting as a template for the organization of a new one. Some evidence would suggest that both DNA and RNA are present in the centriole.

Telophase. Once the chromosomes have reached the poles of the spindle, reformation of the nuclear envelope (from cisternae of endoplasmic reticulum) begins. Subsequently the cytoplasm is divided into two new daughter cells. These remain connected for a time by a narrow stalk of cytoplasm into which some of the remaining continuous microtubules and associated dense substance have been gathered. This temporary, dense isthmus is termed the *midbody*. Chromosomal spindle fibers and the kinetochore structures disappear.

The new daughter nuclei are at first small and very dense. Gradually, these nuclei enlarge and the chromosomes begin to disperse. The reconstruction of the nucleus appears to be the reverse of the changes of prophase: chromosomes become progressively thinner, their presence eventually signified only by the scattered heterochromatin particles characteristic of the interphase nucleus. One or more nucleoli reappear, in association with the nucleolar-organizer regions of certain chromosomes.

General Considerations of Mitosis. Cell division also has an important function in relation to cell growth because without division cells eventually reach a stage where growth ceases. There is no increase in total cell mass during mitosis, but immediately following division the two daughter cells grow rapidly and they continue growing until the mass of cytoplasm reaches a point in relation to nuclear size which is characteristic for a particular cell type. When some of the cytoplasm is removed from an ameba by microsurgery without damage to the nucleus, the cell will regenerate the cytoplasm without nuclear division. For further details on the significance of mitosis, the reader is referred to the excellent article by Mazia (1961).

The constancy of the number of chromosomes, along with other data, indicates that the chromosomes retain their individuality during the intermitotic stage. Earlier in the chapter we reviewed the evidence that the genetic material is not altered during differentiation but that different sites of this material are expressed at different times. Usually the amount of DNA per given chromosome does not vary, no matter what the metabolic variations may be. The DNA molecule is extremely stable, and this stability is the basis for the continuity of life.

Meiosis. As we have just learned, mitosis is the process by which new daughter cells acquire a complete genetic complement identical to that of the parent cell. In man, the set of 46 chromosomes (the *diploid* number) is thus passed on from generation to generation of daughter cells. If this were the case during the formation of the egg and sperm cells, however, the fusion of nuclei at fertilization would lead to a set of 92 chromosomes. Therefore, a somewhat different division process, *meiosis* (or *reduction division*) is at work in the development of each germ cell to provide for the presence of only 23 chromosomes (the *haploid* number). The diploid number of chromosomes is then restored at the time of fertilization. Meiosis is discussed further in Chapter 19.

REFERENCES

GENERAL TOPICS

DeHaan, R. L., and Ursprung, H. (editors) 1965 Organogenesis. Holt, Rinehart and Winston, New York.

Ebert, J. D., and Sussex, I. M. 1970 Interacting Systems in Development. Ed. 2, Holt, Rinehart and Winston, New York.

Harris, H. 1968 Nucleus and Cytoplasm. Clarendon Press, Oxford.

Haynes, R. H., and Hanawalt, P. C. (editors) 1968 The Molecular Basis of Life. Readings from Scientific American. W. H. Freeman and Company, San Francisco.

Kennedy, D. (editor) 1965 The Living Cell. Readings from Scientific American. W. H. Freeman and Company, San Francisco.

Waddington, C. H. 1966 Principles of Development and Differentiation. The Macmillan Company, New York.

Willmer, E. N. (editor) 1965 Cells and Tissues in Culture. vols. 1, 2, and 3. Academic Press, New York.

SPECIAL TOPICS

Tissue Culture

Carrel, A. 1912 On the permanent life of tissues outside of the organism. J. Exp. Med., vol. 15, p. 516.

Fell, H. B. 1951 Histogenesis in tissue culture.

Cytology and Cell Physiology (Bourne, G. H., editor), Ed. 2, pp. 419–443. Clarendon Press, Oxford.

HARRISON, R. G. 1907 Observations on the living developing nerve fiber. Proc. Soc. Exp. Biol. Med., vol. 4, p. 140.

PARKER, R. C. 1961 Methods of Tissue Culture, Ed. 3. Hoeber Medical Division, Harper and Row, Publishers, New York.

PAUL, J. 1960 Cell and Tissue Culture, Ed. 2. The Williams and Wilkins Company, Baltimore.

WHITE, P. R. 1954 The Cultivation of Animal and Plant Cells. The Ronald Press Company, New York.

Experimental Manipulation of Living Cells

AMY, R. L., STORB, R., FAUCONNIER, B., AND WERTZ, R. K. 1967 Ruby laser micro-irradiation of single tissue culture cells vitally stained with Janus green B. Exp. Cell Res., vol. 45, pp. 361–373.

CHAMBERS, R. 1949 Micrurgical studies on protoplasm. Biol. Rev., vol. 24, pp. 246–265.

KOPAC, M. J. 1959 Micrurgical studies on living cells. The Cell; Biochemistry, Physiology, Morphology (Brachet, J., and Mirsky, A. E., editors), vol. 1, pp. 161–191. Academic Press, New York.

ROSE, G. G., (editor) 1963 Cinemicrography in Cell Biology. Academic Press, New York.

ZIRKLE, R. E., AND BLOOM, W. 1953 Irradiation of parts of individual cells. Science, vol. 117, pp. 487–493.

Activities of Living Cells

ALLEN, R. D., AND KAMIYA, N. (editors) 1964 Primitive Motile Systems in Cell Biology. Academic Press, New York.

CLARK, E. R. 1954 The transparent chamber technique for the microscopic study of living blood vessels. Anat. Rec., vol. 120, pp. 241–252.

FAWCETT, D. W. 1966 Transient differentiations associated with surface activity. The Cell. Its Organelles and Inclusions, pp. 389–414. W. B. Saunders Company, Philadelphia.

FURSHPAN, E., AND POTTER, D. 1968 Low resistance junctions between cells in embryos and tissue culture. Current Topics in Developmental Biology (Moscona, A., editor), pp. 95–125. Academic Press, New York.

GROPP, A. 1963 Phagocytosis and pinocytosis. Cinemicrography in Cell Biology (Rose, G. G., editor), pp. 279–312. Academic Press, New York.

HOLTER, H. 1959 Pinocytosis. Int. Rev. Cytol., vol. 8, pp. 481–504.

KAYE, G. I., PAPPAS, G. D., DONN, A., AND MALLETT, N. 1962 Studies on the cornea. II. The uptake and transport of colloidal particles by the living rabbit cornea *in vitro*. J. Cell Biol., vol. 12, pp. 481–501.

KNISELY, M. H. 1938 An improved fused quartz living tissue illuminator. Anat. Rec., vol. 71, pp. 503–508.

LEWIS, W. H. 1931 Pinocytosis. Bull. Johns Hopkins Hosp., vol. 49, pp. 17–27.

SPEIDEL, C. C. 1935 Studies of living nerves. IV. Growth, regeneration, and myelination of peripheral nerves in salamanders. Biol. Bull., vol. 68, pp. 140–161.

TRINKAUS, J. P. 1965 Mechanisms of morphogenetic movements. Organogenesis (DeHaan, R. L., and Ursprung, H., editors), pp. 55–104. Holt, Rinehart and Winston, New York.

Cytological Analysis in Tissue Culture

FITZGERALD, P. H. 1969 Chromosomal abnormalities in man. The Biological Basis of Medicine (Bittar, E. E., editor), vol. 4, pp. 133–178. Academic Press, New York.

HARRIS, H. 1968 Hybrid cells. Nucleus and Cytoplasm, Chap. 5, pp. 89–110. Clarendon Press, Oxford.

HARRIS, M. 1964 Cell Culture and Somatic Variation. Holt, Rinehart and Winston, New York.

HAYFLICK, L. 1968 Human cells and aging. Sci. Amer., vol. 218, (Mar.), pp. 32–37.

KONIGSBERG, I. R. 1963 Clonal analysis of myogenesis. Science, vol. 140, pp. 1273–1284.

MINTZ, B. 1965 Genetic mosaicism in adult mice of quadriparental lineage. Science, vol. 148, pp. 1232–1233.

MITTWOCH, U. 1967 The Sex Chromosomes. Academic Press, New York.

MOSCONA, A., AND MOSCONA, H. 1952 The dissociation and aggregation of cells from organ rudiments of the early chick embryo. J. Anat., vol. 86, pp. 287–301.

PUCK, T. T., MARCUS, P. I., AND CIECIURA, S. J. 1956 Clonal growth of mammalian cells in vitro. Growth characteristics of colonies from single HeLa cells with and without a "feeder" layer. J. Exp. Med., vol. 103, pp. 273–284.

Cell Differentiation

FRENSTER, J. H. 1965 Mechanisms of repression and de-repression within interphase chromatin. In Vitro, vol. 1, pp. 78–101.

GROBSTEIN, C. 1959 Differentiation of vertebrate cells. The Cell; Biochemistry, Physiology, Morphology (Brachet, J., and Mirsky, A. E., editors), vol. 1, pp. 437–496. Academic Press, New York.

GURDON, J. B. 1968 Transplanted nuclei and cell differentiation. Sci. Amer., vol. 219, (Dec.), 24–35.

JACOB, F., AND MONOD, J. 1961 Genetic regulatory mechanisms in the synthesis of protein. J. Mol. Biol., vol. 3, pp. 318–356.

KING, T. J., AND BRIGGS, R. 1965 Serial transplantation of embryonic nuclei. Molecular and Cellular Aspects of Development (Bell, E., editor), pp. 171–192. Harper and Row, Publishers, New York.

LEBLOND, C. P., AND WALKER, B. E. 1956 Renewal of cell populations. Physiol. Rev., vol. 36, pp. 255–276.

LOOMIS, W. F., JR. (editor) 1970 Papers on Regulation of Gene Activity during Development. Harper and Row, Publishers, New York.

WESSELS, N. K., AND RUTTER, W. J. 1969 Phases in cell differentiation. Sci. Amer., vol. 220, (Mar.), pp. 36–44.

Cell Division

Chromosome Morphology

DUPRAW, E. J. 1966 Evidence for a "folded-fibre" organization in human chromosomes. Nature (London), vol. 209, pp. 577–581.

GALL, J. 1963 Chromosome fibers from an interphase nucleus. Science, vol. 139, pp. 120–121.

MOSES, M. J., AND COLEMAN, J. R. 1964 Structural patterns and the functional organization of chromosomes. The Role of Chromosomes in Development (Locke, M., editor), pp. 11–49. Academic Press, New York.

RIS, H. 1967 Ultrastructure of the animal chromosomes. Regulation of Nucleic Acid and Protein Biosynthesis (Koningsberger, V. V., and Bosch, L., editors), pp. 11–21. American Elsevier Publishing Company, New York.

WOLFE, S. L. 1969 Molecular organization of chromosomes. The Biological Basis of Medicine (Bittar, E. E., editor), vol. 4, pp. 3–42. Academic Press, New York.

(*See also* references at end of Chapter 1)

Mitosis

BRINKLEY, B. R., STUBBLEFIELD, E., AND HSU, T. C. 1967 The effects of colcemid inhibition and reversal on the fine structure of the mitotic apparatus of Chinese hamster cells *in vitro*. J. Ultrastruct. Res., vol. 19, pp. 1–18.

DE HARVEN, E. 1968 The centriole and the mitotic spindle. The Nucleus (Dalton, A. J., and Haguenau, F., editors), pp. 197–227. Academic Press, New York.

DEROBERTIS, E. D. P., NOWINSKI, W. W., AND SAEZ, F. A. 1970 Cell Biology, Ed. 5. W. B. Saunders Company, Philadelphia.

INOUÉ, S., AND SATO, H. 1967 Cell motility by labile association of molecules. The nature of mitotic spindle fibers and their role in chromosome movement. J. Gen. Physiol., vol. 50 (Suppl.), pp. 259–288.

KORNBERG, A. 1968 The synthesis of DNA. Sci. Amer., vol. 219, (Oct.), pp. 64–78.

MAZIA, D. 1961 Mitosis and the physiology of cell division. The Cell; Biochemistry, Physiology, Morphology (Brachet, J., and Mirsky, A. E., editors), vol. 3, pp. 77–412. Academic Press, New York.

MCINTOSH, J. R., HEPLER, P. K., AND VAN WIE, D. G. 1969 Model for mitosis. Nature (London), vol. 224, pp. 659–663.

ROBBINS, E., AND GONATAS, N. K. 1964 The ultrastructure of a mammalian cell during the mitotic cycle. J. Cell Biol., vol. 21, pp. 429–463.

SCHRADER, F. 1953 Mitosis, Ed. 2. Columbia University Press, New York.

STUBBLEFIELD, E., AND BRINKLEY, B. R. 1967 Architecture and function of the mammalian centriole. Formation and Fate of Cell Organelles (Warren, K. B., editor), pp. 175–218. Academic Press, New York.

3

General Features of Vertebrate Development

MORPHOGENESIS

The vertebrates, to which man and other mammals belong, may be defined as triploblastic (three layered), metameric (segmented), celomic (body cavity), bilaterally symmetrical animals possessing at some stage a notochord, a dorsal hollow nervous system and pharyngeal clefts.

A brief analysis of the developmental processes which result in a body form having these distinctive characteristics will give the student an outline of the plan of organization of the human body. More detailed information rightly belongs in a textbook of developmental anatomy or of vertebrate embryology.

Normal development begins with a sperm-fertilized egg, a single cell in which the fusion of a male with a female pronucleus has occurred. This cell divides into daughter cells, which continue to divide and adhere, thereby forming a multicellular mass. Although the earlier cell divisions are primarily cleavages of the original egg-cell substance, the process soon becomes associated with actual growth, so that a rapid increase in mass results.

During the early divisions there is little difference among the accumulating cells. Before long, however, the cells, even though not greatly dissimilar in appearance, begin to be arranged in three distinct layers which have been referred to as the three fundamental *germ layers*. Because of their position in the developing embryo they are known as *ectoderm*, *mesoderm* and *entoderm*, terms which mean technically outer, middle and inner skins.

The cells of each of the three germ layers divide, differentiate and group themselves into specialized tissues, which in turn are organized into organs and organ systems. Tissues from different germ layers, although they retain their individuality, frequently associate in the formation of an organ. Through embryological studies we can now name (with only a few exceptions) the original germ layer from which each and every cell of the fully differentiated body has come. The process whereby undifferentiated cells of a germ layer develop into the specialized cells of tissues is termed *histogenesis*. In terms of principal tissue components, the outer epithelia and the nervous system develop from the ectoderm; the lungs, the gut epithelium and its derivatives from the entoderm; the blood, skeleton and muscles, as well as the organs of excretion and reproduction from the mesoderm. A more complete list of derivatives is found at the close of this section.

Several of the most prominent and diagnostic features of the vertebrate are determined in the histogenesis of the mesoderm.

Among these are bilateral symmetry, metamerism and the formation of the celom, commonly called the body cavity. The mesodermal cells first appear bilaterally in a dorsolateral position between the ectodermal and entodermal layers. From this mass of cells a definite tissue layer organizes which pushes its way ventrally between the ectoderm and entoderm of the embryo. On each side of the hollow nerve tube, which has previously organized from ectoderm, the mesodermal cells form a series of compact segments, frequently referred to as mesodermal somites. Later each pair of somites develops a vertebra with its processes and the muscles related to it. Thus, the axial skeleton retains an internal segmented structure, although the subsequent relation of the muscle and skin may obscure any external evidence of segmentation.

The ventral extension of mesoderm splits into two sheets. One adheres to the ectoderm and is known as *somatic mesoderm*. Together with the ectoderm it is referred to as the *somatopleure*. The other associates with the entoderm and is called *splanchnic mesoderm*. Together with the entoderm it forms the *splanchnopleure*. The somatic and splanchnic layers of mesoderm enclose a cavity, the *celom*, which becomes the body cavity of the embryo. In later development this cavity gives rise through partitioning to the pericardial, the pleural and the abdominal cavity. It follows, therefore, that the pericardial, pleural and peritoneal membranes which

form the walls of these cavities are all of mesodermal origin. The epithelium of these internal surfaces is likewise mesodermal and is called *mesothelium*. The student must be on guard to note that *mesothelium* is a term arbitrarily restricted to the *epithelium lining closed body cavities* and that it is not a name for any of the numerous other types of epithelium derived from mesoderm and mesenchyme.

Certain mesodermal elements organize to form the complex system of blood and lymph channels which ramify throughout the body. Their internal cavities are likewise lined with epithelial cells of mesodermal origin, but these cells have been specially designated as *endothelium*. This term is somewhat confusing, and the student must be alert to avoid the error of associating endothelium with entoderm.

The *ectoderm* of the *middorsal line* of the embryo forms the central nervous system. At first, the cells become thicker and form a *medullary (neural) plate* (Fig. 3-1). Then there is further growth and infolding to form a *neural groove*. The groove deepens and its walls rise to meet dorsally, forming a *neural tube*. This tube differentiates into the brain and spinal cord, in which the cavities remain as the brain ventricles and spinal canal. The repeated pairs of cranial and spinal nerves which arise from the original tube again follow for the most part the plan of bilateral symmetry and of a segmented organization of the body.

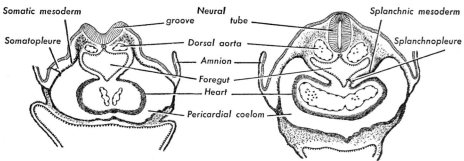

FIG. 3-1. Section through a seven-somite human embryo (*left*) and a 10-somite human embryo (*right*). (Redrawn after Patten.)

The *major portion of the embryonic ectoderm* (i.e., other than that of the middorsal line and that for special regions listed at the end of this chapter) forms the *epidermis* of the skin and its derivatives: *hair, nails, sweat glands* and *sebaceous glands.*

The *entoderm*, or inner tube of embryonic cells, forms the *epithelium of most of the digestive tract* and outgrowths from the digestive tract, such as *liver* and *pancreas.* It also forms the *lining of most of the respiratory tract* and other regions listed at the end of this chapter. Mesoderm is associated with entoderm in the final development of all of these structures in the sense that it contributes their connective tissue, muscle, and blood and lymph vessels.

The adult tissues are not composed of cells only. At a very early stage of differentiation, the cells become separated from each other by the formation of intercellular substance which may be the result of cellular secretion or may represent actual modification of cellular protoplasm. Thus, each tissue is an aggregate of cells with its own characteristic intercellular substance, frequently called a *matrix.* In some tissues the intercellular material is scanty in amount, and the cells are in close contact with one another (epithelium, muscle). In other tissues the intercellular substance may assume large proportions and may contain highly differentiated elements of important physiological significance (bone, cartilage, connective tissue, blood).

The adult tissues are usually classified into four main groups: (1) epithelial tissue, (2) connective tissue with its derivatives, blood and lymph, (3) muscle tissue, (4) nerve tissue.

Of these, epithelium and connective tissue may be regarded as the more elementary tissues. Muscle and nerve are the most highly specialized tissues. Blood is a unique tissue, closely related to the connective tissues, in which the cells are suspended and move freely in a fluid intercellular substance.

A number of tissues are, as a rule, intimately associated with each other in forming the various organs and organ systems of the body.

The student of histology learns the finer organization of the body structures largely from prepared slices of tissue mounted upon glass slides. Here he concentrates his attention upon the more solid remnants of its substance. He is likely to pass lightly over the important fact that the body tissues contain large proportions of fluid which are not evident in the preparations. He may also fail to grasp the fact that the vital, physiological reactions depend upon fluid media, and that fluid-filled cavities and fluid-bathed surface membranes are indispensable in the organization. On numerous occasions one is impressed with the unique manner in which the necessary surface areas are increased by folds, by invaginations and by evaginations. An alert attention to the presence of these developmental processes in the makeup of the various organ systems will repay with a better understanding and finer appreciation of the manner in which the tissues have organized to serve their functions.

GERM LAYER DERIVATIVES

The various tissue derivatives from the primary germ layers are as follows.

Ectoderm. (1) Epithelium of skin and the hair, nails, sebaceous and mammary glands and sweat glands, including the associated smooth muscle fibers (myoepithelial cells).

(2) Epithelium of mouth and anus, of glands opening into mouth, taste buds and enamel of teeth.

(3) Epithelium of nose and of glands and cavities connected with nose.

(4) Epithelium of external auditory canal and of membranous labyrinth.

(5) Epithelium of anterior surface of cornea, of conjunctiva, of lacrimal gland, **of** pars nervosa, and pars ciliaris and pars iridica retinae; also muscle tissue of sphinc-

ter and dilator pupillae and the crystalline lens.

(6) Epithelium of the penile urethra.

(7) The medulla of the suprarenal glands, the pineal gland and all of the lobes of the pituitary gland.

(8) All nerve cells, part of the neuroglia and linings of the central canal and brain ventricles.

Entoderm. (1) Epithelium of the digestive tract (excepting mouth and its glands and anus) and of glands connected with di-digestive tract, including liver, gall bladder and pancreas.

(2) Epithelium of respiratory tract (except nostrils) and of its glands.

(3) Epithelium of bladder (except the trigonum), of female urethra, of vaginal vestibule and vestibular glands, of prostatic portion of male urethra, prostatic glands and bulbourethral glands.

(4) Epithelium of tympanum and of Eustachian tube.

(5) Thyroid and parathyroid glands, and the Hassall's corpuscles and reticulum of the thymus.

Mesoderm. (1) All of the connective or supporting tissues except a part of the neuroglia.

(2) Lymphatic organs (except Hassall's corpuscles and reticulum of the thymus).

(3) Blood cells and bone marrow.

(4) Skeletal, cardiac and smooth muscle (with the exception of smooth muscle of sweat glands and of the pupillary muscles of the eye).

(5) Endothelium lining blood vessels and lymphatics.

(6) Mesothelium lining serous membranes—pleura, pericardium, peritoneum.

(7) Epithelium of genitourinary system, with the exception of the urethra and a large part of the bladder.

(8) The suprarenal cortex.

REFERENCES

AREY, L. B. 1965 Developmental Anatomy, ed. 7. W. B. Saunders Company, Philadelphia.

BELL, E. (editor) 1965 Molecular and Cellular Aspects of Development. Harper and Row, New York.

HAMILTON, W. J., BOYD, J. D., AND MOSSMAN, H. W. 1962 Human Embryology, ed. 3. The Williams & Wilkins Company, Baltimore.

HAY, E. D. 1966 Embryologic origin of tissues. *In*: Histology (Greep, R. O., editor), pp. 56–73. McGraw-Hill Book Company, New York.

LANGMAN, J. 1969 Medical Embryology, Ed. 2. Williams & Wilkins Company, Baltimore.

PATTEN, B. M. 1968 Human Embryology. McGraw-Hill Book Company, New York.

4

Epithelium

The preceding chapters deal with the cell primarily as a structural and functional unit. They present basic information on the constituents commonly found in all cells, and they also point out some specializations related to particular functions, such as, for example, more contractile elements in muscle cells. Chapter 3 briefly outlines the histogenesis of different types of cells and notes that cells of similar function are generally grouped together as tissues. A tissue may be defined as a collection of cells and associated intercellular material specialized for a particular function or functions.

As stated in Chapter 3, tissues are usually classified into four main categories: (1) epithelium, (2) connective tissue, including its derivatives, blood and lymph, (3) muscle and (4) nervous tissue.

Epithelium may be defined as a collection of adherent cells, with very little intercellular material, covering external and internal surfaces of the body. It is in itself avascular, although its functions are dependent on a close relationship to blood vessels.

Epithelium covers the surface of the body as epidermis, and lines all passages leading to the exterior (the lining of digestive, respiratory and urogenital systems). It also lines most of the closed cavities of the body. More specifically, it lines the pleural, pericardial and peritoneal cavities, there known as mesothelium (Fig. 4-2), and it lines blood and lymph vessels, there known as endo-

thelium. An exception to the rule that free surfaces are always covered by epithelium is found in joints: the synovial membranes and bursae of these regions are covered by modified connective tissue cells, which do not form a continuous lining as do the mesothelial cells of the body cavities.

During development, the epithelium covering a surface may send growths into the underlying tissue. These show special characteristics and form glands. They usually contain cavities or passages leading to the surface from which they grew (exocrine glands, Chapter 15). Some ingrowths form deeply lying cords or aggregates of cells which lose their passages or ducts (endocrine glands, Chapter 21).

Epithelium is subjected to different functional demands in different locations. On the surface of the body, it is subjected to abrasion, attrition and drying, and it serves a protective function to a high degree. In less exposed locations, as in the closed body cavities, it is subjected to but little attrition and is covered with a fluid film; in these locations it forms smooth surfaces which glide over each other. In still other locations, it serves not only for protection but also for secretion and absorption. In some places, it is adapted to great changes in surface area, as in the urinary bladder. In correlation with the differences in functional demands, there are marked differences in structure. The epithelial cells vary in shape, in number of cell layers, in physical and structural characteristics and in their mode of attachment to each other.

CLASSIFICATION

Epithelium is classified into different types on the basis of the number of cell layers and the shape of the cells at the surface layer. Thus, epithelia of only one layer are simple, and they are subdivided, according to the height of the cells, into *simple squamous, simple cuboidal* and *simple columnar* (Table 4-1 and Fig. 4-1).

The epithelium of some parts of the body consists of a single layer of cells of variable height and arrangement, with all cells resting on the basement membrane but with only some of the cells reaching the free surface. The nuclei are seen at different levels above the basement membrane, and on first inspection one might conclude that the epithelium is stratified. With careful study and in appropriately stained preparations, one can determine that some of the epithelium which appears to be stratified is really composed of only one layer of cells. It is classified as *pseudostratified* (Fig. 4-1).

An epithelium composed of two or more layers is stratified and is subdivided, according to the shape of the surface cells, into *stratified squamous, stratified cuboidal* and *stratified columnar*. The student should note that stratified squamous is the most commonly found stratified type. He should also note that only the upper layers are squamous; those on the basal lamina and for a considerable distance above are columnar and polyhedral (Figs. 4-1 and 14-4). In epidermis, each of the regions has special functions which are described later (Chapter 14).

A special modification of stratified epithelium is found in the urinary system where the number of cell layers and the shapes of the cells vary with distention and contraction of the organ. This type of epithelium is classified as *transitional* (Figs. 4-1, 4-14).

SPECIAL CYTOLOGICAL CHARACTERISTICS

Attachments between Cells and Internal Supporting Structures. Epithelial cells are held together by special attachment junctions distributed at intervals along apposing cell membranes, in addition to a cohesive force that acts, in general,

TABLE 4-1

TYPES OF EPITHELIUM

Number of cell layers	Shape of surface cell	Examples of location in the body
Simple (one layer of cells)	Squamous	Endothelium of blood vessels, mesothelium of body cavities, thin segment of Henle's loop in kidney
	Cuboidal	Some kidney tubules
	Columnar	Gastrointestinal tract
Pseudostratified (modification of simple; not all cells reach the surface)	Columnar	Trachea, parts of male reproductive system
Stratified (more than one layer of cells)	Squamous	Epidermis, lining of esophagus, vagina
	Cuboidal	Infrequent; found in duct of sweat gland
	Columnar	Infrequent; found in parts of epiglottis and in the male urethra
Transitional (variety of stratified; varies with distention)	Surface cell varies from dome shape in contracted organ to flat in distended state	Lining of renal pelvis, ureter, urinary bladder, and parts of urethra

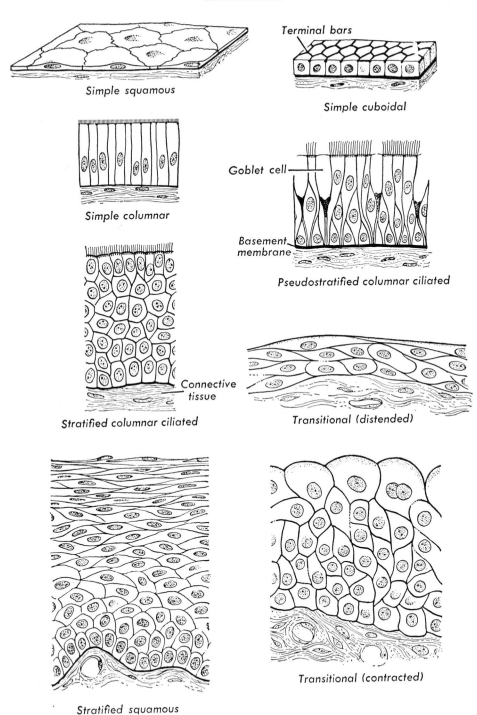

Simple squamous

Terminal bars

Simple cuboidal

Simple columnar

Goblet cell

Basement membrane

Pseudostratified columnar ciliated

Connective tissue

Stratified columnar ciliated

Transitional (distended)

Stratified squamous

Transitional (contracted)

FIG. 4-1. Schematic representation of the various morphological types of epithelium. In each case, the epithelium is shown with some of the underlying connective tissue.

along adjacent cell surfaces. There is also an internal structural support provided by fine filaments within the cytoplasm. Since the system of cytoplasmic filaments is in the form of a meshwork, it is known as the *cell web* or *cytoskeleton*.

Although the cytoplasmic filaments vary in diameter in different locations and in different species, they are regularly too slender to be seen individually with the light microscope. The *tonofibrils* originally observed in epidermal cells with the light microscope represent bundles of *tonofilaments* seen in electron micrographs. Although the filaments are widely distributed in the cytoplasm, they are often more concentrated in particular regions. In columnar epithelial cells of the intestinal tract, the cell web is concentrated chiefly in a narrow zone at the apical or luminal end of the cell and is known as the *terminal web* (Fig. 16-39). Filaments from the web form a "core" in each of the microvilli which project upward from the cells. The tonofilaments of epidermal cells are widely distributed through the cell cytoplasm for general internal structural support and they continue into the special attachment zones at intercellular junctions.

One of the commonest types of epithelial attachments is known either as a *desmosome* (Gr., *desmos*, bond + *soma*, body) or as a *macula adherens* (L. *macula*, spot + *adhaereo*, to stick). Desmosomes are particularly numerous in stratified epithelium where they were first described from light microscope studies as "intercellular bridges." The techniques for preparing tissues for sectioning cause the cells to shrink and pull apart, except in the regions of adherence. Hence, the intercellular spaces are widened and the "bridges" stand out by contrast (Fig. 4-13). Electron micrographs show that the space separating the apposing cell membranes at the desmosome junction is about 200–250 A (Fig. 4-3). The cell membrane is no thicker in this region than elsewhere, but it may appear thicker because there is an electron-

dense plaque of cytoplasmic material subjacent to and parallel with the plasmalemma (Figs. 4-3 to 4-5). Numerous tonofilaments converge in a region of condensed cytoplasm subjacent to the plaque. It was once thought that the tonofilaments terminate in the desmosomes, but further studies of high resolution electron micrographs indicate that many of the filaments form either shallow or hairpin loops that turn backward into the cytoplasm (Kelly, 1966). The substance in the intercellular space between apposing cell membranes at the desmosome level is apparently similar to the coating on the outer leaflet of the plasmalemma in other regions but more abundant. A narrow, electron-dense line, parallel with and midway between the apposing cell membranes, may indicate the junction of the coatings of the membranes. The nature of the mechanisms holding the cells together at the desmosomes is not clearly understood.

In the simple (single layered) epithelia, three different types of intercellular attachments are often found in sequence, forming a *junctional complex*. They can be seen particularly well in the simple columnar epithelium of the intestine. As shown diagrammatically in Figure 4-6 and in electron micrographs (Fig. 16-39), the outer layers of the trilaminar plasma membranes of adjacent cells are fused (or within 20 A of being fused) at their upper or juxtaluminal ends. The union extends around the cell and resembles a zonula or little girdle. It also closes or occludes the intercellular space from continuity with the lumen. Hence, it is named a *zonula occludens*. Filaments in the subjacent cytoplasm are continuous with those of the terminal web, but there is no pronounced condensation of cytoplasm and filaments in this part of the complex. Just below the occludens, the adjacent cell membranes are separated by a narrow space of uniform width, but they adhere firmly to each other. Since the modified zone is in the form of a girdle and since the cells adhere, the region is named a *zonula adherens*. The subjacent cytoplasm is condensed and contains numerous filaments continuous with those of the terminal web. The zonula does not have an electron-dense plaque in the subjacent cytoplasm like that described for the macula; this difference is useful in distinguishing the junctions. Just below the zonula adherens, one often finds one or more maculae adherentes. The latter are identical with the desmosomes described earlier as individual units. They do not form a girdle like the zonula; rather they are spots of adherence, like spot welding. A row of desmosomes is usually present as a part of the junctional complex; additional desmosomes may be found at other levels.

A definite border around the juxtaluminal ends of epithelial cells can be seen under the light microscope in special preparations, particularly after staining with silver nitrate (Fig. 4-2). These zones were originally named terminal bars by light microscopists because it was thought that the stained material consisted of an intercellular substance. Electron micrographs show a lack of intercellular space in the region of the zonula occludens and only a narrow (~200 A) space between apposing cell membranes in the zonula adherens region. It must be concluded that the terminal bars of light microscopy represent the apposing cell membranes plus the rim of subjacent filament-rich, electron-dense cytoplasm of the zonulae seen in electron micrographs (Figs. 4-3, 4-4, and 4-5).

It has been noted above that the type of junctional complex shown diagrammatically in Figure 4-6 is particularly characteristic of intestinal epithelium. However, a similar complex is found in a number of other locations, and each of the three types of junction may occur independently of the others. There are wide ranges in the widths of intercellular spaces in different parts of the body. Intercellular clefts and gaps of unusual size are found in the endothelial lining of lymphatic capillaries; the spaces become sufficiently large to allow intercellular passage of

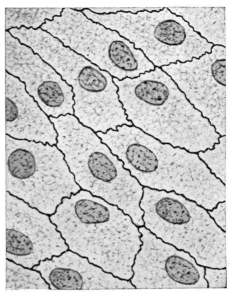

Fig. 4-2. Surface view of mesothelium of mesentery treated with silver nitrate. The cells are sharply outlined by the silver deposit. ×550.

large molecules such as plasma proteins and even entire cells (cancer cells, etc.). At the other extreme one finds the occluded junction. The intermediate ranges include small intercellular gaps of only about 20 A in width and in widths of 200 to 250 A in the zonula adherens and desmosomes. It is not surprising that there are some controversial features about the junctions in some regions. It must be realized that it is very difficult to determine from a study of thin sections whether a junction of a given region is an occluding zonule around its entire perimeter or whether it contains some 20 A gaps.

The ultrastructure of intercellular junctions has been given in detail because it has considerable functional significance (Fig. 4-7). For example, a zonula occludens or tight junction will prevent transfer of substances across an epithelial lining by an intercellular route and limit it to the cells themselves. Tight junctions are also very important as low resistance regions that provide intercellular ionic coupling. The functional significance of wide gaps and clefts,

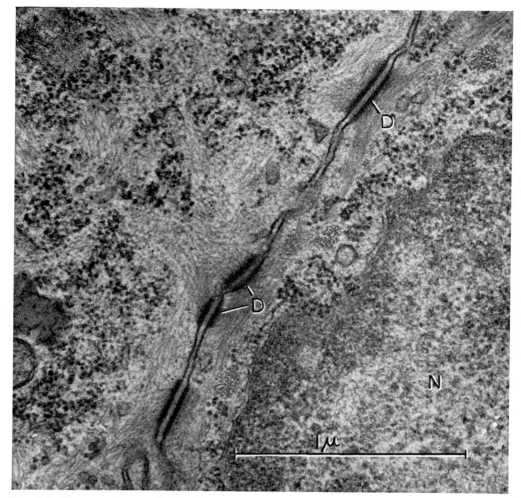

Fig. 4-3. Electron micrograph, showing attachments between epithelial cells of stratified epithelium of esophagus of bat. *D*, desmosome or macula adherens; *N*, nucleus. Fine tonofilaments can be seen in the cytoplasm adjacent to the desmosomes and in other regions of the cytoplasm. ×64,000. (Courtesy of Dr. Keith Porter.)

as in lymphatic endothelium, is noted above. The functions of the different types of junctions in particular locations are discussed further in subsequent chapters on muscle and nervous tissue and on organ systems.

Modifications at the Free Surface. *Microvilli*, or microscopic projections above the free surface, are found in a variety of locations. They are numerous, regularly arranged and uniform in height in the small intestine. Since this region of the intestine

appears vertically striated under the light microscope, it is named a *striated border*. Electron micrographs show that the microvilli composing the border are protoplasmic extensions about 2 μ in height (Fig. 16-40). Each microvillus has a slender core of fine filaments that apparently provide structural support. The microvilli greatly increase the surface area of the cells in correlation with an absorptive function. Biochemical studies have shown that the microvilli also contain enzymes which function in splitting disac-

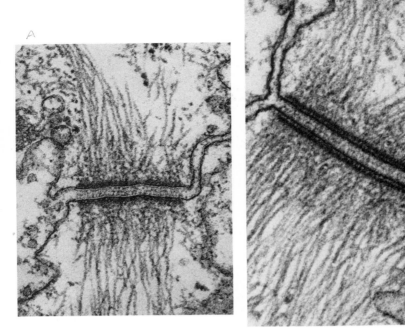

Fig. 4-4. Electron micrographs of desmosomes from stratified squamous epithelium. *A*, the outer and inner layers of the cell membrane and the presence of an electron-dense plaque in each cell subjacent to the inner layer of the plasmalemma at the level of the desmosome. Tonofilaments of the cytoplasm form loops at or in the dense plaque of the desmosome. *B*, another desmosome at higher magnification, clearly portraying the relationship of the looping tonofilaments to the dense plaque. In this picture, a thin electron-lucent line can be seen between the dense plaque and the inner border of the cell membrane. Note that a discontinuous midline is present in the material within the intercellular space at the desmosome level. Both illustrations are from the epidermis of a newt; *A*, ×89,950; *B*, ×115,920. Courtesy of Dr. Douglas E. Kelly.)

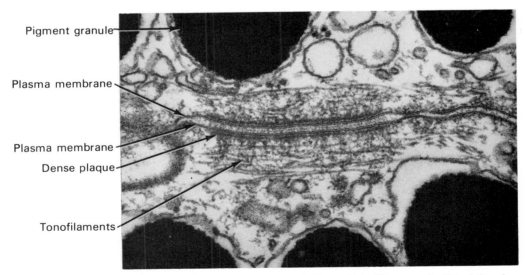

Fig. 4-5. Electron micrograph of a desmosome from epithelium of iris. The outer leaflet of the plasma membrane is specifically more distinct as a result of staining en bloc with uranyl acetate. Note that the looping tonofilaments approach the desmosome in a horizontal direction, in contrast with the pattern seen in Figure 4-4. See Figure 4-7 for variations of desmosomes. Iris of newt. ×90,000. (Courtesy of Dr. A. Tonosaki).

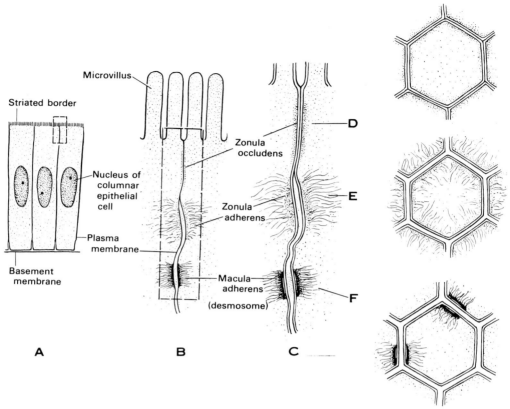

FIG. 4-6. Diagrams of a junctional complex between the adluminal ends of columnar epithelal cells. *A*, the interrelationships of simple columnar epithelial cells of the small intestine as determined by light microscopy. *B*, the structure of the juxtaluminal complex of the region outlined in *A* as deteirmined by electron microscopy. *C*, further details of the junction as determined by high magnification and high resolution electron micrographs. *D*, *E* and *F*, the different regions of the junctional complex in transverse sections. Note that the outer leaflets of the plasmalemma of adjacent cells are in contact around the entire circumference of the cell in the region of the zonula occludens, whereas they are separated by a uniform width around the circumference of the cell in the zonula adherens. The macula adherens of the junctional complex, which resembles the desmosomes of other regions, consists of spots of adhesion. Note that the diagrams of cross sections show the plasmalemma enlarged out of proportion to the cell area; at a similar magnification, the latter would cover more than the width of the page.

charides into monosaccharides—again, an adaptation for absorption. Microvilli are also numerous on the free surfaces of the proximal convoluted tubules of the kidney. In this location, they are somewhat higher and less uniform than in the small intestine, and they appear as a so-called *brush border* under the light microscope (Fig. 18-8). Epithelia of many other locations where no border modification is seen under the light microscope exhibit short and irregularly

distributed microvilli in electron micrographs.

Surface coats are present over the free surfaces of epithelial cells and are particularly well developed over the microvilli of the small intestine and the proximal convoluted tubules of the kidney. They are glycoprotein in nature and give a positive periodic acid-Schiff reaction. The surface coat is also known as *fuzz* or *fluffy coat*. These names characterize its fine filamentous structure as

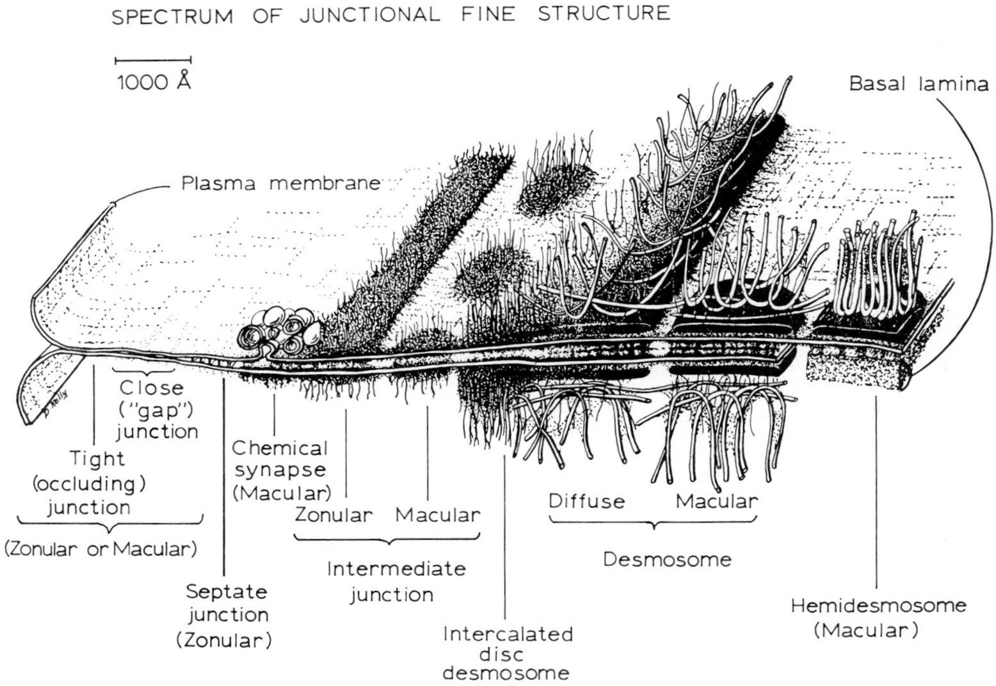

SPECTRUM OF JUNCTIONAL FINE STRUCTURE

FIG. 4-7. Diagram of various types of cell junctions as determined from electron micrographs. The intercalated disc type of junction is characteristic of cardiac muscle, and the chemical synapse is found between neurons; these are described in more detail in the chapters on muscle and nervous tissue. Septate junctions are found primarily in epithelia of invertebrates. (Figure and labels by courtesy of Dr. Douglas E. Kelly.)

seen in high resolution electron micrographs. The filaments of the surface coat in the small intestine are about 25 to 30 A thick, and they form a radiating and branching network for as much as 0.1 to 0.5 μ above the surface (Fawcett, 1966). They are attached to the outer leaflet of the plasmalemma and probably represent an integral part of the cell membrane. The coat probably serves a protective role for the free surface of the cell and may also act as a selective barrier. It apparently keeps large particles away from the microvilli while allowing colloidal particles and dissolved substances to penetrate between them. It also "probably functions as a trap that can concentrate ions and other charged particles to be absorbed by the cell" (Porter and Bonneville, 1968).

Stereocilia are unusually long microvilli found in parts of the male reproductive system. They do not have the structural characteristics of cilia. They increase the surface area of the luminal end of the cell and may aid in secretion and absorption.

Cilia are motile processes, usually 5 to 10 μ in length and about 0.2 μ in diameter. They are readily seen with the light microscope, but their internal structure can be understood only by studies of electron micrographs. The shaft or free part of each cilium is enclosed by a plasmalemma continuous with that of its cell, and each contains longitudinal microtubules arranged in a constant and orderly manner (Figs. 4-8 and 4-9). There are two single central microtubules and nine double peripheral microtubules, or doublets. The fibrils extend from the tip of the cilium to its base, known as the *basal body*, located in the cytoplasm just inside the free surface of the cell. Each basal

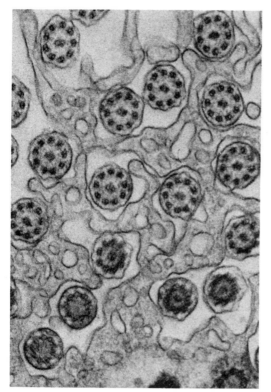

FIG. 4-8. Electron micrograph of a transverse section of cilia. Note that each cilium contains a a pair of central fibrils and nine peripheral fibrils, each of the latter a doublet. Most of the cilia are sectioned through their shaft or free portion, but two at the *lower right corner* of the field are cut near the level of the basal body and lack the central fibrils. From oviduct of a quail. (Courtesy of Dr. Anita Hoffer).

body has a "wall" of nine triplets and is similar to the centrioles which play an important role in mitosis. In the course of the differentiation of a ciliated cell, the centrioles apparently replicate many times to provide a basal body for each cilium. Where the shaft joins the basal body, the two central fibrils end and each of the nine doublets joins a triplet, each doublet continuing with two of the subunits of a triplet. It is interesting to note that the same ultrastructural characteristics are found in the cilia of all animals. Flagella also have the same structure as cilia but are much longer, and are usually present as one per cell.

Cilia are numerous on the surface cells of the epithelium lining the respiratory tract and on some of the cells of the female reproductive system. They beat in a rhythmical manner, producing a forward movement of materials over the cell surfaces. For example, the beating of the cilia in the trachea produces an upward movement of mucus with its entrapped dust particles, thus preventing foreign materials from blocking the lower respiratory regions, which function for exchange of O_2 and CO_2.

Basal Lamina. The basal lamina of epithelium is seen in electron micrographs as a relatively thin layer, about 500 to 1000 A in thickness, subjacent to the basal surfaces of the epithelial cells (i.e., where 2 types of tissue face each other). A light or electron-lucent zone is present between the epithelium and the electron-dense outer zone (Figs. 12-4 and 16-25). The basal lamina is generally described as amorphous, although it contains fine filaments in addition to mucopolysaccharides; the filaments

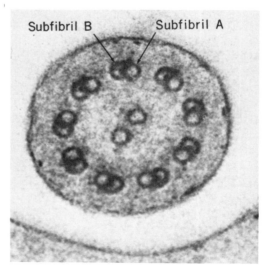

FIG. 4-9. Electron micrograph of a transverse section of a flagellum. The ultrastructure is the same as that of cilia (Fig. 4-8). The high magnification and resolution in this case show the appearance of the subunits of the peripheral fibrils. From a protozoon (*Giardia*). ×175,000. (Courtesy of Dr. Don W. Fawcett).

are very slender and become visible only in very high resolution electron micrographs. At its periphery, the basal lamina blends with a region composed of a meshwork of reticular and collagenous fibers embedded in the mucopolysaccharide matrix. It is named the *reticular lamina*. Beneath most epithelia, it is the combination of the basal lamina and the reticular lamina of electron micrographs that constitutes the *basement membrane* of light microscopy. The combined region stains black in silver preparations because of the presence of reticular fibers, and it stains red after periodic acid-Schiff because of the polysaccharides. The basement membrane of light microscopy is easily seen in hematoxylin-eosin stained sections of the trachea where the reticular lamina is well developed. It is generally not visible in the light microscope, even with special stains, beneath transitional epithelium where the reticular lamina is very thin. The kidney glomerulus is a location where the basement membrane is composed chiefly of basal lamina, but in this case it can be seen by light microscopy because it is formed by fusion of subendothelial and subepithelial layers.

The structural variations in basement membranes are correlated with functional differences. The basement membrane serves as a supporting structure for epithelium and generally holds the basal cells of the epithelium firmly to the underlying connective tissue. They may also serve as "sieves" for modifying the exchange of substances between the epithelium and the blood vessels in the underlying connective tissue.

The basal lamina is not a condensation of underlying connective tissue, as was once assumed. Through histochemical and immunological studies, it has been shown that the basal lamina is formed by the epithelial cells with which it is associated (Midgley and Pierce, 1963). The reticular fibers and mucopolysaccharides of the lamina reticularis seem generally to be formed by connective tissue fibroblasts, although there is

evidence that epithelial cells may also form these elements, either alone or, in concert with fibroblasts.

The basal lamina beneath the epithelium has some similarities to the coat which covers the luminal surface of most epithelial cells. It also has similarities to the coats which form a border or boundary around the majority of the cells of the body. They are all composed of an amorphous substance with an extremely fine filamentous component, and all are apparently derived from the cells which they either cover or surround.

Blood Vessels. With few exceptions, epithelium is entirely avascular. Nutritive materials and oxygen enter it by diffusion through the cells and the intercellular substance. Capillaries are present in the epithelium of the stria vascularis of the internal ear.

SIMPLE EPITHELIA

Simple Squamous Epithelium. Simple squamous epithelium (*pavement epithelium*) consists of flat scale-like or plate-like cells. The edges of the cells are usually serrated but may be smooth. The nucleus, situated in the center of the cell, is spherical or ovoid, causing a bulging of the cytoplasm. On surface view the cells appear as a delicate mosaic which can be demonstrated especially well by the precipitation of silver at the boundaries of the cells (Fig. 4-2). In profile the cells are spindle-shaped, thinner at the ends than at the center where the nucleus is located.

Simple squamous epithelium is widely distributed. It lines the peritoneal, pleural and pericardial cavities (mesothelium), the heart and all blood and lymph vessels (endothelium) and the membranous labyrinth of the internal ear, portions of the uriniferous tubule and of the rete testis.

Endothelium and *mesothelium* are excellent examples of simple squamous epithelium. Pinocytotic vesicles are particularly numerous in the cytoplasm of endothelial cells, and they apparently play a role in the trans-

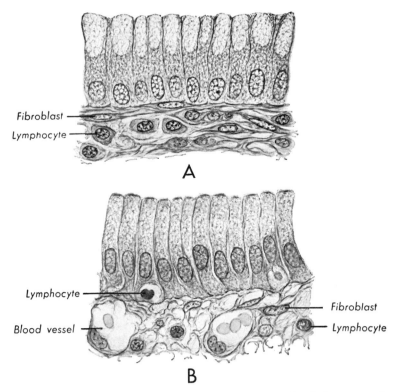

Fibroblast

Lymphocyte

A

Lymphocyte

Blood vessel

Fibroblast

Lymphocyte

B

FIG. 4-10. Simple columnar epithelium. *A*, epithelium of stomach of rhesus monkey. The apical ends of the cells are clear due to the mucin having been dissolved. *B*, epithelium of human gall bladder. ×1200.

port of some substances (e.g., large molecules such as proteins) across the cell. The significance of this in relation to other mechanisms for transport is discussed under the circulatory system (Chapter 12). The regeneration of endothelium is similar to that of most other types of epithelium in that it is replaced only by multiplication and rearrangement of cells of its own type. Mesothelium differs from the other types in that it apparently can be regenerated from cells of the underlying connective tissue. The mesothelial cells can also change into fibroblasts. They seem to be less specialized than other types of epithelial cells and appear to retain some of the multipotency of mesenchyme.

Mesenchymal epithelium is the name given to the simple squamous cells which line certain connective tissue-enclosed cavities: subarachnoid and subdural cavities, the chambers of the eye and the perilymphatic spaces of the ear. The structure of this epithelium is generally similar to that of mesothelium, although in some sites (e.g. surface of the iris) its cells are more loosely joined to each other.

Joints and Bursae. The cells lining the surfaces of structures enclosing the cavities of joints are associated with collagenous fibers and they are more loosely joined to each other than are typical epithelial cells. They are generally described as fibroblasts although electron micrographs show that they differ from ordinary fibroblasts.

Simple Columnar Epithelium. Simple columnar epithelium (Fig. 4-10, *A*, *B*) in its various modifications represents the chief secretory tissue of the body. It forms membranes consisting of a single layer of tall,

prismatic cells resting on a continuous basement membrane. The height of the cells
varies considerably in different locations,
and the term *cuboidal* epithelium is applied
when the height and thickness of the cells
are about equal (isodiametric). All transi-
tions from low cuboidal to high columnar
types of cells are encountered. The tubules
or acini of most glands are lined by epithelium, the cells of which are pyramidal or
conical in shape, with the broad base resting
on the basement membrane and the apex
facing the narrow lumen. This *pyramidal*
or *glandular* epithelium (Fig. 15-7) is a
modification of columnar or cuboidal cells
resulting from their arrangement around a
small lumen. In simple columnar epithelial
cells, the nucleus is oval and usually placed
near the base; in the cuboidal cells, it is
spherical and centrally placed. In the basal
perinuclear portion of the cytoplasm, there
are numerous mitochondria, particularly in
cells that are secretory. The apical portion
may contain various inclusions in the form of
granules or droplets (zymogen, mucin, etc.).

The cytoplasmic constitution varies greatly
under different conditions of cellular activity. A striated border may be absent as
in most glandular epithelium or be very
prominent as in the high columnar epithelium of the small intestine (Fig. 1-9, *C*).

A common and important variation of
simple columnar epithelium is seen in the
form of goblet cells (Fig. 4-11). They become
modified from typical columnar epithelial
cells by the accumulation of membrane-
bounded mucin droplets and by the gradual
disappearance of microvilli. The cytological
events accompanying secretion have not
been as clearly established for mucin of
goblet cells as for zymogen granules produced by pancreatic acinar cells. From com-
parisons, it seems likely that the protein
portion of mucin (a glycoprotein) is synthesized in the rough surfaced endoplasmic
reticulum which is abundant in the basal
half of the cell. It is established that the
carbohydrate moiety of mucin is formed
by the Golgi complex. Autoradiographic
studies show that tritiated glucose injected

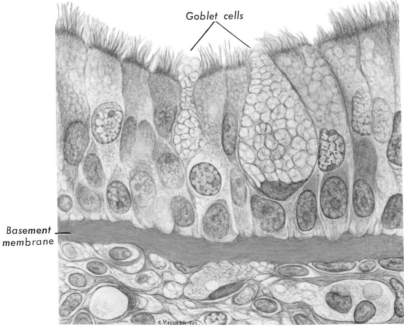

FIG. 4-11. Pseudostratified columnar ciliated epithelium from the trachea

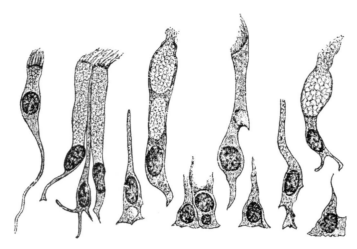

Fig. 4-12. Isolated cells from pseudostratified ciliated epithelium of trachea. Two goblet cells are shown. (Redrawn from Schaffer.)

into laboratory animals appears within minutes, first, over the Golgi complex, next, within the vesicles of the Golgi complex, later as membrane-bounded mucin droplets in the apical cytoplasm, and finally with the mucus in the intestinal lumen. It appears that the protein and carbohydrate moieties of mucin are combined in the Golgi complex and that the membranes of the droplets are derived from membranes of Golgi cisternae which must be replaced continuously. The mucin droplets accumulate in the apical end of the cell and push the nucleus and most of the remaining cytoplasm toward the base. Thus, the cell assumes a goblet shape. The mucin droplets become closely packed but remain membrane-bounded and separate until they escape from the apical end of the cell. It seems that sometimes the goblet cells secrete cyclically and at other times continuously. This probably varies for goblet cells in different locations and with the stimuli and demands in a given location. It should be noted that most mucins are not preserved and stained in the routine preparations for light microscopy. The droplets may wash out of the cell, leaving a clear space, or they may partially dissolve and then fuse into a faintly staining meshwork

composed of remnants of mucin and remaining cytoplasm.

Certain epithelial cells become specialized to serve as sensory cells for the reception of external stimuli (*neuroepithelium*). They are usually tall columnar cells, often carrying on their free surface a number of nonmotile hairlike processes. They are in intimate connection with nerve endings and are described in the chapters on the nervous system and sense organs.

Pseudostratified Epithelium (Figs. 4-11 and 4-12). In this type of epithelium, the nuclei lie at different levels, giving it a stratified appearance. All of the cells reach the basement membrane, but not all of them extend to the free surface. Those which do reach the surface are columnar, with one or more thin processes which extend to the basement membrane. These processes are difficult to see in routine histological preparations. Between the slender processes, there are ovoid or spindle-shaped cells which also reach the basement membrane. This type of epithelium usually has either cilia or stereocilia. It occurs mainly as the lining of the passages of the respiratory and the male reproductive systems.

STRATIFIED EPITHELIA

Stratified Squamous Epithelium. Stratified squamous epithelium (Figs. 4-1 and 4-13) is the main protective epithelium of the body and consists of many cell layers. The number of layers varies considerably in different places, but the shape and arrangement of the cells are quite characteristic. The deepest layer, which rests on a basement membrane, is formed by columnar or prismatic cells which in sections of the tissue appear as a distinct row. Hemidesmosomes are seen along the basal surface of each cell, adjacent to the basal lamina. Nearer to the surface, the cells become irregularly cubical or polyhedral in shape and are usually larger than the cells of the basal layers. As the free surface is approached, the cells are more flattened and at the surface are squamous. The deeper cells of the basal and polyhedral layers are young, soft cells with relatively large nuclei rich in chromatin. The cytoplasm is finely granular and somewhat basophilic due to its content of RNA. The "intercellular bridges" (actually sites of desmosomes) are prominent, giving the cell a prickly appearance ("prickle cells," Fig. 4-13). With special technique, delicate fibrils are demonstrated within the cells. Mitosis is frequently observed in the basal layer.

The extent of the changes in the superficial (surface) cells varies with the location and environment of the stratified squamous epithelium. The epidermis, for instance, is subjected to more attrition and drying than is the epithelium of the mouth, pharynx and esophagus. Its surface cells are nonnucleated, scale-like and keratinized. On the other hand, the epithelium of moist surfaces such as that of mouth, pharynx and esophagus is usually not keratinized. The surface cells become very flat, but usually remain nucleated.

The mitotic activity of the cells in the lower layer and the lack of mitosis in the upper layers may be related partly to in-

FIG. 4-13. Stratified squamous epithelium from esophagus of monkey.

sufficient nutrition of the upper cell layers. The deeper cells are in closer relation to the underlying capillaries which supply the nutritive substances that maintain the epithelial cells. These cells show normal protoplasmic structure and are able to divide mitotically. As more cells are formed, the basal cells are pressed upward. The dead scale-like surface cells are constantly cast off, to be replaced by cells from the deeper strata. In man this is a slow and continuous process; in some of the lower vertebrates (e.g., snakes) there is a periodic shedding of the whole superficial layer of the epidermis.

Stratified squamous epithelium covers the entire surface of the body and the orifices of cavities opening upon it. It lines the mucous membranes of the mouth, pharynx, esophagus, portions of the larynx, external auditory canal and conjunctiva, vagina, vestibule and labia majora and portions of the urethra.

Stratified Columnar and Stratified Cuboidal Epithelium. A *stratified columnar epithelium* is comparatively rare. It consists of columnar surface cells which rest on several layers of irregular cubical cells. Stratified columnar epithelium is found chiefly where a stratified squamous adjoins a pseudostratified columnar type, as for instance at the juncture of the oropharynx with the nasopharynx and with the larynx

(Fig. 17-5). It is said to occur also in part of the penile portion of the male urethra.

In a few locations, a stratified epithelium has surface cells which are definitely cuboidal, thus forming a *stratified cuboidal epithelium*. Examples are the ducts of sweat glands (Fig. 14-6) and the lining of the antra of ovarian follicles (Fig. 20-3). The sebaceous glands are composed of cells which are polyhedral in shape and several layers in thickness

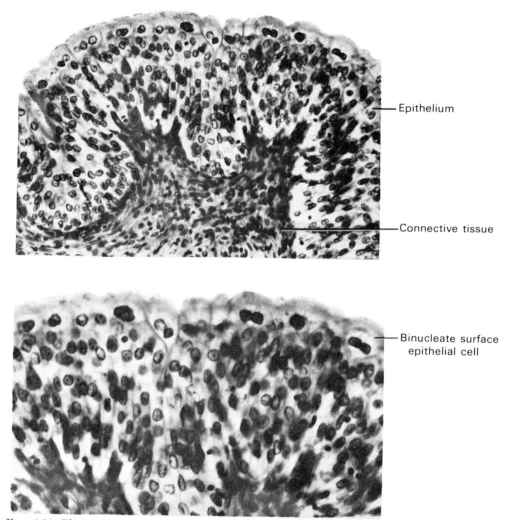

Epithelium

Connective tissue

Binucleate surface epithelial cell

FIG. 4-14. Photomicrographs of transitional epithelium of contracted human bladder. *Upper figure,* ×250; *lower figure,* a portion of the same region at ×390. Note that some of the surface cells have two nuclei and most of the surface cells are umbrella-shaped at their upper border in the contracted bladder. Hematoxylin and eosin stain.

(Fig. 14-13). Although there is no free inner surface, it more closely approximates a stratified cuboidal than any other type of epithelium.

The epithelium of seminiferous tubules of the testis is a highly specialized type (Fig. 19-2). Functionally, it is cytogenic; structurally, it probably approximates a stratified cuboidal type more closely than any other, although certain of its cells (cells of Sertoli) are elongated and extend from the basement membrane to the lumen. The shape of the surface cells varies greatly with stages of growth and differentiation.

Transitional Epithelium (Figs. 4-14 and 4-15). All epithelial cells are somewhat pliable, being able to adjust themselves to influences which increase or decrease the general surface area. These properties are especially striking in the transitional epithelium of the urinary passages and bladder. In the dilated bladder, the epithelium consists of two or three layers of cells. The superficial cells are large, low, cuboidal plates, the lower ones smaller and irregularly cubical. In the contracted bladder, the epithelium becomes five or six layered. The surface cells are large and cuboidal with a

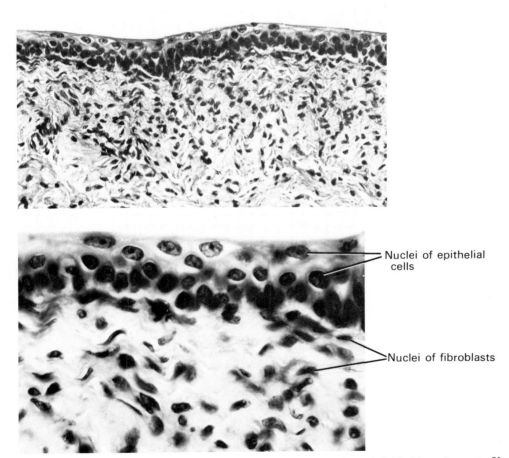

Nuclei of epithelial cells

Nuclei of fibroblasts

Fig. 4-15. Photomicrographs of transitional epithelium from distended bladder of a cat. *Upper figure*, ×250; *lower figure*, a region of the same field at ×390. Note that the cells are arranged in only a few layers and that each stretched surface cell usually covers several of the underlying cells. Transitional epithelium, as indicated by its name, varies in different functional states, and there are numerous gradations between the appearance seen in Figure 4-14 and that seen in Figure 4-15.

superficial layer of cytoplasm which often appears condensed and darker staining. These cells have characteristic convex free surfaces and facet-like indentations in their under surfaces. The lower cells have rearranged themselves, owing to a reduction of the surface area. They overlap each other and have assumed a flask- or pear-shaped form. Some of them fit into the facets of the superficial cells. Electron micrographs show that the luminal surface of transitional epithelial cells is not smooth, as it appears to be under the light microscope, but is uneven as a result of alternating crests and hollows. The cytoplasm contains fairly numerous membrane-bounded, fusiform vesicles which have been shown by experimental studies to be derived from the surface membrane. When the bladder contracts, the tips of the surface crests rise and join, pinching off the intervening troughs into the underlying cytoplasm. This reduces the area of the surface membrane during contraction and may also aid in its rapid renewal or turnover. The worn-out membranes of the vesicles are supposedly digested by lysosomes, and new membrane material must be added, probably by synthesis in the Golgi complex. The surface membrane of the bladder has an important function as a barrier to diffusion of water via the cells from underlying tissues into the hypertonic urine in the lumen. The plasmalemma of the luminal surface is unusual in that its outer leaflet is definitely thicker than its inner leaflet. Tonofilaments within the cytoplasm, particularly numerous beneath the luminal surface of the surface cells, may also aid in preventing diffusion, as well as in providing support. Diffusion via intercellular routes is prevented by juxtaluminal junctional complexes between the surface cells. Desmosomes are scarce between the deeper cells: this seems to be correlated with the ability of the cells to adapt during contraction and distention of the organ. Another structural adaptation for contraction and expansion is the presence of numerous interfoldings and interdigitations of the membranes of the deeper cells. The folds tend to disappear when the bladder is distended.

Transitional epithelium is found only in the urinary system—pelvis of kidney, ureter, bladder and a portion of the urethra.

EPITHELIAL REPAIR

The response of epithelium in the healing of wounds in mammals has been more extensively studied in the epidermis than in other types of epithelium.

Both epithelium and the underlying connective tissue are injured in abrasions and most other wounds, and both have a capacity for cell division and for repair, in contrast with more highly differentiated tissue such as nerve cells and skeletal muscle fibers. The response of the epidermis depends somewhat on the size of the injured surface, but there is generally an enlargement and migration of the deeper cells near the wound. These exhibit a sort of ameboid movement, with the formation of tongue-like processes which grow over the denuded area or, if there is a scab, grow under it and help to absorb it. Mitoses are decreased for the first few (4 to 5) days but soon thereafter exceed the normal rate. In wound repair, as in tissue culture, epithelium exhibits the propensity of forming a cellular layer on a surface.

MEMBRANES

Epithelium assumes its full significance only when considered in conjunction with the underlying connective tissue. In combination with the underlying tissue, it forms structures of varying toughness and thickness, as exemplified by the skin and peritoneum. In conjunction with a stratum of connective tissue, it forms the mucosa of the gastrointestinal, respiratory and genito-urinary systems. In general, the connective tissue lying beneath the epithelium is extremely fine but closely woven. This passes gradually into a stratum of coarser, closely woven fibers. The connective tissue membrane thus formed permits a variable amount of stretching, depending on the location, but prevents an excessive expansion which might separate the epithelial cells. The denseness of the connective tissue varies with the membranes formed; thus, in the mucosa it is not nearly as dense as it is in the skin.

The connective tissue, which with the epithelium forms a membrane, changes with no abrupt transition into a looser stratum, which attaches the membrane to the underlying structures and usually permits a movement over them. This underlying zone of looser tissue is well exemplified by the subcutaneous fascia, the submucosa and a thin stratum of subperitoneal tissue.

Serous Membranes. Serous membranes line the *peritoneal, pleural* and *pericardial* cavities. A serous membrane consists of mesothelium and an underlying layer of delicate fibroelastic tissue. It should be noted that serous membranes line closed cavities and they do not contain glands. They are moistened by a thin fluid similar to lymph.

Mucous Membranes. Mucous membranes (mucosae) line all of those cavities and canals of the body which connect with the exterior; that is, they line the alimentary tract, the respiratory passages and the genitourinary tract. Although differing in details, the mucous membranes of these various locations all have a similarity in the general plan of their structure. The essential parts are (1) surface epithelium, (2) basement membrane and (3) a stratum of connective tissue, the lamina propria.

Although the name mucous membrane suggests that mucous glands are present, this is not always the case. Both mucous and serous glands are present in the mucous membrane of the alimentary and respiratory tracts, but no glands are present in the mucous membrane of most of the genitourinary tract.

REFERENCES

BARLAND, P. NOVIKOFF, A. B., AND HAMMERMAN, D. 1962. Electron microscopy of the human synovial memdrane. J. Cell Biol., vol. 14, pp. 29–42.

BELANGER, L. F. 1954 Autoradiographic visualization of S[35] incorporation and turn-over by the mucous glands of the gastrointestinal tract and other soft tissues of rat and hamster. Anat. Rec., vol. 118, pp. 755–772.

BENNETT, H. S. 1963 Morphological aspects of extracellular polysaccharides. J. Histochem. Cytochem., vol. 11, pp. 2–13.

BISHOP, G. H. 1945 Regeneration after experimental removal of skin in man. Amer. J. Anat., vol. 76, pp. 153–183.

BONNEVILLE, M. A., AND WEINSTOCK, M. 1970 Brush border development in the intestinal absorptive cells of *Xenopus* during metamorphosis. J. Cell Biol., vol. 49, pp. 151–171.

BRANDT, P. W. 1962 A consideration of the extraneous coats of the plasma membrane. Circulation (suppl.), vol. 26, pp. 1075–1091.

CHAMBERS, R., AND DE RÉNYI, G. S. 1925 The structure of the cells in tissues as revealed by micro-dissection. Amer. J. Anat., vol. 35, pp. 385–402.

DiBONA, D. R., CIVAN, M. M., AND LEAF, A. 1969 The anatomic site of the transepithelial permeability barriers of toad bladder. J. Cell Biol., vol. 40, pp. 1–7.

FARQUHAR, M. G., AND PALADE, G. E. 1963 Junctional complexes in various epithelia. J. Cell Biol., vol. 17, pp. 375–412.

FARQUHAR, M. G., AND PALADE, G. E. 1965 Cell junctions in amphibian skin. J. Cell Biol., vol. 26, pp. 263–291.

FAWCETT, D. 1961 Cilia and flagella. *In* The Cell; Biochemistry, Physiology, Morphology (Brachet, J., and Mirsky, A. E., editors), vol. II, pp. 217-297. Academic Press, New York.

FAWCETT, D. W. 1965 Surface specializations of absorbing cells. J. Histochem. Cytochem., vol. 13, pp. 75–91.

FAWCETT, D. W. 1966 An Atlas of Fine Structure. W. B. Saunders Company, Philadelphia.

GABE, M., AND ARVY, L. 1961 Gland cells. *In* The Cell; Biochemistry, Physiology, Morphology (Brachet, J., and Mirsky, A. E., editors), vol. V, pp. 1–88. Academic Press, New York.

GIBBONS, I. R. 1961 The relationship between the fine structure and direction of beat in gill cilia of a lamellibranch mollusc. J. Biophys. Biochem. Cytol., vol. 11, pp. 179–205.

GOODENOUGH, D. A., AND REVEL, J.-P. 1970

A fine structural analysis of intercellular junctions in the mouse liver. J. Cell Biol., vol. 45, pp. 272–290.

GRONIOWSKI, J., BICZYSKOWA, W., AND WALSKI, M. 1969 Electron microscope studies on the surface coat of the nephron. J. Cell Biol., vol. 40, pp. 585–601.

HICKS, R. M. 1965 The fine structure of the transitional epithelium of rat ureter. J. Cell Biol., vol. 26, pp. 25–48.

ITO, S. 1965 The surface coat of enteric microvilli. J. Cell Biol., vol. 27, pp. 475–491.

KELLY, D. E. 1966 Fine structure of desmosomes, hemidesmosomes, and an adepidermal globular layer in developing newt epidermis. J. Cell Biol., vol. 28, pp. 51–72.

LEBLOND, C. P., AND WALKER, B. E. 1956 Renewal of cell populations. Physiol. Rev., vol. 36, pp. 255–276.

MIDGLEY, A. R., AND PIERCE, G. B. 1963 Immunohistochemical analysis of basement membranes of the mouse. Amer. J. Path., vol. 43, pp. 929–943.

PORTER, K. R., AND BONNEVILLE, M. A. 1968 Fine Structure of Cells and Tissues, ed. 3. Lea & Febiger, Philadelphia.

RAMBOURG, A., HERNANDEZ, W., AND LEBLOND, C. P. 1969 Detection of complex carbohydrates in the Golgi apparatus of rat cells. J. Cell Biol., vol. 40, pp. 395–414.

REVEL, J.-P., AND ITO, S. 1967 The surface components of cells. In: The Specificity of Cell Surfaces (Davis, B., and Warren, L., editors), p. 211. Prentice-Hall, Inc. New Jersey.

SCHAFFER, J. 1927 Das Epithelgewebe. Handb. mikr. Anat. Menschen (v. Möllendorff, editor), vol. 2, pp. 1–132. Springer-Verlag, Berlin.

WEISS, P. 1959 Interactions between cells. Biophysical Science—A Study Program (Oncley, J. L., et al., editors). John Wiley & Sons, Inc., New York.

WEISS, P. 1961 The biological foundations of wound repair. The Harvey Lectures, Ser. 55 pp. 13–42.

5

The Connective Tissues

The various types of adult connective tissue, in contrast with epithelium, have relatively few cells and a large amount of intercellular substance. The proportion of cells and intercellular substance shows considerable variation. In some types, especially the loose connective tissue, cells are quite numerous; in other types, they are few in number and the tissue is composed almost entirely of closely packed fibers. The type and the arrangement of the fibers and the nature of the substance in which they are embedded (ground substance) furnish the basis for the subdivision of *adult connective tissue* into three main groups, *connective tissue proper, cartilage* and *bone*. (Scheme 5-1). In connective tissue proper, the intercellular substance is soft; in cartilage, it is firm yet flexible and may be readily cut; in bone, it is rigid because of the deposition of inorganic salts in the matrix.

Connective tissue in the embryo has a different structure and consistency from that of the adult. Some knowledge of the development of connective tissue is important, for in wound healing the stages of repair have considerable similarity to the embryonal developmental stages.

Classification. Since connective tissue in the embryo has a structure very different from that of the adult, it is placed in a separate major category, *embryonal connective tissue*.

Adult connective tissue can be classified into different types because of differences (1) in the relative proportions of the kinds of fibers, (2) in the compactness and in the arrangement of the fibers, (3) in the matrix and (4) in the types of cells. There are numerous gradations between these types, so that the connective tissue in some locations cannot be strictly classified in a certain division. A classification is useful, however, in calling attention to differences that occur in the connective tissue, as well as in organizing the study of this tissue.

EMBRYONAL CONNECTIVE TISSUE

Most of the connective tissues arise from mesoderm. (Exceptions to this are neuroglia, which arises from neural ectoderm, reticulum of thymus, which arises from pharyngeal entoderm, and chromatophores and some cartilages of the head, which arise from the neural crest.)

Mesoderm, as described in Chapter 3, occurs as somites arranged bilaterally along the neural tube and as ventrolateral sheets of somatic and splanchnic layers which enclose the developing body cavities. Some of the mesodermal cells migrate from the somites and from the somatic and splanchnic layers into the spaces between the primary germ layers and form a diffuse network of embryonal connective tissue known as *mesenchyme*. This tissue is composed of irregularly shaped cells with processes extending into a

visceral

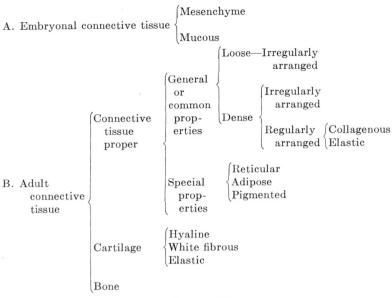

SCHEME 5-1

relatively homogeneous intercellular substance (Fig. 5-1). The processes of the cells often come in contact with each other, but actual protoplasmic continuity between cells is questionable. When mesenchymal cells are grown in tissue culture, one finds that they behave as individual units. They show ameboid movements, detaching themselves from each other and readily reattaching.

In addition to the irregularly shaped branching cells, mesenchyme also contains cells with relatively short processes or pseudopodia. Since these exhibit more ameboid activity than the branching cells, they are known as wandering cells. They are precursors of macrophages.

As development progresses, the mesenchyme gradually assumes the characteristics of adult tissues. In the mesenchyme which is destined to become adult connective tissue, fibers appear on the cell surfaces and become distributed between the cells. The intercellular substance becomes more viscous in correlation with the formation of mucoproteins. The embryonal connective tissue of this stage is known as *mucous connective tissue* and is widely distributed.

The umbilical cord is a classic example of mucous connective tissue, and the term *Wharton's jelly* is frequently applied to it in that location. The number of fibers in the cord will increase during pregnancy, but the umbilical cord has a short life span and an adult type of connective tissue does not form in it.

ADULT CONNECTIVE TISSUE

LOOSE CONNECTIVE TISSUE

Loose, irregularly arranged or areolar connective tissue is widely distributed in the human body. It forms the superficial and most of the deep fascia; it forms a part of the framework (stroma) of most of the organs; it surrounds blood vessels and nerves and fills in any otherwise unoccupied spaces. It generally contains a varying number of fat cells. When the latter are abundant the tissue is designated as adipose or fat tissue. Subcutaneous tissue (superficial fascia) which is heavily laden with fat cells in many parts of the body is often given a special name, panniculus adiposus.

Loose connective tissue, like all of the

other connective tissues, is composed of *cells*, intercellular *fibers* and *ground substance*, which is the material forming the foundation or background. The composition of ground substance is described later under a separate heading, but it should be noted immediately that the ground substance of loose connective tissue is relatively fluidlike, in contrast with that of cartilage and bone. The cells of loose connective tissue are not anchored in position, as might be implied by the term ground substance.

The loose connective tissue derives its name from the fact that its intercellular fibers are loosely arranged, in contrast with the closely packed fibers of dense connective tissue. The name *areolar* is descriptive of the general appearance produced by small spaces which contain only an amorphous ground substance.

Loose connective tissue contains most of the types of cells and all of the kinds of fibers found in the other varieties of connective tissue. Hence, a thorough knowledge of its structure serves not only for understanding its own very important functions but also as a basis for understanding the other types of connective tissue.

Connective Tissue Cells. The cells of loose connective tissue have been objects of intensive histological and experimental study. By means of various methods, the following cell types have been distinguished and found to be more or less constant inhabitants of loose connective tissue: *fibroblasts* or fixed connective tissue cells, *histiocytes* or *macrophages*, *mast cells*, *plasma cells* and *wandering cells from the blood*.

(a) The *fibroblasts* (Figs. 5-2 and 5-3) are one of the two most numerous cell types of loose connective tissue, the other being histiocytes. Fibroblasts, as their name suggests, are responsible for fiber formation. There is evidence that they also form the ground substance.

They are large, somewhat flattened, frequently ovoid cells, with branching processes. Their nuclei are oval and somewhat

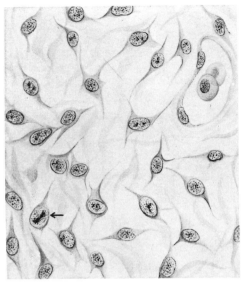

FIG. 5-1. Mesenchyme from subcutaneous tissue from a 10 mm. pig embryo. *Arrow* points to a cell in mitosis. The processes of some cells appear to be continuous with those of other cells when viewed under the light microscope, but experimental studies indicate that they are merely in contact. ×650.

flattened, resembling the shape of the cell. They usually stain lightly in connective tissue spreads. In sections prepared by ordinary methods, the fibroblast nuclei are usually shrunken and stain deeply with basic dyes. The chromatin is distributed through the nucleus, with a tendency to become aggregated at intervals along the inner surface of the nuclear envelope. Since the cytoplasm takes little or no stain in its outer (ectoplasmic) region and since the cell membrane is too thin to be resolved under the light microscope, it is very difficult to identify the cell boundary with the light microscope.

The appearance of the fibroblast varies in relation to its functional activity. When the cell is actively producing intercellular materials, as in normal development and in tissue regeneration after injury, the cell is enlarged in correlation with an increase in its organelles. The nucleus is larger and the nucleoli are more prominent. The cytoplasm

Neutrophil Plasma cells Connective tissue

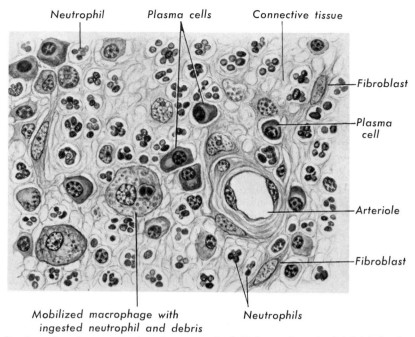

Fibroblast

Plasma cell

Arteriole

Fibroblast

Mobilized macrophage with   Neutrophils
ingested neutrophil and debris

FIG. 5-3. Section of an intratesticular abscess excised 30 days after the initial infection. An intermediate zone of the abscess is figured. Central to the area shown in the figure is a region where neutrophils predominate; peripherally is an extensive fibrosis. Hematoxylin and eosin-azure II. ×753.

stains more deeply and is basophilic in contrast with the lightly staining, slightly acidophilic cytoplasm of the relatively inactive cell. Electron micrographs show that there is a marked increase in rough surfaced endoplasmic reticulum and also in free ribosomes. The Golgi complex is enlarged, and some of its cisternae and vesicles contain electron dense material. There is also an increase in number of vesicles in other regions of the cytoplasm. The cell membrane is difficult to follow (or resolve) in places where aggregates of filamentous material in the peripheral portion of the cytoplasm face aggregates of extracellular, dense material. The significance of these structural changes in relation to fiber formation is discussed further in the section on the origin of fibers. Some investigators prefer to confine the term fibroblast to the active stage of the cell and to use the term fibrocyte for the relatively inactive cell. This seems unnecessary, since they are only different functional states of the same cell.

(b) The *histiocytes* or *macrophages* (Figs. 5-2 and 5-3) are found in all loose connective tissues. The clasmatocytes and resting-wandering cells of various investigators have been found to be identical with these histiocytes. They are irregularly shaped cells with processes which usually are short and blunt but occasionally are long and slender. The nucleus is more rounded and somewhat smaller and darker staining than that of the fibroblast. In the resting cell, the cytoplasm, like that of the fibroblast, stains lightly but may contain a few granules and vacuoles. It should be noted that the diagnostic features just listed are minor. The characteristics of the relatively inactive histiocytes do not differ sufficiently from those of the fibroblasts to enable one to distinguish clearly histiocytes from fibroblasts in most preparations. However, the histiocytes become clearly distinguishable from fibroblasts when they are activated, as in the region of an abscess (Fig. 5-3). The entire cell becomes larger, with a larger nucleus, a more prominent nucleolus and a cytoplasm more or less filled with granules and vacuoles of ingested material. The histiocytes in an area of inflammation are particularly busy engulfing worn-out neutrophilic leukocytes which died in the process of engulfing and destroying bacteria. The neutrophils serve as the "shock troops" and the histiocytes function in "mopping up" operations.

Light microscope studies of macrophages in tissue culture preparations show that foreign material is surrounded by protoplasmic processes and taken into the cell by ameboid-like activity. Electron micrographs show that the engulfed foreign material is membrane-bound. These vesicles combine with lysosomes containing proteolytic enzymes which function in digesting the material. The vesicles are known as phagosomes or digestive vacuoles. Substances which are not digestible may remain in the cytoplasm for a long period. Carbon in the connective tissue macrophages of the lung is an examples of this.

Objects too large to be engulfed by a single cell are attacked en masse and become surrounded by histiocytes, which eventually fuse to form a *multinucleated foreign body giant cell*. These are not to be confused with blood platelet-producing *megakaryocytes* of bone marrow (Fig. 7-11).

The most commonly used experimental method for identifying histiocytes is to study their physiological reaction in supravital preparations and their intravital response to injected trypan blue, colloidal carbon, etc. Sections of tissue from animals which have had one or more injections of trypan blue show extensive ingestion and segregation of the dye in vacuoles in the cytoplasm of histiocytes and relatively little ingested material in fibroblasts (Fig. 5-2).

Macrophages or histiocytes are widely distributed in the body. They are in loose connective tissue and, therefore, they are present in all fascia. They also occur in the connective tissue which is present in organs, although the proportion of them to fibroblasts may vary considerably in different regions of an organ. Certain cells in specific locations, e.g., in the sinusoids of the liver, in lymphoid organs and in bone marrow, are also phagocytic. Together with the histiocytes of loose connective tissue, they form the "macrophage system" or "reticuloendothelial system" which is discussed in more detail at the end of this chapter.

It has been noted above that macrophages become very *active* in regions of inflammation, as in an abscess (Fig. 5-3). They are also more *numerous* in such areas. The increase may result from (1) multiplication of cells already in the area, (2) migration of histiocytes from neighboring areas and (3) transformations of monocytes which migrate into the area from the blood vessels. The macrophages are mobilized so rapidly that it seems likely that monocyte transformation is an important factor. Maximow showed many years ago that monocytes grown in tissue culture can change into macrophages. It is generally accepted that the same change occurs in the body, in the environment of the connective tissue.

The *plasma cells* (Figs. 5-2, 5-3 and 5-5) are relatively rare in most connective tissues under normal conditions, although they are fairly numerous in the connective tissue of the alimentary mucous membrane and greater omentum. They are also fairly numerous in the reticular connective tissues of blood-forming organs. Their number is greatly increased in areas of chronic inflammation. They are ovoid, irregularly shaped cells, smaller than histiocytes but larger than lymphocytes. The nucleus is relatively small and eccentrically placed. The chromatin appears in the form of deep staining, coarse granules. Since most of the chromatin granules are arranged in a regular manner against the nuclear membrane and only a few are present toward the center, the nucleus has a "cartwheel" appearance.

The cytoplasm of the plasma cell is very basophilic, like that of a lymphocyte, but it has a characteristic unstained or lightly stained area at the side of the nucleus where

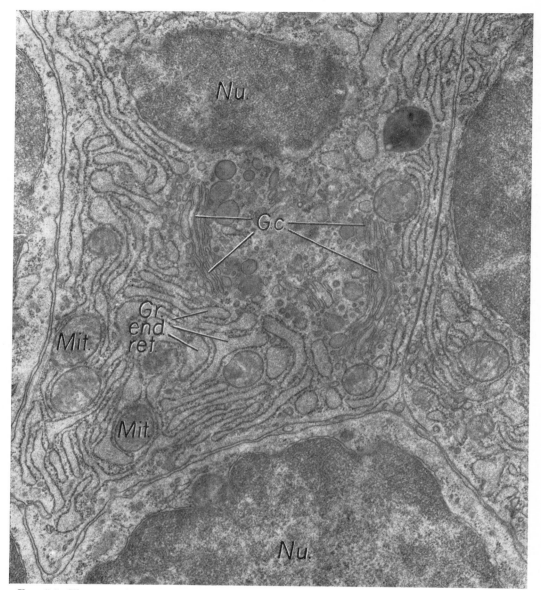

FIG. 5-5. Electron micrograph of a portion of the spleen of a bat, showing parts of two plasma cells (*above*) and a part of a lymphocyte (*below*). *Gc*, Golgi complex; *Gr. end. ret.*, granular endoplasmic reticulum of plasma cell showing relatively wide cisternae and numerous ribosomes associated with the outer surfaces of the membranes of the cisternae; *Mit*, mitochondria; *Nu*, portions of the nuclei. Note that the lymphocyte contrasts with the plasma cell by having very few cisternae of endoplasmic reticulum, although it has numerous ribosomes. ×19,000. (Courtesy of Dr. Keith Porter.)

the cytoplasm is more abundant (Figs. 5-2 and 5-3). The unstained area represents the region of the Golgi complex. The cytoplasm *occasionally* contains acidophilic masses known as *Russell bodies*. They probably arise by degenerative changes, and they may also occur in other types of cells in chronic inflammation. In comparison with a lymphocyte, the plasma cell has more cytoplasm in proportion to the size of the nucleus, i.e., the cytoplasmic-nuclear ratio is greater. The cytoplasm of the two types of cells also shows significant differences in electron micrographs. The plasma cell has an extensive endoplasmic reticulum with associated ribosomes, whereas the lymphocyte contains mostly free ribosomes with little reticulum (Figs. 5-5 and 7-3).

The plasma cell precursor (proplasmacyte) is relatively large and has pyroninophilic cytoplasm. It resembles the large lymphocytes of blood-forming organs and is probably derived from lymphocytes. Although some of the details of the cell relationships remain controversial, it is known that plasma cells, lymphocytes and macrophages of lymphatic organs work together in the immunological mechanisms. It is known from fluorescent antibody techniques and from other lines of evidence that the plasma cell is the major producer of *circulating antibodies*. The mature plasma cell is an end stage, that is, it does not continue to divide. It is derived from pyroninophilic precursors that are actively dividing and reaching stages at which they begin to form antibody. The different roles of the lymphocytes and the macrophages of lymphatic organs in the immune mechanism are discussed in the sections on lymphocytes (Chapter 7) and lymphatic organs (Chapter 13).

(d) *Mast cells* (Figs. 5-2 and 5-4) occur in varying numbers in most loose connective tissue, being especially numerous along the course of the blood vessels. They are large round or ovoid cells with pale staining nuclei and coarse cytoplasmic granules which stain with certain basic dyes such as toluidine blue. They are often known as histogenous mast cells to distinguish them from the hematogenous mast cells (basophilic leukocytes of the blood) which they closely resemble. The mast cell granules of some species, including man, are soluble in water and consequently are seldom preserved and stained in ordinary preparations. The granules contain *heparin*, an anticoagulant, and *histamine*, which produces vasodilation and increases permeability of the capillaries and small venules. The mast cells of a few species, but not of man, also contain serotonin. The first indication that mast cells contain heparin was based on staining reactions. The granules stain metachromatically as heparin does, but this is not conclusive evidence since some other cells also stain metachromatically. However, quantitative studies have demonstrated that tissues with numerous mast cells contain more heparin than do tissues having only a few mast cells. It is also known that mast cell tumors of dogs have a very high content of heparin. The importance of heparin as an anticoagulant in clinical work is obvious, but its role in the normal connective tissues remains obscure.

Mast cells differentiate from mesenchymal cells during embryonic development. Although they may occasionally continue to divide in the adult, it appears that most of the new mast cells in an adult arise from nongranular cells. The cell of origin in this case is controversial. Some workers claim that mast cells arise from undifferentiated cells situated along blood vessels, while other investigators believe that they arise either from fibroblasts or lymphocytes.

(e) *Fat cells* are found singly and in small groups widely distributed in the loose connective tissues. They are similar, except in numbers, to the cells found in masses as *adipose tissue*. The fat content of the cell is dissolved by the reagents generally used in the preparation of sections. Consequently, the cells appear as large empty spaces surrounded by the peripheral portion of the cell and a flattened nucleus (Fig. 5-15).

(e) Besides the cells enumerated, temporary visitors from the blood and lymph stream are seen in varying numbers. These may include lymphocytes, as well as eosinophilic and neutrophilic leukocytes.

Connective Tissue Fibers. Three types of fibers occur in adult connective tissue. Each of these types is present in loose connective tissue, and thus a knowledge of the fibers in this type of tissue gives an understanding of the fibrillar elements of all adult connective tissue.

(a) The *white* or *collagenous* fibers generally course together in bundles of indefinite length and variable thickness ranging from 10 to 100 μ or more. The individual fibers seen in routine preparations vary in diameter from 1 to 12 μ (Fig. 5-2). When these are studied under the higher magnifications of oil immersion objectives, and particularly after special treatment, it is found that they are composed of smaller fibers, the so-called *fibrils of light microscopy*, of only 0.2 to 0.5 μ in diameter. The latter are held together by an amorphous material which can be dissolved by weak alkalis or by trypsin. They are aligned in a parallel direction, giving the appearance of longitudinal striation. The fibers of the loose connective tissue follow an irregular and undulating course; this allows for movement and flexibility of the other tissues with which they are associated. The collagenous fibers themselves are flexible but so slightly elastic as to be practically nonextensible.

Collagen is an albuminous substance which stains with most acid dyes. Hence, the fibers are red in hematoxylin-eosin-stained sections, blue from the aniline blue of Mallory's triple stain, and green or blue in Masson's trichrome, depending on the modification used, i.e., whether the stain contains light green or aniline blue. The fibers are rapidly digested by gastric juice but resist digestion by trypsin in alkaline solution. They swell in dilute acids and are dissolved by strong acids and alkalis. They yield gelatin on boiling; thus, meat with a high content of collagen is made more tender by boiling. Collagen is also a source of glue; animal hides which are composed largely of dense collagenous fibers can be made into leather by tanning.

Electron micrographs show that each of the collagenous fibrils of light microscopy is composed of still smaller *fibrils*. The latter are relatively uniform in diameter in any given connective tissue region but vary in different locations and in different stages of development, ranging from about 200 to 2000 A. In adult human corium, they are about 1000 A diameter. In regions where collagen is being formed, there are slender collagenous fibrils only about 200 A in diameter. In these regions, one may also find very thin *microfibrils* (30 to 150 A) which are collagenous-like but lack the characteristic periodicity of collagen.

The electron microscope fibrils of mature collagen have periodic cross bandings at intervals of about 640 A (Fig. 5-6). Information on the periodicity and the structure of collagen has evolved from the discovery that collagen can be taken apart in vitro and that its constituent molecules can be reassembled either into their previous native form or into other forms. When young or newly formed collagen is taken from the body and placed in cold neutral salt, it readily dissolves. When the solution is incubated at body temperature, fibers form in vitro which have the same 640 A periodicity as native collagen. A solution of young collagen can also be made in weak acetic acid. This will yield native 640 A periodicity collagen by neutralization, or it will give blocks of 2800 A lengths ("segment long spacing collagen") after treatment with adenosine triphosphoric acid. The same solution will yield 2800 A segments arranged end-to-end ("fibrous long spacing") after treatment with glycoproteins. From various studies of this type, using methods of X-ray diffraction, chemical analysis and electron microscopy, it has been established that collagen is composed of macromolecules of about 2800 A in length and 15 A in width. The substance is named tropocollagen (Gr., *trope*, turning, i.e., turning into collagen). The macromolecule is composed of three polypeptide chains in the form of a coiled helix (Fig. 5-9). The chains are composed of amino acids and are joined by hydrogen bonding. The macromolecule is structurally polarized and has a characteristic intraband pattern determined by a

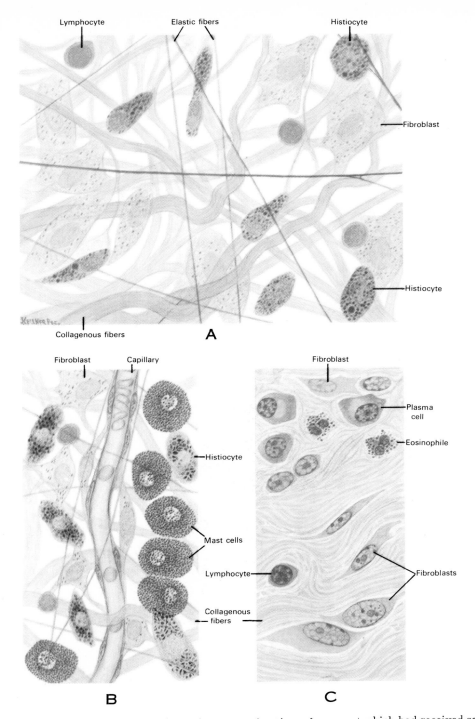

FIG. 5-2. *A*, spread of subcutaneous areolar connective tissue from a rat which had received several intraperitoneal injections of trypan blue over a period of 2 weeks. The animal was autopsied 1 week after the last injection and the spread was made immediately. After fixation in Bouin's fluid, it was stained with resorcin-fuchsin for elastic fibers and with azocarmine to show cells and collagenous fibers. All of the blue color shown in histiocytes and fibroblasts represents the trypan blue which was taken in by the cells preceding autopsy. No trypan blue is present in the nuclei, although a few vacuoles may appear to be within the nuclei when they are in the overlying cytoplasm. ×650. *B*, subcutaneous spread from the same trypan blue rat, stained with neutral red for mast cells. ×650. *C*, a section through the loose connective tissue of the submucosa of the colon. The field shown is directly beneath the muscularis mucosae. Rhesus monkey. Hematoxylin and eosin-azure. ×1250.

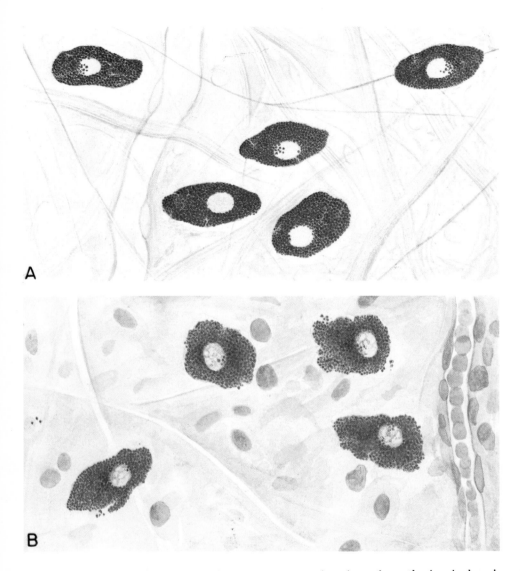

Fig. 5-4. Mast cells in spreads of subcutaneous connective tissue from the inguinal region of a rat. *A*, basophilia of mast cell granules seen after staining with an alcoholic solution of toluidine blue. The pH of the stain was lowered by the addition of HCl and the nuclei of cells remained unstained. Nuclei, connective tissue fibers and the wall of a capillary are visible in the background by their refraction. ×730. *B*, metachromasia of mast cell granules seen after staining in a dilute aqueous solution of toluidine blue. The mast cell granules give a reddish color with the blue dye. Nuclei of fibroblasts, of histiocytes and of capillary endothelial cells (*right side of field*) stain blue. Erythrocytes are bluish green. The pH of the stain in this case was relatively high. ×730.

FIG. 5-6. Electron micrograph of collagen fibrils from the adult human dermis. Chromium shadowed. ×19,300. (Courtesy of Drs. Gross and Schmitt.)

precise linear sequence of the different amino acid residues in the intramolecular strands. In the development of collagen, the macromolecules become aligned parallel with one another to give the 640 A periodicity characteristic of collagen. The most commonly accepted explanation for the 640 A periodicity is that the macromolecules are aligned end to end and with the molecules of adjacent rows arranged in a staggered fashion, overlapping by about one-quarter of their length, as shown in Figure 5-9 (see reviews by Hodge and Schmitt, 1961, and Jackson, 1964). According to another view, the 640 A periodicity is produced by lateral aggregation of macromolecules without staggered overlapping and is due to an alternation of bonding and non-bonding areas between the macromolecules (Grant, Horne and Cox, 1965).

Chemically, the tropocollagen macromolecule consists of about 30% glycine and 25% proline and hydroxyproline, with the remainder consisting of other amino acids, including hydroxylysine. Glycine occupies every fourth position on the chain and is followed by proline and hydroxyproline. Hydroxyproline is not found in significant amounts in any other tissues. Proline and hydroxyproline prevent easy rotation of the strand where they are located, and thus they add stability to the macromolecule.

(b) *Reticular* fibers are small, branching fibers which frequently form a netlike supporting framework or reticulum. Their caliber is so small that they are masked by surrounding structures in ordinary stained preparations, but they blacken intensely after silver impregnation (Bielchowsky's method), whereas collagenous fibers are colored yellow or brown. Because they impregnate with silver, reticular fibers are frequently designated as *argyrophilic* fibers.

Reticular fibers are often continuous with collagenous fibers. At various points, they unite and form bundles which assume the tinctorial characteristics of collagenous fibers. Since reticular fibers are slender, arranged in networks, and often associated with collagenous fibers, it is difficult to obtain any quantity of their substance, known as *reticulin*, for chemical analysis. In most respects, they appear to be chemically similar to collagenous fibers, although they are more resistant to peptic digestion. They also have relatively more carbohydrate, which is apparently associated with each fibril in the form of a surface coat. This explains the fact that reticular fibers give a strongly positive reaction with the periodic acid-Schiff (PAS) technique, while collagenous fibers give only a slight reaction. The associated carbohydrate is also responsible for the more intense reaction with certain silver techniques. The reticular fibers have the same 640 A cross banding as collagenous fibers and are morphologically similar to them except for diameter. In the course of their development, collagenous fibers pass through a stage where they are structurally identical with reticular fibers: they are slender, argyrophilic and have 640 A periodicity.

Reticular fibers are relatively sparse in adult loose connective tissues, except for regions around muscle fibers (Figs. 8-20 and 8-21) and around blood vessels, nerves and epithelial structures. They are numerous in glandular organs (Fig. 16-78).

In lymphatic organs and in red bone marrow, reticular fibers are associated with a special type of cell, the *reticular cell;* the two elements (reticular fibers and reticular cells) form a type of tissue, the *reticular tissue.* In other locations, reticular fibers have the same relationship to fibroblasts as collagenous fibers have.

(c) The *elastic* fibers (Fig. 5-2) are highly refractile fibers which are as a rule thinner than the white fibers but may reach a diameter of 10 to 12 μ in some elastic ligaments (e.g., ligamentum nuchae of an ox). They branch and anastomose freely, forming networks. The smaller fibers are round in cross section, the larger are flat or polygonal. They are highly elastic. When seen in large masses (elastic ligaments) in the fresh state, they have a distinctly yellow appearance. In arteries, the elastic tissue often occurs in the form of fenestrated membranes or lamellae.

Chemically, elastic tissue consists of mucopolysaccharides and a protein known as *elastin* which contains a large variety of amino acids. Elastin differs from collagen in that it has very little hydroxyproline. It has a higher content of valine and contains desmocine, an amino acid not found in collagen. Elastin has a remarkable resistance to most agents. It is not affected by hot or cold water, by dilute acids or alkalis or by gastric juice. It is, however, rapidly digested by *elastase*, an enzyme derived from the pancreas.

Elastic fibers are best demonstrated in the fresh condition by immersing the tissue in dilute acid solutions. The collagenous fibers swell and become transparent. The elastic fibers are then seen as highly refractive, shining threads. The elastic fibers react poorly to most stains, but they are colored specifically by certain dyes such as orcein and resorcin-fuchsin (Fig. 5-2).

Electron micrographs show that elastic fibers are not made up of cross banded fibrils as collagen is. In fact, most electron micrographs give the impression that elastic tissue is composed only of an amorphous substance of varying electron density. However, high resolution electron micrographs of thin sections stained with uranyl acetate and lead citrate show that the elastic fiber substance has two components: homogeneous material of variable electron density and very slender microfibrils (about 30 to 150 A in diameter).

The amorphous material contains the embedded fine fibrils and also forms a surface coat around the fiber. The microfibrils are seen mainly in the peripheral portion of the fiber and are more obvious in young than in mature elastic tissue. Their visibility may also vary with the functional state of the fiber; it is postulated that the fibrils are randomly oriented in relaxed fibers and are more parallel in stretched fibers (Dempsey and Lansing). An analysis of the elastic tissue components, following their separation by extraction of homogenized tissues, shows that the amorphous component has the same amino acid composition as that described for elastin and that the microfibrils consist of protein different from both elastin and collagen (Ross and Bornstein, 1969).

Elastic fibers are generally formed by fibroblasts, although it seems likely that they can also be produced by smooth muscle cells in the walls of arteries. Two different patterns in the development of elastic tissue have been observed. In one type, a lattice-like appearance is produced by a more or less parallel alignment of microfibrils around small aggregates of homogeneous substance (Haust and More, 1967). Another pattern involves the fusion of elastic tissue "units." Each unit consists of a central core of homogeneous material surrounded by fine microfibrils. Elastic fibers and lamellae arise by fusion of the units, and growth occurs by accretion of more units upon the surface.

The surface of an elastic fiber seems to be continually undergoing changes which involve a turnover of material. In the aging of fenestrated membranes (lamellae) of arteries, small regions of degenerating elastic tissue form seeding sites for mineralization in the peripheral portion of the lamella. In elastic fibers of the skin, age changes occur in the associated mucopolysaccharides. There is an increase in chondroitin sulfate B and keratosulfate in proportion to the other mucopolysaccharides, and this gives a loss of resiliency (Yu and Blumenthal, 1967).

Origin of the Connective Tissue

Fibers. The development of connective tissue fibers has been studied extensively both by light microscopy and by electron microscopy. In locations where connective tissue fibers first appear in embryos, one can see with the light microscope that the accompanying cells differ from the more primitive mesenchymal cells from which they are derived. They have prominent nucleoli and basophilic cytoplasm. They resemble the blast cells characteristically found in other regions of differentiation. The name fibroblast, given by early histologists, was based on the belief that the cells participate in some manner in the formation of fibers. However, there were marked differences of opinion as to whether the cells (a) form fibers intracellularly and secrete them into the intercellular regions, or (b) secrete intercellular material which later forms fibers at a distance from the cells and with little or no influence exerted by the cells. Tissue culture studies showed that the first fibers observable with the light microscope are narrow and argyrophilic, and they appear close to the cell surface in at least some instances (Figs. 5-7 and 5-8). The resolution with the light microscope was inadequate to determine whether fibers first seen at a distance from the cells were preceded by more slender precursors.

The advent of electron microscopy, in combination with radioautographic and biochemical methods, has provided a much better understanding of collagen formation. When labeled proline is injected into animals in which new formation of collagen has been stimulated, the labeled material appears first in the region of the rough surfaced endoplasmic reticulum of the fibroblasts, later in the Golgi complex and still later in collagenous fibers outside the fibroblasts. From a variety of studies of this type, it appears that the sequence of collagen formation is as follows: the amino acids (glycine, proline, lysine, etc.) are synthesized into polypeptide chains in the presence of the ribosomes of the endoplasmic reticulum. Some of the proline

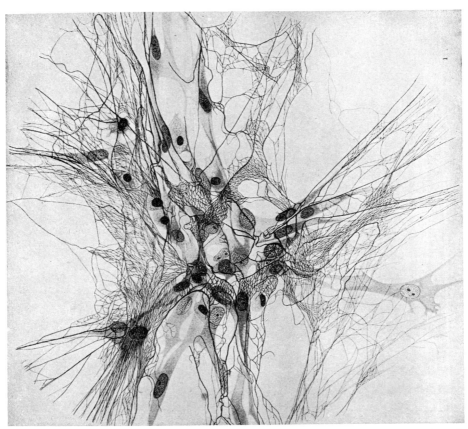

FIG. 5-7. Formation of reticular fibers as seen in a tissue culture preparation. Note that the fibers are closely associated with the cells in some regions and separated from them in others. (After Maximow.)

and lysine is also hydroxylated into hydroxyproline and hydroxylysine, respectively. From the cisternae of the endoplasmic reticulum, the synthesized proteins are transported to the Golgi complex for further processing, and then the collagenous substance is carried in Golgi-derived vesicles to the cell surface, where it is released as macromolecules of tropocollagen. The membranes of the vesicles fuse with the plasmalemma, releasing the electron-dense collagenous material by a merocrine type of secretion, somewhat like reverse pinocytosis. Other electron-dense material is found just inside and just outside the cell membrane. It is difficult to follow the plasmalemma in these regions, and it has been sug-

gested that electron-dense material leaves the cell by partial shedding of the membrane, ecdysis, or by an apocrine-like method (Porter and Pappas, 1959, and Porter, 1964). More recent high resolution micrographs of the electron-dense marginal areas show the presence of very slender microfibrils. They are described as the "smallest organized extracellular components" (Haust and More, 1967), and they vary in diameter in different locations, and according to different investigators, from 30 to 160 A. They have a beaded appearance but lack the periodicity of collagen. It is assumed that they participate in collagen formation. They appear to be a constituent of the electron-dense marginal material previously proposed as a template for

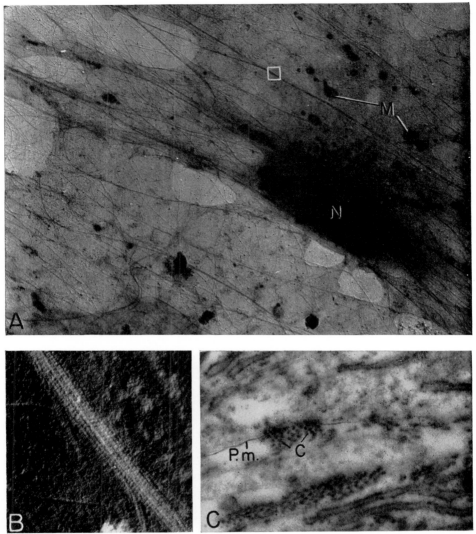

FIG. 5-8. Electron micrographs illustrating the relationship of fibroblasts to collagen fiber formation. *A*, surface view of a fibroblast grown in tissue culture from an explant from the dermis of a 9-day-old chick embryo. The nucleus (*N*) and mitochondria (*M*) are indicated. Collagen fibers formed in association with the cell course from *lower right* to *upper left*. ×3,000. *B*, higher magnification of the fiber shown within the small square of *A*. Note that the fiber is composed of many fibrils. ×20,000. *C*, section through cells of the dermis of a 14-day-old chick embryo. A fiber similar to that illustrated in *B* is shown in a section vertical to the cell surface. No collagen fibrils (*C*) are evident within the cytoplasm; they appear first on the cell surface (*P.m.*). ×20,000. (Courtesy of Drs. Keith Porter and G. D. Pappas.)

initiation and extension of polymerization of collagen (Porter and Pappas, 1959). In other words, the microfibrils which are "shed" from the cell surface may serve as templates on which the monomeric tropocollagen secreted by the vesicles becomes polymerized to form the periodic cross banded collagenous fibrils of about 200 A diameter. Once they are established, these earliest collagenous fibrils themselves apparently act as templates for polymerization of more monomeric tropocollagen from the surrounding medium. The collagenous fibrils increase in diameter by accretion upon their surface to a point characteristic for a given tissue location. The slender and more immature collagenous fibrils are argyrophilic and are similar to the reticular fibers present in adult connective tissue.

The formation of elastic fibers is outlined in the previous section on their structure. The details of their formation are not as clear as for collagen. The elastic fibers make their appearance in the embryo later than collagenous fibers, but this is not to be misconstrued to imply that they may develop from the latter. They contain microfibrils which are morphologically similar to the microfibrils present in regions where collagen is forming. Further studies are needed to determine whether the microfibrils seen in different locations are chemically similar.

In considering the histiogenic functions of fibroblasts, one must not overlook the fact that they secrete the mucopolysaccharides of the intercellular matrix. There is evidence that the protein components are synthesized in the region of the rough surfaced endoplasmic reticulum and that the carbohydrates are added in the Golgi complex.

Ground Substance. The cells and fibers of connective tissue are embedded in an amorphous background material known as *ground substance*. It is a colloidal substance in the form of a gel, and it has the capacity for binding varying amounts of water. The bound water serves as a medium for diffusion of gases and metabolic substances from the blood vessels to the cells of the tissues, and vice versa. Thus the amorphous matrix and the tissue fluids are intimately associated. Most of the extravascular fluid is bound within the matrix and is not present in any appreciable amount as free fluid in the connective tissues under normal conditions. It appears rapidly as free fluid in areas of injury and inflammation.

In fresh spreads of connective tissue, the ground substance has the same refractive index as water and isotonic saline solutions

and, therefore, the ground substance is invisible in spreads mounted in these media. The ground substance is quite soluble in the reagents generally used in preparing tissues for sectioning, and it is not seen in the areolar connective tissue of routinely prepared sections. It is preserved best by fresh frozen and freeze-drying techniques, provided that the tissues are fixed subsequently in vapors of ether-formol. In these preparations, it stains metachromatically, indicating the presence of mucopolysaccharides. In some connective tissues, such as cartilage and bone, the ground substance can be preserved by appropriate fixatives in sufficient quantities for histochemical studies. In fact, the mucopolysaccharide content of cartilage and bone is sufficient to affect the tinctorial results in sections routinely prepared and stained with hematoxylin and eosin (Chapter 6).

The ground substance contains a number of *mucopolysaccharides* (protein-polysaccharides) which are divided into two main categories, *sulfated* and *nonsulfated*, depending upon whether they are esterified with sulfuric acid. The nonsulfated group includes *hyaluronic acid* and *chondroitin*. The sulfated group includes: *chondroitin sulfate A* (chondroitin 4-sulfate), *chondroitin sulfate C* (chondroitin 6-sulfate), *chondroitin sulfate B* (dermatan sulfate) and *keratosulfate* (keratin sulfate). *Heparin*, found in mast cells, is also a mucopolysaccharide, and it has a relatively high content of sulfate. Most of the sulfated mucopolysaccharides are very gel-like, and when they are abundant, as in cartilage, they provide support.

Hyaluronic acid is a viscous, fluidlike mucopolysaccharide isolated by Meyer and Palmer in 1934. It is found in synovial fluid, loose connective tissue, etc. (Table 5-1). Because of its capacity to bind water, it probably has a major responsibility for changes in the viscosity and permeability of ground substance. It probably plays a role in preventing the spread of noxious agents in localized infections. An enzyme, *hyaluronidase*,

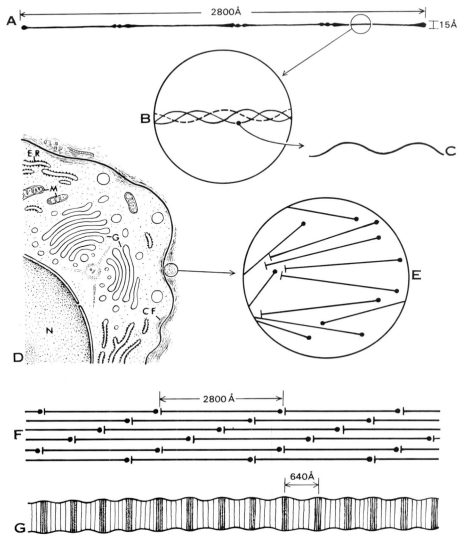

Fig. 5-9. Diagrams of the formation and structure of collagen as determined by electron microscopy, chemical analysis, and X-ray diffraction. A, schematization of the tropocollagen macromolecule, showing structural asymmetry along its length. B, enlargement of a section of the macromolecule, showing that it is composed of three polypeptide chains, with one (indicated by *broken line*) differing from the other two in amino acid composition. C, enlargement of a portion of B, showing that each polypeptide chain has a helical configuration. D, diagrammatic representation of a portion of a fibroblast, showing a portion of the nucleus (N), mitochondria (M), rough surfaced endoplasmic reticulum (ER), Golgi complex (G), and cytoplasmic microfilaments (CF). In the formation of collagen, amino acids taken up by the cell are synthesized into polypeptides at the sites of polyribosomes associated with the endoplasmic reticulum; then the polypeptides are transported via the cisternae of the endoplasmic reticulum to the Golgi complex, where they are assembled into macromolecules which are transported in Golgi-derived vesicles to the cell surface. E, enlarged and schematized representation of a small region of material just outside the cell, showing the irregular distribution of tropocollagen macromolecules. F, diagrammatic representation of the manner in which the macromolecules are postulated as coming together in an aligned and overlapping pattern to form cross banded collagenous fibers as shown in G. (A, B, C, F and G are redrawn and modified from Gross, 1961 and 1964. D and E are based chiefly on descriptions by Porter, 1964, and by Gross, 1964.)

123

TABLE 5-1*

MAIN TYPES OF CONNECTIVE TISSUE MUCOPOLYSACCHARIDES

Name	Some locations where found	Sulfate per disaccharide unit	Hyaluronidase susceptibility	
			Testicular	Bacterial
Hyaluronic acid	Synovial fluid, umbilical cord, vitreous humor, loose connective tissue, group A streptococci capsules	0	+	+
Chondroitin	Cornea	0		
Chondroitin sulfate A (chondroitin 4-sulfate)	Aorta, bone, cartilage, cornea	1	+	—
Chondroitin sulfate C (chondroitin 6-sulfate)	Cartilage, nucleus pulposus, sclera, tendon, umbilical cord	1	+	—
Chondroitin sulfate B (dermatan sulfate)	Aorta, heart valve, ligamentum nuchae, sclera, skin, tendon	1	—	—
Keratosulfate (keratan sulfate)	Bone, cartilage, cornea, nucleus pulposus	1	—	—
Heparin	Mast cells	2	—	—

* Modified from Spicer, Horn and Leppi, 1967.

hydrolyzes it, reducing its viscosity with a consequent increase in the permeability of the tissue. For example, subcutaneous injections of India ink to which hyaluronidase has been added will spread much more rapidly than injections of ink alone. This enzyme (known as "spreading factor") was first isolated from testicles and snake venom. An enzyme with similar effects on hyaluronic acid is produced by some bacteria. Chondroitin differs from hyaluronic acid by having galactosamine in place of glucosamine.

Chondroitin sulfate A differs from chondroitin sulfate C only in that the sulfate moiety is attached at carbon 4. Chondroitin sulfate A and B have a number of chemical differences. When they are found in the same location, as in the aorta (Table 5-1), they can be readily distinguished in histochemical preparations by the fact that A is susceptible to testicular hyaluronidase, whereas B is not.

The sulfated mucopolysaccharides are generally much more metachromatic than the nonsulfated ones in toluidine blue-stained preparations. The sulfated group also stains with hematoxylin when it is sufficiently abundant, as in cartilage, to overshadow the associated acidophilic collagenous fibers. Both types of mucopolysaccharides, sulfated and nonsulfated, give positive PAS reactions.

The PAS Reaction in Connective Tissues. The periodic acid-Schiff technique is based on the fact that free aldehydes will restore the reddish color to basic fuchsin which has been bleached previously with sulfurous acid. In Chapter 1 it is noted that the Schiff reagent (i.e., bleached basic fuchsin) is specific for DNA in the Feulgen reaction because the sections are treated to only a mild hydrolysis which liberates aldehydes from DNA but not from RNA. When a stronger oxidizing agent is used, such as periodic acid, aldehydes are liberated from polysaccharides in general. Cartilage matrix gives a positive PAS reaction, and the ground substances of other connective tissues also give PAS reactions of varying degrees in different locations. However, studies by Glegg, Clermont and Leblond (1952) showed that *pure* hyaluronic acid is PAS-negative, and the same is apparently true for *pure* chondroitin sulfate. More recent studies agree with these earlier findings that PAS methods do not visualize the acid mucopolysaccharides themselves (Spicer, Horn and Leppi, 1967). The PAS reaction that is given by a number of these carbohydrate-protein complexes is apparently due to the associated carbohydrates, such as hexoses, etc. (Leblond, Glegg and Eidinger, 1957). The PAS-positive reaction given by reticular fibers is apparently due to carbohydrates in the surface coat of the fiber.

Functions of Loose Connective Tissue. Loose connective tissue loosely binds structures together and holds them in position. It acts as a padding and serves as a pathway for nerves and blood vessels.

Nutrient substances in their passage from the blood vessels to the cells of the body must traverse connective tissue, as must also those products of metabolism which reach the blood and lymph capillaries (see Fig. 12-23.)

Changes in connective tissues occur in a number of disease states. For example, in a condition known as *scurvy*, collagen is not formed in normal amounts because there is a deficiency of vitamin C which is necessary in order for fibroblasts to hydroxylate normal amounts of proline to hydroxyproline. Many aging changes are closely related to changes in collagen and ground substance. In rheumatoid arthritis, there is an excessive production and abnormal organization of collagen. In fact, the various rheumatic conditions are so intimately related to abnormalities in the formation and repair of connective tissue that they are often spoken of as collagen diseases. Some diseases are clearly related to abnormal function of genes. *Hurler's syndrome*, a condition involving stunted skeletal growth and abnormal fat metabolism, is an hereditary disorder involving an excessive accumulation of chrondoitin sulfate B and heparitin sulfate.

The loose connective tissue plays an extremely important role in limiting the spread of localized infections and in the healing process. The localization invokes all elements of the connective tissue. The ground substance, though permeable, tends to inhibit the passage of the noxious agent. In addition to the phagocytic cells (neutrophilic leuko-cytes and monocytes) which migrate to the area from the blood, the tissue phagocytes (macrophages) multiply and mobilize. The fibroblasts also become active and, after a considerable time, will deposit a surrounding barrier of fibers. An area of infection is shown in Figure 5-3. In repair of wounds, the fibroblasts increase in number and form fibers. Sprouts from the blood vessels penetrate into the delicate regenerating tissue which is known as granulation tissue.

DENSE CONNECTIVE TISSUE

Dense connective tissue is chiefly characterized by the close packing of its fibers. It occurs in the form of sheets, bands and cordlike structures. Examples are the dermis, capsules of certain organs, aponeuroses, ligaments and tendons. Some of the deep fascia is intermediate between dense and loose connective tissue. In most locations, the main component is collagenous fibers but, in a few of the ligaments, elastic fibers predominate.

Dense, irregularly arranged connective tissue occurs in the form of sheets. The main component is coarse collagenous fibers, but elastic and reticular fibers are also present. The fibers interlace and form a coarse tough feltwork, and some of them continue into adjacent tissue. Fibroblasts and some macrophages are present but show no special modifications. Examples of dense irregularly arranged connective tissue are dermis (Figs. 5-10, and 14-1), periosteum and perichondrium and the capsules of some organs. The capsule of the testis (tunica albuginea, Fig. 19-11) is extremely dense.

Dense, regularly arranged connective tissue occurs as cordlike structures and as bands, some of which, as in aponeuroses, may be very broad. The fibers are densely packed and lie parallel to each other, forming structures of great tensile strength. This type of tissue comprises the tendons, ligaments and aponeuroses.

Tendons are composed almost entirely of white fibrous tissue (Fig. 5-11). The fibers

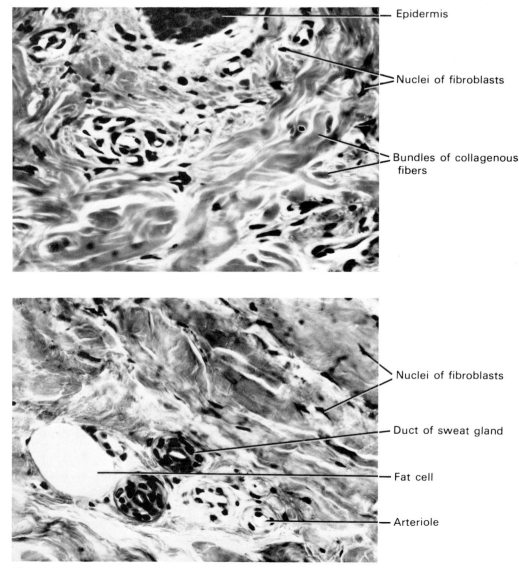

Fig. 5-10. Photomicrographs of dense, irregularly arranged connective tissue in the corium of the dorsum of the thumb. *Upper figure*, a field just below the epidermis; *lower figure*, a deep region of the dermis just above the subcutaneous tissue. Note variations in the diameter and course of the bundles of fibers in different fields. For example, the bundles of fibers are coarse in the deep portions of the dermis and more slender in the subepidermal region. Even greater variations are found in other parts of the body, and there are many gradations between the loose and dense varieties of irregularly arranged connective tissue. Hematoxylin and eosin-stained section of human thumb. ×390.

are parallel and are closely packed in bundles which are so dense that they appear almost homogeneous. Fibroblasts are the only cell type present, and they are few in number as compared to loose tissue. In longitudinal sections of tendon, the fibroblasts or tendon cells are elongated and aligned in rows between the bundles of collagenous fibers (Fig. 5-11). In cross sections, the cells appear stellate in shape, with plate-like extensions between the collagenous bundles (Fig. 5-12).

Around each bundle of fibers is a small

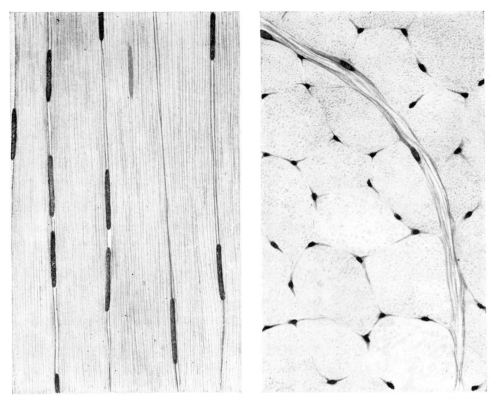

FIGS. 5-11 AND 5-12. Sections of human achilles tendon. Fig. 5-11 (*left*) is from a longitudinal section and shows rows of dense staining nuclei of fibroblasts (tendon cells) between bundles of regularly arranged fibrils. Fig. 5-12 (*right*) is from a cross section. Note that the nuclei and the pale staining cytoplasm of the tendon cells appear stellate in shape. A band of irregularly arranged connective tissue separating tendon bundles is seen in the *right side* of the drawing. Both figures ×575.

epi–, peri–, endo – tendineum

amount of loose tissue, and the whole tendon is surrounded by interlacing fibers.

Aponeuroses have the same composition as tendons but are broad and relatively thin. The fibers may be arranged in several superimposed layers, those of one layer running at an angle to those of adjacent layers. The layers may interweave.

Ligaments in most cases are structurally similar to tendons, being formed predominantly of collagenous fibers, but a few are composed almost entirely of elastic fibers.

The *yellow elastic ligaments* are formed of parallel coursing, yellow, elastic fibers which are bound together by a small amount of loose tissue. The elastic fibers may be very large, as in the ligamentum nuchae (Fig. 5-13). The series of ligaments (ligamenta flava) coursing between the arches of the vertebrae are also of the elastic type.

RETICULAR CONNECTIVE TISSUE

Reticular connective tissue is characterized by the presence of a cellular reticulum (reticular cells) and a fibrillar network. The fibrils are argyrophilic, and they branch and communicate, forming an open, interlacing meshwork. The cells have a stellate shape, with processes which extend in all directions and make contact with the processes of neighboring cells (Fig. 5-14). Most of the protoplasmic processes are wrapped about or extend along the reticular fibers, but many of them lack this association, thus making part of the protoplasmic reticulum independent of the fibrillar one (Fig. 5-14). The fibers are

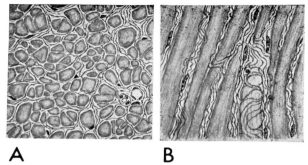

A   **B**

Fig. 5-13. Ligamentum nuchae of an ox. *A*, tissue cut in cross section; *B*, longitudinal section. Slender and irregularly arranged collagenous fibers are present between the unusually large elastic fibers. ×480.

extracellular as in other connective tissue, in close contact with the cells but not a part of them.

Morphologically, *reticular cells* probably have a closer resemblance to embryonic connective tissue or mesenchymal cells than do any other cells in the adult body. They have a large, pale nucleus and rather abundant, lightly staining cytoplasm, but they are without cytoplasmic granules or vacuoles under normal conditions.

Several different functional and developmental potencies have been attributed to reticular cells. It seems likely either that the name includes several distinct types of cells which cannot be distinguished by morphological means alone, or that they are not all in the same physiological state. Some of them may have retained their embryonic or developmental potencies, while others have differentiated into either phagocytic or fibroblastic types of cells. The fibroblastic tendencies are shown by the cells associated with the fibrous elements of the reticular tissue. Other cells are so placed that they seem to make up part of the wall of a lymphatic sinus or blood sinusoid and in this condition may rightly be called reticuloendothelial cells. When an animal is given trypan blue by intravital injection, many of the reticular cells segregate the dye into vacuoles and are therefore part of the "reticuloendothelial system." In fact it is those phagocytic reticular cells which are placed in the walls

of sinuses or sinusoids which have given the "system" its name. However, it should be borne in mind that many of the phagocytic cells are deep in the reticular tissue and have no contact with sinuses or sinusoids, and that none of these phagocytic cells correspond to true endothelium. Reticular cells, in addition to being potentially phagocytic, also may give rise to the early stages of developing erythrocytes and leukocytes in the hemopoietic tissues.

Although reticular fibers are widely distributed in the body in association with fibroblasts, the occurrence of reticular fibers in association with reticular cells, i.e., *reticular tissue*, has a much more limited distribution. Reticular tissue forms the framework of lymphoid tissue (lymph nodes and nodules, spleen, thymus) and bone marrow (Fig. 5-14). In lymphoid tissue, the interstices of the reticular tissue are filled with lymphocytes; in bone marrow, all blood-forming elements are present in the reticular tissue network.

Adipose Tissue (Fat)

Fat is considered by some as a special tissue arising from specific cells (steatoblasts), by others as a modified type of fibrillar connective tissue in which some of the cells have lost their fiber-forming capacity and have assumed the function of fat storage. Fat cells are found isolated or in groups in all loose connective tissue, but in certain places they are present in such large numbers

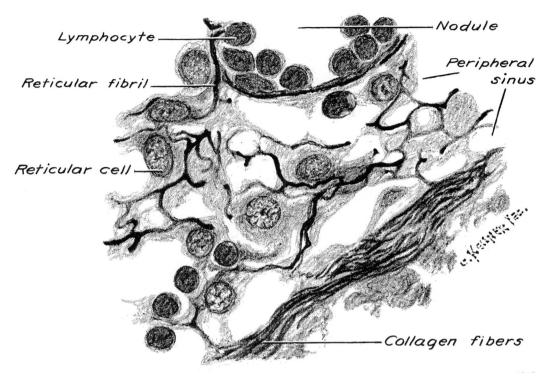

Lymphocyte

Reticular fibril

Reticular cell

Nodule

Peripheral sinus

Collagen fibers

Fig. 5-14. Reticular tissue from lymph node of monkey. Bielschowsky-Foot and eosin-azure. ×1840.

and have an organization which justifies the designation of adipose tissue. The largest deposits of fat are found in the subcutaneous connective tissue (panniculus adiposus), in the kidney region, in the mesenteries and mediastinum and in the cervical, axillary and inguinal regions.

Fat is different from the other connective tissues in that the cells, and not the intercellular substance, make up the bulk and determine the nature of the tissue. The cells are large and have an ovoid or spherical shape. The cytoplasm is displaced to the peripheral region of the cell by the presence of a single large fat droplet (Fig. 5-15). The nucleus, flattened and surrounded by a small amount of cytoplasm, is usually found pressed against the cell wall. In sections of fixed preparations in which the fat has been dissolved out, the cells appear as empty rings or ovals, or they have a "signet ring" shape if

the plane of section passes through the nucleus. When occurring singly or in small groups the cells retain their spherical or ovoid form; in denser masses they become polyhedral as a result of the pressure of adjacent cells. Fat cells are usually arranged in groups or lobules, each lobule being separated from its neighbor by loose connective tissue. Delicate strands of irregularly arranged connective tissue consisting of reticular, collagenous and elastic fibers surround the fat cells and serve as a bed for the numerous capillaries.

The appearance of the adult fat cell can be best understood by a reference to its histogenesis. In places where fat is to be formed, certain cells of the embryonal connective tissue arrange themselves in groups in the meshes of a rich capillary network which marks the end of a small artery. Such groups, each of which is destined to become an adult

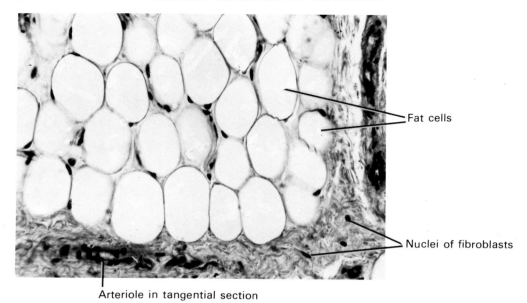

Fat cells

Nuclei of fibroblasts

Arteriole in tangential section

FIG. 5-15. Photomicrograph of fat from human subcutaneous tissue. Since the fat dissolves and escapes from the cell during the dehydration and clearing of the tissue for preparing paraffin sections, the cells appear empty. The cells are large and only a few are sectioned, by chance, in the plane of the nucleus. Hematoxylin and eosin stain. ×250.

fat lobule, can be distinguished in man in the 4th month of embryonic life. The cells enlarge, lose their stellate form, become rich in protoplasm and have the general appearance of secretory cells (steatoblasts). Fine fat droplets are formed in the cytoplasm which increase in number and finally coalesce, forming a larger droplet. By further formation and fusion of fat droplets, the nucleus is pushed to one side and the cytoplasm is gradually reduced to the thin membrane of the adult cell (Fig. 5-15).

The blood supply of fat is rich, and the adult lobule retains its embryonal vascular relations, the vascular supply of each lobule being complete and independent. One artery runs to each lobule, where it breaks up into an intralobular capillary network which in turn gives rise to the intralobular veins, usually two in number.

Chemically, fat consists of the esters of glycerol and certain fatty acids (palmitic, stearic and oleic). It is not soluble in water or cold alcohol but dissolves readily in ether, chloroform, benzol and xylol. Since the latter

reagents are commonly used in histological technique, the fat is usually dissolved, leaving an empty space or vacuole. When properly fixed, fat and fatlike substances stain black with osmic acid (osmium tetroxide). Other specific stains for fat are certain coal tar dyes, as Sudan III and Scharlach R.

The experiments of Schoenheimer have shown that the so-called fat deposits of the body are not inactive storehouses. He labeled or "tagged" molecules of carbohydrates and fats with atoms of heavy water or deuterium and followed their metabolism in the animal body. He found that mice synthesize fats from carbohydrate on a normal diet without overfeeding or fattening. The fats are rapidly replaced; the turnover in mice required only about 6 days.

The fat deposits of the body represent important food reserves which can be tapped in case the normal food supply becomes inadequate. When fat is given up by the cells, at least in the case of isolated fat cells or smaller scattered groups, the cells may revert to a precursor stage and become capable of again storing fat under favorable conditions. In the large fat masses, especially in older individuals, the cells when emptied of their fat sometimes become filled with a serous fluid which also fills the spaces between the cells. This condition is known as serous atrophy of fatty tissue.

Besides its nutritive value, fat has important mechanical functions. It forms plastic, shock-absorbing pads in the subcutaneous tissue of parts exposed to pressure, such as the gluteal region and the soles of the feet. It packs the orbital cavity and the angles of joints, acting as a guard against exaggerated movements. Such fatty pads are especially prominent in the hip, knee, shoulder and elbow joints, where they may be retained even in states of extreme emaciation.

As a nonconductor, fat is also an important agent in the conservation of the body heat.

Rodents and a number of other animals have masses of *brown fat tissue* in addition to the common or white type. Brown fat is found in the interscapular region, in the inguinal area and elsewhere. It was once considered as a *hibernating gland*, but it is present in a number of animals which do not hibernate.

Each cell of brown fat contains a number of small lipid droplets, whereas each cell of adult white fat contains only one large droplet (or vacuole). Therefore, brown fat is described as *multilocular* and white fat as *unilocular*.

Brown fat does not respond to nutritional changes as readily as ordinary fat. On the other hand, hypophysectomy brings about a more rapid lipid depletion in brown than in white fat. *(removal of pituitary)*

PIGMENTED CONNECTIVE TISSUE

Pigmented connective tissue cells occur in the choroid and iris of the eye and in the corium of the dark skinned races (Fig. 5-16). The cytoplasm is filled to a varying degree with brown or black pigment which is usually melanin. Experiments with tissue cul-

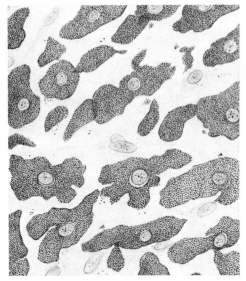

FIG. 5-16. Pigmented connective tissue cells from choroid coat of human eye. Nuclei have been stained with hematoxylin; pigment granules are seen by their natural coloration. A few nuclei of nonpigmented cells are shown among the pigmented cells. ×450.

tures indicate that they are a specialized type of cell. The cells form true pigment in the cultures only if they are explanted from a tissue which would have grown pigment in the body.

BLOOD AND NERVE SUPPLY OF CONNECTIVE TISSUE

Blood vessels and lymphatics are very numerous in loose connective tisue. The rich capillary plexuses are not, however, in the main destined for the tissue itself but for the more active cells of epithelium and muscle. The connective tissue forms the supporting bed for all blood vessels and incidentally receives its own nutrition from them. In the dense connective tissues and tendons, the blood supply is less abundant. In tendons, the blood vessels follow a straight course between the large fascicles and communicate with each other by short branches which run across the fascicles, forming a scanty capillary network with oblong meshes. The fibrous membranes of the periosteum and dura mater are more vascular, but here too the blood vessels are mainly destined for bone.

Lymphatics are numerous and form extensive networks, especially in the submucous, subserous and subcutaneous connective tissue. They are also present in fibrous membranes and tendons, where they form both superficial and deep lymphatic plexuses.

Connective tissue is richly supplied with nerves which end in the tissue itself or go to epithelium and muscle. Special nerve endings are found in the tendons, in fibrous membranes and in the periarticular connective tissue.

THE RETICULOENDOTHELIAL SYSTEM

The anatomical connotation of this name is rather unfortunate because the "system" to which it refers is based on physiological and pathological considerations. The earlier name suggested by Metchnikoff, "macrophages," might better have been retained, but since the former name has become firmly entrenched in a voluminous literature, it will be used in this discussion. The cells in this system do not form true endothelium, and the most widely distributed type of reticuloendothelial cell, the connective tissue histiocyte, is neither a reticular cell nor an endothelial cell.

All highly phagocytic cells of the body, except leukocytes, belong to this system. They have no morphological characteristic which distinguishes them with certainty from other cells. The only certain method of identification is to inject into the living animal certain nontoxic dyes or some inert particulate matter such as the carbon particles of India ink. The macrophages take up the dye or other particles and can easily be identified in microscopic preparations. The injection of nontoxic dyes such as trypan blue or lithium carmine into a living animal is known as *vital* or *intravital staining*. Since the power to take up the dye and segregate it into vacuoles parallels the power to engulf particulate matter such as India ink or colloidal metals, the absorption of the dye has been called

ultramicroscopic phagocytosis. After vital staining, the cells containing dye are found in the loose connective tissue, in the reticular connective tissue and in the dilated blood sinuses of certain organs. In the connective tissue, they correspond to the *histiocytes* described above. They are probably identical with the clasmatocytes of Ranvier, the resting-wandering cells of Maximow, the macrophages of Lewis and Evans, and the splenocytes and endothelial leucocytes of Mallory.

In the liver, the cells containing the dye are found in the sinusoids, either flattened against the wall so as to resemble endothelium or as stellate forms with their processes extending into the lumen after the manner of reticular cells. They are the *Kupffer* cells In the lymphatic system, the phagocytosis is shown particularly by the large *reticular cells* of the sinuses of lymph nodes, but the dye is taken up also by the cells of the reticular tissue of the less organized lymphoid aggregations in many parts of the body. The spleen has a large number of cells which are marked by the dye, both in the reticulum of the pulp and in the walls of the blood sinuses. Some of the reticular cells of the bone marrow and cells in the walls of the sinuses of the suprarenal gland and hypophysis also show the phagocytic activity. The *microglia* of the nervous system take up the dye to some extent and, since they have been shown to be derived from the mesoderm, they should be included in the system. Many of the phagocytic cells in the lymph nodes do actually line the lymph sinuses and at the same time send branching reticular processes into the lumen and into the denser tissue of the nodule. These are properly called reticuloendothelium, but numerically they form only a small portion of the "system."

Macrophages are occasionally found in the blood stream. They apparently represent phagocytic cells which have become detached from their fixed positions in the sinuses of the liver and spleen. They are generally filtered out of the blood in the capillaries of the lung, but some may continue into the peripheral circulation. They are distinguishable from monocytes, which do not exhibit phagocytic characteristics while they are within the circulation. However, it should be recalled that the monocytes assume the characteristics of macrophages when they emigrate into the connective tissues in regions of inflammation. They also behave as macrophages in tissue culture and in fresh preparations of blood with supravital stains, such as neutral red (Fig. 7-2, *C*).

Although cells containing the dye are found in widely separated organs, the *reaction* is quite *specific*. Epithelium, nerve cells, and muscle take up the dye very slightly, if at all. The true endothelial cells, lining the blood cessels and lymphatic capillaries, either fail to react to the dye or react so slightly that, if a macrophage is near an endothelial cell, a quantitative difference is readily seen. The fibroblasts take up the dye more slowly and in smaller amounts than the histiocytes (Fig. 5-2). In the reticular tissue of the spleen, lymph nodes and other lymphoid tissue, there are undifferentiated cells which do not take up the dye, although they are morphologically similar to the active cells.

In the development of the embryo, the mesenchyme gives rise to two types of cells in the connective tissue, fibroblasts and wandering cells (Maximow). After the fibroblasts have once formed connective tissue fibers, they probably remain fibroblasts and do not change into other or more primitive types. The wandering cells, on the other hand, retain some of their primitive properties and may take one of several lines of development according to the stimulus of body needs. Many of them become macrophages; others preserve embryological potencies which can be called forth under abnormal circumstances. The latter are called *undifferentiated mesenchymal cells*.

Some investigators believe that the cells of the reticuloendothelial system retain potentialities for producing other types of cells, particularly blood cells. There is no convincing evidence that they do this under normal circumstances, but it is possible that some of them assume a hemopoietic function under stress. In analyzing the question, one must keep in mind that the reticuloendothelial cell is defined as a macrophage and that it is identified by its ability to take up intravitally injected colloidal dyes. No matter how much colloidal dye one injects into an animal, there are always some reticular cells left in bone marrow which are free of the dye. The hemopoietic stem cells and other cells of the blood series are also free of the dye. The dye-free reticular cells appear to be less differentiated than do the phagocytic ones. They can differentiate in several directions, into macrophages, blood cells, etc. The question is whether a cell that has differentiated into a functioning macrophage reverts to an undifferentiated stage and proceeds on a different developmental course.

The *functional importance* of the macrophages of the reticuloendothelial system is very great. In a normal individual, they are probably responsible for taking the broken down blood cells from the circulation, and they may even store the iron which is to be used in hematopoiesis. In pathological conditions, they are active agents in the removal of foreign bodies, bacteria and broken down tissues or cells.

REFERENCES

BARNETT, R. J. 1962 The morphology of adipose tissue with particular reference to its histochemistry and ultrastructure. *In* Adipose Tissue as an Organ (Kinsell, L. W., editor). Charles C Thomas, Publisher, Springfield, Ill.

BENSLEY, S. H. 1934 On the presence, properties and distribution of the intercellular ground substance of loose connective tissue. Anat. Rec., vol. 60, pp. 93–109.

BLOOM, G. D. 1963 Electron microscopy of neoplastic mast cells: a study of the mouse mastocytoma mast cell. Ann. N.Y. Acad. Sci., vol. 103, pp. 53–86.

CASTRO, C. W., PRINCE, R. K., AND DORSTEWITZ,

E. L. 1962 Characteristics of human fibroblasts cultivated *in vitro* from different anatomical sites. Lab. Invest., vol. 11, pp. 703–713.

DANES, B. S., AND BEARN, A. G. 1965 Hurler's syndrome: demonstration of an inherited disorder of connective tissue in cell culture. Science, vol. 149, pp. 987–989.

DEMPSEY, E. D., AND LANSING, A. I. 1954 Elastic tissue. *In* International Review of Cytology (Bourne, G. H., editor), vol. 3, pp. 437–453. Academic Press, New York.

DOWNEY, H. 1955 The development of histiocytes and macrophages from lymphocytes. J. Lab. Clin. Med., vol. 45, pp. 499–507.

EVANS, H. M., AND SCOTT, K. J. 1921 On the differential reaction to vital dyes exhibited by the two great groups of connective-tissue cells. Carnegie Inst. Contrib. Embryology, vol. 10, no. 47, pp. 1–55.

FAWCETT, D. W. 1952 A comparison of the histological organization and cytochemical reactions of brown and white adipose tissue. J. Morph., vol. 70, p. 363.

FAWCETT, D. W. 1955 An experimental study of mast cell degranulation and regeneration. Anat. Rec., vol. 121, pp. 29–51.

FAWCETT, D. W., AND JONES, I. C. 1949 The effects of hypophysectomy, adrenalectomy and of thiouracil feeding on the cytology of brown adipose tissue. Endocrinology, vol. 45, pp. 609–621.

FOOT, N. C. 1928 Chemical contrasts between collagenous and reticular connective tissue. Amer. J. Path., vol. 4, pp. 525-544.

GLEGG, R. E., CLERMONT, Y., AND LEBLOND, C. P. 1952 The use of lead tetracetate, benzidine, o-dianisidine and a "film test" to investigate the significance of the "periodic acid sulfurous acid" technique in carbohydrate histochemistry. Stain Tech., vol. 27, pp. 277–305.

GRANT, R. A., HORNE, R. W., AND COX, R. W. 1965 New model for the tropocollagen macromolecule and its mode of aggregation. Nature, vol. 207, pp. 822–826.

GROSS, J. 1961 Collagen. Sci. Amer., vol. 204, pp. 120–130.

GROSS, J. 1964 Organization and disorganization of collagen. *In* Connective Tissue: Intercellular Macromolecules, pp. 63–77. J. & A. Churchill Ltd., London.

GROSS, J., AND SCHMITT, F. 1948 The structure of human skin collagen as studied with the electron microscope. J. Exp. Med., vol. 88, pp. 555–568.

HAUST, M. D., AND MORE, R. H. 1967 Electron microscopy of connective tissues and elasto-genesis. *In* The Connective Tissue (Wagner, B. M., and Smith, D. E., editors), pp. 352–376. The Williams & Wilkins Company, Baltimore.

HODGE, A. J., AND SCHMITT, F. O. 1961 The tropocollagen macromolecule and its properties of ordered interaction. Macromolecular Complexes (Edds, M. V., Jr., editor), pp. 19–51. Ronald Press, New York.

HOLMGREN, H., AND WILANDER, O. 1937 Beitrag zur Kentniz der Chemie und Function der Ehrlichschen Mastzellen. Z. Mikr. Anat. Forsch., vol. 42, p. 242.

JACKSON, S. F. 1964 Connective tissue cells. *In* The Cell; Biochemistry, Physiology, Morphology (Brachet, J., and Mirsky, A. E., editors), vol. 6, pp. 382–520. Academic Press, New York.

LEBLOND, C. P., GLEGG, R. E., AND EIDINGER, D. 1957 Presence of carbohydrates with free 1-2 glycol groups in sites stained by the periodic acid-Schiff technique. J. Histochem. Cytochem., vol. 5, pp. 445–458.

LEDUC, E. H., COONS, A. H., AND CONNOLLY, J. M. 1955 Studies of antibody production. II. The primary and secondary responses in the popliteal lymph node of the rabbit. J. Exp. Med., vol. 102, pp. 61–71.

LEDUC, E. H., SCOTT, G. B., AND AVRAMEAS, S. 1969 Ultrastructural localization of intracellular immune globulins in plasma cells and lymphoblasts by enzyme-labeled antibodies. J. Histochem. Cytochem., vol. 17, pp. 211–224.

MAXIMOW, A. A. 1930 Bindegewebe und blutbildende Gewebe. Handb. mikr. Anat. Menschen (v. Möllendorff, editor), vol. 2, pt. 1, pp. 232–583.

MAXIMOW, A. A. 1932 The macrophages or histiocytes. Special Cytology (Cowdry, E. V., editor), vol. 2, pp. 709–770.

MEYER, K. 1946 The biological significance of hyaluronic acid and hyaluronidase. Physiol. Rev., vol. 27, pp. 335–359.

MEYER, K. 1955 The chemistry of the mesodermal ground substances. Harvey Lectures, Ser. 51, pp. 88–112.

MONIS, B. 1963 Variation of aminopeptidase activity in granulation tissue and in serum of rats during wound healing. Amer. J. Path., vol. 42, pp. 301-313.

NAPOLITANO, L. 1963 The differentiation of white adipose cells. An electron microscope study. J. Cell Biol., vol. 18, pp. 663–679.

PADAWER, J. 1969 Uptake of colloidal thorium dioxide by mast cells. J. Cell Biol., vol. 40, pp. 747–760.

PAFF, G. H., AND MERGENTHALER, D. D. 1955 Vacuolation in normal mast cells and in mast cells treated with protamine sulfate. Anat. Rec., vol. 121, pp. 579-591.

PORTER, K. R. 1964 Cell fine structure and biosynthesis of intercellular macromolecules. *In* Connective Tissue: Intercellular Macromolecules, pp. 167–196. J. & A. Churchill Ltd., London.

PORTER, K. R., AND PAPPAS, G. D. 1959 Collagen formation by fibroblasts of the chick embryo dermis. J. Biophys. Biochem. Cytol., vol. 5, pp. 153–166.

RHODIN, J. A. G. 1967 Organization and ultrastructure of connective tissue. *In* The Connective Tissue (Wagner, B. M., and Smith, D. E., editors), pp. 1–16. The Williams & Wilkins Company, Baltimore.

ROSS, R., AND BORNSTEIN, P. 1969 The elastic fiber. I. The separation and partial characterization of its macromolecular components. J. Cell Biol., vol. 40, pp. 366-381.

SCHMITT, F. O., GROSS, J., AND HIGHBERGER, H. J. 1955 Tropocollagen and the properties of fibrous collagen. Exp. Cell Res., suppl., vol. 3, pp. 326–334.

SCHOENHEIMER, R. 1937 The investigation of intermediary metabolism with the aid of heavy hydrogen. Harvey Lectures, Ser. 32, pp. 122–144.

SCHUBERT, M. 1964 Biochemical and biophysical aspects of collagen. *In* Connective Tissue: Intercellular Marcomolecules, pp. 119–138. J. & A. Churchill Ltd., London.

SMITH, D. E. 1963 Electron microscopy of normal mast cells under various experimental conditions. Ann. N.Y. Acad. Sci., vol. 103, pp. 40–52.

SPICER, S. S., HORN, R. G., AND LEPPI, T. J. 1967 Histochemistry of connective tissue mucopolysaccharides. *In* The Connective Tissue (Wagner, B. M., and Smith, D. E., editors), pp. 251–303. The Williams & Wilkins Company, Baltimore.

STEARNS, M. L. 1940 Studies on the development of connective tissue in transparent chambers in the rabbit's ear. Amer. J. Anat., vol. 67, pp. 55–97.

UDENFRIEND, S. 1966 Formation of hydroxyproline in collagen. Science, vol. 152, pp. 1335–1340.

WEST, G. B. 1962 Function of mast cells. J. Pharm. Pharmacol., vol. 14, pp. 618–619.

WISLOCKI, G. B., BUNTING, H., AND DEMPSEY, E. W. 1947 Metachromasia in mammalian tissues and its relationship to mucopolysaccharides. Amer. J. Anat., vol. 81, pp. 1–38.

YU, S. Y., AND BLUMENTHAL, H. I. 1967 The calcification of elastic tissue. *In* The Connective Tissue (Wagner, B. M., and Smith, D. E., editors), pp. 17–49. The Williams & Wilkins Company, Baltimore.

6

The Connective Tissues: Cartilage and Bone

CARTILAGE

Cartilage, like other connective tissues, consists of cells, fibers and ground substance. The last named, however, has physical properties which give to the tissue a compactness and elastic firmness, rendering it capable of withstanding a considerable degree of pressure and tension. In some of the lower vertebrates (e.g., elasmobranchs), the whole adult skeleton consists of cartilage, and in the mammals the greater part of the skeleton is first laid down in cartilage. In the adult body, cartilage covers the articular surfaces of bones, and it forms the sole skeletal support of the larynx, trachea, bronchi and certain other structures.

According to the nature and visibility of the fibrillar elements, cartilage is subdivided into three varieties: (1) hyaline, (2) elastic, and (3) fibrous. Of these, hyaline cartilage is the most widely distributed type.

Hyaline Cartilage

Hyaline cartilage (Figs. 6-1 and 6-2) appears as a bluish white, translucent mass in the fresh condition. It forms the articular cartilage of joints, the costal cartilages and the cartilages of the nose, larynx, trachea and bronchi. In the fetus, nearly all of the skeleton is first laid down as hyaline cartilage and is replaced later by osseous tissue in the formation of the bones.

With the exception of the free surfaces of articular cartilages, hyaline cartilage is always invested by a layer of dense fibrous connective tissue, the *perichondrium* (Fig. 6-1). Hyaline cartilage is composed of cells and an intercellular matrix of ground substance and connective tissue fibers. The term matrix is derived from a Latin word meaning womb, a place where something is formed, and a medium enclosing other bodies.

Cartilage is usually devoid of blood vessels except in areas where vessels may be passing through it to other tissues and in particular zones which are forming ossification centers in intracartilaginous bone development. Exchange of substances between cartilage cells and blood vessels of the perichondrium is mediated by the tissue fluid of the cartilage, i.e., by the bound water which is the dispersion medium of the mucopolysaccharides of the intercellular matrix.

The Cells. The cartilage cells (*chondrocytes*) are situated in smooth walled spaces or *lacunae* (Figs. 6-1 and 6-4). Each cell has a large, centrally placed spherical nucleus with chromatin and one or more nucleoli. The cytoplasm is finely granular and contains fat droplets, glycogen granules and occasionally pigment.

In the living condition, the cells com-

Nucleus of cartilage cell   Capsule   Perichondrium

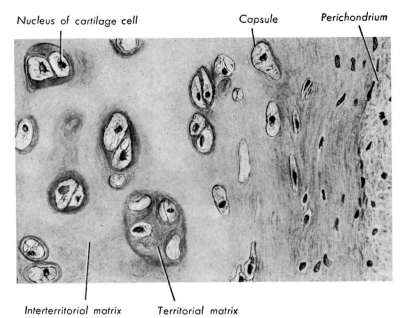

Interterritorial matrix   Territorial matrix

FIG. 6-1. Hyaline cartilage from the trachea of a boy 17 years of age. Delafield's hematoxylin and eosin. ×435.

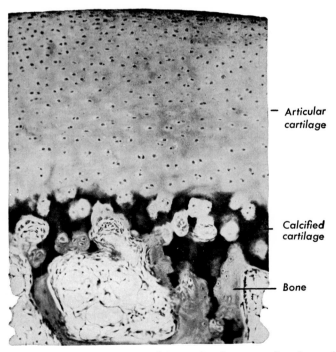

— Articular cartilage

Calcified cartilage

— Bone

FIG. 6-2. Articular cartilage from a metatarsal bone of a rhesus monkey 2 months old. Photomicrograph. ×165.

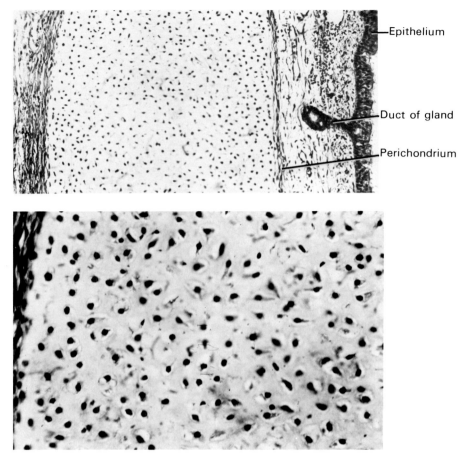

Epithelium

Duct of gland

Perichondrium

Fig. 6-3. Photomicrographs of hyaline cartilage from the trachea of a 5-month human fetus. *Upper figure* is at low magnification to cover a relatively large field. Note that the cartilage cells are distributed singly throughout the fetal cartilage instead of being in groups as they are in later periods (Fig. 6-1). *Lower figure*, a higher magnification of a portion of the field above. Note that the cartilage matrix appears homogeneous and stains uniformly. The irregular shape of the cells is accentuated by the usual shrinkage that occurs during fixation and dehydration for preparing sections. Upper, ×146; lower, ×390.

pletely fill their lacunae, but their large content of fat and glycogen leads to marked structural distortions in fixed preparations, particularly marked in paraffin techniques for light microscopy. Poor preservation of fat and glycogen leaves the cells greatly vacuolated or shrunken into small masses separated by spaces from the walls of the lacunae. Protoplasmic processes often extend to the capsule, giving the cell a branched appearance. In the living condition, the cells of adult cartilage are, however, unbranched.

In the central portion of the cartilage, the cells are generally arranged in groups, each group representing the offspring of a parent cartilage cell (Fig. 6-1). The cells are spherical or ovoid and flattened on adjacent sides, their long axes directed radially to the surface of the plate. Toward the periphery, the cells become progressively flattened and lose their definite grouping, until in the subperichondrial layers they appear as rows of narrow elongated cells whose long axes are parallel with the surface. The cartilage grades insensibly into the fibrous connective tissue of the perichondrium.

In embryonal cartilage (Fig. 6-3), before interstitial mitosis of cartilage cells has begun, the cells are not grouped but scattered singly in the cartilaginous mass. The branching shape which some of the cells show at this stage is lost as the cartilage matures.

The Intercellular Substance. The intercellular substance or *matrix* appears homogeneous in the fresh condition or in ordinary preparations. Only the walls of the lacunae stand out as more highly refractive rings which stain intensely with basic dyes. These so-called capsules are not of the nature of cell membranes but represent a modification of the matrix lining the lacunae.

The apparently homogeneous intercellular substance contains in reality numerous fine collagenous fibers which are masked by a ground substance of a similar index of refraction. By means of trypsin digestion or treatment with dilute alkalis, these fibrils may be demonstrated and their distribution studied. They can also be seen in electron micrographs (Fig. 6-4), and they apparently lack the 640 A banding characteristic of collagenous fibers elsewhere. They are not arranged in bundles but form a fine feltwork. In the superficial portion of the cartilage, they run parallel with the perichondrium and, without sharp transition, they become continuous with the connective tissue of the latter (Fig. 6-5). In the deeper portions they tend to course radially between the cell groups.

The intercellular substance contains *chondromucoprotein*, a polymer of *mucoprotein* and *chondroitin sulfates A* and *C*. Chondroitin sulfate A (chondroitin 4-sulfate) is more abundant than is chondroitin sulfate C (chondroitin 6-sulfate) in the newborn, but the reverse relationship is attained by adulthood. With increasing age there is a decrease in most of the acid mucopolysaccharides, particularly in chondroitin sulfate A. The chondroitin sulfates are bound with the mucoprotein in a macromolecular complex which is closely associated with the collagenous fibrils and soluble collagen. Some *keratosulfate* is present also. It is insignificant in amount at birth but increases with age. It may reach relatively high levels in senile, degenerate cartilage.

Chondromucoprotein stains with basic dyes because of its content of chondroitin sulfate. The latter is abundant throughout the matrix of embryonal cartilage, which is uniformly basophilic (Fig. 6-3). Adult cartilage shows regional differences in staining that correlate with differences in the distribution of the different components of the intercellular materials. The region immediately around a cell group contains more chondroitin sulfate and relatively few collagenous fibrils; it is basophilic and is named *territorial matrix* (Fig. 6-1). The regions between cell groups, or territories, contain less chondroitin sulfates and more collagenous fibers; they tend to be acidophilic and are known as *interterritorial matrices*.

The amorphous ground substance of cartilage is strongly metachromatic with toluidine blue because of its chondroitin sulfate. Metachromasia is most pronounced in the lining of each lacuna and is marked in all of the territorial matrix. The ground substance also gives a positive reaction with the periodic acid-Schiff technique (PAS). Since *pure* chondroitin sulfate is probably not PAS-positive, it is assumed that the PAS response of the ground substance is due to an undetermined carbohydrate component.

Development and Growth. The blastema of cartilage is first recognized as an area of mesenchymal cell concentration resulting from cell proliferation and enlargement. The cells in the interior of the precartilage blastema show a marked increase in cytoplasmic basophilia resulting from an increase in rough surfaced endoplasmic reticulum, and they are known as *chondroblasts*. They form the collagenous fibrils and the ground substance of the matrix. At first, the intercellular substance appears as dark staining lines or partitions in a honeycomb-like pattern between the cells. As the cells of the central region continue to form more matrix, they become separated from each other and become the chondrocytes, while those of the periphery continue as chondro-

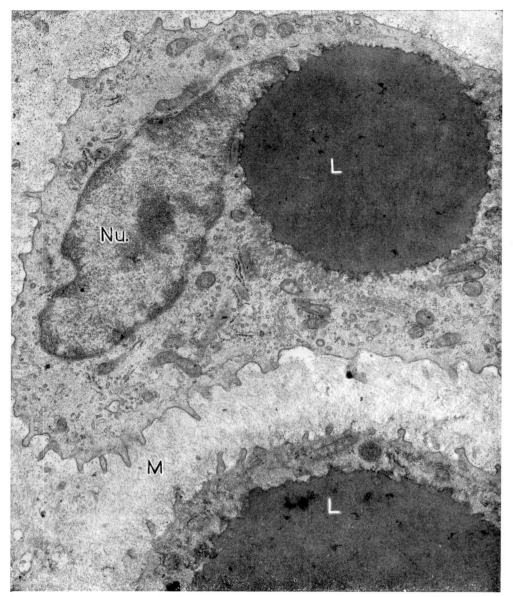

Fig. 6-4. Electron micrograph of hyaline cartilage from the trachea of a bat. Portions of two chondrocytes are seen, one with the nucleus (*Nu*). Large lipid droplets (*L*) are often found in the cytoplasm of mature cartilage cells. Note that the cartilage cells have numerous processes extending into the matrix and that the cells fill the lacunae. A fine feltwork of collagen is seen in the matrix (*M*). ×17,000. (Courtesy of Dr. Keith Porter and the New York Heart Association; see Porter, Biophys. J., vol. 4, 1964.)

blasts. The fibers of the matrix become masked by an increase in ground substance and the matrix becomes homogenous in appearance. It also becomes strongly basophilic. The embryonal cartilage now appears as a plate consisting of cells scattered in a matrix and surrounded by a perichondrium of chondroblasts and embryonal connective tissue (Fig. 6-3).

Electron microscope studies in combina-

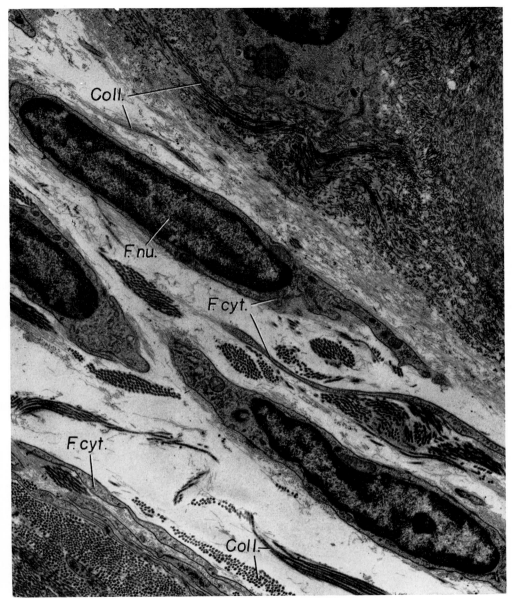

Fig. 6-5. Electron micrograph of junction of hyaline cartilage and perichondrium from the trachea of a bat. A portion of a cartilage cell is seen in the *upper part* of the photograph, and portions of several fibroblasts with their nuclei (*F. nu.*) and cytoplasm (*F. cyt.*) are seen in the *lower part* of the figure. Collagen fibers (*Coll.*) are seen in cross and longitudinal sections. Note that the fibrils adjacent to the surfaces of the fibroblasts are generally smaller than the bundles of fibrils found at some distance from the cells. ×12,250. (Courtesy of Dr. Keith Porter.)

tion with isotope techniques have provided information on the manner in which chondroblasts form the chondromucoproteins. The amino acids, such as glycine and proline, are synthesized into peptide chains in the presence of the ribosomes of the rough surfaced endoplasmic reticulum and are then transported to the Golgi complex. Studies of the pathways taken by tritiated glucose and radioactive sulfate indicate that the carbohydrates enter the cell and pass directly to the Golgi complex for synthesis into polysaccharides. The synthesized proteins and polysaccharides are then combined in the Golgi region to form the chondromucoproteins which are secreted by the cells.

Growth of cartilage takes place in two ways: (1) formation of new cartilage by chondroblasts at the surface, known as *appositional growth;* and (2) expansion of the internal mass of cartilage by division of chondrocytes, known as *interstitial growth.*

In appositional growth, chondroblasts of the perichondrium multiply, and some form cartilage matrix as described above, while others remain as a part of the chondroblast population. New chondroblasts also arise by differentiation from surrounding cells (mesenchyme in embryonal stages and fibroblasts in later stages). In interstitial growth, cartilage cells divide into two, and the daughter cells may divide again, each isogenous group representing the progeny of a single parent cell. The cells become separated from each other, each surrounded by its own capsule and matrix. The old capsules and the territorial matrices merge into the newly formed territorial matrix. Interstitial growth occurs mainly in young cartilage and gradually ceases, further growth being appositional (subperichondrial).

Nutrition of Cartilage. Cartilage is devoid of vascular and lymphatic channels; hence, nutrition is entirely by diffusion and imbibition. That the matrix is permeable even to coarse particles has been definitely shown. It has been demonstrated that injection of indigo carmine into the circulation leads to a deposition of the colored particles within the matrix and in the lacunae.

Age Changes. The poor nutrition is probably responsible for certain degenerative changes found in old cartilage, especially in cartilages of considerable thickness. The deeper portions of the cartilage show areas extending through many cell territories where the homogeneous matrix is replaced by closely packed coarse fibers (*asbestfaserung,* amiantine degeneration). Cavity formation resulting from the softening and liquefaction of these areas may ultimately result.

With old age, cartilage loses its translucency and bluish white color and appears yellowish and cloudy. This change is due to a decrease of acid mucopolysaccharides and an increase in noncollagenous proteins.

Calcification is likewise of common occurrence in old cartilage and is usually associated with degenerative changes of the cartilage cells. Calcification of cartilage is a normal process during bone formation and is subsequently described with the latter.

Regeneration. Regeneration of cartilage is a slow process and occurs primarily by activity of the perichondrium. When cartilage is broken or injured, the wound is invaded by the perichondrial connective tissue which is gradually changed into cartilage. Such growth is in the nature of apposition and depends on the presence of a perichondrium. Regeneration, in part, at least, by interstitial growth has been observed but is doubtless comparatively rare. In many instances of cartilage fracture, the pieces become united by dense fibrous tissue which may partly be replaced by a bony clasp.

ELASTIC CARTILAGE

Elastic cartilage appears more yellow and opaque than hyaline cartilage in the fresh condition because of the large number of elastic fibers in its matrix (Fig. 6-6). These branch and run in all directions and form a dense network of anastomosing and interlacing fibers. In the peripheral layers, the fibers are thin and the network is wide meshed; in the deeper portions, they are thicker and more closely packed. The ground substance also contains some collagenous fibrils.

Elastic cartilage develops from a hyaline-like blastema. Elastic fibrils are formed just peripheral to the cells and traverse the ma-

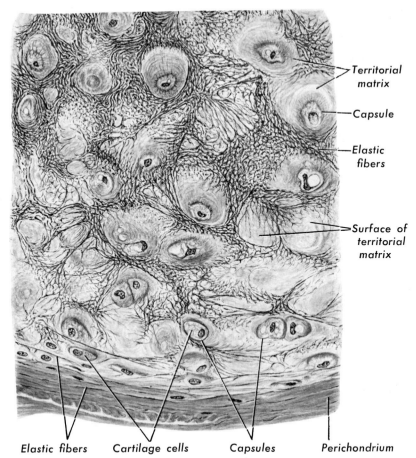

Territorial matrix

Capsule

Elastic fibers

Surface of territorial matrix

Elastic fibers   Cartilage cells   Capsules   Perichondrium

FIG. 6-6. Elastic cartilage of epiglottis of a boy 13 years old. Stained with elastin H, Delafield's hematoxylin and eosin. ×435.

trix as an elastic network. Growth of the cartilage takes place interstitially and subperichondrially. Calcification of elastic cartilage occurs very rarely, if at all.

Elastic cartilage occurs in the external ear, the Eustachian tube, the epiglottis and in some of the laryngeal cartilages.

FIBROUS CARTILAGE

Fibrous cartilage (Fig. 6-7) is a combination of dense collagenous fibers and cartilage cells, the latter lying within lacunae surrounded by variable amounts of hyaline matrix. The relative proportions of collagenous fibers, cartilage cells and hyaline matrix vary greatly. The cartilage cells frequently lie in rows, between which are dense, wavy bundles of collagenous fibers.

Fibrous cartilage occurs in association with some of the joints of the body. It is found where the attachment of a ligament or tendon to bone is adjacent to the hyaline cartilage of the articular surface, or where hyaline cartilage intervenes between the attaching fibers and the bone. It occurs in considerable amounts in articular cartilages, in the glenoid and cotyloid ligaments and in the ligamentum teres of the femur.

The *intervertebral discs* consist largely of fibrocartilage which is continuous above and below with the articular cartilage of the adjacent vertebrae and peripherally with the

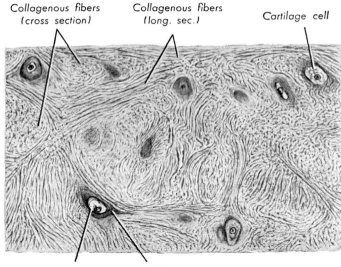

Collagenous fibers (cross section) Collagenous fibers (long. sec.) Cartilage cell

Capsule   Territorial hyaline matrix

FIG. 6-7. Fibrocartilage from the intervertebral disc of a boy 13 years old. The section was cut transversely to the broad (vertebral) surface of the disc. The part drawn is about 5 mm. from the anterior rim of the disc. Near the rim, the tissue is much like tendon. ×435.

spinal ligaments. In the center of each disc is a gelatinous ellipsoid mass of variable extent known as the *nucleus pulposus.* Its center may contain fluid and cellular debris. Rupture of the disc and herniation of the nucleus pulposus into the spinal canal may be the cause of severe pain.

BONE (OSSEOUS TISSUE)

Osseous tissue is a rigid form of connective tissue and is normally organized into definite structures, the bones. These form the skeleton, serve for the attachment and protection of the soft parts and, by their attachment to the muscles, act as levers which bring about body motion.

Bone consists of cells and an intercellular matrix of organic and inorganic substances. The organic matrix is made up of collagen and an amorphous substance known as osseomucoid. The latter consists of protein-polysaccharides containing chondroitin sulfate. The collagenous fibers form the major portion of the organic component of bone, while the chondroitin sulfates form a relatively small but functionally significant part.

Bone matrix gives an acidophilic reaction in stained sections, in contrast with the basophilic reaction of cartilage matrix. This is due to the high content of collagen and low content of chondroitin sulfate in bone.

The inorganic component is responsible for the rigidity of bone and may constitute up to two-thirds of the fat-free dry weight of bone. It is composed chiefly of calcium phosphate and calcium carbonate, with small amounts of magnesium, hydroxide, fluoride and sulfate. The composition varies with age and with a number of dietary factors. X-ray diffraction studies show that the minerals are present as crystals having an *apatite* pattern or structure. More specifically, they are *hydroxyapatites.* Electron microscope studies of developing bone show that the minerals are deposited as contiguous, dense particles aligned in an orderly manner in relation to the cross banded fibrils. They appear at the interband regions of the fibrils, first at the surface and later within the fibrils. In other words, the calcium salts are deposited in a manner which reflects the structural organization of the organic constituents with which

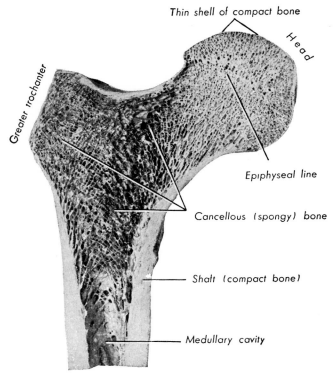

Thin shell of compact bone

Head

Greater trochanter

Epiphyseal line

Cancellous (spongy) bone

Shaft (compact bone)

Medullary cavity

FIG. 6-8. A longitudinal section through the upper end of the femur of an adult male. The epiphyseal line of the great trochanter is not evident. Photograph.

they are combined. Thus, when the organic constituents are completely destroyed by prolonged burning with free access of air (calcination), the inorganic material is left as a white brittle mass retaining the original form and size of the bone.

The shape and size of the bone are similarly retained when the lime salts are removed by decalcification, as with prolonged immersion of the bone in a dilute mineral acid. The bone loses its rigidity, has a silky sheen and is flexible but tough and only slightly extensible.

Gross Organization of Bone Tissue. Grossly, two types of bone may be distinguished: the *spongy* or *cancellous*, and the *dense* or *compact.* When a long bone is cut longitudinally (Fig. 6-8), it will be seen that the head or epiphysis has a spongy appearance and consists of slender irregular bone trabeculae or bars, which anastomose to form a latticework in the meshes of which the marrow is contained. The thin outer shell, however, appears dense and white and, as the shaft is approached, the irregular marrow spaces of the epiphysis become continuous with the central medullary cavity of the shaft whose wall is formed by a thick plate of compact bone.

The spongy and compact varieties of bone have the same types of cells and intercellular substance, but they differ from each other in the arrangement of their components and in the ratio of marrow space to bone substance. In spongy bone, the marrow spaces are relatively large and irregularly arranged, and the bone substance is shaped as slender spicules and trabeculae. In compact bone, the spaces or channels are narrow and the bony substance is densely packed.

With very few exceptions, the compact and spongy forms are both present in every

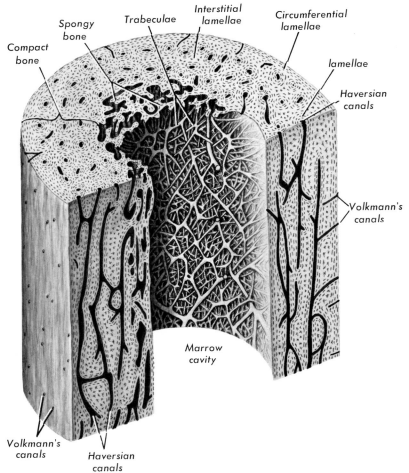

FIG. 6-9. Shaft of human humerus. Drawing is made from undecalcified bone following removal of marrow and other organic components by maceration techniques. (From a chart by H. Poll.)

bone, but the amount and distribution of each type vary considerably. The diaphyses of the long bones consist mainly of compact tissue, only the innermost layer immediately surrounding the medullary cavity being spongy. The tabular bones of the head are composed of two plates of compact bone enclosing a marrow space bridged by irregular bars of spongy bone (diploë). The epiphyses of the long bones and most of the short bones consist of spongy bone covered by a thin outer shell of compact bone.

Each bone, except at its articular end, is surrounded by a vascular fibroelastic coat, the *periosteum*. The so-called *endosteum*, or inner periosteum of the marrow cavity and marrow spaces, is not a well-demarcated layer. It consists of a variable concentration of medullary reticular connective tissue which contains osteogenic cells that are in immediate contact with the bone tissue.

Microscopic Structure. The most characteristic feature of adult bone tissue is its lamellar structure, the fibers and calcified matrix being organized into thin layers or lamellae arranged in various ways. When the compact osseous tissue of a long bone is examined (Figs. 6-9 to 6-11), it is seen to be traversed by longitudinal channels, the *Haversian canals*, which anastomose with each other by oblique and transverse communications. From the periosteal and endosteal surfaces, somewhat narrower channels, *Volkmann's canals,* pierce the bone obliquely or at right angles to its long axis and communicate with the Haversian canals, thus establishing a continuous and elaborate canal system which lodges the blood vessels and nerves of the bone.

In a cross section of the bone, the Haversian canals are seen to be surrounded by a varying number (eight to 15) of concentric lamellae and accompanying bone cells. The concentric lamellae of intercellular substance, the cells and the central canal constitute an *Haversian system* or *osteon* (Figs. 6-10 and 6-11). The whole bone does not, however, consist of such concentric systems. In the periphery, the lamellae run parallel with the surface and form a relatively thin outer layer of the bone. These are the outer *circumferential* lamellae (Fig. 6-9). Similarly arranged inner circumferential lamellae separate the Haversian systems from the marrow cavity. Finally, the intervals between the Haversian systems are occupied by more irregular layers of bone which constitute the *interstitial* lamellae (Fig. 6-10). Adjacent lamellar systems are as a rule sharply delimited from each other by a dark staining, thin layer of modified matrix (cement line, cement membrane).

Compact bone thus consists of branching and anastomosing tubular lamellae whose intervals are filled in by interstitial lamellae and which are covered externally and internally by the more parallel running circumferential lamellae. The channels which pierce the bone from its outer and inner surface and become continuous with the Haversian canals are not lined by concentric lamellae and are known as the *canals of Volkmann.*

The bone cells (*osteocytes*) are placed in flattened, almond-shaped cell spaces or lacunae situated between or within the lamellae (Figs. 6-12 and 6-13). Cytoplasmic processes of the osteocytes project into delicate channels or *canaliculi* which extend at right

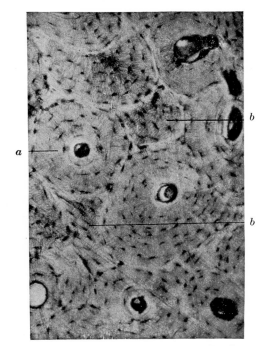

FIG. 6-10. Transverse section from the shaft of an undecalcified, dried long bone. A slab of the dried bone was ground very thin and then mounted in thick balsam. In the spaces within the bone (lacunae, canaliculi and some of the Haversian canals), air was imprisoned so that they appear dark. *a*, Haversian system; *b*, interstitial lamellae. Photomicrograph.

angles from the lacunae. During bone development, the cytoplasmic processes of each cell extend throughout the lengths of the canaliculi that are associated with its particular lacuna, but the extent of the processes in adult bone is variable. The canaliculi from one lacuna connect with those from adjacent lacunae and with Haversian and Volkmann canals. Electron micrographs show that the osteocytes and their processes do not rest directly on the mineralized matrix but are separated from the walls of their lacunae and canaliculi by an amorphous coat. Histochemical studies show that this material is PAS-positive. It probably serves as a medium by which substances can be exchanged between the cells and the blood vessels present in the Haversian canals.

The osteocytes were bone-forming cells

Haversian system   **Partly destroyed**
                   Haversian system

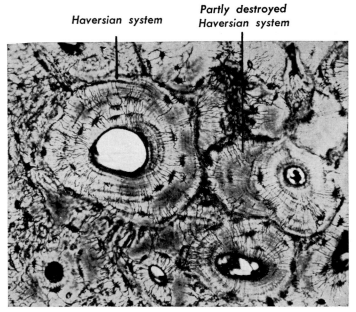

FIG. 6-11. Transverse section through the shaft of the femur of a young adult rhesus monkey. Decalcified, 6-μ section. The walls of the lacunae, canaliculi and Haversian canals are stained with a dye. Schmorl's thionin phosphomolybdic acid method. Photomicrograph. ×270.

(osteoblasts) which became imprisoned in the bone as it was deposited. Osteoblasts and osteoprogenitor cells also persist as an incomplete lining of the Haversian canals and Volkmann's canals and are present in the endosteum and inner layer of the periosteum. With a stimulus such as is supplied by a fracture or physiological stress, they again may become active bone-forming cells.

The distribution of the collagenous fibrils can be studied only in decalcified preparations where proper precautions have been taken to prevent collagenous swelling. Otherwise, the collagen appears as a fused, homogeneous mass. The fibrils are arranged in delicate fascicles and are parallel with one another within a single lamella. They follow a helical course in each lamella, with differences in slope and direction in alternate lamellae. This is apparently the reason why transverse sections of Haversian systems show the concentric lamellae alternately striated and punctuated (Fig. 6-12). In the former, the fibrils are coursing circularly at the level of the section and are cut lengthwise. In the punctuate lamellae, the fibrils are parallel to the long axis of the Haversian system at the level of the section and are cut across.

Besides the lamellar fibers, there are found within the outer layers of the bone the coarser, perforating fibers of Sharpey (Fig. 6-14). They are continuations of the periosteal fibers and pierce the bone obliquely or at right angles to its long axis. They consist of collagenous or fibroelastic bundles with uncalcified or only partly calcified matrix. Purely elastic perforating fibers are likewise found. They extend into the outer circumferential and interstitial lamellae but do not penetrate the Haversian systems. They are especially numerous in places where ligaments and tendons are inserted, and they serve for firmer anchorage of these structures.

Spongy bone shows the same lamellar structure but differs from compact bone in

Canaliculi **Haversian canal** **Lacuna** **Interstitial lamellae**

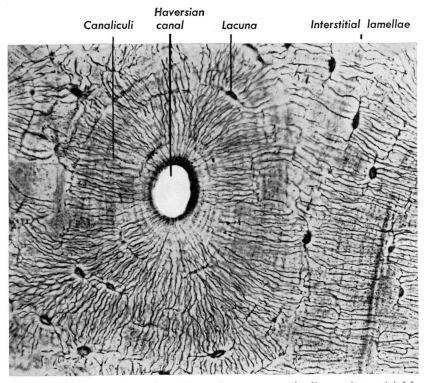

FIG. 6-12. Transverse section through an Haversian system and adjacent interstitial lamellae. Decalcified bone from the shaft of the femur of a young adult rhesus monkey, 6 μ section. Schmorl's thionin phosphomolybdic acid method. Photomicrograph. ×420.

the more irregular arrangement of the lamellae (in trabeculae or spicules) and in the relatively few Haversian systems.

Nonlamellar (Woven) Bone. Although the bone of all vertebrates consists of collagen, ground substance, calcium salts and a permeating system of spaces occupied by cells and their processes, one finds that different samples of bone differ in the manner in which their constituents are combined. Thus, the skeletons of fish, amphibians and birds differ from each other and from those of mammals, and the bone of man shows marked structural changes during ontogenesis. The human embryonic skeleton consists of coarsely bundled *woven bone*, i.e., the collagenous fibers are in coarse bundles and they are irregularly woven or plaited, and the lacunae are irregularly dispersed. Stratified or *lamellar bone*, i.e., with fibrils oriented similarly in any given stratum and in different directions in alternating lamellae, gradually replaces woven bone, beginning before birth and continuing until only traces of woven bone persist in the adult (for example, in tooth sockets, bony sutures, osseous labyrinth and regions of tendon-bone attachment). The first bone formed during repair of fractures is of the woven type.

DEVELOPMENT AND GROWTH OF BONE

According to the embryological origin, there are two types of bone development, *intramembranous* and *intracartilaginous* or *endochondral*. In intramembranous bone formation, the bone develops under or within a connective tissue membrane. It does not involve the removal of cartilage. In endochondral bone formation, cartilage is removed and replaced by bone. The development of

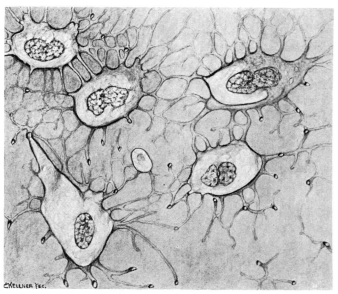

FIG. 6-13. Osteocytes and canaliculi as seen in a tangential section of the peripheral portion of the shaft of the ulna of a 10- to 12-week human fetus. One can follow the extensive network of the canaliculi in the 10-μ section as a result of the staining of the walls of lacunae and canaliculi. Azure II-eosin stain. ×1700.

FIG. 6-14. Fibers of Sharpey in cross section of decalcified phalanx from child of 6 years. The fibers of Sharpey are direct continuations of periosteal fibers. (After Petersen.)

the flat bones of the skull involves only the intramembranous type of bone formation (Figs. 6-15 to 6-19). The development of the bones of the base of the skull, of the face and of the axial skeleton involves both types of bone formation, the bone around a cartilage (subperiosteal bone) being formed by the intramembranous type, and the bone which replaces the cartilage being formed by the endochrondrial method. It should be kept in mind, however, that the fundamental process of bone deposition is the same in both types. In intracartilaginous bone formation, there is the additional feature of the removal of portions of the cartilage preparatory to the deposition of the bone.

CELL TYPES IN OSTEOGENESIS

One can identify different types of cells in sites of bone formation as follows: (1) *Osteogenic* or *osteoprogenitor cells*, (2) *osteoblasts*, (3) *osteocytes* and (4) *osteoclasts*. Since the cells of a given type have similar characteristics regardless of whether they are found in intramembranous or intracartilagenous bone forming regions, the cytological features of the cell types are described before taking up the topographical aspects of bone formation.

Osteogenic or Osteoprogenitor Cells. In regions of mesenchyme where bone formation is beginning and in areas near the surfaces of growing bones, one finds irregularly shaped and somewhat elongated cells which

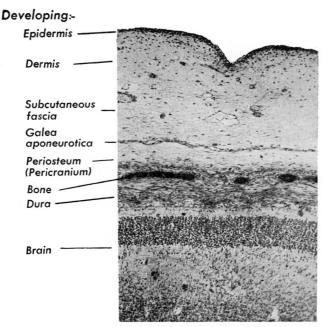

Developing:-
Epidermis
Dermis
Subcutaneous fascia
Galea aponeurotica
Periosteum (Pericranium)
Bone
Dura
Brain

FIG. 6-15. Section showing the first appearance of bone in the parietal region of the developing skull. Human embryo of about 2½ months. Photomicrograph. ×60.

have pale staining cytoplasm and pale staining nuclei. They differ structurally only slightly from the mesenchymal cells from which they have arisen. They are identified chiefly by their location and by their association with osteoblasts. They multiply by mitosis, and some of them change into osteoblasts which change later into osteocytes. It seems established that osteocytes can also change back to osteogenic cells in response to altered conditions in the environment, and the "various types of bone cells represent different functional states of the same cell" (Young, 1962). A temporary change of this type is known as *modulation*, in contrast with differentiation, which involves a more fixed change.

Osteoblasts. These cells are generally larger than the osteoprogenitor cells, and they have a more rounded nucleus, more prominent nucleolus, and cytoplasm which is much more basophilic (Fig. 6-16). The nucleus is often toward one side of the cell and, close to it, in the cytoplasma-rich part of the cell, one can frequently see a clear zone which is the negative image of the enlarged Golgi complex (Fig. 6-26). The cell bodies are separated from each other by amorphous, unstained intercellular substance, but it can be shown by special methods that the processes of adjacent cells come in contact with each other.

The basophilia of the osteoblast cytoplasm is due to its well developed rough surfaced endoplasmic reticulum (Figs. 6-19 and 6-20). As pointed out in Chapter 1, ribonucleoprotein particles are characteristically abundant in cells engaged in protein synthesis. By appropriate techniques, it can be shown that the cytoplasm also contains considerable alkaline phosphatase. Small PAS-positive granules are found both in the cytoplasm and in newly formed matrix. The osteoblasts secrete the organic components of the matrix (collagenous fibers and protein-polysaccharides). They apparently also have some directing influence over the uptake of minerals by the matrix.

The formation of bone in unusual regions of the adult body (metaplastic bone forma-

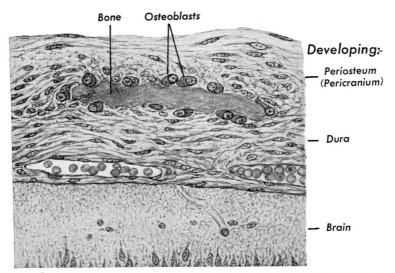

FIG. 6-16. One of the spicules of developing bone. Parietal region of the skull of a human embryo of about 2½ months. Camera lucida drawing. ×420.

tion), as in the walls of sclerotic arteries, calcified foci in the lungs and in connective tissue adjoining transplants of transitional epithelium in experimental animals, is difficult to harmonize with the view that bone formation is accomplished specifically by differentiated osteogenic (osteoprogenitor) cells. The most commonly accepted explanation for metaplastic bone formation is that either fibroblasts or persisting undifferentiated mesenchymal cells can differentiate into osteoprogenitor cells under altered environmental conditions.

Osteocytes. These cells are described above under "Microscopic Structure." It has been pointed out that they arise from osteoblasts by modulation. They apparently have a role in maintaining the constituents of the intercellular matrix at normal levels.

Osteoclasts. On the surfaces of bones where resorption is occurring, one frequently finds large, multinucleated giant cells known as osteoclasts (Figs. 6-17 and 6-18). They are often found in depressions in the bone (Howship's lacunae).

The number of nuclei in osteoclasts varies greatly. The cytoplasm has a foamlike or vacuolated appearance and gives a variable staining reaction. It is less basophilic than the osteoblast cytoplasm and, in some cells, particularly in the older ones, it becomes slightly acidophilic (Fig. 6-25). Electron micrographs show a paucity of granular endoplasmic reticulum, but they reveal clusters of free ribosomes. Lysosomes are seen in material fixed in glutaraldehyde. The surface of an active osteoclast adjacent to bone which is being resorbed has numerous cytoplasmic processes (Fig. 6-21), which are responsible for the irregular brush border appearance observed with the light microscope. Some cells have swollen mitochondria, a decrease in ribosomes and only a few cytoplasmic processes; these are assumed to be the older and less active cells.

The fact that osteoclasts are often present in depressions where bone is being resorbed lends support to the view that they are responsible for the resorption. An increase in numbers of osteoclasts when bone resorption is stimulated by injections of parathyroid extracts has usually been considered as further evidence for this view. On the other hand, electron microscope studies of the sequence of events in bone following injection of parathyroid extracts into rats show that changes occur in osteocytes and osteoblasts prior to changes in osteoclasts

Osteoblasts   Osteoid   Fibrous and osteogenetic layers of periosteum

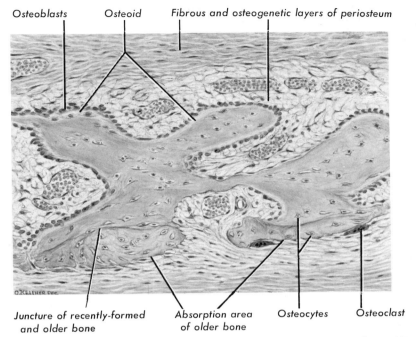

Juncture of recently-formed   Absorption area   Osteocytes   Osteoclast
and older bone   of older bone

FIG. 6-17. Section through parietal bone of human fetus of 3 months. ×115

Osteoid   Osteoblasts   Marrow   Fibrous and osteogenetic
                                      cavity   layers of periosteum

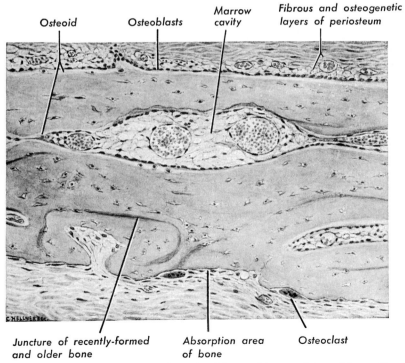

Juncture of recently-formed   Absorption area   Osteoclast
and older bone   of bone

FIG. 6-18. Vertical section through parietal bone of human fetus of 6 months. ×115

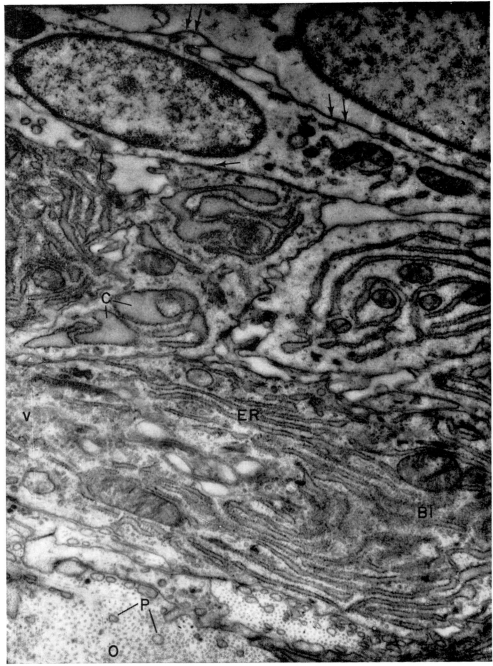

Fɪɢ. 6-19. Electron micrograph of developing bone showing layers of osteoblastic cells in relation to osteoid (O). Note the increasing complexity of the cytoplasm of the osteoblastic cells as the osteoid is approached. Processes (P) of the osteoblasts are seen penetrating the osteoid. Numerous small vesicles (V) are dispersed in the cytoplasm (Bl) of an osteoblast. The granular endoplasmic reticulum (ER) is well developed, and a few cisternae of the reticulum are dilated (C). Arrows point to desmosome-like structures between contiguous cells. Double arrows show another type of cell junction. ×11,000. (Courtesy of Dr. David Spiro, J. Biophys. Biochem. Cytol., 1961.)

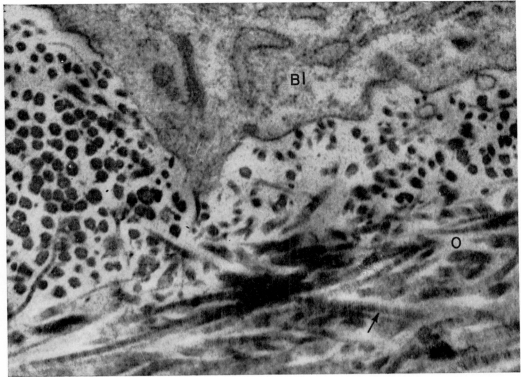

FIG. 6-20. Electron micrograph of developing bone, showing junction of osteoblast (*Bl*) with osteoid (*O*). Note that the collagen fibrils adjacent to the cell surface have smaller diameters than those deeper in the osteoid. Fibrils cut lengthwise show a 640 A repeating periodicity with interperiod bands (*arrow*). ×52,000. (Courtesy of Dr. David Spiro; see Dudley and Spiro, J. Biophys. Biochem. Cytol., 1961.)

(Cameron, Paschall and Robinson, 1967). In fact, resorption can occur without a marked increase in osteoclasts. However, studies of parathyroid-stimulated bone resorption in vitro indicate that osteoclasts excrete lysosomal acid hydrolases and that they are active in the resorption of the organic matrix (Vaes, 1968). Electron micrographs often show apatite crystals between cytoplasmic processes of the cells but not within the cells. Although the exact role of osteoclasts in bone resorption remains controversial, it is generally accepted that they have an important part in the process, probably by secretion of proteolytic enzymes.

Osteocytes and osteoclasts are actually different stages of the same cell type. Osteoclasts arise by fusion of osteogenic cells, including those formed from osteocytes when the latter are released from their lacunae during resorption.

In regions of cartilage resorption, as in stages of endochondral bone development, there are multinucleated cells with the same characteristics as osteoclasts. Since they are associated with cartilage, they are known as chondroclasts. They form by fusion of chondrocytes after the latter are released from their lacunae (Crelin and Koch, 1967).

INTRAMEMBRANOUS BONE FORMATION

Since the development of the flat bones of the skull involves only intramembranous bone formation, it is an excellent place to study the structural features of the deposition of osseous tissue uncomplicated by changes in cartilage. In the locations where

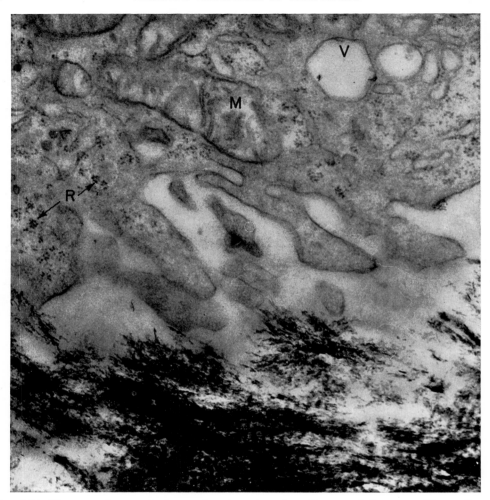

Fig. 6-21. Electron micrograph of osteoclast-bone junction. Clusters of ribosomes (R) are dispersed in the osteoclast cytoplasm between mitochondria (M) and vacuoles (V). Fragments of bone and individual apatite crystals are seen between the processes of the osteoclast. ×40,000. (Courtesy of Dr. David Spiro; see Dudley and Spiro, J. Biophys. Biochem. Cytol., 1961.)

bone is to be laid down, the mesenchyme becomes richly vascularized, and active proliferation of the mesenchymal cells takes place. Within this primitive connective tissue membrane, some of the cells show structural changes which enable one to identify them as osteoprogenitor cells and osteoblasts (Fig. 6-15 and 6-16).

Between the enlarged cells or osteoblasts, an acidophilic hyaline ground substance appears. It masks the fibrils which were already present in the embryonal connective tissue, as well as those that are subsequently

formed by the osteoblasts. The intercellular substance or matrix, which thus is composed of a hyaline ground substance and collagenous fibers, is usually not calcified at first and is soft and easily cut. It is given the name of osteoid (resembling bone) and is the organic part of bone matrix without appreciable inorganic constituent. As the deposition of the matrix progresses, the osteoblasts, with their processes, are imprisoned by matrix being deposited around them, lacunae and canaliculi thus being formed. Since processes of adjoining cells make contact with each other, the canaliculi of adjoining lacunae connect with each other. New osteoblasts, arising by modulation of osteoprogenitor cells, maintain a layer of bone-forming cells at the surface of the newly formed bone. The osteoprogenitor cells multiply by mitosis, and they probably continue to increase for a certain embryonic period by differentiation of undifferentiated neighboring connective tissue cells.

Calcification. In calcification, the minerals are deposited in the form of minute crystals (hydroxyapatites) intimately associated with the collagenous fibers. The crystals are too small to be visible under the light microscope, but electron micrographs show that they appear first on the surfaces of the fibrils and later within them. They are aligned in an orderly manner in relation to the periodic cross bandings of the fibrils.

Calcification of bone is dependent upon (1) the availability of adequate amounts of minerals, particularly phosphorous and calcium, at the region to be calcified and (2) requisite chemical and physical conditions within the calcification site. The minerals are present in the blood and are carried to the calcification site, where calcium and phosphate ions are present in metastable solution under normal conditions. In some disease states, such as *rickets*, the body lacks an adequate amount of vitamine D, which is essential for absorption and maintenance of the minerals at an appropriate level in the blood. In this condition, collagen and mucopolysaccharides continue to form and the increase of uncalcified osteoid at the growing ends of long bones gives abnormal shapes. The lack of sufficient minerals leads to decreased rigidity.

The local factors responsible for calcification are controlled by the cells in the ossification center. Although many of the details remain obscure, there is evidence on some of the requisites. It is noted in Chapter 5 that collagen can be dissolved and reconstituted in vitro, either in its native form or in other types. When different types of recon- stituted collagen are exposed in vitro to metastable solutions of calcium phosphate, calcification occurs only in the 640 A periodicity type (Glimcher, 1961). In other words, a "precise stereochemical configuration" is necessary for the initiation of calcification. This raises a question why calcification does not occur in all 640 A periodicity collagen in the body. Further studies have shown that reconstituted collagen from tendon, which does not calcify in the body, does calcify in metastable solutions of calcium phosphate in vitro, provided that components of the associated ground substance are removed (Glimcher, 1961). Apparently, certain mucopolysaccharides associated with collagen have a role in inhibiting and regulating calcification.

Scurvy is a disease state related to local changes in the calcification site. In this condition, the diet is deficient in vitamin C, which is essential for osteoblasts to form normal amounts of collagen. The collagen which is formed is normal and becomes mineralized, but its deficiency stunts skeletal growth in young individuals and retards healing of fractures.

Further Growth and Resorption of Intramembranous Bone. Osteogenic cells around the foci of newly formed intramembranous bone continue to multiply and change into osteoblasts and osteocytes. By this process, irregular plates and trabeculae are formed. These enclose spaces (primary marrow spaces) which contain blood vessels, reticular cells and primitive marrow cells (Fig. 6-18).

During early development of intramembranous bone, osseous tissue is deposited in both the inner and outer surfaces of the flat bones of the skull and also on their peripheral margins. Deposition in the latter area increases the surface area of the bone and also accompanies an enlargement of the cranial cavity to accommodate the growth of the brain. A further increase in the cranial cavity is achieved by resorption along the inner surface, a process which

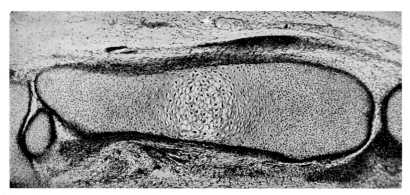

FIG. 6-22. Cartilaginous anlage of metacarpal bone of 4-cm. human fetus, showing changes in the central portion preparatory to ossification. The bone collar is beginning to form. Photograph.

begins relatively early. Continued growth involves new bone deposition, primarily on the outer and marginal surfaces, and resorption, chiefly along the inner surface. However, new bone formation is not entirely absent from the inner surfaces; the processes of formation and resorption accompany each other in the constant remodeling of bone.

INTRACARTILAGINOUS BONE FORMATION

In this form of ossification, an embryonal type of hyaline cartilage precedes the formation of bone, and the shape of the bone will correspond more or less closely to that of the cartilage. During development, this cartilage is replaced by bone, except at the joint surfaces. This will not be completely accomplished, however, until the bone has achieved its full size and growth has ceased.

During the replacement of the cartilage by bone, not only does the supporting function have to be maintained but there is a continual increase in length and diameter as well. The extensiveness of this growth can be realized by comparing the size of the fetal skeleton with that of an adult.

Stages in Intracartilagenous Bone Formation. The first indication of beginning ossification in the cartilagenous model of a long bone is seen near the center of the future shaft, the diaphyseal or *primary ossification center* (Fig. 6-22). The cartilage cells proliferate and hypertrophy, and the lacunae correspondingly increase in number

and size. The matrix between the lacunae becomes reduced in amount and forms but thin partitions. These, except for the cartilage capsules, then become calcified by the deposition of lime salts. This calcified portion stains more intensely with basic dyes than does the unchanged cartilage at either end of the ossification center.

At about the time that these intracartilaginous changes are clearly evident, the fibrocellular membrane of the cartilage (perichondrium) assumes an osteogenetic function. Some of the cells of the inner part of the membrane change into *osteogenic cells* and, in turn, into *osteoblasts*, which deposit a perforated *bony ring* or *collar* around the cartilage of the ossification center. This bone collar is thin walled and short at first but becomes progressively thicker walled and longer as the ossification progresses. It is closely adherent to the cartilage and forms a splint that assists in maintaining the strength of the shaft, which has been weakened by the dissolution of part of the cartilage. It is formed by an intramembranous type of bone development. The fibrocellular membrane which surrounded the cartilage has, in this region of ossification, now become a periosteum.

Vascular connective tissue sprouts from the periosteum, known as *periosteal buds*, grow through apertures in the bone collar, and enter the periphery of the changed cartilage matrix (Fig. 6-23). They contain

Periosteal bud   Primitive marrow cavity   Bone collar

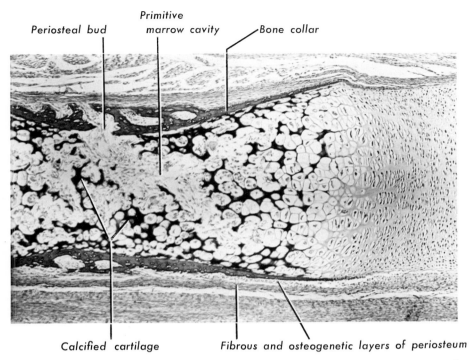

Calcified cartilage   Fibrous and osteogenetic layers of periosteum

FIG. 6-23. Metacarpal bone of human fetus 10 to 12 weeks old. The periosteal bud is only one of several, as shown by an examination of serial sections. The primary marrow cavity is quite extensive The zones of cell and lacunar enlargement and of cell multiplication are evident. Only a small amount of reserve cartilage has been included in the figure. Photograph.

blood vessels and osteogenic cells from the periosteum. They penetrate the thin walled partitions between the hypertrophied cartilage lacunae and thus form cavities, the *primary marrow spaces*. The osteogenic cells multiply by mitosis, and some of them transform into osteoblasts around the periphery of the calcified cartilage remnants.

The literature on the fate of cartilage cells during endochondral bone formation has been controversial. According to a number of authors, the cartilage cells degenerate either before or after they are released from their lacunae by the resorption of cartilage matrix. However, more recent studies on the differentiation of embryonic endochondral bone grown in vitro, in conjunction with isotope labeling at different developmental stages, show that many of the cartilage cells survive (Crelin and Koch, 1967). Some fuse to form *chondroclasts* around the cartilage remnants.

Some persist as small cells which change into osteoblasts. Since the tissues were grown in vitro, there were no penetrating vessels and no periosteal buds. It seems clear that many cartilage cells survive during endochondral bone formation and change into osteogenic cells. This does not deny that osteogenic cells from periosteal buds also contribute osteoblasts in in vivo endochondral bone formation.

The primitive marrow cavity, formed by confluence of cartilage lacunae, retains remnants of calcified cartilage matrix. Some of the osteogenetic cells become aligned on the surfaces of the trabeculae of calcified cartilage and transform into osteoblasts. Through the activity of the osteoblasts, the the calcified cartilage becomes enclosed first by osteoid and then by calcified bone. The trabeculae of calcified cartilage covered by calcified bone will be resorbed subsequently as the marrow cavity enlarges during bone growth. The trabeculae serve as a temporary supporting framework (Figs. 6-24 to 6-26).

The extension of the zone of ossification towards the ends of the cartilage is accompanied by an orderly sequence of changes in the cartilage similar to those which took place in the formation of the primary ossification center, but the changes show a more distinct zonal arrangement (Fig. 6-25).

Several zones can be distinguished in the cartilage. Beginning at the ends of the cartilage and passing towards the ossification center, these zones which overlap each other somewhat are as follows.

1. *Zone of Reserve Cartilage.* In the early phases of ossification, this zone is relatively long but later becomes shorter. It is composed of a primitive type of hyaline cartilage. Cell division and matrix formation occur in

it, and it grows in all directions, although apparently at a slow rate.

2. *Zone of Cell Multiplication.* This zone is composed of cells that are more or less regularly arranged in rows which run parallel to the long axis of the cartilage. The lacunae containing the daughter cells are broad but flattened as are the cells, their long axes being perpendicular to the longitudinal axis of the cartilage. By these divisions of cartilage cells and their distribution in rows, the length of the cartilage is increased more than is its diameter as new matrix is formed.

3. *Zone of Cell Hypertrophy and Lacunar Enlargement.* In this zone there is no further multiplication of the cells, but they mature and enlarge. This still further increases the length of the cartilage of this region. The cytoplasm of the cells contains considerable

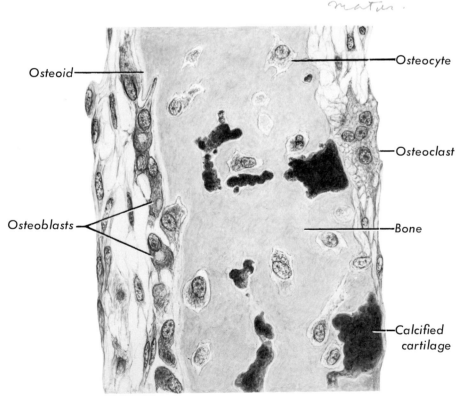

Fig. 6-26. Section of a trabecula in developing endochondral bone. Tibia of human fetus about 3½ months old. Azure II-eosin stain. ×950.

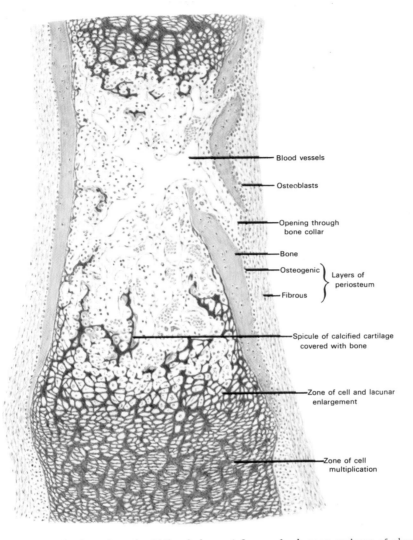

Blood vessels

Osteoblasts

Opening through
bone collar

Bone

Osteogenic ⎫ Layers of
⎬ periosteum
Fibrous ⎭

Spicule of calcified cartilage
covered with bone

Zone of cell and lacunar
enlargement

Zone of cell
multiplication

FIG. 6-24. Longitudinal section of middle phalanx of finger of a human embryo of about 4 months. Hematoxylin and eosin-azure II. ×80.

EPIPHYSIS

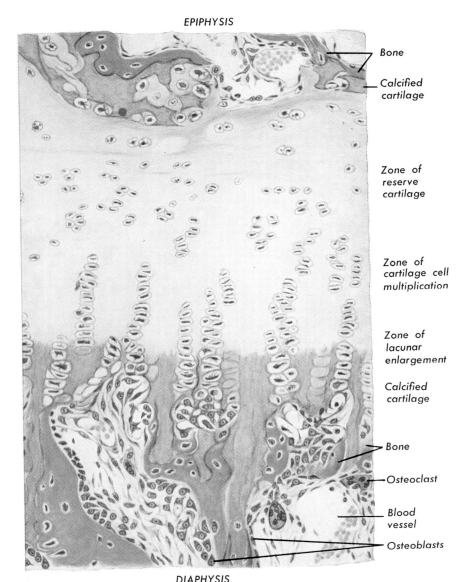

Bone

Calcified
cartilage

Zone of
reserve
cartilage

Zone of
cartilage cell
multiplication

Zone of
lacunar
enlargement

Calcified
cartilage

Bone

Osteoclast

Blood
vessel

Osteoblasts

DIAPHYSIS

Fig. 6-25. Longitudinal section through the distal end of a metatarsal of a rhesus monkey 2 months of age. The epiphyseal (secondary) ossification center is well formed. Bone formation is taking place both at the epiphyseal and the diaphyseal surfaces of the epiphyseal plate, and is particularly pronounced on the diaphyseal side. Delafield's hematoxylin and eosin. ×280.

amounts of glycogen and alkaline phosphatase at this stage. Poor preservation of glycogen in routine preparations for light microscopy is partly responsible for the vacuolated and lightly-stained appearance of the cytoplasm seen in the hypertrophied cartilage cells. The cartilage between adjacent cells within a row, previously small in amount, becomes even thinner.

4. *A Zone of Cartilage Calcification.* This is a zone of variable length, but is always narrow. The matrix between adjacent lacunae within a row has practically disappeared and the matrix between the rows begins to calcify (Fig. 6-25).

5. *A Zone of Cartilage Removal and Bone Deposition.* In the outer part of this zone, the thin partitions between the lacunae within a row undergo dissolution. This is accompanied by death of some of the cartilage cells and it is apparently aided by an erosive action by blood vessels that grow in from the marrow cavity. Longitudinal canals, filled with vessels and marrow, are thus formed in the cartilage matrix. Farther towards the marrow cavity, the calcified cartilage matrix between the newly-formed canals becomes reduced in amount by resorption but remnants of calcified cartilage matrix persist. These are important in endochondrial bone formation. Some osteoblasts (or chondroblasts) are usually present where the cartilage is being resorbed. Osteoblasts appear on the surfaces of the remnants of calcified cartilage and deposit a coating of bone (Figs. 6-24 to 6-26).

The longitudinal remnants of calcified cartilage appear as isolated bars or trabeculae when viewed in sections cut parallel to the long axis of the developing bone. However, they are connected with each other as shown in sections cut transversely, i.e., perpendicular to the long axis of the bone. The remnants of calcified cartilage form a supporting framework and a locus for bone deposition by the osteoblasts. All of the cartilage remnants and their bony coverings will be resorbed subsequently as the marrow cavity enlarges during the growth period.

The region where the diaphysis joins the epiphysis, i.e., where the cartilage is being replaced by bone is known as the *metaphysis.* This includes the region described above as the Zone of Cartilage Removal and Bone Deposition.

While these changes within the cartilage are taking place, the bone collar is increasing in length and in diameter by the deposition of new bone. The marrow cavity also increases in size, not only by its longitudinal extension as a result of cartilage removal, but also in diameter, owing to resorption of the inner part of the bone collar or splint. These processes continue as development proceeds. The zone of reserve cartilage is maintained by continued cell division. However, it becomes relatively reduced in length as the diaphysis continues to increase in length by the same sequence of events as that listed in the description of different zones, i.e., by proliferation of cartilage cells in rows, cell hypertrophy and lacunar enlargement, calcification of cartilage, cartilage removal and bone deposition. This process continues in both directions in the shaft.

At about the time of birth, ossification centers (epiphyseal or *secondary ossification centers*) appear in each end of the long bones. The cartilage in these centers passes through the same changes as in the diaphysis. The proliferation of the cartilage cells leads to nearly equal growth in all directions, however. The cartilage cells, each of which is enclosed in a lacuna, are arranged in irregularly shaped nests and not in rows, and the partitions between the nests run in various directions. As in the diaphysis, the center is invaded by osteogenetic buds, and cartilage removal and bone deposition take place. Bone trabeculae, however, remain in the epiphyseal cavity, giving it grossly a spongy appearance, and the cartilage forming the articular surface persists, anchored to and supported by the underlying bone (Fig. 6-28).

The diaphysis continues its growth in length long after the epiphyseal centers appear. The cartilage plate which separates it from the epiphysis, called the *epiphyseal plate* (Fig. 6-25), continues to form new cartilage which is replaced by bone, a process which, as stated earlier, causes an increase principally in the length of the growing bone. When the cartilage of the epiphyseal plate is absorbed, growth of a bone ceases and the diaphysis is bound to the epiphysis by a bony union. The zone of this union is visible in the adult. It is called the *epiphyseal line*.

Haversian Systems. During the growth of the skeleton, some of the spongy bone becomes transformed into compact bone. In this process, lamellae of bone are deposited progressively inward on the surface of the cavities in the spongy bone until they are reduced to narrow canals. Each canal is traversed by blood vessels which originally were in the large cavity. The system of concentric lamellae with its canal and blood vessels forms an Haversian system.

Haversian systems of the shafts of long bones are formed by a more complicated process than that given above for transformation in areas of cancellous bone. The first step in the formation of Haversian systems in compact bone is the erosion of tunnels in it by vascular sprouts from the medullary and periosteal surfaces. The tunnels thus formed have irregular, roughened surfaces but are of a fairly uniform diameter. When the absorption phase leading to the formation of the tunnel has been completed, osteoblasts arise from the osteogenic cells in the vascular sprouts. They come to lie next to the walls of the tunnel and deposit progressively inward concentric lamellae characteristic of an Haversian system. A narrow canal containing blood vessels is left: the Haversian canal. Parts of the original circumferential lamellae (ground lamellae) remain between the Haversian systems. However, new generations of

Haversian systems keep forming throughout life, although at a reduced rate in later years. In this process, parts of earlier formed Haversian systems, as well as additional parts of the original circumferential lamellae, are destroyed. Stages in the destruction of bone and its replacement by Haversian systems are illustrated in Figure 6-27. Haversian systems have an important function in providing channels for blood vessels through compact bone. They also provide better structural support and presumably make the bone less brittle.

Since bone serves as a storehouse for calcium and phosphate, the rate of bone resorption increases whenever either of these essential elements tends to fall below a normal blood level. This leads to changes in Haversian systems and in the trabeculae at the ends of the long bones. The minerals are not withdrawn from the organic matrix, leaving the latter intact (halisteresis); both minerals and matrix are withdrawn. Destruction of bone can be produced by the experimental administration of parathyroid extract or by a tumor of the parathyroid gland. The latter usually causes pronounced resorption of bone and its replacement by connective tissue (von Recklinghausen's disease).

It has been pointed out that perforating fibers of Sharpey do not enter the Haversian systems. An understanding of the developmental process will make the reason for this clear. Perforating fibers of Sharpey do not grow into bone. Rather they are radially or obliquely directed fibers which have been imprisoned by the advancing deposition of subperiosteal bone in much the same way that a branch of a tree becomes more and more enclosed in the growing trunk. When a vascular sprout forms a tunnel preceding the deposition of an Haversian system, the perforating fibers of Sharpey as well as the bone substance are resorbed, and because of their method of formation the perforating fibers are not replaced.

Development of Short Bones. The

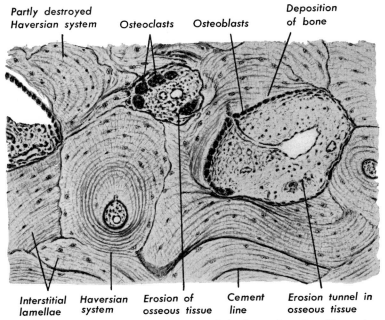

Partly destroyed
Haversian system   Osteoclasts   Osteoblasts   Deposition
                                                                of bone

Interstitial   Haversian   Erosion of   Cement   Erosion tunnel in
lamellae   system   osseous tissue   line   osseous tissue

FIG. 6-27. Figure showing the absorption of bone and the formation of an Haversian system in compact osseous tissue. Proximal phalanx of the thumb of a child 6 years old. ×150. (After Petersen.)

development of the short bones is similar to that of the epiphyses of long bones. Ossification begins in the center of the cartilage and extends in all directions in the wake of the growing cartilage. Near the end of growth, the endochondral bone is invested with a thin compact layer of subperiosteal bone, except at the articular surfaces which remain cartilaginous.

Remodeling of Bone. It is obvious that bone, although dense, hard and rigid, is capable of changing somewhat in shape and also of increasing or decreasing somewhat in amount, in response to environmental conditions. As already pointed out, these changes are not brought about by a remodeling, such as might be done with a plastic wax, but involve the formation of new bone and the removal of bone already formed or the combination of both processes. This capacity to change in shape is well illustrated by the moving of improperly aligned teeth by the orthodontist and by the spontaneous movement of neighboring teeth after a tooth is extracted. The bony socket is

resorbed ahead of the tooth undergoing movement, and the shape and size of the socket is maintained by the formation of new bone back of the tooth. In other situations, as, for instance, in increased muscular development, bone may be remodeled to meet the additional stresses imposed upon it. In old age, resorption of the surfaces of some bones occurs. The changes in bone are slower and less pronounced in the adult than during the period of growth, but they probably occur to some degree throughout life.

Healing of Fractures. A fracture, like any traumatic injury, causes hemorrhage and tissue destruction. The first reparative changes thus are characteristic of those occurring in any injury of soft tissue. Proliferating fibroblasts and capillary sprouts grow into the blood clot and injured area, thus forming granulation tissue. The area also is invaded by polymorphonuclear leukocytes and later by macrophages which phagocytize the tissue debris. The granulation tissue gradually becomes denser and, in parts of it, cartilage is formed. This newly formed connective tissue and cartilage is designated as a *callus*. It serves temporarily in stabilizing and binding together the fractured bone.

As the above described process is taking place, the dormant osteogenic cells of the periosteum enlarge and become active osteoblasts. On the outside of the fractured bone, at first at some distance from the fracture, osseous tissue is deposited. This formation of new bone continues towards the fractured ends of the bone and finally forms a sheathlike layer of bone over the fibrocartilaginous callus. As the bone increases in amount, osteogenic buds invade the fibrous and cartilaginous callus and replace it with a bony one. In the replacement of the fibrocartilaginous callus, the cartilage undergoes calcification and absorption, as described under intracartilaginous bone development. Typical intramembranous bone formation also takes place. The newly formed bone is at first a spongy and not a compact type. It becomes transformed into a compact type, and the callus becomes reduced in diameter. At the time when this subperiosteal bone formation is taking place, bone also forms in the marrow cavity. The medullary bone growing centripetally from each side of the fracture unites, thus aiding the bony union. The process of repair is, in general, an orderly process but varies greatly with the displacement of the fractured ends of the bone and the degree of trauma inflicted. Uneven or protruding surfaces are gradually removed, and the healed bone, especially in young individuals, assumes its original contour.

THE PERIOSTEUM AND ENDOSTEUM

The *periosteum* is a fibrous membrane investing the bones, except at their articular surfaces. Its adherence to the bone varies in different places and at different ages. In the young bone, it is easily stripped off. In the adult bone, it is more firmly adherent and especially so at the insertion of tendons and ligaments, where more periosteal fibers penetrate into the bone as the perforating fibers of Sharpey.

The periosteum consists of two layers, the outer of which is composed of coarse, fibrous connective tissue containing few cells but numerous blood vessels and nerves. The inner layer is less vascular but more cellular and contains many elastic fibers. During growth, an osteogenic layer of primitive connective tissue forms the inner layer of the periosteum. In the adult, this is represented only by a row of scattered, flattened cells closely applied to the bone.

The periosteum serves as a supporting bed for the blood vessels and nerves going to the bone and for the anchorage of tendons and ligaments. Its importance for bone regeneration has been a much disputed topic. If the osteogenic layer is considered a part of the periosteum, the latter undoubtedly furnishes osteoblasts for growth and repair. However, the fibrous periosteum of the adult is itself a differentiated end product of the osteogenic layer, and it probably plays no direct part in bone repair but acts as an important limiting layer controlling and restricting the extent of bone formation.

The *endosteum* lines the surface of cavities within a bone (marrow cavity, Haversian canals) and also the surfaces of trabeculae in the marrow cavity. In growing bone, it is formed of a delicate stratum of myelogenous reticular connective tissue, beneath which is a layer of osteoblasts. In the adult, the osteogenic cells become flattened, and are indistinguishable as a separate layer. They are capable of transforming into osteoblasts when there is a stimulus to bone formation, as after a fracture.

MARROW

Marrow is a soft tissue which occupies the medullary cavity of the long bones, the larger Haversian canals and all of the spaces between the trabeculae of spongy bone. It consists of a delicate reticular connective tissue, in the meshes of which lie various kinds of cells.

Two varieties of marrow are recognized: *red* and *yellow*.

Red Marrow. Red marrow (Fig. 7-10) is the only type found in fetal and young bones, but in the adult it is restricted to the vertebrae, sternum, ribs, cranial bones and the epiphyses of long bones. It is the chief blood-forming organ of the adult body, being the sole normal source of the red blood cells and granular leukocytes. During the fetal and growth period, it forms part of the osteogenic tissue, which furnishes the osteoblasts for bone development. The cells of red marrow are discussed more fully in connection with blood formation (see p. 187).

Yellow Marrow. Yellow marrow consists in the main of fat cells (Fig. 6-28) which have gradually replaced the other marrow elements. Under certain conditions, the yellow marrow of old or emaciated persons loses most of its fat and assumes a reddish color and gelatinous consistency It is then known as *gelatinous marrow*. With an adequate stimulus, yellow marrow may resume the character of red marrow and play an active part in the process of blood development.

BLOOD VESSELS AND NERVES

Bone is richly supplied with blood vessels which pass into it from the periosteum. Near the center of the shaft of a long bone, a canal passes obliquely through the compact bone. This is known as the *medullary* or *nutrient* canal, and its external opening is known as the *nutrient foramen*. A medullary artery

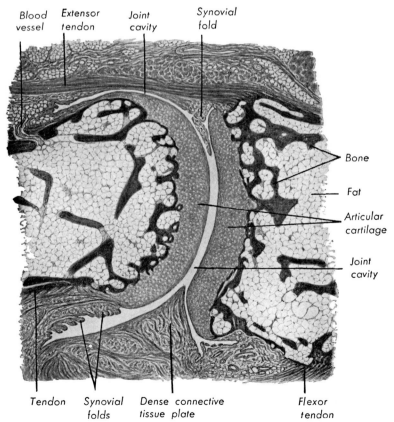

FIG. 6-28. Median sagittal section through the joint between the middle and terminal phalanges of middle toe. Human, 10 years of age. The terminal phalanx is at the *right*. ×14.

runs through this canal to the marrow cavity. In its passage through the compact bone, it communicates by branches with the blood vessels of the Haversian canals. On reaching the marrow cavity, the artery divides into ascending and descending branches which supply all portions of the marrow. The terminal branches of the arterioles connect with *sinusoids*, which differ from capillaries by their larger diameter and by their lining of phagocytic reticuloendothelial cells. There are randomly spaced gaps between the lining cells of some of the sinusoids, and the basal lamina is thin and incomplete. Consequently, the sinusoids are more permeable than are ordinary capillaries.

The capillaries are drained by narrow and thin walled veins which have no valves. The larger medullary veins pass through the medullary canal accompanying the medullary artery and, like the latter, communicate by branches with the veins of the Haversian canals.

Besides the medullary canals, the bone is everywhere pierced by the Volkmann's canals, which serve for transmission of the numerous smaller vessels. In compact bone, these vessels give rise to a network of branches which run in the Haversian canals. In spongy bone, the network lies in the marrow spaces. Branches from these vessels pass to the marrow cavity and there break up into a sinusoidal network which anastomoses freely with that formed by the branches of the medullary artery.

Lymphatics. Lymphatics with distinct walls are present in the outer layer of the periosteum. Cleftlike lymph capillaries lined with endothelium accompany the blood vessels in Volkmann's and in the Haversian canals. The amorphous material which surrounds the osteocytes and cytoplasmic processes in the lacunae and canaliculi serves not only for the exchange of substances between the cells and blood vessels but also as a pathway to the lymphatics of the perios-

teum, of Volkmann's and the Haversian canals and of the bone marrow.

Nerves. Both medullated and nonmedullated nerves accompany the vessels from the periosteum through Volkmann's canals into the Haversian canals and marrow cavities. Periosteum is highly sensitive to painful stimuli, whereas osseous tissue is relatively insensitive.

JOINTS (ARTICULATIONS)

Two main types of connections between bones are distinguished: (1) union without an articular cleft (*synarthrosis*), the joint being immovable or only slightly movable; (2) connection of bones with an articular cleft (*diarthrosis*, movable joint, Fig. 6-28).

1. In **synarthrosis,** union may be by ligaments or dense fibrous tissue (*syndesmosis*) or by means of cartilage (*synchondrosis*).

(a) In *syndesmosis*, the connecting ligaments may be fibrous or elastic. Of the latter type are the ligamenta subflava which unite the vertebral arches. In the immovable articulations of the cranial bones (*sutures*), short fibers which are, in the main, continuations of the fibers of Sharpey unite the serrated edges of adjacent bones.

(b) *Synchondrosis.* The cartilage is usually of the fibrous form, except nearest the bone where it is hyaline (see under "Cartilage"). The intervertebral discs consist of a fibrocartilaginous ring surrounding a central gelatinoid mass, the nucleus pulposus.

2. In **diarthrosis,** the bones are separated by an articular cleft (synovial cavity) and are more or less freely movable. The following structures must be considered: (a) the articular cartilage, (b) the interarticular cartilages or *menisci* and glenoid ligaments, (c) the joint capsule.

(a) The *articular cartilage* (Figs. 6-2 and 6-28) covers the ends of the bones and is usually of the hyaline variety, being the remains of the original cartilage in which the bones were formed. No perichondrium is present. The most superficial cartilage cells are flattened and arranged in rows parallel with the surface. In the deeper portion, the cells are rounded and arranged in typical groups. The deepest layer, firmly apposed to the bone, is calcified.

In the acromioclavicular, sternoclavicular and costovertebral articulations, the cartilage is of the fibrous form. The same is true of the cartilage covering the head of the ulna, while the surface of the radius which enters into the wrist joints is covered not by cartilage but by dense fibrous tissue.

Articular cartilage, like cartilage elsewhere, is devoid of blood vessels. Metabolic exchange is made by diffusion through the ground substance of the cartilage to and from (1) synovial fluid (2) capillaries in the periosteum around the periphery and (3) vessels in the underlying bone. Exchange is chiefly with the synovial fluid.

(b) The *interarticular cartilages* and labra glenoidea serve to deepen the sockets for the articular ends, and they usually consist of fibrous cartilage.

(c) The *joint capsule* consists of two strata: an outer dense *fibrous layer* which blends with the ligaments and periosteum of the articulating bones; and, an inner layer, the *synovial membrane* which lines the joint cavity with the exception of the surfaces of the articular cartilages. Prominent infoldings of the synovial membranes are known as *synovial folds* (Fig. 6-28) and more slender projections are known as *synovial villi*.

The synovial membrane consists of an inner layer composed chiefly of cells and an outer layer of variable types of irregularly arranged connective tissue. On the basis of structural variations, the synovial membranes have been classified as fibrous, areolar, and adipose types. In the fibrous type (e.g., over tendons), a thin cellular layer rests on connective tissue fibers that are intimately blended with the fibrous capsule. The adipose type is found over intra-articular fat pads. The areolar type allows mo-

bility of the synovial membrane over the fibrous capsule. Its outer layer contains irregularly arranged collagenous and elastic fibers plus the usual connective tissue cells, including mast cells and macrophages. Its inner cellular layer is thicker than that of the other types and consists of two to four layers of irregularly arranged cells that are usually described as fibroblasts. Electron micrographs show that the cells have numerous cytoplasmic processes, particularly at the adluminal cell surfaces. No basal lamina is seen between the surface cells and the underlying tissue.

The *synovial fluid, synovia*, is apparently secreted by the synovial cells. It is a viscid, mucoalbuminous fluid, rich in hyaluronic acid. It acts as a lubricating fluid facilitating the smooth gliding of the articular surfaces.

The larger blood vessels of the joint capsule lie in the outer layer of the stratum synoviale whence smaller vessels and capillaries pass to the inner layer and to some of the villi. The inner layer is richly, and the outer layer more poorly, supplied with lymph capillaries. Nonmedullated nerve fibers are found in the connective tissue, some of them ending in end bulbs and Pacinian corpuscles.

REFERENCES

BARLAND, P., NOVIKOFF, A. B., AND HERMERMANN, D. 1962. Electron microscopy of the human synovial membrane. J. Cell Biol., vol. 14, pp. 207–22..

BOURNE, G. H. 1956. The Biochemistry and Physiology of Bone. Academic Press, New York.

CAMERON, D. A., PASCHALL, H. A., AND ROBINSON, R. A. 1967 Changes in the fine structure of bone cells after the administration of parathyroid extract. J. Cell Biol., vol. 33, pp. 1–14.

CLARK, S. M., AND IBALL, J. 1957 The x-ray crystal analysis of bone. Progr. Biophys., vol. 7, pp. 226–252.

CRELIN, E. S., AND KOCH, W. E. 1967 An autoradiographic study of chondrocyte transformation into chondroclasts and osteocytes during bone formation *in vitro.* Anat. Rec., vol. 158, pp. 473–483.

DAVIES, D. V. 1950. The structure and functions of the synovial membrane. Brit. Med. J., vol. 1, pp. 92–95.

DUDLEY, H. R., AND SPIRO, D. 1961 The fine structure of bone cells. J. Biophys. Biochem. Cytol., vol. 11, pp. 627–649.

GLIMCHER, M. J. 1961 The role of the macromolecular aggregation state and reactivity of collagen in calcification. *In* Macromolecular Complexes (Edds, M. V., Jr., editor), pp. 53–84. Ronald Press, New York.

GODMAN, G. C., AND LANE, N. 1964 On the site of sulfation in the chondrocyte. J. Cell Biol., vol. 21, pp. 353–366.

GODMAN, G. C., AND PORTER, K. R. 1960 Chondrogenesis, studied with the electron microscope. J. Biophys. Biochem. Cytol., vol. 8, pp. 719–760.

GOMORI, G. 1943 Calcification and phosphatase. Amer. J. Pathol., vol. 19, pp. 197–210.

HAM, A. W. 1932. Cartilage and bone. Special Cytology (Cowdry, E. V., editor), vol. 2, pp. 979–1051.

HELLER, M., McLEAN, F. C., AND BLOOM, W. 1950 Cellular transformations in mammalian bones induced by parathyroid extract. Amer. J. Anat., vol. 87, pp. 315–348.

HOLMGREN, H. 1950 Normal morphology of the joint fluid. Acta Orthop. Scand., vol. 20, pp. 97–104.

INGALLS, T. H. 1941 Epiphyseal growth: normal sequence of events at epiphyseal plate. Endocrinology, vol. 29, pp. 710–720.

JACKSON, S. F. 1957. The fine srtucture of developing bone in the embryonic fowl. Proc. Roy. Soc. Biol., vol. 146, pp. 270–280.

KIRBY-SMITH, H. T. 1933 Bone growth studies —a miniature bone fracture observed microscopically in a transparent chamber introduced into the rabbit's ear. Amer. J. Anat., vol. 53, pp. 377–402.

LACROIX, P. 1961 Bone and Cartilage. *In* The Cell; Biochemistry, Physiology, Morphology (Brachet, J., and Mirsky, A. E., editors), vol. 5, pp. 219–266. Academic Press, New York.

McLEAN, F. C., AND BLOOM, W. 1940 Calcification and ossification. Calcification in normal growing bone. Anat. Rec., vol. 78, pp. 333–359.

McLEAN, F. C., AND URIST, M. R. 1968 Bone: Fundamentals of the Physiology of Skeletal Tissue, ed. 3. University of Chicago Press, Chicago.

MEYER, K. 1956 The mucopolysaccharides of bone. *In* Ciba Foundation symposium on Bone Structure and Metabolism (Wolstenholme,

G. E. W., and O'Connor, M., editors). Little, Brown & Company, Boston.

MOSS, M. L. 1960 Experimental induction of osteogenesis. *In* Calcification in Biological Systems (Sognnaes, R. F., editor), A. A. A. S. Publ. 64, pp. 323–348.

MOSS, M. L. (editor) 1963 Comparative biology of calcified tissue. Ann. N. Y. Acad. Sci., vol. 109.

NUNNEMACHER, R. F. 1939 Experimental studies on the cartilage plates in the long bones of the rat. Amer. J. Anat., vol. 65, pp. 253–289.

NYLEN, M. U., SCOTT, D. B., AND MOSLEY, V. M. 1960 Mineralization of turkey leg tendon. II. Collagen-mineral relations revealed by electron and x-ray microscopy. *In* Calcification in Biological Systems (Sognnaes, R. F., editor), A. A. A. S. Publ. No. 64, pp. 129–149.

PARK, E. A. 1939 Observations on the pathology of rickets with particular reference to the changes at the cartilage-shaft junctions of the growing bones. Harvey Lectures, Ser. 34, pp. 157–213.

PEACOCK, A. 1952 Observations on the postnatal structure of the intervertebral disc in man. J. Anat., vol. 86, pp. 162–179.

PELEC, S. R., AND GLUCKSMANN, A. 1955 Sulphate metabolism in the cartilage of the trachea, pinna and xiphoid process of the adult mouse as indicated by autoradiographs. Exp. Cell Res., vol. 8, pp. 336–344.

PETERSEN, H. 1930 Die Organe des Skeletsystems. Handb. mikr. Anat., Menschen (v. Möllendorff, editor), vol. 2, pt. 2, pp. 521–676. Springer-Verlag, Berlin.

PORTER, K. R. 1964 Cell fine structure and biosynthesis of intercellular macromolecules. *In* The New York Heart Association Symposium on Connective Tissue. Biophys. J., vol. 4.

PRITCHARD, J. J. 1956 General anatomy and histology of bone. *In* The Biochemistry and Physiology of Bone (Bourne, G. H., editor), pp. 1–25. Academic Press, New York.

REVEL, J. P., AND HAY, E. D. 1963 An autoradiographic and electron microscopic study of collagen synthesis in differentiating cartilage. Z. Zellforsch., vol. 61, pp. 110–144.

ROBINSON, R. A., AND WATSON, M. L. 1955 Crystal-collagen relationships in bone as observed in the electron microscope. Ann. N. Y. Acad. Sci., vol. 60, art. 5, pp. 596–628.

RUTH, E. B. 1947 Fibrillar structure of human bone. Amer. J. Anat., vol. 80, pp. 35–53.

SOGNNAES, R. F. (editor) 1960 Calcification in Biological Systems. A. A. A. S. Publ. No. 64, Washington, D. C.

TERMINE, J. D., WUTHIER, R. E., AND POSNER, A. S. 1967 Amorphous crystalline mineral changes during endochondral and periosteal bone formation. Proc. Soc. Exp. Biol. Med., vol. 125, pp. 4–9.

TRUETA, J. 1963 The dynamics of bone circulation. *In* Bone Biodynamics (Frost, H. M., editor), pp. 245–258. Little, Brown & Company, Boston.

VAES, G. 1968 On the mechanism of bone resorption. The action of parathyroid hormone on the excretion and synthesis of lysosomal enzymes and on the extracellular release of acid by bone cells. J. Cell Biol., vol. 39, pp. 676–697.

YEAGER, J. A., AND KRAUCUNAS, E. 1969 Fine structure of the resorptive cells in the teeth of frogs. Anat. Rec., vol. 164, pp. 1–13.

YOUNG, R. W. 1962 Cell proliferation and specialization during endochondral osteogenesis in young rats. J. Cell Biol., vol. 14, pp. 357–370.

7

Blood and Lymph

Blood may be considered as a tissue consisting of free cells (corpuscles) and a fluid intercellular substance or plasma. Genetically and structurally, blood is related to the connective tissues. The blood cells develop in the reticular connective tissues of blood-forming organs and enter the blood stream in a fully formed condition. Although functioning erythrocytes are limited to the blood stream, the white or colorless corpuscles function in the loose connective tissues and use the blood stream merely as a vehicle of transportation. After migration from the vessels, some of the colorless corpuscles develop into macrophages which cannot be distinguished from the connective tissue histiocytes.

Since the structural components of mammalian blood are not all true cells, they are sometimes designated as the *formed elements*. They include the red corpuscles (*erythrocytes*), the white blood cells (*leukocytes*) and the *blood platelets* (*thrombocytes*). The total quantity of blood (formed elements and plasma) forms about 8% of the body weight. There are some 5 or 6 liters of blood in a man weighing 150 pounds.

Blood may be studied under the microscope in the living animal in such places as the mesentery and the web of the frog's foot. When small vessels are selected, the blood flow is sufficiently slow to enable one to distinguish the individual corpuscles floating in a clear plasma. More detailed observations on living blood cells can be made by placing a fresh drop of blood on a slide beneath a cover slip for studies with the oil immersion objective. By adding relatively nontoxic dyes such as neutral red to a drop of blood removed from the body, i.e., by the use of supravital staining, one can readily study the reactions of the living cells. Tissue culture provides another method for studying living cells for a longer period of time.

In most of the methods commonly used in clinical work, the blood cells are observed in the nonliving state because they are exposed to special techniques for providing particular kinds of information. Thus, to determine what percentage of total blood consists of formed elements, one centrifuges the blood in a graduated tube—the percentage of formed elements is known as the *hematocrit*.

To determine the number of erythrocytes per cubic millimeter of blood, one uses a special pipette to dilute a known quantity of blood by a known amount of isotonic fluid, and a drop of the mixture is placed in the chamber of a *hemocytometer* slide. The bottom of the counting chamber is ruled in fine squares and is at a known depth beneath the cover slip. Since the cubic dimension of the space over each square is known, one can readily calculate the total number of erythrocytes per cubic millimeter from a count of the erythrocytes lying over a given number of ruled squares. This is known as the *total erythrocyte count*, and is of particular importance in studies of different types of anemia. The *total leukocyte count* is done by a similar method, although less dilution is needed for making the observations in the counting chamber because the leukocytes are not as concentrated in whole blood as the erythrocytes are.

To determine the relative proportions of leukocytes, dried blood smears are stained with particular types of compound dyes (e.g., Wright's stain) to give good differentiation of neutrophilic, eosinophilic and basophilic components of the cells. Details on this technique are given in the discussion of the morphology of the formed elements. The determination of different leukocyte percentages by this method is known as the *differential count*.

BLOOD PLASMA

The plasma is a histologically homogeneous, slightly alkaline fluid. Chemically, it contains globulins, albumins and inorganic salts, chiefly the chloride, bicarbonate and phosphate of sodium. Calcium is present in a remarkably constant quantity (1 mg. per 10 cc. of blood). The plasma constitutes 55% of the total quantity of blood and the formed elements constitute 45%, i.e., 45 is the hematocrit value for normal blood. The proportions are altered in a number of pathological conditions; e.g., in microcytic anemia there is a reduction in size and number of erythrocytes, which lowers the hematocrit value.

When blood is exposed to the air or when blood vessels are injured, one of the globulins of the plasma (fibrinogen) precipitates out as a network of delicate filaments, the *fibrin*, leaving a clear yellowish fluid, the *serum*. The blood cells become entangled in the fibrin network and a clot is formed. The clot acts as a plug preventing further hemorrhage. A clot may, however, become of great danger to the individual if it is torn off by the blood stream and circulates in the blood vessels (embolus), in which case it may block the blood supply of vital organs.

The plasma is the fundamental substance mediating all nutrition. In it are dissolved the nutritive substances derived from the alimentary canal, the waste substances from the tissues and the secretions of the various endocrine glands. Even the oxygen which is bound by the red blood cells is first dissolved in the plasma before reaching the cells.

The plasma differs from the tissue fluids by the greater constancy of its constituents. The plasma proteins of the blood are seemingly not destined for nutritive purposes but remain as permanent constituents of the plasma. By experimental methods, it is possible to lower the protein content, but in a few days the normal amount is reestablished.

RED BLOOD CORPUSCLES

The red blood corpuscles or erythrocytes are highly differentiated and specialized for the function of transporting oxygen. In the lower vertebrates, the erythrocyte is a nucleated cell, but in man and all other mammals it is unique in that it normally loses its nucleus, Golgi apparatus, centrioles and most of its mitochondria during the process of maturation before entering the blood stream as a functional element. When fresh preparations of blood are examined under the microscope, it is seen that the individual red corpuscles have a greenish yellow color (Fig. 7-2, *C*); en masse they give the red color characteristic of blood. In dried smears they are acidophilic and stain orange or pink in Wright's stain.

The stains which are commonly used for blood cells consist of mixtures of acid and basic dyes. The development of this procedure stems from the works of Ehrlich published over the period from 1879 to 1898. He added a solution of orange G (an acid dye) to a solution of methyl green (a basic dye) until a precipitate was formed, and then he redissolved the precipitate in an excess of the acid dye for use in staining. Orange G is a sodium salt and methyl green is a chloride. Ehrlich concluded that the mixing of solutions of orange G and methyl green gave sodium chloride plus a new compound, a "neutral" dye consisting of methyl green/orange G, with a dye in both halves of the molecule. He noted that the cytoplasmic granules of some leukocytes took the acid component of his compound dye, while those of other leukocytes took the basic component, and those of a third group took both components of the neutral dye. Hence, he described the leukocytes as acidophilic, basophilic and neutrophilic.

In his later studies, Ehrlich used acid fuchsin and orange G in combination with methyl green (his "triacid" dye). His results stimulated other investigators to try combinations of other acid and basic dyes. A major advance was made by Romanovsky (1891) when he used a mixture of methylene blue and eosin to demonstrate the nucleus of the malarial parasite which had not been seen before. It soon became evident that this gave better staining of blood cells than any of Ehrlich's mixtures. Most of the stains currently used for blood smears are modifications of the Romanosvky stain. The best known modifications are those of Jenner, Leishmann, Giemsa and Wright, the latter being widely employed in clinical work.

The basic dyes used in the preparation of Wright's stain are methylene blue and polychromed (oxidized) methylene blue consisting of methylene azure and methylene violet. When solutions of the basic dyes are added to a solution of the acid dye eosin, a precipitate is formed. The precipitate is dissolved in acetone-free methyl alcohol and, in usage, the alcoholic solution is placed on the slide and water is added during the staining. The alcoholic solution fixes, or preserves, the cells, and the dilution by water permits dissociation of the dye for differential staining. The dye will eventually precipitate in water, but staining should be completed before this occurs.

In Wright's stained blood smears, the erythrocytes are usually colored buff or orange-pink with eosin, the nuclei of leukocytes are stained metachromatically with methylene azure and the cytoplasm of lymphocytes and monocytes is stained blue with methylene blue. The cytoplasmic granules of basophils have an affinity for methylene blue and are metachromatic also, while the granules of eosinophils have an affinity for the acid dye. The explanation for the staining of the neutrophilic granules is not understood as clearly. The cells originally received their name because it was thought that their granules stained with the neutral dye. In the case of Wright's stain, the neutral dye is an eosinate of methylene azure. It is likely that most of this is rapidly dissociated when the dye is diluted with water. The granules of the neutrophils in man usually show a lavender color after Wright's stain, probably from methylene azure and methylene violet. (For further details on compound dyes, see Conn, *Biological Stains*,

and the chapter on blood dyes in Baker's *Principles of Biological Microtechnique*.)

The red corpuscles are biconcave discs. When observed on its flat surface, the corpuscle has a circular outline and the central depression appears as a lighter or darker area, depending on the focus. Seen on edge, the shape resembles that of a dumbbell (Fig. 7-1).

Erythrocytes average about 7.7 μ in diameter and 1.9 μ in greatest thickness in dried smears (Haden, 1940). They are larger in the living state (about 8.6 μ) and smaller in sections (about 7 μ). Although slight variations in size are not uncommon, forms showing marked variations (1 to 2 μ above or below the normal diameter) are relatively rare in normal blood. Large erythrocytes are commonly found in some types of anemia (e.g., pernicious anemia) and are known as macrocytes or megalocytes. Small forms are characteristically present in some other types of anemia (e.g., iron deficiency anemia) and are known as microcytes.

The corpuscles readily change their shape, as may be seen when they squeeze through the narrowest capillaries or pass around the bend of a branching vessel. Experimentally, this has been shown by corpuscles embedded in gelatin. When the latter is stretched, the erythrocytes likewise elongate, only to resume their normal shape when the tension is released. Another interesting physical characteristic is the tendency of the corpuscles to adhere to each other along their concave surfaces, thus forming rows or *rouleaux* like piled up coins (Fig. 7-1). Although the cause of this phenomenon is not entirely clear, it is usually explained as the result of surface tension. Rouleaux formation is a transient phenomenon which is not to be confused with "sludging" of erythrocytes. The latter consists of a clumping of red corpuscles into small masses following severe trauma. As a result of burns of the skin and other types of trauma, there is a leakage of fluid from the blood vessels into

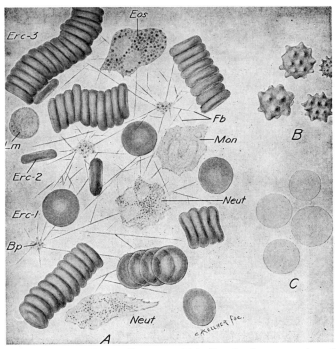

FIG. 7-1. *A*, drawings of human blood cells from a thick film, fresh preparation. (Compare with living cells in thin film preparation, Fig. 7-5.) *Bp*, Blood platelets; *Eos*, eosinophil leukocyte; *Erc-1, 2,* and *3*, erythrocytes in surface view (*1*), in profile (*2*) and in rouleaux (*3*); *Fb*, strands of fibrin; *Lm*, small lymphocyte; *Mon*, monocyte; *Neut*, neutrophil leukocyte. *B*, crenation of erythrocytes after the addition of a few drops of 1.5% NaCl to a fresh preparation. *C*, erythrocytes assuming spheroidal shapes and undergoing hemolysis after the addition of a drop of distilled water to a fresh preparation. All figures ×1540.

the surrounding tissue. The trauma may also produce a generalized reaction in that sludges may circulate and block small vessels in other parts of the body.

Chemically, the erythrocyte consists of a protein and lipoid colloidal complex, of which the most important element is hemoglobin. Hemoglobin has the remarkable property of binding oxygen in a very loose combination (oxyhemoglobin). The hemoglobin becomes saturated with oxygen in the capillaries of the lung, and the circulating blood distributes this oxygen to the cells of the body in exchange for carbonic acid which constantly accumulates in the tissues. The corpuscle does not yield the oxygen directly to the cells, but the oxygen is first dissolved in the plasma at a level held constant by the erythrocytes.

The contents of the corpuscle are normally in osmotic equilibrium with the plasma, hence the plasma is said to be isosmotic or isotonic. Isotonic solutions may be prepared for study of the corpuscles outside the body; a 0.85 % solution of sodium chloride is approximately isotonic for mammalian blood. When *hypertonic* solutions are added to blood, the erythrocytes become shrunken and *crenated* (Fig. 7-1, *B*). This is explained as follows: the membranous coverings of the corpuscles are permeable to water and impermeable to sodium and potassium ions, and therefore water passes from the corpuscles in an attempt to restore the osmotic equilibrium between the corpuscles and the surrounding medium whenever the latter is hypertonic. A few crenated corpuscles are usually found in fresh preparations of blood studied without the addition of hypertonic solutions; this results from evaporation which produces a slightly hypertonic solution and an altered pH. It should be added that crenation has also been produced experimentally in isotonic media and may not be entirely dependent on osmotic phenomena.

When blood is placed in distilled water or any *hypotonic* solution, water enters the corpuscles and they assume a spheroidal shape. The corpuscles lose their color by the escape of hemoglobin into the diluted plasma, and the colorless part which remains is known as the *stroma*, *"blood shadow"* or *"ghost"* (Fig. 7-1, *C*). Eventually, the shadows may also undergo solution. The process of extraction of hemoglobin is called *hemolysis,* and the substances which effect it are known as hemolysins or hemolytic agents. Hypotonic solutions are not the only substances which produce hemolysis. Of particular interest is the fact that the plasma of one species may hemolyze the erythrocytes of another and that, in man, the serum of certain individuals may produce hemolysis in others. Hemolysis is of interest in clinical work since one of the types of anemia, *hemolytic anemia,* occurs when the erythrocytes within the body are hemolyzed at a rate which exceeds that of their formation.

Certain substances also bring about an *agglutination* or clumping of corpuscles. Agglutination may occur within the blood stream during certain pathological and experimental conditions and may thus produce a multiple thrombosis of the smaller vessels. Agglutinins present in the serum of some individuals may bring about an agglutination of erythrocytes in others; on this basis, individuals have been divided into several "blood groups." In giving blood transfusions, it is important to select donors from a blood group which is compatible with that of the recipient in order to avoid accidents which would result if the recipient's serum agglutinated the transfused donor cells.

The cytoplasm of the mature erythrocyte appears homogeneous in the fresh condition, and it is seen as an amorphous, moderately dense material in electron micrographs (Fig. 12-3). The covering or plasmalemma is similar in structure and composition to that of other cells. In fact, membranes from red corpuscles served as a source of material for some of the earliest studies of cell membranes.

A few of the erythrocytes of peripheral blood have a reticulated appearance when supravitally stained with cresyl blue (Fig. 7-2, *B*). They are known as *reticulocytes* or *reticulated erythrocytes.* They are the youngest erythrocytes in the circulating blood, and their reticulated appearance is apparently produced by a clumping of ribosomes by the supravital dye. Electron micrographs of reticulocytes show scattered groups of ribosomes (polysomes) and occasional mitochondria. These cells apparently correspond to the slightly polychromatophilic erythrocytes seen in Wright's stained smears.

The erythrocytes are much more numerous than any of the other formed elements. The average is usually given as 5,000,000 per cubic millimeter of blood in a normal adult male (4,500,000 in females). Actually, the average for healthy adult men is somewhat higher (5,742,000), but normal variations ranging from 4,000,000 to 6,000,000 are not uncommon (Mayers). Normal variations also occur within the same individual in association with physiological changes, e.g., the increase after exercise. Many of these variations apparently represent a redistribution to the peripheral vessels rather than an actual change in total numbers. Life in high altitudes is accompanied by an increase to about 8,000,000. Whereas the initial change in this case may be a redistribution through an outpouring of red cells from the spleen (Chapter 13), there is also a real increase in total numbers in response to the lower oxygen tension. More pronounced variations occur under pathological conditions.

The surface area of a red corpuscle has been given as 128 square microns. From this, one may calculate that the total surface area of 5,000,000 corpuscles in 1 cubic millimeter of blood is 640 square millimeters and that in 6 liters of blood the total area available for respiratory function is 3840 square meters. This enormous area suggests the importance and the rapidity of the exchange phenomena between the corpuscles on the one hand, and the plasma and air on the other.

Under pathological conditions, not only the number but the size, shape and hemoglobin content of the corpuscles may vary strikingly The normal number may be present, but the amount of hemoglobin is reduced, as in some of the *secondary* (chlorotic) anemias. In the *macrocytic anemias* (e.g., pernicious anemia, which results from a deficiency of an erythrocyte maturation factor, vitamin B_{12}, the red cells are reduced in number but are abnormally large (macrocytes), and some of the cells have an increased content of hemoglobin. In *microcytic anemia* (e.g., iron deficiency anemia), there is a decrease both in the number and in the size of the cells. Under most of these conditions, the cells may show a multiplicity of distortions in shape (poikilocytosis).

WHITE BLOOD CORPUSCLES (LEUKOCYTES)

The white blood cells contain no hemoglobin and differ from the red corpuscles in many other important respects. They possess a nucleus and hence are true cells, and they have the power of active ameboid movement which aids in their passage through the walls of blood vessels and enables them to travel within the connective tissues. They are much less numerous than the red cells, the proportion being about one white cell to 600 red cells, or about 8,000 per cubic millimeter of blood, with a normal variation from 6,000 to 10,000. Under pathological conditions, the number may be greatly increased (leukocytosis); more rarely there is a reduction in number (leukopenia). At birth the leukocytes

are more numerous (15,000 to 18,000 per cubic millimeter).

The erythrocytes spend their life span in the blood stream, where their function is performed. Only under abnormal conditions or when they are about to disintegrate are they found outside the blood vessels. It is quite different with the leukocytes. They function in the connective tissue where, as already described, they are wandering elements. They arise, function and die outside of the blood stream, which is to them merely a place of temporary sojourn, a means of transportation from their place of origin to their destination in the connective tissues.

The leukocytes may be subdivided into nongranular forms (*agranulocytes*) and granular leukocytes (*granulocytes*). The cytoplasm of the granular leukocytes is characterized by the presence of numerous granules which may be seen in living cells as well as in fixed and stained preparations. In many of the cells, these granules are fine and only slightly refractile, but in others the cytoplasm is filled with coarse and highly refractile granules. Azurophilic granules may be found in the agranulocytes in Wright's stained dry smears, but these granules are not specific for a particular type of cell as are the neutrophilic, eosinophilic and basophilic granules of the cells that are classified as granular leukocytes.

Types of Nongranular Leukocytes: Agranulocytes. The nongranular leukocytes include the *lymphocytes*, which are small cells about the size of erythrocytes, and a group of larger cells, *monocytes*, which have more cytoplasm and a more indented nucleus. The nongranular leukocytes are comparatively undifferentiated and can reproduce by mitosis. Such division does not take place as a rule in the blood stream itself but may occur in the connective tissues and in blood-forming organs.

The leukocytes seen in routine histological sections appear more or less rounded in shape as they do in the blood circulation, but their diameters are less than in the living state because of shrinkage. However, when leukocytes are spread on slides in preparation for Wright's stain, they are flattened and their diameters are extended to a degree which more than compensates for the shrinkage in technique. Thus, leukocytes in dried smears have diameters greater than those in sections and even greater than the living cells circulating in the blood vessels. On the other hand, the cells in dried smears do not appear as large as living cells in supravital preparations. In the latter case, the leukocytes attach themselves either to the slide or to the underside of the cover slip, show ameboid motion and spread out into thin cells of large diameter. From the foregoing, it becomes obvious that one is justified in comparing the diameter of one cell type with that of another only when both types are studied by the same method. The following descriptions refer to dimensions in dried smears, unless stated otherwise.

Lymphocytes. The lymphocytes of the normal circulation vary from 6 to 10 μ, with the majority being about 7 to 8 μ. They normally constitute about 20 to 25% of the white blood cells (Table 7-1). There is a considerable range for normal individuals, and it is not uncommon to find lymphocyte counts as high as 35 or even 45%. They have a relatively large, spherical nucleus which may have a slight indentation on one side. The densely packed chromatin stains intensely. The *nuclei* have a purplish blue color in many Wright's stained preparations (Fig. 7-2). It is important to realize that the nuclear color varies with different

TABLE 7-1

LEUKOCYTES

	Size	Percentage of leucocytes
Lymphocytes	6–10 μ	20–45
Monocytes	12–20 μ	3–8
Granulocytes		
Neutrophils	9–12 μ	50–75
Eosinophils	10–14 μ	2–4
Basophils	8–10 μ	0.5–1

batches of Wright's stain and with variations in technical procedures. The color generally ranges from purplish blue to reddish purple in the lymphocytes of the normal circulation. It is regularly more on the reddish side in immature lymphocytes of blood formation (Fig. 7-14, *B*). It should be understood that the color of the cytoplasm is much more important in distinguishing different types of leukocytes in stained blood smears than is the color of the nucleus. Morphological characteristics are particularly important in cell identification. These include size and shape of nucleus, coarseness of chromatin and size and number of cytoplasmic granules.

The *cytoplasm* of lymphocytes is very basophilic and is a robin's egg blue (greenish blue) in Wright's stain. It varies in amount according to variations in cell size (Fig. 7-2, *A*). It is usually homogeneous but may be slightly more basophilic at the border of the cell and paler adjacent to the nucleus. The basophilia of the cytoplasm is due to the abundance of RNA, which is found within ribosomes. The ribosomes occur throughout the cytoplasm unassociated with the endoplasmic reticulum as in plasma cells; in fact, the endoplasmic reticulum is very sparse in the lymphocyte of the circulating blood (Fig. 7-3).

Purplish, azurophilic granules are occasionally seen in lymphocytes in Wright's stained dry smears but they are not specific since they are also found in monocytes and in granular leukocytes. The number of lymphocytes containing these granules varies at different times and in different individuals.

It has been noted above that a few of the lymphocytes normally found in blood smears may be as large as 10 to 12 μ. They have a dense chromatic nucleus and differ little from the small cells, except for size. The lymphocytes of different sizes normally present in peripheral blood probably represent different functional stages of the same cell type. The larger lymphocytes seen in peripheral blood under normal conditions

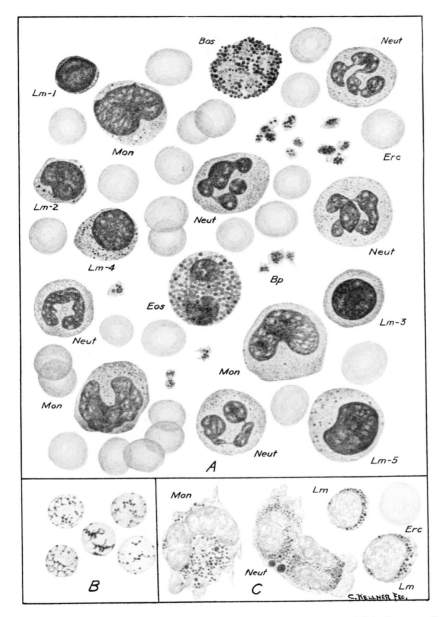

Fig. 7-2. *A*, cells from normal human blood. Wright's stain. *Bas*, Basophil leukocyte; *Bp*, aggregations of blood platelets; *Eos*, eosinophil leukocyte; *Erc*, erythrocytes; *Lm*-1–5, lymphocytes: *1–3* are small and medium sizes, and *4–5* are the less numerous larger forms; *Mon*, monocytes; *Neut*, neutrophil leukocytes. *B*, reticulocytes from normal human blood stained with dilute cresyl blue. *C*, blood cells as seen after about 20 minutes of staining with neutral red and Janus green B in a supravital preparation. *Erc*, Erythrocyte; *Lm*, small lymphocytes with bluish green mitochondria and a few neutral red granules; *Mon*, monocyte with mitochondria and numerous neutral red granules and vacuoles of varying size; *Neut*, neutrophil leukocytes with staining of the neutrophil granules and the formation of a few large vacuoles which frequently appear after 15–20 minutes of staining. All figures ×1550.

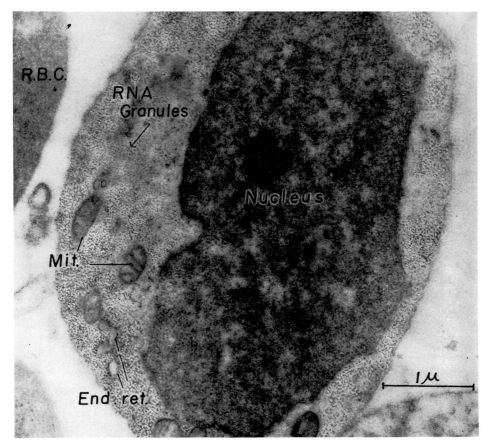

Fig. 7-3. Electron micrograph of a section of a human lymphocyte. Note sparse endoplasmic reticulum (*End. ret.*) and numerous ribosomes. *RBC*, red blood cell; *Mit*, mitochondria. ×23,500. (Courtesy of Dr. J. A. Freeman; refer to *Electron Microscopic Atlas of Blood* by Drs. F. N. Low and J. A. Freeman, Sr.)

should not be confused with the immature large lymphocytes or lymphoblasts found in blood-forming organs. The latter type has a paler staining, undifferentiated nucleus with a prominent nucleolus. The lymphoblast is usually confined to the blood-forming organs but may become abundant in the blood stream in certain pathological states, as in lymphatic leukemia (Fig. 7-14, *B*).

When supravital preparations are studied, the lymphocytes are stationary for a short time, but after 15 or 20 minutes they occasionally move in a manner which differs from that of the other leukocytes. They elongate by sending out a blunt pseudopod and advance by a sort of wormlike motion

with the nucleus usually in front (Fig. 7-5). It should be added that the lymphocytes exhibit their characteristic motility only when the supravital preparations are kept at body temperature; they are usually nonmotile in preparations studied at room temperature. In supravital preparations stained with dilute solutions of neutral red and Janus green B, the mitochondria (stained bluish green by the Janus green B) are in the form of granules and rods (Fig. 7-2, *C*). Most of the lymphocytes also show a few neutral red granules (probably the azurophilic granules of Wright's stained preparations). Medium sized lymphocytes are more motile and form more phagocytic vacuoles of neutral red than do the small lymphocytes. In fact, it is frequently very difficult to differentiate some of the medium sized lymphocytes from the small monocytes in supravital preparations. This is easier to understand if one accepts the view that lymphocytes can differentiate into monocytes.

Lymphocytes appear to have an important role in the mechanism of immunity. In the description of connective tissue cells (Chapter 5), it is pointed out that plasma cells, the principal producers of circulating antibodies, are derived from lymphocyte-like precursors. The immediate precursor cells are larger than the small lymphocytes and they have a more basophilic cytoplasm which stains particularly well with the red basic dye pyronin; hence, they are known as pyroninophilic cells. Evidence in support of the view that lymphocytes can differentiate into the plasma cell precursors has been obtained by the use of tritium-labeled thymidine for tracing cell lineages (Nossal and Mäkelä, 1962). Further studies have shown that this response by the lymphocytes in the spleen and lymph nodes follows a sequence of events, including contact of lymphocytes with phagocytic reticular cells (macrophages), which have an important role in trapping and processing antigen (Chapter 13). The small lymphocytes are apparently of different functional types, even though they appear cytologically similar. Studies of transfused cells, which are identifiable either from isotope labeling or from chromosomal characteristics, show that the small lymphocytes can be divided into two categories on the basis of their life span. Some lymphocytes are *long-lived* and survive for years, perhaps for the life of the individual. Others are *short-lived* and survive for only a few days. The long-lived cells are of the recirculating type, i.e., they pass from the blood to the lymphatic organs and then back to the blood, either directly (spleen) or via lymphatics (lymph nodes). It has been postulated that the long-lived lymphocytes of the spleen and lymph nodes are thymic-derived, i.e., their precursors either were formed in the thymus or passed through it after formation in bone marrow before continuing on to the spleen and lymph nodes (Nossal, 1968). It has been proposed that the long-lived lymphocytes are antigen-reactive cells and that they are responsible for immunological memory. By this latter process, the first antibody response to a given antigen (primary response) is remembered and quickly put into action to stimulate plasma cell formation whenever the body is exposed again to the given antigen (secondary reaction). It has been postulated that many of the short-lived lymphocytes of the lymph nodes and spleen are developed from bone marrow-derived precursors.

When tissues are grafted from one individual to another of the same species (homografts) or from one individual to another of a different species (heterografts), small lymphocytes collect around the graft and change into pyroninophilic cells. In regions of foreign grafts, these cells are known as *graft rejection cells*, and apparently they attack the foreign protein by a localized reaction. The exact mechanism of the reaction is not understood. There is also a generalized response, and conditioned cells are found in the lymphatic organs and in the circulation. It is known from experimental studies, such as thymectomy of newborn animals, that graft rejection is dependent upon the presence of a functioning thymus during early life. Evidence from studies of labeled cells shows that the graft rejection cells are derived from the small long-lived lymphocytes.

Some of the small lymphocytes may retain the potential to develop into other types of blood cells. It has been noted in previous sections that lymphocytes may develop into monocytes in tissue culture and then into macrophages. It seems established that some of the small circulating lymphocytes can also be activated to synthesize DNA and to divide and differentiate into other blood cell types in bone marrow.

Lymphocytes are abundant in the connective tissues beneath the epithelial lining of the digestive and respiratory systems, for example, the Waldeyer's ring of faucial, lingual and pharyngeal tonsils, the Peyer's patches of the ileum and the solitary nodules and scattered lymphocytes along other segments of the digestive and respiratory systems. They multiply by mitosis in a number of these locations and thus contribute to the total body pool of lymphocytes. It seems likely that they also have a localized activity in detoxifying injurious materials in these areas, but the mechanism of action is not understood.

Monocytes or Large Mononuclear Leukocytes Monocytes are large cells which constitute from 3 to 8% of the leukocytes. In dry smears, they usually vary from 12 to 15 μ in diameter, but when extremely flattened and stretched they may reach 20 μ. In supravital preparations, their diameter varies with the activity of the cell. The active monocytes send out numerous pseudopodia and naturally appear larger than the more rounded, inactive forms. The active cells are especially large when flattened in thin film preparations.

The monocyte nucleus is ovoid, kidney- or horseshoe-shaped, very rarely spherical and usually eccentrically placed (Fig. 7-2). Its chromatin network is finer and stains less densely than that of the lymphocytes. The cytoplasm is abundant and has a somewhat reticulated or vacuolated appearance; it is slightly less basophilic than the lymphocyte cytoplasm and is more of a grayish blue after Wright's stain. There are numerous azurophilic granules which are usually smaller than those of the lymphocytes. By special techniques, the cytocentrum and Golgi apparatus can be demonstrated in the cytoplasm near the indentation of the nucleus. Electron micrographs of monocytes show more endoplasmic reticulum but fewer RNA granules than in lymphocytes (Fig. 7-4).

In supravital preparations treated with neutral red and Janus green B, the azurophilic granules are colored by neutral red, and vacuoles of neutral red form by phagocytosis. The vacuoles are often arranged as a rosette around the region containing the cytocentrum and they increase in size as the supravital staining is continued. Mitochondria are stained bluish green and are usually more numerous around the rim of the rosette than in other parts of the cytoplasm (Fig. 7-2, *C*). Large monocytes are more active than small ones, but none of them travels about rapidly like the neutrophilic and eosinophilic granulocytes. The monocytes also exhibit a different type of activity. They continually send out and withdraw pseudopodia and assume an appearance somewhat like an octopus. The pseudopodia are of different shapes, ranging from threadlike processes to broad membranes, and are very transparent. In fact, it usually requires most careful focusing of the microscope and optimal adjustment of the light in order to define the borders of some of the membranous pseudopodia of active cells (Fig. 7-5, *D*).

The largest monocytes have been called *transitionals* because of the supposition that they transformed into granular leucocytes. This view is no longer held, and it seems clear that the larger monocytes merely represent older cells in a more active physiological stage. In tissue cultures, the monocytes can be made to enlarge and take on all the characteristics of typical *macrophages*. In the body, they migrate readily through the capillary walls into the connective tissues where they display their phagocytic characteristics. They develop into histiocytes which cannot be distinguished from those previously present in the connective tissues and, with the latter, they provide the mobilized macrophages found in areas of focal infection (e.g., abscess, Fig. 5-3). The monocytes also function as the chief cells in combating the bacillus of tuberculosis.

Types of Granulocytes. The granular leukocytes are characterized by the presence of specific types of granules in their cyto-

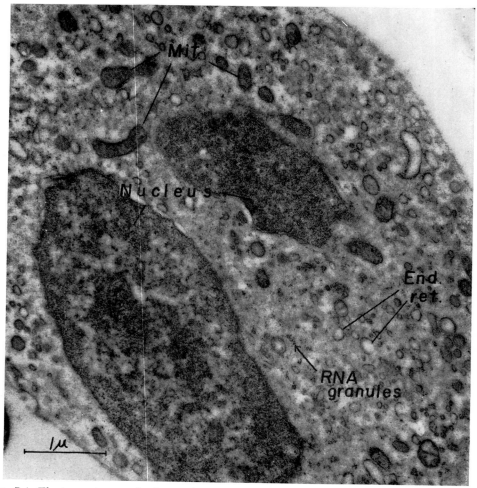

FIG. 7-4. Electron micrograph of a section of a human monocyte. Note well developed endoplasmic reticulum (*End. ret.*) and many small mitochondria (*Mit*). The irregularly shaped nucleus appears in two parts because of the plane of the section. ×23,000. (Courtesy of Dr. J. A. Freeman.)

plasm and, according to the nature of this granulation, they have been subdivided into three groups: the *neutrophilic, eosinophilic* and *basophilic* leukocytes. They are further characterized by the presence of a many lobed (polymorphous) nucleus; hence they are called *polymorphonuclear* leukocytes. The lobes of chromatin are connected by very delicate chromatic strands. Occasionally, some of these strands are broken in dry smear preparations so that a few cells may appear to be polynuclear. The granulocytes also differ from the nongranular leukocytes

in that they are more highly differentiated and cannot reproduce by mitosis.

Neutrophils. The neutrophilic polymorphonuclear leukocytes (Figs. 7-1 and 7-2) vary in size from 9 to 12 μ and are the most numerous of white blood cells. Although they usually constitute about 60 to 70% of the total white blood cells, they have been found to range from 50 to 75% in normal individuals. Under pathological conditions, the range is much greater. The polymorphous nucleus shows a variety of forms, usually consisting of three to five

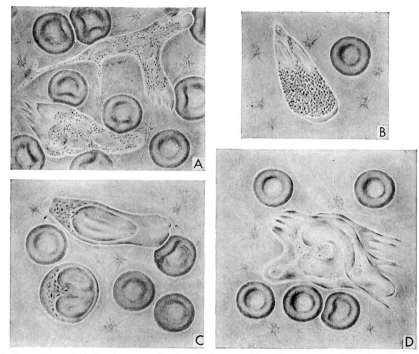

FIG. 7-5. Drawings of living human blood cells from a thin film preparation. *A*, polymorphonuclear neutrophils pushing their way between the red blood cells and the delicate fibrin network extending out from the small platelet masses; *B*, polymorphonuclear eosinophil; *C*, lymphocytes, the round resting stage and the elongated motile stage; *D*, monocyte with pseudopodia in the form of delicate undulating membranes. (Courtesy of Dr. C. M. Goss).

sausage-shaped masses of chromatin connected by fine threads and arranged in the form of an S or a horseshoe. In blood smears from human females, one can see a small appendage attached to the remainder of the nucleus by a narrow filament, giving a drumstick appearance in almost 3% of the neutrophils (Fig. 7-6). The drumstick is composed of the sex chromatin, i.e., the two X chromosomes of the female. Sex chromatin is presumably present in all of the cells in females, but it is closely packed with one of the lobes of the nucleus in most cells and is obscured. Some of the neutrophils of males have hook-shaped and nodule-like appendages, but they generally do not have the drumstick forms.

The cytoplasm is filled with fine granules which are neutrophilic. In some animals, e.g., rabbit and guinea pig, the granules take the acid stain and may be called *pseudo-eosinophils*. Since these cells vary in their staining reactions in different species, they are sometimes called *heterophilic* rather than neutrophilic leukocytes.

It has been known for a long time that the cytoplasmic granules vary greatly in size. Recent studies by electron microscopy and by biochemical assays of particles separated by differential centrifugation show that the granules can be separated into three biochemical and morphological types. There are relatively large, electron-dense granules, identified as azurophilic or primary granules, which contain peroxidases and hydrolysases characteristic of lysosomes (Figs. 7-7 and 7-8). There is another group of smaller and less electron-dense granules, identified as the specific granules, which contain alkaline phosphatase and some antibacterial con-

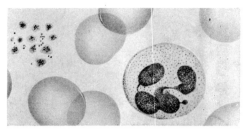

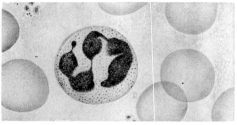

Fig. 7-6. Portions of two oil immersion fields of a Wright's stained blood smear from a human female. Fields have been selected to show the drumstick appearance of the sex chromatin which is seen in a number of the neutrophilic leukocytes in the female. It is seen as a hanging drop of chromatin attached by a thin strand to one of the lobes of the nucleus. A relatively large cluster of blood platelets is seen in the *upper left hand corner* of the figure. ×1335. (From a preparation made by Miss Karen Fu.)

stituents (lysozyme and phagocytin) but little or no acid hydrolases. They are more numerous than the primary granules in the mature neutrophils. There is a third group of particles, heterogenous in size but smaller than the specific granules. They contain acid hydrolysases and qualify as lysosomes, as do the primary granules. They differ from the latter in having little or no peroxidase.

In differential counts, the neutrophils are sometimes divided into subgroups on the basis of the number of lobes to the nuclei. In the Arneth count, the neutrophils are divided into five classes according to whether the nuclei are composed of one, two, three, four or five (or more) lobes. Since there is some increase in nuclear segmentation as myelocytes differentiate into mature neutrophils, it has been claimed that the cells with the most segmented nuclei are the oldest. As originally outlined by Arneth, the count was very complex and there was no definition of what constituted a division into lobes. The count was clarified by Cooke (1914) and by Cooke and Ponder (1927) who gave

diagrams and definitions of the five classes. According to them, two parts of a nucleus are counted as separate lobes when they are connected merely by a thin chromatin strand. When two nuclear segments are connected by a broad band of nuclear material, they are not counted as separate lobes. There have been a number of modifications of the count. The most commonly used modification is the one devised by Schilling. In the Schilling count, the segmented nuclears normally comprise about 57% of the total leukocytes; nonsegmented band or stab nuclears, i.e., those with the nucleus having a band shape or an irregular shape like a stab wound, about 3%; juveniles or metamyelocytes, with an indented nucleus, 0 to 1%; and myelocytes, 0%. An increase in relative numbers of nonsegmented nuclears is designated as a "shift to the left"; an increase in segmented types is a "shift to the right" and is considered a good sign because it is supposed to show that there is no longer any unusual demand on the bone marrow for younger cells.

In supravital preparations, the neutrophilic leukocyte is more active than any other blood cell. It advances by an ameboid movement, usually with the nucleus in the rear. At times, it is difficult to see the strands connecting the nuclear lobes, and the cells may appear to be polynuclear instead of polymorphonuclear. In supravital preparations, the cytoplasmic granules become colored by the neutral red within a few minutes (Fig. 7-2, *C*). After 15 or 20 minutes, some of the neutrophils form phagocytic vacuoles of neutral red that occasionally become as large as one of the nuclear lobes. A few small mitochondria stain with Janus green B.

After migration from the blood stream, the neutrophils phagocytose bacteria and other small particles. They have been called the *microphages*, in contrast with the macrophages, which are larger cells that characteristically engulf larger particles. They are chemotactically attracted by devitalized tissue, bacteria and other foreign bodies, and they migrate to the site of an infection. They engulf bacteria and form vacuoles (phagosomes) in which the bacteria are destroyed by hydrolytic enzymes derived from a breakdown of cytoplasmic granules (lysosomes).

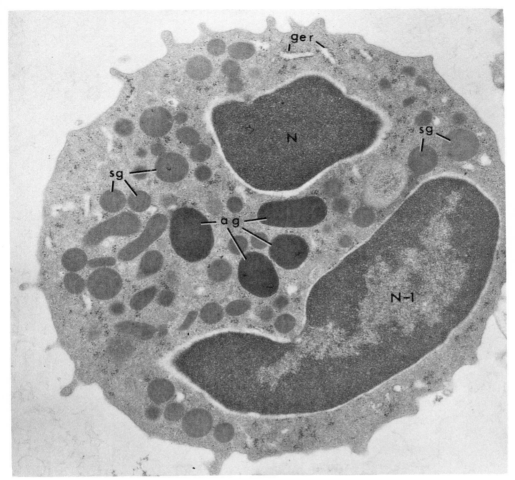

FIG. 7-7. Electron micrograph of a section of a rabbit neutrophilic leukocyte. Note the relatively small specific granules (*sg*) and a few large and dense azurophilic granules (*ag*). The granular endoplasmic reticulum (*ger*) is sparse. Two lobes of the multilobed nucleus (*N* and *N-1*) are seen; the plane of the section did not pass through the connection of the lobes. ×22,500. (Courtesy of Drs. Dorothy Ford Bainton and Marilyn Farquhar, J. Cell Biol., vol. 28, 1966).

The neutrophils also release enzymes which initiate lysis in surrounding tissues. They die in the process of intracellular destruction of bacteria and become the pus corpuscles of an abscess. Although the neutrophils serve as the shock troops or as the first line of defense against invading organisms, they are not equally effective against all types of bacteria. For example, they cannot successfully combat tubercle bacilli; in this case, the macrophages are the efficient agents.

Eosinophils. The eosinophilic leukocytes (Fig. 7-2) normally constitute from 2 to 4% of the white blood cells. They are somewhat larger than the neutrophils (about 10 to 14 μ) and are characterized by an abundance of coarse, refractile granules of a uniform size which stain intensely with eosin or other acid dyes. In electron micrographs, the granules of the eosinophilic leukocytes are characteristically banded (Fig. 7-9). The nucleus is polymorphous, but the average number of lobes is less than in the neutrophils, most commonly two.

In supravital preparations, the eosinophils occasionally travel as rapidly as the

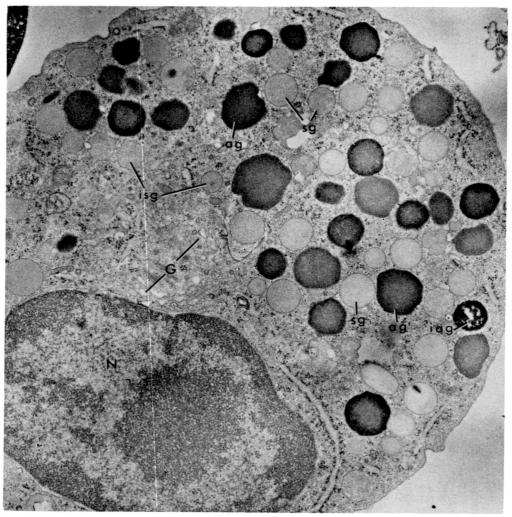

Fig. 7-8. Electron micrograph of a section of a neutrophilic myelocyte from rabbit bone marrow. The tissue was reacted for the enzyme peroxidase during the technical procedure. Note that the reaction product is present in the azurophilic granules (*ag*) but not in the specific granules (*sg*). The reaction product is distributed uniformly throughout most of the mature azurophilic granules, but it is present in flocculent form in an immature azurophilic granule (*iag*) seen at the right. Several small and immature specific granules (*isg*) are seen in the vicinity of the Golgi complex (*G*). The nucleus (*N*) is not lobed at this stage. ×18,000. (Courtesy of Drs. D. F. Bainton and M. G. Farquhar, J. Cell Biol., vol. 39, 1968).

neutrophils but not for as long a period. Their granules stain intensely and uniformly with neutral red, and a few mitochondria can be demonstrated with Janus green B.

The eosinophils are more common in the connective tissue of certain areas (e.g., intestinal mucosa) than in the blood stream. They increase greatly in allergic conditions such as hay fever and asthma, in skin dis-

eases and in parasitic infestations. Their functional role in these conditions is not entirely clear but it has been shown that they ingest antigen-antibody complexes. They are usually not phagocytic for bacteria. They contain some histamine, but are not comparable in this respect to connective tissue mast cells and blood basophils. There is a marked reduction in the number of eosino-

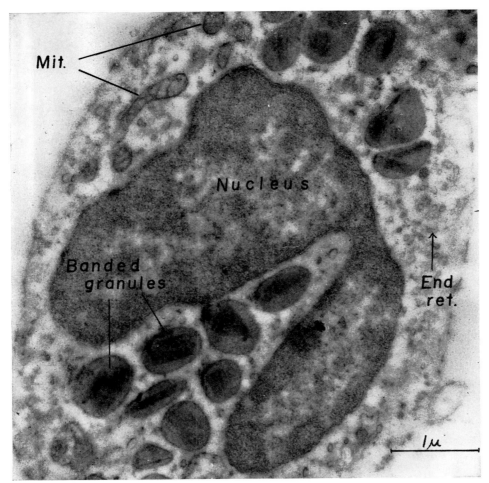

FIG. 7-9. Electron micrograph of a section of a human eosinophilic leukocyte. Note large "banded" granules. *End. ret.*, endoplasmic reticulum; *Mit*, mitochondria. ×23,000. (Courtesy of Dr. J. A. Freeman.)

phils in peripheral blood after the administration of adrenal corticosteroids or after the administration of pituitary hormones which stimulate the adrenal (ACTH). This procedure, often called the Thorn test because of its development by Thorn and his collaborators, provides valuable clinical information on the sites of hormone deficiency.

Basophils. The basophilic leukocytes, (Fig. 7-2) are present in blood in an almost negligible quantity, forming 0.5 to 1% or even less of the total number of leukocytes. In size they vary from 8 to 10 μ. The nucleus is relatively large and irregularly polymorphous. The lobed nature is not as clearly

defined as in other granulocytes, and the chromatin network, which is less compact, takes a lighter stain. The cytoplasm contains a variable number of coarse granules which are basophilic and metachromatic. These granules are variable in size; a few may be as large or larger than the eosinophil granules, but the majority are intermediate between the neutrophil and eosinophil types. Since the granules are soluble in water, they are usually not found in sections prepared by the ordinary routine.

In supravital preparations, the basophils are relatively inactive. The basophilic granules are not as refractile as eosinophilic granules, are more variable in size and do not stain as uniformly. Most of the granules give a deeper red reaction with neutral red than do the eosinophilic granules.

The blood basophils have many structural and chemical similarities to the mast cells of connective tissue. The best evidence indicates that they form the heparin and histamine of circulating blood. They increase in relatively few pathological conditions, e.g., in smallpox, chickenpox and chronic sinus inflammations. They increase along with all other leukocytes in leukemia. Although they normally constitute only about 0.5 % of the leukocytes, their total number in an average individual having 6 liters of blood is approximately 200 million. In some of the lower vertebrates (hellbender, mudpuppy and certain turtles), they are more numerous than the other types of leukocytes.

BLOOD PLATELETS

Blood platelets (thromboplastids or thrombocytes, Fig. 7-2) are minute, colorless bodies from 2 to 4 μ in diameter. In fresh blood their shape is round or ovoid; in fixed preparations they often appear stellate. Their number has been variously estimated, the average being about 200,000 to 300,000 per cubic millimeter. In the blood stream they are separate but show a marked tendency to agglutination when the blood is drawn. The platelets have a central granular area (*chromomere, granulomere*) and a peripheral hyaline zone (*hyalomere*). There is evidence that the platelet clot-promoting factor is associated with the granules.

The thrombocytes of lower vertebrates are larger than those of man and are unquestionably nucleated cells. Their appearance is wholly unlike that of the human platelets, and the relation of the two forms is doubtful.

The platelets presumably liberate an enzyme, *thromboplastin*, which affects the coagulation of the blood. Thromboplastin transforms *prothrombin* into *thrombin* and the latter, in turn, transforms fibrinogen into fibrin. Thromboplastin is present in the plasma, as well as in the platelets. Blood freed from platelets coagulates, though much more slowly, and lymph, which has no platelets, likewise coagulates.

Pathologically, the platelets may by agglutination give rise to colorless intravascular clots or thrombi. Deficiencies of circulating platelets are encountered clinically in various forms of the condition known as thrombocytopenia.

CHYLOMICRONS AND HEMOCONIA

Blood plasma contains very minute globules of fat (chylomicrons, about 1 μ in size) which are best studied by dark field illumination. They are particularly numerous in the plasma after digestion of a meal containing quantities of fat. In addition to the fat globules, blood plasma contains a variable number of small particles which may be observed in dry smears as well as in fresh preparations. These particles are known as hemoconia (blood dust). They are probably produced by disintegration of red corpuscles and leukocytes.

LYMPH

Lymph, like blood, consists of a fluid plasma in which are suspended various corpuscular elements. Red blood corpuscles and platelets are entirely missing and granulocytes are few in number, the chief cellular elements being lymphocytes.

The plasma of lymph is similar to that of blood but of less fixed constitution. It carries carbonic acid but very little oxygen.

During digestion, the lymphatics of the intestine become filled with a large amount of fat globules. The lymph assumes a white color and is known as *chyle*. Many of the fat globules are removed and stored temporarily by the lymphoid organs before the lymph reaches the blood stream.

Lymph coagulates, though much more slowly than blood, the fibrin forming a

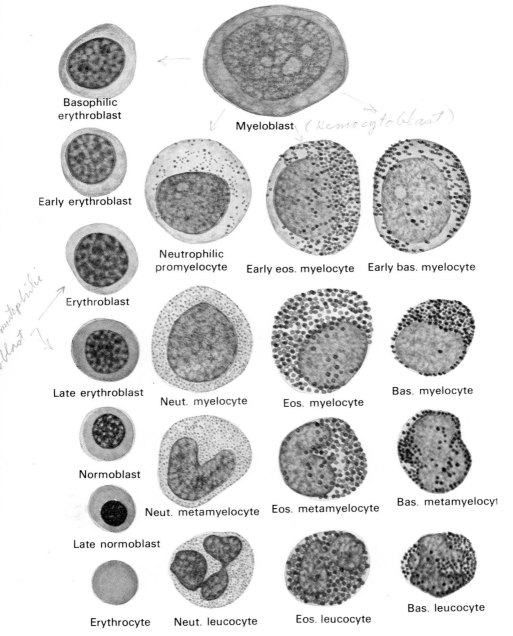

Basophilic erythroblast

Myeloblast *(hemocytoblast)*

Early erythroblast

Neutrophilic promyelocyte

Early eos. myelocyte

Early bas. myelocyte

Erythroblast

monophilic noblast

Late erythroblast

Neut. myelocyte

Eos. myelocyte

Bas. myelocyte

Normoblast

Neut. metamyelocyte

Eos. metamyelocyte

Bas. metamyelocyt

Late normoblast

Erythrocyte

Neut. leucocyte

Eos. leucocyte

Bas. leucocyte

Fig. 7-10. Various stages in blood development as seen in dried smears of marrow from a human rib. Note that the particular myeloblast illustrated is one of the largest cells of this developmental stage; they are often smaller than the promyelocytes. Wright's stain. ×1560.

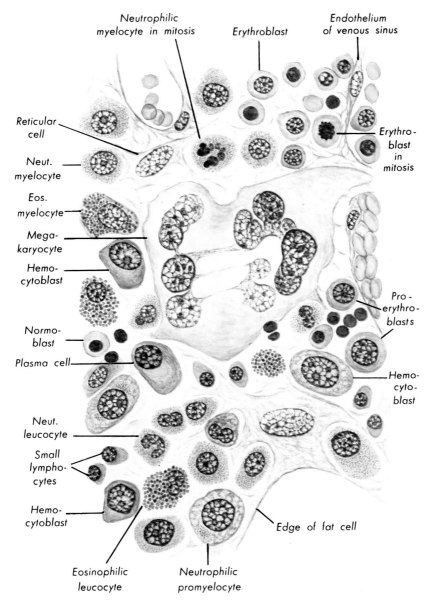

Neutrophilic
myelocyte in mitosis

Erythroblast

Endothelium
of venous sinus

Reticular
cell

Neut.
myelocyte

Eos.
myelocyte

Mega-
karyocyte

Hemo-
cytoblast

Normo-
blast

Plasma cell

Neut.
leucocyte

Small
lympho-
cytes

Hemo-
cytoblast

Erythro-
blast
in
mitosis

Pro -
erythro-
blasts

Hemo-
cyto-
blast

Edge of fat cell

Eosinophilic
leucocyte

Neutrophilic
promyelocyte

Fig. 7-11. Various stages in blood development as seen in a section of marrow from a human rib. Hematoxylin-eosin-azure. ×1365.

colorless clot in which the cells are entangled.

DISPOSAL OF WORN-OUT CORPUSCLES

In contrast with many other cells of the body, the red and white corpuscles of the blood survive for only a relatively short period of time. The life span of the human erythrocyte as determined by tracer doses of radioactive isotopes is about 127 days (Shemin and Rittenberg, 1946). From these data, it is obvious that billions of corpuscles are destroyed daily. The destruction is balanced so well by new blood formation that the characteristic number of corpuscles is constantly maintained under normal conditions.

Destruction of erythrocytes frequently begins within the blood stream itself by a disintegration of corpuscles into small hemoglobin-retaining fragments and is completed by the reticuloendothelial cells of the blood-destroying organs, chiefly by the spleen (see Chapter 13). These cells remove the fragmented forms and also engulf many senile, worn-out erythrocytes in toto. The phagocytic reticular cells break up the hemoglobin into an iron-free portion (*globin*) and an iron-retaining part (*hematin*). Hematin is further separated into *bilirubin* and *iron*. The bilirubin is transported to the liver to be excreted in the bile, and the iron (in protein complexes as ferritin and hemosiderin) is conserved by the macrophages to be used again in new erythrocytes developing in the bone marrow. The exact details of the transfer of iron and its utilization in hemoglobin formation have not been described.

The life span of the various types of leukocytes is quite variable. The length of life within the blood stream is probably about 3 days for the neutrophils. The lymphocytes apparently remain within the peripheral circulation for only a short period at any one time, as judged by the fact that the total number entering the blood stream via the thoracic duct alone each day is greater than the total number in the circulation. However,

this is not an indication of their life span. Studies of transfused labeled lymphocytes show that lymphocytes from the blood return to the lymphoid organs and recirculate over and over (Gowans, 1958). The long-lived ones survive for years.

Fragile and nonmotile leucocytes are frequently found in fresh preparations of blood, but some investigators believe that many of these are produced in the technique of supravital preparations. Senile and dead cells are removed by phagocytosis in the spleen and liver. The migration of neutrophils, especially pronounced during infection, and their disintegration in the connective tissues have already been pointed out (p. 182). They also escape by penetration through the lining epithelia of mucous membranes, as illustrated by their presence in saliva. Eosinophils show a particular tendency for migration into the connective tissues of the respiratory and gastrointestinal tracts, where they eventually disintegrate. Some of the lymphocytes may undergo dissolution in the circulatory system, some may be destroyed while the blood courses through organs where cells of the reticuloendothelial system are particularly numerous, and large numbers migrate into the connective tissues where they apparently disintegrate. Many are lost by migration into the lumen of the intestinal tract. There is also the probability that some lymphocytes develop into other cell types, especially monocytes and macrophages.

DEVELOPMENT OF BLOOD CORPUSCLES: HEMOPOIESIS

Throughout life there is active proliferation of the immature forms of blood cells to replace the mature corpuscles which are constantly being destroyed. The formed elements of the blood may be subdivided into two groups according to the location of their development in the normal adult. Lymphocytes and monocytes proliferate in the lymphoid tissues and to a lesser extent in bone marrow; they are classified as *lymphoid elements.* Erythrocytes and granulocytes normally develop in red bone marrow (myeloid tissue); they are the *myeloid elements.* In certain pathological conditions, the myeloid elements may form in other locations such as spleen, liver and lymph nodes; this is called extramedullary myelopoiesis.

The details of the early stages in blood development are not entirely clear. Similar stages of development have been given different names by different schools which emphasize the theoretical potencies of the developing cells rather than their structural features. For this reason, any description of the early cell types becomes involved with the theoretical considerations. According to one theory all blood cells, red and white, arise from a common stem cell of "lymphoid nature," the *hemocytoblast;* this is the monophyletic or unitarian theory, and it contrasts with the polyphyletic view that the several types of formed elements arise from different stem cells. According to the "dualist" theory, there are two stem cells: a *myeloblast* for all of the myeloid elements, and a *lymphoblast* for the lymphoid elements. The term dualist is also occasionally applied to those who believe that there is one stem cell for the red corpuscles and another one for the white corpuscles. Since investigators supporting the different theories frequently use different terminologies for similar cells, misunderstandings easily arise when the theories are compared. Fortunately, there is uniformity of agreement regarding structural features of the majority of the cells, and the points of controversy are confined to the relationship and characteristics of the earliest stages which are of infrequent occurrence in normal adult marrow. In the account which follows, primary emphasis has been placed on the structural characteristics of the cells, and some of the controversial material has been confined to small print. It is suggested that the developmental stages may be followed more readily by omitting at the first reading all material set in fine print; reference should be made to these sections subsequently for an understanding of various views.

Development of Myeloid Elements

Red bone marrow, like lymphoid tissue, is composed of a framework or stroma of reticular cells and fibers, with free cells located within the meshwork. The stroma of marrow is also characterized by the presence of a varying number of fat cells. The majority of the free cells in red marrow are the immature, developmental stages of the granular leukocytes and erythrocytes. Myeloid tissue may also contain megakaryocytes, mature erythrocytes, granular leukocytes, a few lymphocytes, monocytes and plasma cells. The structure and vascular supply of marrow with its characteristic network of sinusoids have already been described (p. 165).

Granulocytes. The stages of granulocyte development, in order of differentiation, are: *reticular cells, hemocytoblasts (myeloblasts), promyelocytes, myelocytes, metamyelocytes,* and *granular leukocytes.*

Hemocytoblasts (Myeloblasts). The most immature, primitive free cells of marrow are characterized by a deeply basophilic cytoplasm and a relatively undifferentiated nucleus; they are the hemocytoblasts of the unitarian and the myeloblasts of the dualistic theories. Although the primitive cells vary in size, the majority of them are large, up to 15 μ or more. (Fig. 7-10 shows one of the largest cells of the type). The nuclei of these cells are rounded and relatively large, and they contain two or more coarse nucleoli. In dried smears treated with Wright's stain, the nucleoli are very pale, and the arrangement of the granular chromatin frequently gives a characteristic sieve-like appearance (Fig. 7-10). The nucleus of this same cell type has a very different appearance in sections stained with hematoxylin-eosin-azure (see hemocytoblasts in Fig. 7-11). Here the nucleoli are stained intensely, and the chromatin shows as a delicate reticulum enclosing vesicular-like, pale staining areas.

The cytoplasm is very basophilic both in sections and in dried smears and is a definite blue of the lymphocyte type after Wright's stain. Azurophilic granules are occasionally present in the cytoplasm, but there are no granules of the specific leukocyte type.

The myeloblasts of normal adult marrow arise chiefly by mitotic divisions of their own type, but new ones can differentiate from the reticular connective tissue cells which can round up, separate from the reticulum and become free (unattached) cells. Myeloblasts normally constitute only 0.3 to 5.0% of the cells of marrow. In pathological conditions, the myeloblasts may become more numerous and may appear in considerable numbers in the circulating blood, as in myelogenous leukemia. Here the increase is primarily the result of accelerated mitotic activity, but new cells may also arise from the reticulum.

If all of the primitive cells of marrow are identical with the large lymphocytes of lymphoid organs, they obviously constitute a common stem type and may be called hemocytoblasts. According to this theory (unitarian), none of the primitive marrow cells characterized by basophilic, nongranular cytoplasm is definitely restricted to the development of myeloid elements.

On the basis of slight structural differences in dried smears, such as the more delicate nuclear membrane in the primitive marrow cells, the dualists separate these cells from lymphocytes and use the term myeloblast, instead of hemocytoblast.

There is considerable evidence in favor of the unitarian view. Although the large cells in the germinal centers of the lymph nodes can normally be distinguished from the myeloblasts of marrow, these different types probably represent only minor modifications of the cells resulting from environmental factors. There is a good deal of evidence that under abnormal conditions, as in myeloid metaplasia, the large lymphocytes (lymphoblasts) of the lymphoid organs may give rise to granular leukocytes. Furthermore, Downey found that, in acute lymphatic and in mixed leukemias, lymphocytes are derived from myeloblasts, as indicated by the presence of intermediate stages between the latter and the small lymphocytes.

Myelocytes. The myelocytes (marrow cells) receive their name from the fact that they are the most numerous cell in marrow.

They differentiate from the myeloblasts. The earliest myelocytes are known as *promyelocytes* or *progranulocytes*. They are large cells, sometimes even larger than myeloblasts. They have a rounded or oval nucleus with coarser chromatin than that of the myeloblast and less prominent nucleoli. The cytoplasm is very basophilic and has a variable number of azurophilic granules. Electron microscope studies show that azurophilic granules arise by a coalescence of dense-cored vacuoles derived from the inner (adcentriolar) cisternae of the Golgi complex, whereas the specific granules (neutrophilic in this case) form by fusion of dense-cored vacuoles derived from the outer cisternae of the Golgi. Azurophilic granules form only in the progranulocyte (promyelocyte) stage of development and the number of azurophilic granules per cell decreases in the subsequent generations of myelocytes. The first specific granules appear when the promyelocytes differentiate into myelocytes, and new specific granules form throughout the myelocyte generations. As a result of the continued formation of specific granules and the redistribution of previously formed azurophilic granules with each cell division, the proportion of specific granules to azurophilic granules is much greater in the mature leukocytes (Fig. 7-7) than it is in the myelocytes (Fig. 7-12).

In normal marrow, the promyelocytes constitute only about 4% of the cells (range, 1 to 8%). They proliferate and differentiate into the *myelocytes* proper, which make up about 12% of the marrow cells (range, 5 to 20%).

As differentiation proceeds from the promyelocyte stage to the myelocyte proper, specific cytoplasmic granules appear, the basophilia of the cytoplasm gradually decreases, and the chromatin of the nucleus becomes more compact and dense. After a number of generations, the myelocytes eventually reach a stage where they no longer divide. This stage is known as the *metamyelocyte*. It can usually be identified

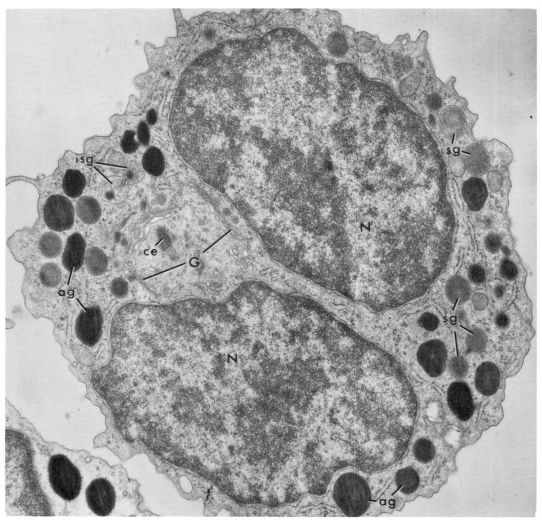

Fig. 7-12. Electron micrograph of a section of a neutrophilic myelocyte from rabbit bone marrow. The indented nucleus is cut in a plane which gives the appearance of two nuclei (*N*). The Golgi complex (*G*) is oriented around the centriole (*ce*) in the region of the nuclear indentation. Note the presence of two types of cytoplasmic granules which are present in about equal numbers at this stage of cell differentiation. The azurophilic granules (*ag*) are dense and relatively large (about 800 mμ), whereas the specific granules (*sg*) are less dense and smaller (about 500 mμ). Immature specific granules (*isg*) are seen near the Golgi complex. ×17,500. (Courtesy of Drs. D. F. Bainton and M. G. Farquhar, J. Cell Biol., vol. 28, 1966).

by its indented or kidney-shaped nucleus. The cells of this stage constitute about 20% of the cells of normal marrow. They differentiate directly into the mature leukocytes, usually within the bone marrow. When they enter the circulation before completing their maturation, they are known as the "juve-nile" leukocytes ("band forms") of the Schilling differential count. Although they are usually scarce in the normal circulation, they become abundant in certain pathological states.

In each of the above myelocyte stages, the neutrophils far outnumber the eosinophils and basophils. All three types of cells are well preserved in Wright's stained dried smears, but the basophils are generally indistinguishable in sections of material fixed in aqueous solutions, since the basophilic granules are water-soluble.

General Considerations of Granulocytopoiesis. When the percentages of the different myelocyte stages are added to the number of mature granulocytes present in marrow (20% or more), it is found that the granular leukocyte line comprises approximately 60% of the cells in normal marrow. Lymphocytes, monocytes, reticular cells, plasma cells and megakaryocytes may constitute another 10 to 20%, leaving only about 20 to 30% of the marrow cells in the erythrocyte line. Although the literature on differential counts for normal marrow gives an even greater range than that listed above, there is general agreement that the progenitors of the leukocytes outnumber those of the erythrocytes. The numerical preponderance of leukocytogenic over erythrocytogenic cells in marrow, in contrast with the opposite relationship in blood, can be explained partly by the fact that the leukocytes survive for a shorter time in the circulation than do the erythrocytes, and they also require a longer period for development and maturation in marrow.

Studies of bone marrow cells by the ultraviolet absorption method have shown that ribonucleic acid (RNA) is more abundant in the myeloblast than in any of the other developmental stages of the granulocyte line (Thorell, 1947). The high concentration of RNA is responsible for the marked basophilia of the cytoplasm at the myeloblast stage. The high concentration of cytoplasmic RNA and the prominence of nucleoli are correlated with the rapid formation of cytoplasmic proteins during the early stages. It has been estimated that the total volume of all of the promyelocytes is about 8 times the total volume of the myeloblasts. This follows from the fact that the promyelocytes are more numerous and often larger than the myelo-

blasts (it has already been noted that the myeloblast illustrated in Figure 7-10 is one of the largest of its type). In the lineage from promyelocyte to myelocyte to metamyelocyte, the cells increase in number with a decrease in size, so that the total volume of all the metamyelocytes is only slightly greater than the total volume of the promyelocytes. Development during these later stages is dominated by differentiation rather than by cell growth. The rapid decrease in cytoplasmic basophilia during these later stages appears to be correlated with the decrease in RNA.

Erythrocytes. The stages of erythrocyte development, in order of differentiation, are: *reticular cells, hemocytoblasts (myeloblasts), basophilic erythroblasts, polychromatophilic erythroblasts, normoblasts,* and *erythrocytes.* The reticular cells and hemocytoblasts are described in the preceding sections.

Basophilic Erythroblasts. The earliest cells which exhibit differentiation in the direction of erythrocytes are smaller than myeloblasts, and their nuclei have a coarser chromatin structure than that seen in myeloblasts (Fig. 7-10). Nucleoli are present but less prominent than in the myeloblast. The presence of hemoglobin is a differential characteristic in identifying the first step in the erythrocyte line, but this can be seen better in living cells than in stained smears, where the hemoglobin is obscured by the basophilia of the cytoplasm. However, hemoglobin usually produces a slightly different shade from that which characterizes the myeloblast.

The terminology of the stages of the erythrocyte line is not as well defined as that for the leukocyte line. Some authors use the term *proerythroblast* for an intermediate stage between the myeloblast and basophilic erythroblast; others include the proerythroblasts within the general category of basophilic erythroblasts. It is unfortunate that the term *megaloblast* has also been used as a synonym for the earliest stage. This usage has led to confusion, since the term megaloblast is regularly employed in clinical work to designate the primitive nucleated red cells of pernicious anemia—cells which differ from those of normal development.

Polychromatophilic Erythroblasts. The basophilic erythroblasts undergo mitotic divisions and give rise to cells in which the hemoglobin is of sufficient quantity to be distinctly observed in stained preparations. There are many generations of erythroblasts and, with each mitotic division, there is a decrease in basophilia of cytoplasm and an increase in quantity of hemoglobin which is acidophilic.

The cytoplasm of the different generations of cells takes varying amounts of the acid and basic components of Wright's stain, and therefore these cells show a "mixed color varying from purplish blue to lilac or gray" and are called polychromatophilic. A few of these stages are illustrated in Figure 7-10.

The nucleus of the polychromatophilic erythroblast has a denser chromatin network than that of the basophilic erythroblast, and the coarse chromatin bodies give a checkerboard appearance which is characteristic of developing erythrocytes, as contrasted with the more irregular arrangement of chromatin in the developing granulocytes. The polychromatophilic erythroblasts are smaller than the basophilic erythroblasts and larger than the normoblasts.

Normoblasts. After an unknown number of divisions, the polychromatophilic erythroblasts reach a stage (normoblast) in which the basophilia of the cytoplasm has decreased and the acidophilic hemoglobin has increased to such an extent that the cytoplasm stains approximately as in the erythrocytes. The normoblasts are only slightly larger than the erythrocytes. Their nuclei are definitely smaller and denser in chromatin than in the erythroblasts. The early normoblasts proliferate actively and eventually reach a late stage in which the nucleus becomes pyknotic and no further division occurs. The chromatin becomes very compact and stains intensely, and some of the

pyknotic nuclei assume bizarre shapes. Finally the nuclei are extruded from the cells. Some investigators believe that the nuclei normally undergo karyolysis and disappear intracellularly, but the fact that extruded nuclei are commonly found in bone marrow does not favor this view. Erythrocytes are occasionally found with small, deep staining bodies (bodies of Howell-Jolly) which apparently are derivatives of nuclear fragmentation. The Cabot ring bodies sometimes found in erythrocytes of anemia were once described as remnants of nuclei, but this has been shown to be incorrect. The configurations observed are laboratory creations and they are the expression of cellular degeneration induced by hemolytic agents in the solutions used in laboratory techniques (Schleicher, 1942).

The youngest erythrocytes (*reticulocytes*) contain a delicate reticulum which can be demonstrated by supravital staining with dyes such as cresyl blue (Fig. 7-2, *B*). Erythrocytes normally lose their reticular structure soon after leaving the marrow; normally, the reticulocyte count of peripheral blood is less than 1% of the erythrocytes. Increased numbers may be called into circulation by repeated hemorrhages. Reticulocyte counts are used as an index of the effectiveness of therapy in pernicious anemia, an increase of reticulocytes after treatment being evidence of an increased production of young erythrocytes.

Extensive cell counts made on normal marrow of the rabbit (Sabin) show that less than 1% of the nucleated reds are of the earliest basophilic erythroblast type. Under pathological conditions, the proerythroblasts may become more numerous, and new ones may develop from a more primitive cell type. The exact details of the development from the primitive cell are controversial. According to the unitarian theory, the primitive cell of origin is the hemocytoblast which, in turn, comes from the undifferentiated reticulum.

Normal marrow, in which normal erythrocytes develop through the stages of normal erythroblasts and normoblasts as described above, is known as *normoblastic marrow*. This contrasts with *megaloblastic marrow*, which occurs in pernicious anemia and other macrocytic anemias.

It has been noted earlier that there is a lack of agreement on terminology for the developmental stages of blood cells. Usage of the term normoblast is an example. If one uses normoblast only for cells which have acquired a sufficient amount of hemoglobin to give a cytoplasmic stain almost equal to that of a normal erythrocyte (i.e., for the immediate precursor of a normal erythrocyte), the terms apply as outlined in the preceding description. On the other hand, if one prefers to use the term normoblast for all stages of normal erythrocyte development in contrast with megaloblastic development in anemia, the names for the stages of development become: basophilic normoblasts, polychromatophilic normoblasts, orthochromatophilic normoblasts, reticulated erythrocytes and mature erythrocytes. It should be noted that the difference in terminology is not related to any controversy involving the appearance of the cells. An erythroblast or polychromatophilic erythroblast is identical with a polychromatophilic normoblast.

General Considerations of Erythropoiesis. It has been found that ribonucleic acid (RNA) is more abundant in the basophilic erythroblast than in the later stages of the erythrocyte line. The concentration of RNA is responsible for the marked basophilia of the cytoplasm in the early stages, and it is apparently correlated with the active synthesis of cytoplasmic proteins during the stages which show the greatest increase in total cell volume.

The normal development of erythrocytes is dependent upon many different factors. Obviously, all of the parent substances which enter into the formation of hemoglobin must be present. The absence of one of these, iron, is responsible for a microcytic type of anemia. Certain additional substances are necessary for the normal maturation of the erythrocytogenic cells. The absence of one of these, vitamin B_{12}, produces pernicious anemia. Vitamin B_{12} has been identified as the antipernicious anemia factor or liver factor. Actually, the real defect in pernicious anemia is the lack of some substance which is normally present in gastric juice, the intrinsic factor. The intrinsic factor facilitates the intestinal absorption of an extrinsic factor present in food (vitamin B_{12} itself). After absorption, B_{12} is stored chiefly in the liver until it is utilized later in bone marrow.

The most potent stimulus for erythropoiesis is hypoxia, or cellular oxygen deficiency: i.e., the oxygen supply to the tissues does not meet the metabolic requirements of the tissues. Extracts from plasma of animals made anemic by experimental methods contain a factor which stimulates erythropoiesis when injected into normal animals. The plasma or humoral factor is known as *erythropoietin*.

Megakaryocytes and Platelet Formation. The megakaryocytes are giant cells (30 to 100 μ) derived from the hemocytoblast, and they apparently give rise to blood platelets. In the normal adult, they are usually said to occur only in marrow. During embryonic development, however, they are also present in other hemopoietic organs (liver, spleen). The nucleus is lobulated in a variable and complicated manner. During the differentiation of a megakaryocyte from a reticular cell (or from a hemocytoblast), the nucleus divides mitotically without accompanying division of cytoplasm. The nuclei usually separate to a late anaphase or early telophase stage and then reunite. In this way a polyploid nucleus is formed with 32N–64N chromosomes instead of the 2N number characteristic of most other cells. The polyploid nucleus is lobulated in a variable and complicated manner, often having only thin strands connecting different lobular units (Fig. 7-11). The megakaryocytes should not be confused with

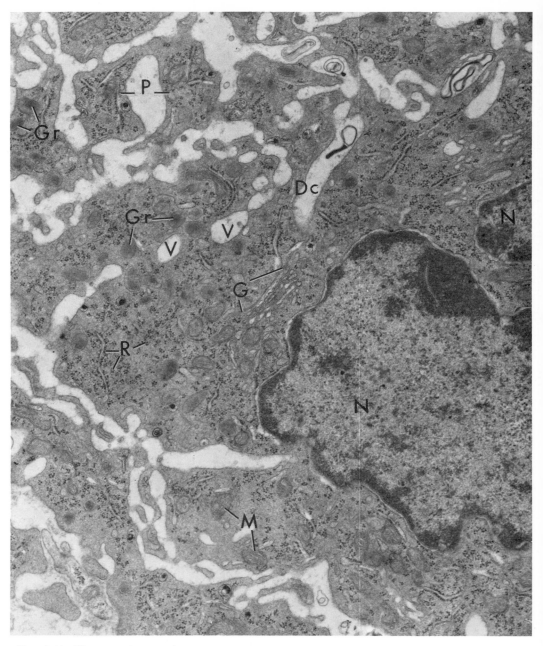

Fig. 7-13. Electron micrograph of a portion of a megakaryocyte. The cell characteristically contains a large multilobed nucleus but only portions of 2 nuclear lobes (N) are present within the field of the micrograph. A portion of one of the Golgi regions (G) is seen adjacent to one of the nuclear lobes. Most of the ribosomes (R) are distributed in clusters through the cytoplasm, and only a few are present along the cisternae of the endoplasmic reticulum. Electron dense granules (Gr) are seen in the cytoplasm of the cell and within the platelets. They are somewhat smaller than the mitochondria (M), and they resemble lysosomes in that they contain acid phosphatase. In the process of platelet formation, portions of the megakaryocyte cytoplasm become partioned off by membranes. First, membrane-lined vesicles (V) develop; later, platelet demarcation channels (Dc) arise by extension and fusion of the vesicles. Finally, the channels become continuous with one another, and membrane-bounded regions of the cytoplasm become detached as platelets. Precursor stage platelets (P), with only a few remaining attachments, are seen in the upper left portion of the micrograph. From the bone marrow of a mouse. ×20,850. (Courtesy of Drs. K. R. Porter and M. A. Bonneville).

osteoclasts of marrow and foreign body giant cells, which are multinucleated and form by fusion of cells.

The cytoplasm of the megakaryocyte contains the usual organelles and numerous fine granules which apparently form in the Golgi complex. The cell has an irregular shape with many pseudopodia. From studies with the light microscope, it appeared that platelets form by fragmentation of pseudopodia. Electron microscope studies have clarified the manner in which this occurs (Fig. 7-13). The peripheral regions of the cytoplasm become gradually subdivided by membranes into compartments, each subdivision having granules. When the partitioning membranes become complete, the compartments readily separate from the parent cell to become free platelets, without any rupture of the cell plasmalemma.

Megakaryocytes are limited in their life span, and stages of degeneration are not uncommon. The nucleus becomes smaller and stains more intensely, and the protoplasm degenerates. The naked, fragmented nuclei may find their way into the blood vessels, to be carried through the right side of the heart into the lung capillaries where they degenerate. In pathological conditions (Minot), entire megakaryocytes may be carried into the lungs and form an embolism of the vessels.

DEVELOPMENT OF LYMPHOID ELEMENTS

Lymphocytes. In the lymphoid organs, some of the undifferentiated reticular cells develop into large and medium sized lymphocytes characterized by basophilic cytoplasm and pale staining nuclei containing one or more large nucleoli (Fig. 7-14). The most immature lymphocytes resemble the primitive cells of bone marrow and, according to the unitarian theory of blood development, they are merely the same cells in different locations and they constitute a common stem type (hemocytoblast). On the other hand, the dualistic theory claims that the large lymphocytes are slightly different from the primitive marrow cells and that they develop only into lymphocytes; therefore, they are known as *lymphoblasts*. These cells have an undifferentiated type of nucleus with coarse nucleoli, and they differ from the large lymphocytes found in the normal circulation (Fig. 7-2, *A*, *Lm-4*). In sections stained with hematoxylin-eosin-azure, the appearance of the most immature lymphocytes is similar to that of the hemocytoblasts (Figs. 7-11 and 7-14).

The lymphoblasts and medium sized lymphocytes (prolymphocytes) proliferate actively and develop into the small lymphocytes commonly found in the circulation. The small lymphocytes enter the circulation by way of the lymphatics and, to some extent, by penetration through the walls of the blood capillaries of lymphoid organs.

The differentiation of reticular cells into lymphoblasts accounts for only a small proportion of the total lymphocytes; their numbers are maintained chiefly by mitotic divisions of the lymphoblasts and prolymphocytes. This proliferation occurs in all parts of the lymphoid tissue and is not confined to the germinal centers, which are intermittent in their activity. Although the small lymphocytes retain the ability to proliferate, their divisions are infrequent under normal conditions.

Monocytes. There are numerous theories for the origin of monocytes. They have been described as being derived from histiocytes, monoblasts, lymphocytes and hemocytoblasts.

As evidence for the development of monocytes from histiocytes, it may be pointed out that, in tissue culture experiments, macrophages have not only been developed from monocytes but have also been made to reassume the appearance of monocytes by varying the culture medium. This, however, is not convincing evidence that the monocytes of the circulating blood normally arise from the connective tissue histiocytes.

According to another theory, undifferentiated reticular cells form primitive free cells which develop into myeloblasts, lympho-blasts and monoblasts. Monoblasts are said to form chiefly in the spleen. The main criticism of this view is that it is extremely difficult to differentiate the monoblast from the lymphoblast. The unitarian theory makes no distinction between these cells and holds that monocytes develop from hemocyto-blasts.

EMBRYONIC DEVELOPMENT OF BLOOD CELLS

Blood development begins shortly after the formation of the germ layers. It is initiated in the 3rd week of development in the extraembryonic mesoderm of the yolk sac by the formation of *blood islands*. These consist of mesenchymal cells which have become less irregular in shape and whose cytoplasm has assumed a definitely baso-philic character. The cells proliferate actively and become more closely packed, forming solid cellular clusters, but they soon show a differentiation in two directions. The peripheral cells of the cluster become flattened and form the primary endo-thelium of the first blood vesesls. The central cells become detached and float freely in the plasma which is gradually accumulating (Fig. 7-15). These isolated mesenchymal cells with their vesicular, pale staining nuclei and basophilic, homogeneous cytoplasm represent the first primitive blood cells or *hemocytoblasts*. In this manner, both endo-thelium and primitive blood cells are formed simultaneously from the mesenchyme.

Some of the hemocytoblasts remain as primitive blood cells characterized by a basophilic cyto-plasm, but the majority of them become trans-formed into *primitive erythroblasts* and primitive nucleated erythrocytes by the elaboration or ac-cumulation of hemoglobin in their cytoplasm (Fig. 7-16). The primitive erythroblasts are character-ized by their large size, and they form a special race of their own which has but a transient exist-ence. Under normal conditions, they develop only in the embryonic yolk sac, but cells of a similar type may develop in adult bone marrow in perni-cious anemia. In some mammals (rat, mouse), the primitive strain is the only type of red cell formed in the yolk sac, but in human embryos a few *defini-tive erythroblasts*—cells identical with the normal erythroblasts of marrow—develop in the yolk sac after 6 or 7 weeks (Bloom and Bartelmez).

The hemocytoblasts are continuously being detached throughout the embryonic period. New ones also can differentiate from the reticular con-nective tissue cells throughout life. For a limited

embryonic period, hemocytobalsts also arise from the primitive endothelium. Among the free cells which are formed, there are some which differ in structure from the hemocytoblasts. They have smaller, darker staining nuclei and a vacuolated cytoplasm which is only slightly basophilic. They are actively phagocytic and readily store vital. dyes. They are the first histoid wandering cells and correspond to the histiocytes of later life.

The liver forms the second important hemo-poietic organ of the fetus. Blood formation begins at about 6 weeks, before the spleen and marrow have appeared. Here too the mother stem cell (hemocytoblast) is a large cell with a pale stain-ing, vesicular nucleus and basophilic cytoplasm. The hemocytoblasts are probably in part brought in by the circulation. In part they are formed from the scanty mesenchyme between the liver cords and from the endothelium of the sinusoids. The hemocytoblasts divide actively and differentiate into nucleated and non-nucleated red cells, granu-lar leukocytes and megakaryocytes. The nucleated red cells (normoblasts) are predominant in the fetal circulation during the 2nd month. Blood de-struction also occurs in the fetal liver, as evidenced by pigment formation, nuclear disintegration and phagocytosis by histiocytes. The liver remains the most active place of blood formation until the middle of fetal life. Then its activity slowly de-creases and, at birth or soon after, hemopoiesis ceases under normal conditions.

The spleen appears as a blood-forming organ in the latter part of the 2nd month and remains ac-tive until the 8th month. After this period, erythropoiesis gradually diminishes and ceases soon after birth, but lymphocytes and monocytes are formed throughout life. In the lymph nodes, the embryonal formation of erythrocytes is of very little extent and does not occur in the parenchyma. Clusters of developing erythrocytes have, how-ever, been observed in the septal connective tissue in the vicinity of blood vessels. The lymph nodes function throughout life as the chief organs of lymphocyte formation. Here again the mother stem cell (lymphoblast) resembles the hemocyto-blast, having the large, pale staining nucleus and nongranular basophilic cytoplasm. These cells are formed by proliferation of their own kind and by new detachment from the reticulum of lymph nodes and spleen.

The most important and permanent hemopoi-etic organ is the red marrow of bones, which be-comes functional in the 3rd fetal month. The perichondral mesenchyme invades the cartilagi-nous primordia of the bones and constitutes the primitive marrow. Again, mesenchymal cells de-tach themselves to become hemocytoblasts (myelo-

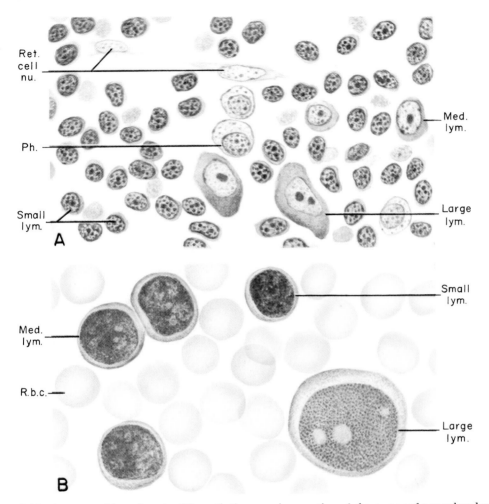

FIG. 7-14. *A*, stages of lymphocyte differentiation seen in a section of the cortex of a monkey lymph node stained with hematoxylin-eosin-azure. Reticular cell nuclei (*Ret. cell nu.*) take a pale stain. Large lymphocytes (*Large lym.*) have prominent nucleoli in an otherwise pale nucleus, with very basophilic cytoplasm. Medium sized lymphocytes (*Med. lym.*) are intermediate in staining characteristics between the large and the small lymphocytes (*small lym.*) A few phagocytes (*Ph.*) are present. *B*, immature lymphocytes in a Wright's stained blood smear from a patient with lymphatic leukemia. The lymphoblast or large lymphocyte (*Large lym.*) has prominent nucleoli which are pale in this stain. Medium sized lymphocytes, with nucleoli, are more numerous than the small lymphocytes. The size difference between the cells in *A* and *B* is due, in part, to differences in technique: *A* is from a section, *B* from a smear which flattens the cells. Both figures, ×1640.

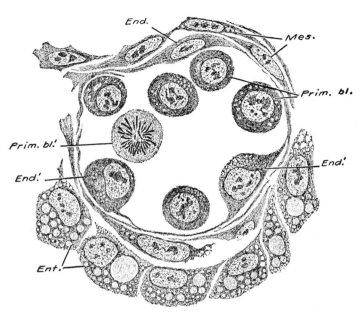

FIG. 7-15. Section through a vessel of the area vasculosa of an 8½ day rabbit embryo. *End*, primitive endothelium; *End'*, primitive endothelial cells rounding off and beginning to differentiate into primitive blood cells; *Ent*, entoderm; *Mes*, mesenchyme; *Prim. bl*, primitive blood cells; *Prim. bl'*, primitive blood cell in mitosis and with cytoplasm showing differentiation toward the primitive erythroblast. (Redrawn from Maximow, Arch. Mikr. Anat., 1909, vol. 73.)

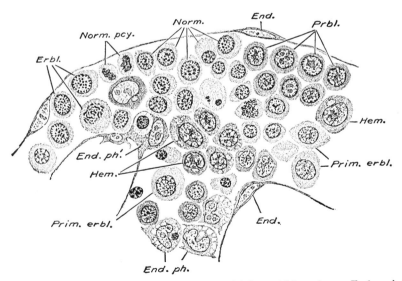

FIG. 7-16. Portion of a vessel from the yolk sac of a 13½ day rabbit embryo. *End*, endothelial cells; *End. ph*, phagocytic cells which have developed from the primitive endothelium and *End. ph'*, a phagocytic cell which is still attached to the endothelium; *Erbl*, erythroblasts; *Hem*, hemocytoblasts; *Norm*, normoblasts; *Norm. pcy*, normoblasts with pyknotic nuclei; *Prbl*, proerythroblasts; *Prim. erbl*, primitive erythroblasts. Magnification is slightly less than that of Figure 7-15. (Redrawn from Maximow, Arch. Mikr. Anat., 1909, vol. 73.)

blasts) and histiocytes, marrow being apparently able when needed to furnish such free elements throughout adult life. From the hemocytoblasts are formed the megakaryocytes and also the erythroblasts and myelocytes, which proliferate and differentiate into the erythrocytes and granulocytes.

With the advent of bone marrow as a hemopoietic organ in the 3rd month, the number of circulating normoblasts is decreased and the nonnucleated erythrocytes become predominant in the circulation.

REFERENCES

ACKERMAN, G. 1963 Cytochemical properties of the blood basophilic granulocyte. Ann. New York Acad. Sci., vol. 103, pp. 376–393.

ACKERMAN, G. A. 1967 The lymphocyte: its morphology and embryological origin. *In* The Lymphocyte in Immunology and Haemopoiesis (Bristol Symposium, Yoffey, J. M., editor), pp. 11–30. Edward Arnold, Ltd., London.

ARCHER, G. T. 1968 The function of the eosinophils. Bibliotheca Haematologica, No. 29, Pt. 1, pp. 71–85.

BAGGIOLINI, M., HIRSCH, J. G., AND DE DUVE, C. 1969 Resolution of granules from rabbit heterophil leucocytes into distinct populations by zonal sedimentation. J. Cell Biol., vol. 40, pp. 529–541.

BAINTON, D. F., AND FARQUHAR, M. G. 1968 Differences in enzyme content of azurophil and specific granules of polymorphonuclear leukocytes. I. Histochemical staining of bone marrow smears. J. Cell Biol., vol. 39, pp. 286–298.

BAINTON, D. F., AND FARQUHAR, M. G. 1968 Differences in enzyme content of azurophil and specific granules of polymorphonuclear leukocytes. II. Cytochemistry and electron microscopy of bone marrow cells. J. Cell Biol., vol. 39, pp. 299–317.

BAINTON, D. F., AND FARQUHAR, M. G. 1970 Segregation and packaging of granule enzymes in eosinophilic leukocytes. J. Cell Biol. vol. 45, pp. 54–73.

BAKER, J. R. 1958 The blood dyes. *In* Principles of Biological Microtechnique, Chap. 14. John Wiley & Sons, Inc., New York.

BENNET, M., AND CUDKOWIZ, G. 1967 Functional and morphological characterization of stem cells: the unipotential role of "lymphocytes" of mouse marrow. *In* The Lymphocyte in Immunology and Haemopoiesis (symposium), pp. 183–194. Edward Arnold, Ltd., London.

BESSIS, M. C. 1963 Cytological aspects of hemoglobin production. Harvey Lectures, Ser. 55, pp. 125–156.

BIERMAN, H. R. (editor) 1964 Leukopoiesis in health and disease. Ann. N. Y. Acad. Sci., vol. 113, pp. 511–1092.

BLOOM, W., AND BARTELMEZ, G. W. 1940 Hematopoiesis in young human embryos. Amer. J. Anat., vol. 67, pp. 21–54.

BRAUNSTEINER, H., AND ZUCKER-FRANKLIN, D. 1962 The Physiology and Pathology of Leukocytes. Grune & Stratton, Inc., New York.

COOKE, W. E., AND PONDER, E. 1927 The Polynuclear Count. J. B. Lippincott Company, Philadelphia.

DAVIDSON, W. M., AND SMITH, D. R. 1954 A morphological sex difference in the polymorphonuclear leucocytes. Brit. Med. J., vol. 2 of 1954, pp. 6–7.

DAVIES, H. G. 1961 Structure in nucleated erythrocytes. J. Biophys. Biochem. Cytol., vol. 9, pp. 671–687.

DIGGS, L. W., STURM, D., AND BELL, B. A. 1956 The Morphology of Human Blood Cells. W. B. Saunders Company, Philadelphia.

DeBRUYN, P. P. H. 1944 Locomotion of blood cells in tissue culture. Anat. Rec., vol. 89, pp. 43–63.

DOWNEY, H. 1938 The Myeloblast. Handbook of Hematology (Downey, H., editor), vol. 3, pp. 1963–2041.

EVERETT, N. B., AND TYLER (CAFFREY), R. W. 1967 Lymphopoiesis in the thymus and other tissues: functional implications. Int. Rev. Cytol., Vol. 21, pp. 205–237.

EVERETT, N. B., CAFFREY, R. W., AND RIEKE, W. D. 1964 Recirculation of lymphocytes. Ann. N. Y. Acad. Sci., vol. 113, pp. 887–897.

FISHER, J. W., AND GORDON, A. S. 1968 Conference: Erythropoietin. Ann. N. Y. Acad. Sci., vol. 149.

FORD, C. E., MICKLIN, H. S., EVANS, E. P., GRAY, J. G., AND OGDEN, D. A. 1966 The inflow of bone marrow cells to the thymus: studies with part-body irradiated mice injected with chromosome marked bone marrow and subjected to antigen stimulation. Ann. N. Y. Acad. Sci., vol. 129, pp. 283–296.

GORDON, A. S. (moderator) 1967 Symposium: Studies of Leucocyte Physiology. Ann. N. Y. Acad. Sci., vol. 136, pp. 779–882.

GORDON, A. S., WINKERT, J., DORNFEST, B. S., AND SIEGEL, C. D. 1959 Studies on the actions and properties of the circulating erythropoietic stimulating factor. *In* Symposium on Hematopoietic Mechanisms. Ann. N. Y. Acad. Sci., vol. 77, pp. 650–676.

GOWANS, J. L. 1958 The recirculation of

lymphocytes from blood to lymph in the rat. J. Physiol., vol. 143, Proc. Physiol. Soc., pp. 84–85.

GOWANS, J. L. 1969 Lymphocytes. Harvey Lectures, Ser. 64.

HADEN, R. L. 1940 Factors influencing the size and shape of the red blood cell. Blood, Heart and Circulation (F. R. Moulton, editor). A.A.A.S. Publ. no. 13, pp. 27–233. Science Press, Lancaster, Pa.

HUDSON, G., OSMOND, D. G., AND ROYLANCE, P. J. 1963 Cell-populations in the bone marrow of the normal guinea-pig. Acta Anat., vol. 53, pp. 234–239.

JONES, O. P. 1916 The influence of disturbed metabolism on the morphology of blood cells. In Functions of the Blood (Macfarlane, R. G., and Robb-Smith, A. H. T., editors), pp. 170–260. Academic Press, New York.

JORDAN, H. E. 1938 Comparative hematology. In Handbook of Hematology (Downey, H., editor), vol. 2, pp. 699–862.

KNISELY, M. H. 1961 The settling of sludge during life; first observations, evidences, and significances; a contribution to the biophysics of disease. Acta Anat., vol. 44, suppl. 41 = 1 ad. vol. 44, pp. 7–64.

LINMAN, J. W., AND BETHELL, F. H. 1960 Factors Controlling Erythropoiesis. Charles C Thomas, Publisher, Springfield, Ill.

LOW, F. N., AND FREEMAN, J. A., SR. 1958 Electron Microscopic Atlas of Normal and Leukemic Human Blood. Blakiston Division of McGraw-Hill, New York.

MACFARLANE, R. G., AND ROBB-SMITH, A. H. T. (editors). 1961 Functions of the Blood. Academic Press, New York.

MAXIMOW, A. 1932 The lymphocytes and plasma cells. Special Cytology (Cowdry, E. V., editor), vol. 2, pp. 601–648.

MENKIN, V. 1955 Factors concerned in the mobilization of leukocytes in inflammation. In Symposium on Leukocytic Functions. Ann. N. Y. Acad. Sci., vol. 59, pp. 956–985.

NOSSAL, G. J. V. 1968 The cellular basis of immunity. Harvey Lectures, Ser. 63, pp. 179–211.

NOSSAL, G. J. V., AND MÄKELÄ, O. 1962 Autoradiographic studies of the immune response. I. The kinetics of plasma cell proliferation. J. Exp. Med., vol. 115, pp. 209–230.

RIEKE, W. O., EVERETT, N. B., AND CAFFREY, R. W. 1963 The sizes and interrelations of lymphocytes in thoracic duct lymph and lymph node of normal and stimulated rats. Acta Haemat., vol. 30, pp. 103–110.

SABIN, F. R. 1923 Studies of living human blood cells. Bull. Hopkins Hosp., vol. 34, pp. 277–288.

SCHILLING, V. 1929 The Blood Picture (translated by Gradwohl). C. V. Mosby Company, St. Louis.

SCHLEICHER, E. M. 1942 The origin and nature of the Cabot ring bodies of erythrocytes. J. Lab. Clin. Med., vol. 27, pp. 983–1000.

SHEMIN, D., AND RITTENBERG, D. 1946 The life span of the human red blood cell. J. Biol. Chem., vol. 166, pp. 627–636.

SPIERS, R. S. 1969 Cellular aspects of immune reactions. Bioscience, vol. 19, pp. 411–417.

THORELL, B. 1947 Studies on the formation of cellular substances during blood cell production. Henry Kempton, London. (Also Acta Med. Scand., suppl. 200.)

TYLER, R. W., EVERETT, N. B., AND SCHWARZ, M. R. 1967 Effect of antilymphocytic serum on rat lymphocytes. J. Immunology, vol. 102, pp. 179–193.

WINTROBE, M. 1961 Clinical Hematology. Lea & Febiger, Philadelphia.

YAMADA, E. 1957 The fine structure of the megakaryocyte in the mouse spleen. Acta Anat., vol. 29, pp. 267–290.

YOFFEY, J. M. 1966 Bone Marrow Reactions. Edward Arnold, Ltd., London.

YOFFEY, J. M. (editor) 1967 The Lymphocyte in Immunology and Haemopoiesis (Bristol Symposium). Edward Arnold, Ltd., London.

8

Muscle

There is a wide diversity of structural configurations among the various muscles of the body. Among these, three broad classes have been traditionally and usefully recognized. They are: *smooth, skeletal* and *cardiac*. Smooth or *nonstriated* muscle lacks the cross striations seen in other muscle, and it is *involuntary*, being especially associated with viscera which are not under voluntary control. Skeletal muscle is *striated* and *voluntary*, making up the bulky muscles of the body. Cardiac or heart muscle is *striated* but *involuntary*.

SMOOTH MUSCLE

Smooth muscle consists of fusiform or spindle-shaped cells with abundant cytoplasm, in whose central thickest portion the nucleus lies. As a rule, the cells are gathered into dense sheets or bands, but they may occur as isolated units scattered among the connective tissue fibers in a tissue such as the dartos tunic of the scrotum.

Within the bands, the cells are roughly parallel to each other but are irregularly and densely packed together, so that the narrower portion of one cell lies against the wider portions of its neighbors. The shape varies according to the organ containing the muscle: for example, very long and slender in the walls of the intestine (Fig. 8-1), short and relatively thick in the walls of small arteries, or thrown into irregular folds and twistings by elastic fibers in the walls of

large arteries. The greatest diameter varies from 3 to 8 μ, the length from 15 to 200 μ, except in the pregnant uterus where it may exceed half a millimeter (500 μ). The complete outlines of the cells cannot be made out with certainty in a longitudinal aspect of either fresh material or prepared sections because of the overlapping. The outlines are easily seen in cross sections, however, where they are round, oval or flattened and vary greatly in size because the individual cells, as a result of their fusiform shape, may be cut through their thick central portions or at the narrow ends (Fig. 8-2). The individual cells can be separated from one another by teasing after treatment with nitric acid (Fig. 8-1) so that the shape of the cells, the central nuclei and faint longitudinal marking or striation can be seen.

The *nucleus* conforms to the outline of the cell, and its shape may therefore be oval, elongated or flattened. It is generally more or less rodlike (Fig. 8-2). The nuclei of contracted muscle cells usually have a folded or pleated outline which can be seen in longitudinal sections.

The *cytoplasm* contains the usual organelles: mitochondria, a Golgi complex, centrioles, endoplasmic reticulum and ribosomes. It also contains some glycogen and occasional fat droplets. In addition, it has longitudinally aligned *myofibrils*, which are specialized structures for contraction. The fibrils are generally not visible in routine

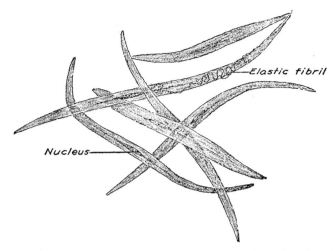

FIG. 8-1. Smooth muscle cells teased from intestine treated with nitric acid. Unstained. ×800

sections, but they can be seen in fresh preparations following maceration in nitric or trichloracetic acid. They represent aggregates of the *myofilaments* which can be seen in electron micrographs (Fig. 8-4). The filaments of smooth muscle cells differ from those in striated muscle in that they are not arranged as orderly and are not preserved as readily. Most of the filaments seen in electron micrographs of vertebrate smooth muscle cells correspond to the *thin* (actin) filaments of striated muscle. Although coarse filaments, interpreted by some investigators as *thick* (myosin) filaments, can be seen in smooth muscles of some vertebrates, there is considerable evidence that most of the myosin of vertebrate smooth muscles is present in an unaggregated form (Panner and Honig, 1970). Some authors (Rice, et al., 1970) postulate that aggregation into visibly thick filaments occurs during tension production and that this state requires special fixation procedures for preservation. Two types of filaments are seen more readily in invertebrate than in vertebrate smooth muscle cells, and some of the so-called smooth muscle cells of invertebrates are intermediate in type between smooth and striated (Rosenbluth, 1967). The actin filaments of smooth muscles (vertebrate and

invertebrate) often course obliquely in the cell, and they generally attach to the inner portion of the plasmalemma at the side of the cell. Electron dense regions are seen at intervals along the bundles of thin filaments and at places where the filaments attach to the cell plasmalemma. These dense areas have been likened to the Z lines of striated muscle where actin filaments appear to be held in register.

In routine sections stained with hematoxylin and eosin, the cytoplasm usually appears more or less homogeneous and takes the eosin stain. The color tone of muscle cytoplasm differs slightly from that of collagen because the ribosomes in the muscle cytoplasm take some hematoxylin, giving the muscle a slight purplish tint, in contrast with a more pure eosin color in collagen. Smooth muscle and collagen also differ in their *intensity* of eosinophilia, but the reactions are variable and the identification of the tissues is based more on morphological characteristics than on tinctorial reactions. Masson's trichrome stain simplifies the differentiation of smooth muscle from collagen because muscle is usually stained red in this technique, whereas collagen is colored blue or green, depending upon the stain modification used. The identification of

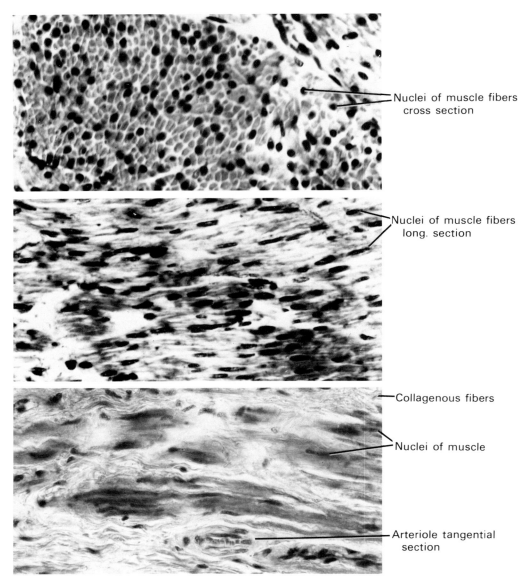

Nuclei of muscle fibers
cross section

Nuclei of muscle fibers
long. section

Collagenous fibers

Nuclei of muscle

Arteriole tangential
section

FIG. 8-2. Photomicrographs of smooth muscle. The *upper figure* shows the muscle fibers cut transversely; the *central* and *lower figures* show the fibers cut longitudinally. In the *central figure*, the fibers are seen in compact arrangement, with a minimum of associated connective tissue whereas in the *lower figure* the fibers are interspersed with considerable connective tissue. *Upper* and *central* micrographs are from human urinary bladder; *lower* micrograph is from human rectum. All figures, ×390.

smooth muscle in routine preparations stained with hematoxylin and eosin is further complicated by the fact that some of the cytoplasmic constituents are not preserved, and consequently the cytoplasm of smooth muscle cells often appears vacuo-lated and pale. The student must be on guard not to confuse bundles of pale stained smooth muscle cells with bundles of nerve fibers.

The *plasma membrane* is seen in high resolution electron micrographs as a trilami-

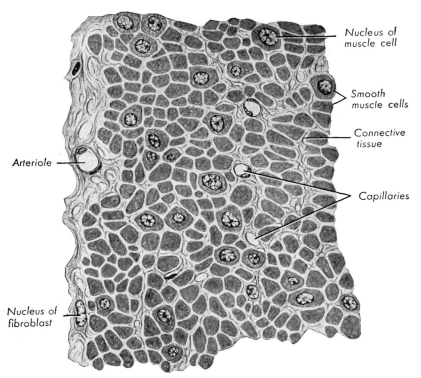

Nucleus of
muscle cell

Smooth
muscle cells

Connective
tissue

Arteriole

Capillaries

Nucleus of
fibroblast

Fig. 8-3. Smooth muscle cut transversely, from the muscularis externa of human stomach. Hematoxylin and eosin. ×1665.

nar membrane resembling that of most other animal cells. In certain regions where adjacent muscle cells come into apposition, the outer layers of the membranes of adjacent cells form specialized zones of contact known as *nexuses, close junctions*, or "gap" junctions (Fig. 8-5, and Chapter 4, Fig. 4–7). The nexus of smooth muscle does not encircle the cells as do the zonulae of epithelial cells; it is more like a band of variable length. The nexus serves as an intimate union of cells (gap junction) and probably facilitates transmission of impulses for contraction from one cell to another.

Individual muscle cells are surrounded by a glycoprotein coat that resembles the basal lamina beneath epithelial cells. It forms a complete covering, except for the regions of gap junctions, and would appear to aid in holding the cells together. It is composed of an amorphous substance with many fine fibrils which blend peripherally with reticular and collagenous fibrils of the connective tissue. The reticular fibers can be demonstrated either by Bielchowsky's silver method or by the periodic acid-Schiff (PAS) technique. By resorcin-fuchsin, elastic fibers can be demonstrated. The latter are occasionally seen in macerated preparations as tiny coils around the cells (Fig. 8-1). Between the larger bundles of fibers there are coarser collagenous and elastic fibers (Figs. 8-2 and 8-3). Since the smooth muscle of mammals either ends in soft parts or forms more or less continuous circular or spiral bands, there is no specialized connective tissue attachment such as the tendon of skeletal muscle.

The *contraction* of smooth muscle is apparently dependent upon the sliding of myofilaments, but the details of the contractile mechanism are not as well under-

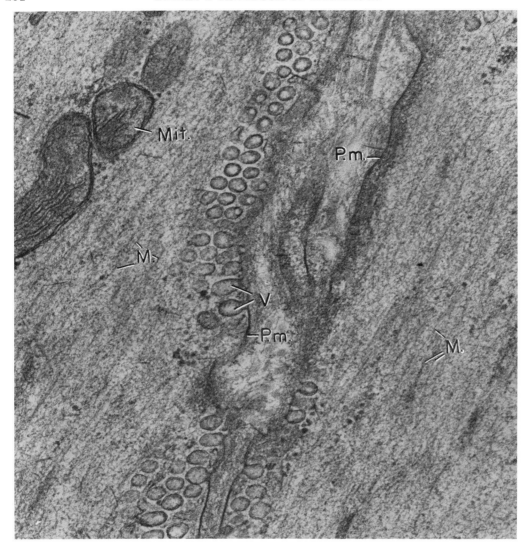

Fig. 8-4. Electron micrograph of portions of two smooth muscle cells from the esophagus of a bat. Note fine myofilaments (*M.*), mitochondria (*Mit.*), pinocytotic vesicles (*V.*) and plasma membranes (*P.m.*). ×57,750. (Courtesy of Dr. Keith Porter.)

stood for smooth muscle as they are for skeletal muscle. As noted above, electron micrographs show numerous actin filaments and some possibly transitory thick filaments. Chemical studies show the presence of both actin and myosin. Although the filaments are not arranged as orderly as they are in striated muscle and most of the myosin is apparently in a nonaggregated form, the contraction appears to be basically dependent upon an interaction of myosin and actin.

The contraction of smooth muscle is slow and sustained; it contrasts with the range of skeletal muscle activity which is generally more rapid and fatiguing. Two types of contraction have been observed. Each individual cell may contract in its entirety, or the contraction may pass over the cell in a wave, only part of each cell being in a state of contraction at a given instant. The oblique direction of the filaments and their attachment at the side of the cell, rather than a

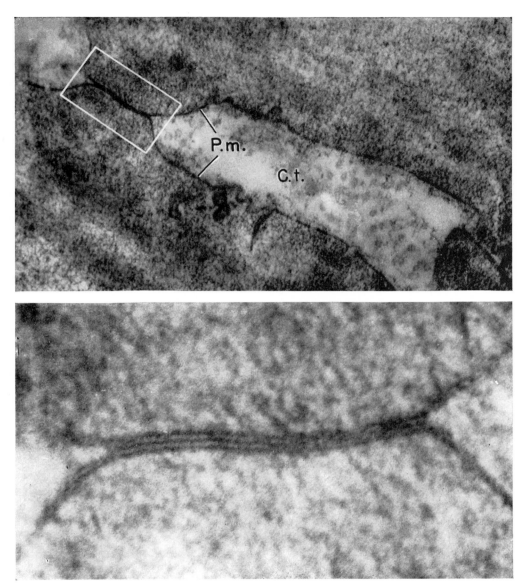

Fig. 8-5. Electron micrograph of portions of adjoining smooth muscle cells from the circular muscle layer of the intestine of a dog. In the *upper figure*, at relatively low magnification, the plasma membranes (*P.m.*) of two cells are seen separated by connective tissue (*C.t.*) in one area and in close approximation in another where they form a nexus. The area outlined by the rectangle is enlarged in the *lower figure* to show the fine structure of the nexus. Note that the plasma membrane of each cell consists of an outer and an inner layer of electron-dense material (protein) separated by a lighter area (lipid). In the region of the nexus, the outer layers of the plasma membranes of adjoining cells form a gap junction. (Courtesy of Drs. Maynard M. Dewey and L. Barr.)

longitudinal end to end arrangement, seems to correlate with the ability for localized contraction. When the cells have been caught in a completely contracted state by the fixative, they appear shortened and stain more intensely. If a wave has been caught passing over the cell by the fixing reagent, the contracted portion is bulged and short-

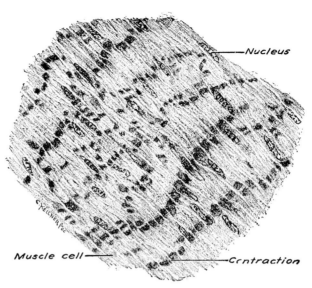

FIG. 8-6. Smooth muscle from human intestine showing contraction nodes. ×500

ened and is more heavily stained than the rest of the cell, so that it looks like a swollen dark segment of the cell. The *contraction bands* have a tendency to extend in lines across the whole sheet of muscle so that the contracted swelling involves the center of one cell and the narrower extremities of its neighbors at the same time (Fig. 8-6).

There are *nerve endings* about smooth muscle cells, but motor terminations for every cell have not been demonstrated. It seems, therefore, that a non-nervous type of transmission must be utilized to stimulate the cells that lack nerve endings. A partial list of the explanations for transmission is as follows: (1) structural union, or nexus as described above; (2) mechanical pull of a contracting cell on its neighbors by their connective tissue investments; and (3) action of chemical agents.

Smooth muscle is not as richly supplied with blood vessels as is skeletal or cardiac muscle. The arteries and veins are carried in the coarser septa of connective tissue. The capillaries lie in connective tissue between thin layers or small groups of cells rather than about individual cells. Connective tissue cells are rare among the reticular fibrils

between the muscle cells, unless associated with the blood vessels or larger connective tissue laminae.

Smooth muscle is found in the wall of the alimentary canal from the middle of the esophagus to the anus; gall bladder and hepatic ducts; dorsal wall of trachea and whole bronchial tree; ureter, bladder, urethra, corpora cavernosa, testes and ducts, prostate and Cowper's glands, broad ligament, oviduct, uterus and vagina; blood vessels, larger lymphatics and spleen. Smooth muscle occurs in the skin in connection with hairs (arrectores pilorum) and occasionally in other places (e.g., corrugator cutis ani). In the eye, it is found in the iris and ciliary body.

Development of Smooth Muscle. Smooth muscle is derived from the loose mesodermal network of the embryo known as mesenchyme. This is most massively manifest in the splanchnic mesoderm surrounding the primitive gut and its appendages. Exceptions are found in the iridic muscle of the eye and in the modified muscle cells in the walls of sweat glands which are derived from the ectoderm. The precursors of the muscle cells cannot be distinguished at first from the mesenchymal cells from which they arise. As differentiation proceeds, some of the cells become recognizable as myoblasts by their elongated nuclei and spindle shape. New myoblasts continue to differentiate from mesenchymal cells during the early stages of development. Later, the division of existing myoblasts gradually takes the place of this differentiation in the production of new muscular elements.

Longitudinal markings may be seen at the surface of some of the elongated cells. This is probably the beginning of differentiation into muscle cells. Later the longitudinal striation can be resolved into fibrillae in the peripheral cytoplasm. At first the myofibrillae are delicate threads; later the peripheral fibrillae become thicker, and fine fibrillae appear in the deeper layers of the cytoplasm.

Scattered oval nuclei around and among the groups of elongated myoblasts mark the presence of connective tissue fibroblasts. As the muscle cells develop into sheets or bundles, the fibroblasts lay down collagenous, elastic and reticular fibers.

Proliferation of smooth muscle cells by mitotic division has been found in the uteri of virgin rabbits treated with female sex hormone. The formation of new muscle cells from undifferentiated cells during pregnancy has been described. The regenerative powers of the muscle coats of the alimentary tract are limited, however, and the healing of wounds takes place principally by scar formation. The muscle cells of the walls of new blood vessels associated with healing processes have been described as coming from primitive types of perivascular connective tissue cells.

SKELETAL MUSCLE

The smallest independent units of skeletal muscle are called fibers. Although they are frequently referred to as cells, the more specific term fiber is preferable. They are grossly more complicated than the cells of smooth muscle; they have many nuclei and are larger than most cells. The fibers are grouped together into bundles called fascic-

uli. In some muscles (gluteus maximus, deltoideus), the bundles are larger than in others, giving the muscle a coarse-grained appearance when seen with the naked eye. The larger muscles are composed of many fasciculi.

Fibers. The *fibers* are cylindrical or prismatic structures which vary greatly in length. A common average length for a fiber in man is 3 cm., but lengths of 4 cm., or more, are not uncommon, and the shortest fibers in small muscles (e.g., stapedius) are less than 1 mm. in length. Lengths of individual fibers can be studied best in teased preparations of excised muscles, particularly in those removed after rigor mortis has set in. The separation is made easier by treatment with nitric acid, which destroys the connective tissues that bind the fibers together. Huber teased all of the fibers of individual fasciculi from rabbit muscles, preserving their entire length intact and at the same time keeping them in their original relationship to the length of the fasciculus. He found three types of fibers: (1) those extending from one end of the fasciculus to the other; (2) those beginning at one or the other end of the fasciculus and terminating within the substance of the bundle; and (3) those having both ends within the muscular substance (Fig. 8-7). It should be noted that the diagram has been simplified by showing a single fasciculus. Actually, each muscle is composed of many fasciculi, and the connections from the different fasciculi to the main tendon are via interfascicular, dense, regularly arranged connective tissue (i.e., by subdivisions of the main tendon).

The *diameter* of the fibers varies from 10 to 100 μ so that, in many cases, they are visible to the naked eye. Although fibers of different thickness are intermingled in the same muscle, there is a more or less typical size for each muscle, and some correlation has been found between the heaviness of the work a muscle performs and the thickness of its fibers. Fibers in the delicate ocular muscles are much smaller than those of a bulky mus-

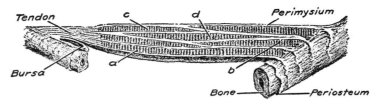

FIG. 8-7. Diagram of attachment of muscle to skeleton and relation of fibers to each other within a fasciculus. *a*, fiber extends the length of fasciculus; *b*, fiber begins at periosteum but ends in muscle; *c*, fiber begins at tendon but ends in muscle; *d*, both ends of fiber within the muscle (Redrawn from Braus.)

A   B

FIG. 8-8. Relative size of muscle fibers. *A*, gastrocnemius; *B*, ocular muscle. Human. The muscles were taken from the same subject, a middle aged adult, and were photographed at the same magnification. ×335.

cle like the gastrocnemius (Fig. 8-8). The fibers of a well nourished individual are thicker than those of one who is emaciated. Moreover, the increase in size of a muscle, which takes place during the growth of an individual or which is brought about by exercise, is due to an increase in the size of its fibers rather than an increase in their number.

Skeletal muscle fibers also vary in diameter in different classes of vertebrates. For example, the fibers of amphibians and fishes are generally thicker, while those of birds are thinner than those of mammals.

Each muscle fiber (or cell) is enclosed by a membrane known as the *sarcolemma* (Gr., *sarx*, flesh + *lemma*, husk). When fresh muscle fibers are teased and broken, a thin, transparent membrane covering each fiber is visible under the light microscope. However, electron micrographs reveal that the membrane seen with the light microscope is composed of a plasmalemma plus a basement membrane which consists of a basal lamina of amorphous material and a reticular lamina. In the light of our present knowledge, it seems proper to use the term sarcolemma for the plasmalemma, or trilaminar cell membrane. The total thickness of the plasmalemma is less than 100 A. Inside the sarcolemma are the nuclei and a cross striated substance composed principally of the *myofibrillae*. Surrounding the fibrillae and accumulated near the nuclei is the more fluid portion of the fiber which is called the *sarcoplasm*. It corresponds to the cytoplasm of other cells.

The skeletal muscle fiber has many *nuclei*,

Nucleus of muscle fiber   Vein   Arteriole

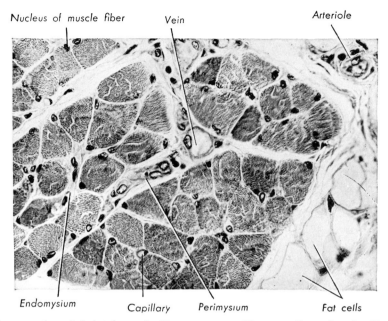

Endomysium   Capillary   Perimysium   Fat cells

FIG. 8-9. Cross section of skeletal muscle. Human tongue. Hematoxylin and eosin. Photomicrograph ×510.

several hundred appearing within a fiber of average size. The characteristic position for these nuclei in mammals is directly under the sarcolemma (Figs. 8-9, 8-10 and 8-11), but occasionally a fiber may be found with some nuclei in the interior. The nuclei are flattened, oval bodies, frequently elongated and of approximately the same size as the nuclei of neighboring connective tissue cells. They are scattered along the fiber in irregular spirals or longitudinal rows. In fresh muscle, they are difficult to see, faintly outlined against the background of striated substance. In fixed preparations, they show a loose network of chromatin threads and granules. The interior position is more frequently encountered in less differentiated muscles, particularly in the so-called dark fibers or those rich in sarcoplasm. Interior nuclei are of common occurrence in the lower vertebrates, and in skeletal muscles of insects it is usual for the nuclei to form an axial column in the center of the fiber.

Myofibrils. Skeletal muscle examined with a comparatively low magnification has

a striking and characteristic appearance resulting from the regular alternation of light and dark stripes or striations across each fiber. These striations are visible whether the muscle is living, freshly removed from the body or fixed and stained, and in either ordinary transmitted light or polarized light. The bands are produced by alternating light and dark segments of longitudinally oriented elements, the myofibrils.

The *myofibrils* range from 1 to 2 μ in diameter for the most part but may be as small as 0.2 μ. They are visible within fibers of teased fresh muscle as well as in sections. Similar segments of adjacent fibrillae are placed side by side in an intact fiber to form the characteristic cross striations.

In a cross section of a fiber, the cut ends of the myofibrils are usually visible as definite areas with individual size and shape. They are separated from each other by narrow regions of *sarcoplasm*. When the sarcoplasm is distributed irregularly, the fibrils appear in groups known as Cohnheim's fields.

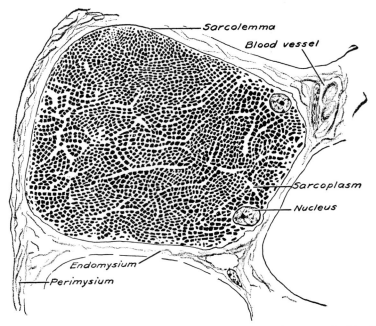

FIG. 8-10. Cross section of human skeletal muscle fiber, drawn with camera lucida. Each dot represents a myofibril. ×1500.

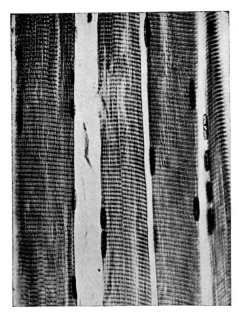

FIG. 8-11. A longitudinal section of human pectoralis minor muscle. Hematoxylin and eosin. Photomicrograph. ×425.

The *cross striations* are confined to the myofibrillae, and they usually stand out

clearly in longitudinal sections of fixed muscle. They color readily with a variety of dyes, but the iron hematoxylin of Heidenhain is a particularly good stain for the minute structure of the striations (Fig. 8-12). The more refractive segments are deeply colored, while the less refractive ones are pale. The dark-staining band is doubly refractive or *anisotropic* when studied under polarized light, and therefore it is known as the *A band*. The light-staining band is relatively mono-refringent or *isotropic* when studied under the polarizing microscope, and therefore it is known as the *I band*. Each of these bands is bisected by a narrow line: that in the I band stains deeply and is designated Z from the German word *Zwischenscheibe*, meaning between disc; the line bisecting the A band is pale and is designated H, both from the German word *Hell*, meaning light, and from the name of the discoverer, Hensen.

The portion of a fibrilla or column between two successive Z lines is called a *sarcomere*. Its length in relaxed mammalian muscle is 2 to 3 μ. It may be stretched to a greater length, and in greatly contracted fibers it may be reduced to about 1 μ. Insect muscles with sarcomeres 14 μ long have been described.

Studies with the electron microscope have revealed all of the cross bands observed with the ordinary light microscope, plus some additional bands. These studies have also established the fact that each of the myofibrils is composed of a number of threadlike elements known as *myofilaments*. Two principal types of myofilaments have been observed. One type has a diameter of about 100 A, whereas the other type is only 50 A in diameter. The *thick (myosin) filaments* have a length of approximately 1.5 μ and extend from one end of the A band to the other. The *thin (actin) filaments* extend from either side of the Z line across the adjacent I band and into the A band as far as the H zone (Figs. 8-14 and 8-15). Thus, the cross bands seen with the light microscope are related to the distribution and overlap of interdigitating myofilaments as revealed by the electron microscope.

The distribution of the myofilaments can be seen to advantage when the myofibrils are sectioned transversely. Sections across the I band show only thin filaments, those through the lateral portions of the A band have both thick and thin filaments and those through the H zone have only thick filaments. The two types of filaments have a precise relationship to each other in the regions where they interdigitate. As seen in cross sections, they have a remarkably constant hexagonal arrangement, with one thick filament in the center of a hexagon of six thin filaments (Fig. 8-16). The thick filaments are arranged as triangles with one thin filament at the center of each triangle.

High resolution electron micrographs indicate that the actin filaments terminate at the Z line. It is also established that the actin filaments are kept in register in this region and that sarcomeres are held firmly together. There are different views on how this is accomplished. According to one model, strands

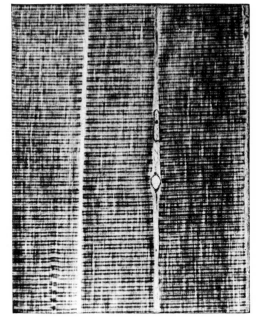

FIG. 8-12. Longitudinal section of human skeletal muscle fibers. Each dark disc (A) is bisected by a very distinct light zone or band (H). Bisecting each light disc (I) is a very narrow but distinct dark line, or Krause's membrane (Z). A capillary and also the nucleus of a fibroblast are evident between two of the fibers. The nuclei of the muscle fibers are not visible. Phosphotungstic acid-hematoxylin. Photomicrograph. $\times$905.

from adjacent actin filaments or from tropomyosin associated with them join in the form of hairpin loops in the Z line region, and the loops from adjoining sarcomeres are interlinked (Kelly, 1967, 1969). According to another model, there are separate filamentous attachments across the Z band linking the tips of the actin filaments (Knappeis and Carlsen, 1962). The myosin filaments are kept in register in the M line region of the H band. Each myosin filament is connected with its neighboring myosin filaments by slender, transversely oriented filaments of about 40 A diameter, and the latter are interconnected and supported by other slender filaments that course parallel to the myosin filaments (Knappeis and Carlsen, 1968). Although the chemical nature of the fine filaments is undetermined, it

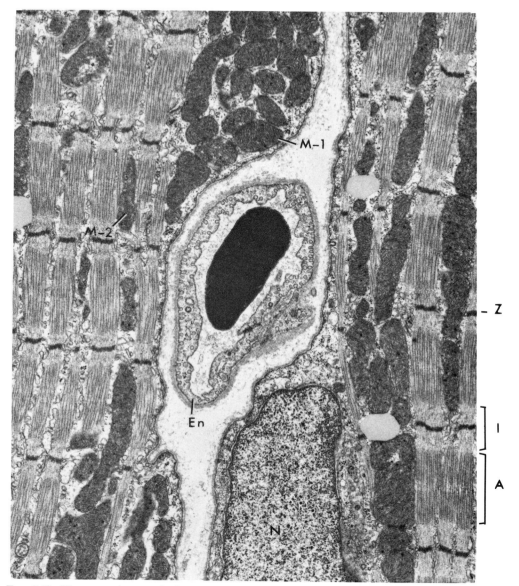

FIG. 8-13. Electron micrograph showing portions of two skeletal muscle fibers. The plane of the section cut only one of the muscle fiber nuclei (*N*). Numerous mitochondria (*M-1*) are seen in the sarcoplasm of the subsarcolemmal region of each fiber and additional mitochondria (*M-2*) are present in the sarcoplasm between myofibrils. The anisotropic or A-bands (*A*) of each myofibril are dark and the isotropic or I-bands (*I*) are relatively light. Each of the latter is bisected by a dense Z-line (*Z*). Caveolae and vesicles can be seen in the cytoplasm of the endothelium (*En*) of a capillary located in the connective tissue between the muscle fibers. Extrinsic eye muscle of slow loris. ×14,000. (Courtesy of Dr. Douglas E. Kelly and Miss Mary Ann Cahill.)

seems obvious from their pattern in stretched and contracted muscle that they have a supporting role. They are not to be confused with cross bridges between myosin and actin filaments, which have an important role in the mechanisms of contraction.

Further details on actin and myosin filaments have been obtained by electron micro-

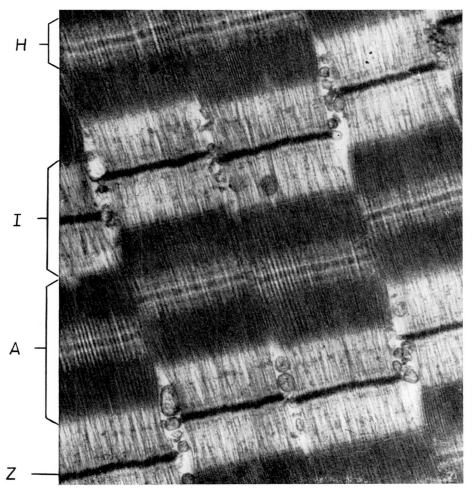

FIG. 8-14. Electron micrograph showing portions of four myofibrils from skeletal muscle, taken from rabbit psoas muscle. The anisotropic bands (A) are dense for most of their extent; they are bisected by lighter bands (H), within which there is a thin dense M band (unlabeled). The isotropic bands (I) are light regions, each bisected by a relatively dense, narrow line (Z). ×26,000. (Courtesy of Dr. H. E. Huxley.)

scope studies of negatively stained, isolated filaments and from X-ray diffraction studies. Each actin filament is composed of two strands of *F actin* (fibrous actin) coiled in a helix. The F actin filaments are polymers of small globular units, *G actin* monomers. *Tropomyosin* and *troponin*, a newly described protein, are associated with the actin filaments.

Myosin filaments are composed of subunits of *light meromyosin* and *heavy meromyosin*. The former are arranged longitudinally, to form the backbone of the myosin filament.

Each subunit of heavy meromyosin consists of a rodlike portion with a globular head. The rod portion lies parallel to the backbone myosin filament in relaxed muscle, and the globular head extends laterally as a cross bridge between myosin and actin (Fig. 8-15). The myosin molecules are polarized in the sense that the heavy meromyocin subunits are always aligned with their globular heads directed away from the midpoint of the backbone filament. Thus, they face in opposite directions on opposite sides of the M lines in relaxed muscle. It is of interest that

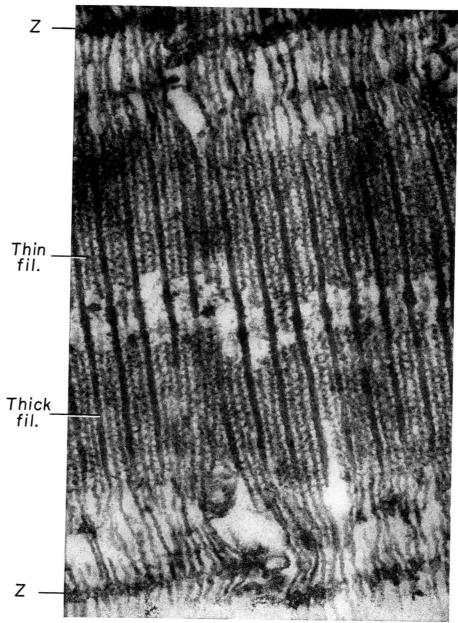

Fig. 8-15. High magnification electron micrograph of longitudinal section of relaxed skeletal muscle, taken from rabbit psoas muscle. The thick myosin filaments (*Thick fil.*) extend throughout the length of the A band and the thin actin filaments (*Thin fil.*) are found in the I band and in a part of A; they do not continue through the H line, although there is some indication of a connecting protein of undetermined nature between the ends of the actin filaments at this level. The actin filaments are twice as numerous as the myosin ones, but they are seen in this manner only when the section passes through the fibers in a plane as indicated in Figure 8-18. Cross linkages from myosin to actin are seen. ×148,000. (Courtesy of Dr. H. E. Huxley.)

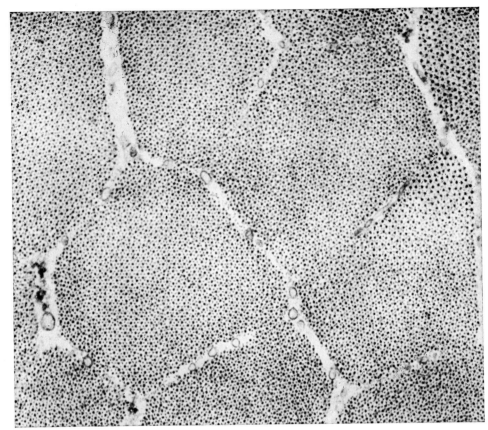

Fig. 8-16. Electron micrograph of a cross section of several myofibrils of skeletal muscle, taken from a rabbit psoas muscle. Note that the thinner (actin) filaments have a hexagonal arrangement around the thicker (myosin) filaments. ×60,000. (Courtesy of Dr. H. E. Huxley.)

the cross bridges are absent from the M line itself, where the myosin filaments are held in register by a latticework of fine cytoplasmic filaments described above. Adenosine triphosphatase and actin-binding sites are apparently located in or on the globular region of the heavy meromyosin.

The Sarcoplasm. This is the name applied to the cytoplasm of muscle fibers. It fills all the interstices between the myofibrils and is also prominent around the nuclei and beneath the sarcolemma. It contains a Golgi complex, variable amounts of mitochondria, and endoplasmic (sarcoplasmic) reticulum, and a few ribosomes. It also contains glycogen and occasional lipid droplets.

Fibers which are rich in sarcoplasm have a dark appearance in the fresh state, whereas those which have less sarcoplasm are lighter in color. In some species, e.g., turkey, the dark fibers are characteristically predominant in particular muscles while the light fibers predominate in other muscles. The two types of fibers are intermingled in human and most other mammalian muscles.

The *sarcoplasmic reticulum* is seen in electron micrographs as a network of cisternae or membranous tubules which course between and around the myofibrils. It is described as an agranular reticulum because the relatively few ribosomes present are scattered through the cytoplasm and are not aligned on the membranes. The cisternae course chiefly in a

Fig. 8-17. Electron micrograph depicting portions of two fibers of amphibian skeletal muscle. The picture shows the interfibrillar components of the muscle fiber in addition to the fine structure of the myofibrils. Note the basal lamina (*Bl*), the mitochondria (*M*), the longitudinally oriented elements of the sarcoplasmic reticulum (*Lsr*), and the dilated transverse components (*Tc*) of the reticulum. The transverse tubules (*Tl*), invaginations of the sarcolemma, are seen also. The *inset* at the *upper left* shows a higher magnification of the relationship of a transverse tubule to the transverse components of the reticulum. The transverse tubule with a dilated cisterna on each side constitutes a triad. A nerve ending (*Ne*) on a muscle fiber is seen in the *lower half* of the picture. Note the presynaptic vesicles, (*psv*) in the nerve terminal and the gutters or junctional folds (*Jf*) of the sarcolemma. ×27,300; *inset*, ×61,870. (Courtesy of Dr. Douglas E. Kelly and Miss Mary Ann Cahill.)

longitudinal direction, i.e., parallel with the direction of the myofibrils. In frog skeletal muscle, in which the sarcoplasmic reticulum has been studied extensively, it is found that lateral anastomoses between longitudinal cisternae form a perforated collar around the myofibrils at the level of the H band and broad *terminal cisternae* on each side of the *transverse tubule* at the level of the Z line (Fig. 8-17). Sections parallel to the long axis of the fiber show the transverse tubule between the terminal tubules from opposite sides of the sarcomere in the form of a *triad* (Figs. 8-17 and 8-18). Studies of mammalian skeletal muscle show a similar pattern but often with transverse tubules and accompanying terminal cisternae at the level of each A-I junction, rather than at the Z line. This provides two sets of tubules and terminal cisternae per sarcomere.

The transverse tubules are actually invaginations of the cell plasmalemma. Their lumen is open to the connective tissue around the muscle fiber and is actually extracellular space. They do not appear to open into the sarcoplasmic reticulum, but in places their lining membranes form junctions, or *couplings*, with the membranes of the terminal cisternae. They serve for rapid transmission of impulses from the exterior to the deepest regions of the cell, thus giving coordinated activity of all myofibrils.

The *mitochondria* or *sarcosomes* are found beneath the sarcolemma, around the nuclei and in the sarcoplasm between the myofibrils. In the latter location, they are generally aligned with their long axis parallel to the direction of the myofibril, although they may be found encircling the myofibril transversely, particularly in the region overlying the Z line.

Changes during Contraction. Morphological changes associated with contraction have been studied both in living and in fixed muscle. In both cases, it is seen that the fiber as a whole becomes shorter and broader when it contracts. Each sarcomere also becomes shorter and broader. The isotropic or I band becomes shorter as the sarcomere becomes shorter, and it disappears when the fibers are stimulated to contract to about 50% of their resting length. The H zone of the A band usually disappears at the same time. The total length of the A band remains constant during most cycles of contraction and relaxation. The A band becomes shorter only when contraction is so extreme that it produces a concentration of dense material along the Z line, forming a dark staining *contraction band*. It is postulated that this is due to a crumpling or folding of the ends of the thick (myosin) filaments against the Z line.

Electron micrographs of contracted muscle show an interdigitation of the thick and thin filaments throughout the length of the sarcomere, in contrast with the arrangement seen in resting muscle. Based on these findings Hanson and Huxley have proposed a *sliding filament* mechanism of contraction (Fig. 8-19). In resting muscle, the thick and thin (myosin and actin) filaments are presumably not firmly attached to each other because a resting or relaxed muscle can be stretched mechanically beyond its normal length. In muscle contraction, the cross bridges of the myosin filaments connect with active sites on neighboring actin filaments and the latter slide farther into the A band.

When a nerve to a muscle is stimulated, a depolarization wave spreads rapidly over the muscle cell membrane and over the membranes lining the T tubules to the deepest regions of the cell. Presumably a change in the membrane potential of the T tubules induces a reaction in some manner in the adjacent terminal cisternae and in other parts of the sarcoplasmic reticulum, with the result that calcium is released from its storage place in the sarcoplasmic reticulum to the sarcoplasm immediately bathing the myofibrils. A certain amount of calcium is necessary for the actin-myosin reaction to occur. According to a recent hypothesis proposed by Huxley (1969), calcium actually works by an effect on the protein troponin

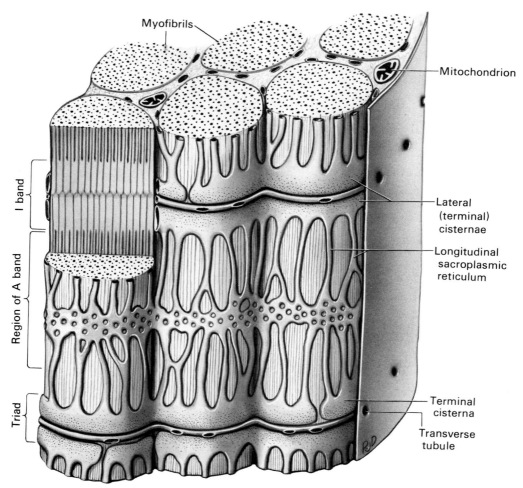

Fig. 8-18. Diagrammatic three-dimensional drawing to show the interrelationships of myofibrils, transverse tubules (T tubules), and elements of the sarcoplasmic reticulum in skeletal muscle. The diagram is based on studies of frog skeletal muscle in which the T tubules are located at the level of the Z line. In man, the T tubules are located at the level of the AI junctions, with two T tubules per sarcomere. The T tubules of cardiac muscle are located at the level of the Z line, as diagrammed here for skeletal muscle. The T tubules of cardiac muscle, however, are of much larger diameter than those of skeletal muscle and the cisternae of the sarcoplasmic reticulum are in a plexiform pattern that is continuous from one sarcomere to another. (Redrawn and modified after Peachey.)

"which functions as a safety catch, preventing activation of myosin adenosine triphosphatase by actin when calcium is absent, but allowing the activation to occur as soon as calcium can be bound by troponin," which is associated with actin. Adenosine triphosphatase, as noted earlier, is present in the cross bridges, or globular heads, of heavy meromyosin molecules. The latter can readily swing to join with active actin sites by reason of the flexible or hinge-like attachment of heavy meromyosin to the light meromyosin filament. In the process of contraction, adenosine triphosphate (ATP) is changed to adenosine diphosphate (ADP) with the release of free phosphate ions which

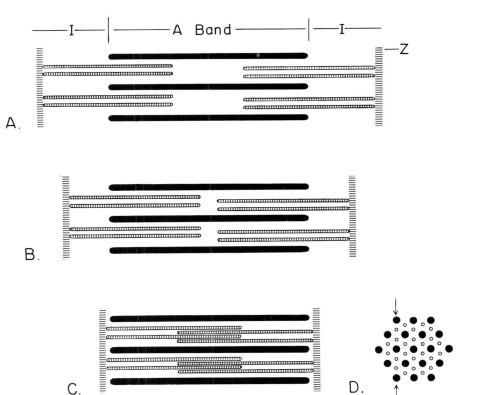

FIG. 8-19. Diagram showing changes in fine structure of skeletal muscle during contraction. *A*, Resting muscle; *B*, partially contracted; *C*, contracted; and *D*, arrangement of myofilaments as seen in a cross section through the anisotropic band. Note that longitudinal sections (*A*, *B*, *C*) will show the thick (myosin) filaments separated by two thin (actin) filaments when the plane of the section corresponds with that shown by the *arrows;* in sections perpendicular to the one indicated, two actin filaments will usually be superimposed and appear as one thin filament for each thick one. Note that the isotropic (*I*) band shortens and disappears during contraction, whereas the anisotropic (*A*) band maintains its length over a wide range of muscle lengths. In extreme contractions, beyond that illustrated, the ends of the myosin filaments of one sarcomere meet with those of adjacent sarcomeres and crumple along the *Z* line, giving rise to new band patterns. (Diagrams are based on illustrations and descriptions by H. E. Huxley.)

supply the source of energy. Apparently a phosphate group is split from ATP each time a cross bridge goes through a cycle. When removal of phosphate groups from ATP stops, there is no further action of myosin-actin cross bridges, and the muscle returns to its resting state. At the same time, calcium is withdrawn from the sarcoplasm to the cisternae of the sarcoplasmic reticulum. ADP is rephosphorylated into ATP before the muscle is ready for contraction again. Sarcosomes (mitochondria) carrying

the enzymes of the citric acid cycle have an important role in the formation and maintenance of ATP.

Connective Tissue. Surrounding each muscle fiber is a sheath irregularly woven out of very delicate reticular fibrils (Fig. 8-20). It is called the *endomysium*. At many points, the delicate fibrils combine into stronger strands which merge with collagenous connective tissue fibers. The collagenous fibers, mingled with elastic fibers, form a more or less complete connective tissue sheath about groups of a dozen or more muscle fibers to make up the fasciculi. The fasciculi are in their turn bound into larger and larger orders of bundles, and the entire muscle has as its outer investment, the deep fascia seen in gross anatomy. The outermost sheath of connective tissue is called the *epimysium*, while the tissue surrounding the fasciculi and dividing the muscle by septa is called the *perimysium*.

Muscle-tendon Attachment. At the ends of a muscle, its fibers are attached securely either to tendon, to periosteum or to some fibrous connective tissue structure. The terminations of the muscle fibers are rounded, abruptly conical or long and tapering and, in certain organs such as the tongue, may be split into digitations.

In sections stained with the ordinary dyes, the fibrillae of the muscle fiber often appear to be continuous with those of the tendon, no definite boundary between them being discernible. The striations of the muscle fiber decrease in distinctness so that the exact point at which they disappear and the tendon fibers begin is uncertain. Sections stained for reticular fibers by the Bielschowsky silver method show that the reticular fibers associated with the sarcolemma become aggregated into strands as they converge around the end of the muscle fiber, and that the strands become continuous with fiber bundles of the tendon (Goss, 1949). From these studies with the light microscope, it was concluded that the connective tissue fibers do not penetrate the sarcolemma but merely extend into indentations (Fig. 8-21). Electron micrographs have confirmed these conclusions and have shown in detail how the connective tissue fibers are inserted into invaginations of the sarcolemma.

Blood Vessels. The larger branches of the arteries penetrate the muscle by following the septae of the perimysium. The arterioles which penetrate the fasciculi give off capillaries at abrupt angles. The capillary supply is very rich (Fig. 8-22), several capillaries having contact with each muscular fiber. The veins follow the arteries; even their smallest branches have valves.

Lymphatic capillaries are not found between the individual muscle fibers. They are present, however, in the connective tissue septa and along the blood vessels.

Nerves. Every skeletal muscle fiber receives at least one motor nerve ending from the efferent cerebrospinal system. The minute anatomy of the motor end plates is described in Chapter 10. The

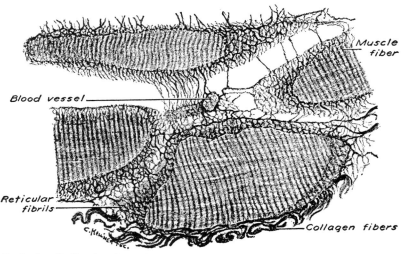

Fig. 8-20. Reticular fibrils of endomysium about skeletal muscle fibers. Foot silver method. ×900.

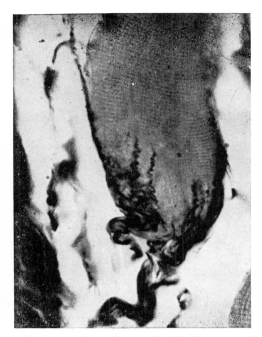

FIG. 8-21. Photomicrograph showing attachment of muscle to tendon. The muscle fiber is enclosed by a network of argyrophilic (reticular) fibers which project into invaginations of the sarcolemma at the end of the muscle fiber, thus giving a firm attachment of muscle and tendon. The argyrophilic fibers become continuous with bundles of collagenous fibers which are seen coursing toward a tendon at the lower left part of the micrograph. Monkey. Bielschowsky silver and Masson's stain. ×900. (After Goss.)

sensory or afferent fibers are principally associated with specialized end organs known as neuromuscular spindles.

Development of Skeletal Muscle. The skeletal muscles of the trunk are derived from the somatic mesoderm of myotomes of the embryonic segments or somites. The limb muscles are formed from the mesenchyme of the limb buds, and the muscles of the tongue are formed from head mesenchyme.

As in the case of smooth muscle, the first evidence of differentiation is the elongation of the nuclei and cell bodies to form myoblasts. Fusion of myoblasts gives rise to multinucleated *myotubes*. Growth occurs by continued fusion of myoblasts and myotubes. There is no evidence of nuclear division either by amitosis or mitosis in the multinucleated muscle cells. The specialized cytological structures, myofilaments, make their appearance in the cytoplasm shortly after the fusion of myoblasts. Actin and myosin filaments appear separately and are arranged randomly at first. They generally arise in the peripheral region of the cytoplasm and become gradually aligned at successively deeper regions within the cytoplasm, first in irregular bundles of filaments, and later with filaments in register at Z

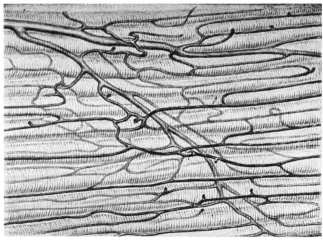

FIG. 8-22. Arterioles and capillaries in skeletal muscle. The vessels were filled with gelatin colored with carmine. ×140.

lines. It has been shown that the cytogenesis of skeletal muscle in vitro is similar to that in vivo and that the organelles (myofilaments and T tubules) can differentiate in the absence of any nerve supply to the muscle.

The number of muscle fibers apparently does not increase during the last month of fetal life or after birth. Increase in the overall size of a muscle is then brought about by the increase in diameter of the fibers through the formation of more myofilaments.

Not all of the primitive muscle fibers survive. Many of them fail to establish themselves as necessary units of the muscle and degenerate.

Regeneration is restricted in adult mammalian muscle by the lack of capacity to produce new fibers. Partial regeneration from remnants of injured or degenerated fibers occurs. The cut end of a fiber may send out a branched pseudopodium containing groups of nuclei, in a manner similar to the behavior of muscle fibers in tissue cultures. The cytoplasm of the pseudopodium is at first without specialized structure but later develops fibrillae and cross striations. Although there is some inherent capacity for growth and regeneration of adult skeletal muscle fibers, union between cut ends of fibers is more commonly effected by the connective tissue elements.

CARDIAC MUSCLE

The myocardium of vertebrate hearts is composed of muscle fibers (cells) which adjoin in an irregular manner to form a network. In mammals, the network of cells is partially subdivided by connective tissue into bundles and laminae that wind about the heart in long spirals, particularly in the ventricles. The fibers within a bundle are roughly parallel, but the bundles themselves course in different directions in the deeper and more superficial layers so that any section through the myocardium will present groups of fibers cut longitudinally, transversely and with varying degrees of obliquity.

Fibers. The cells or fibers of adult cardiac muscle fit together so tightly that they usually appear as a syncytium when examined under the light microscope (Figs. 8-23 and 8-25). Electron micrographs show that cardiac muscle is definitely not a syncytium but is composed of elongated, branching cells with irregular contours at their junctions. The fibers are usually about 14 μ in diameter in a normal adult heart, but they vary during normal growth and under pathological conditions. In a newborn, the fibers are only 6 to 8 μ, or approximately one-half the diameter of those of an adult. In hearts showing hypertrophy, the fibers may be 20 μ or more in diameter.

Each fiber is enclosed by a *sarcolemma* which is similar to that of skeletal muscle. The sarcolemma proper (the plasmalemma) is too thin to be resolved with the light microscope. The structure seen with the light microscope includes a cell membrane, a protein polysaccharide basal lamina outside the plasmalemma, and associated reticular fibers.

The *nuclei* are generally located in the central portion of the fiber, differing in this respect from skeletal muscle. There is usually only one nucleus per cell, or occasionally two, in contrast with the multinucleated condition in skeletal muscle. The nuclei are oval in shape and quite large, sometimes half the diameter of the fibers (Figs. 8-23 and 8-25).

The fibers contain two types of *myofilaments*, *myosin* and *actin*, similar to those in skeletal muscle. The filaments course in longitudinally oriented bundles or fascicles, generally known as *myofibrils*. However, the myofibrils course more irregularly than in skeletal muscle, and they frequently branch. Bundles of myofilaments of one myofibril often become confluent with those of an adjacent myofibril. Consequently, the myofibrils are not as well-demarcated as

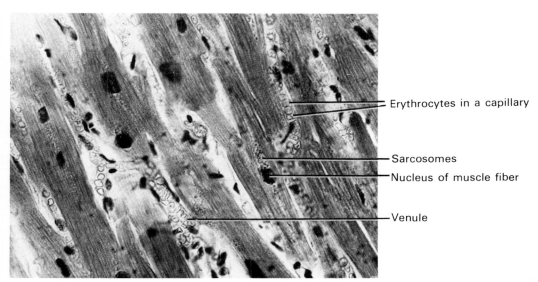

Erythrocytes in a capillary

Sarcosomes
Nucleus of muscle fiber

Venule

FIG. 8-23. Photomicrographs of a longitudinal section of cardiac muscle fibers from human ventricle. Note that the fibers branch and become apposed to each other in a complicated pattern. The intercalated discs at the sites of intercellular attachment are not obvious in this section, and they are frequently obscure in hematoxylin and eosin stained preparations of human cardiac muscle. Cardiac muscle has a rich blood supply and the capillaries and venules are seen clearly in this preparation. The 10μ section is sufficiently thick to show some of the vessels winding around and over the muscle fibers. ×390.

Venule   Nuclei of capillary endothelial cells

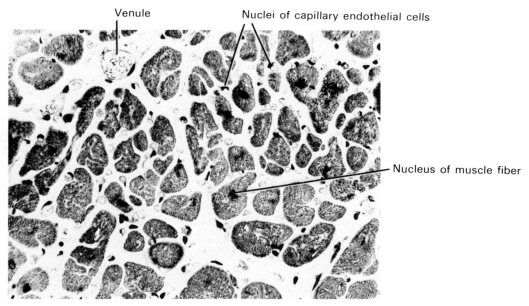

Nucleus of muscle fiber

FIG. 8-24. Photomicrograph of a transverse section of cardiac muscle from human ventricle. Note the central position of the nuclei and the irregular contour of branching fibers cut in cross section. The myofibrils are also cut in cross section, giving the cytoplasm of each fiber a stippled or punctate appearance. Hematoxylin and eosin. ×390.

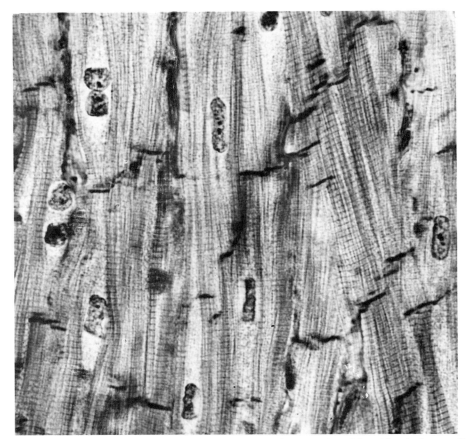

FIG. 8-25. Longitudinal section of muscle from left ventricle of monkey. The wider dark cross lines are intercalated discs. Sarcosomes may be seen in the clearer areas adjacent to the nuclei. Photomicrograph ×920.

they are in skeletal muscle. In longitudinal sections, it is seen that they diverge around the nucleus, leaving a paler staining zone at each pole of the nucleus (Fig. 8-25). In cross sections, the arrangement of the cut ends of the myofibrils often gives the appearance of bands or spokes of a wheel (Fig. 8-24).

The *sarcoplasm*, or cytoplasm, is readily seen with the light microscope in the perinuclear region, which is relatively free of myofibrils (Fig. 8-25). It contains the usual cell organelles plus the bundles of specialized myofilaments. It has a sarcoplasmic reticulum (endoplasmic reticulum), and it also contains fat droplets and glycogen. Lipochrome pigment granules may be present in

older hearts. *Mitochondria* are much more abundant than in skeletal muscle, and they are characterized by their numerous cristae. They are clustered in the area around the nucleus and are also distributed beneath the sarcolemma and between the bundles of myofilaments. In the latter region, there is usually one or two per sarcomere. The *Golgi complex* is located near the nucleus.

The *sarcoplasmic reticulum* consists mainly of smooth surfaced membranes, but small segments occasionally have polyribosomes attached. The cisternae tend to course longitudinally, but they anastomose so frequently that they give a plexiform pattern. The reticulum is continuous from one sarcomere level to another, and there are no dilated terminal cisternae around the Z line or at any other level. The membranes of the cisternae come into close association at various points with the membranes of the T tubules and with the sarcolemma at the cell surface. These junctions function as couplings in the excitation-contraction mechanism.

The *transverse tubules* are formed by invaginations of the sarcolemma into the deepest regions of the fiber. The tubules course in a transverse direction but are often interconnected by longitudinally oriented branches. They are generally at the level of the Z line in all vertebrates studied, similar to the location in frog skeletal muscle and different from mammalian skeletal muscle, which has the transverse tubules located at the A-I junctions. The transverse tubules of cardiac muscle have a much wider lumen than those of skeletal muscle, and their openings at the surface of the fiber are quite obvious in electron micrographs of glutaraldehyde-fixed material. The tubules do not open into the cisternae of the sarcoplasmic reticulum, but their membranes become closely associated at various points with the cisternal membranes. The membranes are separated by a space about 150 A wide, in which poorly defined densities are observed. Since the transverse tubules are associated with only one cisterna at any point, the association is called a *diad*, in distinction from *triads* of skeletal muscle in which a transverse tubule is located between two terminal cisternae. The membranes of the transverse tubule transmit the stimulus for contraction from the surface of the fiber to all depths of the fiber, and the *couplings* at the diads presumably effect a response within the lumen of the sarcoplasmic cisternae that results in the release of stored calcium to the sarcoplasm around the bundles of myofilaments. The presence of calcium is necessary for the actin-myosin reaction in contraction, as described for skeletal muscle.

Cisternae of the sarcoplasmic reticulum lying just beneath the sarcolemma often have couplings with the sarcolemma. These are also diads, and they function as peripheral couplings. Since the membrane of the transverse tubule is an invaginated sarcolemma, the sarcoplasmic cisternae associated with the T tubules, as well as those associated with the surface of the fiber, are actually *subsarcolemmal cisternae* (Fawcett and McNutt, 1969).

The cytological changes during contraction of cardiac muscle are similar to those in skeletal muscle. The sliding of actin filaments farther into the A band during contraction occurs by the same sequence of events. However, there are a number of differences in the functional reactions of these two types of muscle, such as differences in speed and strength of contraction, in factors affecting contraction and in autorhythmicity. For example, the heart muscle is more dependent upon calcium in the surrounding medium than skeletal muscle is. This may be correlated with the fact that heart muscle lacks the dilated terminal cisternae of skeletal muscle and has less space for internal storage of calcium. The contraction of cardiac muscle is relatively prolonged, somewhat like that of the "tonus muscles" of amphibians. In this respect, it is interesting that the myofilaments of cardiac muscle are in poorly defined bundles somewhat like those of the tonus skeletal muscles of amphibians. The ability of cardiac muscle to contract rhythmically at an intrinsic basic rate in the absence of a nerve supply or other external stimuli remains unexplained. Skeletal muscle usually contracts only after an external stimulus that is provided under normal conditions by the motor nerve endings.

Intercalated Discs. Intercalated discs are peculiar to cardiac muscle. They are cross bands 0.5 to 1 μ thick, i.e., less than a cross striation or sarcomere, which are strongly refractive in fresh muscle and deeply stained in fixed material (Fig. 8-25). They often follow an irregular course, giving the appearance of a step formation. Electron micrographs show that the intercalated

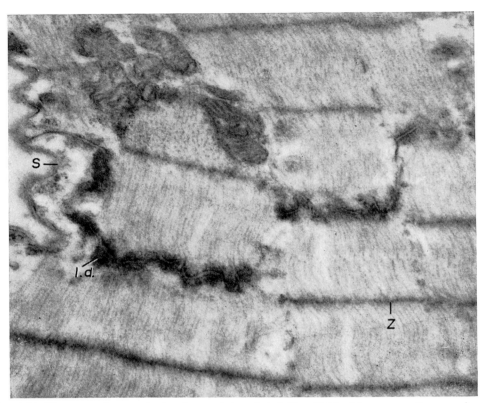

FIG. 8-26. Electron micrograph showing an intercalated disc (*I.d.*) of human cardiac muscle. Note the paired membranes within the disc which represent the cell membranes of adjoining muscle fibers. The membranes of the disc become continuous peripherally with the sarcolemma (*S*). (Courtesy of Dr. D. W. Fawcett.)

discs represent specialized cell junctions with a complex pattern and with a variety of structural characteristics (Figs. 8-26 and 8-27). In some regions, particularly where branches of the muscle fibers meet end-to-end, the cytoplasm along the inner surfaces of the membranes of adjacent cells is very electron-dense. In considerable portions of the electron-dense area, the membranes of apposing cells are separated by a space of uniform width (Fig. 8-27, A II) and the junctions resemble the desmosomes of epithelium (Fig. 4-7). All of the electron-dense regions have sufficient width to be seen as the intercalated discs of light microscopy. The desmosome-like portions of the junctions apparently function chiefly for cell adherence. In other regions of cell contacts, particularly where the cells meet

laterally, there are junctions that have been variously described as nexuses or gap junctions (Fig. 8-27, A III). It was once thought that the outer layers of adjacent cells are fused in nexuses but more recent studies show that there are gaps about 20 A in diameter between the membranes (Fawcett and McNutt, 1969). These gap junctions apparently function in transmission of impulses from one cell to another.

Connective Tissue of Cardiac Muscle.
In the mammalian heart, a net of reticular fibers and fine collagenous fibers surrounds each muscle fiber (Fig. 8-28). This net corresponds to the endomysium of skeletal muscle, but it is more irregular in its arrangement because the cardiac muscle cells are apposed to each other in a complicated

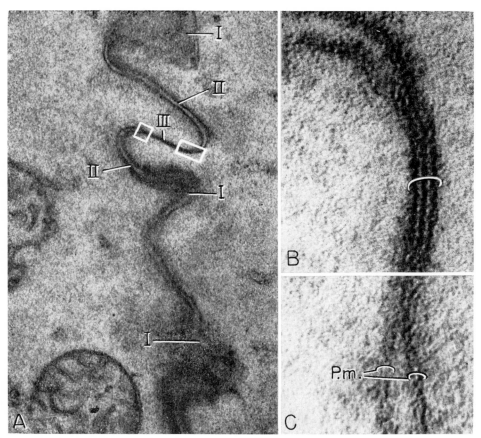

Fig. 8-27. Electron micrographs of an intercalated disc in heart muscle of guinea pig. *A*, different types of junctions: *I*, plasma membranes of adjacent cells are separated by extracellular material of variable width, and cell cytoplasm has electron-dense material; *II*, membranes of adjoining cells are separated by a narrow space of uniform width; *III*, membranes are joined and form a nexus. *B* and *C* show the outlined areas of *A* enlarged and rotated. The plasma membrane (*P.m.*) of each cell consists of an outer and an inner dense layer separated by a lighter zone. *A*, ×45,000; *B* and *C*, ×444,000. (Courtesy of Drs. Maynard M. Dewey and L. Barr.)

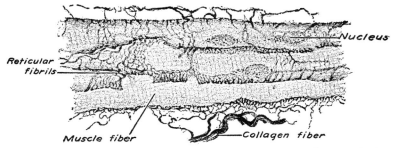

Fig. 8-28. Reticular fibrils about cardiac muscle fibers. Foot silver method. ×900

pattern. Between bundles of muscle fibers, there are coarser collagenous fibers and elastic fibers. These regions correspond to the perimysium of skeletal muscle. The connective tissue is particularly dense at the atrioventricular junction. The topographical arrangement of the connective tissues in the heart is described in Chapter 12.

Blood Vessels and Nerves of Cardiac Muscle. Branches of the coronary arteries and cardiac veins penetrate the myocardium by coursing among the collagenous and elastic fibers of the larger bundles of connective tissue. An extensive plexus of blood and lymph capillaries is found in the connective tissue network surrounding each muscle fiber. The blood supply of cardiac muscle surpasses that of skeletal muscle.

Branches of sympathetic and parasympathetic nerves follow the connective tissue pathways and terminate in fine endings on the muscle fibers. The frequency of muscle contraction is accelerated by stimulation of the sympathetics and retarded by the parasympathetics.

Conduction System. Cardiac muscle fibers, because of their intimate contact in a network and their inherent capacity to conduct, are capable of transmitting a contractile impulse over the entire heart. However, some of the fibers are modified in structure and conduct at a rate surpassing that of the typical cardiac fibers. The special conduction elements are known as *Purkinje fibers;* a description of their structure and distribution is given in Chapter 12.

Development of Cardiac Muscle. The heart muscle or myocardium is derived from the splanchnic mesoderm. It is recognizable at a very early age in mammals. At this stage, the cell boundaries can be distinguished in both living and fixed material under the light microscope. Cardiac muscle fibers arise by differentiation and growth of single cells, not by a fusion of cells as is the case for skeletal muscle fibers. Growth of the fibers occurs by formation of new myofilaments, particularly in the peripheral portion of the cytoplasm. The binucleate cells found frequently in the conduction system and occasionally in the working heart muscle cells probably arise by mitotic division of the nucleus without accompanying division of the cytoplasm.

Regeneration of Cardiac Muscle. There is little or no regenerative capacity of cardiac muscle fibers following injury or destruction. Healing is accomplished by scar formation.

Hypertrophy of the heart following any condition which places an excessive functional demand on the organ is accomplished by an increase in the size of the fibers rather than by an increase in their numbers. Likewise, growth of the heart during childhood is accomplished by an increase in the size of the fibers.

REFERENCES

BENNETT, H. S. 1960 The structure of striated muscle as seen by the electron microscope. *In* The Structure and Function of Muscle (Bourne, G. H., editor), vol. 1, pp. 137–181. Academic Press, New York.

BENDALL, J. R. 1969 Muscles, Molecules and Movement. (An Essay on the Contraction of Muscles). American Elsevier Publishing Company, Inc., New York.

BOURNE, G. H. (editor) 1960 The Structure and Function of Muscle. Three volumes. Academic Press, New York.

BOZLER, E., AND COTTRELL, C. L. 1937 The birefringence of muscle and its variation during contraction. J. Cell. Comp. Physiol., vol. 10, pp. 165–182.

BRANDT, P. W., LOPEZ, E., REUBEN, J. P., AND GRUNDFEST, H. 1967 The relationship between myofilament packing density and sarcomere length in frog striated muscle. J. Cell Biol., vol. 33, pp. 255–263.

DEAMER, D. W., AND BASKIN, R. J. 1969 Ultrastructure of sarcoplasmic reticulum preparations. J. Cell Biol., vol. 42, pp. 296–307.

DEWEY, M. M., AND BARR, L. 1962 Intercellular connection between smooth muscle cells: the nexus. Science, vol. 137, pp. 670–672.

EISENBERG, B., AND EISENBERG, R. S. 1968 Selective disruption of the sarcotubular system in frog sartorius muscle. A quantitative study with exogenous peroxidase as a marker. J. Cell Biol., vol. 39, pp. 451–467.

FAWCETT, D. W. 1960 The sarcoplasmic reticulum of skeletal and cardiac muscle. Circulation, vol. 24, pp. 336–348.

FAWCETT, D. W., AND MCNUTT, N. S. 1969 The ultrastructure of the cat myocardium. I. Ventricular papillary muscle. J. Cell Biol., vol. 42, pp. 1–45.

FISHMAN, A. P. (editor) 1960 The myocardium; its biochemistry and biophysics. Circulation, vol. 24, suppl. 2, and American Heart Association, New York.

GODMAN, G. C. 1957 On the regeneration and redifferentiation of mammalian striated muscle. J. Morph., vol. 100, pp. 27–82.

GOSS, C. M. 1944 The attachment of skeletal muscle fibers. Amer. J. Anat., vol. 74, pp. 259–289.

HALL, C. E., JAKUS, M. A., AND SCHMITT, F. O. 1946 An investigation of cross striations and myosin filaments in muscle. Biol. Bull., vol. 90, pp. 32–50.

HANSON, J., AND HUXLEY, H. E. 1955 The structural basis of contraction in skeletal muscle. Sympos. Soc. Exp. Biol., vol. 9, pp. 228–264.

HODGE, A. J. 1956 The fine structure of striated muscle. J. Biophys. Biochem. Cytol., vol. 2 (suppl.), pp. 131–142.

HUXLEY, H. E. 1964 The fine structure of striated muscle and its functional significance. Harvey Lectures, Ser. 60, pp. 85–117.

HUXLEY, H. E. 1969 The mechanism of muscular contraction. Science, vol. 164, pp. 1356–1366.

ISHIKAWA, H. 1968 Formation of elaborate networks of T-system tubules in cultured skeletal muscle, with special reference to the T-system formation. J. Cell Biol., vol. 38, pp. 51–66.

ISHIKAWA, H., BISCHOFF, R., AND HOLTZER, H. 1969 Formation of arrowhead complexes with heavy meromyosin in a variety of cell types. J. Cell Biol., vol. 43, pp. 312–328.

JOHNSON, A. J., AND SOMMER, J. R. 1967 A strand of cardiac muscle. Its ultrastructure and the electrophysiological implications of its geometry. J. Cell Biol., vol. 33, pp. 103–129.

KELLY, D. E. 1967 Models of muscle Z-band fine structure based on a looping filament configuration. J. Cell Biol., vol. 34, pp. 827–839.

KELLY, D. E. 1969 Myofibrillogenesis and Z-band differentiation. Anat. Rec., vol. 163, pp. 403–425.

KELLY, R. E., AND RICE, R. V. 1969 Ultrastructural studies on the contractile mechanism of smooth muscle. J. Cell Biol., vol. 42, pp. 683–694.

KNAPPEIS, G. G., AND CARLSEN, F. 1962 The ultrastructure of the Z disc in skeletal muscle. J. Cell Biol., vol. 13, pp. 323–336.

KNAPPEIS, G. G., AND CARLSEN, F. 1968 The ultrastructure of the M-line in skeletal muscle. J. Cell Biol., vol. 38, pp. 202–211.

LEGATO, M. J., AND LANGER, G. A. 1969 The subcellular localization of calcium ion in mammalian myocardium. J. Cell Biol., vol. 41, pp. 401–423.

MCNUTT, N. S., AND WEINSTEIN, R. S. 1970 The ultrastructure of the nexus. Jour. of Cell Biol., vol. 47, pp. 666–688.

MOMMAERTS, W. F. H. M., WITH BRADY, A. J., AND ABBOTT, B. C. 1961 Major problems in muscle physiology. Ann. Rev. Physiol., vol. 23, pp. 529–576.

MONOMURA, Y. 1968 Myofilaments in smooth muscle of guinea pig's taenia coli. J. Cell Biol., vol. 39, pp. 741–745.

PANNER, B. J., AND HONIG, C. R. 1967 Filament ultrastructure and organization in vertebrate smooth muscle. Contraction hypothesis based on localization of actin and myosin. J. Cell Biol., vol. 35, pp. 303–321.

PANNER, B. J., AND HONIG, C. R. 1970 Locus and state of aggregation of myosin in tissue sections of vertebrate smooth muscle. J. Cell Biol., vol. 44, pp. 52–61.

PEACHEY, L. D. 1965 The sarcoplasmic reticulum and transverse tubules of frog's sartorius. J. Cell Biol., vol. 25 (no. 3, part 2), pp. 209–231.

PEACHEY, L., AND PORTER, K. R. 1959 Intracellular impulse conduction in muscle cells. Science, vol. 129, pp. 721–722.

POGOGEFF, T. A., AND MURRAY, M. R. 1946 Form and behavior of adult mammalian skeletal muscle in vitro. Anat. Rec., vol. 95, pp. 321–336.

PORTER, K. R. 1956 The sarcoplasmic reticulum in muscle cells of Amblystoma larvae. J. Biophys. Biochem. Cytol., vol. 2 (suppl.), pp. 163–170.

RICE, R. V., MOSES, J. A., MCMANUS. G. M., BRADY, A. C., AND BLASIK, L. M. 1970 The organization of contractile filaments in a mammalian smooth muscle. J. Cell Biol., vol. 47, pp. 183–196.

ROSENBLUTH, J. 1963 Fine structure of epineural muscle cells in Aplysia californica. J. Cell Biol., vol. 17, pp. 455–460.

ROSENBLUTH, J. 1967 Obliquely striated muscle. II. Contraction mechanism of Ascaris body muscle. J. Cell Biol., vol. 34, pp. 15–33.

SHIMADA, Y., FISCHMAN, D. A., AND MOSCONA, A. A. 1967 The fine structure of embryonic chick skeletal muscle cells differentiated in vitro. J. Cell Biol., vol. 35, pp. 445–453.

SPIRO, D. 1962 The ultrastructure of heart muscle. Trans. N. Y. Acad. Sci., Ser. II, vol. 24, pp. 879–885.

SZENT-GYÖRGYI, A. 1953 Chemical Physiology of Contraction in Body and Heart Muscle. Academic Press, Inc., New York.

9

Organization of Nervous Tissue

Every nerve cell of the body is an integral part of a single organized system, the *nervous system*. The typical nerve cell has the capability of generating and conveying a form of electrical activity called a nerve impulse, and these impulses provide a means of rapid signaling between various regions of the body. By combining many nerve cells into a single system, the organism is able to receive information from its environment, analyze this information and respond in an appropriate manner.

An understanding of the organization of nervous tissue is aided by a brief consideration of nervous system development. The primitive nervous system forms on the dorsal surface of the developing embryo as the surface layer (the ectoderm) thickens and then folds up to form a deep groove. This groove closes over and becomes a long hollow tube (the *neural tube*) extending over the entire length of the developing embryo (Fig. 9-1). Proliferation along the internal aspect of this tube leads to a rapid increase in the number of nerve cells. Relatively greater proliferative activity anteriorly leads to the formation of the *brain;* posteriorly, the basic developmental pattern persists in the *spinal cord* (Fig. 9-2). Later, cellular proliferation along the neural tube provides the companion cells of the neurons, the *neuroglia.* Together these derivatives of the neural tube comprise the *central nervous system.* The central nervous system is later surrounded and invaded by mesoderm derivatives that contribute to the ensheathing *meninges* and provide the blood vessels.

To bring this central mass of nerve tissue into contact with other parts of the body, nerve fibers grow out from certain of the cells in the brain and spinal cord (and some nerve cell bodies migrate out into peripheral tissues) to make functional contact with the *effectors* of the body—the muscles and glands. These outgrowing fibers will carry impulses from the central system to peripheral structures. They are the *output* of the nervous system and are called *efferent* or *motor* because they control the activities of the outlying tissues.

Other neurons develop from a cord of tissue dorsal and lateral to the developing neural tube, a group of cells called the *neural crest* (Fig. 9-1). These nerve cells take permanent residence in ganglia outside the central nervous system and develop fibers which will connect the periphery with the central nervous system. These fibers provide an *input* for the central neurons; they carry impulses from the periphery back to the central nervous system and are therefore called *afferent* or *sensory.* The motor and sensory nerves become intermixed to form the *cranial* and *spinal nerves* of the *peripheral nervous system* (Fig. 9-2).

THE NEURON

The functional unit within both the central and peripheral nervous systems is the

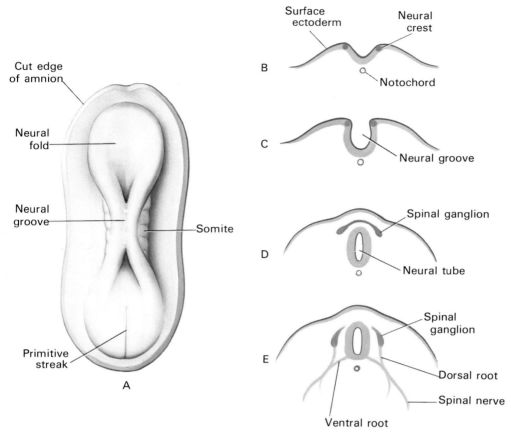

FIG. 9-1. Surface and cross-sectional views of the development of the neural tube on the dorsal surface of the embryo. The lips of the neural fold fuse to enclose a hollow tube, the neural tube. This fusion progresses anteriorly and posteriorly until the neural tube is completely shut off from the amnionic fluid. Parts *B*, *C*, *D*, and *E* show cross-sections through the neural tube at various stages of development. The derivation of the spinal ganglion from the neural crest, and the joining together of the dorsal and ventral nerve root to form the spinal nerve are shown.

nerve cell or *neuron*. Although these cells exhibit a great variety of forms, every neuron is characterized by having one or more cytoplasmic processes. Some of these processes are specialized to receive signals from other neurons. These processes are called *dendrites*, and this part of the neuron is termed the *receptive* portion. Other processes (*axons*) are specialized for the specific function of generating the nerve impulse (frequently termed the *action potential*) and conducting this impulse to the most distal regions of the axon. In these terminal regions, the typical central nervous system axon forms a special contact, a *synapse*, with the dendritic portion or the cell body of another nerve cell. Many neurons receive a great number of signals from a variety of sources on their dendritic, or receptive, surface. Those incoming signals may be *inhibitory* or *excitatory*. The summation of these influences will determine whether the neuron will fire (i.e., generate its own action potential) and thus influence the dendritic portion of the next nerve cell in the pathway. The cytoplasmic processes of the nerve cell (the axons and the dendrites together) are sometimes referred to as *nerve fibers;* during development these processes are often called *neurites*.

BASIC ORGANIZATION

An arrangement whereby a motor and a sensory neuron are linked together synaptically as a receptor-effector mechanism constitutes the simplest type of *reflex arc*. An example of this type of combination is illustrated in Figure 9-3, *A*, which represents a cross section through the spinal cord and a spinal nerve. The cell body of the sensory neuron is located outside the spinal cord where, together with other similar cell bodies, it forms a spinal ganglion. The sensory neuron is unipolar: that is, it has only one process. A short distance from the cell body, this single process, which is structurally an axon, divides into a peripheral process with a receptor ending in the skin and a central process which enters the spinal cord by way of the *dorsal root* of the spinal nerve. The central process may terminate in contact with either the dendrites or the cell body of a multipolar motor neuron located in the ventral part of the cord. The axon of this second neuron leaves the cord by way of the *ventral root*, joins the sensory fibers to form the *spinal nerve* and courses peripherally to terminate on an effector (skeletal muscle, in the example illustrated in Fig. 9-3, *A*).

The two-neuron reflex, described above, although theoretically possible, is a much more simple arrangement than that which is usually found in mammals. More commonly, a series of neurons is interposed between the sensory and motor neurons of the basic reflex arc. These are commonly called interneurons (or internuncial neurons). Simpler nervous systems, as in some invertebrates, often have relatively few interneurons interposed between receptors and effectors, and the reactions of the organism are quite stereotyped and predictable. In higher animals, the pathways provided by interneurons can be very complex; and nerve impulses generated in receptors

in the periphery are carried to many levels of the nervous system, including the highest centers (the cerebral cortex) of the brain. In the various parts of the brain, incoming information is sorted, stored and used in determining the appropriate motor responses. Complex interneuronal pathways lead from the brain back to the cranial or spinal motor neurons and are influential in determining whether these neurons will fire, i.e., generate a nerve impulse (and thus cause a muscle to contract or a gland to secrete). In the vertebrate nervous system, the cranial or spinal motor neuron is the chief executive; these cells constantly receive "advice" in the form of hundreds or thousands of inhibitory and excitatory synapses applied to their dendritic portion or to their cell bodies. These motor neurons provide the *final common pathway* from the central nervous system to its effector organs. When they fire, there is no mechanism of recall; the muscle contracts or the gland secretes.

THE SPINAL NERVE

The arrangement of the nerve cells and fibers within the spinal cord makes it possible to differentiate two distinct areas of tissue: a thick peripheral layer of *white matter* and a central column of *gray matter* (Fig. 9-3). The white matter is composed primarily of longitudinally directed nerve fibers, many of which are covered by sheaths of a white, fatty substance, *myelin*. The gray matter is composed principally of nerve cells and their fibers and neuroglia. Many of the fibers of the gray matter are unmyelinated, but a considerable number of myelinated ones are present also. In transverse section, the gray matter is shaped like the letter H. Its dorsal wings constitute the *dorsal horns* and its ventral ones the *ventral horns* in which lie the cell bodies of the motor neurons. The two lateral gray areas are connected across the midline by a transverse bar, the *gray commissure*, in which lies the small central canal. It is, of course, evident that the dorsal and ventral horns seen in

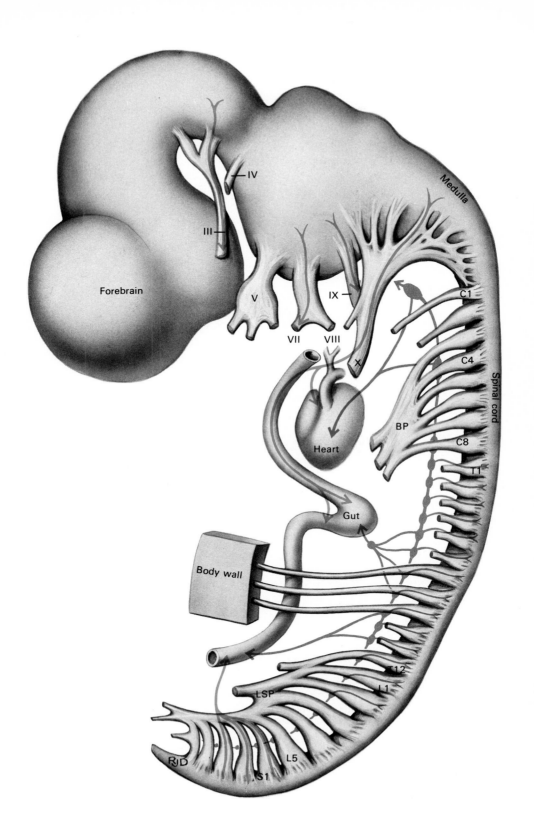

Fig. 9-2. This diagram shows the derivatives of the neural tube after brain parts have begun to form and after the cranial and spinal nerves have developed. Cranial nerves shown are given Roman numerals, the spinal nerves of the cervical (C), thoracic (T), lumbar (L), and sacral (S) regions are indicated by numbers. The craniosacral (blue) and thoracolumbar (red) parts of the autonomic nervous outflow are shown to emphasize how these divisions derive from the "head and tail" and the "middle" part of the neuraxis to provide dual innervation to visceral structures. The chain of autonomic ganglia extending from head to tail is shown; this is the method by which thoracolumbar nerve fibers can be distributed to all parts of the body. The dominance of the vagus nerve (X) in the innervation of the trunk viscera is also apparent. The fact that autonomic outflow is always a two-neuron system is not shown.

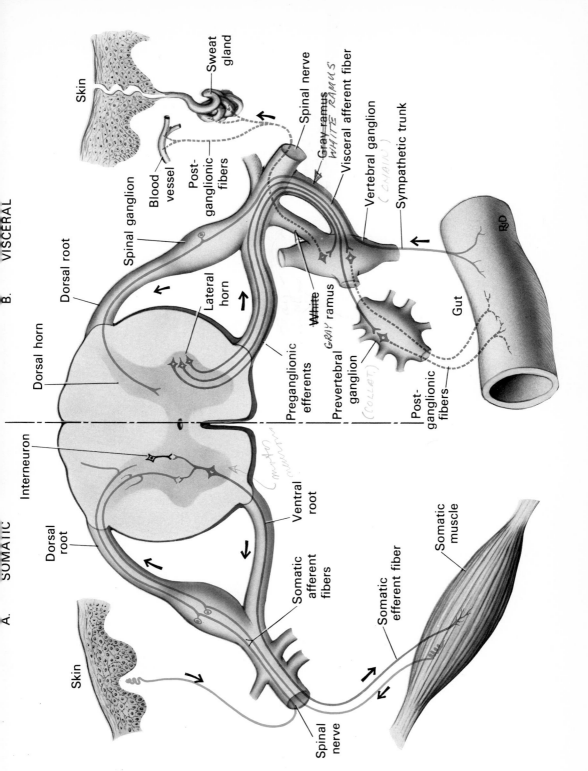

A. SOMATIC   B. VISCERAL

Labels in figure:

Skin
Sweat gland
Blood vessel
Post-ganglionic fibers
Spinal ganglion
Dorsal root
Spinal nerve
Gray ramus
WHITE RAMUS
Visceral afferent fiber
Vertebral ganglion (CHAIN)
Sympathetic trunk
Lateral horn
Dorsal horn
White
GRAY ramus
Preganglionic efferents
Prevertebral ganglion (COLLAT)
Post-ganglionic fibers
Gut
Interneuron
Dorsal root
Ventral root
motor nerve
Somatic afferent fibers
Somatic efferent fiber
Somatic muscle
Skin
Spinal nerve

FIG. 9-3. *A*, somatic nerves. *B*, visceral nerves. A cross-section of spinal cord is shown connected via dorsal and ventral roots to the spinal nerve and to one of the ganglia of the autonomic system. The pattern of afferent (blue) and efferent (red) nerve fibers in both the somatic and visceral system may be directly compared. For details see text.

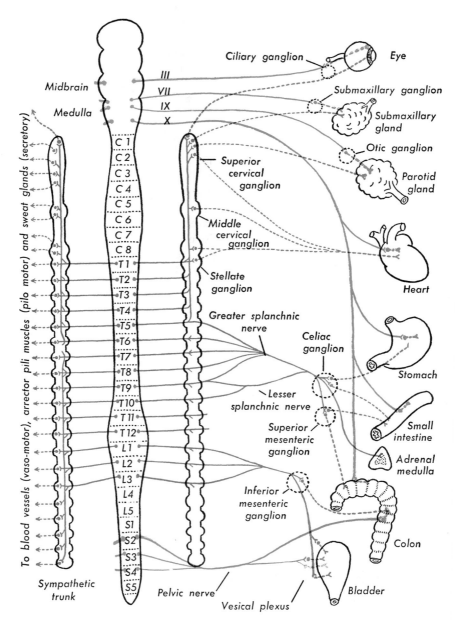

FIG. 9-4. Diagrammatic representation of some of the chief conduction pathways of the autonomic nervous system. For clearness, the nerves to blood vessels, arrector pili muscles and sweat glands are shown only on the *left side* of the figure and the pathways to other visceral structures only on the *right side*. The sympathetic division is shown in red, the parasympathetic division in blue. Solid lines represent preganglionic fibers; broken lines represent postganglionic fibers.

cross section actually are continuous columns of gray matter extending the length of the cord.

The *dorsal roots* are composed of the afferent or sensory fibers; these fibers have their cell bodies grouped into an enlargement of the dorsal root called the *dorsal root ganglion* (Fig. 9-3). The *ventral roots* contain the efferent or motor fibers and these join the dorsal root to make up the *spinal nerve*. Those afferent fibers which are distributed to sensory endings in the body, exclusive of the viscera, are termed *somatic afferent* fibers; those providing the sensory innervation of the viscera are the *visceral afferent* fibers. Both functional types have their cell bodies in the spinal ganglia (Fig. 9-3).

A great many of the efferent fibers are distributed to the voluntary skeletal muscle of the body and are therefore termed *somatic efferent* fibers. Other efferent fibers terminate on smooth or cardiac muscle and glandular epithelium of visceral structures; these are the *visceral efferent* fibers.

THE AUTONOMIC NERVOUS SYSTEM

The visceral efferent components of both the cranial and the spinal nerves pursue a different course than do the somatic efferent fibers, for two neurons are always involved in the conduction of a visceral impulse from the central nervous system to the effector organ. They also differ physiologically in that the essentially visceral reflexes which they mediate are often not subject to direct voluntary control and are also more or less diffuse, rather than localized, in their effects. Because of these and certain other differences, it has been found convenient to consider the visceral efferent neurons of the body as a separate physiological system for which the name first given by Langley, the *autonomic nervous system,* is commonly used. According to the original definition, the autonomic system included only the visceral efferent (motor) innervation and did not include either the

visceral afferent (sensory) fibers or those higher centers in the central nervous system which influence the visceral activities. In recent years, however, the usage of the term "autonomic" generally has included all of the neural apparatus concerned with visceral function. In this sense, the term becomes more synonymous with "visceral" or "vegetative."

It must be emphasized that the autonomic nervous system is purely a functional grouping of efferent neurons and is in no sense an anatomical division. Some neurons lie within the central nervous system; others (which have migrated peripherally during development) are located in visceral ganglia in distant regions of the body. Autonomic nerve fibers are present in all spinal nerves and in most of the cranial nerves. The reflexes which they govern may be initiated by sensory impulses flowing over somatic afferent or visceral afferent fibers or coming from any receptor organ. The stimuli may be in the external environment or they may arise within the body.

The efferent fibers to visceral structures leave the central nervous system at three levels, making it possible to recognize three divisions of the autonomic nervous system (Fig. 9-3). In the *cranial division,* fibers leave by way of the third, seventh, ninth, 10th and 11th cranial nerves. Other visceral efferent fibers emerge through the thoracic and the upper lumbar spinal nerves; these constitute the *thoracolumbar division.* The *sacral division* includes visceral efferent fibers in the second, third and fourth sacral nerves.

Whatever their level of origin, all visceral efferent pathways involve two successive neurons (Figs. 9-3 and 9-4). The first of these has its cell body within the central nervous system and its axon terminating in a peripheral autonomic ganglion; it is therefore termed a *preganglionic* neuron. In the ganglion, it makes synaptic connection with a second multipolar neuron whose axon terminates in the effector organ (muscle or epithelium). This is the *post-ganglionic* neuron.

In the cranial and sacral divisions, the preganglionic fibers generally end in *terminal* ganglia which lie near or within the walls of the structures that they innervate. In this and other respects, as well as in their response to certain drugs, the cranial and sacral divisions resemble each other and differ from the thoracolumbar components. They are therefore grouped together as the craniosacral or *parasympathetic* division of the autonomic nervous system.

The thoracolumbar visceral efferent outflow is the *sympathetic* division of the autonomic nervous system. Its preganglionic fibers terminate in either *vertebral* or *prevertebral* ganglia. The vertebral ganglia are a series of ganglia, connected linearly by nerve fibers, that lie along the ventrolateral aspects of the vertebral column and thus form two *sympathetic trunks* extending on either side the length of the vertebral column. The prevertebral, or *collateral*, ganglia are aggregations of postganglionic neurons associated with visceral nerve plexuses in the abdomen (Figs. 9-3 and 9-4).

It can be said in general that most visceral organs are innervated by both the parasympathetic and sympathetic divisions, the effects of which are usually antagonistic. For example, the parasympathetic fibers to the heart transmit impulses which tend to slow the heart rate; impulses from the sympathetic fibers, on the other hand, accelerate it. In the case of the stomach, parasympathetic impulses excite muscular contraction, and sympathetic impulses inhibit it. The stimulation of the parasympathetic contributes to the conservation of bodily energy; the stimulation of the sympathetic assists the body in meeting emergencies.

Sympathetic Division. The sympathetic trunks are composed of a series of vertebral ganglia containing the cell bodies of postganglionic neurons and connected in linear order by ascending or descending nerve fibers (Figs. 9-2 to 9-4). In the cervical region there are three ganglia: the *superior cervical* ganglion, which is the largest; the *middle cervical*, sometimes absent; and the *inferior cervical*, which may be fused with the first thoracic to form the *stellate ganglion*. In the thoracic region, the ganglia, 10 or 11 in number, are segmentally arranged. Three or four ganglia are associated with the lumbar level and four or five with the sacral region.

Each sympathetic trunk is connected with the spinal nerves of its side by a series of communicating rami composed of nerve fibers. These are of two types. One type, the *gray communicating rami*, consists of fibers mostly devoid of myelin; these are found connecting the trunk to every spinal nerve. The other type, the *white communicating rami*, is limited to the thoracic and first three or four lumbar nerves and is not present at cervical or sacral levels (Fig. 9-3).

Preganglionic fibers of the sympathetic division have their cell bodies located in the *intermediolateral cell column (lateral horn)* of the thoracic and upper lumbar levels of the spinal cord (Fig. 9-3). The myelinated fibers emerge through the ventral roots and reach the nearby sympathetic trunk by way of the white communicating rami. Within the sympathetic trunk the preganglionic fiber may take one of three courses:

1. It may terminate in this level of the trunk in synaptic relation to a postganglionic neuron whose nonmyelinated axon joins the corresponding spinal nerve by way of the gray communicating ramus. With the various other fibers of this nerve, the postganglionic fiber courses peripherally to terminate in the smooth muscle of a blood vessel (vasomotor), the arrector pili muscle of a hair (pilomotor) or among the epithelial cells of a sweat gland (secretory) (Fig. 9-3).

2. Many of the preganglionic fibers from the white rami pass directly through the sympathetic trunk without interruption and continue to the prevertebral (collateral) ganglia, from which postganglionic fibers course to the visceral organs. Preganglionic

fibers such as these give the appearance of forming branches from the sympathetic trunks. Those from the fifth to 10th thoracic ganglia form the *splanchnic nerves*, which terminate in the *celiac ganglia*, which are prevertebral. The postganglionic fibers contribute to the formation of the celiac plexus and pass directly to their terminations in the viscera.

3. A great many of the preganglionic fibers, upon reaching the sympathetic trunk, course either caudally or cephalically in this trunk before they have a synaptic juncture with postganglionic neurons. These fibers form the pathways for the visceral efferent outflow to regions of the trunk which do not possess white rami. For example, preganglionic fibers originating at levels as low as the seventh thoracic terminate in the superior cervical ganglion. From this ganglion, nonmyelinated postganglionic nerve fibers run to various visceral structures. Some accompany the internal carotid artery as the internal carotid plexus and furnish the pathway by which impulses reach the dilator pupillae muscle of the eye. Other fibers form the superior cervical cardiac nerve to the cardiac plexus and conduct impulses which accelerate the rhythm of the heart.

Other pathways of the sympathetic division are shown diagrammatically in Figure 9-4.

Parasympathetic Division. It has already been noted that most structures innervated by the autonomic system receive a double nerve supply in the form of fibers from its sympathetic and parasympathetic divisions, and that the action of these two divisions is generally antagonistic.

The cranial parasympathetic preganglionic neurons lie in the midbrain and medulla, sending their axons out over the oculomotor, facial, glossopharyngeal, vagus and accessory cranial nerves (Fig. 9-2). These preganglionic fibers are myelinated and course in their respective nerves to terminal ganglia located near or within visceral structures.

In the case of the oculomotor nerve, the preganglionic fibers enter the orbit with this nerve but diverge to reach the ciliary ganglion, forming its short motor root. The ciliary ganglion, which lies against the lateral surface of the optic nerve, contains the postganglionic neurons whose axons course in the short ciliary nerves to the eyeball. In the eyeball, they are distributed to the ciliary muscle of accommodation and the sphincter muscle of the iris. The antagonistic action of parasympathetic and sympathetic nerves is here evident, for the parasympathetic fibers bring about contraction of the pupil. It has already been noted that sympathetic postganglionic fibers from the superior cervical ganglion cause dilation of the pupil.

The vagus nerve contains many preganglionic fibers. The cell bodies lie in the medulla, and many of the fibers pass to the cardiac plexus and terminate in synaptic relation to ganglion cells located on the surface of the atria and roots of the great vessels or in the subepicardium of the atrial walls. The axons of these cardiac ganglion cells are short postganglionic fibers which end in the heart muscle. They are inhibitory in function.

The parasympathetic innervation of the gastrointestinal tract and other abdominal viscera is through efferent fibers of the vagus nerve and also the pelvic nerve, which arises from nerve cells in the lateral horn of the second, third and fourth sacral segments of the spinal cord. These are preganglionic fibers. Those which innervate the gastrointestinal tract course without interruption to terminate in its wall. Here they are synaptically related to postganglionic neurons which, with associated plexuses of nerve fibers, form two extensive ganglionated plexuses, the *enteric ganglionated plexuses*. One of these, the *myenteric plexus* or *plexus of Auerbach*, is situated between the longitudinal and circular layers of muscle. The other, the *submucosal plexus* or *plexus of Meissner*, lies in the submucosa. These plexuses are composed of small ganglia connected to each other by strands of nerve fibers. Other strands connect the plexuses with each other.

Preganglionic fibers which pass to pelvic reproductive and urinary organs terminate in synaptic relation to the cell bodies of postganglionic neurons located in or near the walls of these viscera.

The nerve fibers of the enteric plexuses fall into the following classes:

1. *Postganglionic sympathetic fibers*, derived from postganglionic neurons located chiefly in prevertebral ganglia. They end on the smooth muscle of the gut and among epithelial cells. Their impulses usually inhibit gastrointestinal activity.

2. *Preganglionic parasympathetic fibers*. These are fibers of the vagus or, in the descending colon and rectum, the visceral branches of sacral nerves. They end in synapses with the ganglion cells of the myenteric or submucosal plexuses.

3. *Postganglionic parasympathetic fibers*, which are axons of the above mentioned ganglion cells. They innervate smooth muscle and epithelium of the gut, and their impulses usually excite gastrointestinal activity.

4. *Visceral afferent fibers*. These fibers are sensory and intermingle with the visceral efferent fibers. They play an important part in gastrointestinal reflexes. Some of the sensory fibers from the gut course in the vagus to the sensory ganglia of this nerve and from there to the medulla. Other sensory fibers course in the visceral nerves, then through the vertebral sympathetic ganglia and the white rami communicantes to their cell bodies in the spinal ganglia and then to the spinal cord (Fig. 9-3).

REFERENCES

ARIËNS KAPPERS, C. U., HUBER, G. C., AND CROSBY, E. C. 1960 The Comparative Anatomy of the Nervous System of Vertebrates, Including Man. 3 volumes. Hafner Publishing Company, New York.

BOURNE, G. H. (editor) 1968–1969 The Structure and Function of Nervous Tissue. Three volumes. Academic Press, New York.

BULLOCK, T. H., AND HORRIDGE, G. A. 1968 Structure and Function in the Nervous Systems of Invertebrates. Two volumes. W. H. Freeman and Company, San Francisco.

CANNON, W. B. 1939 The Wisdom of the Body. W. W. Norton & Co., Inc., New York.

CANNON, W. B., AND ROSENBLUETH, A. 1937 Autonomic Neuro-effector Systems. The Macmillan Company, New York.

CROSBY, E. C., HUMPHREY, T., AND LAUER, E. W. 1962 Correlative Anatomy of the Nervous System. The Macmillan Company, New York.

HERRICK, C. J. 1931 An Introduction to Neurology. W. B. Saunders Company, Philadelphia.

KUNTZ, A. 1953 The Autonomic Nervous System. Lea & Febiger, Philadelphia.

NOBACK, C. 1967 The Human Nervous System. McGraw-Hill Book Company, New York.

RAMON Y CAJAL, S. 1909–1911 Histologie du Système Nerveux de l'Homme et des Vertébrés. Two volumes. A. Maloine, Paris.

TRUEX, R. C., AND CARPENTER, M. B. 1969 Strong and Elwyn's Human Neuroanatomy. The Williams & Wilkins Company, Baltimore.

WHITE, C., SMITHWICK, R. H., AND SIMEONE, F. A. 1952 The Autonomic Nervous System. The Macmillan Company, New York.

10

Nervous Tissue

In higher animals, the great majority of nerve cells are within central nervous tissue. The histology of this tissue reflects its origin. Like other epithelia, its cells are closely packed with little extracellular space or substance and are connected by frequent cell to cell junctions. Unlike most epithelia, however, nervous tissue is comprised of enormous numbers of cells, many of great complexity, and it contains a special type of junction: the synapse (from a Greek word meaning clasp). Neurons must be connected into the synaptic network to survive, and a cell is identified as a neuron if it receives or provides synapses. The human brain contains billions of neurons, and certain of these receive thousands of synapses. The enormous number of neurons in the human body and the complexity and specificity of their synaptic networks provides for the functional capabilities of the nervous system and gives man his rich variety of reaction and behavior.

In the central nervous system (CNS), the neuronal somas are the most conspicuous elements, and they tend to occur in groups. These groups of cell bodies are called *nuclei* (not to be confused with the nucleus of a single cell) if they occur as a cluster, *layers* if they occur in a laminar array and *columns* if they occur in a linear configuration. Related to the nerve cell bodies are great entanglements of nerve cell processes (or fibers) called *neuropil* where many of the synaptic contacts occur. Nerve fibers grouped into bundles that travel to other parts of the nervous system are called *tracts*.

Although a variety of special techniques is required to work out the "wiring diagrams" of nervous tissue, much can be learned from standard preparations. Neurons can generally be identified, and their organization into nuclei, layers and columns can be analyzed. The "cytoarchitecture" will reveal whether there has been abnormal development or injury to the nervous system. More specialized techniques delineate the whole of the neuronal contour, demonstrate synapses or detect certain types of neurotransmitters; other procedures demonstrate degenerating cell processes. Only when electron microscopy is used in addition to these basic techniques, however, is the full complexity of the nervous system apparent.

The CNS is marked by compactness, in contrast with the peripheral nervous tissues in which nerve cell bodies and nerve fibers are interspersed with distinctive connective tissue elements. Groups of nerve cells in the peripheral nervous system are termed *ganglia*, entanglements of nerve fibers are termed *plexuses* and a bundle of parallel nerve fibers is a *nerve* or *nerve root*.

Detailed study of the synaptic networks of the nervous system will be found in textbooks of neuroanatomy. It is the purpose of this chapter to describe the histology and cytology of the cellular elements of the nervous system, not only of the neuron but also of the supportive cells and the connective tissue. Supportive cells—the *neuroglia*—are the helper cells of the neuron. These cells include the neuroglia of the central nervous system, the neurilemma (or Schwann) cells of the peripheral nerve fibers and the satellite cells of the cerebrospinal and sympathetic ganglia. *Connective tissue* is associated with the above elements in the structure of some parts of the nervous system. Connective tissue forms part of the membranous investments (the meninges) of the central nervous system and provides tubular investments around peripheral nerves. It also contributes to the capsules of the ganglia and is associated with the sensory nerve fiber endings in the formation of sense organs.

THE NEURON

The neuron may be defined as the nerve cell body with all of its extensions. Neurons are generally elongated—some may be over 5 feet long—to provide for their function of communicating between various regions of the body (Fig. 10-1). Despite their elongation, neurons generally are not multinucleated (as are skeletal muscle cells), and it is important to recognize the portion of the nerve cell which contains the nucleus (the perikaryon), for this region is vital for the survival of the entire cell. The processes extending from the perikaryon are specialized for three primary functions (Fig. 10-2): (1), *reception* of various stimuli: this is generally the function of the dendrites, although areas of the cell body or the axon may also receive signals from other cells, (2) *conduction* of the nerve impulse to regions distant from the receptive area: this is generally the function of the axon, but parts of some dendrites and cell bodies may also propagate impulses, and (3) *synaptic transmission* of the signal to subsequent neurons in the neural pathways, or to muscle or gland. This *effector* function generally

occurs in the nerve terminals where minute amounts of chemical compounds called *neurotransmitters* are released. Each neuron is thus equipped to receive information, to act on the basis of this information to signal its distant portions and then to influence other neurons or other tissues.

Classification of Neurons by Shape. The general form of the neuron is best studied after staining thick sections of nervous tissue with heavy metals such as silver or gold (Fig. 10-3). Adaptation to different functional needs in various parts of the body leads to a great spectrum of neuronal shapes and sizes (Fig. 10-1). *Multipolar neurons* (Fig. 10-1, *B*, *C*, *D*, *F*, *G* and *H*) frequently have a number of dendrites arising directly from the cell body. The axon may also arise from the cell body or from the proximal part of one of the dendrites. The axon sometimes branches soon after its formation to provide recurrent collateral branches which return to the region of the cell body (Fig. 10-2). Except for these collaterals, there is often no further branching until the axon reaches the region of terminal arborization and transmitter release (Figs. 10-1 and 10-2). In *bipolar neurons*, one process emerges from each pole of an elongated cell body (Fig. 10-1, *E*). The receptor and effector portions of these cells are often limited to the extreme ends; the entire intermediate portion, including the cell body, is conductile in function. In *unipolar neurons* (as found in most sensory ganglia), the nerve cell body possesses a single process which divides not far from the cell body into two branches, one proceeding to some peripheral structure and the other entering the central nervous system (Fig. 10-1, *A*). Both arms of the single process have the structural and functional characteristics of an axon; together they form the conductile portion of the cell. The receptor part is located in some peripheral sense organ and the central part arborizes within the CNS to provide effector influence upon the dendrites of various CNS cells. It should also be noted that in

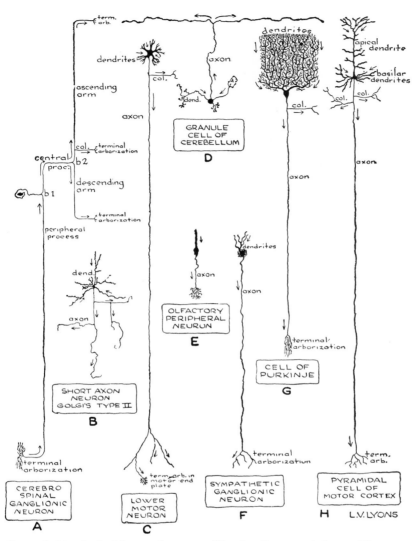

FIG. 10-1. Some of the principal forms of neurons. The sheaths are not shown. The axons, except in *B*, are shown much shorter in proportion to the size of body and dendrites than they actually are. The direction of conduction is shown by the arrows. *Col*, collateral branch; *proc*, process; *term. arb*, terminal arborization.

various specialized areas of the CNS there appear to be cells which do not possess axons. There are small cells, called *anaxonic neurons*, which have both receptor and effector regions on their dendritic portions. They thus require no conductile portion to convey receptor influences to distant regions. One example, the amacrine cell of the retina, is discussed in Chapter 22.

The Nerve Cell Body. As in most other cells, the nerve cell body consists of a mass of cytoplasm surrounding a nucleus. There is little distinctive in the content of the nerve cell body, for only the usual cell organelles are present; it is the quantity of certain components and their disposition which indicate the special functional capacities of the neuron. The generally accepted

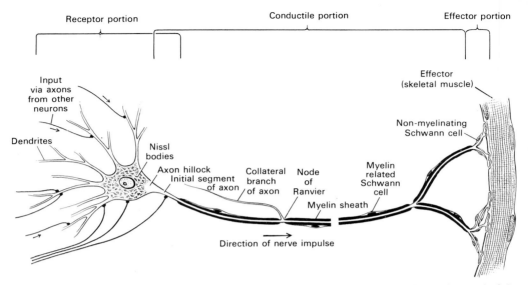

FIG. 10-2. This diagram illustrates the receptor, conductile and effector portions of a typical large neuron. The effector endings on skeletal muscle identify this as a somatic motor neuron; in many neurons the effector endings are applied to the receptor portions of other neurons. The presence of the myelin sheath on the conductile portion of the neuron (the axon) increases conduction velocity. The axon is shown to be interrupted for it is much longer than can be illustrated here.

neuron doctrine states that the vertebrate neuron soma, with its nucleus, is the genetic center of the neuron, and that the various nerve cell processes depend on the neuronal soma for their survival. If these processes are cut off from the nucleated portion, they degenerate and ultimately disappear.

Nerve cell bodies vary considerably in size. The small granule cells of the cerebellum are about 4 μ in diameter, whereas large motor cells in the ventral horn of the human spinal cord may attain diameters of 135 μ (certain invertebrate neurons may be 4 times this size). The size of the neuron cell body generally reflects the amount of cytoplasm being supported in the cell processes. Thus, some of the largest neuronal cell bodies are those with the longest and thickest axons.

Nucleus of the Nerve Cell. The *nucleus* of the nerve cell is spherical in form, and its size is generally proportional to the size of cell it occupies. It is generally pale, with widely dispersed chromatin, suggesting a high volume of transcriptional activity. Certain large neurons are known to contain a

tetraploid amount (i.e., twice the normal amount) of DNA. Usually the nucleus is situated approximately in the center of the cell body in large nerve cells, the most striking exceptions being its eccentric position in the cells of Clarke's column in the spinal cord and in cells of sympathetic ganglia. Eccentric nuclei are also seen in various pathological conditions and when the axon of the cell is injured. Although a single nucleus is the rule, binucleate cells occur in sympathetic and sensory ganglia.

The *nucleolus* is relatively large and appears particularly prominent because the remainder of the nucleus stains lightly. In tissues from females, the sex chromatin (or Barr body) is often clearly visualized within the lightly staining nucleoplasm. In some animals (such as the cat, in which it was first observed), this body is seen as a satellite of the nucleolus about 1 μ in diameter; in human females it is adjacent to the nuclear envelope. The appearance of this body is described in Chapter 1 on the cell and in Chapter 7 on the blood.

Cytoplasm of the Nerve Cell Body. The

cytoplasm in the region of the nerve cell perikaryon contains: (1) chromophilic or Nissl substance (ribosomes and endoplasmic reticulum), (2) the Golgi apparatus, (3) mitochondria, (4) filaments, (5) microtubules, (6) lysosomes and (7) cytoplasmic inclusions such as fat, glycogen, lipofuscin and sometimes the pigment melanin.

When neurons are grown in tissue culture to allow their direct visualization in the living state, exceptionally clear regions in the cytoplasm may be observed (Fig. 10-4). These appear distinct from the granular images provided by lysosomes and mitochondria, and the clear linear areas formed by aggregates of filaments and microtubules. These regions absorb the same wavelengths of ultraviolet light as do nucleic acids. They stain strongly with basophilic dyes, and this staining does not occur after prior treatment with RNAase (Fig. 10-5). The German histologist Nissl, who first noted these distinctive areas in neurons after fixation and staining with basic aniline dyes, called the stained material chromophilic substance. After fixation and staining, the "Nissl" substance appears as very small granules clumped together in a variety of shapes (Fig. 10-5). These clumps of stained material are usually larger in motor than in sensory neurons. The *Nissl bodies*, as these structures are now commonly called, are one of the hallmarks that guide the light microscopist in identifying neurons. Nissl bodies are found in the perikarya and in the proximal parts of the dendrites of all large and many small nerve cells, but they are absent from the axon and the axon hillock (Fig. 10-2).

Electron micrographs show that the Nissl bodies are composed of clusters of endoplasmic reticulum cisternae and ribosomes (Fig. 10-6). The ribosomes are found on the outer surfaces of the cisternae and in the cytoplasm between them, frequently arranged in rosettes or linear arrays of five or more granules (Fig. 10-7). The basophilic

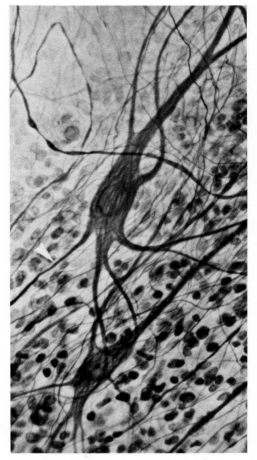

FIG. 10-3. This photomicrograph shows two large neurons that have matured in tissue culture. The culture has been fixed and then stained with silver. In the lower neuron the nucleolus is stained deeply, as are many of the nuclei of the surrounding supporting cells. Within the neurons neurofibrils are seen interlacing in the nerve cell body and extending into the numerous dendrites. The axon of the upper neuron is indicated by a *white arrowhead*. ×310. (Courtesy of Dr. C. D. Allerand.)

staining of Nissl bodies depends upon the presence of RNA in the ribosomes, not upon components in the membranes of the cisternae. Certain cisternae of endoplasmic reticulum come to lie unusually close to the plasma membrane of the neuron soma. These have been termed *subsurface cisternae*, and they are a distinctive characteristic of neu-

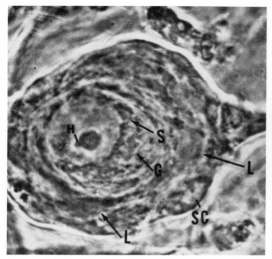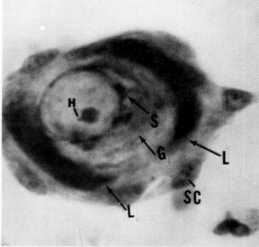

FIG. 10-4. These are photomicrographs of the same neuron before (*left*) and after (*right*) fixation and staining of Nissl substance. The picture on the *left* is of a living chick neuron in tissue culture photographed with a phase microscope. The large, relatively homogeneous masses (*L*) apparent in the phase microscope are seen to be heavily stained by the basic dye employed to stain Nissl substance (*right*). *S* marks a patch of Nissl material often found near the nuclear envelope and commonly called the nuclear cap. *H* calls attention to heterochromatin adjacent to the nucleolus. *G* points to some granular material seen in the living state that proved not to be Nissl material after staining. *SC* marks a satellite cell nucleus. *Left*, ×1800; *right*, ×2000. (From Deitch, A. D., and Murray, M. R. 1956 J. Biophys. & Biochem. Cytol., vol. 2, p. 433.)

rons visible only in electron micrographs (Fig. 10-6).

The fact that neurons exhibit a large nucleolus and abundant arrays of granular endoplasmic reticulum would indicate that they are actively synthesizing proteins. This may seem surprising because mature neurons are not increasing in size or number. There is evidence, however, that virtually all protein synthesis for the nerve cell and its extensions is accomplished in the region of the cell body (and the proximal dendrites). Material constantly moves from these areas of production to the farthest reaches of the axon and dendrite. This intracellular transport, so important in neurons because of their unusual configuration, is discussed in detail below.

Following repeated electrical stimulation, or after amputation of a substantial part of the axon, the disposition of the chromophilic substance in the nerve cell body is altered. In this condition, known as *chro-*

matolysis, the nucleus becomes eccentric and the basophilic material in the cytoplasm is concentrated in the cell periphery (Fig. 10-5). Certain types of neurons undergo this change as a prelude to degeneration, but others are able to gradually reverse the chromatolytic pattern, regenerate amputated parts and return to their former organization. Chromatolysis may be observed as early as the first day after an axon is cut and is most marked at about 2 weeks. Cytochemical studies have shown that there is little change in the total quantity of RNA in the perikaryon during the early stages of regeneration, although its concentration decreases. This is explained by the fact that the cell imbibes water and increases in volume by more than 200%. In neurons capable of axon regeneration, the amount of RNA and protein in the neuron increases after several days, and the amputated part is slowly regenerated. The neuronal cytoplasm then returns to normal. The extent

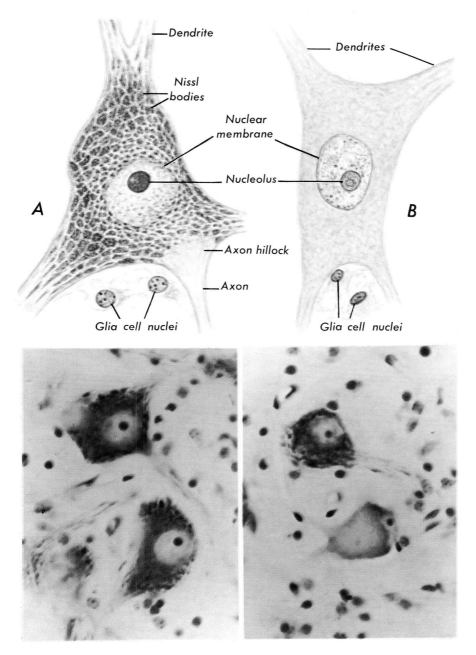

FIG. 10-5. These neurons from the ventral horn of the spinal cord are stained for Nissl substance by the toluidine blue method. *A* is a drawing of a normal neuron illustrating the absence of Nissl substance in the axon hillock region; *B* is a drawing of a neuron similarly stained after treatment with the enzyme ribonuclease to remove RNA. This preparation is counterstained with erythrosin. The pictures below are photomicrographs showing three normal neurons and one neuron showing chromatolysis in response to axon section several days earlier (*lower right*). The comma shaped nucleus is at the soma periphery and the center of the neuron soma stains very lightly. *Above,* ×1,000; *below,* ×750.

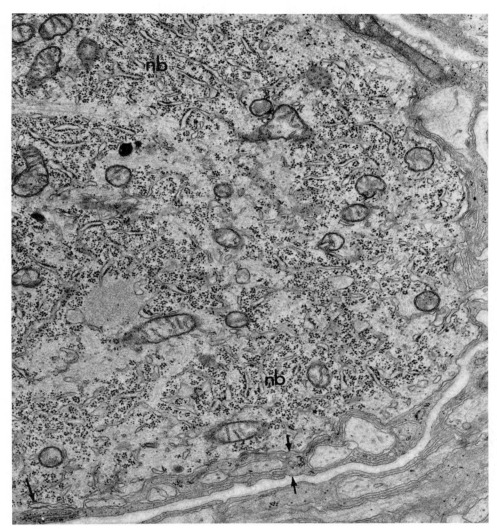

FIG. 10-6. This electron micrograph shows a portion of a neuron soma ensheathed by satellite cell processes. The Nissl bodies seen in Figure 10-5 are shown here to be aggregates of ribosomes and endoplasmic reticulum cisternae (as at *nb*). Light, often linear areas (sometimes called roads) separate the Nissl material. Cisternae of endoplasmic reticulum lying very near the surface of the neuron are referred to as subsurface cisternae (*single arrow*). The width of the satellite cell investment is indicated by the *paired arrows*. Rat sensory ganglion neuron. ×21,500.

and rapidity of the changes depend upon the type of neuron and upon the nature and location of the injury, an injury near the cell body causing more effect than one at a distance. Injury very near the cell body is more likely to lead to cell death.

The clear areas of neuronal cytoplasm between Nissl bodies (Fig. 10-6), as well as in both axons and dendrites, contain numerous minute *filaments* and *microtubules*. The microtubules are similar to those found in other cell types. Typically, the filaments are linear elements about 70 A in diameter, occurring in groups interspersed with microtubules (Fig. 10-7). They are often called *neurofilaments*, but it is not clear whether

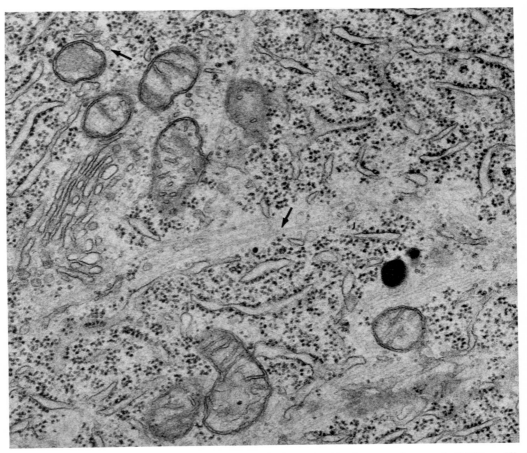

FIG. 10-7. A typical region of neuronal cytoplasm is shown in this electron micrograph. Within a Nissl body, many of the ribosomes are in polysomal aggregates that either lie free in the cytoplasm or are arrayed on cisternal membrane. Also illustrated are a Golgi region (*left*), microtubules in cross and longitudinal section (*arrows*) and two small, dense lysosomes. Rat sensory ganglion neuron. ×43,000.

they are chemically distinct from filaments in other cell types. These filaments and the prominent Nissl bodies are the most characteristic features of the nerve cell cytoplasm. The filament content of neurons varies between species as well as between regions of the nervous system, and the success of silver staining is sometimes related to these variations. Successful silver preparations characteristically show dark, slender elements called *neurofibrils*. The neurofibrils visible in the light microscope are aggregates of filaments on which silver has been deposited. These neurofibrils course parallel with one another in the axon and dendrite but cross and interlace in the cell body (Fig. 10-3). The frequent association between filaments and microtubules and their location between Nissl bodies and in axons and dendrites suggests a possible role in intracellular transport.

The *Golgi apparatus* is limited to the cell body of the neuron. Its prominence in neurons remains unexplained, for it is known that a substantial part of the protein manufactured by the neuron is not channeled through the Golgi region, as it is in secretory cells. The protein that does pass to the

Golgi region in neurons may be related to functioning of the lysosomal system (see Chapter 1). *Mitochondria* are plentiful in the nerve cell body, as well as in the dendrites and axons. Neither the mitochondria nor the lysosomal elements of nerve cells are morphologically distinctive. It has long been recognized that *lipofuscin* pigment accumulates in neurons with advancing age. This pigment is naturally yellow or brown and stains with lipid stains. The significance of this "wear and tear" pigment is not known, but it may simply represent the end product of incessant lysosomal activity during the long life of the nerve cell (see Chapter 1).

Some nerve cells contain granules of a dark brown pigment, *melanin*. This occurs in certain cells of the olfactory bulb, the locus ceruleus in the floor of the fourth ventricle, the substantia nigra of the midbrain and in certain cells of the reticular formation. Melanin is also present in some spinal and sympathetic ganglion cells.

Dendrites. Like a tree spreading its limbs to allow each leaf exposure to the sun, the highly branched dendrites (Gr., *dendron*, meaning tree) allow an expansion of the neuron surface for the reception of many axon terminals. Dendrites are generally shorter than axons, but they branch repeatedly and their surface is often studded with fine spiny or knobbed excrescences (*spines* or *gemmules*, Fig. 10-8); this elaboration of surface area allows large neurons to receive as many as 100,000 separate axon terminals on their dendritic surfaces. At the point of axon contact, the dendritic membrane is often modified (see "Synapses," below). These axon inputs are not randomly arranged; axons from one source occupy a specific region of the dendritic tree, whereas axons from another source terminate elsewhere. The contents of the dendrites resemble those of the cell body except that Nissl substance is generally restricted to the more proximal regions. Microtubules, filaments and mitochondria are conspicuous

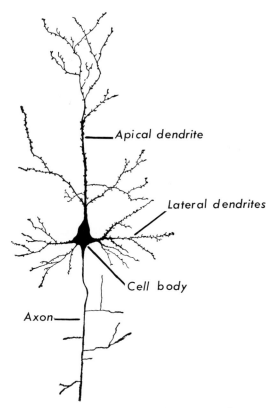

Fig. 10-8. This drawing shows part of a pyramidal cell from human cerebral cortex, including the dendritic portion, the cell body and the proximal part of the axon. The tiny protuberances on the dendrites are called spines or gemmules. Gold chloride method.

components (Fig. 10-9). In the dendrite, as in the axon, there are fine, tortuous channels of smooth membrane, the function of which is not yet known.

Axons. Axons (sometimes termed axis cylinders) arise either from the nerve cell body (Fig. 10-3) or from the proximal part of a dendrite. They are slender extensions with a smoother contour and a more uniform diameter than have dendrites. The axon may have side or *collateral* branches along its length, but its most prominent branching generally occurs shortly before its termination. These terminal branches are termed

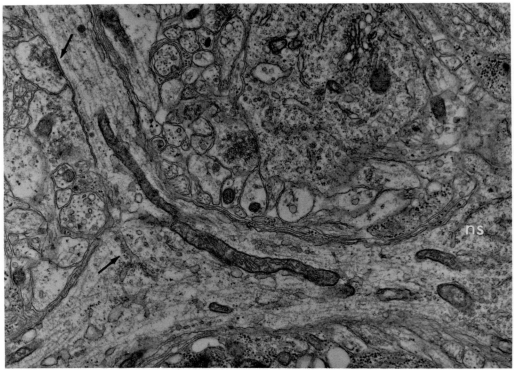

Fig. 10-9. This electron micrograph shows a primary dendrite arising from a cell body (*right*) and branching into two secondary dendrites (*left*). Nissl substance in the periphery of the parent neuron is marked *ns*. The *upper arrow* indicates an axodendritic synapse. The *lower arrow* points to endoplasmic reticulum related to polysomes within the dendrite. Note that the dendritic shaft is covered in many places by flattened processes of astrocytes. The compactness and complexity of the cellular elements is characteristic of central nervous tissue. Rat spinal cord. ×17,000. (From Bunge, R. P., *et al*. 1965 J. Cell Biol., vol. 24, p. 163.)

telodendria, and the actual point of ending, where the axon is frequently enlarged, is called the *terminal*. The plasma membrane of the axon is often referred to as the *axolemma;* morphological specializations of this membrane have been observed in the region of the initial segment of the axon, at nodes of Ranvier and at the terminals. The axon contents are termed the *axoplasm,* and this cytoplasm differs from that of the cell body in that the only formed organelles normally observed are mitochondria, filaments, microtubules and channels of smooth membrane. Nissl substance and Golgi elements are lacking. At the point of egress of the axon from the nerve cell body (or dendrite), there

is generally a region of cytoplasm from which Nissl bodies are conspicuously absent (Fig. 10-2). This region marks the emerging process as the axon (rather than a dendrite) and is called the *axon hillock*.

That portion of the axon between the cell body and the point at which the myelin sheath begins is termed the *initial segment* (Figs. 10-2 and 10-10). In many neurons, this region is known to have a much lower threshold of electrical excitability than has the dendrite or the perikaryon (see below). Morphologically, it is characterized by three special features: (1) a dense layer of finely granular material undercoating the axolemma, (2) scattered clusters of ribo-

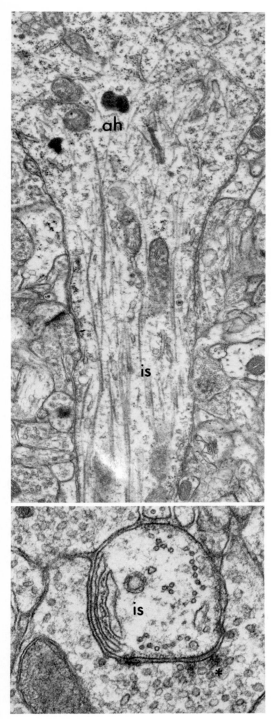

somes but no discrete Nissl bodies and (3) microtubules gathered into slender fascicles (Fig. 10-10).

Axoplasmic Transport. Although there is evidence that some axons contain minute amounts of nonmitochondrial RNA and that they undertake a small amount of protein synthesis, the acknowledged protein assembly center of the neuron is the cell body. The transport of manufactured material into the processes of the cell, especially the long axon, presents special problems. From observations on constricted axons, and from radioautographic studies after labeling of the proteins formed in the cell body, it is known that materials constantly travel from the cell body into the axon and are transported peripherally. The microtubules (and perhaps the filaments) are believed to be involved in this transport. A small amount of material travels rapidly (at rates of 40 mm. per day or more), but the bulk moves slowly at a rate of about 1 mm. per day in mammals. The latter figure is also the approximate rate of axon regrowth after cutting. Normally, the transported materials are presumed to be destined for the replenishment of proteins involved in the ion transport mechanisms of the axolemma, in the release and uptake mechanisms for neurotransmitters and per-

FIG. 10-10. These electron micrographs show the initial segment of an axon of a rat cerebral cortex neuron in longitudinal (*above*) and in cross (*below*) section. The upper figure shows the initial segment (*is*) arising from the axon hillock (*ah*). Characteristic features of the initial segment include (1) the absence of Nissl bodies (but note that occasional ribosomes are present), (2) the presence of dense material undercoating the axolemma and (3) the formation of fascicles of microtubules. In cross section (*below*) bridges between fasciculated microtubules within the initial segment (*is*) may be seen. At this level the initial segment is partially surrounded by a large axon terminal that forms a synaptic complex in the region of the *asterisk*. The initial segment also contains two flattened cisternae of membrane sandwiching dense material between them; similar structures are sometimes found in dendritic spines. *Above*, ×23,000; *below*, ×49,000. (From Peters, A., *et al.* 1968 J. Cell Biol., vol. 39, p. 604.)

haps in the trophic effect of nerve on innervated tissues (see below). There is also
thought to be transport of some material or
signal from the periphery back to the cell
body, for the nerve cell body responds to
changes in the distal regions of the axon.

AXON TERMINALS, SYNAPSES, RECEPTORS, AND NEURO- TRANSMITTERS

As the electrical activity of the axon is
carried into the region of its terminal, the
mechanism of signaling is generally changed
from electrical to chemical. In certain special
terminals (especially in invertebrates and
lower vertebrates), however, the electrical
signal may be carried directly to an adjacent
cell via a special structural adaptation called
variously a *gap junction*, an *electrotonic junction* or an *ephapse*. Here the membranes of
both cells are brought into especially close
contact (Fig. 10-11), and special channels
are established between the two cells to
allow the ionic currents involved in the
electrical signal to pass directly between cell
interiors with little resistance. This type of
cell to cell communication has the advantage
of great rapidity. These junctions are akin
to those observed in various epithelial cell
layers and in portions of the intercalated
disc of the heart.

More commonly, the electrical signal
entering the axon terminal has no direct
electrical effect on the adjacent cell. Instead,
it causes the release of a *neurotransmitter*
from the axon terminal. This chemical
diffuses across the intercellular space to
react with a specialized region on the adjacent cell called a *receptor*. It is the interaction of neurotransmitter with receptor
that leads to electrical activity in the second
cell. The site at which this "chemical" form
of transmission (as opposed to the "electrical" transmission discussed above) takes
place is called a *synapse*.

A synapse is defined as a region of specialized contact between nerve cells or between
nerve cells and effector organs. Light micro-

scopic observations established that synapses are generally areas of axon enlargement
containing mitochondria and neurofibrillar
material. Electron microscopic studies have
added the observation that the axon characteristically contains clusters of tiny vesicles in the region of the synapse and that the
plasma membrane of both the axon and the
contacted cell is often modified in this area.
These membrane modifications consist of
dense material applied to the inner surface
of either one or both of the apposed membranes, in addition to the presence of demonstrable extracellular material between the apposed membranes (Fig. 10-13). Unlike
epithelial junctions such as desmosomes,
the intracellular dense material is not disposed similarly on both membranes. This
difference, and the presence of vesicles in
the axon, make the synapse asymmetrical.
This asymmetry is thought to correlate with
the physiological observation that the synapse transmits the nerve signal in one direction only—from the axon to the cell contacted. The electrical junctions discussed
above are known to transmit the impulse
with equal efficacy in either direction.

At the *synapse*, the axon is termed the
presynaptic element, the cell being contacted
is called the postsynaptic element and the
intervening extracellular space is designated
the synaptic cleft (Figs. 10-12 and 10-15).
At the point of synapse, the axon enlargements are called *boutons terminaux* (or end
feet) if they are terminating, or *boutons en
passage* if they continue on to make additional contacts elsewhere (Fig. 10-12). Thus,
a single axon may make contacts with many
different neurons. The dense material within
the synaptic cleft apparently attaches the
pre- and postsynaptic elements. This attachment is strong enough to survive tissue
homogenization and differential centrifugation, and it is possible to prepare a tissue
fraction comprised, in large part, of the axon
terminals still attached to cleft substance
and postsynaptic membrane. Such prepara-

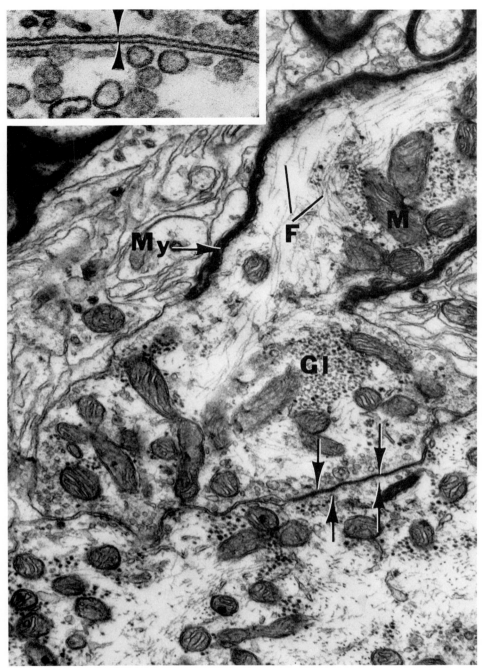

Fig. 10-11. These electron micrographs illustrate the type of close apposition of cell membranes that allows direct electrical coupling between nerve cells. This is a section of an axosomatic electrotonic synapse from the medulla of a gymnotid fish *Sternopygus*. Filaments (*F*), mitochondria (*M*) and glycogen (*Gl*) are present in the axon. Termination of the myelin sheath (*My*) may be seen. At the *paired arrows* the axon and soma membranes are very closely apposed. The inset (*upper left*) shows a similar junction at higher magnification to illustrate that the closely apposed membranes (at *arrows*) are separated by a space of about 25 A. ×27,500; inset, ×110,000. (Courtesy of Dr. George Pappas.)

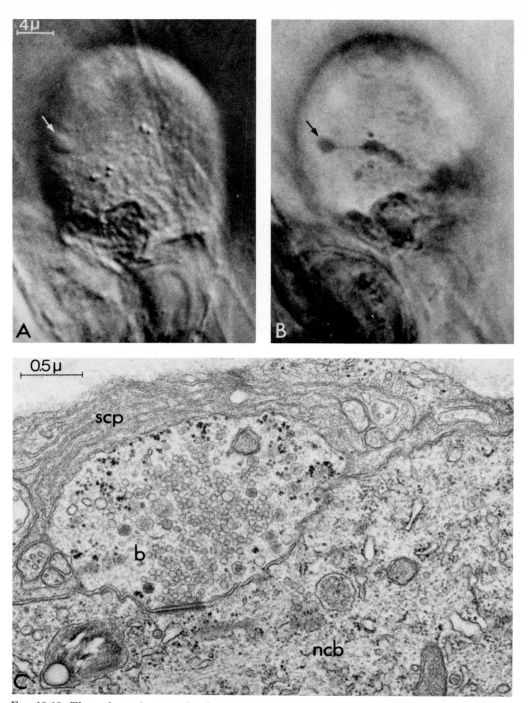

Fig. 10-12. These three photographs show a synaptic bouton in living tissue (*A*), after vital staining (*B*) and after preparation for electron microscopy (*C*). *A* shows a bouton (*arrow*) on the cell body of a parasympathetic neuron in the interatrial septum of the frog heart. The septum has been removed from the heart and pinned out in tissue culture medium, and is viewed with a Nomarski differential interference contrast optical system. *B* shows the same nerve cell 15 minutes after adding a dilute solution of methylene blue to the medium. The terminal synaptic bouton (*arrow*) seen in *A* and two others (apparently boutons en passage) not visible in the unstained preparation have taken up the dye. *C* is an electron micrograph of this type of bouton. A bouton (*b*), contains a mitochondrion, glycogen particles, a few granular vesicles and numerous small agranular vesicles, some of which are clustered next to a region of specialized membrane. Layers of Schwann cell processes (*scp*) cover the bouton, except where it is in contact with the postsynaptic nerve cell body (*ncb*). (From McMahan, U. J., and Kuffler, S. W. 1970 *In* Excitatory Synaptic Mechanisms, edited by P. Andersen and J. K. S. Jansen, p. 57.)

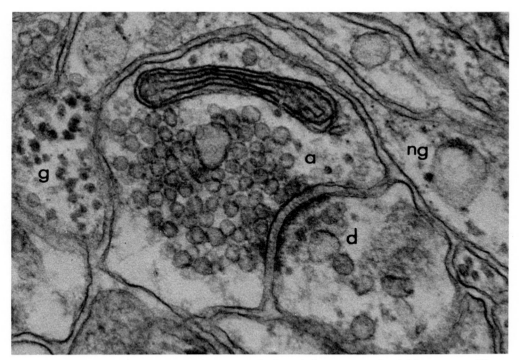

Fig. 10-13. This electron micrograph from rat spinal cord shows an axodendritic synapse. The presynaptic (axonal) element (a) contains numerous round vesicles and a single mitochondrion. It is in contact along a curved face with a smaller postsynaptic element, presumably a dendrite (d). At the synapse the intercellular gap is somewhat increased, there is extracellular material visible between the two processes, and there is a considerable amount of dense material applied to the cytoplasmic side of the membrane of the postsynaptic process. The synaptic complex is partially surrounded by a neuroglial process (ng) which contains glycogen (g) particles in its tip. ×99,000. (From Bunge, R. P., et al. 1965 J. Cell Biol., vol. 24, p. 163.)

tions are termed synaptosomes and are now widely used in biochemical studies.

Synapses may be classified on the basis of (1) position, (2) membrane specialization or (3) organelle content. On the basis of position, they are termed *axodendritic, axosomatic* or *axoaxonic*, thus indicating whether they end on dendrites, on the nerve cell body or on another axon. Axoaxonic synapses are most often found in the initial segment region, or near the axon terminal in what is termed a preterminal position. Differences in membrane specialization at the site of synapses have been noted. Some axodendritic synapses are distinguished by an increased amount of dense material coating the synaptic membranes and a widening of the synaptic cleft (Fig. 10-15).

Variations in the *synaptic vesicle* content of the axon terminal also aid in the classification of synapses. Although the vesicle content of the terminal is often not homogeneous, one type generally predominates. At neuromuscular junctions (where nerve contacts skeletal muscle) and in many CNS terminals, the majority of synaptic vesicles are 300 to 600 A in diameter and are spherical with clear centers (Figs. 10-12 and 10-13). In axon terminals of autonomic nerve fibers supplying smooth muscle (as in the intestine and ductus deferens), the synaptic vesicles may be slightly larger. They are also round but contain a prominent dense particle or short rod (Fig. 10-47). This allows the distinction between terminals with "clear" and those with "dense cored" (or

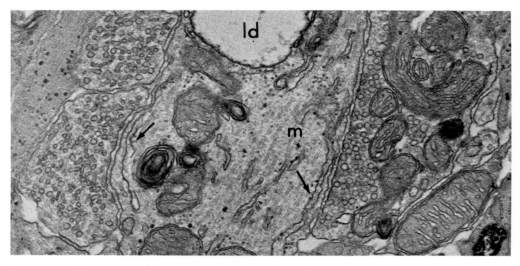

Fig. 10-14. This electron micrograph from rat spinal cord shows a dendrite contacted by three axonal boutons. The dendrite contains microtubules (*m*), mitochondria, a large lipid droplet (*ld*) and cisternae of endoplasmic reticulum underlying its surface membrane (*arrows*). Note that the axon terminal on the right contains predominantly round synaptic vesicles, whereas the two terminals on the left contain vesicles that are generally somewhat smaller and somewhat flattened. These differences in synaptic vesicle morphology are revealed only after primary fixation in aldehyde. ×46,000. (From Bunge, M. B. *et al.* 1967 Brain Res., vol. 6, p. 728.)

granular) vesicles. It has been observed that synapses known to release the neurotransmitter acetylcholine (i.e., cholinergic synapses) always contain clear vesicles, whereas terminals known to release noradrenalin (i.e., adrenergic synapses) always contain vesicles with dense cores. It has recently been observed that aldehyde fixation of nervous tissue allows further classification of endings which contain predominantly clear vesicles. In these preparations, the clear vesicles in certain axon endings appear smaller and are shaped like discs (or red blood cells) instead of spheres. Clusters of this type of vesicle have been observed in axon terminals that are known to be inhibitory in function (Fig. 10-14), but the demonstration of this type of vesicle is not considered sufficient evidence, by itself, to identify a synapse as inhibitory.

The demonstration of vesicles in nerve endings and the physiological observation that certain transmitters are released in "packets" (i.e., in pulses of several thousand molecules rather than in a continuous stream) have led quite naturally to the suggestion that the vesicles contain or bind the neurotransmitter. It was also suggested that vesicles release the neurotransmitter by dumping it into the synaptic cleft after fusing with the presynaptic membrane, i.e., by pinocytosis in reverse. It now seems quite certain that neurotransmitters are located in synaptic vesicles, but the mechanism of their release is not clear and may differ in cholinergic and adrenergic synapses.

The synaptic complex is also known to contain mechanisms for the breakdown and/or uptake of released neurotransmitter. Certain cholinergic synaptic areas are known to contain the enzyme acetylcholinesterase in the pre- and postsynaptic elements, in the synaptic cleft and in the adjacent tissues. This enzyme hydrolyzes acetylcholine with the formation of acetate and choline. Part of the choline is taken up by the presynaptic element and reutilized in subsequent acetylcholine synthesis. In adrenergic endings, the

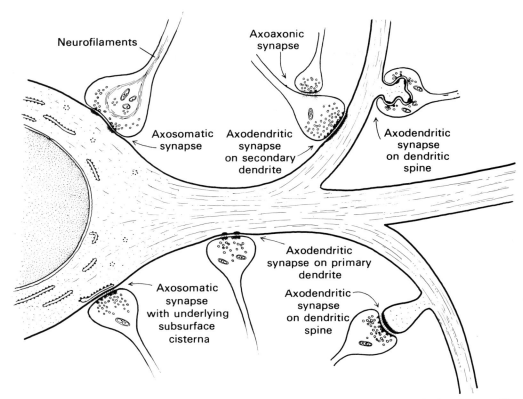

Neurofilaments

Axoaxonic synapse

Axosomatic synapse

Axodendritic synapse on secondary dendrite

Axodendritic synapse on dendritic spine

Axodendritic synapse on primary dendrite

Axosomatic synapse with underlying subsurface cisterna

Axodendritic synapse on dendritic spine

FIG. 10-15. The types of synapses occurring on various parts of the neuron are depicted here. Note that the degree of membrane "thickening" varies in different types of synapses, and that the material applied to the cytoplasmic side of the presynaptic membrane is often seen as a regular pattern rather than as a solid plaque. Variations in synaptic vesicle morphology are not shown.

transmitter has not been observed to be similarly broken down, but it is simply taken up intact from the surrounding extracellular spaces for reuse.

The number of clearly identified neurotransmitters is few, including acetylcholine, norepinephrine, γ-aminobutyric acid, serotonin and possibly glycine. These are all small molecules which, after release, combine with specific areas on the postsynaptic membrane called *receptor sites*. The receptor sites react with a specific neurotransmitter and not with others, and this reaction engenders a permeability change to certain ions. If this permeability change leads to a decrease in the electrical polarization of the postsynaptic membrane, the effect is excitatory, for it makes it more likely that the postsynaptic

element will generate an action potential. When recording from the postsynaptic cell, the physiologist then observes an excitatory postsynaptic potential (often abbreviated EPSP). If the effect is to increase electrical polarization of the membrane, making it less likely that the postsynaptic element will "fire," the effect is said to be inhibitory and an inhibitory postsynaptic potential (IPSP) is recorded. The specificity of synaptic action depends upon the receptor site rather than on the neurotransmitter, for a transmitter may have an excitatory influence at one synapse and an inhibitory effect at another.

It seems certain that molecules other than neurotransmitters must also pass between cells at synaptic junctions, for many synapses also have a *trophic action* on the postsynaptic element. The normal state of skeletal muscle, for example, is dependent upon the continuing presence of neuromuscular junctions; if the nerve is cut, the neuromuscular contact degenerates and the electrical, chemical and anatomical properties of the muscle fiber are permanently altered unless nerve regeneration occurs. Certain neurons of the CNS do not survive if a substantial portion of their synaptic input is removed.

The junction between nerve terminal and skeletal muscle has many of the properties of the basic synaptic apparatus described above. The functional relationship between nerve and cardiac or smooth muscle, on the other hand, presents some basic differences, and these are discussed below under the heading of "Nerve Terminations."

Functional Considerations. Neurons, like many other cells, maintain a negative electrical potential across their plasma membrane, the inside of the cell being about 70 millivolts (mv) more negative than the outside. If this potential is made progressively less negative, a point is reached at which major permeability changes in the surface membrane cause the generation of an action potential and, once generated, this action potential tends to be propagated rapidly and with little loss of amplitude over the neuron surface. On many neurons, however, there is a limited number of sites at which action potentials are generated. The dendritic tree and the cell body are often not very excitable. The action of synaptic contacts in these areas leads to transient local shifts, some inhibitory and some excitatory, in the properties of the postsynaptic membrane. Generally, only when several excitatory synaptic inputs act together (and are not canceled by inhibitory influences) does a change in membrane potential reach sufficient strength to be carried down over the dendrite and cell body to excite the initial axon segment. In most neurons, this region is much more sensitive to membrane potential shifts than is the dendrite or the cell body, and it is here—at the initial segment—where the all or none action potential of the axon is initiated.

NEUROGLIA

Most organs of the body have a connective tissue framework which not only serves as a vascular bed but also provides a supporting skeleton for the particular cellular elements of the organ. Peripheral nerve has such a framework (as discussed below), whereas the CNS does not. The CNS has less need for this type of support because the brain and spinal cord are "floated" in a fluid environment: the cerebrospinal fluid. In the brain and spinal cord, the connective tissue is limited to the enveloping membranes (the meninges) and to a small amount which accompanies the blood vessels. The remainder of the non-neuronal elements form the interstitial tissue of the nervous system: the neuroglia (Gr., *neuron*, nerve + *glia*, glue). The neuroglia are thought to assist the neurons in their activities. The most direct method by which neuroglia influence neuronal function is by investing the axon with a myelin sheath which dramatically increases the speed of impulse conduction. Other functions of glia are less clearly defined. It has been suggested that they provide direct assistance for the metabolic activities of the neuron by providing high energy compounds, for example, or by assisting in the control of the neuronal environment (by reacting to changes in ion concentration in the extracellular spaces or by aiding in the elimination of CO_2). Neuroglia do not generate action potentials, and they have never been observed to provide or to receive synapses. Studies of glial function are presently a fertile frontier in neurobiological research.

Prior to the era of the electron microscope, neuroglia could not be studied except by special and often difficult selective staining methods. Electron microscopy has provided the great advantage of allowing all elements of nervous tissue to be observed simultaneously and allowing the membrane relationships to be clearly delineated. Much of the description given below is derived from electron microscopic studies; many of the features described are not visible in ordinary light microscopic preparations.

In routine microscopic preparations of CNS tissue, many nuclei are seen which belong neither to nerve cells nor to vascular tissue (Fig. 10-5). These nuclei belong to neuroglial cells, and careful study of their morphology often will allow indentification of a particular glial type. The neuroglia, frequently referred to simply as the glia, may be divided into the following classes: (1) astrocytes, (2) oligodendrocytes, (3) microglia and (4) ependyma (Fig. 10-16). The neurilemma cells (or cells of Schwann) of peripheral nerves and the satellite cells which surround the cell bodies of the spinal and cranial ganglia are also sometimes called neuroglia.

Astrocytes. As the name implies, the astrocytes are stellate cells with many cytoplasmic processes (Fig. 10-17). They are divided into two general types, protoplasmic and fibrous, which have in common their shape (which provides a large surface area), the presence of characteristic cytoplasmic filaments and glycogen, a generally loosely packed cytoplasm and a tendency to have one or more processes applied to a blood vessel (as perivascular feet). In both astrocytic types, the nucleus is irregularly ovoid and less compact than in other glial cell types.

Protoplasmic astrocytes are found principally in the gray matter of the brain and spinal cord. In addition to the perivascular disposition of some cellular extensions (as mentioned above), these cells also provide flattened processes which cover much of the nonsynaptic neuronal surface, and they circumscribe synaptic zones, suggesting that they may function to separate the activities of synaptic regions from adjacent tissues (Fig. 10–13). In some areas of the brain, protoplasmic astrocytes are known to be connected to one another by low resistance gap junctions.

The *fibrous astrocytes* differ from the protoplasmic type in having fewer processes which are much straighter and longer (Fig. 10–16). They possess many more of the filaments which course through their cytoplasm in bundles (Fig. 10-18). When specially stained in light microscopic preparations, these filamentous bundles appear as fine, straight, unbranched fibers called astroglial fibers. The fibrous astrocytes are found chiefly in the white matter. Like the protoplasmic astrocytes, they bear perivascular feet. They are the scarring cells of the nervous system, filling in the gaps after tissue is lost in various disease processes. Connective tissue may also participate in CNS scarring. The result is generally a hardened mass of tissue within the normally soft brain tissue. This scarring process is termed sclerosis ("hardening").

Oligodendrocytes or oligodendroglia (Gr., *oligos*, few + *dendron*, tree + *glia*, glue). These cells were given their name by del Rio-Hortega because of the fact that their branches were small and few as compared with the astroyctes. They differ from astrocytes in the following ways: (1) their nuclei are generally smaller, rounder and more dense than astrocytic nuclei; this is the chief identifying characteristic in the standard histological preparation, (2) the entire cell body is smaller and the processes are fewer and more delicate, (3) their cytoplasm is more dense, containing chiefly ribosomes, mitochondria and microtubles; the filaments and glycogen prominent in astrocytic cytoplasm are absent (Figs. 10-19 and 10-20).

Oligodendrocytes are of three general types. When found in groups adjacent to blood vessels, they are termed *perivascular;* their function in this position is unknown. When found directly adjacent to neuron cell bodies (as in gray matter), they are termed *perineuronal*. This close relationship

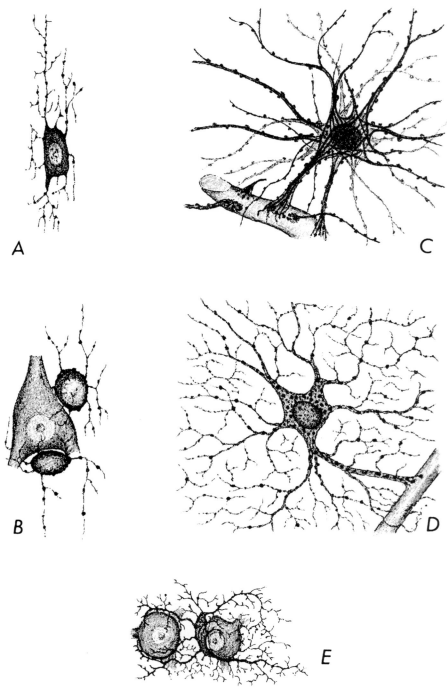

Fig. 10-16. *A*, oligodendrocyte in white matter (interfascicular form) (see also Fig. 10-33); *B*, two oligodendrocytes lying against a nerve cell (perineuronal form); *C*, astrocyte of fibrous type with processes forming foot plates against a neighboring blood vessel. Astrocytic fibrils (bundles of filaments) are visible in the cell body and the processes. *D*, astrocyte of protoplasmic type with foot plate on blood vessel; *E*, microglial cell in vicinity of two nerve cell bodies. Redrawn from a preparation by Penfield; del Rio-Hortega's modified silver method.

suggests some type of symbiosis between glia and neuron, but efforts to identify positively what might exchange between them have not yet been successful.

When oligodendrocytes are found in white matter, they are termed *interfascicular*. Many of these are directly related to myelin in a manner in many ways similar to that of the peripheral Schwann cell. The differences are discussed below. Although the anatomical connection between the myelin supporting oligodendrocyte and the myelin sheath is tenuous, it is thought to be permanent and to provide a route through which may pass the necessary materials for the maintenance of the myelin sheath. Thus, the myelin sheath appears to be metabolically related to the oligodendrocyte cell body in much the same way that the axon is related to the neuron soma (Fig. 10-34).

Certain of the smaller cells in nervous tissue (which may be classified as small oligodendrocytes) may be multipotential "stem" cells capable of reacting to various types of nervous system damage to provide whatever type of glial cell is needed for repair.

Microglia. In the past, this third type of neuroglial cell has been described as being a small, dense cell with a deeply staining nucleus. As shown in Figure 10-16, microglia bear delicate tortuous processes with small spines. These cells have generally been considered to be histiocytes belonging to the reticuloendothelial system (and thus mesodermal in origin), and they are therefore incidental visitors in nervous tissue. They are often found in relation to blood vessels. Normally inactive, they are considered to respond with phagocytic activity for the removal of cellular debris.

There is at present a controversy regarding this interpretation, for electron microscopic studies have revealed few cells clearly identified as microglia in normal nervous tissue, and it has been suggested that stains considered selective for microglia were, in fact, staining certain oligodendro-

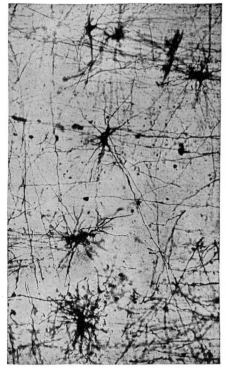

FIG. 10-17. This photomicrograph shows several astrocytes in the white matter of spinal cord. The straight unbranched processes are characteristic of the fibrous astrocytes of this region. Golgi's chrome-silver method.

cytes in many instances. It does seem clear that (1) there are relatively few histiocytes resident in normal nervous tissue, (2) invasion of the nervous system by monocytes derived from the blood is common in extensive nerve tissue injury and (3) all neuroglial cells can participate to some extent in the phagocytic activity required for the removal of cell debris. In many cases of minimal injury, astrocytes take up the debris, and no monocytic invasion occurs.

In extensive injury when a great deal of dead tissue must be disposed of, the phagocytic cells become greatly enlarged and stuffed with debris so that the nucleus appears compressed or indented (Fig. 10-21). These cells are called compound granular corpuscles or gitter cells (lattice-like cells). It remains controversial whether cells of

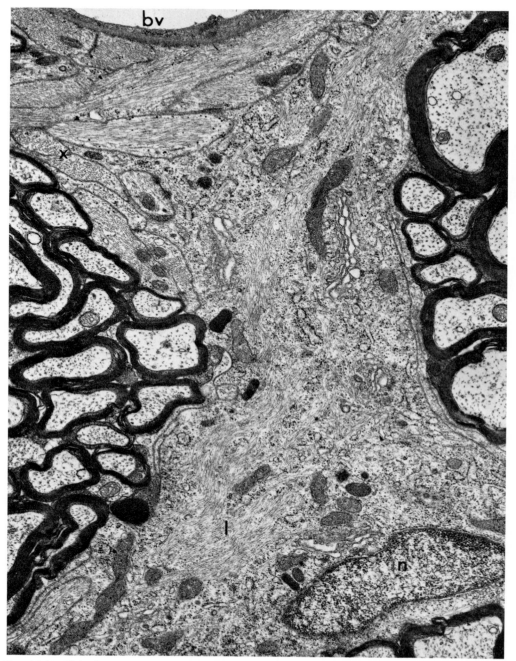

Fig. 10-18. This electron micrograph from rat optic nerve shows a fibrous astrocyte interposed between myelinated axons (cut in cross section). Part of the astrocyte nucleus (n) is shown as well as astroglial filaments cut in longitudinal (l) and in cross (x) section. A series of filament filled astrocytic processes are applied to a blood vessel (bv) at the top of the picture. Some of these processes contain glycogen particles. ×15,000. (From Vaughn, J. E., and Peters, A. 1968 J. Comp. Neurol., vol. 133, p. 269.)

this type, many of which are known to derive from monocytes, may also arise from small, dense glial cells of ectodermal origin. Gitter cells are capable of taking up impressive amounts of cellular remnants (especially myelin); laden with this material, they take up positions around blood vessels, and the contained material is slowly digested over several weeks or months.

Ependyma. The ependyma (Figs. 10-22 and 10-23) in ordinary preparations appears to consist of closely packed cells with elongated nuclei, lining the cavities of the spinal cord and brain (central canal and ventricles). Their long axes are perpendicular to the cavity, and they present the appearance of a columnar epithelium. These cells have inner processes ramifying more or less deeply into the neural tube. They may have, in certain forms and in certain places at least, cilia which protrude into the neural cavity (Fig. 10-23).

NERVE ENSHEATHMENT

As *peripheral nerves* course among various body tissues, they are found everywhere in association with companion cells which provide various types of nerve ensheathment. When these companion cells are in association with a nerve cell body (as in the peripheral ganglia of the autonomic or sensory system), they are called *satellite cells;* when they provide ensheathment for axons, they are called *neurilemma cells,* or *cells of Schwann.* Whereas the former term is considered more acceptable by many workers, the term Schwann cell is more widely used at the time of this writing. During development, these companion cells arise from neural crest tissue and migrate peripherally along with the outgrowing nerve fiber (and in relation to the nerve cell body) and provide a covering sheath which everywhere encloses the nerve, except at certain axon tips, as discussed below (Fig. 10-55). The basic form of ensheathment provided for the axon is shown in Figures 10-24 and 10-25. The Schwann cell embraces

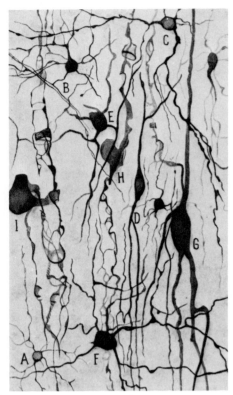

FIG. 10-19. This drawing by del Rio-Hortega shows the various types of oligodendrocytes found in white and gray matter. Note that the cells have few processes but that these may be very complex. The elaborate interfascicular forms of oligodendrocytes shown at H and I are depicted in more detail in Figure 10-33. (From del Rio-Hortega, P. 1928 Mem. Real. Soc. Espan. Hist. Nat., vol. 14, p. 5.)

the axon and cradles it in a trough formed from its plasma membrane. The axons remain outside the Schwann cell but are surrounded by it. The region in which the lips of the encircling Schwann cell processes approach each other is termed the *mesaxon* (Fig. 10-26). Because no special junctions are formed, the space between the axon and the encircling process is in continuity with the general extracellular space. Each Schwann cell extends over a distance of several hundred microns along the axon. This basic pattern of ensheathment, with a single Schwann cell embracing from one to a dozen separate axons, is found throughout

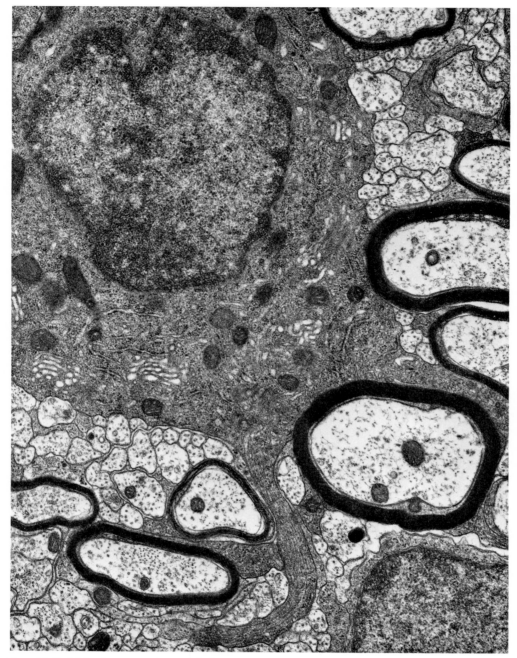

FIG. 10-20. This electron micrograph from neonatal rat spinal cord shows an oligodendrocyte in apposition to both myelinated and unmyelinated axons. Oligodendrocytes present this dense appearance after aldehyde fixation. They characteristically contain many ribosomes and microtubules and lack bundles of filaments. The slender processes of this cell are related to myelin segments (as is shown schematically in Fig. 10-34). ×16,000. (Courtesy of Drs. P. L. Hinds and J. E. Vaughn.)

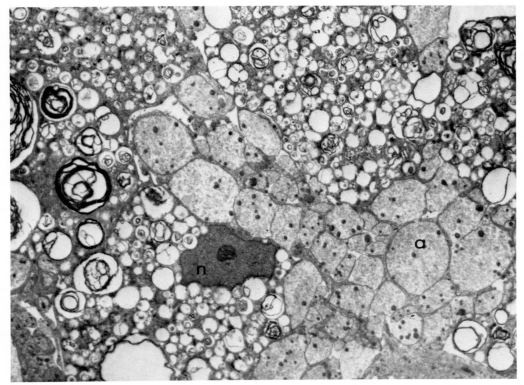

FIG. 10-21. Microglial cells (gitter cells) engorged with remnants of degenerating myelin are shown in this electron micrograph from a demyelinating lesion in cat spinal cord. Cross sectioned axons which have lost their myelin sheaths occupy the lower right and central areas of the picture (e.g., *a*). The remainder of this field is filled with the cytoplasm of four microglial phagocytes. These become so engorged with debris that the nucleus may be indented (as in *n*). ×4500. (From Bunge, R. P., *et al.* 1960 J. Biophys. Biochem. Cytol., vol. 7, p. 685.)

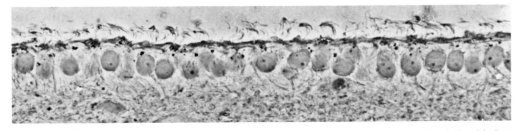

FIG. 10-22. This photomicrograph shows the row of ependymal cells lining the wall of the third ventricle of an adult rabbit. Bundles of cilia protrude from the ventricular surfaces of these cells. (From Tennyson, V. M., and Pappas, G. D. 1968 *In* Pathology of the Nervous System, edited by J. Minckler, p. 518, McGraw-Hill, New York.)

the peripheral nervous systems of both invertebrates and vertebrates. In many species, this is the highest form of peripheral nerve ensheathment found.

Nerve fibers ensheathed in this manner are termed unmyelinated, and they comprise the majority of the axons of the autonomic ganglia and axons from the smaller neurons of the sensory ganglia. These unmyelinated peripheral nerve fibers are sometimes called

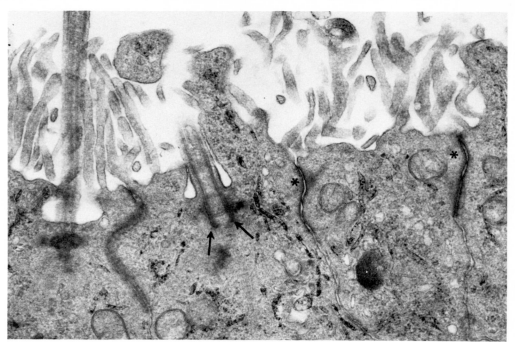

FIG. 10-23. This electron micrograph shows both microvilli and cilia projecting from the surface of ependymal cells lining the spinal cord central canal in a human fetus. The arrows indicate a basal body at the base of the cilium. Junctional complexes (*) occur between lateral cell borders near the free cell surface. ×23,500. (From Tennyson, V. 1970 *In* Developmental Neurobiology, edited by W. A. Himwich, p. 47, C. C. Thomas, Springfield, Illinois.)

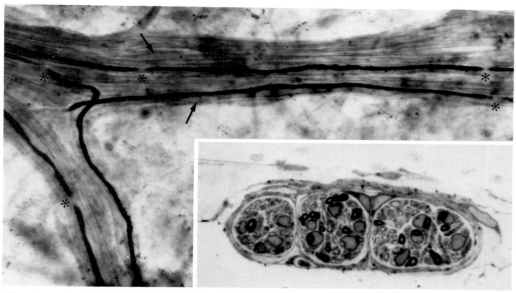

FIG. 10-24. These light micrographs show a small nerve fascicle viewed longitudinally (*above*) and in cross section (*inset*). The tissue has been fixed in OsO₄ which preserves and blackens myelin. In the upper picture individual segments of myelin are delineated by nodes (*). The remainder of the fascicle is composed of unmyelinated nerve fibers and their associated Schwann cells. Cell nuclei (*arrows*) are not stained but are visible as elliptical structures between the nerve fibers. In the cross section a perineurial sheath is seen around each of three small nerve fascicles. Myelin sheaths, some with related Schwann cell nuclei, and individual unmyelinated fibers, with Schwann cell investments, are shown. ×500; *inset*, ×1600.

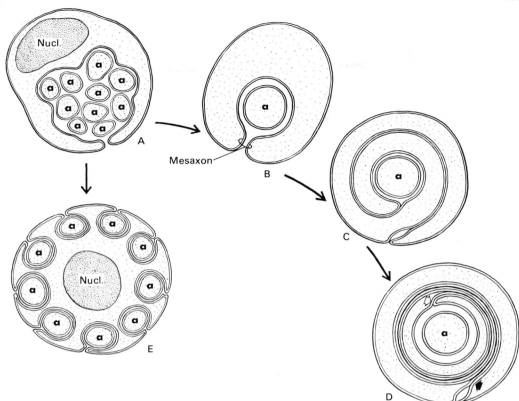

Fig. 10-25. Forms of ensheathment in peripheral nerve. During development the small embryonic nerve fibers are surrounded in groups by Schwann cells (A). Those fibers which will become myelinated enlarge and become ensheathed by individual Schwann cells (B). The encircling lips of the Schwann cell slide by one another, and the mesaxon is elongated (C). As the mesaxon is compacted (D), myelin is formed. Note that the apposition of the cytoplasmic surfaces of the plasma membrane forms the major dense line of the myelin sheath; the apposition of the external surfaces of the plasma membrane forms the intraperiod line (D). Axons which will not be myelinated remain small and obtain ensheathment within individual troughs in the Schwann cell (E). a = axon; nucl. = nucleus; inner mesaxon marked by white arrow; outer mesaxon marked by black arrow.

C fibers or fibers of Remak. They conduct nerve impulses at the rate of about 1 meter per second. In light microscopic observations of routine histological preparations, these smaller diameter unmyelinated fibers are often not directly visible, but the presence of a nerve fascicle in the tissue can be distinguished by the elongated nuclei of the ensheathing Schwann cells, as well as by the connective tissue layers, discussed below, which are external to the Schwann cell ensheathment (Fig. 10-24). The function of Schwann cell ensheathment of unmyelinated nerve fibers is not known, but it is known that the axolemma, and not the plasmalemma of the Schwann cell, is the membrane responsible for the propagation of the action potential.

Peripheral Myelinated (or Medullated) Nerve Fibers. In many higher animals, the basic form of nerve ensheathment described above is modified for elaboration of the myelin sheath. Peripheral myelin is the spirally disposed plasma membrane of the Schwann cell compacted together to provide a highly resistant but regularly interrupted sleeve of insulation around the axon. During early development

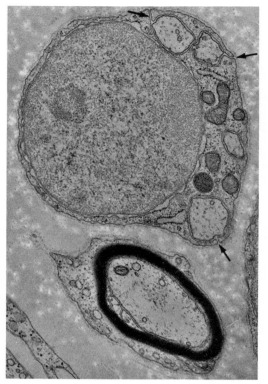

FIG. 10-26. This electron micrograph shows four unmyelinated nerve fibers ensheathed by one Schwann cell. The mesaxons (where the trough of Schwann cell membrane is open to the extra-cellular space) are marked by *arrows*. A myelinated axon appears below. Rat peripheral nerve. ×23,000.

(about the time of birth), axons which will become myelinated become thicker in diameter and, as the diameter exceeds 1 μ, they are ensheathed by their own individual Schwann cells. The apposing lips of the embracing Schwann cell slide by one another, and a spiral of membrane is formed as the original mesaxon is elongated (Fig. 10-25). There is some evidence that this "jelly roll" configuration of myelin is accomplished by the repeated circumnavigation of the axon by the outer mass of Schwann cell cytoplasm—that part containing the nucleus. This leaves behind a great length of spiraled plasma membrane which becomes compacted together into lamellae to form myelin. As compaction occurs, the

outer surface of the membrane from one turn of the spiral is applied to the outer surface of the membrane from the next, to form the *intraperiod line* of compact myelin; the apposition of the cytoplasmic surfaces as the cell cytoplasm is eliminated forms the *major dense line* of the myelin sheath (Fig. 10-25). By this mechanism, one Schwann cell forms one segment or *internode* of myelin, with the Schwann cell nucleus located external to the compacted lamellae and about midway along the myelin segment. At each end of the internode, there is a gap of a few microns called a *node of Ranvier*, and then another internode of myelin begins (Fig. 10-24). As nerves elongate during growth, the diameter of the axon is further increased and the segments of myelin are increased in length and in diameter so that the thickest axons will eventually have the longest (and thickest) segments of myelin and thus the greatest distance between the interrupting nodes of Ranvier.

At the node of Ranvier, the lamellae of myelin are separated because Schwann cell cytoplasm has been retained. Each myelin lamella is brought successively into contact with the axon (Fig. 10-30) so that the outermost lamellae of myelin approach the axon nearest the node. At the node itself, loosely interdigitating Schwann cell processes partially fill the nonmyelinated interval (Figs. 10-29 and 10-30).

Initially, the myelin segment is quite smooth and regular. If not injured, the myelin-Schwann cell unit, like the neuron, is thought to be maintained for the lifetime of the individual. As it ages, myelin develops distortions and redundancies in its basic tubular form. In addition, there develop oblique, funnel-shaped clefts, called *Schmidt-Lanterman* clefts, which interrupt the smooth contour of the internode. These clefts have been observed in the living myelin sheath, and electron microscopic examination has established they represent "faults" through which the myelin lamellae pass without interruption, i.e., they are focal areas of incomplete membrane compaction where Schwann cell cytoplasm is retained (Fig. 10–27).

Figures 10-27 and 10-30 illustrate that myelin is an integral part of the Schwann cell, and that Schwann cell cytoplasm is retained both external and internal to the compact myelin layers and in the paranodal areas. The amount of cytoplasm in these regions decreases with development, but substantial amounts remain in the region of the Schwann cell nucleus and near the nodes of Ranvier. The cytoplasm external to the compact myelin is visible in the light microscope and has frequently been termed the neurilemma sheath. Unfortunately, this term has been used in the past to include various connective tissue elements external to the Schwann cell, including the basal lamina that borders all Schwann cells. It is important to distinguish between the cytoplasm of the myelin-related Schwann cell and the adjacent connective tissue sheath.

The finer details of the myelin sheath are not visible in the routine histological preparation. If a fixative that preserves lipid (such as osmium tetroxide) has been used, followed by a lipid stain, the compacted regions of myelin will be visualized as a tight sleeve around the axon. In preparations involving the use of lipid solvents, much of the myelin sheath is dissolved, leaving a proteolipid residue called neurokeratin. In silver-stained preparations, the axon appears in cross sections as a central density apparently surrounded by a space because the myelin has been largely extracted. These points are illustrated in Fig. 10-28.

Myelin-containing tissues can be fractionated and a relatively pure myelin preparation prepared. This is found to contain about 80 % lipid, including cholesterol, phospholipids, glycolipids and plasmalogens, and about 20 % protein, including some proteolipids. The high lipid content gives myelin a whitish appearance in the fresh state. This explains the whiteness of peripheral nerves (e.g., the white rami of the autonomic nerves, as compared with the gray rami that contain primarily unmyelinated fibers), as well as the distinction between white and gray matter of the CNS.

The myelinated axon is the superhighway of the nervous system, the periodic interruptions at the nodes of Ranvier providing the "limited access" to current flow which allows myelin ensheathment to speed greatly the process of impulse conduction. In the typical myelinated nerve fiber, the action potential is first generated in the initial segment of the axon (Fig. 10-2). This current flows through the axon to depolarize and "fire" the first node of Ranvier. The action potential thus generated forces a pulse of current into the axon interior. Because of the high resistance and low capacitance of the surrounding myelin, the current remains confined to the axon and flows forward, not radially, until the next node is reached. Thus, the myelinated fiber forces ionic currents to flow great distances before regeneration of the action potential. This leaping or jumping of the current has led to the term *saltatory conduction*. This process is not only faster than the sequential depolarization of unmyelinated fibers but more economical of ionic interchange between the inside and outside of the fiber.

Myelinated fibers vary considerably in size, from large (10 to 20 μ in overall diameter) to medium (4 to 10 μ) to small (2 to 4 μ) (Fig. 10–31). In recent physiological classification, the large and medium fibers are type A, the small myelinated fibers are type B and unmyelinated fibers are type C. The largest diameter fibers have the longest myelin segments (between 1 and 2 mm.); they thus have the greatest spacing between nodes and hence the fastest nerve conduction rates (up to 140 meters per second).

Central Myelinated Nerve Fibers. The major differences between peripheral and central myelin are: (1) there is little cytoplasm associated with the mature central myelin sheath, (2) the cell which forms

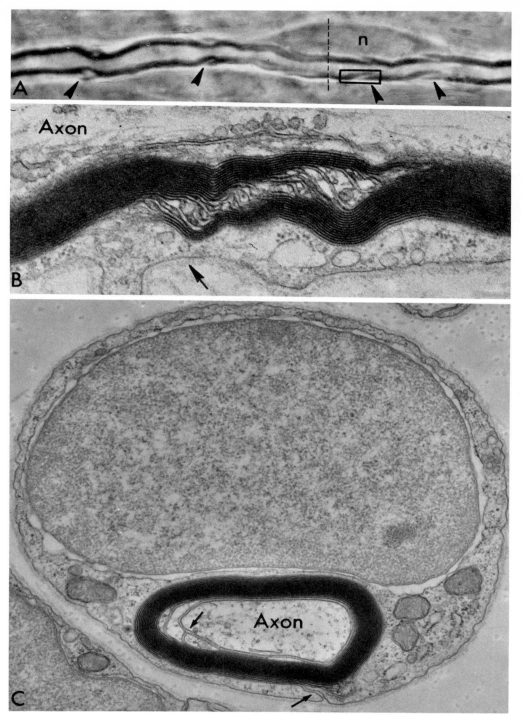

Fig. 10-27. The upper figure (A) is a photomicrograph of part of a living myelin segment (in tissue culture) displaying a series of Schmidt-Lanterman clefts (*arrowheads*), and also the nucleus (*n*) of the Schwann cell related to this internode. In an electron micrograph (B) a cleft as in the box in A is seen to be a region where the myelin lamellae are separated by cytoplasm but retain their continuity. The *arrow* in the middle picture indicates the basal lamina adjacent to the Schwann cell. Figure C is an electron micrograph of a myelin sheath cut in cross section at the level of the dotted line in A. The *arrows* indicate the inner and outer mesaxons, the points where the membrane spiral which forms the compact myelin begins and ends. The axons depicted are small, between 1 and 2 μ in diameter. Rat peripheral nerve.

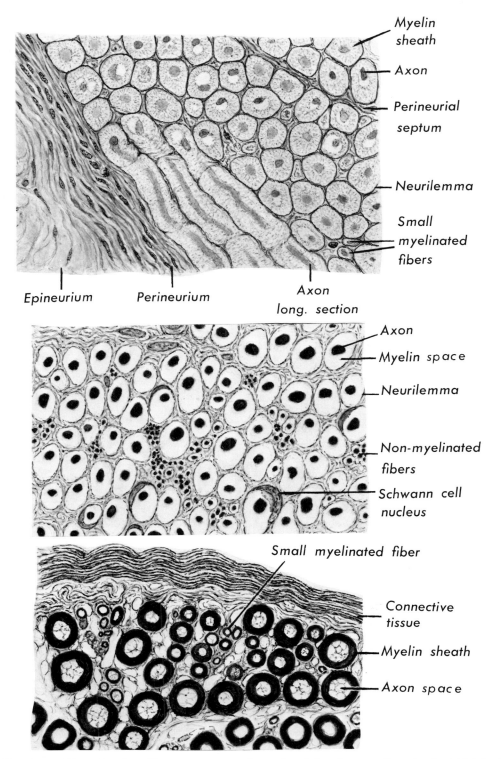

Fig. 10-28. These drawings illustrate cross sections of peripheral nerve after standard histological preparation and H and E staining (*top*), after silver staining to show the axons (*middle*), and after fixation with OsO₄ to preserve the myelin sheaths (*bottom*). The spoke-like remnants of myelin seen in H and E preparations are called neurokeratin.

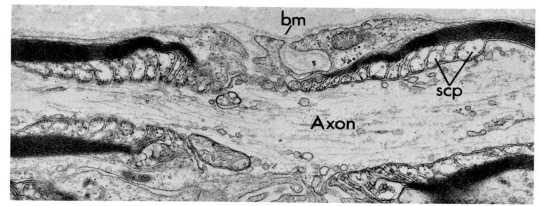

Fɪɢ. 10-29. This electron micrograph shows a node of Ranvier on a small axon of a rat sensory ganglion cell. The myelin lamellae terminate in loops in which a small amount of Schwann cell cytoplasm
is retained. The innermost lamellae terminate farthest from the node. *bm* = basal lamina; *scp* =
Schwann cell processes. ×27,500.

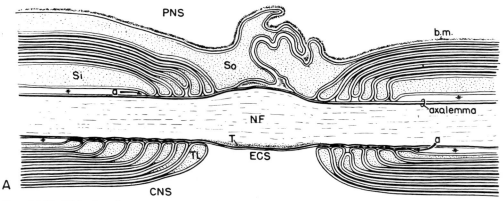

Fɪɢ. 10-30. This drawing compares nodal regions from PNS (*above*) and CNS (*below*). In the PNS
the Schwann cell provides both an inner collar (*Si*) and an outer collar (*So*) of cytoplasm in relation to
the compact myelin. The outer collar (*So*) extends into the nodal region as a series of loosely interdigitating processes. Terminating loops of the compact myelin come into close apposition to the axolemma in regions near the node apparently providing some barrier (*arrow at a*) for movement of materials
into or out of the periaxonal space (*). The Schwann cell is covered externally by a basal lamina. In the
CNS the myelin ends similarly in terminal loops (*tl*) near the node and there are periodic thickenings of
the axolemma where the glial cell membrane is applied in the paranodal region. These thickenings may
serve to confine material in the periaxonal space (*) so that movement in the direction of the arrow at *a*
would be restrained. At many CNS nodes there is considerable extracellular space (*ECS*). (From Bunge,
R. 1970 Physiol. Rev., vol. 48, p. 197.)

central myelin—the oligodendrocyte—is not
as directly apposed to central myelin
segments as is the Schwann cell in the
periphery and (3) the myelin supporting
oligodendrocyte may be related, at least
during development, to more than one
axon and to more than one segment of

forming myelin (Figs. 10-32 to 10-34).
Whereas the overall pattern of myelin
deposition is the same, the relation of the
oligodendrocyte to more than one axon
indicates that the myelin membrane spiral
cannot be formed by cell circumnavigation
around the axon; the actual mechanism of

myelin deposition is unknown. The very small amount of cytoplasm external to the central myelin sheath has led to the frequent statement that there is no neurilemma cell in the CNS. There is, in fact, some cytoplasm related to central myelin both internally and externally and at the nodes of Ranvier (Figs. 10-30 and 10-34). The amount of cytoplasm is too small to be seen in the light microscope, however, and it can be clearly visualized only with the electron microscope. Myelinated central fibers have no connective

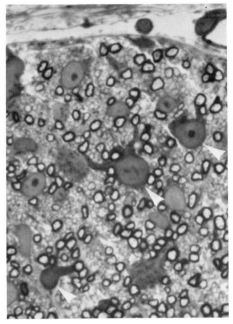

FIG. 10-32. This is a photomicrograph of 5 day old kitten spinal cord with the surface of the cord above. Myelin sheaths in varying stages of formation have been cut in cross section. Three myelin-related cells (*arrowheads*) each display two processes which appear to be related to at least two different myelinated axons. A 1 μ section of OsO₄ fixed material embedded in plastic and stained with toluidine blue. ×1200.

tissue coats, as found in peripheral nerves (Fig. 10-34).

The integrity of myelin depends upon both the axon (as discussed below) and the myelin-supporting cell—the Schwann cell or the oligodendrocyte. If the myelin-supporting cell is damaged, as in certain demyelinating diseases, the myelin will break down even though the axon is preserved. If the axon is preserved, remyelination sometimes occurs in both central and peripheral nervous tissue.

THE PERIPHERAL NERVES

The nerve fibers, coursing from their cell bodies to their terminations in some peripheral structure, are grouped together in bundles to form the peripheral nerves. The fibers connected with the spinal cord form

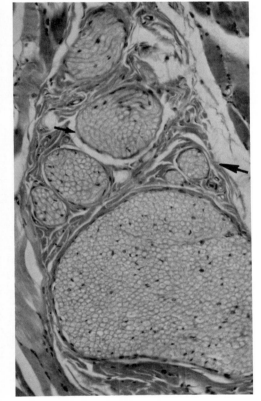

FIG. 10-31. This photomicrograph shows seven peripheral nerve fascicles of varying sizes within the muscles of the tongue. At places, the encasing epineurium (*large arrow*) is separated from the underlying perineurium (*small arrow*). The nuclei of Schwann cells and endoneurial cells are visible as darkly stained elements within the fascicles. The outline of individual myelinated fibers is seen but much of the myelin has been extracted in the tissue preparation. H and E stain. ×130.

FIG. 10-33. This is a diagram by del Rio-Hortega of the oligodendrocytes in white matter of cat central nervous tissue. The cells labelled *AD*, *BC*, *E*, *F* and *G* are related to underlying myelin sheaths which are not stained in this preparation. Oligodendrocytes that appear not to be related to myelin sheaths are labelled *H* and an astrocyte appears at *I*. (From del Rio-Hortega, P. 1928 Mem. Real. Soc. Espan. Hist. Nat., vol. 14, p. 5.)

the spinal nerves, and those connected with the brain comprise the cranial nerves.

　　When the spinal cord is viewed grossly, it is readily observed that the rootlets which form the peripheral nerve leave from both its dorsal and its ventral regions. The

dorsal root is distinguished from the ventral by an enlargement containing nerve cell bodies, the dorsal root ganglion. The dorsal root contains the sensory or afferent nerve fibers from both somatic and visceral

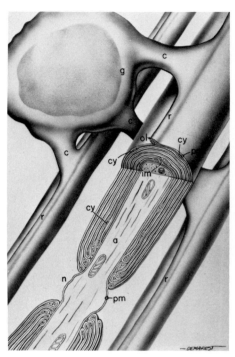

FIG. 10-34. This diagram illustrates the relationship of the oligodendrocyte to the central myelin sheath. The trilaminar plasma membrane (*pm*) is here designated as two lines separated by a space except in the mitochondrion, where it is represented by a single line. The inner mesaxon (*im*), formed as a glial process completes the initial turn around an axon (*a*) and starts a second, is retained after myelin formation is completed. Some cytoplasm of the glial process is present here. Cytoplasm is trapped occasionally at *cy*. On the fully formed sheath exterior, a bit of glial cytoplasm is also retained. In transverse sections, this cytoplasm is confined to a loop (*ol*) but, along the internode length, it forms a ridge (*r*) which is continuous with a glial cell body (*g*) at *c*. When viewed transversely, the sheath components are oriented in a spiral, only the innermost and outermost layers ending in loops; in the longitudinal plane, every myelin unit terminates in a separate loop near a node (*n*). Within these loops glial cytoplasm is also retained. (From Bunge, M., *et al.* 1961 J. Biophys. Biochem. Cytol., vol. 10, p. 67.)

structures; the ventral root contains the motor or efferent fibers to somatic muscles and fibers to the visceral effectors: smooth muscle (as in the wall of the gut), cardiac muscle and glands (Fig. 9-3). The dorsal and ventral roots join together to form the spinal nerves; the spinal nerve is thus a mixed nerve of both sensory and motor fibers. Some of the sensory fibers are myelinated, whereas others are not; and the same applies to motor fibers. For this reason, it is generally not possible in the standard histological preparation to distinguish afferent from efferent fibers or visceral from somatic fibers.

Of the cranial nerves, some are purely efferent, others are purely afferent, while still others contain both efferent and afferent fibers. The same fundamental relations hold for the cranial nerves as for the spinal nerves. The afferent fibers arise from cell bodies in ganglia outside the CNS and the efferent fibers arise either from neuron bodies lying within the brain or from cells in autonomic ganglia. The optic "nerve" and parts of certain other cranial nerves form exceptions to this statement. The optic nerve actually is a fiber tract connecting the retina—an outlying evaginated part of the neural tube—with the brain.

In all peripheral nerves, the delicate nerve fibers, both myelinated and unmyelinated, are strengthened and protected by the substantial connective tissue components (Fig. 10-31). In histological sections, the connective tissue sleeves in which the nerve fibers course are often the most conspicuous elements. Enclosing the entire nerve is a thick sheath of connective tissue, the *epineurium*. It is composed of irregularly arranged collagenous and elastic fibers, together with fibroblasts and histiocytes. When the nerve fibers are arranged in several distinct fascicles, as is often the case, these bundles are separated by extensions of the epineurium. Inside the heavy epineurial layer is a more delicate sleeve of connective tissue, the *perineurium*. Recent studies

indicate that flattened cells on the inner aspect of this layer form a continuous sheet of epithelium, which provides an effective barrier to the penetration of material into the nerve (Fig. 10-35). Thus, when marker proteins are applied to the nerve externally, they are excluded from the inner regions not by the heavy and coarse connective tissue of the epineurium but by the continuous cellular sleeve of the inner part of the perineurium.

Inside the perineurium are the scattered cells (fibroblasts and histiocytes) and the delicate connective tissue fibers of the *endoneurium*. The basal lamina surrounding the neurilemma or Schwann cells (which ensheath both myelinated and unmyelinated fibers) is considered to be a component of the endoneurium (Figs. 10-26 and 10-27).

THE GANGLIA

Cranial and Spinal Ganglia. The cranial and the spinal ganglia consist of aggregates of afferent neurons situated on the sensory roots of their respective nerves. Each ganglion is surrounded by a connective tissue capsule which is continuous with the epineurium and perineurium of the peripheral nerve. Connective tissue trabeculae extend from the capsule into the ganglion to form a framework. Within the ganglion, the nerve cells are separated into irregular groups by strands of connective tissue and by bundles of nerve fibers (Fig. 10-36).

Each ganglion cell is invested with both cellular and connective tissue elements. The inner aspect of this investment consists of flattened cells closely applied to the plasma membrane of the neuron. These cells are termed *satellite* cells, and they form a mosaic which completely envelops the neuronal soma. These cells are akin to the neurilemma (Schwann) cells of the nerve fibers, and both derive from neural crest tissue. The outer aspect of the satellite cell investment is made up of a basal lamina reinforced externally by connective tissue fibers intermingled with flattened fibroblasts (sometimes called capsule cells) (Fig. 10-38). These connective tissue elements are continuous with the endoneurium of the contiguous nerve fibers.

The nerve cells of the cranial and spinal ganglia are unipolar neurons. The cell bodies vary in size from 15 to 100 μ. The smaller neurons, which give rise to unmyelinated

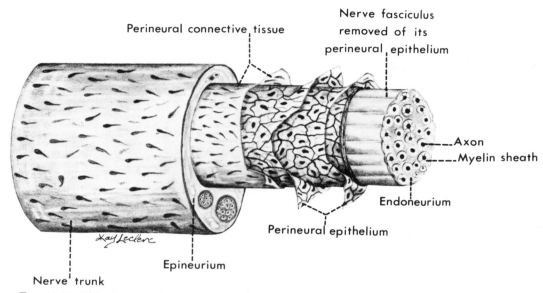

FIG. 10-35. This diagram illustrates the connective tissue sheaths around a peripheral nerve. The perineurial cells are seen disposed as an epithelium, and thus form a barrier against penetration of certain materials into the nerve fascicle. (Courtesy of Drs. T. R. Shantha and G. H. Bourne.)

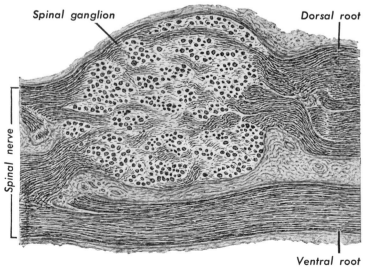

FIG. 10-36. Longitudinal section through a spinal ganglion of an infant, two months of age. Cajal silver. ×28.

fibers, contain quite closely packed Nissl substance, giving these cells a dark appearance in conventional stains. The large neurons, on the other hand, have Nissl bodies separated by groups of microtubules and neurofilaments which course through the cell body and extend into the axonal process. The "dilution" of the Nissl material by these poorly staining elements gives these cells a lighter appearance (Fig. 10-37).

Most of the large ganglion cells have one principal myelinated process that, at some distance from the cell body, divides into a peripheral branch which courses in the peripheral nerve and a central branch which enters the CNS. The course of the axon in the neighborhood of the cell body varies for different neurons. In some cases, the axon is coiled and looped around the cell body to form an intracapsular "glomerulus"; in other cases, it follows a relatively straight course from its cell body to the point where it divides into a central and a peripheral process. The majority of the large ganglion cells have axons of the "glomerular" type, whereas most of the small, darkly staining cells have the uncoiled type. These cell bodies do not receive synapses; the sensory ganglion is not an integrative center but merely a collection of nerve cell bodies.

The Autonomic (Sympathetic and Parasympathetic) Ganglia. The majority of the autonomic ganglia resemble the cranial and spinal ganglia in having a similar connective tissue capsule and framework. Unlike sensory ganglia, these ganglia contain synapses, for they are the way stations where certain of the first neurons of the two-neuron sympathetic efferent system form a synapse with the second neuron of the visceral motor pathway (Fig. 10-12).

The neurons are multipolar cells with numerous branched dendrites and a single axon which forms the unmyelinated postganglionic visceral efferent fiber (Fig. 10-39). The cell bodies vary in size from 15 to 60 μ. The nucleus is relatively large and pale, round or oval in shape and often eccen-

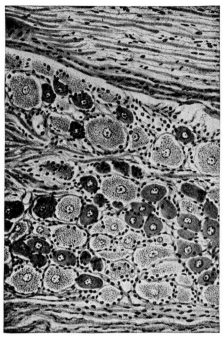

FIG. 10-37. Drawing of a section of a human spinal ganglion. Two principal types of ganglion cells are shown, a large clear type with well marked Nissl bodies and a smaller more darkly staining type. This dichotomy reflects a closer packing of Nissl material in the smaller neuron. The nuclei of the surrounding satellite cells are also evident. (Ph. Stöhr, Jr., from v. Möllendorff, Handbuch der mikroskopischen Anatomie des Menschen.)

trically placed. Binucleate cells are not uncommon. The Nissl bodies may be distributed uniformly throughout the cytoplasm or may be confined either to the perinuclear zone or to the peripheral cytoplasm. In the larger ganglia, each cell is surrounded by a layer of satellite cells as in the spinal ganglia (Fig. 10-39). Often, two ganglion cells may share a single satellite cell-connective tissue investment.

Located in a confusing array throughout these ganglia are frequent axosomatic and axodendritic synapses. The preganglionic elements contain numerous round, clear vesicles as would be expected in a synapse known to be cholinergic (see above). It has recently been demonstrated that there are

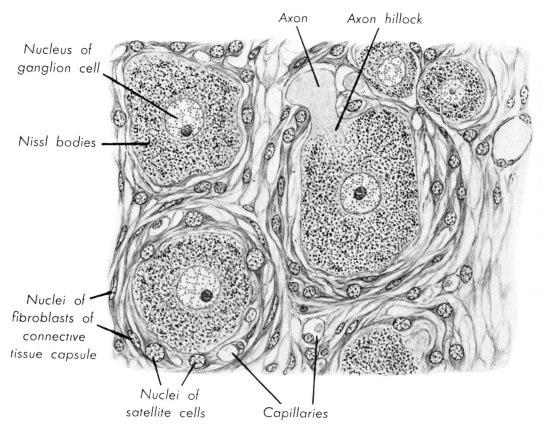

FIG. 10-38. Unipolar nerve cells from a Gasserian (cranial) ganglion stained by the Nissl method. Human, 19 years of age. ×640.

small, densely staining interneurons in certain sympathetic ganglia which apparently allow some integrative activity within the ganglion itself.

It will be recalled from the discussion in Chapter 9 that the synaptic contact between the first and second neuron of the parasympathetic system is frequently not in a discrete ganglion but directly in the wall of the organ innervated (heart, gut, bladder, etc.). Here presynaptic fibers make contact with neurons in isolated groups. The postsynaptic neurons often have no definitive dendrites. The synapse frequently occurs on the cell body of the second neuron; it is the activity of the axons of this postsynaptic neuron, then, that results in neurotransmitter release in relation to the smooth muscle or glands of the visceral structures of the body (Fig. 10-12).

DEGENERATION AND REGENERATION OF NERVE FIBERS

The individuality of the neuron and the interdependence of its parts are strikingly exemplified by its behavior when injured. When a nerve trunk is cut across, certain changes take place in the cut ends for a short distance on either side of the cut. These are degenerative changes of a traumatic nature, involving necrosis of the injured parts. On the proximal side of the injury (toward the cell body), degenerative changes may extend the distance of a few internodes, but very soon regenerative

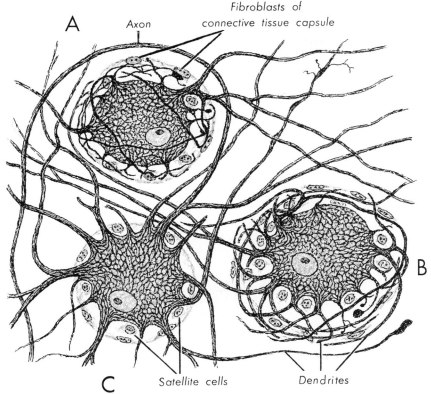

A — Axon — Fibroblasts of connective tissue capsule

B

C — Satellite cells — Dendrites

FIG. 10-39. Sympathetic nerve cells, human, 36 years of age. Cajal's silver stain. *A* and *B*, cells whose dendrites form a pericellular plexus. *C*, cell with long dendrites. Redrawn from Cajal.

processes are initiated, leading to a new growth from the end of this central stump.

Distal to the site of injury, however, the degenerative changes are progressive and in time lead to the complete breakdown and disappearance of this portion of the nerve fibers, including their terminal arborizations. This process is known as *secondary* or *Wallerian degeneration*. In terms of the neuron concept, this means that an axon cut off from its cell of origin degenerates and disappears, and this behavior of the axon accords with the fact that the cell body is the trophic center of the neuron.

The first changes seen in the distal portion of the cut nerve occur in the axons themselves. They lose their uniform contour and become swollen. This swelling is generally intermittent rather than uniform, and the nerve fiber takes on a beaded appearance.

Within 3 to 5 days after section of a peripheral nerve, the axons break up into irregular, twisted segments which finally undergo complete disintegration. In the CNS, this axon breakdown is often very much slower, and special stains (e.g., the Nauta stain) which selectively delineate the degenerating axons and their terminals are useful in tracing fiber pathways in neuroanatomical studies.

Coincident with these changes in the axon are degenerative changes in the myelin sheath. During the first few days, there is a fragmentation of the myelin so that it becomes broken into spherical, oval or elongated segments which surround the fragments of the axon (Fig. 10-40). In the succeeding days, these myelin fragments undergo further breakdown within Schwann cells or invading histiocytes. The myelin fragments appear as smaller and smaller droplets until finally they disappear (Fig. 10-40). The chemical changes taking place as the myelin is digested are the basis of the selectivity of the Marchi stain for degenerating myelin. This stain allows degenerating tracts (which contain myelin) to be identified, and it is a useful adjunct to the axonal stains mentioned above.

In peripheral nerve tissue, the degeneration of the axon and myelin sheath occurs within the confines of the connective tissue framework. The endoneurial elements which originally surrounded the axon-Schwann cell unit forms a tubular envelope within which the reacting Schwann cells are confined (Fig. 10-40). While the breakdown and digestion

of axon and myelin are progressing, certain Schwann cells enlarge and undergo mitosis. Confined by the sleeve of connective tissue mentioned above, these cells accumulate in tubular or bandlike arrays along the length of the nerve. These cylindrical cellular aggregates are known as "band fibers" or "protoplasmic bands." This tubular framework is very important in supplying pathways for regenerating axons as they grow out of the proximal and into the distal stump of the damaged nerve.

The extensive degenerative processes in the peripheral stump are not the only changes which follow nerve section. The primary or traumatic degeneration occurring in the proximal stump at the site

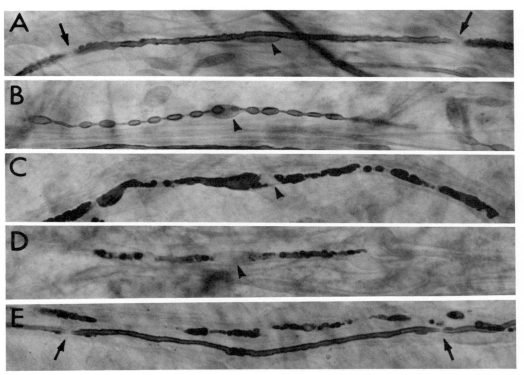

Fig. 10-40. *A*, normal short myelin segment delineated by two nodes of Ranvier (*arrows*) and showing the myelin-related Schwann cell nucleus (*arrowhead*). Myelin segments are shown breaking down several hours after the axon has been cut (*B*), several days later (*C*) and about one week later (*D*). In each case the Schwann cell involved in disposal of the myelin remnants is marked by an *arrowhead*. *E*, a small nerve fascicle containing one normal myelinated nerve fiber and remnants of a myelinated axon severed about one week earlier. If larger amounts of myelin must be digested macrophages invade the tissue and assist the Schwann cells. Cultured rat sensory ganglia fixed in OsO_4 and stained with Sudan black. ×520.

of the injury has already been mentioned. Degenerative changes also occur in the neuron body itself. An apparent *chromatolysis* may be observed as early as the first day after nerve section and is marked at about 2 weeks. The cytological changes that characterize chromatolysis have been discussed above. It should be noted that this response to axon section is another useful anatomical tool in identifying neurons whose axons have been damaged. Thus, if a neuron is observed in chromatolysis after a particular neurological lesion, it is presumed that this neuron supported an axon which coursed through the lesion area.

Regrowth from severed axons is generally considered to be especially vigorous in the autonomic nervous system and active in the somatic peripheral nervous system but minimal and generally ineffective in the CNS. If the neuron cell body which supports

nerve fibers within the peripheral nervous system survives, regeneration can be expected. The axons of the proximal stump of the severed nerve form bulbous enlargements and axonal sprouts within a few days (Figs. 10-41 and 10-42). Usually it takes about 2 weeks for the axonal sprouts to cross the scar to enter the endoneurial tubes of the distal stump of the severed nerve. The growing tip of the axonal sprout advances more rapidly after it has entered the endoneurial tube. Axon growth across the scar is facilitated by bridges which are formed chiefly by proliferation and migration of the Schwann cells and fibroblasts. The axonal sprouts are unable to cross the gap when it is too long or when it becomes filled with dense collagenous fibers. Nerve transplants are made in order to facilitate the growth of axonal sprouts across gaps of any appreciable size (e.g., after gunshot wounds);

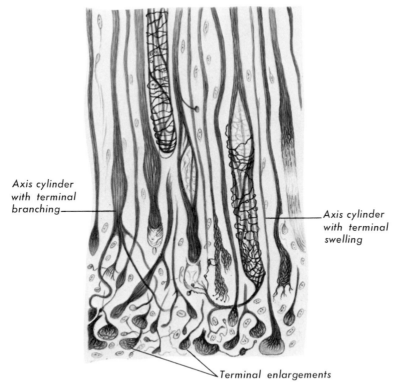

Axis cylinder with terminal branching

Axis cylinder with terminal swelling

Terminal enlargements

Fig. 10-41. Regenerating axons in the central stump of the sciatic nerve of a cat two and one-half days after section of the nerve. (Redrawn from Ramon y Cajal.)

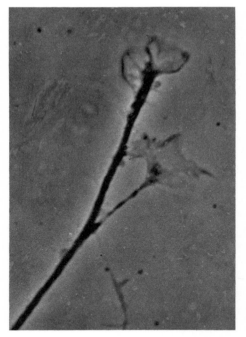

FIG. 10-42. This photomicrograph shows nerve fibers which have grown out from a rat autonomic ganglion in tissue culture. The leading tips of the fibers are expanded and when watched over a period of time can be observed to move actively. These tips are called growth cones. ×1340. (Courtesy of Dr. Dennis Bray.)

the transplanted nerve provides the important guiding connective tissue framework and thus may be effective even though it contains no viable cells.

Each sprout from the proximal end of a severed nerve usually splits into a number of branches, sometimes as many as 50. This increases the chance of appropriate connections. A number of branches may enter a single Schwann tube. Some of these branches enlarge, others degenerate. In fibers which will become myelinated, generally only one axon is left per tube.

When only a fraction of the nerve fibers of a peripheral nerve are cut, the remarkable process of *collateral sprouting* appears. If 75 of 100 nerve fibers innervating a region are cut, the 25 remaining fibers will sprout numerous collateral branches (at the point of the node of Ranvier in myelinated fibers),

and these will attempt to take up the positions of the 75 lost fibers. This attempt is often at least partially successful, and the 25 remaining fibers then have expanded regions of nervous influence. In practical terms, this means that the number of muscle fibers supplied by each motor nerve fiber will be increased, or that the field of sensation served by a sensory neuron will be enlarged. This type of regeneration is common after motor neuron loss in poliomyelitis and helps to explain the partial recovery of motor function that occurs.

In the CNS of mammals, where Schwann cells are lacking and no band fibers are formed, regeneration does not occur as readily as in the peripheral nervous system. Recent studies have shown, however, that axons will bridge the gap between the cut ends of a transected spinal cord in mammals when special efforts are made to prevent connective tissue from growing into the gap. Even under the best conditions, however, effective regeneration accompanied by functional recovery does not occur.

NERVE TERMINATIONS

The axons which form the peripheral nerve fibers terminate in peripheral structures to which or from which they convey nerve impulses. The *efferent* fibers terminate in tissues in which they excite activity by releasing a neurotransmitter. In the somatic effectors (skeletal muscle), the transmitter released is acetylcholine. By reacting with special sites on the muscle membrane, acetylcholine causes the generation of an action potential in the muscle fiber, with subsequent muscle contraction. In many of the visceral effectors, two different transmitters are involved: acetylcholine released by the parasympathetic nerve terminals and norepinephrine released by sympathetic endings. It should be recalled that in the former case the endings contain small, round, clear vesicles; in the latter case they contain dense-cored vesicles of slightly larger size. The dual anatomic innervation provides for shifts in organ activity; parasympathetic nerves stimulate digestive action in the intestine after eating, whereas sympathetic nerves inhibit intestinal activity during exercise. In the case of afferent fibers, on the other hand, the receptor portions are located in the peripheral parts of the body. These nerve fibers end freely in the tissues or in specially organized structures where, in either case, they receive stimuli which cause them to convey nerve impulses to the CNS.

Terminations of Somatic Efferent Fibers. The cell bodies of these fibers lie in the ventral gray matter of the spinal cord or in the motor nuclei of cranial nerves in the brain. The axons are myelinated and form part of the ventral roots and efferent fibers of the peripheral nerves, terminating in the skeletal muscles of the body and head. The nerve fibers enter the perimysium, in which they may bifurcate several times, thus permitting one neuron to innervate more than one muscle fiber. Finer muscles con-

cerned with precise movement generally receive a more abundant supply of nerve fibers. In muscles which move the eyeball, the proportion of nerve fibers to muscle fibers may approach a one to one ratio. In most muscles, however, the ratio is much lower, and as many as 1600 muscle fibers are innervated by the terminal branches of one nerve fiber.

After repeated branchings in the perimysium, the nerve fibers pass to the individual muscle fibers, where they terminate in structures known as *motor end plates* (Fig. 10-43). At the end plate region, the myelin is lost and the endoneurium becomes continuous with a layer of reticular fibers over the sarcolemma. The fiber terminates in a series of bulbous expansions, and in these regions the Schwann cell covering (which has replaced the myelin as an axon sheath) is withdrawn from between the nerve and muscle fiber (Fig. 10-44). At the regions of termination, the nerve indents the muscle fiber, forming a "synaptic gutter." Within

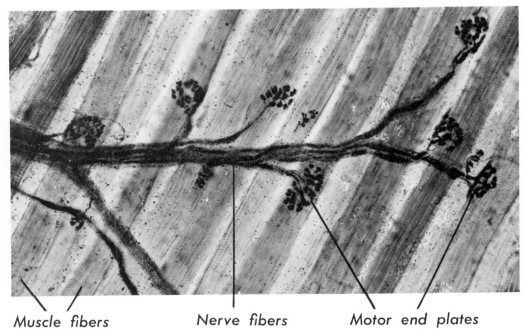

Muscle fibers   Nerve fibers   Motor end plates

FIG. 10-43. Photomicrograph of motor nerve ending in intercostal muscle. Gold chloride method. ×215.

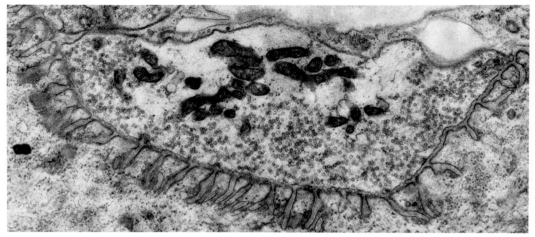

FIG. 10-44. This is an electron micrograph of a portion of the region of contact between an axon terminal and a somatic muscle cell. The underlying muscle is of the "fast" or "twitch" type. The sarcolemma of the muscle cell below is regularly folded. Note that the material of the basal lamina which overlies the sarcolemma is continued into the space between the axon and the sarcolemma, and into these folds. The bulbous axon expansion contains many small vesicles and a number of mitochondria. A sheath formed by the flattened process of a Schwann cell overlies the axon. At regions of axon contact on "slow" somatic muscle fibers there is generally less folding of the sarcolemma. ×16,000. (From Hess, A. 1965 J. Cell Biol., vol. 26, p. 467.)

the nerve terminal are a multitude of small, round, clear vesicles about 450 A in diameter, and an abundance of mitochondria. Details of this junction, which has many similarities to the synapses of the CNS, are shown in Figures 10-45 and 10-46. It has been suggested that the general configuration (rather than the ultrastructural details) of nerve endings on "fast" muscle fibers differs from that of endings on "slow" fibers and, in fact, that the "trophic" characteristics of the nerve terminal determine whether the muscle fiber contacted is of the slow or fast type.

In the part of the muscle fiber beneath the motor end plate region, there is an increase in number of muscle nuclei. In ordinary sections, the muscle nuclei may appear adjacent to or even between some of the Schwann cell nuclei where nerve fibers course in grooves of the muscle fiber, but electron micrographs have clearly shown that the axon terminals do not penetrate the sarcolemma and, therefore, they do not intermingle with the constituents of the muscle cell (Fig. 10-44).

Terminations of Visceral Efferent Fibers. The visceral efferent fibers from the autonomic ganglion cells terminate in the following effectors: heart muscle (cardiomotor); smooth muscle of viscera (visceromotor), of blood vessels (vasomotor) and of hairs (pilomotor); and glandular epithelia (secretory). These fibers are unmyelinated.

In heart muscle and in smooth muscle, the fibers form plexuses around the muscle bundles. From these plexuses, fine nerve fibers course in relation to individual muscle fibers. Electron microscopic examination indicates that no special junctions are formed but that bulbous enlargements of the nerve fiber in the vicinity of, and in some cases directly adjacent to, smooth muscle fibers contain aggregates of synaptic vesicles (Fig. 10-47). Some enlargements contain the small, clear vesicles, others contain the larger, dense-cored variety; the former are considered characteristic of parasympathetic fibers, the latter are components of sympathetic nerve fibers (see above). Ap-

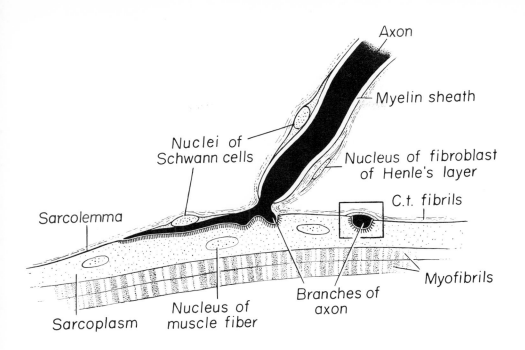

Axon

Myelin sheath

Nuclei of
Schwann cells

Nucleus of fibroblast
of Henle's layer

C.t. fibrils

Sarcolemma

Myofibrils

Branches of
axon

Nucleus of
muscle fiber

Sarcoplasm

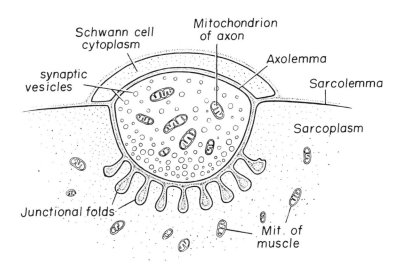

Schwann cell
cytoplasm

Mitochondrion
of axon

Axolemma

Sarcolemma

synaptic
vesicles

Sarcoplasm

Junctional folds

Mit. of
muscle

FIGS. 10-45 and 10-46. FIGURE 10-45 (*above*) illustrates a somatic motor nerve ending on a skeletal muscle fiber. The sheath of Henle (part of the endoneurium) extends onto the muscle fiber. The myelin ends just before the axon reaches the muscle fiber. Schwann cells associated with myelin end at the same point. Other Schwann cells, sometimes described as teloglia, continue onto the branches of the axon. Their cytoplasm is so thin that it can be seen under the light microscope only at the level of the nuclei. The branches of the axon lie in invaginations of sarcolemma known as synaptic gutters, or primary synaptic clefts. The subneural sarcolemma and subjacent sarcoplasm, often described as a "subneural apparatus," may appear as a series of rodlets in special preparations under the light microscope.

Figure 10-46 (*below*) diagrams a portion of the motor end plate (enclosed in the box in Fig. 10-45) showing a branch of an axon in a synaptic gutter as seen in electron micrographs. Secondary clefts or junctional folds extend inward from the primary cleft or gutter. The axon is covered by a thin layer of Schwann cell cytoplasm on the side away from the muscle but no Schwann cell cytoplasm extends into the gutter. The space between the axolemma and sarcolemma contains an amorphous material, continuous with the basal lamina material around the muscle cell. (Diagram based on descriptions and illustrations by Robertson, 1960, and Couteaux, 1947 and 1960.)

281

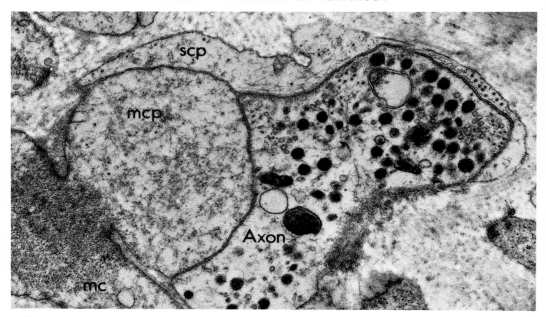

Fig. 10-47. This is an electron micrograph of a region of contact between a smooth muscle cell and a nerve fiber in the small intestine of a toad. A bulbous process (*mcp*) protrudes from the muscle cell (*mc*) containing conspicuous fine filaments. This process is in direct contact with an axon containing a variety of vesicles, including many granule containing vesicles. The axon is partially covered by a Schwann cell process (*scp*). In this type of "visceral" neuromuscular junction neither membrane specialization nor vesicle accumulation near the presynaptic membrane is apparent. ×22,500. (Courtesy of Dr. J. Rosenbluth.)

parently, neurotransmitter released from these areas is able to influence responsive cells in the surrounding tissues without establishing discrete neuromuscular junctions.

In glandular epithelium, the visceral efferent fibers form a plexus beneath the basement membrane, through which the fibers pass to terminate in relation to individual gland cells.

Classification of Terminations of Afferent Fibers. Those parts of the body which receive stimuli and contain the terminations of peripheral afferent fibers are known as receptors. The receptors have the function of responding to various physical and chemical stimuli, and furthermore, certain receptors have the function of reacting primarily to one particular kind of stimulus. The mechanism of reception must provide for the initiation of a nerve impulse, and in this sense the action of a receptor is con-

sidered analogous to the chemical excitability of the dendritic portion of the typical neuron. In some receptors (as in the taste bud), special cells receive the stimulus and respond with receptor potentials which, in turn, activate the nerve ending. In other receptors (as in the Pacinian corpuscle), the nerve ending itself receives the stimulus and develops a generator potential which triggers the action potential of the nerve fiber. The concept that each type of sensation (touch, heat, etc.) has its own specific receptor has been modified, for it has been observed that different receptors may respond to the same stimulus (e.g., both Pacinian corpuscles and free nerve endings respond to tactile stimuli).

The receptors may be classified in several more or less overlapping ways:

1. Some receptors are found widely distributed over the body. These may be termed collectively receptors of general body

or *somaesthetic* sensibility (touch, pressure, pain, temperature, position, movement, visceral). Other receptors are found aggregated only in certain places in the head, where they constitute the *organs of special senses* (smell, sight, taste, hearing and head position and movement).

2. Another distinction may be made between *exteroceptors*, the receptors affected by external stimuli (touch, light pressure, cutaneous pain and temperature, smell, sight and hearing): the *proprioceptors*, which are affected by stimuli arising within the body wall, especially those of movement and posture; and the *enteroceptors*, which are affected by stimuli arising within the viscera.

The modes of termination of the peripheral processes of the cranial or spinal ganglion cells in receptors are so varied and complicated as to make impracticable any structural classification except in the broadest sense. The terminal arborizations of the afferent fibers, however, follow one of two structural arrangements. Either they terminate freely among the body tissues or they are surrounded by special connective tissue capsules. The distinction can thus be made between *free* or *nonencapsulated* sensory endings and *encapsulated* ones.

Nonencapsulated Afferent Endings. These endings are found in practically all epithelia of the body, in connective tissue, in muscle and in serous membranes. They are the most common type of sensory ending in the body.

In the skin and in those mucous membranes which are covered by stratified squamous epithelium, the nerve fibers of a given branch separate as they approach the epithelium, lose their myelin sheaths and form a subepithelial plexus. From this plexus, axons or their branches enter the epithelial layer and split into minute arborizations, which terminate between the cells in little knoblike swellings. In the skin, the nerve endings do not penetrate beyond the cells of the stratum granulosum.

Essentially similar free nerve endings are seen in other epithelial surfaces, such as the mucosa of the respiratory tract (Fig. 10-48).

Another form of free nerve ending is the *peritrichial* ending, in which sensory fibers encircle the hair follicle and terminate principally in the connective tissue sheath and vitreous membrane of the follicle. Fine nerve fibers may also extend into the outer epithelial root sheath.

In general, these intraepithelial endings

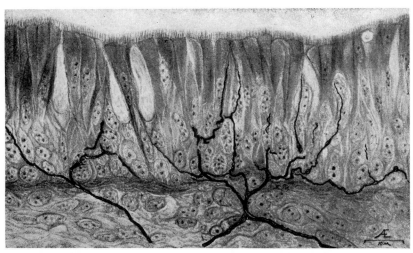

FIG. 10-48. Nerve endings in bronchial epithelium (pseudostratified ciliated columnar epithelium). Reduced silver method of Cajal. (After A. Elftman.)

terminate among epithelial cells that do not differ from the adjoining epithelial cells. In the deeper epithelial layers of the skin, however, there may be seen leaflike expansions of a nerve terminal, each of which forms a *meniscus* in contact with an epithelial cell which stains differently from the other cells. This is a *tactile cell*, and the whole apparatus is known as a *tactile corpuscle of Merkel*.

Sensory fibers also terminate diffusely in connective tissue. Although these terminations may vary in form, they have in common the fact that they all end by a branching of the sensory fibers among the fibers and cells of the connective tissue. Such endings are found extensively in the dermis and subcutaneous tissue and in the connective tissue of mucous and serous membranes, the periosteum and blood vessels, to name a few instances.

In addition to arborized terminations in the interstitial connective tissue of muscle, nonencapsulated sensory nerve endings are also found around the individual muscle fibers themselves (Fig. 10-49).

Encapsulated Afferent Endings. These include such structures as the *end bulbs*, the *tactile corpuscles of Meissner*, the *Pacinian corpuscles*, the *muscle spindles* and the *tendon organs* (or *organs of Golgi*).

Of the encapsulated sensory endings, probably the simplest are the so-called end bulbs. These are spherical or oval in shape and consist of a thin, lamellated capsule of flattened connective tissue cells and fibers surrounding a central cavity, the *inner bulb*. Within the inner bulb, the naked axons of one or more myelinated fibers end. In some inner bulbs, the axon may terminate in a number of branches which twist and interlace to form a spherical, skeinlike mass known as a glomerulus. An example of this type is seen in the *end bulbs of Krause* in the conjunctival connective tissue.

End bulbs are found in the lips, in the mucous membranes of the tongue, cheeks, soft palate, epiglottis, nasal cavities, lower end of rectum, peritoneum, serous membranes, tendons, ligaments, connective tissue of nerve trunks, synovial membranes of certain joints and the external genitals, especially the glans penis and clitoris.

Fig. 10-49. Afferent nerve endings in muscle (smooth) of one of the larger bronchi. Seven-day-old puppy. Reduced silver method of Cajal. (After A. Elftman.)

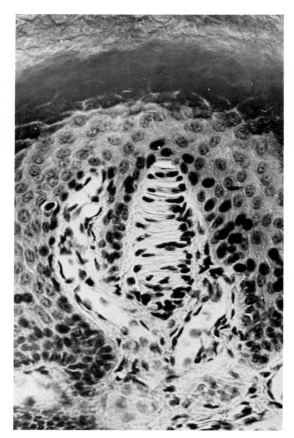

Fig. 10-50. Photomicrographs of Meissner's corpuscles in dermal papillae of human skin. At *left*, stained with silver, showing the axon; at *right*, stained with hematoxylin and eosin, showing the connective tissue elements of the nerve ending. Only a portion of the epidermis is included in the field. (Courtesy of Dr. A. Elwyn.)

The *tactile corpuscle of Meissner* (Fig. 10-50) offers an example of a more complex encapsulated tactile corpuscle. It occurs especially in the hairless portions of the skin and is most numerous in the finger tips, the palms of the hands and the soles of the feet. Lying within the connective tissue of the dermal papillae, these corpuscles are oval bodies which are composed of flattened connective tissue cells in the form of horizontal lamellae surrounded by a connective tissue capsule. Two or more myelinated nerve fibers are distributed to each corpuscle. As the fibers reach the corpuscle, the connective tissue sheath of the nerve joins the connective tissue capsule, the myelin sheaths disap-

pear and the naked axons pass into the corpuscle where they branch and pursue a spiral course among the connective tissue elements. In addition to the myelinated fibers, many tactile corpuscles and other encapsulated receptors may also contain the endings of unmyelinated fibers, the significance of which is not known. The corpuscles of Meissner are known to respond to tactile stimuli.

The *Pacinian corpuscles* are laminated elliptical structures which differ from the simpler end bulbs already described chiefly in the greater development of the connective tissue capsule. They are relatively large structures which are visible to the naked eye (Fig. 10-51). The capsule is formed by a large

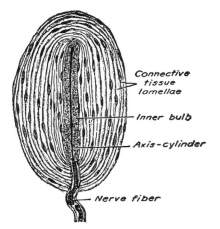

Connective
tissue
lamellae

Inner bulb

Axis-cylinder

Nerve fiber

FIG. 10-51. Pacinian corpuscle. Human. (Redrawn from Cajal.)

number of concentric lamellae, each lamella consisting of connective tissue fibers lined by a single layer of flat connective tissue cells. The lamellae are separated from one another by a clear fluid or semifluid substance. As in the simpler end bulbs, there is a central cavity within the capsule known as the inner bulb. Each Pacinian corpuscle is supplied by a single myelinated nerve fiber. After losing its myelin sheath, the axon extends through the center of the inner bulb, terminating in a knoblike expansion.

Fine blood vessels enter the base of the corpuscle along with the nerve fiber and break up into capillary networks among the lamellae. They do not enter the inner bulb.

The Pacinian corpuscles are found in the deeper subcutaneous connective tissue, especially of the hand and foot, in the parietal peritoneum, pancreas, mesentery, penis, clitoris, urethra, nipple, mammary gland and in the connective tissue in the vicinity of tendons, ligaments and joints. Their form and to some extent their position indicate that they are stimulated by deep or heavy pressure.

In skeletal muscle, sensory nerves terminate in end bulbs and in complicated end organs called *muscle spindles*. The muscle spindle (Fig. 10-52) is an elongated cylindrical structure within which are one or several

small muscle fibers, connective tissue, blood vessels and myelinated nerve fibers (Fig. 10-52). The whole is enclosed in a connective tissue capsule which is pierced at various points by one or more nerve fibers. The thinner nerve fibers are generally motor fibers and end on the muscle fibers in typical motor end plates. The thicker myelinated fibers are sensory fibers which lose their myelin as they branch repeatedly within the spindle. The axons then terminate around the enclosed muscle fibers in close apposition to the sarcolemma. Frequently, the ending is in the form of a spiral; it may also form a series of rings or an arborization.

The muscle fibers of the spindle are thinner than ordinary fibers and are richer in sarcoplasm. They also contain more nuclei, particularly in the regions surrounded by nerve fibers. They are referred to as intrafusal fibers, as opposed to the extrafusal fibers of of the muscle proper. The motor neurons of the spinal cord that innervate the intrafusal fibers are termed gamma motor neurons; the motor neurons supplying the remainder of the muscle fibers are termed alpha motor neurons. Information conveyed to and from the muscle spindle is not consciously received, but it is important in the reflex regulation of muscle tone. Details of the structure of the muscle spindle are given schematically in Figure 10-53.

At the junction of muscle and tendon are found the elaborate sensory structures known as the *tendon organs* or *organs of Golgi* (Fig. 10-54). These are spindle-shaped bodies composed of several tendon bundles covered by a thin capsule. Into this there enter one or several afferent nerve fibers which break up into complicated arborizations upon the tendon bundles.

The proprioceptive stimuli of position and movement resulting from the constant or varying tension of voluntary muscles and their attached tendons are received by the muscle spindles and tendon organs. The information gathered in these receptors guides the CNS in determining how to use the at-

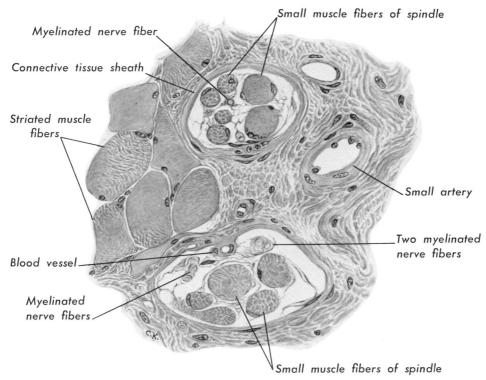

Small muscle fibers of spindle

Myelinated nerve fiber

Connective tissue sheath

Striated muscle fibers

Blood vessel

Myelinated nerve fibers

Small artery

Two myelinated nerve fibers

Small muscle fibers of spindle

FIG. 10-52. Cross section of two muscle spindles in skeletal muscle of monkey.

tached muscle in the fine degrees of contraction or relaxation necessary for precise motor control.

HISTOGENESIS OF NERVE TISSUE

The formation of the neural tube from ectoderm on the dorsal surface of the embryo is discussed in Chapter 9 (Fig. 9-1). This tubular cell mass and the adjacent neural crest (together with the accessory sensory placodes for the ear, the eye and the nose) provide the source of neurons and supporting cells of both the CNS and the peripheral nervous system (Fig. 10-55). The upper (or anterior) end of the neural tube develops three dilations which form the forebrain, the midbrain and the hindbrain of the CNS. In these regions, additional cell proliferation and cell migration lead to the development of surface (cortical) areas containing large numbers of neurons.

The development of the posterior neural tube is less complex. As cellular proliferation proceeds, three regions become apparent within the wall of the tube (Fig. 10-55). The most internal (subventricular) region is termed the *matrix* layer and contains actively dividing cells. After division, cells take up positions in the intermediate (or *mantle*) layer; those destined to become neurons send processes toward the exterior. These axons may grow out of the neural tube to form ventral root motor fibers or, in the case of interneurons, they may course up and/or down longitudinally along the tube to form the relatively acellular outermost *marginal* layer. In the fully differentiated CNS, these three layers (marginal, mantle and matrix) become, respectively, (1) the white matter, (2) the gray matter and (3) the ependyma and an immediately adjacent layer of tissue in which proliferation of glial cell precursors continues into adulthood.

Within these layers, the neurons develop

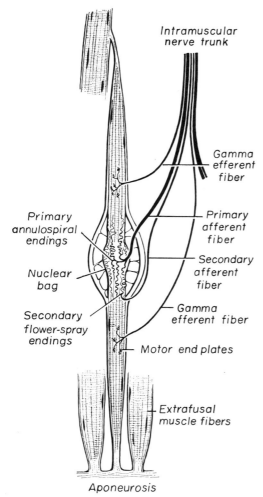

Intramuscular
nerve trunk

Gamma
efferent
fiber

Primary
annulospiral
endings

Primary
afferent
fiber

Secondary
afferent
fiber

Nuclear
bag

Secondary
flower-spray
endings

Gamma
efferent fiber

Motor end plates

Extrafusal
muscle fibers

Aponeurosis

FIG. 10-53. Diagram of a muscle spindle. Each spindle contains several slender muscle fibers (intrafusal) enclosed by a connective tissue sheath which becomes continuous at its ends with the connective tissue endomysium of regular muscle fibers (extrafusal). For purposes of clarity, only one intrafusal fiber is shown. The polar regions of each intrafusal fiber are striated and contractile, whereas the central region of each fiber is expanded and contains more nuclei; hence it is known as the nuclear bag. In the latter region, the connective tissue sheath is separated from the sarcolemma by a space filled with tissue fluid and traversed by connective tissue fibers and nerve fibers. The intrafusal muscle fibers are supplied by three types of nerve fibers: (1) small *efferent* fibers (gamma efferents) which terminate in motor end plates; (2) primary *afferents* which are large and wind around the muscle fibers to form annulospiral endings; and (3) secondary *afferents* which are small and

first, the astrocytes later and the oligodendrocytes last of all. The precursor cell of the neuron is termed the *neuroblast;* that of the glial cells is called the *glioblast* (or spongioblast). After an initial period of proliferation, neuron formation is thought to cease, and thereafter the number of neurons gradually decreases with age. Generally, motor neurons develop and muscles are innervated very early in development. Later, sensory fibers from the neurons of the peripheral ganglia grow into the gray matter of the spinal cord, and only then is the reflex arc formed and the embryo able to respond to stimuli.

It has been stressed in Chapter 9 that the basic reflex arc is not controlled by local sensory influences alone but by information converging on the motor neurons from many levels of the CNS, including the cerebral cortex, the midbrain and the hindbrain. How these complex synaptic networks become organized is one of the most challenging questions in neurobiology. There is no doubt that some synaptic contacts are genetically deter-

branch to terminate in clusters known as flower spray endings.

Since the intrafusal fibers are parallel with the extrafusal fibers, they are stretched and their afferent nerves are stimulated whenever the extrafusal fibers of the muscle as a whole are stretched. Hence, the spindle afferents function as stretch receptors. Contraction of extrafusal fibers reduces tension on the spindle, whereas localized contraction in the poles of the intrafusal fibers under stimulation of gamma efferents increases tension on the nuclear bag region and stimulates the stretch receptors.

The afferents have their neuron cell bodies in the spinal ganglion. The central processes from the cells having annulospiral receptors form synapses in the spinal cord with alpha motor neurons which send axons to motor end plates on extrafusal muscle fibers. Thus, a two-neuron (monosynaptic) path is established, functioning as a stretch or myotatic reflex. This type of reflex activity maintains muscle tonus and provides a background for voluntary movements following stimulation of the alpha motor neurons from higher centers. Stretch receptor reflexes associated with the flower spray endings are more complicated and involve polysynaptic pathways. (Diagram based on illustration by Barker, D. 1948 Quart. J. Micr. Sci., vol. 89, p. 143.)

mined, for certain synapses form in nerve tissue completely isolated from the other tissues of the body and from sensory influences.

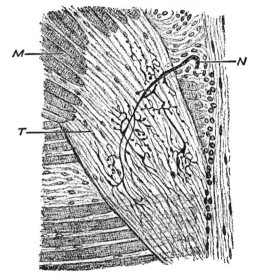

FIG. 10-54. Musculotendinous bundle from a six months human fetus. *M*, Muscle fibers; *N*, nerve fiber, *T*, tendon fibers. (Redrawn from Tello.)

Some investigators believe that, after having been guided to the correct region by mechanical forces and by chemical gradients, the axon makes contact with another neuron because of affinities of surface macromolecules. Certain synapses appear to require some degree of use to be retained, others do not. Are most synapses permanent? Are new synapses formed with learning? Are some synapses superfluous? Are more synapses formed in animals exposed to an "enriched" environment? How is memory stored in our nervous systems? These are some of the questions that present neurobiological experimentation is attempting to answer.

REFERENCES

AKERT, K., AND WASER, P. G. (editors) 1969 Mechanisms of synaptic transmission. Progr. Brain Res., vol. 31.

BARKER, D. (editor) 1962 Symposium on Muscle Receptors. Hong Kong University Press, Hong Kong.

BODIAN, D. 1962 The generalized vertebrate neuron. Science, vol. 137, pp. 323–326.

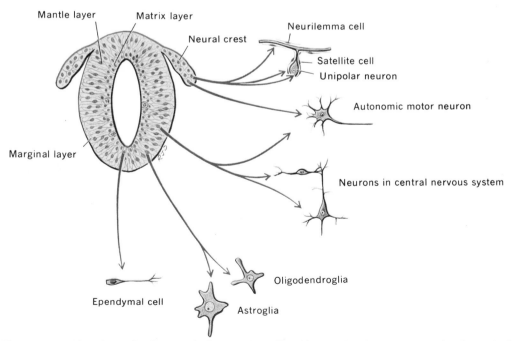

FIG. 10-55. This schematic diagram indicates the cells which derive from the neural tube and the neural crest. Note that mitotic activity in the neural tube is restricted to cells of the matrix layer adjacent to the central canal. (From Noback, C. 1967 The Human Nervous System, McGraw-Hill, New York.)

BOURNE, G. (editor) 1968, 1969 Structure and Function of the Nervous System, vols. 1 and 2. Academic Press, New York.

BUNGE, R. 1968 Glial cells and the central myelin sheath. Physiol. Rev., vol. 48, pp. 197–251.

CAUSEY, G. 1960 The Cell of Schwann. E. and S. Livingstone, Ltd., Edinburgh.

CLEMENTE, C. D. 1964 Regeneration in central nervous system. Int. Rev. Neurobiol., vol. 6, pp. 257–301.

COUTEAUX, R. 1960 Motor end-plate structure. In The Structure and Function of Muscle (Bourne, H. G., editor), vol. 1, pp. 337–380. Academic Press, New York.

DAVIS, H. 1961 Some principles of sensory receptor action. Physiol. Rev., vol. 41, pp. 391–415.

DEITCH, A. D., AND MURRAY, M. R. 1956 The Nissl substance of living and fixed spinal ganglion cells. J. Biophys. Biochem. Cytol., vol. 2, pp. 433–444.

DE ROBERTIS, E. D. P. 1964 Histophysiology of Synapses and Neurosecretion. The Macmillan Company, New York.

DOUGLAS, W. W., AND RITCHIE, J. M. 1962 Mammalian nonmyelinated nerve fibers. Physiol. Rev., vol. 42, pp. 297–334.

DROZ, B. 1969 Protein metabolism in nerve cells. Int. Rev. Cytol., vol. 25, pp. 363–390.

ECCLES, J. C. 1957 The Physiology of Nerve Cells. Johns Hopkins Press, Baltimore.

ECCLES, J. C. 1964 The Physiology of Synapses. Academic Press, New York.

GASSER, H. S. 1955 Properties of dorsal root unmedulated fibers on the two sides of the ganglion. J. Gen. Physiol., vol. 38, pp. 709–728.

GEREN, B. B. 1956 Structural studies of the formation of the myelin sheath in peripheral nerve fibers. In Cellular Mechanisms in Differentiation and Growth (Rudnick, D., editor), pp. 213–220. Princeton University Press, Princeton.

GLEES, P. 1955 Neuroglia; Morphology and Function. Charles C Thomas, Publisher, Springfield, Ill.

GRAY, E. G., AND GUILLERY, R. W. 1966 Synaptic morphology in the normal and degenerating nervous system. Int. Rev. Cytol., vol. 19, pp. 111–182.

GUTH, L. 1956 Regeneration in the mammalian peripheral nervous system. Physiol. Rev., vol. 36, pp. 441–478.

HILD, W. 1959 Das Neuron. In Handbuch der mikroskopischen Anatomie des Menschen (von Möllendorff, W., and Bargmann, W.,

editors), Springer-Verlag, Berlin, vol. 4, part 4, pp. 1–184.

HYDÉN, H. 1960 The Neuron. In The Cell; Biochemistry, Physiology, Morphology (Brachet, J., and Mirsky, A. E., editors), vol. 4, pp. 215–323. Academic Press, New York.

HYDÉN, H. (editor) 1967 The Neuron. Elsevier Publishing Company, Amsterdam.

KATZ, B. 1966 Nerve, Muscle and Synapse. McGraw-Hill Book Company, New York.

KUFFLER, S. W., AND NICHOLLS, J. G. 1966 The physiology of neuroglial cells. Ergebn. Physiol., vol. 57, pp. 1-90.

LANGMAN, J. 1963 Medical Embryology. The Williams & Wilkins Company, Baltimore.

MUGNAINI, E., AND WALBERG, F. 1963 Ultrastructure of neuroglia. Ergebn. Anat. Entwicklungsgesch., vol. 37, pp. 194–236.

MURRAY, M. R. 1965 Nervous Tissue in vitro. In Cells and Tissues in Culture (Willmer, E. N., editor), vol. 2, pp. 373–455. Academic Press, New York.

NOBACK, C. R. 1967 The Human Nervous System. McGraw-Hill Book Company, New York.

PALAY, S. L., AND PALADE, G. E. 1955 The fine structure of neurons. J. Biophys. Biochem. Cytol., vol. 1, pp. 69–88.

PAYTON, B. W., BENNETT, M. V. L., AND PAPPAS, G.D. 1969 Permeability and structure of junctional membranes at an electrotonic synapse. Science, vol. 166, pp. 1641–1643.

PENFIELD, W. (editor) 1932 Cytology and Cellular Pathology of the Nervous System, vols. 1, 2 and 3. Paul B. Hoeber, New York.

PENFIELD, W. 1932 Neuroglia: normal and pathological. In Cytology and Cellular Pathology of the Nervous System (Penfield. W., editor), vol. 2, pp. 421–479. Paul B. Hoeber, New York.

PETERS, A., PALAY, S., AND WEBSTER, H. de F. 1970 The Fine Structure of the Nervous System. Paul B. Hoeber, New York.

QUARTON, G. C., MELNECHUK, T., AND SCHMITT, F. O. 1967 The Neurosciences. Rockefeller University Press, New York.

RAMON Y CAJAL, S. 1928 Degeneration and Regeneration of the Nervous System. Oxford University Press, London.

RICHARDSON, K. C. 1962 The fine structure of autonomic nerve endings in smooth muscle of the rat vas deferens. J. Anat., vol. 96, pp. 427–442.

ROBERTSON, J. D. 1955 The ultrastructure of adult vertebrate peripheral myelinated nerve fibers in relation to myelinogenesis. J. Biophys. Biochem. Cytol., vol. 1, pp. 271–278.

Robertson, J. D. 1958 The ultrastructure of Schmidt-Lanterman clefts and related shearing defects of the myelin sheath. J. Biophys. Biochem. Cytol., vol. 4, pp. 39–46.

Shanthaveerappa, T. R., and Bourne, G H. 1966 Perineural epithelium: a new concept of its role in the integrity of the peripheral nervous system. Science, vol. 154, pp. 1464–1467.

Sperry, R. W. 1963 Chemoaffinity in the orderly growth of nerve fiber patterns and connections. Proc. Nat. Acad. Sci. USA, vol. 50, pp. 703–710.

Truex, R. C., and Carpenter, M. B. 1969 Human Neuroanatomy. The Williams & Wilkins Company, Baltimore.

Uzman, B. G., and Nogueira-Graf, G. 1957 Electron microscope studies of the formation of nodes of Ranvier in mouse sciatic nerves. J. Biophys. Biochem. Cytol., vol. 3, pp. 589–598.

Weiss, P. (editor) 1950 Genetic Neurology; Problems of the Development, Growth, and Regeneration of the Nervous System and Its Functions. University of Chicago Press, Chicago.

Weiss, P., and Hiscoe, H. B. 1948 Experiments on the mechanism of nerve growth. J. Exp. Zool., vol. 107, p. 314–395.

Windle, W. F. 1956 Regeneration of axons in the vertebrate central nervous system. Physiol. Rev., vol. 36, pp. 427–440.

Wolstenholme, G. E. W., and O'Connor, M. (editors) 1968 Growth of the Nervous System. Little, Brown and Company, Boston.

Young, J. Z. 1942 The functional repair of nervous tissue. Physiol. Rev., vol. 22, pp. 318–374.

11

The Spinal Cord, Cerebellar Cortex and Cerebral Cortex

The central nervous system is an array of various types of cell assemblies specialized to carry out their specific functions. Groups of nerve cell bodies carrying out similar functions are termed *nuclei* (or *ganglia*). If linearly arranged (as in the spinal cord), such cell groups may be termed *columns*. Groups of nerve fibers interconnecting these neuronal groups are called *tracts*. Myelinated tracts form the *white matter* of the central nervous system (CNS). When neuronal cell bodies occupy the surface of the brain, these areas are termed cortical regions or *cortex*. The CNS is covered with connective tissue and supported in a special fluid, the cerebrospinal fluid (CSF). It is the purpose of this chapter to present the cytology of several typical CNS regions and to describe the connective tissue investments that act both as a vessel for the CSF and as a protective covering for the fragile CNS tissues.

INVESTMENTS OF THE BRAIN AND CORD AND THE FLUID SPACES

The brain and spinal cord are enclosed by two connective tissue investments, the *dura mater* and the *pia-arachnoid*, the latter usually being subdivided into two layers, the *pia mater* and *arachnoid* (Figs. 11-1 and 11-2). These "membranes" are collectively known as the *meninges*, the dura mater

being the *pachymeninx* and the pia-arachnoid the *leptomeninx*, or *leptomeninges*.

The *dura mater*, which is the outer of the two investments, consists of dense fibrous tissue (Fig. 11-2). The *cerebral dura* serves both as an investing membrane for the brain and as periosteum for the inner surfaces of the cranial bones. It consists of two layers. The inner layer is composed of dense connective tissue lined on its inner surface by a single layer of flat cells. The outer layer, which forms the periosteum and is similar in structure to the inner layer, is much richer in blood vessels and nerves. The *spinal dura* corresponds to the inner layer of the cerebral dura, the vertebrae having their own separate periosteum. It contains more elastic tissue than the inner layer of the cerebral dura but otherwise resembles it in structure. The outer surface of the spinal dura is covered with a single layer of flat cells and is separated from the periosteum by the *epidural space*, which contains anastomosing, thin walled veins lying in connective tissue rich in fat (Fig. 11-1). The inner surface of the spinal dura is also lined by a single layer of flat cells. Beneath the spinal dura, between it and the arachnoid, is the *subdural space*, a narrow cleft containing fluid. It has no direct communication with the subarachnoid space.

The *pia mater* (Fig. 11-2) closely invests

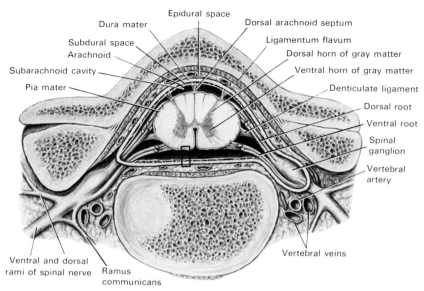

FIG. 11-1. This is a diagram of a transverse section through the fourth cervical vertebra showing the coverings of the spinal cord and related structures. An area comparable to that within the box is shown at higher magnification in Figure 11-2. (From Rauber-Kopsch, Anatomie.)

the brain and cord, extends into the convolutions of the brain and protrudes into the ventricles at the thin walled portions of the brain, where in combination with modified ependymal cells it forms the choroid plexus (described below). The pia consists of white fibrous tissue and contains the blood vessels that send branches into the nerve tissue.

The *arachnoid* (Fig. 11-2) passes over the convolutions of the brain without dipping into them. It is partly separated from the pia by a substantial space, across which trabeculae pass connecting pia and arachnoid. This is the *subarachnoid space*, and it is filled with a clear fluid, the CSF. The trabeculae and arachnoid contain delicate strands of connective tissue covered with a single layer of flat or low cuboidal cells which also extends over the outer pial surface. This layer of cells (mesenchymal epithelium) lines the subarachnoid spaces. The cells ordinarily have large, pale, oval nuclei.

The spinal dura and the inner layer of the cerebral dura are poor in blood vessels. The outer layer of the cerebral dura, forming as it does the periosteum of the cranial bones,

is rich in blood vessels which pass into and supply the bones. The pia is very vascular, especially its inner aspect from which vessels pass into the brain and cord. The arachnoid is nonvascular (Fig. 11-2).

The Cerebrospinal Fluid. The CSF in the subarachnoid space is in continuity with the CSF of the brain cavities (the ventricles) and the central canal of the spinal cord. This continuity is effected through an aperture in the caudal part of the thin roof of the fourth ventricle (the foramen of Magendie) and an aperture in each of the thin walled lateral recesses of the fourth ventricle (the foramina of Luschka).

The CSF is a clear, colorless fluid which is very slightly viscous and of low specific gravity (1.004 to 1.006). It contains small quantities of inorganic salts, chiefly sodium chloride and potassium chloride, as well as small amounts of dextrose and traces of proteins. It normally contains very few cells. Its quantity in an adult man is about 150 cc. The bulk of the CSF is probably formed by the activity of the epithelial cells lining the choroid plexus, from which it passes

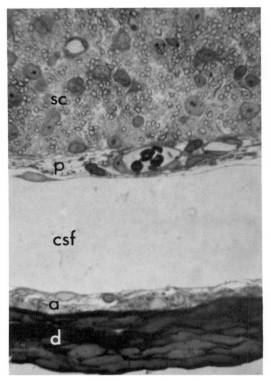

FIG. 11-2. This is a photomicrograph illustrating the histology of the region outlined by the box in Fig. 11-1. The white matter of the spinal cord (*sc*) shows a variety of neuroglia cells in the process of forming myelin. Many small myelin sheaths are seen in cross section. Immediately overlying the cord tissue is the pia mater (*p*) containing two blood vessels, one of which contains several red blood cells. The space between the pia mater and the arachnoid (*a*) contains the cerebrospinal fluid (*csf*). The heavy connective tissue layers of the dura mater (*d*) form the outermost investment. The arachnoid is shown in its normal close apposition to the dura; only in abnormal conditions does fluid accumulate in the potential space between these two membranes. Kitten spinal cord.

into the ventricles and thence by the foramina of Magendie and Luschka into the subarachnoid spaces. The drainage of the fluid appears to be chiefly by passage through the walls of arachnoid villi (see below) into the cerebral venous sinuses.

Choroid Plexuses. Certain parts of the wall of the brain are composed solely of modified ependymal cells forming a thin epithelial membrane, a lamina epithelialis, which is covered externally by a highly vascularized pia mater. These two layers together constitute the *telae choroideae*, which form the roof of the fourth ventricle, the roof of the third ventricle and parts of the walls of the lateral ventricles. Projecting into the ventricles are complex folds and invaginations from the telae choroideae containing tortuous networks of small vessels and capillaries, the *choroid plexuses* (Fig. 11-3). The term "choroid plexus" is often used in referring to the entire mass of infolded membranes, rather than to the network of blood vessels alone.

The modified ependymal epithelium covering the choroid plexuses is a simple cuboidal to low columnar type with a rather granular cytoplasm. In electron micrographs, the free surface of the cells appears to be thrown

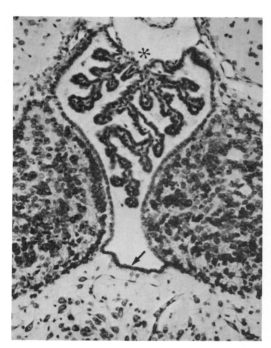

FIG. 11-3. This photomicrograph shows tufts of choroid plexus protruding downward from the roof (*) of the third ventricle into the ventricular cavity. The *arrow* points to the ependymal cells that form the lining of the third ventricle. Rat brain. ×130.

into fine irregular cytoplasmic projections, resembling a brush border. These cells play an important role in the production of the CSF. It should be noted that the cells of this modified ependyma, unlike ependyma elsewhere, are joined together along their lateral borders by a zone of tight membrane apposition. Thus, although the capillaries of this region are known to be quite "leaky" (as compared with capillaries elsewhere in brain parenchyma), extravascular material is prevented from entering the CSF directly because of the seal along the lateral edges of the cells of the choroid plexus epithelium.

The Arachnoid Villi. In certain places, the arachnoid sends prolongations into the dura which protrude into a venous sinus or venous lacuna. The prolongations contain spaces, traversed by trabeculae, which may be regarded as continuations of the subarachnoid space. These arachnoidal outgrowths, which are covered with the usual layer of low cells, are known as *arachnoid villi* (Fig. 11-4). They are most numerous along the longitudinal fissure of the cerebral hemispheres where they protrude into the superior longitudinal venous sinus. They are also sometimes found along the transverse, cavernous and superior petrosal sinuses.

It is thought that these villi have small one-way valves which permit the intermittent flow of CSF from the subarachnoid space into the venous sinuses (which have a very low fluid pressure).

The Fluid Compartments and the Blood-Brain Barrier. As is pointed out in the above discussion, the CSF occupies both the cavities of the CNS and the spaces around the brain and spinal cord. It is now known that neither the lining of the brain ventricles (the unspecialized ependyma) nor the covering of the brain surface (the pia) provides a tight barrier against the entry into or egress of fluids from the substance of the brain. The narrow extracellular clefts between neurons and glia of the CNS are therefore in continuity with CSF (Fig. 11-5). Thus, clinical sampling of the CSF with analysis of its composition provides a useful index of cellular changes in CNS diseases.

The perivascular spaces are also thought to be in continuity with this fluid system (Fig. 11-5). Near the surface of the brain, where pial tissue is carried down into brain substance with the penetrating blood vessels, this perivascular space is substantial and provides a common site of cell invasion in brain disease. Deeper within the brain

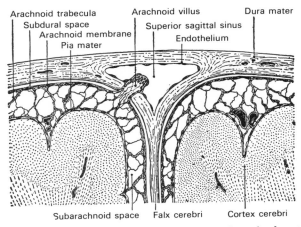

Arachnoid trabecula   Arachnoid villus   Dura mater
Subdural space   Superior sagittal sinus
Arachnoid membrane   Endothelium
Pia mater

Subarachnoid space   Falx cerebri   Cortex cerebri

Fig. 11-4. Schematic diagram of coronal section of meninges and cerebral cortex, to show relation of arachnoid villus to dural venous sinus. The potential subdural space is necessarily shown of greater size than is normal; the subarachnoid space is also increased in width to illustrate the character of the subarachnoid mesh. The nuclei of the cells lining the subarachnoid space are faintly shown. (After Weed.)

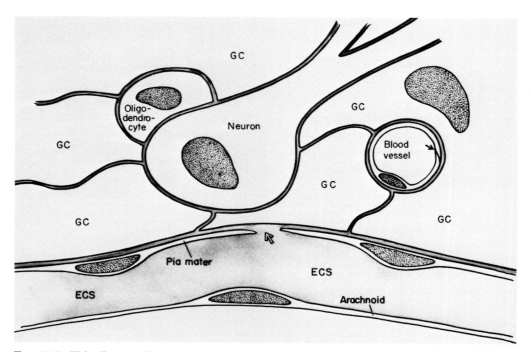

FIG. 11-5. This diagram illustrates the continuity between the cerebrospinal fluid within the sub-arachnoid space and the fluid filling the extracellular space within the nervous tissue parenchyma. Protein markers placed in the cerebrospinal fluid pass between the cells of the pia mater (*hollow arrow*) and into the narrow extracellular space of the nervous tissue. On the other hand, markers placed within the blood vessels of nervous tissue are confined to the vessel lumina by the presence of tight junctions between the overlapping processes of endothelial cells (*solid arrow*). Thus the cerebrospinal fluid represents a type of extracellular fluid (*ECS*) for nervous tissue cells. *GC* = neuroglial cell. (From Bunge, R. 1970 The Neurosciences: Second Study Program, edited by F. O. Schmitt, p. 782, Rockefeller University Press, New York.)

parenchyma, the pericapillary spaces are scarcely larger than the other cleftlike intercellular spaces of nervous tissue. In these deeper areas, the basal lamina of the capillaries is often surrounded by flattened cellular extensions of astrocytes. This application of astrocytic processes to the capillary wall led to the suggestions that (1) these "sucker-feet" are avenues of nutrient passage from blood vessel to neuron, and/or (2) that the mosaic of applied cellular processes constitutes the barrier for the passage of materials from blood vessels to brain parenchyma (*the blood-brain barrier*).

The use of the electron microscope has demonstrated the precise site of the blood-brain barrier for certain types of molecules.

When proteins (which can be rendered visible in the electron microscope) are injected into the vascular system, their entry into brain tissue is prevented by the minute, tight junctions between the lateral edges of the endothelial cells. When this protein marker is placed within brain substance, it passes between all cells (including the perivascular astrocyte processes and even through synaptic clefts) but does not enter blood vessels. Thus, the blood-brain barrier for this protein is in the wall of the CNS capillaries and is not provided by the perivascular tissues (the astrocytic processes and the basal lamina). Whether the perivascular astrocytic feet function in nutrient transport is not known (see Chapter 10).

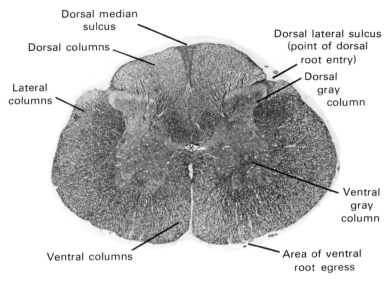

Fig. 11-6. This is a photomicrograph of a cross section of the spinal cord in the lumbar region of a cat. The H-shaped central region is the gray matter and it is surrounded by the tracts of nerve fibers which form the white matter. The central canal is marked with an asterisk.

THE SPINAL CORD

In transverse section (Fig. 11-6), the spinal cord appears oval in shape and slightly more flattened on its ventral than on its dorsal surface. It is surrounded by the pia mater spinalis, which extends into the deep longitudinal *ventral median fissure*. Dorsally, the cord is partitioned longitudinally by the *dorsal median septum*, which is composed principally of neuroglia and over which the pia mater passes without entering. At the entrance of the dorsal root fibers on either side, there is a *dorsolateral groove* or *sulcus*.

The *gray matter* occupies the central part of the section, where it is arranged somewhat in the form of the letter H. Dorsally, the gray matter extends almost to the surface of the cord as the *dorsal gray columns* (*posterior horns*). The *ventral gray columns* (*anterior horns*) are shorter and broader and do not so nearly approach the surface of the cord. Surrounding the gray matter is the *white matter* which, in each lateral half of the cord, is divided by the dorsal column into two parts. The part lying between the horn and the dorsal median septum is the

dorsal funiculus (*dorsal* or *posterior white column*); the other part, comprising the remainder of the white matter, is the *ventrolateral funiculus* (*ventrolateral* or *anterolateral white column*).

The ventrolateral white column is again divided, rather indefinitely, by the ventral horn and nerve roots into a *lateral funiculus* (*lateral white column*) and a *ventral funiculus* (*ventral* or *anterior white column*). In the thoracic segments of the cord there is usually a lateral protrusion of the gray matter slightly dorsal to the dorsal boundary of the ventral horn. This is called the *lateral horn* and this region contains the nerve cell bodies of the CNS neurons of the thoracodorsal portion of the autonomic nervous system.

Gray Matter. In the cross portion of the H structure is seen the *central canal*, usually partially obliterated in the adult and represented only by a group of epithelial cells (ependyma). The central canal divides the gray matter connecting the two sides of the cord into a *ventral gray commissure* and a *dorsal gray commissure*.

The components of the lateral portions of the H are, as noted above, the *dorsal horns*, which are primarily concerned with sensory input, and the *ventral horns*, which are concerned with motor activity. Between these two, and lateral to the gray commissures, is the *intermediate* (or *middle*) *gray*, which is associated largely with visceral innervation. The neuron cell bodies in these regions of gray matter are arranged in longitudinal columns, each a linear aggregate of neurons specialized for a particular function.

The dorsal horn contains three major nuclear groups specialized for the reception of the sensory impulses carried into the spinal cord by the axons of dorsal root ganglia neurons. The various modalities of somatic sensation are handled differently in this region, some of the incoming axons synapsing locally and others being carried upward toward the brain before synapsing. Thus the sensory information available to the organism via the *first order* sensory neurons of the dorsal root ganglia is carried to *second order* sensory neurons and is distributed widely throughout the CNS.

Visceral sensibilities, on the other hand, appear to be channeled primarily to the poorly defined nuclear columns of the intermediate gray. As has been noted, in certain regions of the cord this same intermediate zone contains motor neurons of the visceral system (in the lateral horn cell column). Thus, the visceral areas of the gray matter are generally more medially located than are the somatic regions.

The ventral horn contains many motor cells (ventral or anterior horn cells) arranged in columns in relation to the portion of the body musculature that they innervate. Motor neurons providing fibers to trunk musculature are more medially disposed in ventral gray matter, and motor neurons to the muscles of the limbs are located laterally. Certain of these motor neurons are the largest neurons in the spinal cord. Their dendritic portions, which are generally multipolar, extend some distance up and down the cord to receive a variety of signals from local (spinal) interneurons as well as from distant (e.g., cortical) parts of the CNS. In higher animals, very few first order sensory neurons make direct contact with motor neurons. The large axons of the motor neurons can be seen passing out through the ventrolateral white matter to form, along with the fibers of the visceral motorneurons in the intermediate gray, the ventral spinal root at the surface of the cord.

White Matter. In order to carry nerve signals to and from gray matter at different levels of the spinal cord and to the higher centers in the brain, fibers must course up and down the long axis of the cord. These fibers (axons) leave the gray matter and form the more superficial white matter. The white matter is thus composed of myelinated and a few unmyelinated nerve fibers and neuroglia, along with blood vessels and inward continuations of the pia mater. White matter contains no neuron cell bodies or dendrites. If the section has been cut through a *dorsal (posterior) nerve root*, a small bundle of *dorsal root fibers* can be seen entering the white matter of the cord along the dorsal and medial side of the posterior horn. Ventral to the anterior gray commissure is a bundle of transversely disposed myelinated fibers, the *ventral white commissure*. In the dorsal part of the dorsal gray commissure there are also fine, similarly disposed myelinated nerve fibers, the *dorsal white commissure*. Both of these commissures are composed of fibers crossing from one side of the spinal cord to the other.

THE CEREBELLAR CORTEX

General Structure. The cerebellum, connected with the rest of the brain by its three peduncles, consists of two lateral lobes or hemispheres connected by a median lobe, the vermis. These are divided by transverse fissures into lobules, each lobule consisting of a median portion belonging to the vermis and two winglike extensions belonging to the hemispheres. The surfaces of the lobules are marked by folds (*laminae* or *folia*) running approximately parallel to the fissures and thus transversely to the longitudinal axis of the brain. The surface of the cerebellum is composed of gray matter, the cortex, which envelops the white matter.

In the *cerebellar cortex* there can be distinguished, with ordinary stains (hematoxylin-eosin, Nissl), an outer or *molecular layer* containing few cells and no myelinated fibers, an inner *granular layer* and, between the two, a single row of large flask-shaped cells, the *cells of Purkinje* (Fig. 11-7). Below the granular layer is an area of white matter containing the fibers that carry signals to or from the neuronal machinery of the cortex.

The major input of nerve fibers to the cerebellum arrives in the granule cell layer. With routine stains, this layer appears to be comprised of closely packed cell nuclei, but there are clear spaces here and there which are called *islands* or *glomeruli*. The cell nuclei belong to small neurons, the *granule cells*, and the glomeruli are regions where the granule cell dendrites receive synapses from axons arriving from outside the cerebellum. The incoming fibers, which are highly branched, are called *mossy fibers* (Fig. 11-8). Each granule cell possesses three to six short dendrites for the reception of the mossy fiber input.

The granule cell sends its fine, unmyelinated axon to ascend into the molecular layer, where it divides into two branches running longitudinally along the folium and terminating in varicosities (Fig. 11-8). These are the *parallel fibers* of the molecular layer. They thus run at right angles to and through the dendritic expansions of the Purkinje cells, and their cross sections, together with the terminal dendritic aborizations of the Purkinje cells, give the molecular layer its punctate appearance. During their course in the molecular layer, the parallel fibers make synaptic contact (known to be excita-

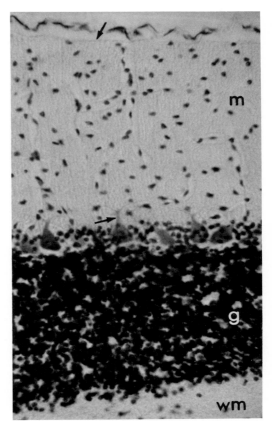

FIG. 11-7. This photomicrograph shows the layers of neurons within the cerebellar cortex of a rat. The *upper arrow* indicates the surface of the cerebellum which is covered by remnants of the pia. The *lower arrow* indicates the dendrite of a Purkinje cell. The soma of this cell and adjacent Purkinje cells are also visible. The molecular layer (*m*) contains a considerable number of capillaries. *g* = granule cell layer; *wm* = white matter. Compare with Figure 11-8.

tory) with dendrites from a number of different Purkinje cells.

The Purkinje dendrite also receives excitatory input from *climbing fibers*, many of which are recurrent collaterals from neurons of the deep cerebellar nuclei (see below). These climbing fibers, which entwine the dendritic trunk (Fig. 11-8), have a powerful excitatory influence on the Purkinje cell.

Other granule cell axons are known to make contact with smaller neurons, the

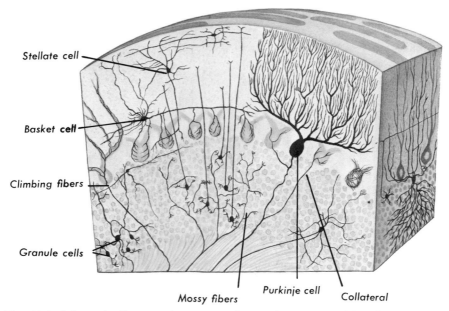

Stellate cell

Basket cell

Climbing fibers

Granule cells

Mossy fibers   Purkinje cell   Collateral

FIG. 11-8. Schematic diagram of structure of cerebellar cortex. (After Bargmann.)

basket cells, which are located in the region of the Purkinje layer. These cells are so named because their axons form basket-like skeins around the bodies and initial axonal segments of the Purkinje cells (Fig. 11-8). They are thus well disposed to exert an inhibitory influence on Purkinje cell activity. We have thus described two excitatory inputs and one inhibitory input to the Purkinje cell.

The Purkinje cell possesses several main dendrites, which enter the molecular layer and form a remarkably rich arborization extending to the surface. The dendritic arborization is fan-shaped, extending at right angles to the laminae. The axon is given off from the end of the cell opposite to the dendrites and passes into the granular layer. Here axon collaterals may turn back to enter another part of the cerebellar cortex, but the main axon continues on to neurons deep within the cerebellum that are known as the deep cerebellar nuclei. The influence of the Purkinje axons on the neurons of the deep cerebellar nuclei is thought to be inhibitory. It is the neurons of the deep cere-

bellar nuclei that have axons leaving the cerebellum to provide the cerebellar output to other regions of the nervous system.

As complex as the above interneuronal connections may appear at first reading, it should be noted that the cerebellar circuitry is much more complex than this short review would indicate. This complexity is achieved not by unique cytology but by repetition of basic neurocytological components (elaboration of the cell surface to provide a dendritic zone, development of basic synaptic types, extension of the cell as an axon with specializations at the axon terminal). The same statement can be made regarding the more complicated cerebral cortex discussed below.

Function. The cerebellum contributes to nervous system function by serving to modulate and coordinate skeletal muscle activity. Among other activities, it assists in preventing muscle "overshoot" so that a muscle contraction once started will not become too gross by being carried too far; thus, fine movements are facilitated. The cerebellum is not involved in sensation or in intellectual processes.

Even a beginning understanding of how the cellular assemblies of the cerebellar cortex participate in this type of control must await the student's study of the origins of the fibers that enter the cerebellum and the destinations of fibers that comprise the cerebellar output.

From the viewpoint of the neurocytologist, it is particularly interesting to note the results of recent electron microscopic observations on cerebellar tissues after aldehyde fixation. Under appropriate conditions, all of the cells known to provide inhibitory influences (e.g., the basket cell contacts with Purkinje cell bodies) have been found to contain primarily flattened synaptic vesicles in their nerve endings, and all of the cells known to provide excitatory influences (e.g., the climbing fiber contacts with Purkinje dendrites or granule cell contacts with Purkinje dendritic spines) have been found to contain primarily spheroid synaptic vesicles (see chapter 10).

THE CEREBRAL CORTEX

General Structure. The cerebral cortex (or pallium) is the external layer of gray matter covering the convolutions and fissures of the cerebral hemispheres. It has an area of about 200,000 sq. mm. and varies in thickness from about 1.5 to 4.0 mm. It contains, in addition to nerve fibers, neuroglia and blood vessels, the bodies of nearly 14 billion neurons. The older, less elaborate olfactory cortex is termed the *allocortex*, the rest the *neocortex* or *isocortex*.

The chief types of neurons found in the cortex are (1) *pyramidal cells*, (2) *stellate* or *granule cells*, (3) *horizontal cells* and (4) inverted or *Martinotti cells* (Figs. 11-9, 11-10). The pyramidal cells (Fig. 11-10) are characterized by a pyramid-shaped perikaryon with an apical dendrite directed toward the surface of the brain and an axon leaving the base of the perikaryon to course into the white matter as a projection or association fiber. These axons provide the principal

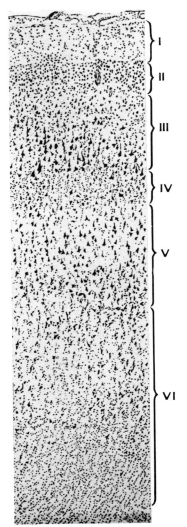

FIG. 11-9. Photograph of cell layers of Nissl-stained preparations of cerebral cortex. (After Bargmann.)

output of the cortex. The granule or stellate cells are characterized by their relatively small size, numerous dendrites coursing in various directions and a relatively short axon. Many of the axons providing an input to the cortex are thought to end on their dendrites. The horizontal cells, found mostly in the outer layer, are characterized by their horizontally disposed dendrites and axons, which presumably serve to interconnect neighboring cortical regions. The inverted or Martinotti cells, which are located in the deeper cortical layers, have axons directed toward the surface, to be distributed entirely intracortically.

When viewed in a section cut perpendicu-

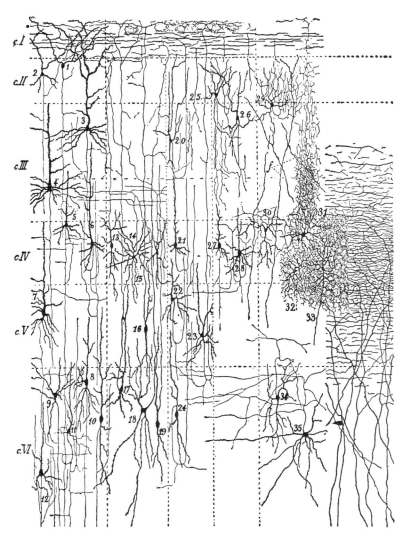

Fig. 11-10. Various forms of nerve cells of the cerebral cortex. From various figures of Cajal, especially of the temporal cortex. *cI*, Zonal layer of cortex; *cII*, external granular layer; *cIII*, pyramidal layer; *cIV*, internal granular layer; *cV*, ganglionic layer; *cVI*, multiform layer. *1* to *12*, cells, mostly pyramidal, whose axons enter the white matter (corticofugal cells); *13* to *35*, cells whose axons do not leave the gray matter (or cortex); *13* to *19*, cells with directly ascending axons; *20* to *24*, cells with arciform ascending axons; *25* to *28*, cells with short descending axons, with or without ascending collaterals; *29, 30*, short axon cells properly speaking (Golgi's type II); *31* to *33*, cells with bushy axons (bipenicillate and neuroglia form), some forming terminal nests around the small granule cells; *34, 35*, large stellate cells of layer *VI* with extensively branching axons, especially extending horizontally; *f*, fibers of unknown origin. On the right are shown corticopetal fibers and their terminal plexus, especially dense in layer *IV*. (After Bonne.)

lar to the cortical surface, the most striking aspect of the cerebral cortex is the lamination of its cellular components in layers horizontal to the surface. The neocortex is characterized by a laminated appearance in which six layers can be identified (Fig. 11-9). The layers are as follows: (1) The outermost *molecular layer* made up chiefly of cell processes and of horizontal cells; (2) the *external granular layer*, composed chiefly of small, triangular neurons; (3) the *pyramidal layer*, composed chiefly of relatively large pyramidal cells plus many granule cells; (4) the *internal granular layer*, made up chiefly of the stellate or granule cells; (5) the *ganglionic layer* of large and medium sized pyramidal cells; and (6) the *multiform layer* containing neurons of widely varying shape, including Martinotti cells.

The laminar arrangement of cortical neurons so clearly visible in histological sections is deceptive in view of what is now known regarding the functional properties of certain cortical regions. From electrophysiological studies, it is now known that the functional organization of some cortical areas receiving sensory stimuli (e.g., the cortex at the back of the head, which receives signals from the visual system) invovles *columns* of neurons oriented vertical to the cortical surface. Stimuli arriving in this cortical region activate a specific column of cells, each column being 0.3 to 0.5 mm. in diameter. The intrinsic morphological basis for these functional columns has not been clearly defined.

The thickness of the various cell layers differs considerably in different areas of the cerebral cortex. Some areas exhibit such marked modification in the layers of cells that they are known as *heterotypic*, in contrast with *homotypic* areas, which show all of the six layers outlined in Fig. 11-9. On the basis of differences in structure and function, the cortex has been mapped into a number of areas. In some regions, the cytoarchitecture of a particular area of cortex corresponds quite precisely to the functional modality known to be processed in that cortical region. This is true, for example, in cortical regions concerned with vision and with hearing. In other cases, cortical regions of different function have virtually identical cytological arrangements.

The input to the cortex comes from a great variety of sources. Many of the sensory modalities have cortical representation in discrete cortical regions which provide surface representations for the different body parts. Other cortical regions are concerned with the initiation and/or control of motor activities; these regions are also *somatotopically* organized, each part of the body being represented in a discrete area of cortex. There are also discrete cortical regions associated with special faculties, e.g., speech. In the human, there are in addition substantial cortical areas, called association areas, which have connections with the motor and sensory regions of the cortex. These association areas provide additional orders of circuitry to assist in the analysis of sensory input and the programming of motor output.

Function. The discussion of nervous tissue begins in Chapter 9 with the suggestion that higher animals use multiple sets of interneurons to effect their more discriminating and exact behavior. Between the primary sensory neurons in various sensory ganglia and the motor neurons of the "final common path," there are interposed, in the higher animal, circuit upon circuit of neuronal "wiring." By these circuits, sensations reach cortical levels. This wiring system provides for the convergence and association of many kinds of stimuli from all parts of the body. This cortical mechanism not only associates many stimuli prior to the performance of a motor activity, but it also dissociates, i.e., discriminates, and thus, by inhibition, it enables motor activity to be limited only to the necessary movements. There is also plasticity in cortical mechanisms, for the neurons are somehow changed by their activities. Whatever their nature, the acquired changes of the cortex, because of its plasticity and consequent capacity for "learning," affect the action of subsequent stimuli reaching the cortex and furnish the basis of memory, of personal experience and of individually acquired neural mechanisms, as opposed to germinal or inherited neural mechanisms. Cortical mechanisms are also involved in the transmission, by educational processes using complex symbols, of acquired experience to the plastic cortex of other individuals. Animals other than man "learn," i.e., acquire and utilize individual experience, but it is doubtful that any animal other than man significantly *summates* experience, i.e., transmits it to other individuals and generations. The cortex is thus, in a sense, the organ of human culture and conduct. This supermaze of neuronal interconnections provides for the origin and expression of the highest faculties of the mind. If it is possible for the human cerebral cortex to understand the mechanisms of its own function, the concentrated study of many generations will certainly be required to accomplish this task.

REFERENCES

BRIGHTMAN, M. W., AND REESE, T. S. 1969 Junctions between intimately opposed cell membranes in the vertebrate brain. J. Cell Biol., vol. 40, pp. 648–677.

CHOW, K. L., AND LEIMAN, A. L. 1970 The structural and functional organization of the neocortex. Neurosci. Res. Progr. Bull., vol. 8, pp. 157–220.

CROSBY, E. C., HUMPHREY, T., AND LAUER, E. W. 1962 Correlative Anatomy of the Nervous System. The Macmillan Company, New York.

ECCLES, J. C., ITO, M., AND SZENTAGOTHAI, J. 1967 The Cerebellum as a Neuronal Machine. Springer-Verlag, New York.

ECONOMO, C. 1929 The Cytoarchitectonics of the Human Cerebral Cortex. Oxford University Press, London.

LAJTHA, A., AND FORD, D. H. (editors) 1968 Brain Barrier Systems. Progr. Brain Res., vol. 29.

NOBACK, C. R. 1967 The Human Nervous System. McGraw-Hill Book Company, New York.

PETERS, A., PALAY, S. L., AND WEBSTER, H. 1970 The Fine Structure of the Nervous System. Hoeber Medical Division, Harper & Row, Publishers, New York.

SHOLL, D. A. 1956 The Organization of the Cerebral Cortex. Methuen and Company, Ltd., London.

TRUEX, R. C., AND CARPENTER, M. B. 1969 Human Neuroanatomy, ed. 6. The Williams & Wilkins Company, Baltimore.

WEED, L. H. 1934 Certain anatomical and physiological aspects of the meninges and cerebrospinal fluid. Brain, vol. 58, pp. 383–397.

WISLOCKI, G. B. 1932 The cytology of the cerebrospinal pathway. Special Cytology (Cowdry, E. V., editor), vol. 3, pp. 1485–1521.

12

The Circulatory System

The circulatory apparatus consists of a blood vascular system and a lymph vascular system. The *blood vascular system* consists of (1) the *heart*, which is a pump for propelling the blood, (2) the *arteries*, which are tubes for conveying the blood toward the organs and tissues, (3) the *capillaries*, which are anastomosing channels of small caliber and with thin walls providing for interchange of substances between the blood and tissue fluids, and (4) the *veins* which serve for the return of blood to the heart.

The lymph vascular system consists of lymphatic capillaries and various sized lymphatic vessels which ultimately drain into two main trunks: the thoracic duct and the right lymphatic duct, which empty into the large veins in the neck.

THE BLOOD VASCULAR SYSTEM

The entire system—heart, arteries, veins, capillaries—has a common and continuous lining which consists of a single layer of endothelial cells. In the capillaries, this single layer of cells forms the main component of the wall. In the heart, arteries and veins, the endothelium is invested with accessory coats of muscle and connective tissue. Since the structure of the capillary is simpler than that of any of the other parts of the vascular system, it has become customary to describe the capillaries first, instead of following the system in its functional order of heart, arteries, capillaries and veins.

CAPILLARIES

The capillaries are delicate tubes with an average diameter of about 7 to 9 μ. They branch extensively without much change in caliber, and the branches anastomose to form networks which vary in density and pattern in different tissues and organs. The tissues with the highest metabolic activity have networks of elaborately branched and closely packed capillaries. This is so in the lungs, liver, kidney and most glands and mucous membranes. The capillaries of the network nearest to the arterioles supplying them are called arterial capillaries, and those nearest to the venules draining them are called venous capillaries. This division is based on topography and function and not on structural differences.

The capillary network between arterioles and venules often contains a central or *thoroughfare channel* where the blood flow is continuous, in contrast with the branches of the network where the flow tends to be intermittent (Fig. 12-1). The proximal portion of the central channel, i.e., the part just beyond the arteriole proper, is known as a *metarteriole* (Gr., *meta*, beyond). The metarteriole has isolated smooth muscle cells dispersed at intervals along the outer surface of its endothelial cells. These smooth muscle cells are surrounded by a glycoprotein coat which is continuous with the basal lamina of the endothelium. They have branching processes and tend to be oriented

305

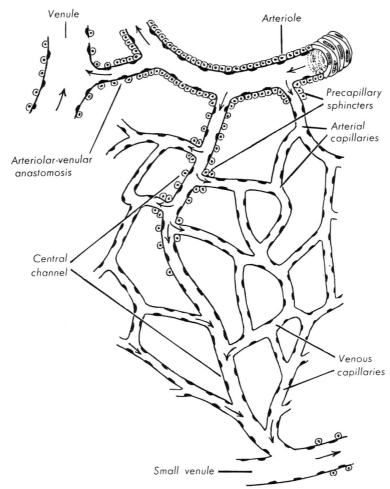

Fig. 12-1. Diagram showing relationship of capillaries to arteriole and venule. The proximal portion of the central channel through a capillary bed is surrounded by scattered smooth muscle fibers and has been named the "metarteriole" (Chambers and Zweifach, 1944); the distal portion of the central channel is structurally a true capillary.

longitudinally on the vessel, in contrast with the transversely oriented muscle cells of the arterioles proper (compare Figures 12-5 and 12-7). These cells, like the smooth muscle fibers of the rest of the system, are supplied with postganglionic sympathetic nerve fibers. The venous end of the thoroughfare channel resembles other capillaries except for its wider lumen.

The thoroughfare channels differ from the branched portions of the capillary networks in their functional behavior, and they can be differentiated more readily in living than in fixed preparations. The thoroughfare channels convey an active flow of blood at all times, although the amount of flow varies with vasoconstriction and vasodilation of the metarteriolar segment. Flow in the branches of the network is intermittent during relatively inactive metabolic periods; in other words, the branches do not all function at once, except when there is an increased demand. The amount of blood entering the branches is controlled by the state of contraction of smooth muscle cells of the *precapillary sphincters* which are located wherever arterial capillaries arise from any of the arterioles, whether from metarterioles or from arterioles proper. The number of thoroughfare channels in proportion to the number of branched capillaries differs for different regions of the body; in skin, for example, the direct channels are numerous, whereas in skeletal muscle they are relatively infrequent in comparison with the branches of the meshwork.

The wall of the capillary consists of a single layer of flat endothelial cells which rest on a basement membrane, and an outer discontinuous layer of pericapillary cells and fibers which form a thin adventitia. Electron micrographs show that the basement membrane described by light microscopists is made up of a *basal lamina* of amorphous material and fine filaments plus a *lamina reticularis* of reticular fibers, as described in Chapter 4. In surface view, the endothelial cells appear as a delicate mosaic which can be demonstrated by the precipitation of silver at the cell margins (Fig. 12-2). The cell borders are usually serrated or wavy. The cells tend to be arranged with their long axes parallel with the long axis of the tube. The cytoplasm is clear or finely granular, and the nucleus is elongated and centrally placed. The cells are thicker in the region of the nucleus. In fixed preparations, this condition may be accentuated, and there is fre-

quently a more pronounced bulging of the nuclei into the lumen. Two endothelial cells, and occasionally even one, suffice to form the complete circumference of small capillaries. For the larger ones, three to five cells may be required.

Electron micrographs show that endothelial cells contain the usual cell organelles. They also show that the cells frequently have caveolae and vesicles which are generally known as pinocytotic vesicles. The name signifies that the vesicles form by invaginations of cell membranes during a process of cell drinking known as *pinocytosis* (Fig. 12-3). The vesicles are bounded by unit membranes, and they are usually about 650 to 750 A in overall diameter. Some are found entirely within the cell cytoplasm, while others are seen as caveolae, open either to the inner (luminal) surface or to the outer (tissue) side. They may occur singly or in short chains of two or more. Electron micrographs of tissues fixed following injection of colloidal particles, which serve as markers, show the presence of tracer material within some of the pinocytotic vesicles. This supports the view that the vesicles have a role in the transport of some substances, e.g., large molecules and other macromaterials. However, it should be noted that other mechanisms have a major role in the transport of substances across the endothelium. Furthermore, many of the so-called pinocytotic vesicles appar-

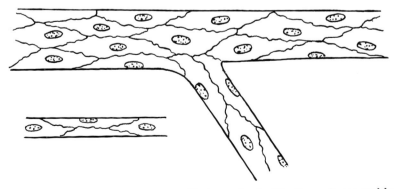

FIG. 12-2. Surface view of large and small capillaries stained with silver nitrate and hematoxylin to show outlines of endothelial cells and their nuclei.

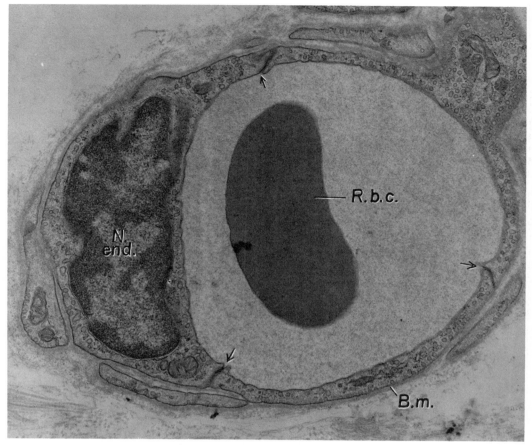

Fɪɢ. 12-3. Electron micrograph of blood capillary from lamina propria of bat esophagus. Junctions of endothelial cells are indicated by *arrows*. The nucleus (*N. end.*) of one endothelial cell is seen. Within the cytoplasm of the endothelial cells, there are numerous vesicles. These are particularly clear in the *upper right hand corner* of the photograph where the plane of the section is tangential to the surface of the cell. Basement membrane material (*B.m.*) surrounds the endothelium and also encloses some processes of pericytes, shown on the *left*. A red blood cell (*R.b.c.*) is seen in the lumen of the vessel. ×63,000. (Courtesy of Dr. Keith Porter.)

ently have functions other than that of pinocytosis.

Adjacent endothelial cells may meet in a simple end-to-end pattern, but more often the edge of one cell overlaps that of another along an oblique course (Fig. 12-3) or in more complicated S-shaped patterns. The walls of adjacent cells are separated from each other by about 200 A along parts of their course but, at intervals, they come into closer association by junctions which differ somewhat from the junctional complexes of simple columnar epithelium (Chapter 4).

True *zonulae occludentes* are present in cerebral capillaries (Reese and Karnovsky, 1967) but not in capillaries of muscles and other regions. The capillaries of muscles have *maculae occludentes* separated by gaps where there is a 20 to 40 A space between apposed membranes; that is, the outer leaflets of the trilaminar membranes of adjacent cells are in contact only in spots and do not form rings of complete occlusion at the adluminal ends of the cells (Karnovsky, 1967). It has been suggested that the 40 A width spaces may correspond to the "small pores" proposed by physiologists as routes for diffusion of small lipid-insoluble molecules.

Pericapillary cells are closely associated with the capillaries. This category includes *fibroblasts, histiocytes* and *pericytes*. Fibroblasts and histiocytes are present in the connective tissue associated with the capillaries in most parts of the body, but there are some locations where the capillaries are so closely related to the tissues with which they function that there is little or no intervening space for connective tissue. For instance, in the glomeruli of the kidney, the basal lamina of the endothelium is fused with the basal lamina of the epithelium of the visceral layer of Bowman's capsule. *Pericytes* are irregularly shaped, isolated cells distributed at intervals along the capillaries in a pattern resembling that of the modified muscle cells on metarterioles. In electron micrographs, the pericytes appear within the basement membrane of the endothelium because each pericyte is enclosed by a glycoprotein coat which is fused with the basal lamina portion of the endothelial basement membrane. In the literature on capillaries, some investigators use the term pericyte as synonymous with Rouget cell. The latter was named in honor of Rouget, who first observed it in 1875 as a contractile cell on amphibian "capillaries" studied in vivo. Rouget and subsequent investigators undoubtedly observed contractile cells on small vessels, but it seems likely they were looking at modified smooth muscle cells on vessels subsequently identified as metarterioles. No convincing evidence has been presented thus far that the pericytes of true capillaries are contractile. Some authors have suggested that the pericytes are relatively undifferentiated cells and that they may, under stimulus, be able to differentiate into other cell types, including smooth muscle cells of regenerating vessels after injury. This is not to say that they form endothelium; the latter arises by multiplication and migration of preexisting endothelial cells.

Fenestrated capillaries are found in a number of locations known for their fluid transport (e.g., intestinal villi, ciliary processes of the eye and choroid plexus). Their endothelium has numerous fenestrae or pores of about 300 to 800 A in overall diameter, in which cell cytoplasm is absent and the endothelial wall consists solely of a thin diaphragm. The lining of these capillaries differs from that of the capillaries of muscle and most other parts of the body in which, as described above, there is a continuous endothelium, i.e., a complete layer of cytoplasm throughout the cell. The pores of the fenestrated capillaries are closed by diaphragms thinner than the cell membrane, and they are also covered by the basal lamina of the endothelium (Fig. 12-4). One manner in which the pores may develop is by formation of plasmalemmal vesicles and fusion of membranes. Stages in the process of fenestrae formation have been described by Palade and Bruns, 1968.

Sinusoidal capillaries and *sinusoids* differ in a number of respects from ordinary capillaries. The *sinusoidal capillaries* of the carotid gland and of endocrine glands (e.g., adrenal cortex, anterior hypophysis and thyroid) are usually of larger diameter than ordinary capillaries, and they have less adventitial covering so that they become more closely associated with the parenchymal cells of the gland. Their endothelial cells are also attenuated and have pores similar to those described above for the ciliary processes. The *sinusoids* of the liver, spleen and blood-forming organs are of larger diameter than the sinusoidal capillaries of the endocrine glands, and their lining cells are markedly phagocytic and belong to the reticuloendothelial system. The stellate cells of Kupffer in the liver are of this type. The lining cells of the sinusoids, unlike those of the sinusoidal capillaries, have relatively wide intercellular gaps, and they lack a complete basal lamina.

Exchange of substances between the blood and surrounding tissues is accomplished pri-

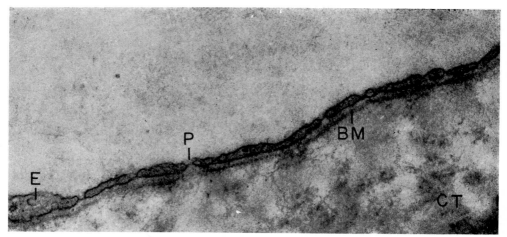

FIG. 12-4. Electron micrograph of a portion of a capillary from the ciliary processes of the eye of an adult rabbit. The endothelial cell (*E*) has fenestrae or pores (*P*). The pore space is traversed by a diaphragm thinner than the endothelial cell membrane. On the outer surface of the endothelium, there is a continuous basal lamina (*BM*). Outside of this, there is connective tissue (*CT*). ×35,000. (Courtesy of Drs. George Pappas and Virginia Tennyson.)

FIG. 12-5. Modified smooth muscle cells on precapillary arterioles (metarterioles) of human heart. The irregular shapes of the cells and their numerous processes are demonstrated by a chrome silver impregnation method. *Left*, several muscle cells with their processes surrounding a metarteriole; *right*, higher magnification of one muscle cell at junction of metarteriole and capillary. (Redrawn and modified from Zimmermann, Z. Anat. Entwicklungsgesch., vol. 68.)

marily in the capillaries and small venules. The passage of fluid across the capillary wall is partially dependent on the blood pressure within the capillaries and on the colloid osmotic pressure of the blood (Lan-

dis, 1937). The former factor promotes passage from the vessels to the tissues, and the latter factor favors reabsorption. The blood pressure in the arterial capillaries is normally higher than in the venous capillaries, and the blood pressure on the arterial side also exceeds the colloid osmotic pressure of the blood plasma. Based on the pressure relationships, fluids normally pass by diffusion from the vessels to the tissues in the arterial part of the capillary bed and return to the vessels in the venous capillaries and small venules (Fig. 12-23). Pressure within the capillaries can be modified at the local level by vasoconstriction and vasodilation through contraction and relaxation of smooth muscle cells in the walls of arterioles, metarterioles and precapillary sphincters (Fig. 12-5).

Electron microscope studies have clarified our understanding of the correlation of structure and function in the mechanism for exchange across the vascular wall. Pinocytosis has a role in the transport of substances across the endothelium, although this is apparently not the major pathway for exchange. Physiologists have proposed a small pore system for the diffusion of small, lipid-insoluble molecules across membranes. On the basis of studies of capillaries of cardiac and skeletal muscle, it is found that substances of low molecular weight pass through intercellular gaps about 40 A in width which are located between maculae occludentes, and it has been suggested that these gaps may correspond to the small pore system proposed by the physiologists (Karnovsky, 1967). On the other hand, studies of capillaries of intestinal mucosa show that passage of low molecular weight substances occurs primarily across the endothelial cells rather than at intercellular junctions, and it has been proposed that intact diaphragms of fenestrae correspond to the small pore system of the physiologists and that diaphragm-free or deficient fenestrae may correspond to the large pore system (Clementi and

Palade, 1969). On the basis of studies of the type just cited, it seems likely that there is more than one ultrastructural equivalent of the small pore system and that it differs in capillaries of different locations.

It has been noted earlier that endothelial cells of most capillaries are not joined by zonulae occludentes but by maculae adherens and maculae occludentes and by close junctions. Under altered conditions, the narrow intercellular spaces between the membranes of apposed cells may become widened to form much larger gaps. When vascular permeability is increased by injections of substances such as histamine and endotoxin, relatively large intercellular gaps appear in the endothelium of venous capillaries and small venules (Fig. 12-6). Substances readily pass through these gaps, be-

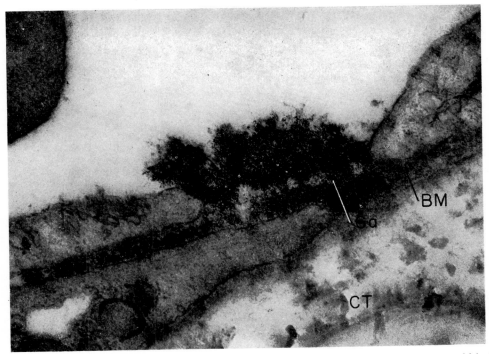

FIG. 12-6. Electron micrograph of a portion of a venule from a ciliary body of the eye of a rabbit. The animal had received an injection of *Shigella* endotoxin which alters the normal aqueous humor secretion in the eye. Thirty minutes before the tissue was fixed, the animal also received an intravenous injection of saccharated iron oxide. This serves as a marker which can be seen in electron micrographs. It is found in gaps (*Ga*) between endothelial cells, in the basement membrane (*BM*) and in the surrounding connective tissue (*CT*). It seems clear that the increased permeability of the vessel wall in this case is largely caused by the formation of gaps between neighboring endothelial cells. ×55,000. (Courtesy of Drs. George Pappas and Virginia Tennyson.)

come concentrated against the basement membrane and eventually pass into the surrounding connective tissues (Fig. 12-6). Under conditions of inflammation, substances pass from the blood to surrounding tissues on the venous side of the capillary bed.

Changes in the physical consistency of the capillary walls which favor emigration of leucocytes were observed in living animals by the Clarks (1935). These authors showed that various mechanical and chemical stimuli make the endothelial wall sticky and that, as the stickiness increases, the leukocytes adhere to the endothelial wall and later migrate into the surrounding tissues.

ARTERIES

The wall of an artery is composed of three tunics or coats which are most distinct in vessels of medium caliber. (1) The innermost coat, the *intima*, consists of an inner endothelial lining continuous with and similar to that found in the walls of the capillaries, an intermediate layer of delicate connective tissue, which is absent in the smaller vessels, and an external band of elastic fibers, the *membrana elastica interna*, which marks the boundary between the intima and media. (2) The middle coat, or *media*, consists mainly of smooth muscle cells with varying amounts of elastic and collagenous tissue. (3) The outer coat, *adventitia* or *externa* is composed chiefly of connective tissue.

The structure and relative thickness of each of the tunics varies according to the size of the artery. Although the changes along the arterial tree are gradual and never abrupt, one may readily distinguish different types of arteries according to size, structure and function. Following the blood vessels from the heart to the capillaries, we recognize (1) large, elastic arteries, (2) medium sized, muscular arteries, (3) small arteries (terminal arteries) and arterioles. Working backwards from the capillaries which have been described, we will consider the structure of the arterioles first.

Arterioles and Small Arteries. The transition from a capillary to an arteriole is marked by the appearance of isolated smooth muscle fibers which are arranged spirally. These small arterioles of transitional type are called precapillary arterioles or metarterioles (Fig. 12-1). As the vessels become larger, the muscle cells are increased in number and form a complete coat of one or two layers of circularly arranged fibers (Figs. 12-7 and 12-8). Outside of the muscle, the connective tissue is condensed to form a fibrous layer which is composed of flattened fibroblasts and longitudinally arranged collagenous fibrils. Thus, in the walls of the *arterioles*, the three coats are already distinguishable: an endothelial intima, a muscular media and an adventitia of connective tissue. Although a few scattered elastic fibers can be demonstrated in the walls of very small arterioles, an internal elastic membrane sufficiently thick to be visible under the light microscope does not begin until the vessels have reached a diameter of about 40 μ.

The coats become thicker and more definitely organized as the blood vessels increase in caliber. In small arteries of about 130 μ, the media contains three or four layers of muscle cells among which are found scattered elastic fibrils. The more distinct internal elastic membrane is composed of a delicate net of elastic fibrils. The adventitia contains, besides collagenous fibers, longitudinally disposed elastic and reticular fibers. The elastic fibers are aggregated mainly in the inner portion of the coat, close to the media. As the vessels become larger, the muscle and elastic tissue components increase so that, in arteries of about 300 μ, the wall shows all of the structural features described in medium sized arteries.

Some authors use the term arteriole for small arteries ranging in caliber from about 300 μ to the very small precapillary vessels. Under this definition, the term arteriole encompasses most of the small, unnamed arteries and consists of vessels in which the

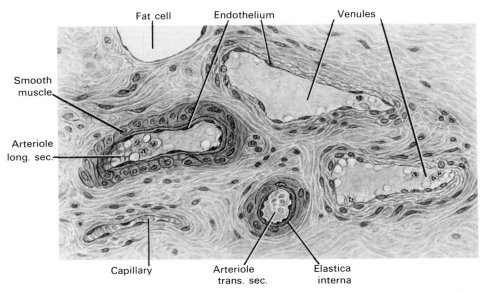

Fat cell   Endothelium   Venules

Smooth muscle

Arteriole long. sec.

Capillary   Arteriole trans. sec.   Elastica interna

FIG. 12-7. Arterioles and accompanying venules from the submucosa of a human rectum. The arteriole at the *left* is cut longitudinally in the central part of its course where its walls show the circularly arranged muscle fibers cut across, but farther to the *left*, where it passes out of the plane of the section, the wall of the arteriole is cut tangentially and shows muscle fibers extending over the lumen. The vacuoles in the blood plasma just beneath the endothelium of the vessels are artifacts produced by shrinkage. ×250.

tunica media ranges in thickness from one to several layers of muscle cells. Other authors prefer to restrict the term arteriole to the vessels which have only one or two layers of muscle cells (Fig. 12-1) and to use the term small artery, or terminal artery, for the vessels which connect the arterioles proper with the medium sized or muscular arteries. The latter usage seems preferable.

The arterioles are able to regulate the distribution of blood to different capillary beds by vasoconstriction or vasodilation in localized regions. Widespread vasoconstriction or vasodilation of the arterioles alters the peripheral resistance to flow from the larger arteries and hence plays an important part in regulating blood pressure. The arterioles are structurally adapted for vasoconstriction and vasodilation since their walls are composed primarily of circularly arranged muscle fibers which are controlled by the autonomic nervous system. Elasticity is not as important in these vessels as in the

larger arteries in which the blood pressure is much higher. Hence, the sparseness of elastic tissue in arterioles is another example of correlation between structure and function.

Medium Sized Arteries. These include all of the named arteries of gross dissections except the very large ones. There is a gradual transition between the branches of the medium sized arteries and the small arteries described above. Examples of medium sized arteries are the radial, tibial, popliteal, axillary, splenic, mesenteric and intercostal arteries. The walls of these blood vessels are relatively thick, mainly as a result of the large amount of muscle in the media (Fig. 12-9). They are therefore called *muscular* arteries, in contrast with the *elastic* arteries like the aorta, in the wall of which elastic tissue predominates. The muscular arteries have also been called *distributing arteries* because they distribute the blood to different organs and, by contraction or relaxation,

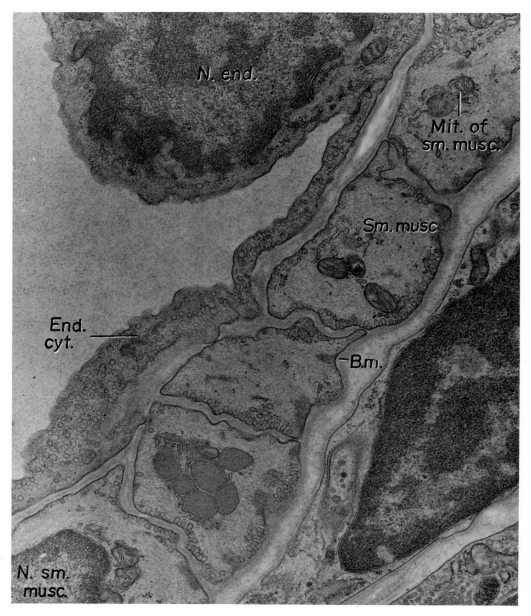

Fig. 12-8. Electron micrograph of a portion of an arteriole from the cervical region of a bat. The nucleus (*N. end.*) of one endothelial cell is seen, and numerous pinocytotic vesicles are present in the cytoplasm of the endothelial cells (*End. cyt.*). Since the circularly arranged smooth muscle cells are cut transversely, one may conclude that the plane of the section is longitudinal to the axis of the vessel. A nucleus (*N. sm. musc.*) is seen in one of the muscle cells, and their mitochondria (*Mit. of sm. musc.*) are shown. Numerous vesicles are seen at the periphery of the muscle cells. A basal lamina (*Bm.*) can be seen beneath the endothelium and around the muscle cells. Fibroblasts and fine connective tissue fibrils are seen in the adventitial coat at the *right.* ×22,500. (Courtesy of Dr. Keith Porter.)

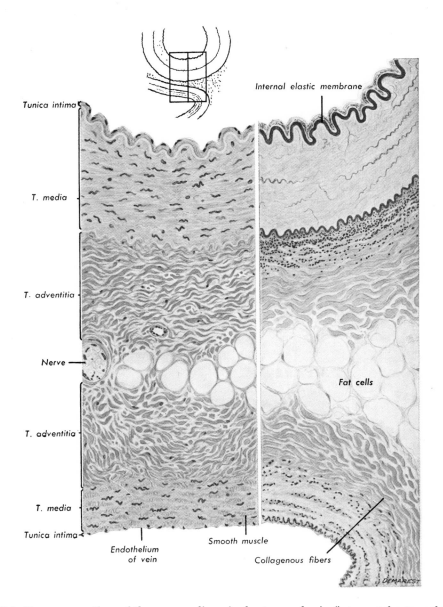

Tunica intima

T. media

T. adventitia

Nerve

T. adventitia

T. media

Tunica intima

Internal elastic membrane

Fat cells

Endothelium
of vein

Smooth muscle

Collagenous fibers

J. DEMAREST

FIG. 12-9. Two cross sections of the same medium sized artery and vein (intercostal artery *above*, vein *below*). The line drawing at *upper left* gives orientation of regions drawn. Section on the *left* is stained with hematoxylin-eosin, that on the *right* with resorcin-fuchsin to show elastic tissue. *T.*, tunica. ×215.

they aid in regulating the supply to different regions in response to different functional demands.

The *intima* exhibits three definite layers: endothelium, intermediate layer and internal elastic membrane. The intermediate layer consists of delicate elastic and collagenous fibrils and a few fibroblasts. The *internal elastic membrane* is a thick, fenestrated band formed of closely interwoven elastic fibers. In certain arteries, it splits in places and appears in section as a double membrane. It is intimately connected with the media and marks the boundary between the latter and the intima. In the smaller muscular arteries, the intermediate layer is thin and the endothelium is close to the elastic membrane.

Owing to the large amount of muscle in their walls, the postmortem contraction of arteries throws the elastic membrane into longitudinal folds; hence, in transverse sections it has the appearance of a corrugated or wavy band.

Isolated longitudinal smooth muscle fibers are occasionally found in the intima, especially in places where the artery branches. Larger longitudinal bundles close to the elastic membrane are prominent in the coronary arteries, and they have also been described in some of the larger muscular arteries (femoral, popliteal, axillary, hepatic, splenic, renal).

The *media* is the thickest coat and consists of 25 to 40 layers of circularly disposed muscle fibers. The thickness of the muscle coat is to some extent proportional to the size of the vessel, but there are considerable variations in arteries of the same size. Between the layers of muscle, there are small amounts of connective tissue composed of elastic, collagenous and reticular fibers and fibroblasts.

The amount and distribution of elastic tissue in the media are closely correlated with the caliber of the vessel. In the smaller vessels, the elastic fibers are scattered between the muscle cells, but in the larger vessels they form circularly oriented elastic nets which permeate the entire media. In the larger vessels of the group there is a fenestrated membrane or network of elastic tissue, the *external elastic membrane*, at the junction of the tunica media with the adventitia (Fig. 12-9). The largest vessels of the group contain circularly disposed fenestrated membranes of elastic tissue (Fig. 12-10); hence, these vessels are transitional between the muscular and elastic types in structure.

Radial elastic fibers likewise occur in some arteries. In transverse section they appear as vertical fibers which penetrate the media for varying depths, sometimes extending from the adventitia to the internal elastic membrane.

The *adventitia* is a coat of considerable thickness, occasionally as thick as the media. It is composed of connective tissue containing collagenous and elastic fibers, most of which course longitudinally. The elastic fibers are concentrated in the inner layer of the coat, where they form a coarse network. The outer layer of the adventitia blends gradually with the surrounding connective tissue which attaches the artery to other structures.

A few longitudinal smooth muscle fibers are occasionally found in the inner layer of the adventitia, between the elastic fibers. In some arteries (splenic, dorsalis penis), bundles of longitudinally disposed muscle fibers occur in close proximity to the media.

Large Arteries. The large arteries belong to the *elastic* type. They have also been called *conducting arteries* because they conduct the blood from the heart to the medium sized distributing arteries. The wall is relatively thin for the size of the vessel. There is a tremendous accretion of elastic tissue and a great reduction in the amount of smooth muscle. While in the medium sized arteries the various elements are arranged circularly or longitudinally, the muscle fibers, elastic and collagenous tissue, have in the main a spiral disposition in the large

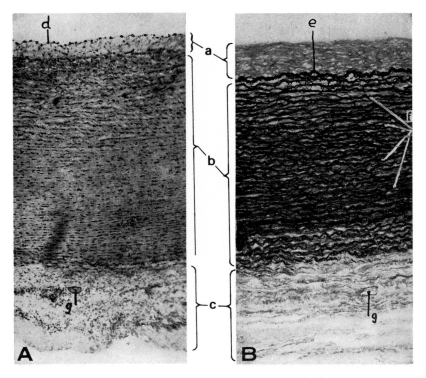

FIG. 12-10. Cross section through internal carotid artery. Retouched photograph. ×85. *A*, stained with hematoxylin-eosin; *B*, with resorcin-fuchsin; *a*, intima; *b*, media; *c*, adventitia; *d*, endothelium; *e*, internal elastic membrane; *f*, elastic membranes in media; *g*, vasa vasorum.

arteries. The chief representative of this group is the aorta (Fig. 12-11).

The endothelial cells of the *intima* are short and polygonal in shape. Below the endothelium there is a layer of connective tissue containing fine collagenous and elastic fibers and a few fibroblasts. The deeper portion of the intima contains coarser collagenous fibers, some longitudinally oriented smooth muscle cells and many elastic fibers which are also arranged longitudinally (Fig. 12-11). The amount of elastic tissue and the character of the internal elastic membrane change with age. The inner elastic membrane is usually split into two or more lamellae which merge with other similar membranes, both in the intima and in the media. Hence it is generally difficult to identify this membrane in the aorta with exactness.

The *media* is distinguished by numerous distinct elastic membranes which course spirally and which anastomose to form complex elastic nets. The elastic layer at the junction of the media with the adventitia does not differ from the elastic membranes found throughout the media, and hence it is not as clearly demarcated as the external elastic membrane of medium sized arteries. The narrow spaces between the lamellae are permeated by a finer elastic network, in the meshes of which the muscle fibers are contained. The muscle tissue is greatly reduced in amount and its fibers are short, flat cells of irregular · outline. They unite to form branching bands which, like the elastic lamellae, pursue a spiral course. The muscle fibers are surrounded and supported by a small amount of collagenous and reticular fibers.

The *adventitia* is a thin coat and consists of connective tissue composed mostly of

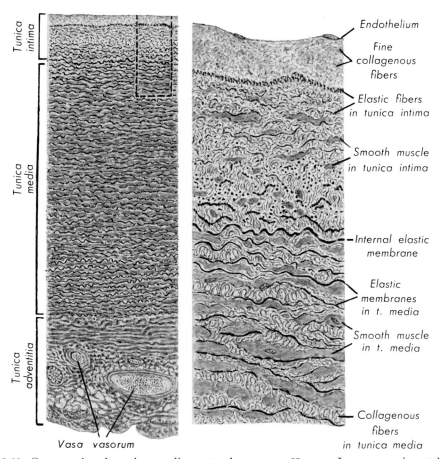

FIG. 12-11. Cross section through ascending aorta, human, age 23 years. Low power view at *left* shows layers of tissue present in total thickness of vessel. Region outlined by broken line is enlarged in the figure at the *right* to show structure of tunica intima and a portion of the adjacent media. Weigert's elastic tissue and Van Gieson's stains to differentiate elastic fibers, collagenous fibers and smooth muscle. Left, ×60; right, ×285.

collagenous fibers arranged in longitudinal spirals. It contains relatively few elastic fibers. A few longitudinally arranged smooth muscle fibers are occasionally found in the adventitia of some of the large arteries.

Besides the aorta, the large arteries include the innominate, common carotid, subclavian, vertebral and common iliac. These resemble the aorta in structure, but they have less elastic tissue and more smooth muscle. As these arteries branch and become smaller, they gradually assume the structure of a medium sized artery.

Since the blood is propelled through the blood vessels by the rhythmic contractions of the heart, the rate of flow is not uniform. When the heart contracts and forces blood into the aorta, the walls of the elastic arteries stretch and a part of the force of the beat is converted into potential energy in the form of increased elastic tension. During diastole of the ventricles, the potential energy of the expanded arterial walls is transformed into kinetic energy which keeps the blood moving forward. Thus, the elasticity of the large arteries makes the blood flow less irregularly than it would if the vessels were rigid tubes. The most marked irregularity is found at the beginning of the arterial system; the flow becomes more uniform in the terminal parts of the arterial system.

Special Forms of Arteries. There are certain arteries which exhibit pronounced structural peculiarities. The *cerebral* and *dural* arteries, which are protected from external mechanical forces, are thin walled for their caliber. They have a well developed internal elastic membrane but almost no elastic fibers in the media. The adventitia is poorly developed and consists mainly of collagenous fiber bundles.

The arteries of the *lung* have thin walls, owing to a reduction of both muscle and elastic tissue. This is probably associated with the lower blood pressure in the pulmonary circulation.

In the *penile* and *pudic* arteries, a hyperplasia of the intima and media manifests itself after puberty, while the adventitia remains relatively thin. The intima especially becomes greatly thickened and contains many longitudinal muscle fibers in its outer layer.

The *umbilical* arteries have a media composed of two muscle layers, an inner longitudinal and an outer circular. The internal elastic membrane is indistinct and entirely missing in some places. A true adventitia is lacking in the segment which is in the umbilical cord and is but poorly developed in the intra-abdominal portion of the artery.

Aging of the Arteries. The arteries undergo age changes which differ in type and in degree in different vessels of the same individual. The elastic arteries, especially the aorta, show more changes than do the muscular arteries of the extremities such as the femoral or brachial. Particularly pronounced and early changes occur in the arteries of the brain and heart.

In a 4-month human fetus, the aorta has a tunica intima composed only of endothelium and one elastica interna. By the end of fetal life, the internal elastic membrane has become thicker, and after birth it splits into two or more layers. Additional elastic and collagenous fibers develop between the endothelium and elastica interna, and the elastic layers of the media also increase in number. The layers of the aorta are not completely differentiated until about 25 years of age. It is difficult to separate some of the final stages of differentiation from regressive changes resulting from use. In fact, some authors think that arteriosclerosis may be a physiological rather than a pathological process. In the aging or wearing out process, the tunica intima becomes thicker, the elastic layers of the media change chemically and

become less elastic, and fat gradually accumulates between the elastic and collagenous fibers.

The anterior descending branch of the left coronary artery furnishes another interesting example of age changes. In this vessel, the internal elastic membrane is already split at the time of birth, definite hyperplasia of the elastic tissue occurs during the first decade, and calcification of the media begins in the third decade. It is interesting to note that similar changes in another branch of the coronary arteries—the posterior descending branch of the right coronary—do not occur until considerably later. The calcification of the media is one of the main changes in the arteries of muscular type.

The Carotid and Aortic Bodies. These structures were formerly included with the paraganglia as a part of the endocrine system. They were erroneously thought to contain chromaffin cells similar to those of the adrenal medulla.

The *carotid bodies* are small, paired organs which lie in or near the bifurcation of each common carotid. Each one is frequently divided, a half lying on either side of the bifurcation. They are very vascular and contain numerous sinusoidal capillaries. The parenchyma is composed of epithelial-like cells which are pale staining and show no particular characteristics in the usual hematoxylin and eosin preparations. For cytological details that can be observed with special technical methods, reference should be made to the work of Hollinshead (1943). The cells contain cytoplasmic granules which can be particularly well stained with neutral red and other basic dyes in supravital preparations. They do not give the chromaffin reaction, and no fat, cholesterol or glycogen can be demonstrated in them. They exhibit no Nissl substance, neurofibrils or other evidence of similarity to neurons.

Afferent nerve fibers from the carotid body form the sinus branch of the glossopharyngeal nerve or sinus nerve. The fibers have delicate endings on the epithelioid cells which are in close contact with the sinusoidal capillaries. The mechanism is spoken of as a *chemoreceptor*, since nerve impulses are initiated in response to changes in the pH of the circulating blood.

The *aortic bodies* vary somewhat in position in different species. In the rabbit, in which their structure and innervation have been described in detail by Nonidez (1935), the right aortic body is in the angle formed by the subclavian and common carotid, whereas the left aortic body is closely applied to the roof of the arch of the aorta. Histologically, they appear to be similar to the carotid bodies, and they are thought to have a similar function: that is, they are responsive to changes in the chemical composition of the blood, and stimuli initiated by these changes are carried to the central nervous system by the afferent nerves.

The Carotid Sinus. This sinus is an enlargement at the bifurcation of each common carotid. In this region, the media of the wall of the artery is relatively thin and the adventitial layer has a rich supply of specialized sensory nerve endings derived from the carotid sinus branch of the glossopharyngeal nerve. The nerves have reticulated swollen endings in contact with the cells of the adventitial layer and appear as terminal menisci. They are stimulated by distention of the vessel wall (by an increase in blood pressure), and they bring about reflex dilation of splanchnic vessels, slowing of the heart and a fall in systemic blood pressure.

VEINS

The caliber of veins is as a rule larger than that of arteries, but their walls are much thinner because of a great reduction of the muscular and elastic elements. The collagenous connective tissue, on the other hand, is present in much larger amounts and constitutes the bulk of the wall. The relatively sparse circular muscle of the media is more loosely arranged and separated into layers by abundant collagenous fibers. The internal elastic membrane is not a compact fenestrated layer but consists of a network of elastic fibers which becomes distinct only in the larger veins. The three coats—intima, media and adventitia—are present, but their boundaries are often indistinct for lack of definite limiting membranes. The entire wall is flabbier and more loosely organized than in arteries, and it tends to collapse when not filled with blood.

A histological classification of veins is quite difficult as their structure varies extensively. The variations are not always related to the size of the vessels but depend on local mechanical conditions. The structure may be quite different in veins of the same caliber and even in different portions of the same vein. A description of the venous wall can therefore enumerate only the most general features.

Small Veins. The transition from capillary to vein is a very gradual one, the connective tissue elements appearing first and the smooth muscle cells somewhat later. The smallest veins (*venules*) are endothelial tubes surrounded by an outer sheath of collagenous fibrils with a few fibroblasts (Fig. 12-7).

Isolated, circularly disposed muscle fibers make their appearance in vessels of 40 to 50 μ, although the presence of muscle fibers is variable and is not always dependent on caliber. In venules of 0.2 to 0.3 mm., the circular muscle fibers form a continuous layer and the adventitia is a relatively thick coat of longitudinally disposed collagenous fibers. In its inner portion, just outside the muscle, are scattered elastic fibrils.

As the veins increase in size, the muscle becomes many layered and the individual layers are separated by loose collagenous tissue. The elastic fibers gradually invade the whole media and form longitudinal elastic nets between the muscle layers. The innermost elastic net comes to lie directly underneath the endothelium and constitutes a poorly defined inner elastic membrane.

Medium Sized Veins. These include practically all of the named veins and their branches, excepting the main trunks found in the thoracic and abdominal cavities (Fig. 12-9).

The *intima* is thin. The endothelial cells are short and polygonal in shape. A subendothelial layer of delicate collagenous and elastic fibers is present in the larger veins but missing in many of the smaller ones. The internal elastic layer consists of a dense network of longitudinal fibers. Often the layer is so indistinct that there is no demarcation between media and intima.

The *media* is thin as compared with that of arteries of the same size. It is composed of circular muscle fibers and collagenous and elastic connective tissue. In the larger veins, the muscle is arranged in bundles or layers separated by collagenous fibers. The muscle layers alternate with nets of longitudinal elastic fibers which are especially distinct in the outer portions of the media.

The media is thickest in the veins of the lower extremity, where it resembles more nearly the media of an artery. In the veins of the head and abdomen, it is very thin, and in some it is missing entirely.

The *adventitia* is well developed and forms the bulk of the wall. It consists of collagenous and elastic tissue, and often it contains a few bundles of longitudinal muscle fibers.

Large Veins. In the large venous trunks of the thoracic and abdominal cavities, the circular muscle is greatly reduced, while the longitudinal muscle bundles of the adventitia are strongly developed (Fig. 12-12). Unusually stout bundles are found in the portal vein and hepatic portion of the inferior

vena cava. The media is thin and poorly defined. To this group belong the superior and inferior venae cavae, the innominates, the internal jugulars, portal, splenic, azygos, superior mesenteric, renal, adrenal and external iliac veins.

Special Features of Certain Veins. Very little or no muscle whatever is found in the following veins: the subpapillary veins ("giant capillaries") of the skin and nail bed, the trabecular veins of the spleen, the dural sinuses, most pial and cerebral veins, the veins of the retina and of the bones and the deeper veins of the maternal placenta.

Especially rich in muscle are the veins of the *gravid uterus*, which contain muscle fibers in all three coats. The *umbilical* vein has an inner longitudinal and outer circular muscle layer.

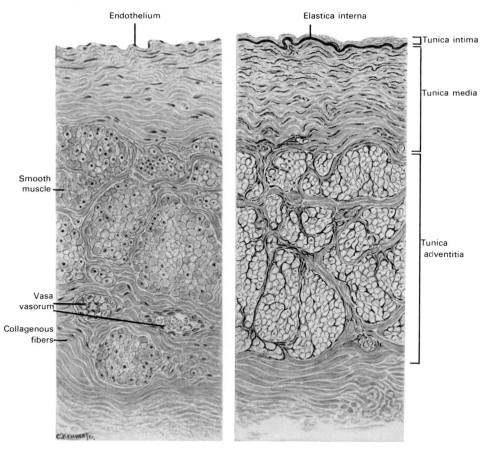

FIG. 12-12. Two cross sections of the same internal jugular vein; *left*, stained with hematoxylin-eosin; *right*, stained with resorcin-fuchsin and picro-fuchsin to differentiate elastic fibers, collagenous fibers and smooth muscle. ×180.

Smooth muscle   Leaflet of valve

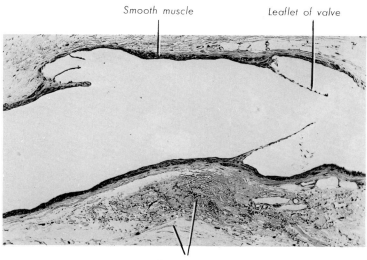

Collagenous fibers

FIG. 12-13. Longitudinal section of a vein from human subcutaneous tissue showing valves. The valve at *upper left* is in a small tributary which curves out of the plane of the section. A part of the lower leaflet of the valve at *right* is enlarged in Figure 12-14. Photomicrograph. ×84.

Occasionally, longitudinal fibers are also found outside the circular coat.

Longitudinal smooth muscle fibers are found in the intima of the saphenous, popliteal, femoral, basilic, cephalic, median, internal jugular, umbilical and some mesenteric veins; also in the veins of the gravid uterus.

Near their entrance into the heart, the adventitia of the venae cavae and pulmonary veins is invested with a layer of cardiac muscle, the fibers coursing spirally or circularly around the tube.

Valves. Veins over 2 mm. in diameter are provided at intervals with valves (Figs. 12-13 and 12-14). These are semilunar flaps or pockets which project into the lumen, their free margin being directed towards the heart. As the blood flows towards the heart, it flattens the flaps against the wall and thus passes without obstruction towards the heart, but if it starts to flow in the reverse direction, the valves float up, approach each other and occlude the cavity.

The valves are derived from the intima and consist of connective tissue covered by a layer of endothelium. Beneath the endothelium of the surface of the valve directed against the blood current is a rich network

of elastic fibers continuous with the elastic tissue of the intima. The connective tissue of the side facing the wall of the vein is entirely free from or contains but few elastic fibers. Adjacent to the valve, on the side toward the heart, the wall of the vein is usually distended and thin; this region is called the *sinus of the valve*. The smooth muscle of the vein at the base of the valve and along the sinus region runs mostly in a longitudinal or spiral direction. Valves are especially numerous and strong in the larger veins of the lower extremities. They are absent in the veins of the brain and spinal cord and their meninges as well as in the umbilical vein, in most of the visceral veins with the exception of some branches of the portal, and in the superior and inferior venae cavae and their branches.

Portal Vessels. In most parts of the body, arteries are connected with veins via capillary plexuses. Modifications of this pattern occur in some locations in adaptation to special functions. When capillaries lead to vessels which in turn supply a second set of capillaries (or sinusoids) before returning

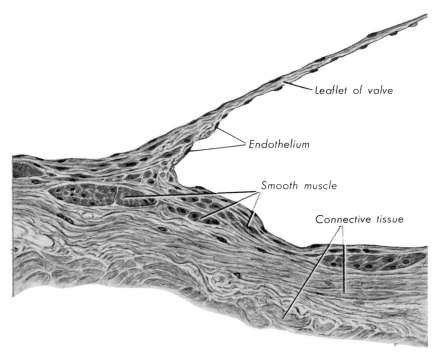

FIG. 12-14. Higher magnification of a part of the valve of the vein shown in Figure 12-13. ×447

the blood to the systemic veins, the arrangement of vessels is known as a *portal system.* The liver is an example of a venous portal system, with a set of capillaries between veins. In this instance, the portal vein receives blood by its tributaries from the capillaries of most of the abdominal viscera and empties into the hepatic sinusoids that lead to the hepatic veins. The anterior pituitary gland is another example of a venous portal system. Capillaries from the infundibulum drain into veins which supply the sinusoidal capillaries of the anterior lobe. The kidney glomerulus is an example of an arterial portal system, with a capillary plexus between arteries. In this case, afferent glomerular arterioles supply glomerular capillaries which drain into efferent glomerular arterioles and thence to a capillary plexus around the uriniferous tubules.

Arteriovenous Anastomoses. In addition to the capillary and sinusoidal connections of vessels already described, arteries sometimes empty directly into veins—*ar-*

teriovenous anastomoses. Such connections have been found in pathological conditions resulting from injury, in vascular neoplasms and in developmental anomalies. They also occur normally in certain parts of the body. They are especially numerous in the sole of the foot, in the palm of the hand, in the skin of the terminal phalanges and in the nail bed. The arteriovenous anastomoses are usually surrounded by a connective tissue sheath, and the arterioles generally follow a convoluted course, forming a structure known as a *glomus* (Chapter 14, Fig. 14-17). The smooth muscle fibers are modified in shape and structure and are epithelioid in appearance.

When the arteriovenous anastomoses are open, they shunt a considerable amount of blood directly into the veins and decrease the flow through adjacent arterioles leading to the capillary bed, but in the normal behavior of the peripheral vessels, they are contracted a large part of the time.

Blood Vessels, Lymphatics and Nerves of the Blood Vessels

Vasa Vasorum. Arteries and veins with a diameter over 1 mm. are supplied with small nutrient blood vessels, the *vasa vasorum*. These vessels enter and branch in the adventitia and terminate in a capillary network that penetrates the media, probably reaching its deepest layers. No capillaries are found in the intima.

Lymphatics. Lymphatics have been found in the adventitia of many of the larger arteries and veins. Extensive *perivascular lymph spaces* surround the thin walled blood vessels of the pia-arachnoid of the brain and spinal cord.

Nerves. The walls of blood vessels have a rich nerve supply. The nerve fibers are mainly unmyelinated axons from sympathetic ganglia and are known as vasomotor nerves, since they control the caliber of the blood vessel. They form a plexus in the adventitia, from which are given off secondary plexuses that permeate the entire media. Here the fibers branch extensively and end on the muscle fibers with delicate knoblike terminations.

Scattered ganglion cells have been found in the adventitia of the aorta.

Besides the vasomotor nerves, the blood vessels receive myelinated sensory nerve fibers which are the peripheral arms of spinal or cranial ganglion cells. The larger fibers run in the connective tissue surrounding the blood vessel. They enter the adventitia, divide repeatedly, lose their myelin sheaths and terminate in free sensory endings. In some blood vessels, they can be traced into the intima.

The Heart

The heart is a pump for propelling the blood through the blood vessels. It is composed of four chambers in the following sequence in relation to blood flow: (1) the *right atrium* receives venous blood from the superior and inferior vena cavae and from the coronary sinus; (2) the right ventricle receives blood from the right atrium through the right atrioventricular (A-V) orifice which is guarded by the tricuspid valve and it pumps blood into the pulmonary artery; (3) the *left atrium* receives blood from the pulmonary veins and opens into the left ventricle via the left AV orifice guarded by the bicuspid (mitral) valve (Fig. 12-15); and (4) the left ventricle which pumps blood into the aorta.

Although the different chambers of the heart vary to some extent in their microscopic structure, the arrangement of tissues in each conforms to a general plan. The wall of each chamber consists of three layers: an inner layer or *endocardium*, a middle layer or *myocardium*, and an outer layer or *epicardium*. The myocardium forms the main mass of the heart.

Endocardium. The endocardium is a thin, glistening membrane covering the inner surface of the atria and ventricles. It is thick in the atria, especially in the left atrium, and thin in the ventricles; this explains the whiter color of the inside of the atria as contrasted with the red appearance of the inside of the ventricles, where the color of the cardiac muscle shows readily through the thin endocardium. At the arterial and venous orifices, it becomes continuous with the intima of the vessels, with which it is comparable in structure. It is lined by an endothelium of irregularly shaped, polygonal cells with oval or round nuclei. Beneath the endothelium is a thin layer of exceedingly fine collagenous fibrils and, outside of this, a stouter layer containing abundant elastic tissue and varying numbers of smooth muscle cells (Fig. 12-16). In most parts of the heart, the deepest layer of the endocardium is composed of loose connective tissue which binds the endocardium proper to the myocardium. This layer, known as the *subendocardium*, contains collagenous fibers, elastic fibers and blood vessels. In the ventricles, it also contains some of the specialized muscle fibers of the impulse conducting system. This layer

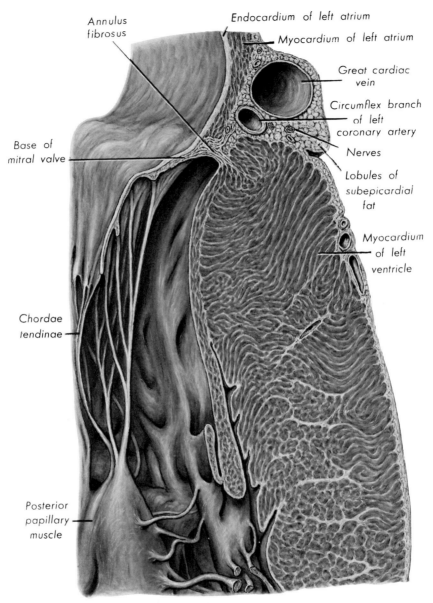

Annulus fibrosus

Endocardium of left atrium

Myocardium of left atrium

Great cardiac vein

Circumflex branch of left coronary artery

Nerves

Base of mitral valve

Lobules of subepicardial fat

Myocardium of left ventricle

Chordae tendinae

Posterior papillary muscle

Fig. 12-15. Low power, three dimensional view of the zone of juncture of the left atrium with the left ventricle in the human heart. The region illustrated is from the posterior part of the heart and shows the posterior papillary muscle and the posterior cusp of the bicuspid (mitral) valve. ×3.5.

is absent from the papillary muscles and chordae tendinae.

Myocardium. The myocardium consists of a special form of striated muscle tissue already described as cardiac muscle (Chapter 8). Its thickness varies in different parts of the heart, being thinnest in the atria and thickest in the left ventricle. The atrial muscle tends to be arranged in bundles in a sort of latticework with spaces where the connective tissue of the subendocardium joins with that of the subepicardium. The

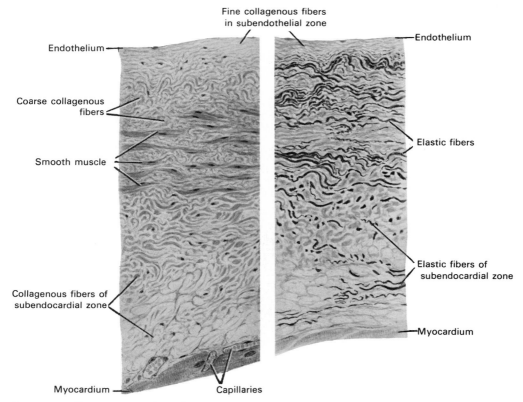

Fine collagenous fibers
in subendothelial zone

Endothelium

Endothelium

Coarse collagenous
fibers

Elastic fibers

Smooth muscle

Elastic fibers of
subendocardial zone

Collagenous fibers of
subendocardial zone

Myocardium

Myocardium

Capillaries

FIG. 12-16. Cross sections through the endocardium of the left atrium of an adult. Section on the *left* is stained with hematoxylin and eosin; the one on the *right* is stained for elastic fibers. ×206.

muscle bundles of the outer part of the atrial wall are oriented chiefly in a transverse or oblique direction and continue over both atria. The bundles in the deeper portions of the atrial wall are more independent for each atrium and are oriented approximately at right angles to the bundles of the outer layer. The innermost bundles stand out as ridges (pectinate muscles) in the auricular portions of the atria.

The disposition of the muscle tissue of the ventricles is much more complicated. It is usually described as composed of several layers, the fibers of which run in different directions. The arrangement of these fiber layers can be readily determined by dissecting hearts in which the connective tissue has been broken down by maceration. The muscle of the ventricles consists mainly of two

sets of fibers, a *superficial* set and a *deep* set. These run at approximately right angles to each other. Both sets of fibers take their origin from fibrous connective tissue of the A-V rings. The superficial fibers follow a spiral course from the base of the ventricles to the apex of the heart, where they turn inward to terminate in the papillary muscles. The deeper layers follow a circular course on each ventricle, with some of the fibers making an S-shaped pattern as they pass from one ventricle to the other by way of the interventricular septum. (The arrangement of these layers was well illustrated by Robb et al., 1935.)

The cardiac muscle of the atria is separated from that of the ventricles by strong fibrous rings, the *annuli fibrosi*, which surround the A-V ostia. The fibrous rings are composed mainly of dense bundles of collagenous fibers. They also contain some elastic fibers, fibroblasts and fat cells which become continuous with the subepicardial adipose tissue in the region of the coronary sulcus (Fig. 12-15).

The fibrous rings show structural variations in different persons and at different ages. They exhibit more marked variations in different species, e.g., they contain hyaline cartilage in sheep and bone in the ox.

The *annuli fibrosi of the atrioventricular ostia* form a part of a dense connective tissue supporting structure known as the *cardiac skeleton*. Other parts of this system are: the *annuli fibrosi at the arterial foramina*, the *trigona fibrosa*, and the *septum membranaceum*.

Epicardium. The epicardium is the visceral layer of the pericardial sac in which the heart is placed. It is lined by a single layer of mesothelial cells which may be flat or cubical, depending on the contraction state of the heart. Below the mesothelium is a layer of connective tissue containing a considerable number of elastic fibers in its deeper portion. At the venous and arterial openings, the connective tissue fibers pass over into the adventitia of the blood vessels. The epicardium is attached to the myocardium by the *subepicardial* connective tissue containing blood vessels, nerves and varying amounts of fat.

Valves of the Heart. The atrioventricular valves (tricuspid and mitral) are attached at their bases to the annuli fibrosi (Figs. 12-15 and 12-17). They consist of folds of endocardium covering a central plate of

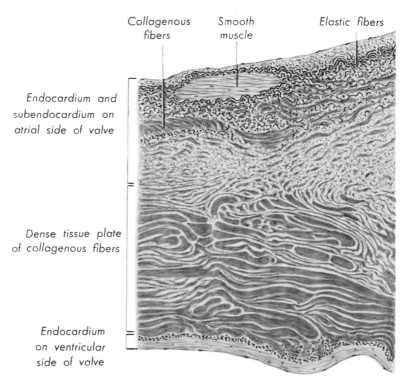

Fig. 12-17. Cross section through a human mitral valve. The region shown is from the base of the valve, with the right side of the illustration facing the A-V junction and annulus fibrosus. (Compare with Fig. 12-15 for orientation.) Weigert's elastic tissue and Van Gieson's stains to differentiat elastic fibers, collagenous fibers and smooth muscle. ×110.

dense bundles of collagenous fibers which are continuous with the fibrous tissue of the annuli fibrosi and chordae tendinae. The endocardium is thicker on the atrial than on the ventricular side and contains more elastic tissue. Some smooth muscle fibers are present on the atrial side, but these are rarely distinguishable except in specially prepared slides.

The semilunar valves of the pulmonary artery and aorta resemble the A-V valves in their microscopic structure, but they are much thinner and contain no smooth muscle fibers.

Impulse-conducting System. Besides its ordinary musculature which furnishes the energy for the movement of the blood, the heart possesses a system of special muscle fibers whose function is to regulate the proper succession of contractions of atria and ventricles. It is known as the impulse-conducting system. A part of the system extending from the right atrium into the ventricles may be easily demonstrated by gross dissection and is known as the *atrioventricular bundle*, or *bundle of His*. This bundle has its origin in the *atrioventricular*

node (node of Tawara) which is found in the subendocardium of the median wall of the right atrium close to the termination of the coronary sinus (Fig. 12-18). From the node, a common bundle or stem, the *crus commune*, is continued into the membranous septum of the ventricles, where it divides into two trunks which go respectively to the left and right ventricles. Each trunk ultimately breaks up into a large number of fine branches which radiate to all parts of the ventricle and form an extensive network of fibers in the subendocardial tissue. From the subendocardial plexus, numerous branches extend into the myocardium and eventually terminate by connecting with the working myocardial fibers of the ventricles.

The A-V bundle and its branches consist of modified muscle fibers, *Purkinje fibers*, which surpass the ordinary cardiac fibers in their rate of conduction. Although the histological differences between Purkinje fibers and ordinary cardiac muscle fibers are less pronounced in human hearts than in ungulate hearts, they are sufficient for identification of the fibers in the majority of human cases studied (Fig. 12-19). In comparison

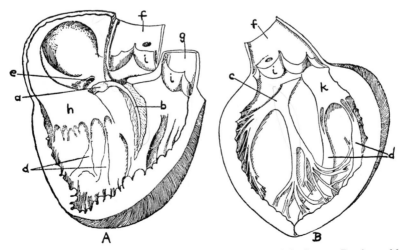

FIG. 12-18. Atrioventricular bundle of human heart. *A*, view of right heart; *B*, view of left heart. *a*, atrioventricular node; *b*, right trunk of bundle; *c*, left trunk of bundle; *d*, papillary muscles; *e*, coronary sinus; *f*, aorta; *g*, pulmonary artery; *h*, flap of tricuspid valve; *i*, semilunar valve; *k*, flap of mitral valve. (After Tandler.)

Connective tissue
of endocardium

Purkinje fibers

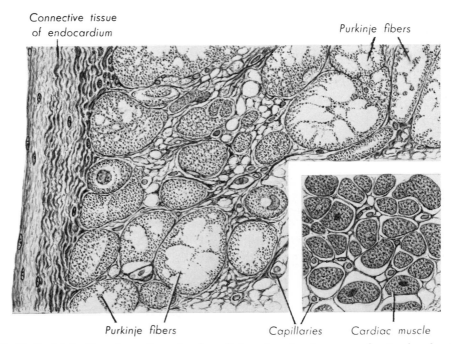

Purkinje fibers   Capillaries   Cardiac muscle

FIG. 12-19. Purkinje fibers from the subendocardial region of a human moderator band cut transversely. The cardiac muscle illustrated in the *inset* is taken from the same section as the Purkinje fibers but is located at a greater distance beneath the endocardium. The magnification of the two figures is the same. ×500. (Redrawn from preparations of Truex and Copenhaver.)

with ordinary cardiac fibers, the distinguishing characteristics of Purkinje fibers are: their myofibrils are reduced in number and usually limited to the periphery of the fiber; they contain relatively more sarcoplasm; their nuclei are more rounded and more often in groups of two or more; they usually have a larger diameter, particularly in the peripheral branches of the system; they apparently lack the transverse tubules of cardiac muscle; they give a positive reaction for acetylcholinesterase; and they generally have more glycogen. The myofibrils resemble those of ordinary fibers in that they are cross striated. Electron micrographs show that the Purkinje fibers, like ordinary cardiac muscle fibers, are separate cells and that the intercalated discs seen under the light microscope are electron dense areas along the membranes of cell junctions. The Purkinje fibers ultimately lose their specific characteristics and terminate by coming into

contact with ordinary cardiac fibers (Fig. 12-20). Since the cell membranes are thin, the cell junctions are not readily seen under the light microscope.

The A-V node is composed of a group of irregularly arranged, branching fibers (*nodal fibers*) which have a smaller diameter and fewer myofibrils than ordinary cardiac muscle fibers (Fig. 12-21). On the side of the A-V node adjacent to the A-V fibrous ring, the nodal fibers become continuous with Purkinje fibers of the A-V bundle; on the opposite side of the node, they are continuous with ordinary cardiac muscle fibers of the atrium.

Another division of the specialized system, the *sinoatrial* (S-A) *node* of Keith and Flack, is found in the subepicardium at the junction of the superior vena cava and right atrium in the region of the terminal sulcus. (Fig. 12-22). This node is composed of slender, fusiform fibers which have the general

Cardiac muscle   Transition of Purkinje fibers into cardiac muscle   Purkinje fibers

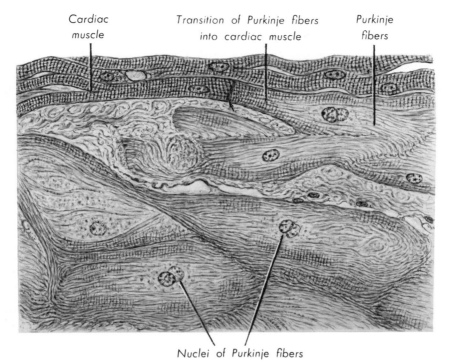

Nuclei of Purkinje fibers

FIG. 12-20. Longitudinal section of a beef moderator band showing transition of Purkinje fibers into cardiac muscle fibers in the myocardial portion of the band. The transition occurs near cell junctions and does not indicate a syncytium of cells. An intercalated disc can be identified in the region indicated by the *arrow*, although the discs are not stained in most parts of this preparation. ×500. (Redrawn from preparation of Truex and Copenhaver.)

structure of the fibers of the A-V node. A plexus of fibers extends from the S-A node into the myocardium of the right atrium.

It is well established that the stimuli for cardiac contraction are normally initiated in the S-A node. Since some of the fibers of this node come into close association with the typical cardiac fibers and since the latter, as already described, are arranged as a meshwork of contiguous cells, the impulse initiated in the S-A node may spread as a contraction wave (Lewis) over the typical cardiac fibers of both atria and then into the special fibers of the A-V node. On the other hand, electrophysiological studies of canine and rabbit hearts indicate that the impulse initiated in the S-A node is transmitted by special pathways to the A-V node (Hoffman, 1961, 1965). Results of microscopic studies to determine whether

the fibers of the atrial conduction pathways differ cytologically from the ordinary atrial fibers remain somewhat controversial. The atrial preferential conduction pathways described from physiological and pharmacological studies contain a number of cells which are intermediate in their histological characteristics between working myocardial fibers and conduction fibers of the ventricles. In comparison with typical cardiac fibers, they contain fewer myofibrils and give a different tinctorial reaction with a modified Masson stain. The preferential pathways also contain some cardiac fibers which stain similarly to the typical fibers, but this is not sufficient reason to conclude that they do not participate in conduction. In fact, it seems likely that most atrial fibers have the potentiality to conduct. The preferential pathways are located primarily in the regions which com-

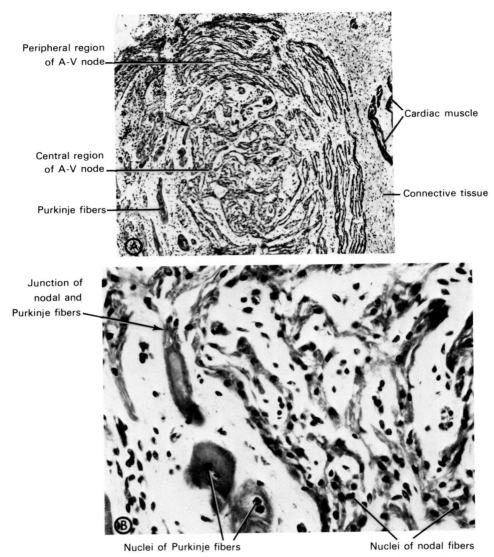

Peripheral region of A-V node

Central region of A-V node

Purkinje fibers

Cardiac muscle

Connective tissue

Junction of nodal and Purkinje fibers

Nuclei of Purkinje fibers

Nuclei of nodal fibers

FIG. 12-21. Photomicrographs of a section through the atrioventricular node of a sheep heart. *A* shows a low magnification micrograph of an area from the wall of the right atrium medial to the opening of the coronary sinus and just above the origin of the atrioventricular bundle. Only a few atrial muscle fibers are seen in this section. The junctions of nodal fibers with atrial fibers occur chiefly in the preceding sections, at a greater distance above the origin of the A-V bundle. *B* shows a higher magnification micrograph of a portion of the field seen in *A*. For orientation, note that the *arrows* to the junctions of nodal fibers with Purkinje fibers are directed to the same cells in *A* and *B*. The fibers of the A-V node are very similar in size and structure to those of the S-A node but the former are arranged in a different pattern. The presence of Purkinje fibers of large diameter in the A-V nodal area is characteristic of hearts of ungulates; the special conduction fibers of the human heart do not attain the large diameter typical of ventricular Purkinje fibers until the branches of the A-V system are reached. Hematoxylin and eosin. *A*, ×63; *B*, ×146. (From preparations of Copenhaver and Truex, Anat. Rec., vol. 114, 1952.)

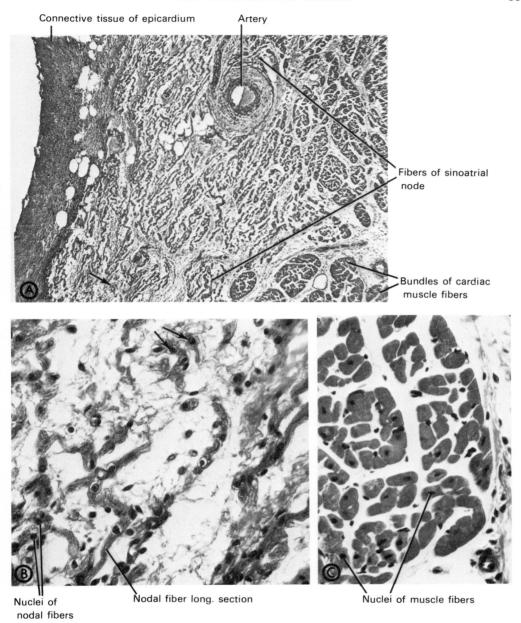

Connective tissue of epicardium   Artery

Fibers of sinoatrial
node

Bundles of cardiac
muscle fibers

Nuclei of
nodal fibers

Nodal fiber long. section

Nuclei of muscle fibers

FIG. 12-22. Photomicrographs of a section through the sinoatrial node and adjacent cardiac muscle of a sheep heart. *A* is a low magnification micrograph of an area from the wall of the right atrium near the junction of the atrium and the superior vena cava. *B* shows a portion of *A* at higher magnification. For orientation, note that the *arrows* in *B* point to the same nodal cells that are indicated by the *arrow* in *A*. *C* shows a section of typical atrial myocardial fibers at the same magnification as that of the nodal fibers in *B*. Note that the diameter of the nodal fibers is less than that of the atrial muscle fibers. The nodal fibers are also interspersed with more loose connective tissue and they course in a very irregular pattern. With higher magnification, one would also see that the myofibrils are less numerous and more irregularly arranged within the nodal fibers than they are in the atrial muscle fibers. Hematoxylin and eosin stain. Greater contrast between the fiber types can be obtained by the use of special stains. *A*, ×63, *B* and *C*, ×146. (From preparations of Copenhaver and Truex, Anat. Rec., vol. 114, 1952.)

pose the junction of the sinus venosus and atrium in the embryonic heart.

After the conduction impulse reaches the A-V node, it is conducted at a relatively slow rate through the node to reach the A-V bundle of His, where it travels rapidly to the ventricles. If this bundle is injured or destroyed, the normal rhythm in the succession of atrial and ventricular beats is lost. Branches of the bundle transmit the impulse at a relatively high velocity over both ventricles and terminate with typical cardiac fibers. The branches of the bundle are composed of typical Purkinje fibers with structural characteristics distinctly different from typical cardiac fibers.

Blood Vessels. Blood for the nutrition of the heart is supplied through the two coronary arteries. Each coronary artery sends a branch to its respective atrium and then courses between the ventricles to the apex of the heart, giving numerous branches to both ventricles. The major blood supply is for the myocardium which has a very rich capillary network. Small vessels also supply the subepicardial connective tissue and the endocardium. The blood in the capillaries is collected by veins which unite to form the cardiac veins. These empty into the right atrium by way of the coronary sinus. A number of small veins, the *venae minimae*, empty directly into the lumen of the heart, especially in the right atrium. Additional direct connections between the vessels and the heart chambers have been described (see review by Wearn, 1940).

The atrioventricular valves apparently have only a few or no vessels in the dense, fibrous, central plates. The supply in the subendothelial layers differs for the different leaflets of the valve: it is richer in the aortic cusp of the mitral valve than in others. The supply is also richer in infants than in normal adults.

The bundle of His is, according to some investigators, supplied by special fine branches of the coronary arteries. The capillary net is less dense than in the ordinary musculature of the heart.

Lymphatics. The heart is richly supplied with lymph channels which form networks in the subendocardial and subepicardial tissue. In the myocardium, the exact distribution of lymphatics is not definitely established. According to some, lymph capillaries occur in close association with the blood capillaries. Others maintain that lymphatics are found only in the interfascicular connective tissue, and that the lymph channels between the individual muscle fibers are merely tissue clefts unlined by endothelium.

Nerves. The heart receives nerve fibers from the vagus and the sympathetic division of the autonomic system. These fibers form an extensive cardiac plexus at the base of the heart. The vagus and sympathetic fibers have antagonistic functions, the former inhibiting, the latter accelerating the action of the heart.

The efferent vagus fibers do not go directly to the cardiac muscle but arborize around parasympathetic ganglion cells scattered in the wall of the heart, chiefly in plexuses in the subepicardium. These cells are especially numerous in the dorsal wall of the atria, in the coronary sulcus near the larger coronary vessels and at the base of the aorta and pulmonary artery. The ganglion cells send out delicate, nonmyelinated nerve fibers which branch and end in terminal varicosities on the muscle fibers.

Some of the sensory nerve fibers are derived from the vagus; others have their cell bodies in the spinal ganglia of the first to the fourth thoracic nerves. The fibers of the latter group pass through the white rami, up the sympathetic trunk to the cervical sympathetic ganglia and thence to the heart by way of the cardiac nerves.

THE LYMPH VASCULAR SYSTEM

Besides the blood vessels, the body contains a collateral system of endothelial-lined channels which collect the tissue fluid and return it by a circuitous route to the blood stream. The fluid in these vessels is called lymph. Unlike the blood, the lymph circulates in one direction only, from the periphery toward the heart. The *lymphatic capillaries* end blindly in the tissues from which the lymph is collected (Fig. 12-23). They, as well as the larger vessels which conduct the lymph to the blood stream, freely anastomose along their course, gradually fuse to form fewer lymph channels and are ultimately gathered into two main trunks, the large *thoracic duct* and the smaller *right lymphatic duct*. The thoracic duct empties into the left subclavian vein, and the right lymphatic duct drains into the right subclavian, in each case near the point where the subclavian joins with its respective internal jugular vein. In the pathways of the lymph vessels there are groups of lymph nodes containing lymph sinuses in which the lymph is filtered before reaching the thoracic and lymphatic ducts.

Lymphatic capillaries and vessels occur in most tissues and organs. They have not been demonstrated in the central nervous system, the bone marrow, the intralobular portion of the liver, the coats of the eyeball, the internal ear and the fetal placenta.

Lymph Capillaries. The lymph capillaries, like those of the blood, are delicate tubes with walls which consist of a single layer of endothelial cells. The tubes are larger, however, and instead of having a uniform diameter, they vary greatly in caliber within short distances. The exceedingly thin cells have a flattened, oval nucleus and a very irregular outline which can be demonstrated with silver impregnations. Electron microscope studies of lymphatic capillaries do not show endothelial pores which are

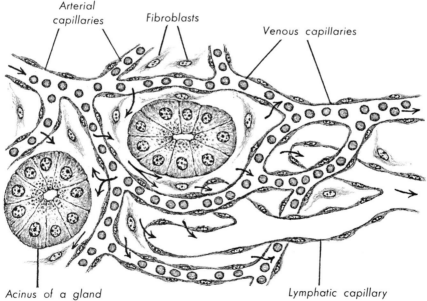

Fig. 12-23. Diagram showing the relationship of lymphatic capillaries to blood capillaries and to the tissue fluids around the acini of a gland. Similar relationships exist in most of the organs of the body. *Arrows* indicate the direction of flow of fluid leaving the arterial capillaries, permeating the connective tissue spaces as tissue fluid and reentering the blood capillaries on the venous side. The lymphatic capillaries supplement the venous capillaries in the drainage of fluid from the tissues to the circulatory system.

found in some blood capillaries. Gaps between endothelial cells of lymph capillaries appear readily under altered conditions and undoubtedly play an important role in the marked permeability of these vessels. The basal lamina is relatively thin and incomplete in lymphatic capillaries; according to some investigators, it is absent. This may be another factor in the permeability of lymphatic capillaries.

The lymph capillaries anastomose to form extensive networks in the spaces between the blood capillaries. In the skin and in the mucous and serous membranes, the lymph capillaries are usually more deeply placed than are the blood capillaries. Toward the surface the lymph capillaries often end in blind swollen or looped projections.

Lymph Vessels. The lymph vessels resemble the veins in structure, but their walls are as a rule thinner than those of veins of a corresponding caliber. In the smaller lymph vessels, the endothelium is surrounded by collagenous and elastic fibers and a few muscle cells. In the larger ones, three coats may be distinguished: intima, media and adventitia. The intima is composed of the endothelial lining, underneath which is a delicate network of elastic fibers disposed longitudinally. The media consists mainly of circularly disposed smooth muscle fibers and a few longitudinal ones. Between the muscle fibers are relatively few, delicate, elastic fibrils. The adventitia, which is the thickest coat, is composed of longitudinally coursing collagenous fibers, among which are bundles of longitudinal muscle and elastic fibers.

The lymph vessels contain numerous valves which are usually arranged in pairs and whose free margins are always directed centrally, i.e., in the direction of the lymph flow. The valves are infoldings of the intima.

Thoracic Duct. The thoracic duct has a considerable amount of muscle tissue. The *intima* consists of an endothelial lining, a thin intermediate layer of fibroelastic tissue in which are bundles of longitudinal muscle fibers, and an internal elastic membrane composed of a longitudinal network of elastic fibers. The elastic membrane is best developed in the caudal portion of the duct and is much thinner or missing altogether in the cervical portion.

The *media* is the thickest coat and consists of longitudinal and circular muscle bundles, the former predominating. The muscle bundles are separated by abundant connective tissue composed mainly of collagenous fibers. Elastic fibrils are scarce in the inner layer of the media but become more numerous in the outer portion.

The *adventitia* is poorly defined. Near the media is a layer of coarse collagenous fibers, mainly longitudinally disposed and containing considerable elastic tissue and occasional longitudinal muscle fibers. The outer layer is more finely fibrillar and merges with the surrounding connective tissue.

DEVELOPMENT OF THE CIRCULATORY SYSTEM

Blood Vessels and Heart. The myocardium of the heart develops from bilaterally localized regions of splanchnic mesoderm. The endothelium of the heart and vessels differentiates from mesenchymal cells derived from mesoderm. The heart and the main trunks of its accompanying large vessels (e.g., aorta) develop independently of the peripheral vessels with which they unite later. While the heart develops within the embryo, the earliest vessels and earliest blood cells develop from extraembryonic mesenchyme. The earliest vessels have the structure of capillaries. They appear first near the periphery of the area vasculosa which surrounds the developing embryo. Here groups of cells known as *"blood islands"* differentiate from the rest of the mesenchymal cells, appearing in the chick by the end of the first day of incubation. The superficial cells of these islands become flattened to form the endothelium; and the central cells develop into the primitive blood cells. The channels, which are at first unconnected, anastomose and give rise to a network of channels which are the earliest capillaries. These develop rapidly in the area vasculosa, and some of them increase in size to become arteries and veins, the smooth muscle and connective tissue of their walls being differentiated from the surrounding mesenchyme. These grow toward, and finally into, the embryo where they unite with intraembryonic vessels which have developed from mesenchyme in situ. After a primary system of closed vessels has been established and after the embryonic circulation has been initiated, new vessels develop as outgrowths from preexisting vessels. New vessels arise by a similar method in the adult, e.g., the outgrowth of new vessels into granulation tissue.

The *heart* in the earliest human embryos (2 to 3 mm.) consists of an *endothelial tube* surrounded by a layer of splanchnic mesoderm which forms the *myoepicardial mantle*. The two layers are at first separated by a considerable space filled with a gelatinous fluid (cardiac jelly) and they are connected to each other only by occasional protoplasmic strands. As development proceeds, the two layers become firmly united, the endothelium now forming the lining of the myoepicardial mantle. The endothelium and its underlying connective tissue form the endocardium. From the myoepicardial mantle are formed both myocardium and epicardium.

Lymphatics. According to one view, the lymph vessels arise originally as evaginations or buddings from veins. By further sprouting of the original anlagen, the whole system of lymphatics is ultimately formed.

According to the more widely accepted view, the lymphatics first appear as tissue clefts in the mesenchyme. These clefts elongate and become dilated by pressure of accumulated fluid and finally fuse to form the primary lymph vessels which later on establish communication with the veins.

Whatever the primary origin, it is certain that, in later development, formation of lymph vessels takes place in large part by budding from the walls of already existing lymphatics.

REFERENCES

BENNETT, H. S., LUFT, J. H., AND HAMPTON, J. C. 1959 Morphological classification of vertebrate blood capillaries. Amer. J. Physiol., vol. 196, pp. 381–390.

BRUNS, R. R., AND PALADE, G. E. 1968 Studies of blood capillaries. I. General organization of blood capillaries in muscle. J. Cell Biol., vol. 37, pp. 244–276.

CHAMBERS, R., AND ZWEIFACH, B. W. 1944 Topography and function of the mesenteric capillary circulation. Amer. J. Anat., vol. 75, pp. 173–207.

CLARK, E. R. 1938 Arterio-venous anastomoses. Physiol. Rev., vol. 18, pp. 229–247.

CLARK, E. R., AND CLARK, E. L. 1935 Observations on changes in blood vascular endothelium in the living animal. Amer. J. Anat., vol. 57, pp. 385–438.

CLEMENTI, F., AND PALADE, G. E. 1969 Intestinal capillaries. I. Permeability to peroxidase and ferritin. J. Cell Biol., vol. 41, pp. 33–58.

COPENHAVER, W. M., AND TRUEX, R. C. 1952 Histology of the atrial portion of the cardiac conduction system in man and other mammals. Anat. Rec., vol. 114, pp. 601–626.

DAVIES, F. 1942 The conducting system of the vertebrate heart. Brit. Heart J., vol. 4, pp. 66–76.

DAVIES, F., AND FRANCIS, E. T. B. 1952 The conduction of the impulse for cardiac contraction. J. Anat., vol. 86, pp. 302–309.

FRENCH, J. E., FLOREY, H. W., AND MORRIS, B. 1960 The absorption of particles by the lymphatics of the diaphragm. Quart. J. Exp. Physiol., vol. 45, pp. 88–103.

HOFFMAN, B. F. 1961 Physiology of atrioventricular transmission. Circulation, vol. 24, pp. 506–517.

HOFFMAN, B. F. 1962 Electrophysiology of the conducting system of the heart. Trans. N. Y. Acad. Sci., vol. 24, pp. 886–890.

HOFFMAN, B. F. 1965 Atrioventricular conduction in mammalian hearts. *In* Comparative Cardiology (Hecht, H. H., and Detwiler, D. K., Conference Chairmen). Ann. N. Y. Acad. Sci., vol. 127, pp. 105–112.

HOGAN, P. M., AND DAVIS, L. D. 1968 Evidence for specialized fibers in the canine right atrium. Circ. Res., vol. 23, pp. 387–396.

HOLLINSHEAD, W. H. 1943 A cytological study of the carotid body of the cat. Amer. J. Anat., vol. 73, pp. 185–215.

JAMES, T. N., SHERF, L., FINE, G., AND MORALES, A. R. 1966 Comparative ultrastructure of the sinus node in man and dog. Circulation, vol. 34, pp. 139–163.

JAMES, T. N. 1967 Anatomy of the cardiac conduction system in the rabbit. Circ. Res., vol. 20, pp. 638–648.

KARNOVSKY, M. J. 1967 The ultrastructural basis of capillary permeability studied with peroxidase as a tracer. J. Cell Biol., vol. 35, pp. 213–236.

LANDIS, E. M. 1937 The passage of fluid through the capillary wall. Harvey Lectures, Ser. 32, pp. 70–91.

LANDIS, E. M., AND PAPPENHEIMER, J. R. 1963 Exchange of substances through the capillary walls. *In* Handbook of Physiology (Hamilton, W. F., and Dow, P., editors), sect. 2, vol. 2, pp. 961–1034. American Physiological Society, Washington, D. C.

LEAKE, L. V., AND BURKE, J. F. 1968 Ultrastructural studies on the lymphatic anchoring filaments. J. Cell Biol., vol. 36, pp. 129–149.

LHAMON, R. M. 1912 The sheath of the sino-ventricular bundle. Amer. J. Anat., vol. 13, pp. 55–70.

MAJNO, G., PALADE, G. E., AND SCHOEFL, G. I. 1961 Studies on inflammation. II. The site of action of histamine and serotonin along the vascular tree: a topographic study. J. Biophys. Biochem. Cytol., vol. 11, pp. 607–626.

MAJNO, G., SHEA, S. M., AND LEVENTHAL, M. 1969 Endothelial contraction induced by histamine-type mediators. An electron microscopic study. J. Cell Biol., vol. 42, pp. 647–672.

NONIDEZ, J. F. 1935 The aortic (depressor) nerve and its associated epithelioid body, the glomus aorticum. Amer. J. Anat., vol. 57, pp. 259–301.

PALADE, G. E. 1961 Blood capillaries of the heart and other organs. Circulation, vol. 24, pp. 368–384.

PALADE, G. E., AND BRUNS, R. R. 1968 Structural modulations of plasmalemmal vesicles. J. Cell Biol., vol. 37, pp. 633–649.

PAPPAS, G. D., AND TENNYSON, V. M. 1962 An electron microscope study of the passage of colloidal particles from the blood vessels of the ciliary processes and choroid plexus of the rabbit. J. Cell Biol., vol. 15, pp. 227–239.

PAPPENHEIMER, J. R. 1953 Passage of molecules through capillary walls. Physiol. Rev., vol. 33, pp. 387–423.

PHELPS, P. C., AND LUFT, J. H. 1969 Electron microscopical study of relaxation and constriction in frog arterioles. Amer. J. Anat., vol. 125, pp. 399–428.

REESE, T. S., AND KARNOVSKY, M. J. 1967 Fine structural localization of a blood-brain barrier to exogenous peroxidase. J. Cell Biol., vol. 34, pp. 207–217.

RHODIN, J. A. G. 1967 The ultrastructure of mammalian arterioles and precapillary sphincters. J. Ultrastruct. Res., vol. 18, pp. 181–223.

RHODIN, J. A. G. 1968 Ultrastructure of mammalian venous capillaries, venules, and small collecting veins. J. Ultrastruct. Res., vol. 25, pp. 452–500.

ROBB, J. S., HISS, F., AND ROBB, R. C. 1935 Localization of cardiac infarcts according to component ventricular muscles. Amer. Heart J., vol. 10, pp. 287–292.

SOMMER, J. R., AND JOHNSON, E. A. 1968 Cardiac muscle. A comparative study of Purkinje fibers and ventricular fibers. J. Cell Biol., vol. 36, pp. 497–526.

TRUEX, R. C. 1966 Anatomical considerations of the human atrioventricular junction. In Mechanisms and Therapy of Cardiac Arrythmias (Dreifus, L. S., and Likoff, W., editors), pp. 333–340. Grune & Stratton, Inc., New York.

TRUEX, R. C., AND COPENHAVER, W. M. 1947 Histology of the moderator band in man and other mammals, with special reference to the conduction system. Amer. J. Anat., vol. 80, pp. 173–201.

WALLS, E. N. 1945 Dissection of the atrioventricular node and bundle in the human heart. J. Anat., vol. 79, pp. 45–48.

WEARN, J. T. 1940 Morphological and functional alterations of the coronary circulation. Harvey Lectures, Ser. 35, pp. 243–269.

ZIMMERMAN, J., AND BAILEY, C. P. 1962 The surgical significance of the fibrous skeleton of the heart. J. Thorac. Cardiov. Surg., vol. 44, pp. 701–712.

13

Lymphatic Organs

LYMPHATIC TISSUE

Lymphatic (lymphoid) tissue is not one of the fundamental tissue types of the body but is merely a particular variety of connective tissue. It consists of a framework of reticular cells and reticular fibers infiltrated with lymphocytes. In many parts of the body, such as the gastrointestinal and respiratory tracts, some of the so-called lymphatic tissue is not sharply outlined from the surrounding connective tissues, and the lymphocytes are not packed closely together. This is often spoken of as diffuse lymphatic tissue, in contrast with the denser form (*lymphatic nodules* or *follicles*) in which the lymphocytes are densely aggregated. Various gradations exist between these two types and also between lymphatic tissue and an infiltration of lymphocytes into the connective and epithelial tissues of the mucosa. The lymphocytes that are dispersed in small groups within the connective tissues are readily identified in sections by their small, dense staining, and uniformly-rounded nuclei.

The more or less circumscribed, spherical aggregations of densely packed lymphocytes forming the *lymphatic nodules* have been called the structural units of lymphatic tissue. Each nodule may contain a lighter staining central area, the *germinal center*. The solitary nodules or follicles of the intestinal tract are examples of isolated lymphatic nodules. The lymphatic nodules may also be found in aggregations in definitely encapsulated organs having a characteristic lymphatic and blood vascular system as in the lymph nodes. Nodules may also be aggregated into less highly organized structures that are intermediate in complexity between the isolated nodules and the lymph nodes. The nonencapsulated aggregations forming the Peyer's patches of the intestine and the partially encapsulated aggregations forming the tonsils are examples of this intermediate type. The various circumscribed aggregations of lymphatic tissue forming the lymphatic organs include the lymph nodes, tonsils, thymus and spleen.

The chief characteristic common to all lymphatic organs is the presence of large numbers of lymphocytes in a stroma of reticular cells and fibers. The lymph nodes are the only lymphoid or lymphatic organs which are located in the course of lymphatic vessels; that is, they are the only ones that have both afferent and efferent lymphatic vessels. They are also the only ones that contain lymphatic sinuses, and they are the only structures for filtering the lymph. The spleen, thymus and tonsils resemble most other organs in their relationship to lymphatic vessels. They have efferent lymph vessels draining from them, but they have neither afferent lymphatic vessels nor lymphatic sinuses.

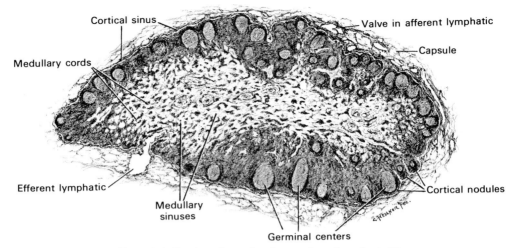

FIG. 13-1. Section through a human lymph node. ×10

THE LYMPH NODES

The lymph nodes are variable in number but are more or less constantly found in certain definite regions of the body such as the mesentery, axilla and groin. Frequently they are found in groups or in a series, as in the inguinal and axillary regions. They vary considerably in size, ranging from very minute bodies to as much as 1 inch in length. They are usually oval or bean-shaped, with an indentation, the *hilum*, on one side where the blood vessels enter and leave the node. The lymphatic vessels coming from the node, the *vasa efferentia*, are also found at the hilum, but the entering vessels, the *vasa afferentia*, are found at various points along the convex surface of the node.

Lymph nodes are covered by a very definite *capsule* of connective tissue. At its outer surface, the capsule blends with the surrounding connective tissue, and in this way the organ is attached in position. The capsule consists of rather closely packed bundles of white fibrous connective tissue and scattered elastic fibers, which are more numerous in its inner layer. A few smooth muscle fibers can be found in the capsule around the points of entrance and exit of lymphatic vessels. At the hilum, there is a depression where the capsule is thickened and extends deep into the node. At various points over the surface of the node, the capsule gives off septa or *trabeculae* that extend into the substance of the organ. Both the trabeculae of connective tissue and the elements of the lymphatic tissue are arranged differently in the outer or cortical and the inner or medullary part of the node.

The Cortex. In the cortex, the trabeculae are more or less perpendicular to the surface, and they partly subdivide this region into compartments (Figs. 13-1 and 13-2) which are continuous centrally with the more irregularly arranged anastomosing subdivisions of the medulla. The cortical compartments also communicate laterally with each other through spaces between the trabeculae. The degree of development of the trabeculae and of separation into compartments varies in nodes taken from different parts of the body and in nodes of different animals. In some of the other mammals (e.g., ox), the trabeculae are more highly developed and they more definitely mark off compartments than in man.

In the cortical compartments, most of the lymphocytes are closely packed together to form *cortical nodules* (*cortical follicles, primary nodules*) which are continuous

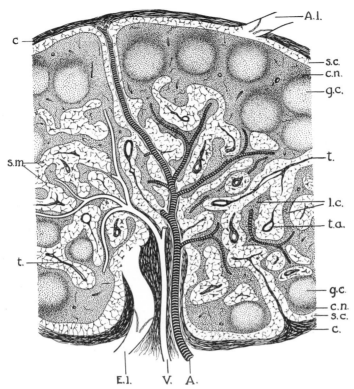

FIG. 13-2. Diagram of a lymph node. *A.*, artery, entering at hilum; *A.l.*, afferent lymphatic with valve; *c*, capsule; *c.n.*, cortical nodules; *E.l.*, efferent lymphatic with valve; *g.c.*, germinal centers (secondary nodules); *l.c.*, lymph cords of medulla; *s.c.*, lymph sinus of cortex; *s.m.*, lymph sinuses of medulla; *t*, trabeculae; *t.a.*, artery in trabecula; *V*, vein, leaving node at hilum. (Modified after a drawing by M. Heidenhain, from Heudorfer.)

centrally with the cords of lymphatic tissue found in the medulla. When the cortical areas are well separated by trabeculae, the lymphatic nodules are more or less spheroidal or pear-shaped as shown in Figure 13-6, *D*, but when trabeculae are not well developed, the cortical nodules are more irregular in shape and are frequently continuous with each other laterally, forming a more continuous mass of lymphatic tissue as shown in Figures 13-1 and 13-2.

The cortical nodules often contain lighter staining central areas known by the following names: *germinal centers*, *secondary nodules* and *reaction centers*. The region was named a germinal center because it was once thought that its chief function was lymphocyte formation. It is recognized

now that lymphocytes also develop in other areas of the node and that the centers have additional important functions. The name secondary nodule indicates that the centers are located within the primary nodules. The term reaction center was applied to the areas when it was found that they contain numerous free macrophages during certain pathological conditions. The centers vary in their activity at different ages and under different physiological conditions. They may contribute at certain times to the origin of new lymphoblasts from undifferentiated reticular cells, whereas at other times they may have numerous macrophages in reaction to foreign material. The centers do not appear until after birth, they are numerous during childhood and they decline in number

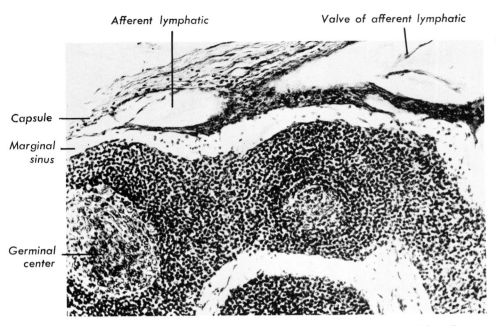

Fig. 13-3. Portion of cortex of human lymph node. Photomicrograph. ×260. (After Petersen.)

and activity with age. There is substantial evidence that they appear in response to antigens and that they disappear in the absence of antigens. They reappear in the same regions after subsequent stimulation from antigens. When animals are placed in a germ-free environment at the time of birth, germinal centers fail to develop. They also remain relatively inactive in animals thymectomized at birth.

The central region of the germinal center stains lighter than does its marginal region because of the combined effects of its component cells as follows: (1) it has undifferentiated reticular cells in which both nucleus and cytoplasm stain lightly; (2) it has activated reticular cells or macrophages that are not particularly basophilic; and (3) it has large lymphocytes (lymphoblasts) which have large, pale staining nuclei that counteract the overall effect of their basophilic cytoplasm. The marginal zone contains numerous closely packed, small lymphocytes which have nuclei with coarse and deeply staining chromatin as well as basophilic cytoplasm. Although some of the small

lymphocytes of the marginal zone may arise by multiplication of the larger cells of the central region, their chief source is apparently recirculating lymphocytes which enter this area from the blood vessels. The recirculation of lymphocytes is described in Chapter 7.

The cortical nodules are separated from the capsule and trabeculae by channel-like spaces, *lymphatic sinuses*, through which the lymph circulates. The peripheral or marginal sinus (Figs. 13-2 and 13-3) between the capsule and the nodules receives the lymph from the afferent lymphatics. From the peripheral sinus the lymph flows centrally through sinuses, passing around the nodules to enter the sinuses of the medulla.

Although the cortical tissue is usually found completely surrounding the medulla except at the hilum, it varies considerably in thickness. At times it may extend for a considerable depth into the node, while at other times medullary substance may approach the surface more closely. Frequently the cortical nodules form a single layer at the periphery but, where the cortex

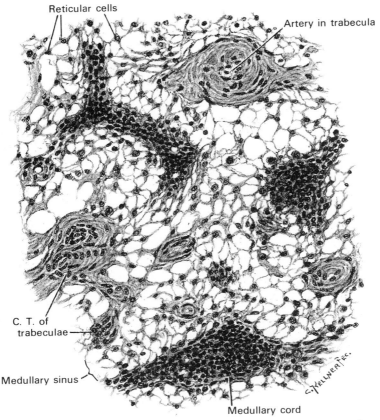

Reticular cells

Artery in trabecula

C. T. of trabeculae

Medullary sinus

Medullary cord

Fig. 13-4. A portion of the medulla of a human lymph node, showing arrangement of connective tissue (*c.t.*) trabeculae, lymph cords and medullary sinuses. ×290.

is thickened, they may be found in layers and be more deeply situated.

Medulla. The cytological components of the medulla and cortex are very similar except for the difference in arrangement. Contrasted with the more regular arrangement in the cortex, the trabeculae in the medulla are very irregularly arranged and they anastomose frequently. The lymphocytes are not aggregated in the form of nodules as they are in the cortex, but are arranged as anastomosing cords, *medullary cords*, which course through the communicating divisions outlined by the meshwork of trabeculae (Figs. 13-2 and 13-4). Lymphatic sinuses, which are relatively broad and numerous in the medulla, separate the medullary cords and trabeculae at all points.

The relationship of these three parts—dense lymphatic tissue, sinuses and trabeculae—is therefore similar throughout the node.

Components of Lymphatic Tissue. The lymphatic tissue of the node consists of reticular cells and fibers, which form the framework or stroma, and free cells contained in the meshwork. The reticular meshwork (Fig. 13-4) extends throughout the node, although it varies in density in different parts. Its reticular fibers are continuous with the collagenous fibers of the trabeculae. Its reticular cells have an irregular shape with processes often in apposition, and they have pale staining nuclei with very little chromatin (Fig. 13-5). They form a part of the reticuloendothelial system (Chapter 5). They readily take up vital

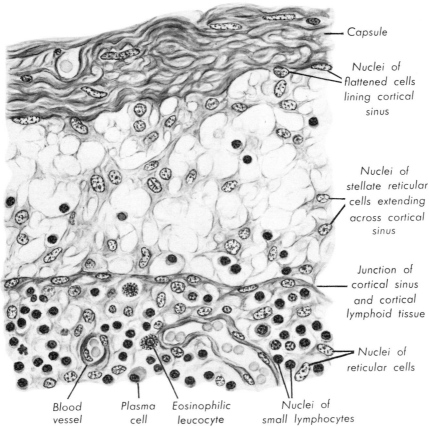

Fig. 13-5. A portion of the cortex of a human lymph node showing cortical (marginal) lymphatic sinus and adjacent dense cortical lymphatic tissue. ×725.

dyes such as trypan blue and normally may be found with engulfed materials such as degenerated lymphocytes. They may become detached from adjoining cells of the network and assume a more rounded form as free macrophages. The reticulum also contains some cells that remain free of phagocytosed material, even after prolonged vital staining (Maximow). These cells are supposed to be less differentiated than the more numerous phagocytic cells of the reticulum. By proliferation, the undifferentiated cells give rise to daughter cells which may follow any one of the following courses: some remain undifferentiated as a reserve line, while others differentiate into phagocytic cells and still others into lymphocytes.

The majority of the free cells are lymphocytes. Free macrophages and plasma cells are also fairly numerous. Various types of granulocytes which have migrated from the blood vessels are found in small numbers. Occasionally a few red blood cells may be found which have escaped from the blood vessels by diapedesis. Usually they are soon engulfed by the macrophages.

The lymphocytes of the node consist of small, medium sized and large forms. These same types, which are also found in the other lymphatic organs, are illustrated in a germinal center of the spleen (Fig. 13-23). The small lymphocytes are the most numerous and are the typical lymphocytes of adult blood and lymph. They are found throughout the node but are especially numerous and closely packed at the periphery of the germinal centers. The medium sized lymphocytes contain more cytoplasm than do the small ones, and their nuclei contain finer chromatin and are lighter staining. In structure as well as in size, they are intermediate between the small and large lymphocytes. The large lymphocytes are not as numerous as the other forms. They may be found throughout the node but are present more consistently in the germinal centers. They may be as much as 15 or 20 μ in diameter. They have a wider zone of cytoplasm which is more basophilic than that of the small lymphocyte on account of its greater content of RNA. The nucleus is quite different from that of the small lymphocyte: it is larger and lighter staining, and it contains one or more large nucleoli (Fig. 7-14). The medium sized and large lymphocytes are frequently found in stages of mitosis. Evidence also indicates that the small lymphocytes, which seldom undergo mitosis as such, may hypertrophy and change into large and medium sized lymphocytes which do divide. There is evidence that this may also occur with the small lymphocytes which have returned to the lymphatic tissues after circulation in the blood stream. In addition to the proliferation of preexisting lymphocytes, which occurs throughout the node, lymphocytes also form in the germinal centers from the undifferentiated cells of the reticulum.

The cell that has been described as the large lymphocyte of the lymph node is often called a "lymphoblast." It is a stage in the development of small lymphocytes. According to the dualistic and polyphyletic theories of blood development, the lymphoblast is differentiated to such an extent that it cannot develop into any blood cells other than lymphocytes. On the other hand, as described in Chapter 7, the monophyletic or unitarian theory of blood development holds to the view that the so-called lymphoblast is really a hemocytoblast and that it retains the potency to differentiate into all types of blood cells. Whatever its potential, the lymphoblast is usually found only in blood-forming organs under normal conditions. However, it occurs in considerable numbers in circulating blood under certain pathological conditions, e.g., lymphatic leukemia.

Lymphatic Vessels and Sinuses. The afferent lymphatic vessels pierce the capsule on the convex side of the node and open into the marginal or peripheral sinus. The lymph circulates slowly through the sinuses of the cortex and medulla, which afford a greatly enlarged area for the circulating lymph, as compared with the afferent vessels. From the medullary sinuses, a plexus of vessels arises which penetrates the connective tissue of the hilum and forms the efferent lymphatic vessels. The efferent lymphatic vessels are usually wider but less numerous than the afferent vessels. The afferents possess valves which open toward the node, while the efferent lymphatics have valves which open outward from the node.

In the walls of the sinuses there are flattened cells (Fig. 13-5), sometimes described as endothelium, which become continuous at the periphery of the node with the endothelial cells lining the afferent and efferent lymphatic vessels. Like the cells lining the venous sinuses of the spleen, they differ from the ordinary endothelial cells of blood and lymph vessels. They have many similarities to reticular cells and are classified by most authors as flattened reticular cells rather than as endothelium. They are associated with reticular fibers and are joined with the network of reticular cells of the medullary cords and cortical nodules and also with the cells and fibers which bridge the sinuses. They are very phagocytic and belong to the reticuloendothelial system (Chapter 5).

Blood Vessels. An artery enters the lymph node at the hilum and gives off some branches that go directly to the medullary cords of lymphatic tissue, whereas other branches enter the trabeculae (Fig. 13-2). The branches entering the medullary cords, giving off capillaries along the way, continue into the cortex, where an arterial branch penetrates each cortical nodule and breaks up into diverging capillaries to form a plexus around the germinal center and the peripheral part of the nodule. The arteries entering the trabeculae supply the trabecular connective tissue and continue into the capsule. They also give off branches which cross the medullary sinuses to join in the supply of the medullary cords and cortical nodules. From the capillaries the blood is collected into veins that follow the same general course as the arteries and leave the node at the hilum.

Nerves. The nerves, which are not abundant, enter the node at the hilum and accompany the blood vessels. Some of them terminate in the trabeculae and capsule, while others form perivascular networks that follow the vessels into the lymphatic tissue.

Functions. One of the functions of lymph nodes is the production of lymphocytes. The lymph of the efferent vessels contains many more lymphocytes than does that of the afferent vessels. The smallest lymphatic vessels, whose lymph has not yet passed through any lymph nodes, contain very few lymphocytes. The lymphocytes found in the efferent lymphatic vessels consist partly of cells newly formed in the node and partly of recirculating lymphocytes which enter the node via the blood vessels and afferent lymphatic vessels. Lymphocytes also leave the node by way of blood vessels, in addition to the large numbers leaving by the efferent lymphatic vessels.

As already pointed out, the lymph nodes contain numerous phagocytic reticular cells and free macrophages. In this way the nodes act as filters to remove degenerating cells and other particulate matter from the lymph. The bronchial lymph nodes are good examples of this function. Inhaled carbon particles are removed in the lungs and eventually reach the bronchial lymph nodes, where they are found accumulated in phagocytic cells, especially in the medullary sinuses. Eventually, such accumulations become very extensive and blacken the entire node. Since the lymphatic capillaries

that lead to the afferent vessels are permeable to large molecules and even to entire cells, the sinuses of lymph nodes may contain erythrocytes that escaped from blood vessels into surrounding tissues by internal hemorrhage. They may also contain cancer cells transported via their afferent lymphatics from areas of malignancy.

One of the major functions of lymph nodes is the production of antibodies. This is a subject of active investigation, and numerous details of the mechanism of antibody formation are still unresolved. However, recent research has provided a much better understanding of some of the intercellular reactions involved. There are various ways in which antigens may be handled by the body. Some may be excreted, some may be taken up by macrophages and be subjected to degradative enzymes and some may be trapped by adherence to reticular cells within the nodules (follicles) of the lymph nodes and spleen. The trapped antigen apparently undergoes some type of processing. It has been proposed that *antigen-reactive lymphocytes* which come in contact with the trapped and processed antigen are stimulated to divide and to manufacture something that stimulates other lymphocytes to develop into plasma cells that form a specific antibody to the particular antigen (see review by Nossal, 1968). The antibody-forming plasma cells are nondividing end stages, whereas some of the antigen-reactive lymphocytes survive as the cells with immunological memory.

Development. The first indications of lymph node formation are found in the axilla and groin, toward the end of the third month of development. In connective tissue closely associated with plexuses of lymphatic vessels, condensations of mesenchymal cells occur around capillary loops, as shown in Figure 13-6, *A*. Since the cellular condensation is very vascular from the beginning, it is difficult to determine with certainty whether the lymphocytes migrate from the blood vessels or whether they develop in situ from the mesenchymal cells, although the latter is now the generally accepted manner of origin. In addition to lymphatic plexuses which are in continuity from

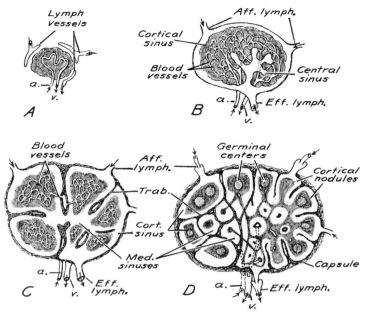

FIG. 13-6. Diagrams illustrating stages in the development of a lymph node. *A*, early stage, showing aggregation of lymphatic tissue around a capillary loop and surrounded by a plexus of lymphatic vessels; *B*, *C*, and *D*, later stages showing development of sinuses, etc. *a*, artery; *Aff. lymph.*, afferent lymphatics; *Cort. sinus*, cortical sinus; *Eff. lymph.*, efferent lymphatics; *Med. sinus*, medullary sinuses; *v*, vein. (Slightly modified after Braus.)

the beginning with lymphatics that become the afferent and efferent vessels, there are apparently other blind or isolated lymph spaces that develop in situ in the mesenchyme. The isolated lymph spaces and the different parts of the plexuses gradually all fuse together to form lymph sinuses. The marginal or peripheral sinus forms first (Fig. 13-6, *B*). From the marginal sinus, subdivisions penetrate centrally into the lymphatic tissue as central sinuses (Fig. 13-6, *B*), which subdivide and eventually form a system of anastomosing sinuses throughout the node (Fig. 13-6, *C*, *D*). The connective tissue outside the marginal sinus becomes thickened to form the capsule. From the capsule, projections of connective tissue extend into the marginal sinus and later into the other sinuses to form the trabeculae. The trabeculae penetrate the central parts of the sinuses and always remain separated from the lymphoid tissue by the sinuses.

HEMOLYMPH NODES

In certain animals, structures have been described that are very similar to lymph nodes, except that afferent and efferent lymphatic vessels are absent and the sinuses contain blood instead of lymph. True hemal

nodes of this type occur in the sheep. In the pig, hemolymph nodes have been described which have sinuses connected with both lymphatic and blood vessels, and so they appear to be intermediate between lymph nodes and the hemal nodes of sheep. In man, the occurrence of organs of this type has been questioned and seems very doubtful. Normal lymph nodes usually contain a few red blood cells, some of which may have been brought in by the afferent lymphatics, while others probably enter from the blood vessels within the node by diapedesis. It is true that nodes may be found in man with considerable numbers of red blood cells, but there have been no descriptions of connections between the sinuses and the blood vessels. It seems very probable that the presence of an unusual number of erythrocytes may be the result of hemorrhage from vessels either within the node or in the neighborhood of the afferent lymphatics.

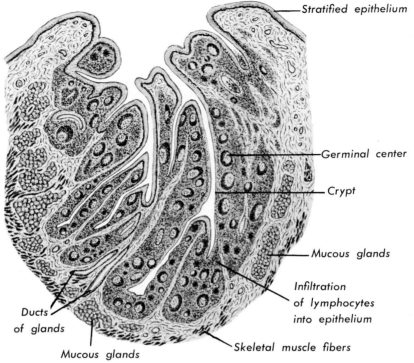

Fig. 13-7. Section through the palatine tonsil of man. ×9

THE TONSILS

The Palatine Tonsils. The palatine tonsils are paired, oval-shaped bodies located in the oropharynx between the glossopalatine and pharyngopalatine arches. They consist of dense accumulations of lymphatic tissue in the connective tissue of the mucosa. They are covered on their free surface by a stratified squamous epithelium which is continuous with the epithelium of the rest of the pharynx. This epithelium has the same structure as elsewhere in the pharynx: flat surface cells, beneath which are irregular cells, while the deepest cells are cuboidal or more or less columnar and rest upon a basement membrane. A very thin layer of fibrous connective tissue with papillae is usually found between the basement membrane and the underlying lymphatic tissue. At various places on the surface of the tonsil, deep indentations or pockets occur. These depressions, 10 to 20 in number, are known

as the *crypts* of the tonsil (Fig. 13-7) and are lined by a continuation of the surface epithelium that becomes thinner as the deeper part of the crypt is reached. Passing off from the bottoms and sides of the main or primary crypts are frequently several secondary crypts, also lined with the same type of epithelium.

Surrounding each crypt there is a zone of varying thickness, consisting of a rather diffuse lymphatic tissue in which are embedded *nodules* of compact lymphatic tissue similar to those of the lymph nodes. The nodules are frequently more or less fused together. The nodules, like those of lymph nodes, may contain *germinal centers* that consist of a lighter staining central area and a surrounding zone of more closely packed cells.

There is a *capsule* of connective tissue over the attached or basal surface of the lymphatic tissue which is firmly adherent

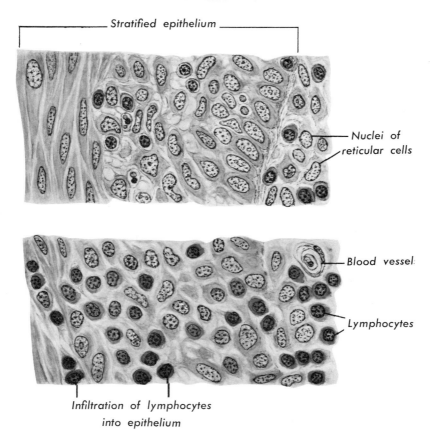

Stratified epithelium

Nuclei of reticular cells

Blood vessel

Lymphocytes

Infiltration of lymphocytes into epithelium

FIG. 13-8. Two fields from different depths along the crypts of a human tonsil. The squamous epithelial cells, facing the lumen of the crypt, are toward the *left*. The *upper figure* shows only slight lymphocytic infiltration of the epithelium. The *lower figure* shows an extensive infiltration that makes it difficult to distinguish the junction of epithelium and underlying connective tissue. ×932.

on the one side to the tonsillar tissue and on the other to the surrounding structures from which it separates the tonsils. From the capsule there are *septa* of loose connective tissue that separate the various crypts with their surrounding zones of lymphatic tissue from one another. Infiltrated into this connective tissue are various sized lymphocytes, plasma cells, mast cells and, frequently, neutrophil leukocytes.

At various points on the surface of the tonsil, and especially in the crypts, there occurs what is known as *lymphocytic infiltration of the epithelium* (Fig. 13-8). This consists of an invasion of the epithelium by the underlying lymphocytes. It varies

from only a few lymphocytes scattered in the epithelium to an almost complete replacement of epithelium by lymphocytes. In this way, the latter reach the surface and are discharged into the crypts. These cells probably form the bulk of the so-called salivary corpuscles. Surface regions of tonsillar tissue may also contain cells with polymorphic nuclei (Kingsbury, 1945). These cells differ from the blood neutrophils, since their cytoplasm usually lacks granules. They may arise from lymphocytoid (mononuclear) cells either through partial nuclear fragmentation or through differentiation from a "blast" stage. In inflammation, the tonsillar tissue also contains numerous polymorphonuclear neutrophilic leukocytes which emigrate from the blood.

Small mucous glands, similar to those found in other parts of the pharynx, are numerous in the connective tissue adjacent to the tonsil. The bodies of these glands are separated from the tonsils by the capsule. Their excretory ducts usually open on the free surface, but occasionally they may open into the tonsillar crypts.

The Lingual Tonsils. These are spherical aggregations of lymphatic tissue situated on the dorsum and sides of the back part of the tongue between the circumvallate papillae and the epiglottis (Fig. 16-4). They contain rather wide-mouthed, deep crypts which may be branched and which are lined with a continuation of the surface stratified squamous epithelium. As in the palatine tonsils, each crypt is surrounded by an aggregation of lymph nodules containing distinct germinal centers, or secondary nodules. In most crypts, there is marked lymphoid infiltration of the epithelium with free salivary corpuscles. Ducts of some of the mucous glands of the tongue frequently open into the crypts (Fig. 16-5).

The Pharyngeal Tonsil. There is a median aggregation of lymphatic tissue in the posterior wall of the nasopharynx which forms the pharyngeal tonsil. The lymphatic tissue is similar to that of the palatine tonsils. The epithelium over the free surface, as is characteristic for the nasopharynx and other respiratory passages, is largely pseudostratified columnar ciliated. There are patches of stratified squamous epithelium, which become more numerous in the adult. Hypertrophy of the pharyngeal tonsil, with consequent obstruction of the nasal openings, is common, especially in children, constituting what are known as adenoids.

Blood Vessels of Tonsils. These have a distribution similar to that of the blood vessels of the lymph nodes, but they enter the organ along its entire attached side and not at a definite hilum.

Lymphatic Vessels. The tonsils have no afferent lymphatic vessels and no lymph sinuses. At the peripheral surface of the lymphatic tissue, there are plexuses of lymph capillaries which form the beginnings of efferent lymphatic vessels. The tonsils, therefore, unlike the lymph nodes which are situated in the course of lymphatic vessels, are situated at the beginnings of lymphatic vessels.

Nerves. The nerves of the palatine tonsils are derived from the glossopharyngeal nerve and from the sphenopalatine ganglion, and they enter the organ along its attached side.

Functions. The mitoses in the germinal centers show that the tonsils participate in the development of lymphocytes. The lymphatic tissue of the tonsils, along with that of other parts of the digestive tract, is believed to aid in some manner in the destruction of microorganisms and to have a local detoxifying action. The tonsils apparently aid in the protection of the body. On the other hand, the deep tonsillar crypts, which are often imperfectly lined by epithelium, can serve as regions where microorganisms invade and proliferate, leading to general infections.

Development. The palatine tonsils make their first appearance during the third month of development. Evaginations of entoderm begin to grow down into the underlying mesenchyme at the site of the second entodermal pouch and, at the same time, there is a subepithelial condensation of mesenchyme. The cells of the inner part of the mesenchymal condensation become arranged around the epithelium of the evaginations and gradually develop the reticulum and lymphocytes of the lymphatic tissue, while the entodermal evaginations become the crypts of the tonsil. At the outer part of the mesenchymal condensation, fibrous connective tissue develops, to form the capsule separating the lymphatic tissue from the underlying structures.

The lingual and pharyngeal tonsils begin their development during the later months of fetal life. In the pharyngeal tonsil, definite nodules appear at about the time of birth or during the first or second year. In the lingual tonsil, the nodules are not fully formed until the fifth or sixth year.

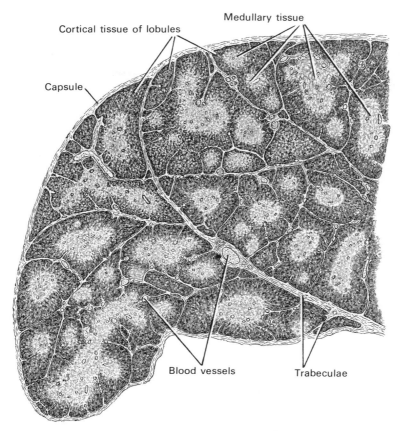

Cortical tissue of lobules

Medullary tissue

Capsule

Blood vessels

Trabeculae

Fig. 13-9. Section through a part of the human thymus at birth. ×12

THE THYMUS

The thymus varies in size and development with the age of the individual. It grows very rapidly until the end of the second year, after which there is a much slower growth and only a slight increase in weight until about the 12th to the 14th year. Following this, the thymus begins to decrease in size (undergoes "age involution") and gradually becomes replaced by fat and connective tissue until in old age very little thymic tissue is left. (Compare Figures 13-9 and 13-10.)

As a rule, the thymus consists of two lobes which are closely applied to each other and joined in the midline by connective tissue. The lobes are surrounded by a connective tissue *capsule*, which gives off numerous *septa* that partially subdivide each lobe into many lobules (Fig. 13-9). Each lobule consists of a *cortex* and a *medulla*. In random sections, some of the lobules appear to be completely separated from adjacent lobules, and the medulla appears to be entirely surrounded by the cortex. From a study of serial sections it can be seen that, at least until involution is well advanced, the lobules are only partially separated and that, by means of medullary cords, the medullary tissue is continuous from one lobule to another throughout each lobe.

The cortex consists of a compact, dense lymphatic tissue in which the reticular cells are obscured by the abundance of closely packed free cells. The latter, sometimes called thymocytes, seem to be identical with small lymphocytes. The lymphatic tissue, unlike that of the lymph nodes, is not ar-

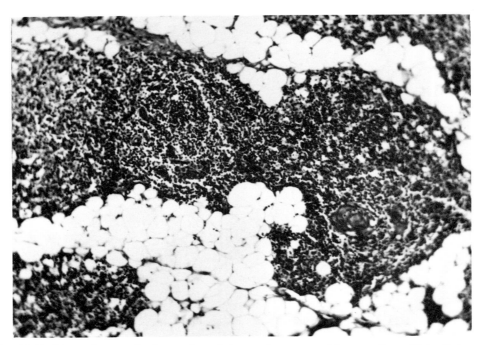

Fig. 13-10. Photomicrograph of a portion of thymus from a man 36 years of age. Note that portions of the organ have undergone involution and have been replaced by fat. ×110.

ranged in nodules and, although mitoses occur, there are no germinal centers.

The fetal thymus contains lymphocytes before its blood supply is established, and this indicates that the earliest thymic lymphocytes arise locally. Some investigators believe that the thymic lymphocytes differentiate from entodermal-derived reticular cells but this has not been substantiated. Most of the evidence indicates that the earliest thymic lymphocytes are derived from lymphocytic precursors which appear in the mesenchyme around the primordial thymus and subsequently migrate into the thymic parenchyma where they undergo further differentiation. In late fetal and postnatal life, many lymphocytes enter the thymus via the blood vessels. It appears that these are derived chiefly from bone marrow. The lymphocytes proliferate at a high rate within the thymus. Some of these leave by way of the blood vessels to circulate to other lymphatic organs, but large numbers also degenerate within the thymus. The func-

tional significance of the rapid degeneration of cells within the thymus is not clear.

In the medulla, the thymocytes or lymphocytes are less numerous and not so closely packed together. The medulla contains a number of spherical or oval bodies which are composed of concentrically arranged cells (Fig. 13-11). These bodies are known as *thymic corpuscles* (*Hassall's corpuscles*). They are characteristic of the thymus. Their average diameter in the fully developed thymus is from 20 to 50 μ, but they vary considerably in size, and much smaller as well as much larger corpuscles may be found. The cells composing the corpuscles are polygonal or flattened. They are concentrically arranged, and frequently hyalinized, and they take a bright red stain with hematoxylin-eosin. In the center of the corpuscle, the cells may be completely degenerated, whereas at the periphery some of the cells usually retain protoplasmic contacts with cells of the surrounding reticulum.

The reticular connective tissue of the thy-

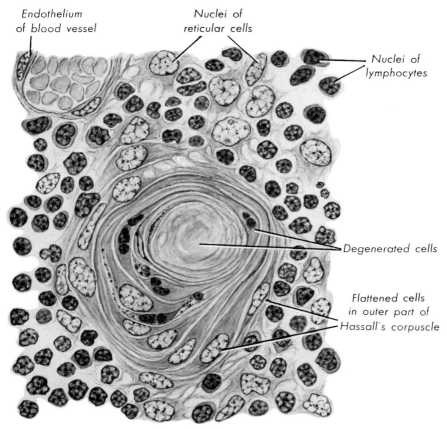

Endothelium
of blood vessel

Nuclei of
reticular cells

Nuclei of
lymphocytes

Degenerated cells

Flattened cells
in outer part of
Hassall's corpuscle

FIG. 13-11. Portion of medulla of thymus at birth, showing Hassall's corpuscle. ×1134

mus differs in some respects from that of other lymphatic organs. Reticular fibers are sparse and are found chiefly around blood vessels. The reticular cells have an unusual origin, arising from entoderm rather than from mesenchyme. They constitute a special strain of cells, and they maintain themselves by mitotic divisions. They are large cells of irregular shape and resemble other reticular cells in that they have pale staining nuclei (Fig. 13-11). However, in tissue culture preparations from the thymus, the reticular cells reassume epithelioid characteristics in keeping with their entodermal origin. These epithelial reticular cells of the thymus do not phagocytose colloidal dyes (e.g., trypan blue) as readily as other reticular cells do, but this may be due to a lack of escape of colloidal dyes from the blood vessels in the

thymus. The capillaries of the thymus are unusually competent (Weiss, 1963). They have a complete endothelium, a thick basement membrane and an encircling layer of reticular cells. This may not constitute a blood-thymus barrier equal to the blood-brain barrier, but it does seem that the thymus is isolated from corporal factors to a greater degree than other lymphatic organs are.

In addition to lymphocytes and epithelial-derived reticular cells in different stages of activity, the thymus contains some free macrophages, plasma cells and mast cells. The latter are found chiefly in the connective tissue of the septa and capsule.

Blood Vessels. The blood vessels supplying the thymus are branches of the internal mammary and inferior thyroid arteries. The larger vessels follow the connective tissue septa and give off branches that penetrate the cortex of the lobules and break up into capillary networks in the cortex and medulla. The medulla is more vascular than the cortex. The capillaries collect into thin walled veins in the medullary tissue, which converge to form larger veins that pass into the connective tissue septa to accompany the arteries. They empty into the left innominate and thyroid veins.

Lymphatics. There are no lymph sinuses. Lymphatic vessels are not found penetrating the lymphoid tissue. They arise around the lymphoid tissue of the lobules and fuse to form larger vessels that accompany the arteries in the connective tissue septa.

Nerves. The nerves are branches of the vagus and cervical sympathetics. They are distributed mainly to the walls of the blood vessels. A few fine fibers, terminating freely in the lymphatic tissue of the cortex and medulla, have been described.

Functions. The thymus is a very active center of lymphocyte proliferation during fetal and early postnatal life. This has important significance in relation to the function of lymphocytes in the other lymphatic organs. Insight into the function of the thymus has been aided particularly by studies of the effects of thymectomy of newborn animals (Miller, 1962, and others). Mice thymectomized on the first day after birth develop a wasting disease within a few months that gradually leads to their death. There is a marked deficiency in the development of the other lymphatic organs, with few or no germinal centers, and there is evidence of a general lack of development of the mechanism for immunity. The thymectomized mice accept skin grafts from other strains of mice and from rats, whereas normal mice reject foreign grafts. When thymectomized animals are given injections of lymphatic tissue from other strains and species, the injected cells react against the host, whereas normal animals reject foreign cells. Although results of thymectomy in other species, e.g., rats and hamsters, show some minor varia-

tions from findings in mice concerning the degree of deficiency in the other lymphatic organs, they support the conclusion that the thymus regulates the development of the immune mechanism.

It was proposed at first that thymectomized animals fail to develop a mechanism for immunity because their lymphatic organs lack colonizing cells from the thymus. In further studies which appeared to support this view, it was found that implantation of thymic tissue (lymphocytes and thymic reticular cells) into thymectomized animals restores the ability for forming antibody. However, still further studies showed that thymectomized animals also regain their antibody-forming function when the thymic implants are enclosed in Millipore filters, which prevent the escape of cells. On this basis, it was proposed that a humoral factor from the thymus is sufficient to stimulate the immunological mechanism in the lymphatic organs. It has been pointed out earlier that lymphocytes developing in the thymus plus bone marrow-derived lymphocytes sojourning in the thymus do circulate to the other lymphatic organs. Thus, there is evidence that the thymus exerts an influence on the other lymphatic organs both by a migration of cells and by humoral factors, but many of the details remain obscure. It should be noted that the thymus itself does not form antibodies and does not have germinal centers, and that it has a partial blood-thymic barrier. It has been suggested that the thymus, in addition to stimulating the development of the immunological mechanism, maintains a pool of noncommitted cells that are available whenever the body is exposed to a new antigen.

The thymus has some interrelationships with the gonads, adrenals and thyroids. As stated earlier, the thymus reaches its greatest development during childhood and begins to undergo some involution at the time of puberty. When the gonads are removed from experimental animals, thymic involution is delayed. Thyroidectomy hastens involution, while adrenalectomy not only delays involution but brings about some thymic regeneration.

Development. The thymus arises as a paired entodermal outgrowth from the median and ventral portions of the third pair of pharyngeal pouches. Each outgrowth contains a narrow, cleft-like lumen at first, but this is soon obliterated by proliferation of the epithelial cells. In the thymus, most of the reticular cells are derived from epithelial cells and not from mesenchyme as in the other lymphatic organs. Transformation of epithelial cells into a reticulum begins at about the end of the second month in the central portion of the outgrowth. In this transformation, the epithelial cells become more loosely arranged and form protoplasmic contacts. Small thymic cells similar to small lymphocytes also appear at about this same time. Although there are different theories with regard to the origin of the thymic lymphocytes, most investigators support the view that these cells arise from mesenchyme rather than from the entodermal (epithelial) cells. Studies of thymic glands fixed at successive stages of development show that lymphocytes are present in the mesenchyme around the gland earlier than in the parenchyma. In embryos 50 to 60 mm. in length, the medulla begins to become differentiated from the cortex as the lymphocytes become more densely aggregated in the peripheral regions of the gland and less numerous at the center. At about this same time, the lobules begin to form and become separated by the septa of connective tissue. As already stated, the connective tissue septa subdivide the cortical tissue but do not completely subdivide the medullary tissue.

Hassall's corpuscles make their first appearance during the first half of fetal life. At first they are few in number and small in size, but they increase rapidly in diameter, and new ones continue to form until the time when thymic involution begins. Hassall's corpuscles apparently are formed from hypertrophic and degenerating entodermal reticular cells.

THE SPLEEN

The spleen is the largest lymphatic organ in the body. Unlike the lymph nodes, however, it has no afferent lymphatic vessels and no lymph sinuses.

Except at the hilum, the spleen is covered by a serous membrane, the peritoneum. Beneath this is a *capsule* of fibrous tissue containing numerous elastic fibers and some smooth muscle. From the capsule (Figs. 13-12 and 13-13), dense connective tissue trabeculae, similar to the capsule in structure, extend into the interior of the organ. These branch and unite with one another to form very incomplete anastomosing chambers. At one point on the surface of the spleen a deep indentation occurs, which is known as the *hilum*. This marks the entrance and exit of the splenic vessels. Accompanying the vessels, broad strands of capsular tissue extend deep into the organ where they radiate and subdivide to form, with the smaller trabeculae which extend in from other parts of the capsule, the connective tissue framework of the organ. Because of the abundance of elastic tissue together with some smooth muscle, and because of the arrangement of fibrous connective tissue in wavy bundles, the organ is distensible and capable of considerable change in volume.

The spaces within the connective tissue framework shown in Figure 13-13 are filled with a soft, sponge-like tissue known as the *splenic pulp*. On the basis of color differences seen in fresh preparations, different regions of the splenic pulp have been named *red pulp* and *white pulp*. Both types consist of lymphoid tissue (that is, reticular connective tissue and lymphocytes), together with other cell types described below under "The Splenic Pulp."

The red pulp is traversed by a plexus of *venous sinuses* (Figs. 13-14 and 13-15) by which it is broken up into anastomosing cords known as *pulp cords* (*cords of Billroth*). The lymphatic tissue of the pulp cords is almost always infiltrated with some erythrocytes, the number varying under different conditions. The venous sinuses contain erythrocytes which are packed particularly close together when the sinuses are in a storage phase (see below). Thus the red pulp as a whole, venous sinuses plus pulp cords, contains large numbers of erythrocytes which are responsible for its color in fresh preparations.

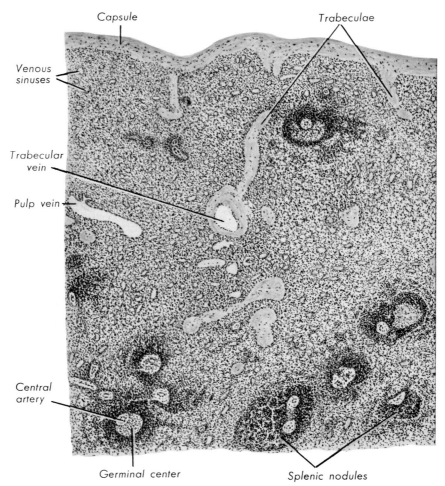

Capsule

Trabeculae

Venous
sinuses

Trabecular
vein

Pulp vein

Central
artery

Germinal center

Splenic nodules

FIG. 13-12. Section through a portion of human spleen to show general topography. ×40

The white pulp is composed of compact lymphatic tissue arranged around certain divisions of the arteries in the form of a *periarterial sheath*, with ovoid enlargements at intervals which are known as *lymphatic nodules, splenic nodules* or *Malpighian corpuscles*. The junction of a lymphatic nodule with the surrounding red pulp has characteristic features in the pattern of its vessels and reticulum and is known as the *marginal zone*. Except for their larger blood vessels, the lymphatic nodules of the spleen are very similar to those found in lymph nodes and, like the latter, they may contain germinal centers. In children, a germinal center is

usually found in each nodule or follicle, but in the adult spleen the germinal centers are less numerous.

The structure of the spleen depends largely upon the characteristic arrangement of the blood vessels, which are described before considering further the minute structure of the organ.

Blood Vessels. The arteries enter the spleen at the hilum and divide into branches which enter the trabeculae to become the *trabecular* or *interlobular arteries* (Fig. 13-15). These are accompanied by the trabecular branches of the splenic veins. After following the trabeculae for a short distance, the

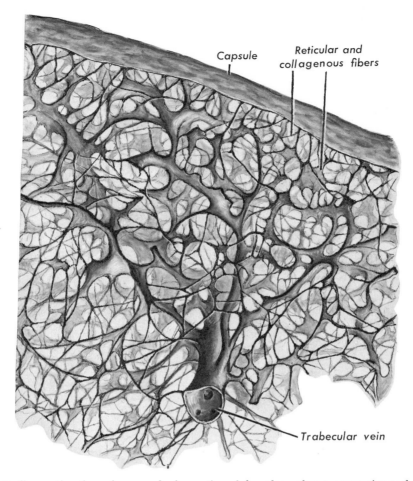

Capsule   Reticular and collagenous fibers

Trabecular vein

FIG. 13-13. Connective tissue framework of a portion of the spleen after a maceration technique which has removed all of the cells of the red and white pulp. ×15. (Preparation and drawing by Mr. Kellner.)

arteries leave the veins and the septa and pursue an entirely separate course through the splenic pulp. The adventitial coat of these smaller arteries takes on the character of reticular tissue and becomes infiltrated with lymphocytes, forming a periarterial sheath. At various points along the course of the vessels, the lymphatic tissue is increased in amount and forms the splenic corpuscles already mentioned. These arteries are called the *central arteries*, although they are eccentrically located with reference to the splenic corpuscles. When a corpuscle is located at a point where the artery divides, as frequently happens, two or more arteries

will be seen in a cross section of the nodule. As they pass through the white pulp, the arteries give off numerous capillaries which nourish the lymphatic tissue. The capillaries of the lymphatic nodules continue into the marginal zone, where some terminate and some continue directly to the sinuses of the red pulp. Drainage from the marginal zone is via the sinuses of the red pulp; in other words, there is no venous return through the white pulp. India ink injected intravascularly readily enters the meshes of the reticulum in the marginal zone.

After a number of divisions, the central arteries become reduced in size, lose their

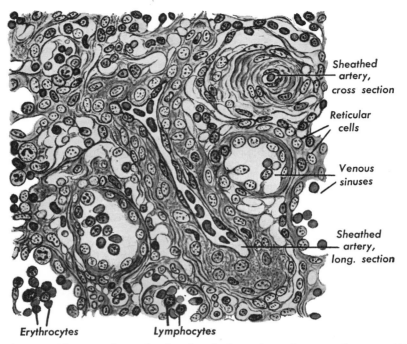

FIG. 13-14. Section of human spleen, showing sheathed arteries and venous sinuses. ×619. (Redrawn after Hartmann.)

surrounding coat of compact lymphoid tissue and enter the cords of the red pulp. At this point, each artery divides into a number of rather straight branches that lie close together like the bristles of a brush or *penicillus*. The arteries of the penicilli consist of three successive portions: *pulp arteries, sheathed arteries* and *terminal arterial capillaries*. The pulp arteries are the longest of the three divisions and possess a thin tunica of smooth muscle which is immediately surrounded by the tissue of the red pulp. The pulp arteries become smaller and divide into the sheathed arteries (Figs. 13-14 and 13-15) which have an unusually thickened wall, the *Schweigger-Seidel sheath*. The sheath is not as well developed in man as in some of the lower animals such as the pig and dog. These arteries have no muscular layer. The sheath or thickening consists of a compact mass of concentrically arranged cells and fibers continuous externally with the reticulum of the red pulp. The sheath apparently repre-

sents a local modification and condensation of the reticulum. The sheathed arteries have a lumen of about 6 to 8 μ, and they are very uniform in size.

Each of the sheathed arteries divides into two or more arterial capillaries which may have conical enlargements (ampullae) at their terminations. The exact manner in which these vessels terminate has been a controversial subject. Some authors believe that the capillaries empty into intercellular spaces of the red pulp reticulum and that the blood finds its way from the pulp spaces into the venous sinuses through perforations in the walls of the sinuses. Other authors believe that the capillaries empty directly into the venous sinuses. However, openings of terminal arterioles into the intercellular spaces of the red pulp can be seen in electron micrographs (Fig. 13-16) and it is evident that at least some of the arterioles terminate in this manner.

The *venous sinuses* (terminal veins, cav-

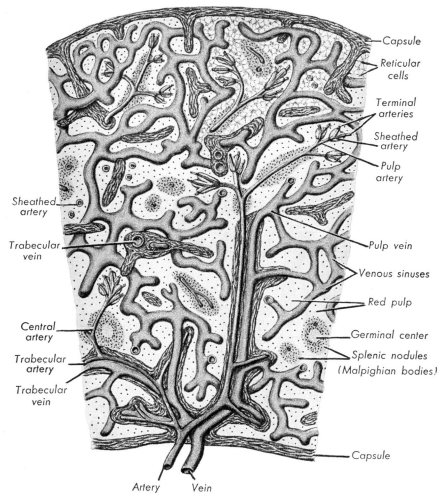

Capsule

Reticular
cells

Terminal
arteries

Sheathed
artery

Pulp
artery

Sheathed
artery

Trabecular
vein

Pulp vein

Venous sinuses

Red pulp

Central
artery

Germinal center

Splenic nodules
(Malpighian bodies)

Trabecular
artery

Trabecular
vein

Capsule

Artery   Vein

FIG. 13-15. Schema of the structure of the spleen. The diagram shows a portion of the organ extending from the hilum to the opposite (convex) surface. The structural components (vessels, nodules, etc.)
that would be contained in such a large section have not been drawn to scale, but have been increased in
size and decreased in numbers for clearer illustration. (Redrawn and modified from Hartmann.)

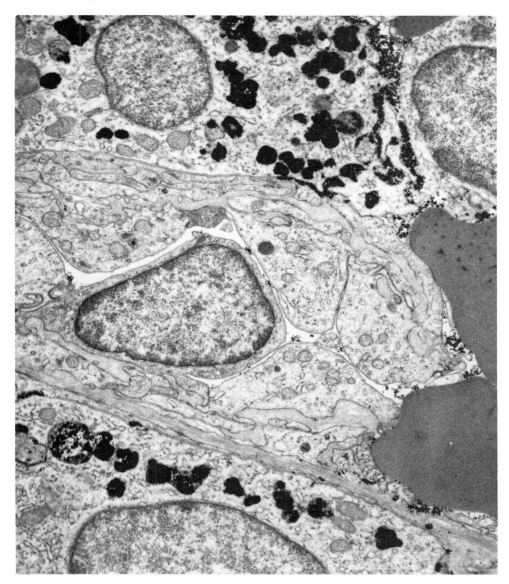

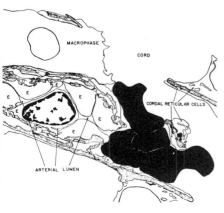

Fig. 13-16. Electron micrograph of a terminal arteriole of the red pulp of a rabbit spleen. The structures seen in the micrograph are identified in the tracing at the left; the latter includes a slightly larger area than that shown in the micrograph. The endothelial cells (*E*) of the arteriole bulge into the lumen of the vessel. The arteriole ends by opening into the spaces between the reticular cells. A few erythrocytes (*black*) are seen in the pulp. Some thorotrast that was injected intravenously several minutes prior to splenectomy is seen within the lumen of the vessel and in the pulp spaces; it is particularly abundant in the macrophages. Extracellular reticulum (*stippled*) is associated with the reticular cells and with the wall of the arteriole. A layer of the reticulum contributes to the basement membrane beneath the endothelium. ×15,000, (Micrograph and labeled tracing, courtesy of Dr. Leon Weiss. Amer. J. Anat., vol. 113, 1963.)

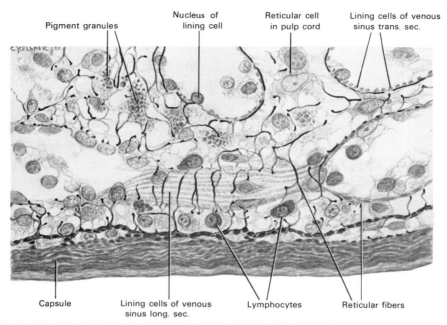

FIG. 13-17. Section of spleen of rhesus monkey stained with silver to show reticular fibers and with hematoxylin-eosin-azure to show cell types. The venous sinus in the *lower part* of the field is cut longitudinally and tangentially so that the section gives a surface view of part of the sinus wall. The two *upper* sinuses are cut transversely. Granules of hemosiderin pigment are unusually abundant in this particular field. ×950.

ernous veins) form an anastomosing plexus throughout the red pulp, breaking it up into the pulp cords. The lining cells are phagocytic and belong to the reticuloendothelial system (Chapter 5). Although they are often described as endothelial cells, they have many of the characteristics of reticular cells. They differ from the ordinary stellate reticular cells in that they are more elongated and more regularly arranged as structural adaptations to the sinus wall (Fig. 13-17). Their shape changes with the state of contraction or expansion of the sinus. These cells have received a number of names: *lining reticular cells, littoral cells* or *special endothelial cells.* Electron micrographs show an incomplete basal lamina of variable thickness beneath the lining cells (Fig. 13-18).

The outer part of the sinus wall also contains relatively coarse, circularly arranged reticular fibers, which are quite obvious in

silver-stained preparations under the light microscope (Fig. 13-17). Electron micrographs show that these fibers are embedded in a perforated layer of ground substance (Weiss, 1963). This layer, plus the incomplete basal lamina, probably corresponds to the perforated basement membrane described by some light microscopists and denied by others. Although the perforations of the basement membrane and the clefts between littoral cells seen with the light microscope (Fig. 13-17) are exaggerated by shrinkage of cells during the fixation and preparation of tissues, their presence has been confirmed by electron microscope studies (Weiss, 1963, Roberts and Latta, 1964, and others).

The terminal veins or venous sinuses unite to form larger *pulp veins,* or *collecting venules,* lined by endothelium. The collecting venules enter the trabeculae to become the

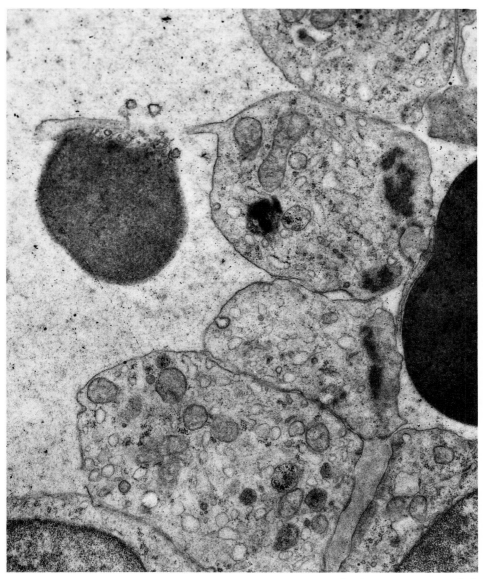

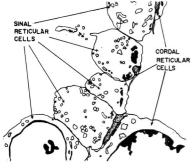

FIG. 13-18. Electron micrograph of a venous sinus of the red pulp of a rabbit spleen. The wall of the sinus is cut transversely and the lining cells are therefore seen in cross section. The structures are identified in the tracing at the left. Note that the lateral surfaces of the contiguous lining cells (sinal reticular cells) touch one another along most of their course, but that there are no desmosomes or other forms of firm intercellular attachment. Dense material (*black* in the tracing) is seen, at intervals, in the lower parts of the lining cells. The basement membrane (*stippled*) of the lining cells is incomplete and is therefore seen only at intervals in sections. Portions of reticular cells of the red pulp cords are seen at the right. ×30,000. (Micrograph and labeled tracing, courtesy of Dr. Leon Weiss, Amer. J. Anat., vol. 113, 1963).

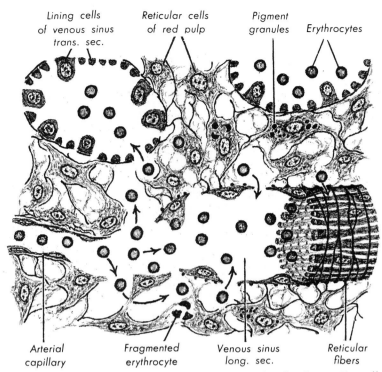

Lining cells of venous sinus trans. sec.

Reticular cells of red pulp

Pigment granules

Erythrocytes

Arterial capillary

Fragmented erythrocyte

Venous sinus long. sec.

Reticular fibers

FIG. 13-19. Schema of union of arteries and veins in splenic pulp, showing an "open" type of circulation. The venous sinus at *lower right* is drawn to give a three-dimensional view to show the longitudinal orientation of the lining cells surrounded by circularly arranged reticular fibers. Granules in the reticular cells represent hemosiderin resulting from the phagocytosis of senile erythrocytes.

trabecular or *interlobular veins*, which follow the trabeculae toward the hilum where they unite to form the splenic veins.

Union of Arteries and Veins. The relationship between the terminal arterial capillaries and the venous sinuses deserves a more detailed discussion with regard to the question whether the splenic circulation is an open or closed system. As noted above, some authors believe that the capillaries open into the intercellular spaces of the reticulum of the red pulp (Fig. 13-19), whereas others believe that all capillaries open directly into venous sinuses (Fig. 13-20).

Most light microscope studies of sections of fixed tissues and most electron microscope studies indicate that a considerable number of the terminal capillaries are open to spaces in the red pulp and that relatively few open directly into venous sinuses. This is a modified version of the open system theory in that it accepts the view that some terminal vessels connect directly to sinuses. It also visualizes the flow of blood as normally following preferential channels, rather than as flowing freely throughout the red pulp like water passing through a swamp. Endothelial cells of the terminal capillaries make contacts with processes of reticular cells, and the latter in turn make contacts with the lining cells of the venous sinuses, as diagrammatically illustrated in Figure 13-19, except that the intercellular spaces are exaggerated in the diagram. The actual appearance of intercellular gaps and clefts as seen under the electron microscope is shown in Figure 13-18.

The view that the splenic circulation is closed receives its strongest support from studies of blood flow in living animals. Using a quartz rod method of transillumination, Knisely (1936) observed arterial capillaries emptying directly into the venous sinuses and also into the collecting venules of the pulp (Fig. 13-20). He found that the venous sinuses show cyclic activity in which different phases can be recognized. In the *conducting phase*, all physiological sphincters are open and whole blood enters at the afferent end and leaves at the efferent end. At the beginning of the filtration-filling phase, the sphincter at the effer-

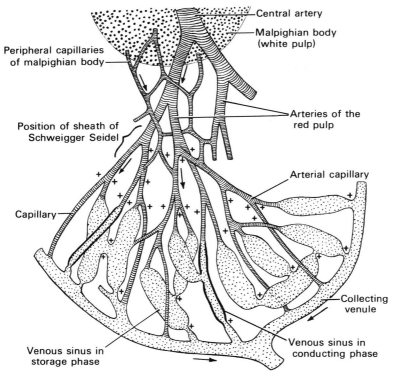

Fig. 13-20. Diagram of the different types of vascular connections that have been observed in the spleens of living animals. *Plus signs* indicate positions of physiological sphincters. (Redrawn and slightly modified from Knisely.)

ent end closes. Whole blood continues to enter at the afferent end, blood fluid passes rapidly across the sinus wall into the pulp, and the sinus becomes a distended, cucumber-shaped structure packed with blood corpuscles. When the sinus is nearly filled with cells, the afferent sphincters constrict and the *storage phase* begins. This phase lasts from a few minutes to several hours. The sinus walls are very thin during this phase, and Knisely observed a few erythrocytes passing through the sinus wall in this stage. They appeared to "snap" forward as they passed through a visible membrane wall. At the end of the storage phase, the physiological sphincters open, packed cells are washed out of the sinuses and a new conducting phase begins.

Further studies of spleens of living animals by other investigators using Knisely's methods have given conflicting results. One group of investigators (MacKenzie, Whipple and Wintersteiner, 1941) described the circulation as open, whereas another group (Peck and Hoerr, 1951) supported Knisely's conclusion that the circulation is of a closed type.

The quartz rod method for studying spleens in living animals has made significant contributions to our understanding of splenic function. However, it will be readily appreciated that the method cannot provide the resolution necessary to see the intercellular gaps and clefts more recently observed by electron microscopy. It is not difficult to understand that observations on living animals often show the blood passing through preferential pathways that appear to be closed. Although there are a number of unanswered questions, most of the evidence currently available favors the view that the splenic circulation is chiefly of an open type.

The Splenic Pulp. As already stated, the splenic pulp fills in all of the spaces between the connective tissue trabeculae, and it has been subdivided into white pulp, consisting of compact lymphatic tissue surrounding the central arteries, and red pulp, containing an abundance of erythrocytes and broken up into pulp cords by the

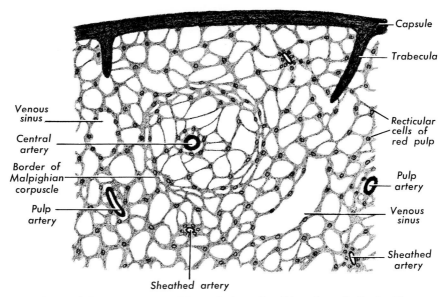

FIG. 13-21. Schema of the arrangement of the reticular cells of the spleen. Reticular fibers are omitted. No structural details are shown for the capsule, trabeculae and walls of arteries, but the positions of these structures are shown as the darkest parts of the schema. (Redrawn from Hartmann.)

venous sinuses. A meshwork of reticular connective tissue extends throughout both the red and white pulp, although its density and arrangement vary in different parts. The reticular cells (Fig. 13-21) and also the fibers (Fig. 13-22) are more numerous and more closely arranged around the arteries and at the marginal zone of the lymphatic nodule than they are elsewhere.

The *cells of the reticulum*, like those of lymph node reticulum, can be subdivided into reticular cells with phagocytic properties and the more undifferentiated mesenchyme-like cells. The former belong to the reticuloendothelial system and represent fixed or attached histiocytes. They frequently lose their connections with the reticulum and become free histiocytes or macrophages. Both the free and attached histiocytes may be found to contain various foreign particles, degenerating leucocytes, fragmented and whole erythrocytes, etc. Frequently, they contain reddish or brownish pigment granules (hemosiderin) derived from the hemoglobin of erythrocytes that have been phagocytosed (Fig. 13-17).

The undifferentiated cells of the reticulum easily transform themselves into reticular cells with phagocytic properties, or they may become primitive free cells that develop into lymphocytes in the germinal centers of the white pulp just as in the germinal centers of lymph nodes.

Lymphocytes of large, medium and small sizes are numerous and compactly arranged in the white pulp, the first two types being especially numerous in the germinal centers (Fig. 13-23). In the red pulp, the lymphocytes are less numerous and more loosely arranged.

Monocytes and *plasma cells* are also fairly numerous. Monocytes are brought into the spleen by the circulating blood and are also formed within the spleen, both by proliferation of existing monocytes and by differentiation from a more embryonic cell type. The monocytes have phagocytic properties and, when very active, they may enlarge and become similar in appearance to the free macrophages already described, which arise from the reticular cells of the pulp cords and from the cells lining the sinuses.

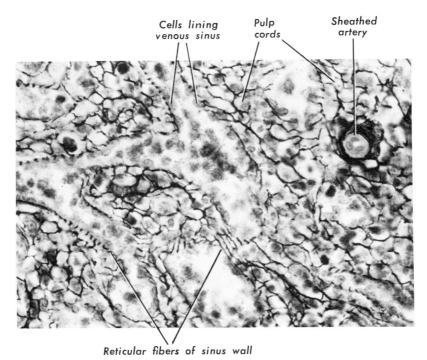

Cells lining venous sinus   Pulp cords   Sheathed artery

Reticular fibers of sinus wall

FIG. 13-22. Photomicrograph of spleen of rhesus monkey. Stained with Bielschowsky-Foot silver for reticular fibers and with hematoxylin-eosin-azure for cell types. ✕540.

The red pulp also contains the various types of *granular leucocytes* and a variable number of *erythrocytes*. Because of the thinness of the walls of the sinuses and the presence of some erythrocytes outside the sinuses, it is frequently difficult in ordinary sections to distinguish between the sinuses and pulp cords.

Giant cells or *megakaryocytes*, similar to those of bone marrow, are found in the splenic pulp of a number of animals (e.g., cat, rat). They are present in man during fetal life but are usually absent in the adult.

Lymphatics. Efferent lymphatic vessels are present in the connective tissue of the capsule and trabeculae. Contrary to previous views, it has been found that deep efferent lymphatic vessels are present also in the white pulp, coursing parallel with the arteries (Snook, 1946).

Nerves. These are mainly nonmyelinated, although a few meylinated fibers are present. The latter are probably sensory in function.

The nonmyelinated fibers—axons of sympathetic neurons—accompany the arteries, around which they form plexuses. From these plexuses, terminals pass to the muscle cells of the arteries, to the septa, to the capsule and to the splenic pulp.

Functions of the Spleen. The spleen is not essential for life and can be removed without giving very definite evidence concerning its functions, since various other organs, particularly the bone marrow, readily take over its functions.

The spleen acts as a filtering organ for the blood in much the same way as the lymph nodes function as organs of lymph filtration. The phagocytic cells of the spleen, both the free and attached histiocytes, remove foreign particles, including bacteria, degenerating leukocytes, etc., from the circulating blood.

The phagocytic reticular cells also remove fragmented and whole erythrocytes and in this way the spleen functions as an organ

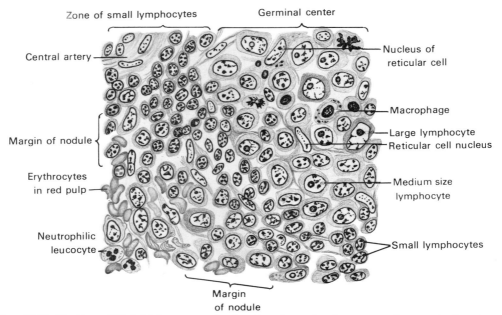

FIG. 13-23. Portion of Malpighian corpuscle of cat's spleen, showing a part of a germinal center and various types of lymphocytes. *a*, central artery; *erc.*, erythrocytes in red pulp; *g.c.*, germinal center; *l.l.*, large lymphocytes; *m.l.*, medium size lymphocytes; *n*, outer border of splenic nodule (junction of red and white pulp); *n.lk.*, neutrophil leukocytes; *p*, phagocyte; *r*, nuclei of reticular cells; *s.l.*, small lymphocytes; *z.sl.*, compact zone of small lymphocytes around germinal center. ×570. (Redrawn from Hartmann.)

for blood destruction. Many of the cells engulfed have already begun to fragment in the peripheral circulation, but the spleen is thought also to play a part in making the cells more fragile. Regardless of what initiates the fragmentation or determines which erythrocytes are to be destroyed, the spleen is of importance in blood destruction as an organ for the removal and phagocytosis of the cells.

Engulfed erythrocytes are digested by the phagocytic cells, and iron is recovered from the hemoglobin and temporarily stored in the cells. In this way the spleen plays a part in the iron metabolism of the body. The stored iron is given up as needed and is utilized by the body in the formation of new hemoglobin.

The spleen functions as an organ for blood development during a part of fetal life, but after birth the only blood cells normally formed in the spleen are lympho-cytes and monocytes. In certain pathological conditions, the splenic pulp reassumes its earlier function as a blood-forming organ for all types of cells and becomes similar to bone marrow in appearance, containing all types of myelocytes, erythroblasts and megakaryocytes.

As already described, the framework of the spleen includes elastic fibers and smooth muscle and the organ is able to make rapid changes in volume. Contraction of the spleen expels erythrocytes and increases the number of these corpuscles in the general circulation. Contraction and decrease in volume occurs under many different conditions (e.g., during exercise, following hemorrhage) and, although this reservoir function of the spleen is not necessary for life, there are a great variety of conditions both normal and pathological in which it may be of considerable value (Barcroft and Stephens, 1927).

The white pulp of the spleen has an important role, similar to that described for lymph nodes, in the formation of antibodies and in the production of immunity.

Development. The spleen appears as a thickening of the mesenchyme in the left side of the mesogastrium (greater omentum) during the fifth week of embryonic development. When the primordium of the spleen first appears, the cells of the mesothelium are not sharply separated from the underlying mesenchyme, and it is thought that some of the mesothelial cells are added to the mesenchymal thickening. By continued growth, the primordium becomes a larger elevation from the mesentery and extends into the body cavity. The attachment to the mesentery gradually becomes constricted and finally forms only a narrow band of tissue surrounding the splenic vessels.

The mesenchymal cells differentiate into the reticulum and into primitive free cells resembling lymphocytes. Slightly later, the tissue becomes myeloid in type, containing all stages in the development of erythrocytes, granulocytes and megakaryocytes. The development of lymphocytes continues throughout life, but the formation of erythrocytes and granulocytes normally ceases shortly after birth.

In its early stages of development, the primordium of the spleen is supplied with a capillary plexus connecting the afferent and efferent vessels. Following the development of the characteristic distribution of vessels, lymphocytes gradually become more compactly arranged around the arteries to form the beginning of the white pulp. The enlargements of the white pulp forming definite splenic corpuscles are not found until toward the end of fetal development. The characteristic adult structure of the red pulp is not attained until after birth, when the myeloid characteristics of the tissue are lost as the development of erythrocytes and granulocytes ceases.

REFERENCES

ACKERMAN, G. A. 1967 The lymphocyte: its morphology and embryological origin. *In* Bristol Symposium: The Lymphocyte in Immunology and Haemopoiesis (Yoffey, J. M., editor), pp. 11–20. The Williams & Wilkins Company, Baltimore.

ACKERMAN, G. A., AND HOSTETLER, J. R. 1970. Morphological studies of the embryonic rabbit thymus. Anat. Rec., vol. 166, pp. 27–46.

ALEXANDER, J. W., AND GOOD, R. A. 1970 Immunology for Surgeons. W. B. Saunders Company, Philadelphia.

AUERBACH, R. 1961 Experimental analysis of the origin of cell types in the development of the mouse thymus. Develop. Biol., vol. 3, pp. 336–354.

BARCROFT, J., AND STEPHENS, J. G. 1927 Observations on the size of the spleen. J. Physiol., vol. 64, pp. 1–22.

BURNET, F. M. 1962 The thymus gland. Sci. Amer., vol. 207, pp. 50–57.

CLARK, S. L., JR. 1962 The reticulum of lymph nodes in mice studied with the electron microscope. Amer. J. Anat., vol. 110, pp. 217–257.

CLARK, S. L., JR. 1964 The penetration of proteins and colloidal materials into the thymus from the blood stream. *In* The Thymus (Defendi, V., and Metcalf, D., editors), Wistar Institute Symposium Monograph 2, pp. 9–32. Wistar Institute Press, Philadelphia.

CLARK, S. L., JR. 1966 The synthesis and storage of protein by isolated lymphoid cells, examined by autoradiography with the electron microscope. Amer. J. Anat., vol. 119, pp. 375–404.

COONS, A. H., LEDUC, E. H., AND CONNOLLY, J. M. 1955 Studies on antibody formation. J. Exper. Med., vol. 102, pp. 49–60.

EVERETT, N. B., AND TYLER (CAFFREY), R. W. 1967 Lymphopoiesis in the thymus and other tissues: functional implications. Int. Rev. Cytol., vol. 22, pp. 205–237.

FORD, C. E., MICKLEM, H. S., EVANS, E. P., GRAY, J. G., AND OGDEN, D. A. 1966 The inflow of bone marrow cells to the thymus. Studies with part-body irradiated mice injected with chromosome marked bone marrow and subjected to antigen stimulation. Ann. N. Y. Acad. Sci., vol. 129, pp. 283–296.

GOOD, R. A., AND GABRIELSON, A. E. (editors) 1964 The Thymus in Immunology. Hoeber Medical Division, Harper & Row, Publishers, New York.

HARTMANN, A. 1930 Die Milz. *In:* Handb. mikr. Anat. Menschen (v. Möllendorff, editor), vol. 6, pt. 1, pp. 397–563. Springer-Verlag, Berlin.

HELMANN, T. 1930 Die Lymphknötchen und die Lymphknoten. *In:* Handb. mikr. Anat. Menschen (v. Möllendorff, editor), vol. 6, pt. 1, pp. 233–396. Springer-Verlag, Berlin.

HOSTETLER, J. R., AND ACKERMAN, G. A. 1969 Lymphopoiesis and lymph node histogenesis in the embryonic and neonatal rabbit. Amer. J. Anat., vol. 124, pp. 57–76.

KALPAKTSOGLOU, P. K., YUNIS, E. J., AND GOOD, R. A. 1969 The role of the thymus in development of lympho-hemopoietic tissues. The effect of thymectomy on development of blood cells, bone marrow, spleen and lymph nodes. Anat. Rec., vol. 164, pp. 267–282.

KINGSBURY, B. F. 1945 Lymphatic tissue and regressive structure, with particular reference to degeneration of glands. Amer. J. Anat., vol. 77, pp. 159–188.

KLEMPERER, P. 1938 The spleen. *In:* Handbook of Hematology (Downey, H., editor), vol. 3, pp. 1587–1754. Paul B. Hoeber, Inc., New York.

KNISELY, M. H. 1936 Spleen studies. Anat. Rec., vol. 65, pp. 23–50; 131–148.

MacKENZIE, D. W., WHIPPLE, A. O., AND WINTER-STEINER, M. P. 1941 Studies on the microscopic anatomy and physiology of living transilluminated mammalian spleens. Amer. J. Anat., vol. 68, pp. 397–456.

McMASTER, P. D. 1961 Antibody formation. *In* The Cell; Biochemistry, Physiology, Morphology (Brachet, J., and Mirksy, A. E., editors), vol. 5, pp. 323–404. Academic Press, New York.

MILLER, J. F. A. P., MARSHALL, A. H. E., AND WHITE, R. G. 1962 The immunological significance of the thymus. Advances Immun., vol. 2, pp. 111–162.

NOSSAL, G. J. V. 1968 The cellular basis of immunity. Harvey Lect. Ser. 63, pp. 179–211.

PECK, H. M., AND HOERR, N. L. 1951 The intermediary circulation in the red pulp of the mouse spleen. Anat. Rec., vol. 109, pp. 447–478.

PETTERSEN, J. C., AND ROSE, R. J. 1968 Marginal zone and germinal center development in the spleens of neonatally thymectomized and non-thymectomized young rats. Amer. J. Anat., vol. 123, pp. 489–500.

ROBERTS, D. K., AND LATTA, J. S. 1964 Electron microscopic studies of the red pulp of the rabbit spleen. Anat. Rec., vol. 148, pp. 81–101.

SANEL, F. T. 1967 Ultrastructure of differentiating cells during thymus histogenesis. Z. Zellforsch., vol. 83, pp. 8–29.

SNOOK, T. 1946 Deep lymphatics of the spleen. Anat. Rec., vol. 94, pp. 43–56.

SNOOK, T. 1958 The histology of the vascular terminations in the rabbit spleen. Anat. Rec., vol. 130, pp. 711–729.

WAKSMAN, B. H., ARNASON, B. G., AND JANKOVIĆ, B. D. 1962 Role of the thymus in immune reactions in rats. III. Changes in the lymphoid organs of thymectomized rats. J. Exp. Med., vol. 116, pp. 187–206.

WEISS, L. 1963 Electron microscopic observations on the vascular barrier in the cortex of the thymus of the mouse. Anat. Rec., vol. 145, pp. 413–438.

WEISS, L. 1963 The structure of the intermediate vascular pathways in the spleen of rabbits. Amer. J. Anat., vol. 113, pp. 51–92.

YOFFEY, J., AND COURTICE, F. 1956 Lymphatics, Lymph, and Lymphoid Tissue. Harvard University Press, Cambridge.

YOFFEY, J. M. (editor) 1967 Bristol Symposium: The Lymphocyte in Immunology and Haemopoiesis. The Williams & Wilkins Company, Baltimore.

14

The Integument

The integument comprises the skin that covers the entire body, together with certain accessory organs which are derivatives of the skin, such as nails, hair and glands of various kinds.

The skin performs many important functions. It protects the body from injurious substances and dessication, helps in the regulation of the body temperature, excretes water, fat and some other substances and constitutes the most extensive sense organ of the body for the reception of tactile, thermal and painful stimuli.

THE SKIN

The skin or cutis consists of two main parts: (1) the *epidermis*, a stratified epithelial layer derived from the ectoderm, and (2) the *dermis, corium*, or cutis vera, a connective tissue derivative of the mesoderm. Below the corium is a layer of loose connective tissue, the *subcutaneous tissue* (superficial fascia), which attaches the skin to the underlying organs (Fig. 14-1). In certain places this layer is so richly infiltrated with fat as to be called the *panniculus adiposus*. The subcutaneous tissue makes possible an easy movement of the skin and, where such mobility is slight or absent, as for instance in the soles, palms and finger tips, this tissue is more dense.

The thickness of the skin varies considerably in different parts of the body. The relative proportions of epidermis and dermis vary also, and a thick skin is found in regions where there is a thickening of either or both layers. On the interscapular region of the back, where the dermis is particularly thick, the skin may be more than 5 mm. in thickness, whereas on the eyelids it may be less than 0.5 mm.; the usual thickness is 1 to 2 mm. The skin is generally thicker on the dorsal or extensor surfaces of the body than on the ventral or flexor surfaces, but this is not true for the hands and feet where the skin of the palms and soles is thicker than on any dorsal surface except the interscapular region. The palms and soles have a characteristically thickened epidermis, in addition to a thick dermis (Fig. 14-1). The epidermis of these regions is not only thicker than that of other regions but it also differs structurally from the thin epidermis present elsewhere.

The whole surface of the skin is traversed by numerous fine furrows which run in definite directions and cross each other to bound small fields of a rhomboid or rectangular form. These furrows correspond to similar ones on the surface of the corium so that, in section, the boundary line between epidermis and corium appears wavy. On the thick skin of the palms and soles, the fields form long, narrow ridges separated by parallel coursing furrows, and in the fingertips these ridges are arranged in the complicated loops, whorls and spirals that give the fingerprints

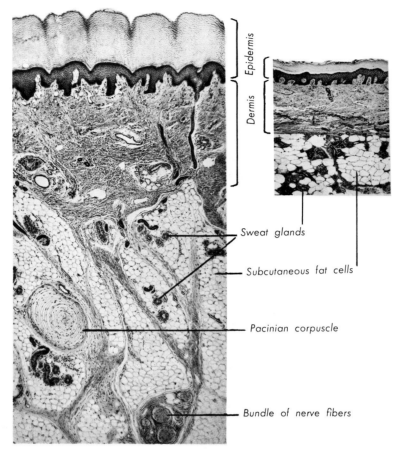

FIG. 14-1. Low power photomicrographs of vertical sections of skin. Thick skin from fingertip, at *left*; skin of medium thickness from dorsal surface of finger, at *right*. The fields shown do not include the total thickness of the subcutaneous tissue. ×30.

characteristic for each individual. In those regions where the epidermis is thickest, these ridges are more prominent.

Each of the epidermal ridges of the palms and soles has an underlying ridge of connective tissue known as the *primary dermal ridge*. Each primary ridge is divided into *secondary* dermal ridges by a downward projection of epidermis known as a *rete peg* because it appears peglike in sections (Fig. 14-1). The secondary dermal ridges appear as papillary-like elevations in sections and are known as *papillae* (Figs. 14-1 and 14-2). In the palms and soles, the dermal papillae are numerous, tall and often branched, varying in height from 0.05 to 0.2 mm. They are

likewise numerous and tall in the lips, clitoris, penis, labia minora and nipples. Where the mechanical demands are slight and the epidermis is thinner, as in the skin of the abdomen, chin and face, the papillae are low and few in number.

THE EPIDERMIS

The epidermis is composed of stratified squamous epithelium whose thickness varies in different parts of the body.

Epidermis of Palms and Soles. The epidermis of the palms, soles and volar surfaces of the digits is particularly thick and highly differentiated. In these regions, several components can be identified: (1) the *stratum*

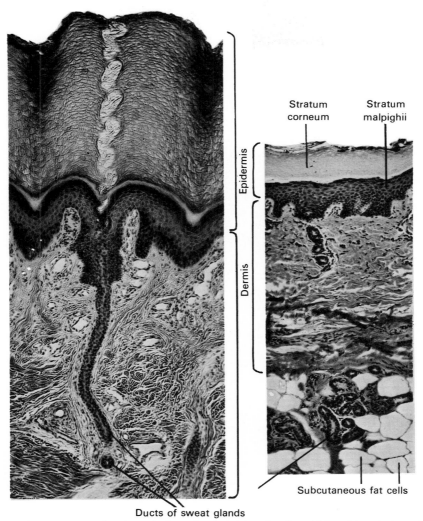

Stratum corneum

Stratum malpighii

Epidermis

Dermis

Subcutaneous fat cells

Ducts of sweat glands

FIG. 14-2. Photomicrographs of vertical sections of skin, showing thick epidermis from fingertip, at *left*, and thinner epidermis from dorsal surface of finger, at *right*. ×94.

basale (*stratum cylindricum*), (2) *stratum spinosum*, (3) *stratum granulosum*, (4) *stratum lucidum* and (5) *stratum corneum* (Figs. 14-2 and 14-3). The stratum basale and stratum spinosum together compose the *stratum Malpighii*. The name stratum germinativum is often used as synonymous with stratum basale since the basal layer is normally the chief region of mitosis. Stratum germinativum is an ambiguous term, because it has also been used synonymously with stratum Malpighii.

(1) The *stratum basale* consists of columnar or high cuboidal cells arranged in a single layer (*stratum cylindricum*) which rests on a basement membrane composed of a basal lamina and lamina reticularis, as described in Chapter 4. The lamina reticularis portion of the basement membrane of light microscopy is relatively thin in mammals but is thicker and more complex in some of the lower animals. Electron micrographs show that the border of the cell and of its underlying basement membrane follows an

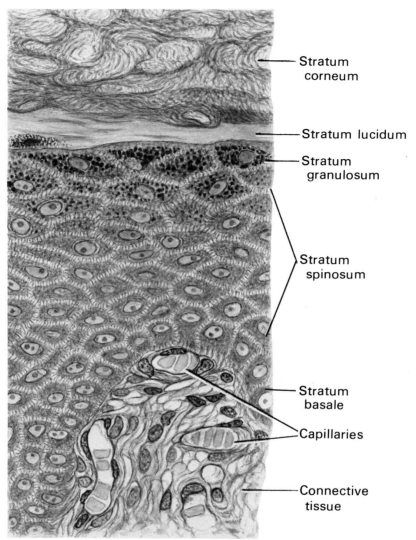

Stratum
corneum

Stratum lucidum

Stratum
granulosum

Stratum
spinosum

Stratum
basale

Capillaries

Connective
tissue

Fig. 14-3. Vertical section of thick epidermis of fingertip as seen under the oil immersion objective. The field includes only a small fraction of the total thickness of the stratum corneum and it does not include all of the stratum spinosum at the sides of the connective tissue papilla. ×815.

irregular course. They show slender strands of connective tissue penetrating spaces between infoldings of the cell membrane, and they show half-desmosomes at the base of the cells similar to those illustrated for stratified epithelium of the esophagus in Figure 16-25. Adherence between the epithelium and its underlying connective tissue is aided by the irregularity of the boundary between the two tissues and by the half-desmosomes.

(2) The *stratum spinosum* is composed of cells of polygonal shape. The plasma membranes of adjacent cells are normally in close apposition throughout most of their extent, but they tend to pull apart except in the region of the desmosomes (Figs. 4-3 and 4-4) when the cells shrink during technical procedures used in the preparation of routine sections. Thus, the cells seen in sections have an irregular outline, with delicate processes or

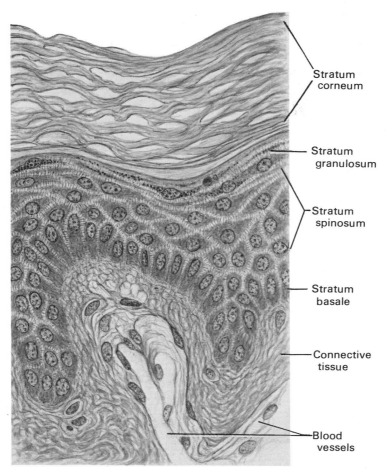

Stratum corneum

Stratum granulosum

Stratum spinosum

Stratum basale

Connective tissue

Blood vessels

Fig. 14-4. Vertical section of relatively thin epidermis from the median side of the lower extremity. The field includes the total thickness of the stratum corneum. The stratum corneum is very much thinner than that of the finger tip. The stratum granulosum is also thinner than that of thick epidermis and the stratum lucidum is barely discernible. Compare with Figure 14-3. ×815.

spines projecting from their surface. For this reason, these cells are often called "prickle cells" and the whole region is known as the *stratum spinosum.* Prior to the time of electron microscope studies, it was thought that the spinous processes formed protoplasmic connections between cells, the so-called intercellular bridges. Electron micrographs show that the points of apposition between epidermal cells do not represent bridges of protoplasmic continuity but typical *maculae adherens* or *desmosomes* (Chapter 4, Fig. 4-3).

The nuclei of the cells of the stratum Mal-

pighii are deeply chromatic. Their shape varies with that of the cells, being ovoid in the stratum cylindricum and round in the stratum spinosum. Some of the nuclei of the deeper layers are found in various stages of mitosis. This is the means by which new cells are formed to replace those which migrate outward and eventually slough from the superficial layer of the stratum corneum.

The cytoplasm of the cells of the stratum Malpighii is basophilic in its staining reaction, particularly in the deeper cell layers. There is evidence that this is correlated with the ribosomal content of the cytoplasm and hence with active protein synthesis. Electron micrographs show that the cytoplasm of the cells contains numerous fine filaments which are apparently composed of polypeptide chains of keratin precursor proteins. Bundles of the filaments are randomly distributed throughout the cytoplasm, and they are found consistently in the cytoplasm adjacent to the desmosomes, often coursing in a direction toward these points of cell adhesion (Fig. 4-4). Aggregates of the filaments are visible with the light microscope and, as such, they were originally described by light microscopists as *tonofibrils*. In keeping with this terminology, the individual filaments seen with the electron microscope are often called *tonofilaments*. The epidermal filaments of the deeper cells become the fibrous elements of the filament-matrix complex of the stratum corneum.

(3) The *stratum granulosum* consists of two to five rows of flattened, rhombic cells with their long axes parallel with the surface of the skin (Figs. 14-3, and 14-4). The cytoplasm contains numerous *keratohyalin* granules that stain intensely with hematoxylin. These should not be mistaken for pigment granules, which have color in the natural, unstained state. Electron micrographs show that the keratohyalin granules which appear so well defined under the light microscope are actually irregularly shaped masses of electron-dense material in close association with bundles of filaments. Chemical studies have shown that the keratohyalin granules are relatively rich in proline and in sulfur-containing amino acids. These granules are the precursors of the amorphous portion of the filament-matrix complex of stratum corneum.

(4) The *stratum lucidum* is a thin, light staining zone located between the stratum granulosum and the cornified surface layer. The lucidum is readily seen in the epidermis of the palms and soles but is usually not identifiable in most parts of the body. The nuclei begin to degenerate in the outer cells of the granulosa layer and disappear in the lucidum. The cytoplasm of the cells is said to contain a refractile substance known as eleidin, but little is known about this. Electron micrographs show that the tonofilaments have become more aggregated and more orderly arranged than in the granulosa cells.

(5) The *stratum corneum* is very thick in the palms and soles and is composed of clear, dead, scale-like cells which become more and more flattened as the surface is approached, the most peripheral layer containing flat, horny plates which are constantly desquamated. The cells have a thickened membrane or husk and they are closely interdigitated. The nuclei have disappeared, but some of the spaces that they occupied can be seen.

The cytoplasm has been replaced by keratin proteins. Electron micrographs show that these dead cells are composed of filaments tightly packed in orthogonal arrays that lie parallel to the skin surface and embedded in an opaque, electron-dense, interfilamentous material. Desmosomes, though modified, persist and are thought to play a role in the spatial arrangement. The structural changes in the keratinization process involve changes in the aggregation and arrangement of filaments, the formation of keratohyalin granules as the precursors of the interfilamentous material of keratin and the loss of cell organelles after the keratohyalin granules have reached their maximal size. The structural changes in the cells as they move from the stratum basale to the cornified layer are correlated with chemical changes. These include the formation of disulfide groups in keratin from sulfhydryl groups in the filaments of the deeper layers.

The thickened membranes or husks which envelop the horny cells are resistant to keratinolytic agents and they provide integrity for the filament-matrix complex within the cell. The filamentous portion of the complex, derived from protein synthesis within the basal epidermal cells, provides for flexibility and elastic recovery of the cell content. The amorphous portion of the filament-matrix complex, derived from keratohyalin granules, is primarily responsible for the chemical resistance of the horny cells (Matoltsy and Matoltsy, 1970).

The cornified layer of the epidermis is composed of "*soft keratin*," which contrasts with "*hard keratin*" found in the nails and in the cortex of the hairs. Hard keratin contains relatively more sulfur, is less elastic and is more permanent in the sense that it does not desquamate as the epidermis does.

The peripheral region of the stratum corneum which is constantly being desquamated is often referred to as the *stratum disjunctum*. The desquamated cells are replaced by new cells that formed by mitosis in the germinative layers and moved toward the surface during the process of keratinization.

Epidermis of the General Body Surface. The epidermis of the rest of the body is considerably thinner than that of the palms, soles and volar surfaces of the digits. All layers of the epidermis are reduced, and the stratum corneum and stratum Malpighii are the only layers that are constantly present in all parts of the body. A thin stratum granulosum, composed of only one or two cell rows, is frequently present, but a definite stratum lucidum is generally absent. The structure varies with the region studied. On the leg, for example (Fig. 14-4), where the epidermis is thicker than that of abdominal or pubic skin yet much thinner than that of the fingertip, a faint stratum lucidum may be found. The reduction in the thickness of layers in thin epidermis is probably due to the fact that keratinization is far less marked and occurs not as a continuous process but only at certain times.

Color of the Skin. The color of the skin is dependent upon the blood in the capillaries of the connective tissue beneath the epidermis and on the presence of varying amounts of *melanin* pigment. Certain patches of skin are especially rich in pigment, such as the circumanal region, the areolae and nipples, the axilla, the labia majora, the penis and scrotum, while practically no pigment is present in the palms and soles. The pigment is stored as fine granules within the cells of the Malpighian layer, although some granules may be deposited between the cells. In white races, the granules occur only in the deepest cell layers and chiefly in the cylindrical cells of the basal row. In colored races, pigment is found throughout the entire Malpighian layer and even in the stratum granulosum.

Melanin is formed in specialized cells known as *melanocytes*, which differentiate from *melanoblasts* that migrate from the neural crest to the dermoepidermal junction during embryonic development. The melanoblasts and melanocytes lack tonofilaments and desmosomes, and the former also lack pigment granules. Several intermediate stages can be recognized in the differentiation of a melanocyte from a melanoblast (Seiji *et al.*, 1963, and Starico, 1963). Morphological differentiation involves a change from the relatively round melanoblasts and premelanocytes to the melanocytes which have numerous long processes. Cytological differentiation encompasses the formation of melanin granules. There are several theories on this. According to one view, the polypeptides, which eventually become tyrosinase, are synthesized in association with ribosomes and are transferred to the region of the Golgi complex where they are condensed and packaged into units surrounded by membranes. Next, the protyrosinase molecules become arranged in an orderly manner in the membrane-bound units, giving the latter a lamellar pattern in electron micrographs. The units at this stage of differentiation have dimensions of about 0.7 by 0.3 μ, and they are known as premelanosomes. When the protyrosinase becomes activated as tyrosinase, melanin biosynthesis begins, and the units which now contain melanin in addition to tyrosinase are known as *melanosomes*. The melanin continues to increase in the melanosomes until the latter are transformed into amorphous melanin granules that lack the lamellar pattern seen in electron micrographs of melanosomes; they also lack demonstrable tyrosinase. The differentiation of melano-somes is accompanied by a change in their intracellular position: the premelanosomes appear in the region of the Golgi complex, the melanosomes appear in the basal portion of the cytoplasmic cell processes and the melanin granules are chiefly in the peripheral portions of the processes. Thus, the body or perikaryon of the melanocyte is relatively free of melanin and appears relatively clear in routine preparations, whereas the proces-ses contain melanin granules. From the mela-nocyte processes, the melanin granules are distributed to the cytoplasm of the epidermal cells of the Malpighian layer.

The melanocytes can be identified by their reaction to the "dopa" reagent, dihydroxy-phenylalanine: they oxidize the solution and stain black. The intracellular substance re-sponsible for the reaction is an oxidase, ty-rosinase, which is an enzyme involved in the synthesis of melanin from a precursor, pre-sumably tyrosine. It should be noted that the dopa reaction does not occur for the fully formed melanin granules present in the epi-dermal cells of the Malpighian layer, or in dermal chromatophores which have obtained their pigment by phagocytosis of melanin synthesized by melanogenic cells. As noted earlier, the mature melanin granules lack tyrosinase, which is presumably the oxidase responsible for the dopa reaction.

The cell bodies of the melanocytes are nor-mally confined to the basal layer of the epi-dermis, near their place of origin from the primitive melanoblasts. However, melano-cyte processes extend for some distance be-tween epidermal cells. When melanin forma-tion is stimulated, e.g., by ultraviolet radia-tion, or by X-irradiation, the cell bodies of the melanocytes also appear in the supra-basal layers of the epidermis.

The melanocytes supposedly wear out and slough off with the epidermal scales, but their number is maintained by proliferation of cells which are presumably melanocytes in an active phase of melanogenesis. By the use of a gold chloride technique, it is pos-sible to demonstrate a few branched cells in the suprabasal region of the Malpighian layer that are known as the *cells of Langer-hans*. It was once thought that they repre-sent a stage of worn-out melanocytes. Elec-tron micrographs show that these cells have characteristic granules which differ from melanin and that they are not degenerating cells. The best evidence available at this time, however, indicates that they are de-rived from melanocytes (Breathnach, 1965).

THE DERMIS OR CORIUM

The dermis varies from 0.2 to 4 mm. in thickness and is composed of dense, irregu-larly arranged connective tissue. It contains the three types of connective tissue fibers and fibroblasts and histiocytes. Two layers can be distinguished, although they blend without distinct demarcation. The deeper one is relatively thick and is known as the reticular layer. The superficial layer is thin-ner and is named the subepithelial or papil-lary layer.

The *reticular layer* is characterized by coarse collagenous fibers and fiber bundles which often unite to form secondary bundles of considerable thickness (nearly 100 μ in diameter). The fibers cross each other to form an extensive feltwork with rhomboid meshes, the direction of the fibers in the main being parallel to the surface of the skin. The elastic fibers form complex elastic nets per-meating the entire corium. Here too the course of the main fibers is parallel with the surface, although vertical and oblique fibers are present in considerable number. The elastic fibers form basket-like, capsular con-densations around the hair bulbs, sweat and sebaceous glands.

The *papillary* or *subepithelial layer* is sim-ilar in structure to the reticular layer, but the fibers are finer and more closely ar-ranged.

Although the connective tissue fibers of the corium form complex nets and meshes, those bundles which course parallel with the lines of tension of the skin are more numerous and better developed than the others. The lines of skin tension, which are caused by the direction of the predominant fibers, are known as *Langer's lines*. These lines have different directions in the various parts of the body. Their direction is of surgical importance because incisions made parallel with the lines gape less and heal with less scar tissue than do incisions made across the lines.

As has been mentioned, the surface of the corium is studded by numerous papillae that indent the underside of the epidermis. These papillae vary in structure and content. Some are simple, others branched. Some contain loops of capillary blood vessels (vascular papillae), others contain special nerve terminations (nervous papillae) (Fig. 10-50).

In addition to the usual types of connective tissue cells, the corium of certain regions may contain a few branched, pigmented connective tissue cells, the *dermal chromatophores*, which resemble the pigmented cells of the choroid coat of the eye. The dermal chromatophores are normally scarce in the white race. They occur chiefly in regions where the epidermis itself is richly pigmented, and their pigment is apparently obtained from melanogenic cells of neural crest origin.

Smooth muscle is found in the skin in connection with the hair (arrector pili muscles). Smooth muscle fibers also occur in considerable number in the skin of the nipple, prepuce, glans penis, scrotum (tunica dartos) and parts of the perineum. The fibers are arranged in a network parallel to the surface, and contraction of the fibers gives the skin of these regions its wrinkled appearance. In the face and neck, skeletal muscle fibers from the mimic musculature likewise penetrate the dermis. Both smooth and skeletal fibers end in delicate, elastic bands that are continuous with the general elastic network of the corium.

GLANDS OF THE SKIN

Two kinds of glands occur in the skin: sweat glands and sebaceous glands.

Sweat Glands (Glandulae sudoriferae). Most of the sweat glands are of the eccrine (merocrine) type, i.e., the product of the cell is secreted without destruction of any part of the cell. Eccrine sweat glands are found over the entire body surface, excepting the margin of the lips, the ear drum, the inner surface of the prepuce and the glans penis. They are most numerous in the palms and soles and are the only glands found in these places. They are simple, coiled, tubular glands. The coiled, ball-shaped portion usually lies in the subcutaneous tissue, although it may lie partly or wholly in the deeper portion of the reticular layer of the dermis. The excretory duct runs a straight or oblique course through the derma and enters the epidermis between two papillae. In the epidermis, the duct takes a spiral course to the surface where it opens into a minute pit just visible to the naked eye, the *sweat pore* (Fig. 14-2).

The coiled secretory portion of the gland is lined with a simple columnar or high cuboidal epithelium (Figs. 14-5 and 14-6), the height varying with the activity of the cells. The nuclei are round and stain deeply; the protoplasm contains secretory granules, fat

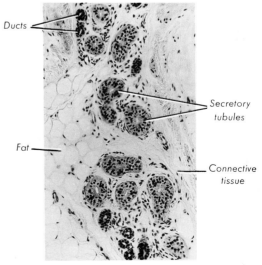

FIG. 14-5. Section of sweat glands of human fingertip. Field shown is at junction of dermis and subcutaneous tissue. Photomicrograph. ×110.

droplets and occasionally pigment granules. Distinct intercellular secretory channels (canaliculi) can be demonstrated (Fig. 14-6, *A*). Dark and light cells have been recognized, in the sense that the cytoplasm of some cells stains more intensely than that of others. Electron microscope studies show that these represent two cell types rather than different functional stages of the same cell (Munger, 1961). The dark cells have more ribosomes and have numerous secretory droplets. Histochemical studies show the presence of protein-polysaccharides in the secretory droplets and in the lumen. The clear cells are associated with the intercellular canaliculi and apparently function in fluid transport. A well defined basement membrane is present, but it is separated in places from the epithelial cells by *myoepithelial cells* (Fig. 14-6*A*). The latter have processes that spiral around the epithelial cells. They differ from the isolated smooth muscle cells around the endothelium of metarterioles (Chapter 12) in that they arise from ectoderm and they are not encircled by a basal lamina. Electron micrographs show that they have thin myofilaments however (Ellis, 1965). It is assumed that their contraction aids in forcing the secretion toward the duct.

The wall of the duct consists of a two-layered (stratified) cuboidal epithelium resting upon a delicate basement membrane which is surrounded by a network of elastic and collagenous fibers (Fig. 14-6, *B*). The cells of the inner layer of the duct epithelium have a refractile, cuticular-like border facing the lumen where the cytoplasm is more acidophilic. This is actually the apical ends of the cells where filaments are aggregated in a manner similar to that of the terminal web of many other types of epithelial cells (Chapter 4). On reaching the epidermis, the duct loses its own wall and becomes a mere channel through the epithelium (Fig. 14-2).

Especially large sweat glands are found in the axilla, mammary areola, labia majora and circumanal region (Figs. 14-7 and 14-8). They yield a thicker secretion than the sweat formed by the smaller glands. To this group belong also the wax-secreting *ceruminous* glands of the external auditory canal and the glands of Moll in the margin of the eyelid.

Glands of axillary type are known as *apocrine sweat glands* because histologists once felt certain that these glands secrete by an apocrine method, i.e., by portions of the apical ends of the cells breaking off. It is a useful name for the glands, in spite of the

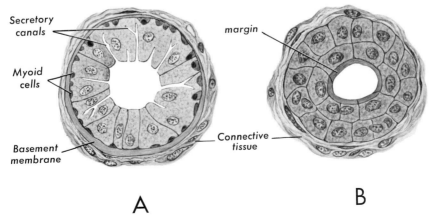

A   B

FIG. 14-6. Sections through a terminal secretory tubule (*A*) and a duct (*B*) of a sweat gland. Myoepithelial (*myoid*) cells are seen between the secretory cells and the basement membrane in *A*. ×650. (Redrawn and slightly modified from Schaffer.)

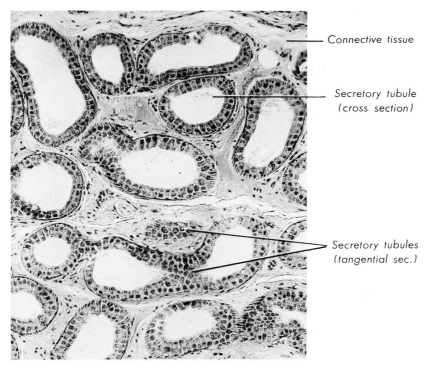

Connective tissue

Secretory tubule
(cross section)

Secretory tubules
(tangential sec.)

FIG. 14-7. Section of human circumanal glands. Note that these glands are much larger than the typical sweat glands illustrated in Figure 14-5. Photomicrograph. ×110.

fact that there is more question now regarding the exact mode of secretion. The apical ends of the cells appear intact in phase microscope studies of frozen sections. Electron microscope studies show that the apical ends of the cells have microvilli of variable length, and it has been suggested that secretion occurs either by a release of material from the microvilli or by a pinching off of the ends of microvilli, i.e., by an apocrine method at a submicroscopic level.

Sebaceous Glands. These are usually associated with the hair follicles and are described in that connection.

THE HAIR

The hairs are elastic, horny threads developed from the epidermis. They are placed in deep narrow pits or pockets that traverse the dermis to varying depths and usually extend into the subcutaneous tissue (Fig. 14-9). Each hair consists of a *shaft* that projects

above the surface and a *root* that is imbedded within the skin. At its lower end, the root presents a knoblike expansion, the *hair bulb*, in the under surface of which is a flask-shaped indentation of the connective tissue, the *papilla* of the hair. Enclosing the hair root is the *hair follicle*, which consists of an epidermal (epithelial) and dermal (connective tissue) portion.

Structure of the Hair. The hair is composed entirely of epithelial cells, which are arranged in three definite layers: the medulla, cortex and cuticle.

(1) The *medulla* forms the central axis of the hair, varying in thickness from 16 to 20 μ. It consists of two or three layers of cells which vary in appearance in different parts of the hair. In the lower portion of the root of the hair, the cells are cuboidal and have rounded nuclei (Fig. 14-10). In the shaft, the cells of the medulla are cornified and shrunken and the nuclei are rudimentary or

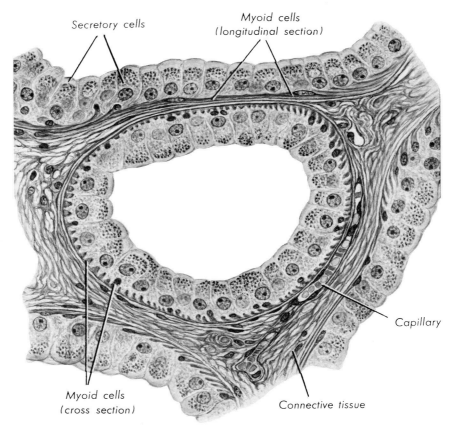

Secretory cells

Myoid cells
(longitudinal section)

Capillary

Myoid cells
(cross section)

Connective tissue

FIG. 14-8. Higher magnification of a portion of the circumanal gland shown in Figure 14-7, showing prominent secretory granules. × 420.

absent (Fig. 14-11, *A* and *B*). The intercellular spaces are usually filled with air. The medulla is absent from the finer, shorter (lanugo) hairs and also from some of the hairs of the scalp. It frequently fails to extend the whole length of the hair.

(2) The *cortex* makes up the main bulk of the hair and consists of several layers of cells. In the lower part of the root of the hair, the cortex is composed of cuboidal cells with nuclei of normal appearance (Fig. 14-10). The cells become progressively flattened and modified at higher levels. In the upper part of the root of the hair and in the shaft, the cortex is composed of cornified, elongated cells with longitudinally striated cytoplasm and shrunken, degenerated nuclei (Fig. 14-11). In colored hair, pigment granules are found in and between the cells. Air also ac-

cumulates in the intercellular spaces and modifies the hair color.

(3) The *cuticle* of the hair is exceedingly thin and is composed of a single layer of clear cells. In the deeper part of the hair root, the cuticular cells are nucleated (Fig. 14-10). In the upper part of the root and on the shaft, the cuticular cells are clear, scale-like and non-nucleated (Fig. 14-11). The cells overlap like shingles on a roof, giving the surface of the hair a serrated appearance.

The color of the hair is determined primarily by the amount of pigment but to some extent also by the presence of air, since the latter appears white in reflected light. Hair in which the pigment has faded and the medulla has become filled with air appears silvery white.

Hair Follicle. The hair follicle consists of

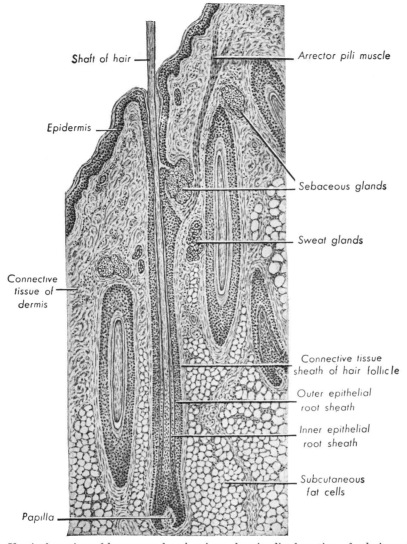

Shaft of hair

Arrector pili muscle

Epidermis

Sebaceous glands

Sweat glands

Connective tissue of dermis

Connective tissue sheath of hair follicle

Outer epithelial root sheath

Inner epithelial root sheath

Subcutaneous fat cells

Papilla

FIG. 14-9. Vertical section of human scalp, showing a longitudinal section of a hair and its follicle. Reconstructed from serial sections to show a complete follicle cut through its longitudinal axis. ×36.

the inner and outer epithelial root sheaths, derived from the epidermis, and the connective tissue sheaths, derived from the derma.

(1) The *inner epithelial root sheath* is composed of three distinct layers: the cuticle of the root sheath, Huxley's layer and Henle's layer.

The *cuticle of the root sheath* lies against the cuticle of the hair and is similar to the latter in structure (Fig. 14-10). It consists of thin, scale-like, overlapping cells, nucleated in the deeper parts of the sheath, non-nucleated nearer the surface. The free edges of the scales project downward and interdigitate with the upward projecting edges of the hair cuticle.

Huxley's layer lies immediately outside the cuticle of the root sheath and consists of several rows of elongated cells whose protoplasm contains eleidin-like granules (trichohyalin). In the deeper portion of the hair follicle, these cells contain nuclei (Fig. 14-12). Nearer

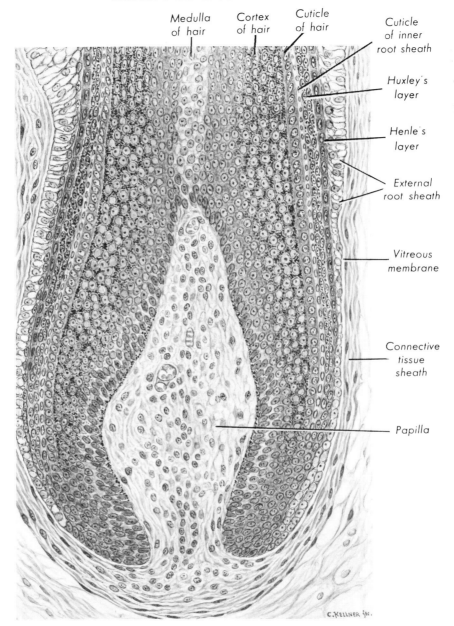

FIG. 14-10. Longitudinal section of lower end of root of hair, including hair follicle and connective tissue papilla. ×310.

the surface the nuclei are rudimentary or absent (Fig. 14-11, *C*).

Henle's layer is a row of rectangular, somewhat flattened, clear cells. The cytoplasm contains longitudinal horny fibrils, and nuclei are present only in the deepest portions of the follicle (Figs. 14-10 and 14-12). Between the cells are sometimes seen short, wedge-like processes which extend from the cells of Huxley's layer.

(2) The *outer epithelial root sheath* is a direct continuation of the Malpighian layer of

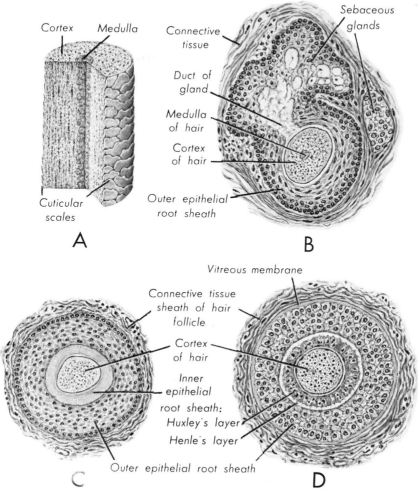

Fig. 14-11. Structure of hair and hair follicles from human scalp. *A*, a portion of the shaft of a hair reconstructed from a surface view and from longitudinal sections. *B*, *C* and *D*, cross sections of hairs and their follicles at various levels: *B*, at the level of the sebaceous glands; *C*, midway between epidermis of scalp and papilla of hair root; *D*, through the lower third of follicle. No medulla was present in the hairs illustrated in *C* and *D*. *A*, ×280; *B*, *C* and *D*, ×175.

the epidermis, to which it corresponds in structure. The outermost cells, adjacent to the connective tisue, are tall and they are arranged in a single row (the stratum cylindricum). The rest of the cells are more polygonal in shape. They have spinous processes and resemble the prickle cells already described for the stratum spinosum of the skin.

(3) The *connective tissue sheath* is derived from the dermis and consists of an inner, middle and outer layer.

The inner layer is a homogeneous, narrow band, the hyaline or *vitreous membrane*, and is closely applied to the cylindrical cells of the outer root sheath. The middle layer is thickest and is composed of fine connective tissue fibers which are arranged circularly. The outer layer is poorly defined and consists of rather coarse, loosely woven bundles of white fibers which run in a longitudinal direction.

In the deeper portion of the root, some

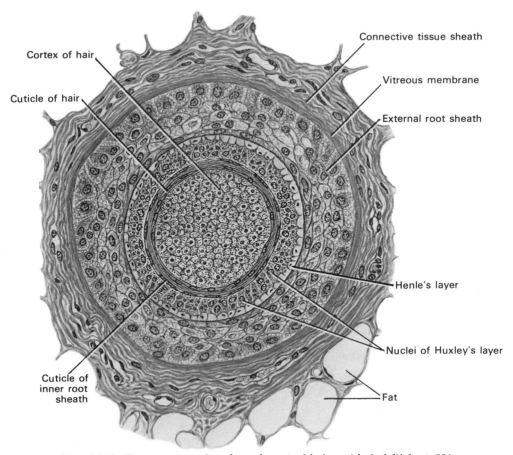

Cortex of hair

Cuticle of hair

Connective tissue sheath

Vitreous membrane

External root sheath

Henle's layer

Nuclei of Huxley's layer

Cuticle of inner root sheath

Fat

FIG. 14-12. Transverse section through root of hair and hair follicle. ×334

little distance above the bulb, all of the layers of the hair and its follicles can be distinctly seen. The differentiation of the layers becomes less marked as one passes in either direction. At the level of entrance of the ducts of the sebaceous glands (Fig. 14-9), the inner epithelial root sheath disappears and the outer root sheath passes over into the Malpighian layer of the epidermis. The connective tissue follicle ceases as a distinct structure at about the level of insertion of the *arrector pili* muscles.

Marked changes are also noted as the bulb is approached. The outer root sheath thins down to two and finally to one layer of rather flat cells and then disappears. The layers of the inner root sheath retain their iden-

tity until the neck of the papilla is reached, at which point the different layers coalesce.

The bulbous thickening of the hair root which surrounds the papilla is not organized into layers but constitutes a matrix of growing, multiplying cells that superficially become transformed into the horny cells of the hair and the inner root sheath. Laterally, the cells of the bulb become continuous with the outer root sheath which, like the Malpighian layer of the epidermis, grows by mitosis of cells in the deeper layers, i.e., the external layers of the root sheath. Thus, the growth of the outer root sheath is radial, while the hair and inner root sheath grow upward from the thickened base of the follicle. The hair papilla, although much larger, is simi-

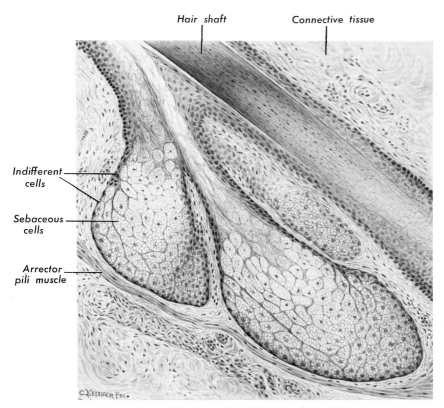

Hair shaft   Connective tissue

Indifferent cells

Sebaceous cells

Arrector pili muscle

FIG. 14-13. Sebaceous gland from scalp. ×130

lar in structure to other dermal papillae and contains delicate elastic and collagenous fibrils, cellular elements, blood vessels and nerves.

Muscles and Glands of the Hair Follicle. The erectors of the hairs (*arrectores pilorum*) are oblique bands of smooth muscle fibers, from 50 to 220 μ in diameter, which arise in the subepithelial tissue and are usually inserted in the connective tissue follicle of the hair, about the middle of the follicle or a little above. Each muscle, at its origin, is attached to several delicate connective tissue strands, runs for a distance as a compact bundle and then divides into several bundles that go to the individual hairs of a hair group. The muscles usually arch around the sebaceous glands which fill the angle between the muscle and hair, although large sebaceous glands occasionally penetrate the mus-

cle. The thickness of the muscle bands corresponds roughly to the thickness and length of the hair. They are poorly developed in the hairs of the axilla and in certain parts of the face where the muscles of facial expression apparently take over the function of arrectors. The eyebrows, eyelids and lashes have no arrectors.

The hairs and hair follicles are not perpendicular to the skin but slope distinctly. The *arrector pili* muscle is situated in the obtuse angle between the hair follicle and surface. When the muscle contracts, the hair becomes more vertical to the surface and, at the same time, a small groove appears in the skin at the place where the muscle is attached. This gives rise to the so-called "goose flesh."

The *sebaceous* glands are with few exceptions connected with the hair follicles (Fig. 14-13). They are simple or branched alveolar glands. Their size varies considerably and bears no relation to the size of the hair, the largest glands being frequently connected with the smallest hairs. The glands are spherical or ovoid in shape, and each is encapsulated in connective tissue. The excretory duct is wide and empties into the neck of the follicle. It is lined with stratified squamous epithelium continuous with the outer root sheath and the Malpighian layer of the epidermis. The lower end of the duct opens into several simple or branched alveoli, at the mouths of which the epithelium becomes thinner. The alveoli themselves are completely filled with a stratified epithelium.

The most peripheral cells are rather small and cubical in shape and occasionally show mitotic figures. Toward the interior the polyhedral or spheroidal cells become progressively larger as a result of the accumulation of numerous fat droplets in their cytoplasm. Their secretion, an oily substance called *sebum*, appears to be the direct product of disintegration of the alveolar cells (holocrine mode of secretion), and all of the stages of the process are seen in the various layers of cells. The smaller peripheral cells contain only a few small fat droplets or none at all. The most central ones and those in the lumen of the duct show the most marked changes. Their cytoplasm is almost wholly converted into fat, and their nuclei are shrunken or disintegrated. In the middle zone are cells showing intermediate stages.

The replacement of cells lost in secretion is accomplished chiefly by mitotic divisions of the indifferent cells at the periphery of the gland (Fig. 14-13). The stages in this process, as well as the proliferation of new alveoli from the cells of the excretory ducts, can be demonstrated in animals in which the growth of the sebaceous glands is stimulated experimentally (Montagna and Kenyon, 1949). In fetal development, the glands and their ducts arise by proliferation and differentiation from the outer epithelial root sheath of the hair follicle (See Fig. 14-18 under Development of Skin).

Sebaceous glands unconnected with hair follicles occur along the margin of the lips, in the nipple, in the glans and prepuce of the penis and in the labia minora.

Replacement of Hairs. Shedding of hair takes place in most mammals at regularly recurring periods. In man there is constant though gradual loss and replacement of hairs. The scalp hairs have the longest duration of life, from 2 to 5 years, while those of the eyebrows and ears last only from 3 to 5 months. Even shorter is the age of the eyelashes.

When a hair is about to be shed, proliferation of cells above the papilla slows down and finally ceases. The bulb develops into a solid, club-shaped mass and becomes completely keratinized, its lower end splitting brushlike into numerous fibers. The club-shaped bulb, firmly fused with the lower ends of the inner root sheath which likewise cornifies, becomes detached from the papilla and is slowly shifted towards the surface of the skin, to about the level of the entrance of the sebaceous ducts. There it may remain for some time, until pulled out or shed or pushed out by a replacing hair. Such hairs are called *club hairs* to distinguish them from hairs that possess papillae.

The papilla atrophies and may completely disappear. The outer root sheath collapses and forms a cord of cells extending between the atrophied papilla and the lower end of the shedding hair.

The formation of a new hair starts with the proliferation of cells of the outer root sheath in the region of the old papilla. The papilla becomes larger and invaginates the cell mass or, according to some authors, a new papilla is formed. From this new matrix or "hair germ," the new hair develops in a manner similar to embryonal hair formation. The new hair grows toward the surface, under or to one side of the dead hair which it finally replaces.

THE NAILS

The nails are composed of flat, horny scales which form protective coverings for

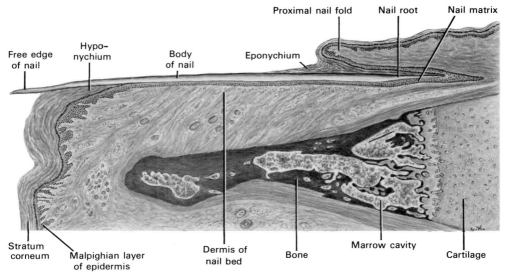

FIG. 14-14. Longitudinal section of a finger nail of a newborn infant. ×22

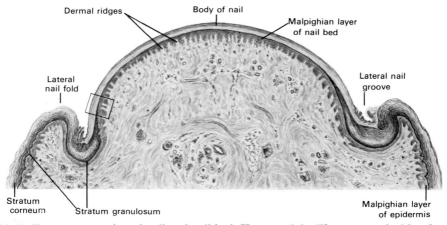

FIG. 14-15. Transverse section of nail and nail bed. Human adult. The area marked by the *square* is enlarged in Figure 14-16. ×20.

the distal phalanges of the fingers and toes. Each nail consists of (a) a *body*, the attached uncovered portion of the nail, (b) a *free edge*, the anterior unattached extension of the body, and (c) the *nail root*, the posterior or proximal part of the nail which lies beneath a fold of the skin (Fig. 14-14). Most of the body of the nail is pink because it is sufficiently translucent to transmit the color from the underlying vascular tissue. The proximal part of the nail is ,whitish and is called the *lunula* because of its shape.

The fold of skin which extends around the proximal and lateral borders of the nail constitutes the *nail fold*, and the skin which lies beneath the nail forms the *nail bed*. The furrow between the nail bed and nail fold is the *nail groove* (Figs. 14-14 and 14-15).

The nail itself is hard and horny and consists of several layers of clear, flat cells that contain shrunken and degenerated nuclei. The striated appearance observed in sections cut perpendicular to the surface is produced by the arrangement of the cells in layers.

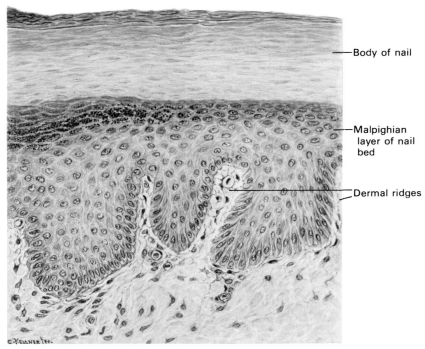

Body of nail

Malpighian layer of nail bed

Dermal ridges

Fig. 14-16. Transverse section through the lateral part of a nail, near the lateral nail groove, as outlined in Figure 14-15. ×365.

The nail bed consists of epithelium and corium continuous with the epidermis and dermis of the skin of the nail folds. The epidermis of the nail folds usually has the zones characteristic of palmar skin, although the stratum lucidum may be thin or absent in some cases. The stratum corneum of the proximal nail fold turns into the nail groove, spreads over the upper surface of the nail root and continues for a short distance onto the surface of the body of the nail as the *eponychium* (Fig. 14-14). The stratum corneum of the lateral folds ends in the lateral grooves in contact with the borders of the nail (Figs. 14-15 and 14-16). The stratum granulosum and lucidum terminate in the lower part of the grooves.

The epithelium of the nail bed corresponds to the Malpighian layer of the skin and, like the latter, consists of polygonal prickle cells and a stratum cylindricum resting upon a basement membrane. The epithelium of the posterior part of the nail bed, the part that lies beneath the root and the proximal portion of the body corresponding to the lunula, is thicker than elsewhere and is called the *matrix* because it functions for nail growth. Growth of the nail takes place by a transformation of the more superficial cells of the matrix into true nail cells. In this process, the outer, harder layer is pushed forward over the Malpighian layer, the latter remaining always in the same position.

Under the distal free edge of the nail, the epithelium of the nail bed becomes continuous with the Malpighian layer of the skin, and the other layers characteristic of the epidermis begin. The stratum corneum of the skin beneath the free edge of the nail is thickened and is known as the *hyponychium* (Fig. 14-14).

The corium of the nail bed differs somewhat from that of ordinary skin. Its connective tissue fibers are arranged partly longitudinal to the long axis of the nail and partly in a vertical plane extending from the periosteum to the nail. Dermal papillae are found beneath the proximal part of the nail root but disappear beneath the distal part of the root, to be replaced by longitudinal dermal ridges which, increasing in height as they pass forward, continue to the distal end of the nail bed. Since the dermal ridges run longitudinally, the boundary between the epithelium and connective tissue appears smooth in longitudinal sections and irregular and papilla-like in cross sections (Fig. 14-15).

BLOOD VESSELS, LYMPHATICS AND NERVES OF THE SKIN

Blood Vessels. From the larger arteries in the subcutaneous tissue, branches penetrate the reticular layer of the dermis, where they anastomose to form cutaneous networks. The latter give off branches that pass to the papillary layer of the dermis and there form a second series of networks, the subpapillary, just beneath the papillae. From the cutaneous networks arise two sets of capillaries, one supplying the fat lobules, the other supplying the region of the sweat glands. From the subpapillary networks are given off small arteries that break up into capillary networks for the supply of the papillae, sebaceous glands and hair follicles. The return blood from these capillaries first enters a horizontal plexus of veins just under the papillae. This communicates with a second plexus just beneath the first. Small veins from this second plexus pass alongside the arteries of the deeper part of the corium, where they form a third plexus with larger, more irregular meshes. Into this plexus pass most of the veins from the fat lobules and sweat glands, although one or two small veins from the sweat glands usually follow the duct and empty into the subpapillary plexus. The blood next passes into a fourth plexus in the subcutaneous tissue, from which arise veins of considerable size. These accompany the arteries.

As noted in Chapter 12, arteriovenous anastomoses are especially numerous in

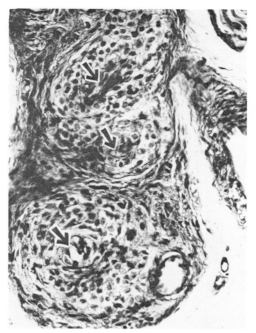

Fig. 14-17. Photomicrograph of a glomus from the dermis of thick skin. A small artery is seen at the right of the glomus in longitudinal and tangential section. The artery coils in the glomus and is cut at different levels (*arrows*); its wall is thickened by epithelioid cells. ×290. (From a preparation contributed by Dr. T. E. Hunt.)

the dermis of the fingers and toes. In these areas, the arterial part of the anastomosis often forms a part of a specific organ known as a glomus. The artery is coiled or ball-like and its media contains epitheloid cells (Fig. 14-17). The internal diameter of the narrowest part of the anastomosis is usually 20 to 40 μ; thus, the anastomoses convey much more blood than capillaries do. By contraction or relaxation, they influence the amount of blood flowing through localized regions. They play an important role in conserving heat and in regulating the temperature of peripheral areas. In this respect, their high degree of development in the feet of penguins is noteworthy.

Small arteries from the plexuses of the skin and subcutis pass to the hair follicle. The larger arterioles run longitudinally in the outer layer of the follicle. From these are given off branches which form a rich plexus of small arterioles and capillaries in the middle vascular layer of the follicle. Capillaries from this plexus also pass to the sebaceous glands, the arrectores pilorum muscles and the papillae.

Lymphatics. The lymphatics of the skin begin as clefts in the papillae which open into a horizonatal network of lymph capillaries in the papillary layer. This communicates with a network of larger lymph capillaries with wider meshes in the subcutaneous tissue. The latter also receives lymph capillaries from plexuses that surround the sebaceous glands, the sweat glands and the hair follicles.

Nerves. The nerves of the skin are mainly sensory. Efferent sympathetic axons supply the smooth muscle of the walls of the blood vessels, the arrectores pilorum and the secretory cells of the sweat glands. The sensory nerves are peripheral processes of somatic ganglion cells. The larger trunks lie in the subcutis, giving off branches which pass to the corium, where they form a rich subpapillary plexus of both myelinated and nonmyelinated fibers. From the subcutaneous nerve trunks and from the subpapillary plexus are given off fibers which terminate in more or less elaborate special nerve endings (Chapter 10). Their location is as follows. (1) *In the subcutaneous tissue:* Vater-Pacinian corpuscles. They are most numerous in the palms and soles. (2) *In the dermis:* tactile corpuscles of Meissner are found in the papillae, especially of the fingertip, palm and sole. Krause's end bulbs are usually in the dermis just beneath the papillae, more rarely in the papillae themselves. (3) *In the epithelium:* free nerve endings among the epithelial cells.

Branches of the cutaneous nerves supply the hair follicles, which are important in sensory reception. As a rule, only one nerve passes to each follicle, entering it just below the entrance of the duct of the sebaceous gland. As it enters the follicle, the nerve fiber loses its myelin sheath and divides into two branches, which further subdivide to form a ringlike plexus of fine fibers encircling the follicle. From this ring, small varicose fibrils run for a short distance up the follicle, terminating mainly in slight expansions on the vitreous membrane.

DEVELOPMENT OF THE SKIN AND ITS APPENDAGES

The *epidermis* develops from the ectoderm and consists at first of a single row of cuboidal cells. By the second month it has differentiated into two layers. The outer layer, the periderm or epitrichium, consisting of flattened cells, is a transient structure and is lost shortly before or after birth. The inner layer, composed of irregular cells with large nuclei and abundant protoplasm, gives rise to the entire epidermis. The cells multiply by mitosis and soon form a stratified epithelium. True keratinization, however, begins only in the fifth month.

The *dermis* develops from the parietal mesoderm and consists at first of typical mesenchyme. In the second month, cell differentiation begins, some of the cells becoming fibroblasts. Toward the end of the second month, fibrils make their appearance, at first reticular and collagenous and, soon after, elastic as well. Some time later the whole mass shows a differentiation into two layers, an upper, denser one, giving rise to the corium proper, and a deeper, looser one that forms the subcutaneous tissue.

Hair appears in human embryos at the end of the second month, the first places being the brows, upper lips and chin. By the seventh month, lanugo hairs are distributed all over the body.

Each hair develops as a thickening of the germinative layer that grows down obliquely into the derma, forming a slender solid cord of cells, the *hair germ* or *hair plug* (Fig. 14-18). The connective tissue cells of the corium surrounding the cord condense to form the dermal follicle, while an invagination of connective tissue into the lower end of the hair germ forms the papilla.

The cells surrounding the papilla become differentiated into two zones, a central conical mass whose apex is directed toward the surface (the hair bulb) and an outer layer of epithelial cells which becomes the outer root sheath. The cells of the hair bulb grow toward the skin, the axial cells forming the hair and the peripheral cells giving rise to the inner root sheath. The various sublayers are formed from these by subsequent differentiation. Above the apex of the cone, the axial cells of the hair plug cornify and disintegrate; and a channel is formed that penetrates the epidermis. The hair grows into this channel and, when first

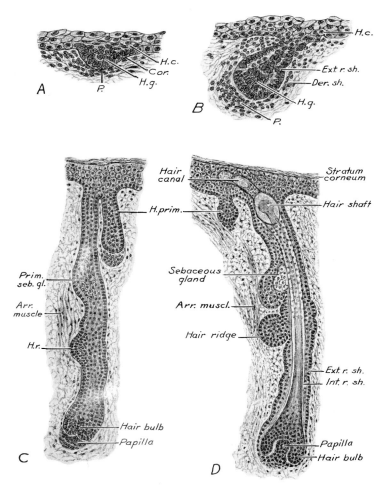

FIG 14-18. Four stages in the development of a human hair. *A* and *B*, early stages from a frontal skin of a 3-month embryo. *C* and *D*, later stages from chin of a 5-month embryo. *Arr.muscl.*, primordium of arrector muscle; *Cor.*, border of the corium; *Der.sh.*, primordium of dermal sheath (connective tissue follicle); *Ext.r.sh.*, external root sheath; *H.c.*, hair canal cells; *H.g.*, hair germ; *H.prim.*, primordia of young hairs; *H.r.*, hair ridge for attachment of arrector muscle; *Int.r.sh.*, internal root sheath; *P.*, primordium of papilla; *Prim.seb.gl.*, primordium of sebaceous gland. (Redrawn after Shaffer.)

formed, lies wholly beneath the surface. As the hair reaches the surface, its pointed extremity pierces the surface epithelium and emerges as the hair shaft.

The *sebaceous* gland develops from the outer root sheath and appears first as a thickening in the upper portion of the hair germ (see above). It soon develops into a flask-shaped, solid mass of cells which later differentiate to form the ducts and alveoli of the gland.

The *sweat* glands first appear as solid ingrowths of the epithelium into the underlying corium. The lower end of the ingrowth becomes thickened and convoluted to form the coiled portion of the gland,

and somewhat later the central portion becomes channeled out to form the lumen. The myoepithelial cells, which lie between the epithelium and the basement membrane, are derived from the ectodermal cells of the ingrowth and not from mesoderm.

REFERENCES

BREATHNACH, A. S. 1965 The cell of Langerhans. Int. Rev. Cytol., vol. 18, pp. 1–28.

BREATHNACH, A. S., BIRBECK, M. S. C., AND EVERALL, J. D. 1963 Observations bearing on the relationship between Langerhans cells and melanocytes. Ann. N. Y. Acad. Sci., vol. 100, pp. 223–238.

CUMMINS, H. 1964 Dermatoglyphics; a brief review. In The Epidermis (Montagna, W., and Lobitz, W. C., Jr., editors), pp. 375–386. Academic Press, New York.

ELLIS, R. A. 1965 Fine structure of the myoepithelium of the eccrine sweat glands of man. J. Cell Biol., vol. 27, pp. 551–563.

GIROUD, A., AND LEBLOND, C. P. 1951 The keratinization of epidermis and its derivatives, especially the hair, as shown by x-ray diffraction and histochemical studies. Ann. N. Y. Acad. Sci., vol. 53, pp. 613–626.

HUTCHINSON, C., AND KOOP, C. E. 1956 Lines of cleavage in the skin of the newborn infant. Anat. Rec., vol. 126, pp. 299–310.

LAIDLAW, G. F. 1932 The dopa reaction in normal histology. Anat. Rec., vol. 53, pp. 399–413.

LERNER, A. B., AND FITZPATRICK, T. B. 1950 Biochemistry of melanin formation. Physiol. Rev., vol. 30, pp. 91–126.

LEWIS, T. 1937 The Blood Vessels of the Human Skin and Their Responses. Shaw and Sons Ltd., London.

MASSON, P. 1948 Pigment cells in man. The Biology of Melanomas. N. Y. Acad. Sci., Special Publ., vol. 4, pp. 15–51.

MATOLTSY, A. G., AND MATOLTSY, M. N. 1970 The chemical nature of keratohyalin granules of the epidermis. J. Cell Biol., vol. 47, pp. 593–603.

MENTON, D. N. 1970 The effects of essential fatty acid deficiency on the fine structure of mouse skin. J. Morph., vol. 132, pp. 181–206.

MENTON, D. N., AND EISEN, A. Z. 1971 Structure and organization of mammalian stratum corneum. J. Ultrastruct. Res., vol. 35, pp. 247–264.

MONTAGNA, W. 1962 The Structure and Function of Skin. Academic Press, New York.

MONTAGNA, W., AND KENYON, P. 1949 Growth potentials and mitotic division in the sebaceous glands of the rabbit. Anat. Rec., vol. 103, pp. 365–380.

MONTAGNA, W., AND LOBITZ, W. C. (editors) 1964 The Epidermis. Academic Press, New York.

MOYER, F. H. 1963 Genetic effects on melano-some fine structure and ontogeny in normal and malignant cells. Ann. N. Y. Acad. Sci., vol. 100, pp. 584–606.

MUNGER, B. L. 1961 The ultrastructure and histophysiology of human eccrine sweat glands. J. Biophys. Biochem. Cytol., vol. 11, pp. 385–402.

ODLAND, G. F. 1964 Tonofilaments and keratohyalin. In The Epidermis (Montagna, W., and Lobitz, W. C., Jr., editors), pp. 237–249. Academic Press, New York.

RAWLES, M. E. 1948 Origin of melanophores and their role in development of color pattern in vertebrates. Physiol. Rev., vol. 28, pp. 383–408.

ROGERS, G. E. 1964 Structural and biochemical features of the hair follicle. In The Epidermis (Montagna, W., and Lobitz, W. C., Jr., editors), pp. 179–236. Academic Press, New York.

ROTHMAN, S. 1954 Physiology and Biochemistry of the Skin. University of Chicago Press, Chicago.

ROTHMAN, S. 1964 Keratinization in historical perspective. In The Epidermis (Montagna, W., and Lobitz, W. C., Jr., editors), pp. 1–14. Academic Press, New York.

SEIJI, M., SHIMAO, K., BIRBECK, M. S. C., AND FITZPATRICK, T. B. 1963 Subcellular localization of melanin biosynthesis. Ann. N. Y. Acad. Sci., vol. 100, pp. 497–533.

SELBY, C. C. 1955 An electron microscope study of the epidermis of mammalian skin in thin section. J. Biophys. Biochem. Cytol., vol. 1, pp. 429–444.

STARICO, R. G. 1963 Amelanotic melanocytes in the outer sheath of the human hair follicle and their role in the repigmentation of regenerated epidermis. Ann. N. Y. Acad. Sci., vol. 100, pp. 239–255.

TROTTER, M. 1939 Classification of hair color. Amer. J. Phys. Anthrop., vol. 25, pp. 237–260.

WILLIER, B. H., AND RAWLES, M. E. 1940 The control of feather color pattern by melanophores grafted from one embryo to another of a different breed of fowl. Physiol. Zool., vol. 13, pp. 177–199.

ZELICKSON, A. H. (Editor) 1967 Ultrastructure of Normal and Abnormal Skin. Lea and Febiger, Philadelphia.

15

Glands

STRUCTURE AND CLASSIFICATION

All cells of the body take up oxygen and nutritive substances from the blood, via intercellular fluid, and give off waste products. In this sense, all cells secrete and excrete. Certain cells of the body, in addition to carrying on these metabolic processes necessary for their own existence, also manufacture specific substances not for their own use but to be extruded from the cells and used elsewhere in the body (secretions, e.g., gastric juice) or discarded (excretions, e.g., urine). Such cells are known as *gland cells* or *glandular epithelium,* and an aggregation of these cells into a definite structure for the purpose of carrying on secretion or excretion is known as a *gland.*

A gland may consist of a single cell, as for example, the goblet cell (see Chapter 4) or the *unicellular glands* of invertebrates. Such a cell produces within itself a substance which is to be used outside the cell. The appearance which this cell presents depends upon the stage of secretion. It is thus possible to differentiate between a "resting" and an "active" cell or between an "empty" and a "loaded" cell.

Most glands are composed of more than one cell (*multicellular glands*). Usually there is a large number of cells, and these cells, instead of lying directly upon the surface, line more or less extensive invaginations into which they pour their secretions.

General Structure and Function of

Secretory Cells. The goblet cell of the intestine is one of the simple columnar cells that constitute the surface epithelium of the mucous membrane. It is distinguishable as a mucous cell only after the formation of secretion has begun. When filled with secretion, the apical portion of the cell becomes dilated while the basal portion remains slender, giving the cell a goblet shape. The swollen apical portion in the living cell contains droplets of premucin or mucigen. The mucigen droplets are not generally visible in sections prepared by routine methods because the commonly used fixatives dissolve the mucigen, leaving a loose filamentous network in the cytoplasm. However, the mucigen droplets can be seen readily under the light microscope in sections prepared by appropriate technical procedure (Fig. 15-1).

At the height of the "active" phase of secretion, the mucigen droplets are released at the apical end of the cell (Figs. 15-1 and 15-2) and are dissolved and immediately converted into mucin. In some cases, the droplets are released gradually while new droplets are formed, and the goblet shape of the cell is retained for a considerable length of time. In other cases, the droplets are released rapidly and the cell quickly loses the goblet shape and reverts to a more slender form. After a period of rest, the same cell may become active again and pass through the same stages of secretion.

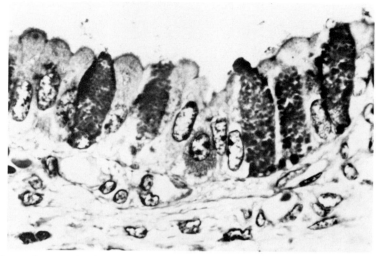

FIG. 15-1. Photomicrograph of a portion of a pancreatic duct of a guinea pig showing several goblet cells interspersed among the columnar lining cells. The mucigen is preserved in droplet form but the resolution of the light microscope is not sufficient to show whether the plasmalemma is complete at the apical end of the cell. Compare with eiectron micrograph in Figure 15-2. Chrome hematoxylin and phloxine stain. ×1125.

Our knowledge of the processes involved in the synthesis and release of secretory materials by gland cells is based on biochemical studies and on a combination of electron microscopy and radioautography. Biochemical studies show that three classes of RNA are involved in the secretory process: ribosomal RNA, messenger RNA and transfer RNA. The ribosomes of the cytoplasm are composed of protein combined with ribonucleic acid of nuclear origin. Messenger RNA, formed in association with DNA of the chromosomes, migrates to the cytoplasm where it becomes associated with ribosomes in the form of polysomes. The messenger RNA carries information from the DNA of the nucleus to the polysomes of the cytoplasm to direct the particular sequence of amino acids necessary for the formation of a particular protein. Transfer RNA picks up the amino acids (building materials) taken into the cell from the blood via the intercellular fluid and transports them to the region of the polyribosomes. There is biochemical evidence for a specific transfer RNA for each of the amino acids. In association with the polyribosomes of the endoplasmic reticulum, the amino acids are assembled to form molecules and marcomolecules of proteins. (See Chapter 1 and Figure 1-16.)

The intracellular transport of secretory proteins from their site of synthesis to their exit from the cell has been studied by cell fractionation methods and by electron microscopic radioautography. Stages in this process are illustrated in Figures 15-3 to 15-6 inclusive, from studies by Jamieson and Palade (1967). By using slices of pancreas incubated in vitro, they were able to expose pancreatic exocrine cells to labeled leucine for only a short period of time, followed by post incubation in a medium in which there was no further incorporation of labeled amino acids into proteins. In other words, changes in location of the label at successive intervals of post incubation could be due only to movement of protein synthesized during the pulse labeling. Figure 15-3 shows that pancreatic cells of slices incubated in vitro for as long as 3 hours have normal ultrastructural characteristics. Figure 15-4 shows radio-

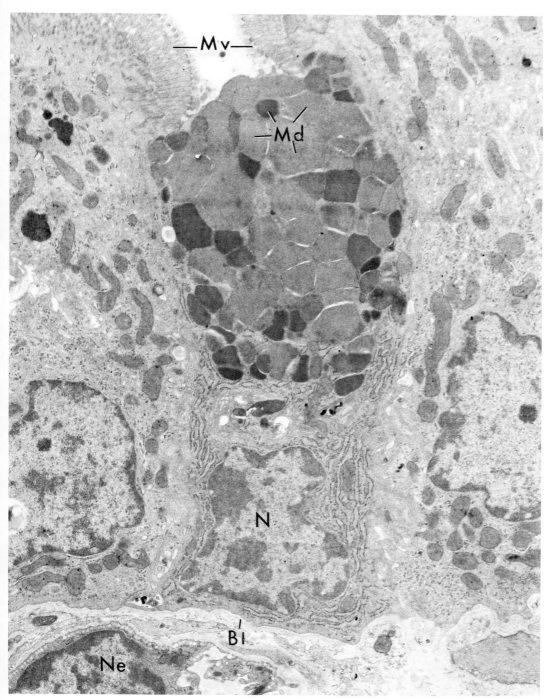

Fig. 15-2. Electron micrograph of a section of the small intestine of a bat showing a goblet cell between two columnar absorbing cells. Mucigen droplets (*Md*) fill most of the cell above the nucleus (*N*). An intact plasmalemma, with a few microvilli, is seen at the adluminal surface of the goblet cell. Numerous microvilli (*Mv*) are present on the adluminal surface of the absorbing cells. *Bl*, basal lamina beneath the intestinal epithelium; *Ne*, nucleus of an endothelial cell of a capillary blood vessel within the connective tissue of the lamina propria. ×11,440. (Courtesy of Drs. Keith Porter and Mary Bonneville).

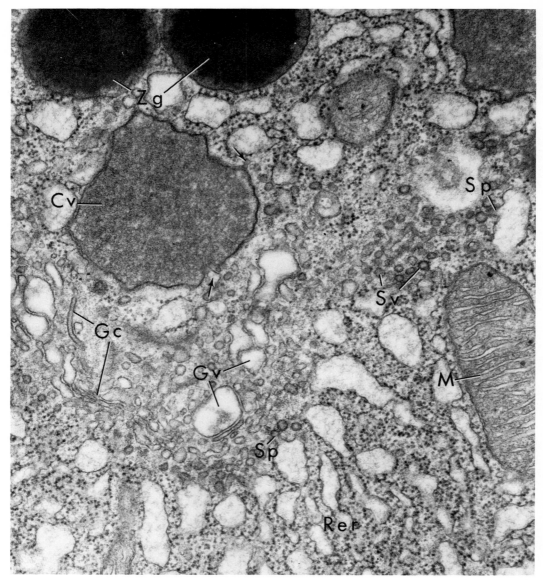

Fig. 15-3. Electron micrograph of a portion of a pancreatic exocrine cell from a slice of a guinea pig pancreas incubated for 3 hours in vitro. The ultrastructure of the incubated cell is approximately the same as that of pancreatic cells fixed at biopsy. Note that the rough-surfaced endoplasmic reticulum (*Ser*) is composed partly of rough-surfaced and partly of smooth-surfaced cisternae. The latter have projections (*Sp*) into the Golgi complex, toward clusters of smooth-surfaced veiscles (*Sv*). Some of the latter are in contact (at *arrows*) with the limiting membrane of a condensing vacuole (*Cv*). *Gc*, Golgi cisternae; *Gv*, Golgi vacuoles; *M*, mitochondrion; and, *Zg*, zymogen granules. This is a control specimen for comparison with pancreatic slices that were pulse-labeled with leucine-³H and then post incubated for varying periods in order to study the secretory cycle by electron microscopic radioautographs. See next three figures. ×43,400. (Courtesy of Drs. J. D. Jamieson and G. E. Palade, J. Cell Biol., vol. 34, 1967).

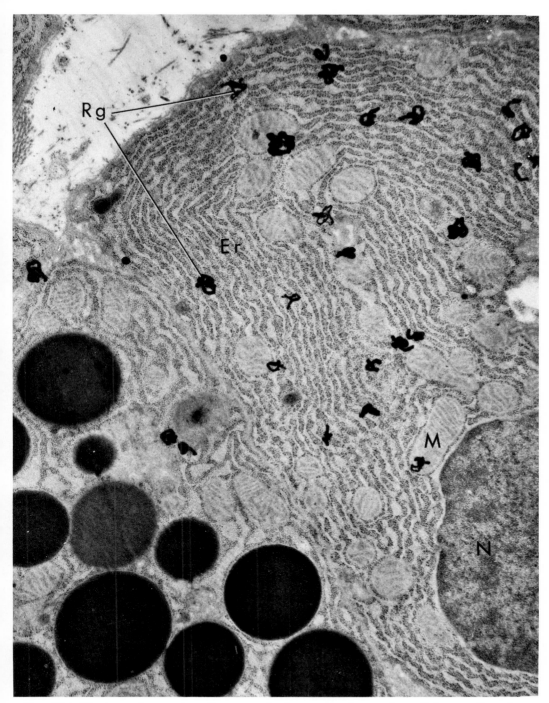

FIG. 15-4. Electron microscopic radioautograph of a pancreatic exocrine cell from a slice of pancreatic tissue that was pulse labeled in vitro for 3 minutes with L-leucine-^{3}H. Note that the radioautographic grains (Rg) are present chiefly over the rough surfaced endoplasmic reticulum (Er). M, mitochondrion; N, nucleus. ×17,500. (Courtesy of Drs. J. D. Jamieson and G. E. Palade, J. Cell Biol., vol. 34, 1967).

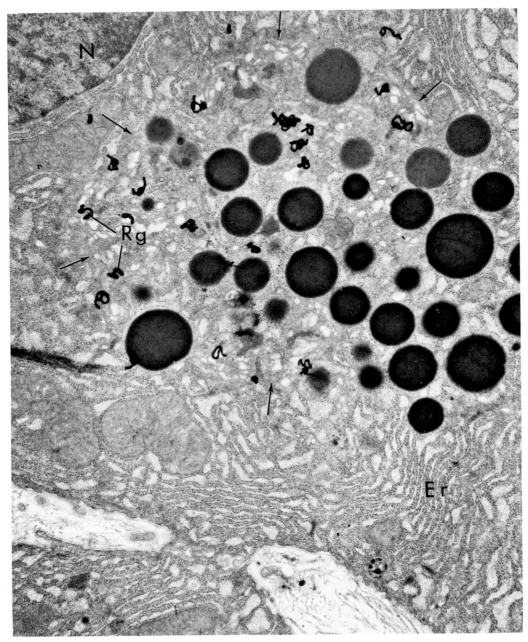

Fig. 15-5. Electron microscopic radioautograph of a pancreatic exocrine cell after 3 minutes of pulse labeling, similar to that used for the cell shown in Figure 15-4, plus 7 minutes of post-incubation. Note that most of the radioautographic grains (*Rg*), indicating the position of the labeled leucine, are present at the periphery of the Golgi complex (marked by *arrows*). *Er*, endoplasmic reticulum. ×16,700. (Courtesy of Drs. J. D. Jamieson and G. E. Palade, J. Cell Biol., vol. 34, 1967).

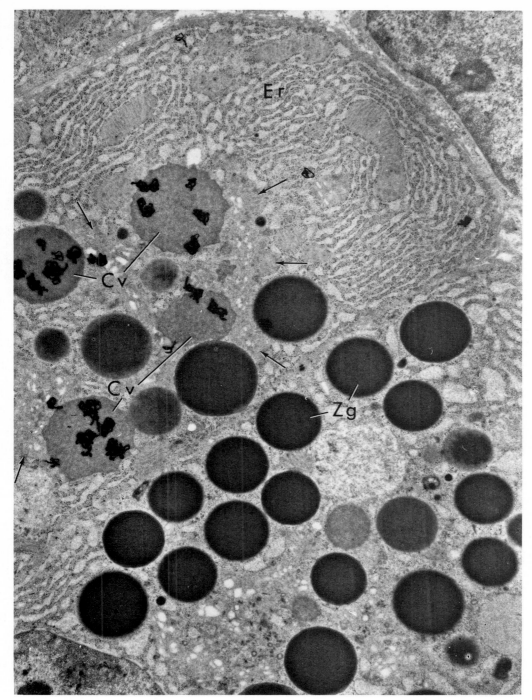

FIG. 15-6. Electron microscopic radioautograph of a pancreatic exocrine cell after 3 minutes of pulse labeling, as shown in Figure 15-4, plus 37 minutes of post-pulse incubation. The periphery of the Golgi complex is indicated by *arrows*. Note that most of the radioautographic grains are present over condensing vacuoles (*Cv*). This series of radioautographs shows that the secretory material, synthesized from leucine and other amino acids at the sites of ribosomes of the rough surfaced endoplasmic reticulum, *Er*, is transported via cisternae to the Golgi region where it is concentrated within condensing vacuoles which become zymogen granules (*Zg*). ×12,500. (Courtesy of Drs. J. D. Jamieson and G. E. Palade, J. Cell Biol., vol. 34, 1967).

autographic grains over the rough surfaced endoplasmic reticulum of cells fixed after 3 minutes of incubation in labeled leucine, demonstrating that labeled amino acid has been incorporated rapidly into newly synthesized proteins. Studies of tissues fixed at subsequent intervals of post incubation show that the proteins move via cisternae of the endoplasmic reticulum to smooth surfaced vesicles at the periphery of the Golgi complex and thence to condensing vacuoles that become zymogen granules.

Secretory proteins of most cells have a carbohydrate moiety and those of some cells (e.g., goblet cells) have an appreciable amount of carbohydrate. Hence, goblet cells are advantageous for studies on the synthesis of carbohydrates and their conjugation with proteins. Radioautographic studies of goblet cells of tissues taken from animals at intervals following injection of labeled glucose show that sugars are transported to saccules of the Golgi complex where they are conjugated with the secretory proteins (Neutra and Leblond, 1969). (For further details on secretion, see sections on The Granular Endoplasmic Reticulum and The Golgi Apparatus, Chapter 1.)

Classification of Glands. As has been mentioned, a gland may consist of a single secretory cell (unicellular gland), or it may be composed of many cells (multicellular gland), the secretory cells usually lining an invagination from the free surface. In the simplest form of a glandular invagination, all of the cells lining the lumen are secreting cells. In more highly developed glands, secretion is primarily by the deeper cells and remainder of the gland serves to carry the secretion to the surface. This latter part is then known as the *duct*, in contradistinction to the deeper *secreting portion*. In both the duct portion and secreting portion of a gland, the epithelium rests upon a more or less definite *basement membrane*. Beneath the basement membrane, separating and supporting the glandular elements, is a fine vascular connective tissue.

Glands are sometimes classified, according to the nature of their secretion, into *mucous* (producing a viscous, slimy secretion), *serous* (producing a thin, watery secretion) and *mixed glands* (producing both types of secretion). Although this classification is particularly useful for some of the glands, such as those of the oral cavity, it cannot be satisfactorily used for all glands of the body, such as the sebaceous and mammary glands and the kidney.

The cells of mucous and serous glands differ in structure. The structure of the unicellular mucous gland or goblet cell has already been described. In the multicellular mucous glands or *mucous alveoli* (e.g., of the palatine glands) the cells are usually more or less pyramidal in shape as a result of their arrangement around the lumen of the terminal tubule. When the cell is filled with secretion, the nucleus is flattened against the basal part of the cell. As already described for the goblet cell, the mucigen of these cells is not well preserved with ordinary techniques and is dissolved, leaving a loose network that, with hematoxylin and eosin, remains unstained or stains very faintly with hematoxylin.

The cells of *serous alveoli* secrete a clear, watery, albuminous product. The secretion of many serous glands (e.g., pancreas and parotid gland) contains digestive enzymes. In these cells, the secretory granules are the enzyme precursors, or *zymogen granules* (Figs. 15-7 and 15-8), and the cells are therefore known as *serozymogenic cells*. Serous cells are usually pyramidal, with rounded nuclei lying in the basal half of the cells. The cells pass through active and resting phases of secretion, similar to the mucous cells. During the resting phase, the secretory granules may become so numerous as to almost fill the cell, but the nucleus does not become flattened as in the mucous cell. The secretory granules, if they are preserved, are acidophilic. Chromophilic material (RNA) is found in high concentration in the basal portion of serozymogenic cells, giving that part of the cell a strongly basophilic, striated appearance (Fig. 15-7).

The alveoli of mixed glands (e.g., mandibular and sublingual) contain both mucous and serous cells.

According to whether the secretion is merely a product of the cell or whether it consists of gland cells, the glands may be classified as *eccrine* (merocrine), *apocrine* or *holocrine*. The majority of the glands are eccrine. The secretion is a product of the cell, but no part of the cell itself is extruded with the secretion. In the sebaceous glands, entire cells laden with secretory material are extruded as the secretion. This is the holocrine type of secretion. An intermediate type of secretion known as apocrine may be found in axillary and circumanal modified sweat glands. In these glands, an ultramicroscopic portion of the cell may be released along with the secretory material. The gonads (ovary and testis) produce very highly specialized secretions consisting of living cells (ova and sperm) that continue to develop after extrusion from the gland. Since they secrete living cells, the ovary and testis are sometimes called *cytogenic* glands.

Glands may also be classified according to whether they possess ducts which carry their secretions to an epithelial surface (*exocrine glands, glands of external secretion*) or whether they are ductless and pour their secretions into the blood or lymph (*endocrine glands, glands of internal secretion*).

The exocrine glands may further be subdivided and classified in accordance with the type of duct system contained. When a gland consists of a single secretory passage or a single system of secretory passages opening into an unbranched duct, it is called a *simple gland* (Fig 15-9, *A–G*). When a gland contains a duct system that is elaborate and branched, it is called a *compound gland* (Fig. 15-9, *H–J*). Both the simple and compound glands may be subdivided in accordance with the form of the terminal secretory portions. When the

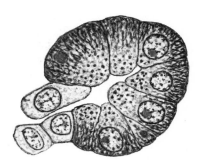

Fig. 15-7. Acinus of human pancreas. Acinar enlargement produced by the increase in height of the secretory cells, while the lumen remains narrow. All secretory cells in same functional stage. Zymogen granules in apical portion of cells; chromophilic material in basal portion of cells. Chrome hematoxylin and phloxine stain. ×1100.

secreting portion is a tubule, the lumen of which is of fairly uniform diameter, the gland is known as a *tubular gland* (Fig. 15-9, *A–C*). When the secreting portion is dilated in the form of a sac or alveolus, the gland is known as a *saccular, alveolar* or *acinar gland* (Fig. 15-9, *E, F, G, J*). In many glands, the secretory passages are neither typically tubular nor alveolar but intermediate in type and combine certain characteristics of both; such glands are called *tubuloalveolar* or *tubuloacinar* (Fig. 15-9, *D, I*). The serous salivary glands and pancreas are typical examples of this type and have acinar enlargements which are produced by an increase in the height of the secretory epithelium while the lumen remains undilated and tubular (Figs. 15-7 and 15-9, *I, a, e, f,* and *g*). In some of the glands usually included in this group, such as the mucous salivary glands, mucous portions of the mixed salivary glands and Brunner's glands of the duodenum, the secretory passages vary in type of lumen from tubular forms to dilations resembling elongated alveoli (Fig. 15-9, *I, b, c*).

Glands may thus be classified as follows:

A. Exocrine glands (or glands with ducts)
   1. Simple glands

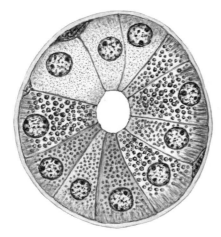

Fig. 15-8. Serous alveolus of human subman-dibular gland. Cells are shown in different func-tional stages; the cells containing zymogen gran-ules are taller than those without. Myoepithelial cells are seen between the secretory cells and the basement membrane. Hemalum-mucicarmine-au-rantia. (Redrawn after Zimmerman.)

(a) Tubular { straight
coiled
branched
(b) Tubuloalveolar (tubuloacinar)
(c) Alveolar (acinar, saccular)
2. Compound glands
(a) Tubular
(b) Tubuloalveolar (tubuloacinar)
(c) Alveolar
B. Endocrine glands (or glands without ducts)

EXOCRINE GLANDS

Simple Tubular Glands. These glands consist of simple, epithelial-lined tubules which open to the surface. All of the cells may be secreting cells, or only the more deeply situated ones may be. In the more highly developed of the simple tubular glands, we distinguish a mouth opening upon the surface, a neck which is usually some-what constricted, and a fundus, or deep secreting portion of the gland.

Simple tubular glands are divided accord-ing to the behavior of the fundus into (1) straight, (2) coiled, or (3) branched.

(1) A *straight tubular gland* is one in which the entire tubule runs a straight unbranched course, e.g., the glands of the large intestine (Fig. 15-9, *A*).

(2) A *coiled tubular gland* is one in which the deeper portion of the tubule is coiled or convoluted (Fig. 15-19, *B*). The sweat glands of the skin are the most typical examples.

(3) A *branched tubular gland* is a simple tubular gland in which the deeper portion of the tubule divides into branches that are lined with secreting cells and that open into a superficial portion which serves as a duct (Fig. 15-9, *C*). Examples of branched tubular glands are the fundic, pyloric and cardiac glands of the stomach and the glands of the mucous membrane of the uterus. Many of the pyloric glands are also slightly enlarged and coiled at their terminations so that they resemble to some extent both the convoluted tubular and the tubuloalveolar glands.

Simple Tubuloalveolar Glands. Simple tubuloalveolar or tubuloacinar glands are found only in the branched form (Fig. 15-9, *D*). Included in this group are the smaller glands of the following types: sali-vary glands of the oral cavity, seromucous glands of the respiratory tract, mucous glands of the esophagus and the Brunner's glands of the duodenum. Many of these, such as the esophageal and Brunner's glands, are classified by some authors as branched tubular but, since they are frequently en-larged at their terminations, they may be included in the branched tubuloalveolar group.

Simple Alveolar Glands. The simplest form of alveolar gland, consisting of a single sac with a dilated lumen and connected with the surface by a constricted portion, the neck, is shown in Figure 15-9, *E*. This simple form of alveolar gland is found in the skin of certain amphibians but does not occur in man. Simple alveolar glands in which there are several saccules are repre-sented by the smaller sebaceous glands (Fig. 15-9, *F*). In the sebaceous glands, as pointed out in Chapter 14, the secreting cells undergo fatty degeneration, are pushed centrally by new cells and are finally ex-truded as the secretion. Consequently, there are a number of layers of cells filling

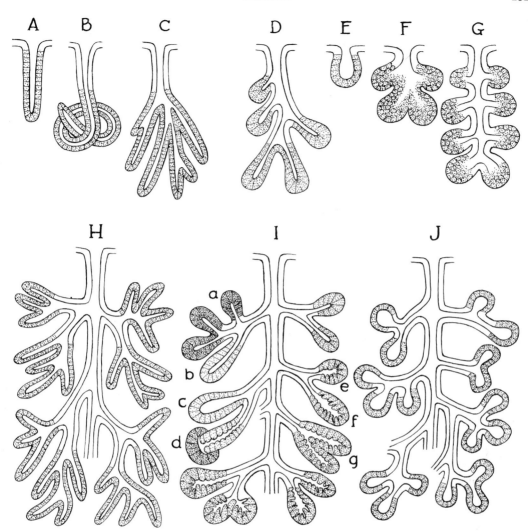

Fig. 15-9. Schema of various types of exocrine glands. *A* to *G*, simple glands: *H* to *J*, compound glands. *A*, simple nonbranched tubular; *B*, simple coiled tubular; *C*, branched tubular; *D*, branched tubuloacinar (tubuloalveolar); *E*, simple nonbranched alveolar; *F* and *G*, branched alveolar as in sebaceous glands; *H*, compound tubular; *I*, compound tubuloacinar, showing some of the various types of terminations. *a*, serous acinus with simple nonbranched canal; *b* and *c*, variations in size of lumen of mucous terminations, as in sublingual, etc.; *d*, tubuloalveolus of mucous tubule and serous demilune; *e*, *f* and *g*, serous terminations with branched canals, or intercellular secretory canaliculi as in parotid, etc.; *J*, compound alveolar gland.

the space that would otherwise represent the lumen of the alveolus. Simple branched alveolar glands (Fig. 15-9, *G*), in which a common duct gives rise to a number of saccules, are seen in the larger sebaceous glands and in the Meibomian glands.

Compound Tubular Glands. The compound tubular glands consist of a number of distinct duct systems, which open into a common or main excretory duct (Fig. 15-9, *H*). The kidney and testis are examples of compound tubular glands. Some authors, as already stated, classify the smaller mucous glands of the esophagus, etc., as branched tubular glands and, accordingly, the larger of the mucous glands of the esophagus, mucous terminations of the salivary glands and Brunner's glands of the duodenum are then classified as compound tubular, but since these glands frequently terminate in enlargements they are usually classified as compound tubuloalveolar.

Compound Tubuloalveolar Glands. The glands of this type (Fig. 15-9, *I*) are numerous and widely distributed, and they include the parotid, pancreas, mandibular, sublingual, the larger of the mucous glands of the esophagus and seromucous glands of the respiratory tract, many of the duodenal (Brunner's) glands, etc. The structure of the terminal tubules and duct systems varies somewhat in the different glands and, for the finer structure, reference may be made to the special sections dealing with some of the more typical glands of the group, such as the parotid and the pancreas, in Chapter 16.

Compound Alveolar Glands. The compound alveolar glands resemble the compound tubular and compound tubuloalveolar glands in having a large number of duct systems, but the terminal ducts, instead of ending in tubular and tubuloacinar secreting passages, end in alveoli with dilated, saclike lumina (Fig. 15-9, *J*). The mammary gland is the best example of a compound alveolar gland.

Architecture of Compound Glands. All compound glands are surrounded by connective tissue which forms a more or less definite *capsule*. From the capsule, connective tissue *septa* or *trabeculae* extend into the gland. The broadest septa usually divide the gland into a number of compartments or *lobes*. Smaller septa from the capsule and from the interlobar septa divide the lobes into smaller compartments, usually microscopic in size, the *lobules*. A lobule is not only a definite portion of the gland separated from the rest of the gland by connective tissue but represents a definite grouping of tubules or alveoli with reference to one or more terminal ducts. The glandular (epithe-

lial) tissue is known as the *parenchyma* of the gland, in contradistinction to the connective tissue or *stroma*.

DEVELOPMENT OF GLANDS

The relations of the glandular tissue proper to the connective tissue are best understood by reference to development. Glands originate as ingrowths from a surface covered with epithelium. The epithelial invagination grows down into the underlying connective tissue. As the invagination grows and subdivides, the main portion, which is connected with the epithelium at the original point of outgrowth, becomes the excretory duct, while the subdivisions form the larger and smaller ducts and finally the secreting tubules or alveoli. During the development of the gland tubules, the connective tissue is also developing but is being largely replaced by the more rapidly growing tubules. The gland tubules do not develop irregularly but in definite groups, each group being dependent upon the tubule (duct) from which it originates. Thus the main excretory duct gives rise to a few large branches which may lie either between or within the developing lobes (interlobar and intralobar ducts, respectively), a lobe being formed by all of the subdivisions of one of the lobar branches. From each intralobar duct there arise within the lobe a large number of smaller branches, each of which gives rise to subdivisions which make up a lobule of the gland. These branches lie first between lobules (interlobular ducts) and finally within the lobules to which they give rise (intralobular ducts). As groups of tubules develop into lobes and lobules, the largest strands of connective tissue are left between adjacent lobes (interlobar connective tissue), smaller strands between lobules (interlobular connective tissue), and the finest connective tissue between the tubules or alveoli within the lobule (intralobular connective tissue).

ENDOCRINE GLANDS

Certain glands, as already stated, are lacking in ducts and are called *endocrine glands* or glands of internal secretion, in contrast to those with ducts, the exocrine or external secreting glands. Some glands such as the pancreas and testis secrete both externally by way of ducts and internally by way of the blood stream. The endocrine glands secrete specific substances called *hormones* which have specific effects on the other tissues or organs of the body. The endocrine glands include the thyroid, parathyroid, adrenal, hypophysis, islands of Langerhans of the pancreas and parts of the ovary and testis. The pineal gland is also usually included in this group. For a detailed description of the endocrine glands, see Chapter 21.

REFERENCES

GABE, M., AND ARVY, L. 1961 Gland cells. *In* The Cell; Biochemistry, Physiology Morphology (Brachet, J., and Mirsky, A. E., editors), vol. 5, pp. 1–88. Academic Press, New York.

JAMIESON, J. D., AND PALADE, G. E. 1967 Intracellular transport of secretory proteins in the pancreatic exocrine cell. I. Role of the peripheral elements of the Golgi complex. J. Cell. Biol., vol. 34, pp. 577–596.

JAMIESON, J. D., AND PALADE, G. E. 1967 Intracellular transport of secretory proteins in the pancreatic cell. II. Transport to condensing vacuoles and zymogen granules. J. Cell Biol., vol. 34, pp. 597–615.

NEUTRA, M., AND LEBLOND, C. P. 1969 The Golgi apparatus. Sci. Amer., vol. 220, no. 2, pp. 100–107.

PALADE, G. E. 1956 The endoplasmic reticulum. J. Biophys. Biochem. Cytol., vol. 2, no. 4, suppl., pp. 85–98.

PALADE, G. E., SIEKEVITZ, P., AND CARO, L. G. 1962 Structure, chemistry and function of the pancreatic exocrine cell. *In* The Exocrine Pancreas (deReuck, A. V. S., and Cameron, M. P., editors), pp. 23–99. Little, Brown and Company, Boston.

PALAY, S. L. 1958 Morphology of secretion. *In* Frontiers in Cytology. Yale University Press, New Haven.

PETERSON, M., AND LEBLOND, C. P. 1964 Synthesis of complex carbohydrates in the Golgi region as shown by radioautography after injection of labeled glucose. J. Cell Biol., vol. 21 pp. 143–148.

PORTER, K. R., AND BONNEVILLE, M. A. 1968 Fine Structure of Cells and Tissues. 3rd Edition, Lea & Febriger, Philadelphia.

SCHAFFER, J. 1927 Das Epithelgewebe. Die Drüsen, Handb. mikr. Anat. (v. Möllendorff, editor), vol. 2, pt. 1, pp. 132–231. Springer-Verlag, Berlin.

SCHARRER, E. 1966 Principles of neuroendocrine integration. *In* Endocrines and the Central Nervous System. The Williams & Wilkins Company, Baltimore.

SJÖSTRAND, F. S., AND HANZON, V. 1954 Ultrastructure of Golgi apparatus of exocrine cells of mouse pancreas. Exp. Cell Res., vol. 7, pp. 415–429.

TURNER, C. D. 1966 General Endocrinology. W. B. Saunders Company, Philadelphia.

WARSHAWSKY, H., LEBLOND, C. P., AND DROZ, B. 1963 Synthesis and migration of proteins in the cells of the exocrine pancreas as revealed by specific activity determination from radioautography. J. Cell Biol., vol. 16, pp. 1–23.

ZIMMERMAN, K. W. 1927 Die Speicheldrüsen der Mundhöle und die Bauchspeicheldrüse. Handb. mikr. Anat. Menschen (v. Möllendorff, editor), vol. 5, pt. 1, pp. 61–244. Springer-Verlag, Berlin.

16

The Digestive System

The *digestive system* consists of the alimentary tract and such structures as the tongue, teeth and accessory glands which are associated with it. The alimentary tract is conveniently divided by structural variations and topographical locations into a series of regions: mouth, pharynx, esophagus, stomach, small intestine and large intestine, including the rectum and anal canal. The structural modifications of the various regions are associated with the function of the tract, namely, the forwarding of the food through the tube, where in transit it can be mechanically altered and acted on by enzymes, a portion of it absorbed and the residue eliminated as feces.

GENERAL FEATURES OF THE ALIMENTARY CANAL

The innermost layer of the digestive tract is a *mucous membrane* or *mucosa*. This has two constantly occurring components, an *epithelial lining* and a stratum of connective tissue, the *lamina propria*. The lamina propria is formed of interlacing connective tissue fibers, which are usually fine. It contains fibroblasts and macrophages, is frequently infiltrated with lymphocytes and may also contain plasma cells and eosinophils. Beginning with the esophagus, a thin stratum of smooth muscle (*muscularis mucosae*) appears subjacent to the lamina propria and forms a third component of the mucosa.

A *submucosa*, formed of loose connective tissue, is invariably present beneath the mucosa from the beginning of the esophagus to the lower end of the anal canal. This layer is absent from parts of the mouth and pharynx. It contains rather coarse collagenous fibers which are usually loosely interwoven and among which are elastic and reticular fibers and connective tissue cells. The submucosa attaches the mucosa to the underlying firm structures but allows considerable movement in much the same way that superficial fascia allows movement of the skin. In regions where no definite submucosa is present, the mucosa attaches directly to the firm underlying structures as, for example, in the gums.

Throughout most of the alimentary canal, there is a rather thick layer of muscle (*muscularis externa*) which has a very regular arrangement. In the mouth the muscle layer has no uniform arrangement and is absent in certain regions.

Beginning with the pharynx, there is an external layer composed of connective tissue (*fibrosa*) or of connective tissue and mesothelium (*serosa, serous membrane*).

THE MOUTH

The *mouth* or oral cavity is an irregularly shaped structure which is bounded by and contains a number of different parts, such as the lips, cheeks, teeth, gums, tongue and palate. Except over the surface of the teeth,

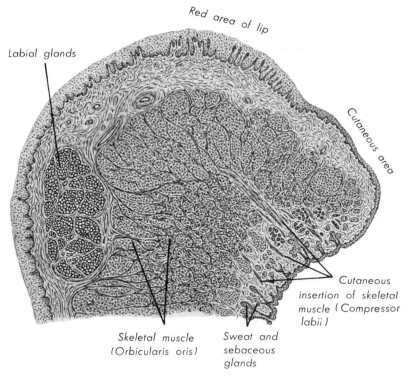

Labial glands

Red area of lip

Cutaneous area

Cutaneous insertion of skeletal muscle (Compressor labii)

Skeletal muscle (Orbicularis oris)

Sweat and sebaceous glands

FIG. 16-1. Transverse section through lower lip of newborn infant. Van Gieson strain. The oral surface of the lip is at the *left*. ×12.

the mouth is lined throughout by stratified squamous epithelium; the lamina propria is rather dense, and a submucosa is present only in certain regions.

Lips and Cheeks. The lips may be divided into three rather distinct regions: the cutaneous area, the red area and the oral mucosa (Fig. 16-1). The cutaneous area of the lips is covered by typical thin skin with cornified epithelium, hair follicles and sebaceous and sweat glands. The red area is covered by noncornified, relatively translucent stratified squamous epithelium which is indented by tall vascular connective tissue papillae (Figs. 16-1 and 16-2). The red color of the lip is due to the blood in the vessels of the tall papillae and the translucency of the epithelium. Glands are absent in the red area, except for an occasional sebaceous gland. The red area is continuous

with the skin externally and with the mucous membrane of the lips internally.

The inner surfaces of the lips and cheeks are similar in structure. The epithelium is not cornified, and connective tissue papillae of moderate length indent it. The lamina propria is rather compact and is connected by a submucosa to the underlying skeletal muscle (orbicularis oris in the lips, buccinator in the cheeks). The submucosal fibers are thick and are so arranged that they closely bind the mucosa to the underlying structures, preventing the formation of folds and thus reducing the chance of biting the mucous membrane during mastication. In the area where the mucosa of the lips and cheeks becomes continuous with that of the gums (fornix vestibuli), the submucosa is very loose, allowing movement.

Numerous glands of a mixed (mucous

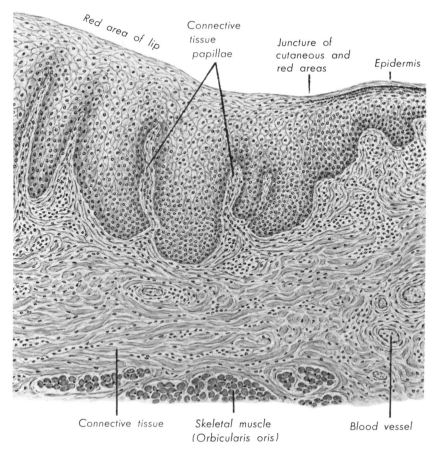

FIG. 16-2. Transverse section through the contiguous cutaneous and red areas of lip of newborn infant. ×110.

and serous) type and a mucous type are present in the submucosa of the lips and cheeks, and they also penetrate into the buccinator muscle.

Gums. The epithelium of the *gums* or *gingivae* is cornified to a variable degree. Cornification is most pronounced in those areas which are subject to the greatest amount of abrasion from mastication or brushing, i.e., on the free margin of the gums. Numerous long vascular papillae deeply indent the epithelium and are responsible for its pink color. At the gingival sulcus, the epithelium of the gums is continuous with the epithelial attachment of the tooth (see section on "The Teeth" and Fig. 16-9). The lamina propria of the gums is formed of

coarse, interweaving collagenous fibers which bind it closely to the periosteum of the alveolar processes of the maxillae and mandible. The lamina propria is also attached to the gingival fibers of the periodontal membrane. No submucosa and no glands are present in the gingiva.

Hard Palate. The epithelium of the *hard palate* is much like that of the gums. It has a cornified layer in which the cells are hard and scale-like (Fig. 16-3), and it usually has a stratum granulosum. Long vascular papillae deeply indent it, giving a pinkish color. Except in the area adjacent to the gums and in the midline, a submucosa is present. Its fibers are coarse and run largely in a vertical direction, thus binding the lamina propria firmly to the periosteum of the hard palate. In the anterior region of the hard palate, a considerable amount of fat is present in the submucosa (the fatty zone); in the posterior two-thirds are many mucous glands (the glandular zone). In the narrow longitudinal zone of the raphe, glands are absent. Spherical or ovoid aggregations of flattened, concentrically arranged epithelial cells occasionally occur near the midline. They are remnants of the embryonic fusion of the palatine processes. Structures of this type are called epithelial pearls.

Soft Palate. The oral surface of the *soft palate* and *uvula* is lined by noncornified stratified squamous epithelium. This type of epithelium extends over the free margin and for a variable distance onto the pharyngeal surface, where it becomes continuous with pseudostratified ciliated columnar epithelium. The submucosa is loose and contains many glands: mucous on the oral side and mixed (mucous and serous) on the upper (respiratory) side. A number of small skeletal muscles enter into the formation of the soft palate and uvula.

Floor of the Mouth. The *floor* of the *mouth* is lined by a noncornified epithelium. The submucosa is loose and contains the sublingual glands.

THE TONGUE

The main bulk of the tongue, particularly of the anterior two-thirds, is skeletal muscle. The interlacing muscle fibers course chiefly in three directions, longitudinally, transversely and vertically, an arrangement which gives maximal mobility and physical control. In the posterior third of the tongue, there are aggregations of lymphatic tissue, the lingual tonsils (Figs. 16-4 and 16-5).

Lower Surface of the Tongue. The *lower surface* of the tongue is covered by a stratified squamous epithelium which is not cornified. The lamina propria is thin and closely bound down to the underlying muscle.

Dorsum of the Tongue. The *dorsal*

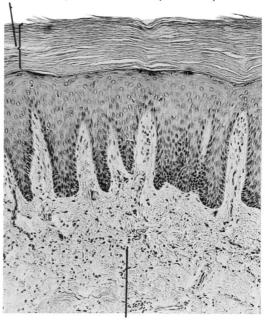

Cornified layer of stratified squamous epithelium

Lamina propria

FIG. 16-3. Mucous membrane from anterior region of hard palate. Human. Photomicrograph by Mr. L. Koster. ×110.

surface of the tongue is divided into an anterior two-thirds and a posterior one-third by a V-shaped row of circumvallate papillae (Fig. 16-4). Some structural features are very different in the two regions. On the *anterior two-thirds*, there are numerous projections, the *lingual papillae*. These papillae are virtually small organs and should not be confused with the connective tissue papillae which indent stratified squamous epithelium. The lingual papillae are formed of a central core of connective tissue and a covering layer of stratified squamous epithelium (Figs. 16-5 to 16-7). The connective tissue core may give rise to small (connective tissue) papillae which indent the epithelium. According to their shape, the lingual papillae are divided into three types: *filiform, fungiform* and *circumvallate*.

The *filiform papillae* are by far the most numerous and are quite evenly distributed

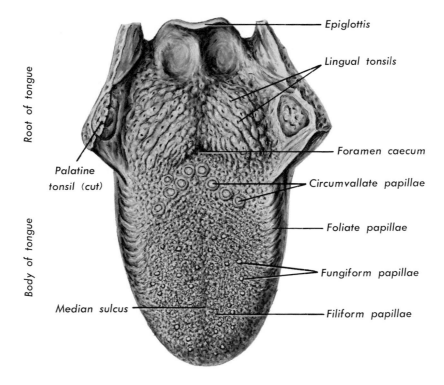

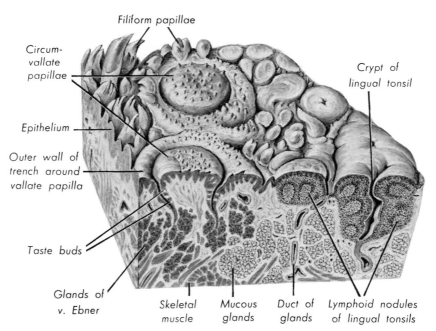

FIG. 16-5. Reconstruction of the surface of the tongue at the juncture of the dorsum and root. ✕13. (Redrawn from Braus.)

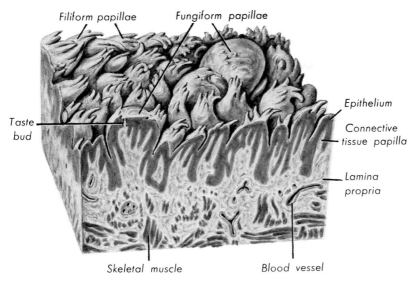

Filiform papillae   Fungiform papillae

Epithelium

Connective
tissue papilla

Taste
bud

Lamina
propria

Skeletal muscle   Blood vessel

FIG. 16-6. Reconstruction of the surface of the dorsum of the tongue. The front surface represents a sagittal section, with the root of the tongue at *right*. ×16. (Redrawn from Braus.)

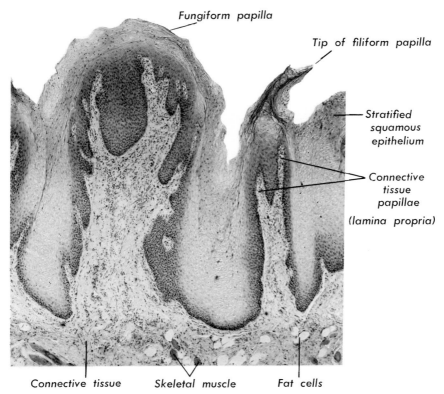

Fungiform papilla

Tip of filiform papilla

Stratified
squamous
epithelium

Connective
tissue
papillae

(lamina propria)

Connective tissue   Skeletal muscle   Fat cells

FIG. 16-7. Section of human tongue showing a fungiform papilla (*left*) and a filiform papilla (*right*). Photomicrograph. ×56.

over the dorsal surface of the anterior two-thirds of the tongue. Each consists of a slender vascular core of connective tissue covered by stratified squamous epithelium which is cornified. The epithelium forms one or more secondary projections which taper into threadlike points (Fig. 16-7).

The *fungiform papillae* are relatively few in number and are interspersed among the filiform papillae. Their summits are rounded and are broader than the bases. They are covered by noncornified epithelium which is indented with connective tissue papillae. The connective tissue core is highly vascular. This and the thinness of the epithelium are responsible for their red color.

The *circumvallate papillae*, usually nine to 12 in number, are arranged along a V-shaped line, the apex of the V pointing posteriorly. They resemble the fungiform papillae but are much larger and are surrounded by a trench and a wall; hence their name, vallate or circumvallate. The wall is somewhat lower than the papilla, thus allowing the latter to project slightly above the surface. Connective tissue papillae indenting the epithelium are limited to the upper surface, the sides being free of them. The circumvallate papillae, the trench and the wall are covered by noncornified stratified squamous epithelium. In the epithelium of the lateral wall and sometimes in that of the trench also, are small oval bodies, *taste buds* (Figs. 16-5 and 16-8), which serve as receptor organs of taste (see Chapter 22).

Along the posterolateral border of the tongue there are folds of the mucous membrane, sometimes called the foliate papillae

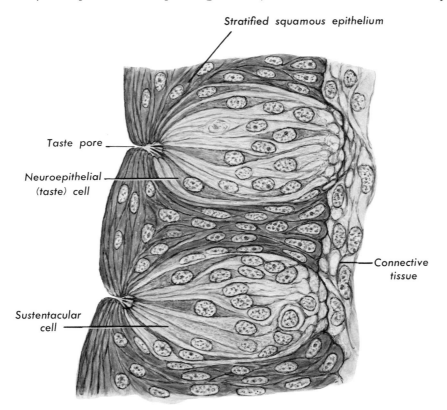

Stratified squamous epithelium

Taste pore

Neuroepithelial (taste) cell

Sustentacular cell

Connective tissue

FIG. 16-8. Taste buds from wall of circumvallate papilla of a rhesus monkey. Masson's trichrome stain. ×800.

(Fig. 16-4). They are not well developed in man.

The *dorsal surface* of the *posterior third* of the tongue is free of papillae but has mucosal ridges and *lingual tonsils*. The latter appear as low eminences caused by the underlying aggregations of lymphatic nodules (Figs. 16-4 and 16-5). Each tonsil usually has a centrally placed pit or crypt lined by stratified squamous epithelium. The epithelium is infiltrated with lymphocytes.

No submucosa is distinguishable on the dorsum of the tongue.

Glands of the Tongue. The glands of the tongue can be divided into three main groups according to their structure and location.

A paired group of mixed mucous and serous glands are located in the anterior part of the tongue near the apex (*glands of Nühn*). They are embedded in the muscle but are closer to the ventral than to the dorsal surface. They have several ducts which open on the ventral surface.

A group of serous glands located in the region of the vallate papillae are known as the *glands of von Ebner*. They extend into the muscle. Their ducts open into the trenches of the vallate papillae (Fig. 16-5).

Mucous glands of the root of the tongue are the most numerous. They lie in the posterior third of the tongue and extend far enough forward to mingle with the serous (von Ebner's) glands. Their ducts open into the crypts of the lingual tonsils and into depressions between the tonsils.

Nerve Supply. The *nerve supply* of the oral cavity is complex. The skeletal muscle of the lips and cheeks is supplied by the seventh cranial nerve, that of the tongue by the 12th nerve. The fibers carrying ordinary sensation are from the lingual branch of the fifth nerve and from the ninth nerve. The fibers carrying the special sense of taste are from the seventh nerve (through the chorda tympani) and from the ninth nerve.

THE TEETH

A *tooth* has three anatomic divisions, *crown, root* and *neck* or *cervix* (Fig. 16-9).

The *clinical crown* refers to that part which is visible with the tooth in situ. In early life the gums cover a part of the enamel so that the clinical crown consists of only a part of the anatomical crown. More of the enamel normally becomes exposed with the aging process so that later in life the clinical crown includes all of the anatomical crown and even a part of the anatomical root.

The root is embedded in a cavity (the *alveolus* or *socket*) in the alveolar process of either the mandible or the maxilla, and it is firmly attached to the bony wall of its socket by connective tissue, the *periodontal membrane* or *ligament*.

Structurally, a tooth has four components: *enamel, dentin, cementum* and *pulp*.

Enamel. Enamel is the hardest substance in the body and, by weight, is composed largely (96%) of inorganic salts, of which the greater part (about 90%) is calcium phosphate. By volume, however, the organic component of enamel is very considerable, nearly equaling the inorganic element. Enamel is somewhat brittle but, because of the support of the underlying dentin and also because of its internal structural arrangement, it does not fracture from the amount of stress produced by the contact relation (occlusion) of opposing maxillary and mandibular teeth during normal mastication. Enamel is present in greatest amounts on the cusps of the permanent bicuspids and molars, where it is 2 to 2.5 mm. in thickness.

Structurally, enamel is composed of *enamel rods* or *prisms* and *interprismatic substance*.

The *enamel rods* are elongated columns, each of which extends throughout the thickness of the enamel layer from the dentinoenamel juncture to the surface of the anatomical crown. When seen in cross section, some rods are hexagonal, oval or polyg-

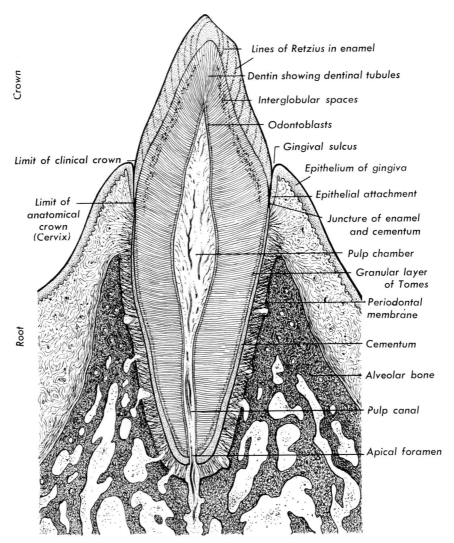

Crown

Root

Lines of Retzius in enamel

Dentin showing dentinal tubules

Interglobular spaces

Odontoblasts

Gingival sulcus

Epithelium of gingiva

Epithelial attachment

Juncture of enamel
and cementum

Pulp chamber

Granular layer
of Tomes

Periodontal
membrane

Cementum

Alveolar bone

Pulp canal

Apical foramen

Limit of clinical crown

Limit of
anatomical
crown
(Cervix)

Fig. 16-9. Diagram of a section through an incisor tooth and surrounding structures. The enamel at the tip of the crown shows some abrasion.

onal, but most are arcade or scale-shaped with a depression on one side (Fig. 16-10). The average diameter of the enamel rods is about 4 μ, i.e., about one-half that of a red blood cell. The diameter increases as they course toward the periphery, since the area of the outer surface of the enamel is greater than at the dentinoenamel juncture.

Each enamel rod is composed of sub-microscopic crystals of inorganic material embedded in a sparse framework of organic material. A thin peripheral region, the *rod sheath*, contains a higher proportion of organic material than does the bulk of the rod (Fig. 16-11). Between the rods is a small amount of a calcified organic substance, the *interprismatic* or *interrod substance*, which appears to act as a cementing substance.

Enamel rods are transversely striated, the striations being evenly spaced at intervals of about 4 μ (Fig. 16-12). This is due to the rhythmic longitudinal growth of the

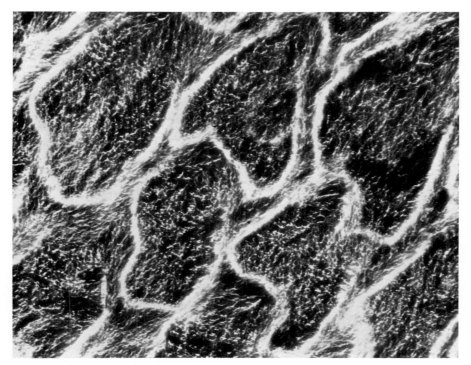

FIG. 16-10. Electron micrograph of demineralized enamel. The field includes cross sections of several enamel rods. Note the submicroscopic fibrillar network of the organic matrix and the more dense peripheral rod sheaths. Human. ×5000. (Courtesy of Dr. D. B. Scott.)

rods during development. In addition to the closely spaced striations on the individual rods, there are more widely and somewhat more variably spaced continuous lines in the enamel, the *incremental lines of Retzius* (Fig. 16-9). In coronal sections through the crown, these appear as concentric circles. In longitudinal sections, they form arches over the apex of the dentin. In the deciduous teeth and in the first permanent molar, an especially prominent line, the *neonatal line*, marks the boundary between the enamel formed before and after birth. The incremental lines are due to variations in the rate of enamel deposition and are roughly analogous to the growth rings of a tree. The neonatal line is an accentuated incremental line resulting from a disturbance in the deposition of enamel at the time of birth.

The course of the enamel rods is usually wavy or, especially on the occlusal surfaces, they may entwine, forming *gnarled enamel*. This is a functional adaptation which adds strength to the enamel by reducing the danger of cleavage between the rods.

An awareness of the direction and course of the enamel rods in different regions of a tooth is important in the technique of cavity preparation, both from the standpoint of ease in removing portions of the enamel and also of maintaining the strength of the surrounding wall.

A membrane, *Nasmyth's membrane* or *enamel cuticle*, covers the exposed surface of the crown for a short time after eruption (see p. 423).

Dentin. Dentin is hard, yellowish and elastic. It forms the bulk of a tooth and also gives the main strength to it. Chemically, it contains more mineral than bone but less than enamel (69 % by weight, as compared with 46 and 96 %, respectively). Morphologically, it resembles bone in that

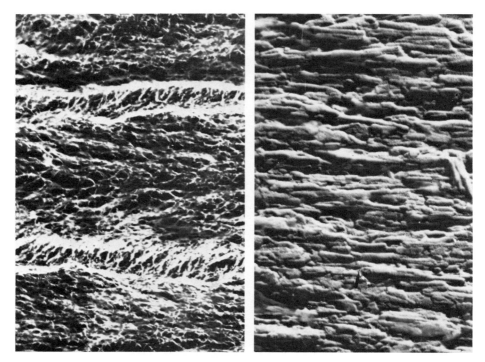

Fig. 16-11. Electron micrographs of longitudinal sections of mature enamel. *Left*, demineralized enamel. The field shows the entire width of one enamel rod and parts of two adjacent rods. Note the submicroscopic fibrillar network of enamel rods and rod sheaths. Extending crosswise between the rods (prisms) are interprismatic fibrils. ×10,000. *Right*, pseudoreplica of acid-etched, ground longitudinal section of mature enamel. The field shows the surface layers of crystallites and the crystalline pattern within a single enamel rod. ×21,000. (Courtesy of Dr. D. B. Scott.)

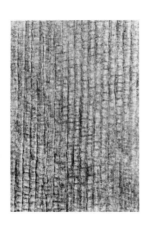
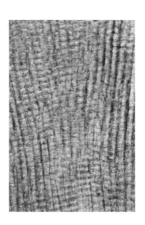

Fig. 16-12. Photomicrographs of ground section through enamel of human bicuspid tooth. *A*, lateral area in which the prisms are regularly arranged. *B*, cuspal area in which the prisms entwine. ×380.

A   B

it is composed of collagenous fibers in a calcified ground substance. It differs from bone in that it contains no cells but has only processes of cells (odontoblasts) whose bodies lie adjacent to the dentin in the pulp cavity.

The cells responsible for the deposition of dentin, the *odontoblasts*, are arranged in

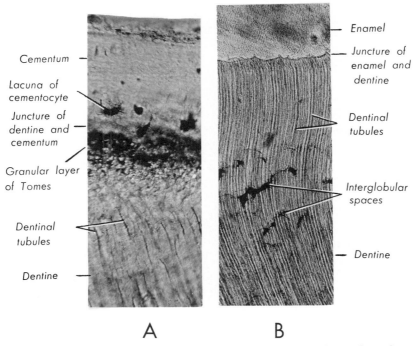

Cementum

Lacuna of
cementocyte

Juncture of
dentine and
cementum

Granular layer
of Tomes

Dentinal
tubules

Dentine

Enamel

Juncture of
enamel and
dentine

Dentinal
tubules

Interglobular
spaces

Dentine

A B

FIG. 16-13. Photomicrographs of ground section of human bicuspid tooth; *A*, through root, showing dentin and adjoining cementum; *B*, through crown, showing dentin and adjoining enamel. The dark areas in the enamel are not due to pigment or discoloration but to refraction of the rods. ×265.

an epithelial-like layer on the inner surface of the forming dentin. Unlike osteoblasts, the odontoblasts do not become imprisoned but retreat progressively as the layers of dentin are deposited, each one leaving a single branching process embedded in the dentin matrix. These *odontoblastic processes* or *dentinal fibers* (of Tomes) become increasingly elongated as the odontoblasts recede with the formation of successive layers of dentin. The dentinal fibers thus occupy narrow, tubular channels within the dentin, the *dentinal tubules*. The dentinal fibers branch and anastomose somewhat but, in general, they run parallel to one another in a slightly wavy course through the dentin. This is well shown in ground sections of dentin in which the dentinal canals are filled with air and thus appear dark in transmitted light (Fig. 16-13). The odontoblastic processes probably completely fill the dentinal tubules in the

living tooth; the spaces which appear between the processes and the walls of the tubules in fixed sections are very likely artifacts (Fig. 16-14). The rim of dentin matrix bordering on the tubule stains darker than the remainder of the dentin and is known as *Neumann's sheath*.

In each layer of dentin, the meshwork of collagenous fibers in the matrix runs perpendicular to the long axis of the tubules, i.e., parallel or tangential to the outer surface of the tooth. The mineral salts are in the form of crystals and have two types of arrangement: (1) the long axes of the crystals are parallel to the collagenous fibers, and (2) the crystals radiate out from a center in spherulitic arrangement. The ground substance of dentin is composed of mucopolysaccharides.

In certain regions of the tooth, there are areas which have less inorganic material than elsewhere, as a result of a failure

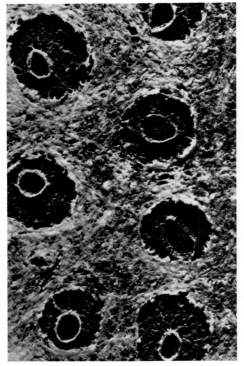

FIG. 16-14. Electron micrograph of thin section of demineralized dentin, showing organic matrix and cross sections of dentinal tubules with their enclosed odontoblastic processes (dentinal fibers). The space between each process and the rim of organic matrix (Neumann's sheath) is probably largely artifact. Human. ×5500. (Courtesy of Dr. D. B. Scott.)

of the individual areas of calcification to meet and fuse. The matrix in such regions shrinks in ground (dried) sections, and a space is formed which becomes filled with air and so appears dark in transmitted light. One such constantly occurring region is in the root of the tooth close to the dentinocementum juncture. It has a granular appearance and is known as the *granular layer of Tomes* (Figs. 16-13, *A*, and 16-9). A second location, the *interglobular spaces* (Fig. 16-13, *B*), occurs chiefly in the crown (Fig. 16-9) but may be present in the root also. It lies a short distance from the dentinoenamel (or dentinocementum) juncture. Each area is irregular in shape

and much larger than the areas forming the granular layer of Tomes.

Parallel incremental growth lines (*contour lines of Owen, imbrication lines of von Ebner*) which are due to the deposition of dentin in successive lamella-like layers are present. In cross sections of a tooth, they appear like annual rings of a tree.

Dentin, unlike enamel, forms throughout life. The dentin that forms prior to the completion of root development is known as *primary dentin* in contrast with that which arises subsequently, the so-called *secondary dentin*. The former consists of relatively straight dentinal tubules whereas the latter has tubules which follow a more wavy course. The distinction between the two types is somewhat arbitrary. The dentin that arises after severe stimuli, such as caries or erosion, is composed of elements that are very irregularly arranged; it is known as *reparative dentin*. The deposition of dentin induced by stress may be so extensive that it obliterates the pulp chamber and even part of the root canal. It is an important protective response.

Dentin is sensitive to a number of painful stimuli. Despite this well known fact, nerve fibers have not been demonstrated penetrating its matrix to any appreciable extent. The odontoblastic processes presumably convey impulses to the pulp, where many nerve endings are located.

Cementum. Cementum is similar to bone both in morphology and in composition. It is darker than enamel but lighter in color than dentin. It forms a thin sheath on the surface of the dentin of the anatomical root of the tooth (Fig. 16-9). It is usually somewhat thicker at the apex of the root, and sometimes it covers the inner surface of the dentin for a short distance at the apical foramen.

Cementum may either be free of cells, *acellular cementum*, or it may be *cellular*, containing cells similar to osteocytes (*cementocytes*) which lie in irregularly shaped lacunae in the matrix (Fig. 16-13, *A*). Except at the apex of the root, the acellular type is usually adjacent to the dentin. The ground substance of cementum resembles that of bone. Collagenous fibers of the matrix extend into the surrounding connective tissue (periodontal membrane) and, as in bone, are known as *Sharpey's fibers*. Cementoblasts on the surface continue to form cementum throughout life. The added layers are irregular in thickness and may be either cellular or acellular. Hypertrophy of cementum frequently occurs in response to unusual stress or movement of a tooth.

Although the bond between dentin and cementum is a firm one, the mode of attachment is not clear. Cementum forms a protective covering over the dentin and serves to attach the tooth to the surrounding structures. Movement of teeth without injury to the tooth structures is possible in orthodontic procedures because cementum is more resistant to resorption than is the alveolar bone.

Periodontal Membrane. The *periodontal membrane* or *ligament* is composed of connective tissue which surrounds the root of the tooth. It attaches the root to: (1) the wall of its alveolus, (2) the gingival connective tissue, (3) the more superficial parts of the roots of adjacent teeth. Fibers extending into the cementum of the tooth interweave with those extending into the alveolar bone, thus binding the tooth to the bone. The fibers do not course in the same direction at different levels (Fig. 16-9) but are arranged in a way that makes them most effective in maintaining the tooth in position and in serving as a suspensory ligament. The fibers are collagenous but, because of their waviness, some temporary physiological movement of a tooth is possible without morphological alterations in its root and socket.

In the periodontal membrane are fibroblasts, osteoblasts and cementoblasts. There are also groups of cells which are remnants of Hertwig's epithelial root sheath, a derivative of the enamel organ. Blood vessels and nerve fibers, particularly proprioceptive endings, are present.

The density and strength of a periodontal ligament varies with the stress to which a tooth has been subjected. Thus, if there is no opposing tooth, the fibers of the membrane become more delicate, a change which is accompanied by a rarefaction of the bone of the alveolus. When this is allowed to occur, restorative measures become more difficult.

Pulp Cavity and Dental Pulp. The shape of the *pulp cavity* is quite similar (in miniature) to that of the tooth in which it occurs. It consists of an expanded *pulp chamber*, which lies in the crown portion and adjacent part of the root, and a narrow *pulp canal* or *root canal* in each root (Fig. 16-9). The pulp cavity is relatively much larger in teeth of young than of old individuals, for there is a continuous deposition of dentin throughout life. A root canal communicates with the periodontal tissues through one or more foramina at or near the apex, the *apical foramina*.

The *dental pulp* is essential to the nourishment and vitality of the tooth. It consists of fine connective tissue, which fills the pulp cavity. In addition to fibroblasts and histiocytes, it contains the specialized connective tissue cells, odontoblasts, which are responsible for dentin formation.

The pulp is richly vascular. An arteriole entering at the apical foramen forms a profuse capillary network close to the odontoblast layer, the blood being returned by one or more venules.

The dental pulp contains both myelinated and unmyelinated nerve fibers. The sensory fibers terminate as free nerve endings among the odontoblasts. They are pain receptors (eliciting a sensation of pain regardless of the type of stimulus).

Attachment of Gingiva to Teeth. The gums are attached to the teeth in two ways. One has been described under "Periodontal Membrane," namely, the attachment of the subepithelial connective tissue to the cementum. The other is a direct attachment of the gingival epithelium to the tooth, the *epithelial attachment* (Figs. 16-9 and 16-21). At the gum line the epithelium turns inward and follows along the surface of the tooth, to which it is attached. Although the structural features of this attachment are not clear, it is certain that there is a definite adhesion of the epithelium to the tooth. In contrast with the epithelium of the expsoed part of the gums, the epithelium of this zone of attachment is not indented by connective tissue papillae.

With advancing age, an increasing proportion of a tooth becomes exposed, i.e., the clinical crown increases in size. This is due to a continued but slow rate of eruption and also to a normal recession of the gums. As more of the crown becomes exposed, the epithelial attachment gradually grows apically for a short distance over the surface of the anatomical root. Thus, in young individuals, the epithelial attachment is on the enamel only; with increased exposure of the crown, it is partly on the cementum; late in life, it may attach to the cementum only. Mild mechanical stimulation, such as massage and brushing, strengthens the epithelium at its attachment by increasing keratinization of its surface layers.

The Development of the Teeth

In man there are normally two sets of natural teeth, the *primary dentition* or deciduous teeth and the *secondary dentition* or permanent teeth. Each tooth develops from a *tooth germ* which is derived from ectoderm and mesoderm. The enamel organ, derived from oral epithelium, forms the enamel. The dental papilla, a condensation of mesenchyme which becomes partially enclosed by the enamel organ, gives rise to the dentin and pulp. The sac of connective tissue that surrounds the enamel organ and papilla, the dental follicle, produces the cementum and periodontal membrane.

The first indication of tooth development in man occurs during the sixth or seventh week of intrauterine life, at which time the embryo measures slightly over 1 cm. in length. At this time, an epithelial ingrowth into the underlying mesenchyme forms along the future dental arch of each jaw. This is the *dental lamina*. Slightly external to this lamina, but in close association with it, is a continuous epithelial ingrowth, the *labiogingival lamina,* in which a groove (Fig. 16-15) and then a deep separation will form (Fig. 16-16). This will divide the dental arch from the lips and cheeks. The dental lamina is of nearly uniform thickness at first, but proliferations soon form at intervals on its outer side close to the oral epithelium. These proliferations are the primordia of the *enamel organs* of the deciduous teeth. They develop into cap-shaped and then into bell-shaped structures (Figs. 16-15 and 16-16). Within and beneath the concavity of an enamel organ, a proliferation and condensation of the mesenchyme take place and forms the *dental papilla*. It is the primordium of the pulp. Its peripheral cells, i.e., those adjacent to the enamel organ, will become odontoblasts.

Somewhat later in development, there appear the primordia of the enamel organs of those permanent teeth that correspond to the milk teeth. Each primordium arises as an inner or lingual growth from the dental lamina at a point coexistent with the enamel organ of a milk tooth. Later, as the dental arch lengthens, the dental lamina also grows dorsally, and from this dorsal extension arise the primordia of the enamel organs of the molars. The primordium of the last molar (wisdom tooth) does not form until the fourth or fifth year. The developmental pattern of the permanent teeth is the same as that of the deciduous teeth.

During the development of an enamel organ, the dental lamina, which connected the enamel organ with the oral epithelium, disintegrates. The developing tooth thus becomes entirely separated from the oral epithelium and does not again come into relationship with it until eruption.

The mesenchyme surrounding the enamel

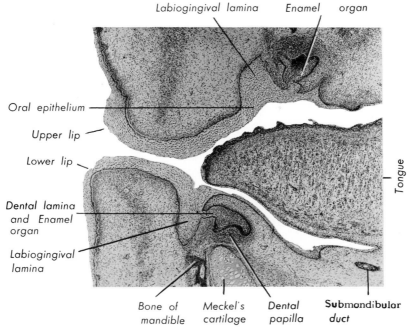

FIG. 16-15. Sagittal section through developing upper and lower medial deciduous incisor teeth of a 50-mm. human embryo. Age about 10 weeks. Photomicrograph. ×34.

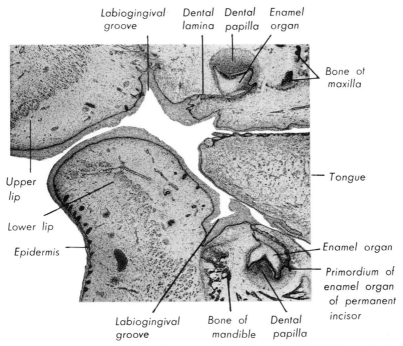

FIG. 16-16. Sagittal section through developing upper and lower medial deciduous incisor teeth of an 86-mm. human embryo. Age about 3 months. Photomicrograph. ×34.

organ and dental papilla plays a role in tooth development. It thickens and forms a capsule-like structure named the *dental sac* or *dental follicle*. From the relationship in the developing tooth, it is evident that the segment of the dental sac adjacent to the papilla has the position of the future periodontal membrane. From it arise the cells associated with the deposition of cementum. Its peripheral part serves as the periosteum of the wall of the future alveolus.

All of the teeth do not show the same degree of development at any one time. The most anterior ones are usually the most advanced in development. In any one tooth, the future occlusal area develops more rapidly than do the more apically situated regions. Thus, at the time of eruption, the crown is fully formed but the root is still in the process of development.

Formation of Dentin. Dentin is the first hard substance formed in a developing tooth. Preceding its actual deposition, several changes occur in the dental papilla. Reticular fibers form in the papilla, more especially in the peripheral zone adjacent to the enamel organ. The outer portions of these fibers (Korff's fibers) fuse with the delicate basement membrane which separates the papilla from the enamel organ, and the thickened membrane thus formed is known as the *membrana preformativa.* The mesenchymal cells closest to the membrane enlarge and form a continuous layer of columnar cells, *odontoblasts.* The Korff's fibers which lie between the odontoblasts become collagenous and change their direction so that they become largely parallel to the membrana preformativa. Around them is deposited a gel-like ground substance. The final stage in the formation of dentin is the deposition of lime salts in the ground substance. Dentin is deposited in lamella-like layers. The incremental or growth lines are known as *contour lines of Owen* or *imbrication lines of von Ebner.*

The apical ends of the odontoblasts prior to the deposition of dentin were in contact with the membrana preformativa. As dentin is deposited, the odontoblasts are not imprisoned but remain on the advancing surface of the dentin. Each, however, leaves a process, the *odontoblastic process* (fiber of Tomes), in the path of its retreat. As more and more dentin is deposited, these processes increase in length, for they extend through the entire thickness of the dentin. The odontoblasts remain functionally active throughout the life of a tooth and, as a consequence, secondary dentin can be formed.

Enamel Organ and Deposition of Enamel. The enamel organ* is structurally rather complex (Figs. 16-17 to 16-21). Four layers are usually described which, from its concavity outward, are as follows. (1) The *inner enamel epithelium* is a single layer of columnar cells, the future *ameloblasts.* A basement membrane separates these from the dental papilla. (2) The *stratum intermedium* is composed of two or more layers of squamous or cuboidal cells. (3) The *stellate reticulum (enamel pulp)* is composed of loosely arranged branching cells. (4) The *outer enamel epithelium* is a single layer of cuboidal cells, adjacent to which is a rich vascular plexus in the connective tissue.

The margin of the bell-shaped enamel organ is called the *cervical loop* (Fig. 16-18). After completion of the crown, the inner and outer enamel epithelial layers of the cervical loop grow apically to form *Hertwig's epithelial root sheath.* This structure determines the shape of the future root or roots and stimulates the differentiation of odontoblasts from the underlying mesoderm. The root

---

* Some authors prefer to substitute the term *epithelial dental organ* for enamel organ, since this structure, although primarily concerned with enamel formation, does contribute to the form and development of the entire tooth, particularly in the formation of root dentin by means of Hertwig's epithelial root sheath. Similarly, there is some justification for the use of the terms *inner* and *outer dental epithelium* in place of inner and outer enamel epithelium.

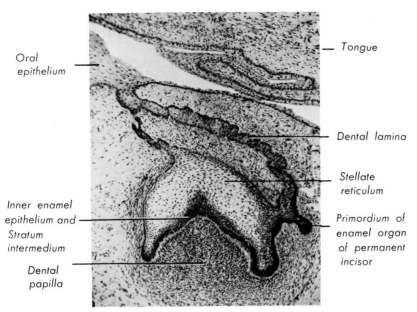

Oral epithelium

Tongue

Dental lamina

Stellate reticulum

Inner enamel epithelium and Stratum intermedium

Primordium of enamel organ of permanent incisor

Dental papilla

FIG. 16-17. Higher magnification of the developing lower incisor tooth shown in Fig. 16-16 (86-mm. human embryo). Photomicrograph. ×73.

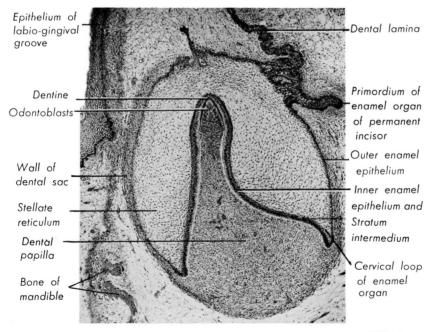

Epithelium of labio-gingival groove

Dental lamina

Dentine

Odontoblasts

Primordium of enamel organ of permanent incisor

Outer enamel epithelium

Wall of dental sac

Inner enamel epithelium and Stratum intermedium

Stellate reticulum

Dental papilla

Cervical loop of enamel organ

Bone of mandible

FIG. 16-18. Sagittal section of medial deciduous incisor tooth of an 111-mm. (C-R) human embryo. Age about 14½ weeks. Photomicrograph. ×57.

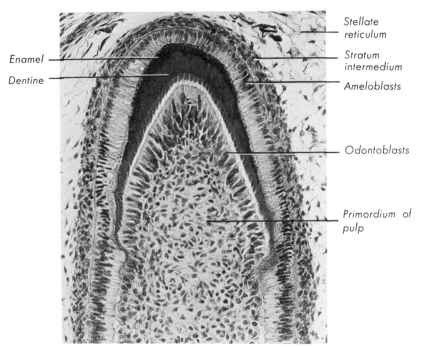

Stellate reticulum

Enamel

Stratum intermedium

Dentine

Ameloblasts

Odontoblasts

Primordium of pulp

FIG. 16-19. Sagittal section through the developing crown of a medial deciduous incisor tooth of a 170-mm. human fetus. Age about 5 months. Photomicrograph. ×180.

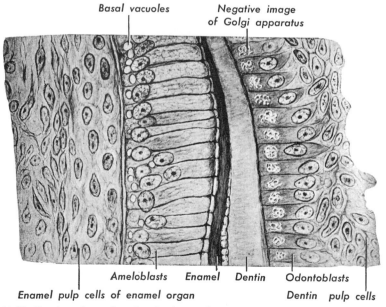

Basal vacuoles   *Negative image of Golgi apparatus*

Ameloblasts   *Enamel*   *Dentin*   *Odontoblasts*

Enamel pulp cells of enamel organ   *Dentin pulp cells*

FIG. 16-20. Section through a developing molar tooth of a 5-day-old rat (Beams)

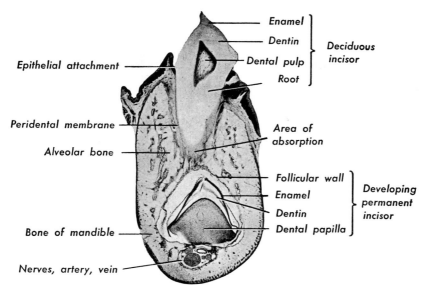

Enamel ⎤
Dentin ⎥ Deciduous
Dental pulp ⎥ incisor
Root ⎦

Epithelial attachment

Peridental membrane

Alveolar bone

Area of absorption

Follicular wall ⎤
Enamel ⎥ Developing
Dentin ⎥ permanent incisor
Dental papilla ⎦

Bone of mandible

Nerves, artery, vein

FIG. 16-21. Section through the mandible of a kitten, showing deciduous tooth and developing permanent tooth germ.

sheath later disintegrates, leaving nests of cells in the periodontal membrane.

Deposition of enamel begins only after a layer of dentin is formed. At this time, the cells of the inner enamel epithelium elongate and differentiate into *ameloblasts*. Enamel is elaborated in the form of rods or prisms cemented together by an interprismatic substance. A short segment at the dentinal end of each ameloblast becomes more granular. This part of the cell is then known as *Tomes' process*. As each process becomes transformed into enamel rod matrix, the ameloblast lengthens and recedes, and a new portion of cytoplasm becomes a process. In this way, Tomes' processes always remain the same length. As the enamel prisms increase in length, there is a progressive mineralization, an uncalcified segment always remaining next to the ameloblast. The interprismatic substance derived from the terminal bars between the processes also becomes calcified. The amount of mineral deposited at this time, however, is only about one-fourth that of mature enamel. Complete calcification takes place after the rods have reached full length. At

that time, *maturation* of the enamel matrix takes place, water is withdrawn and there is a crystallization and further deposition of salts. Maturation always begins at the occlusal region and progresses toward the cervix.

After completion of enamel formation, the ameloblasts deposit on its surface a thin(0.2 μ), homogeneous, protective covering, the *primary enamel cuticle*. The enamel organ then regresses but remains as a few layers of cuboidal cells, the *reduced enamel epithelium*. As the tooth erupts, it is covered by a thicker (up to 10 μ) keratinous layer, the *secondary enamel cuticle*, produced by the reduced enamel epithelium. These two cuticles together form *Nasmyth's membrane*, which covers the surface of the enamel until it is worn off by mastication or brushing. When the tooth erupts, the reduced enamel epithelium fuses with the oral epithelium at the gingival margin and forms the *epithelial attachment* or *attached epithelial cuff*. As the tooth continues to erupt and more of the crown becomes exposed, the epithelial attachment gradually separates from the exposed enamel. Concomitantly, the epithelial attachment grows apically on the tooth so that the extent of the attachment does not materially decrease.

Deposition of Cementum. The developing tooth is surrounded by a condensation of embryonal connective tissue which forms the *dental follicle* or *dental sac.* That portion of the follicle adjacent to the dental papilla occupies the position of the future periodontal membrane. It is separated, however, from the papilla by the apically directed extension of the enamel organ, Hertwig's epithelial root sheath. Following the first deposition of dentin of the root, the epithelial root sheath disintegrates. At this time, cells of the dental sac differentiate into *cementoblasts,* following which cementum is deposited on the surface of the root. Cells in the outermost zone of the dental sac differentiate into osteoblasts of the periosteum of the alveolus. Collagenous fibers also develop in the follicular tissue. Some are attached to the cementum, others to the alveolar bone or gingival connective tissue. Together they form the fibrous component of the *periodontal membrane* or *ligament.*

THE PHARYNX

The *pharynx* extends from the level of the base of the skull to the level of the cricoid cartilage, where it becomes continuous with the esophagus. It is 5 to 6 inches in length. Its cavity is continuous with the cavities of the nose, mouth and larynx, and it continues caudally as the lumen of the esophagus. Superiorly and laterally, the Eustachian tubes open into it. The cavity of the pharynx is incompletely divided by the soft palate and uvula into upper (pars nasalis) and lower (pars oralis and pars laryngea) regions.

The *wall of the pharynx* consists of three coats: mucosa, muscularis and fibrosa. There is no submucosa except in the superior lateral region and near the juncture with the esophagus.

The *epithelium* lining the pharynx is not the same throughout. That lining the nasopharynx is the ciliated pseudostratified columnar type, except near the juncture with the oropharynx where the soft palate and uvula come in contact with the posterior wall. There the epithelium changes to a stratified squamous type which continues through the lower region. The *lamina propria* of the pharynx is a tough, fibroelastic layer, subjacent to which is a strongly developed layer of elastic fibers which course mainly in a longitudinal direction. Fibers from it penetrate between the skeletal muscle bundles and thus bind the lamina propria to the muscularis.

The *muscle* of the pharynx is skeletal and is quite irregularly arranged. The *fibrosa* is a tough, fibroelastic layer which, with varying degrees of firmness, attaches the pharynx to the surrounding structures.

In the *nasopharynx,* lymphatic tissue is very abundant, being arranged both diffusely and as aggregations. These aggregations, the *pharyngeal tonsils,* frequently become enlarged and are then known as adenoids. Mixed glands which often penetrate deeply into the muscular layer are present. (See also Chapter 17, under "Nasopharynx.")

In the *oral* and in the *laryngeal pharynx,* scattered nodules of lymphatic tissue occur. The glands are a mucous type and are few in number.

PLAN OF THE ESOPHAGUS, STOMACH AND INTESTINES

Except for the mucosa, no layer has been constantly present throughout the mouth and pharynx. Beginning with the esophagus, however, four layers are constantly present through the remainder of the alimentary tract (Fig. 16-22): *mucosa, submucosa, muscularis externa* and *fibrosa* or *serosa* (peritoneum). The chief structural modifications in the different segments of the tract occur in the mucosa, and these modifications are closely correlated with differences in function. An additional component, the

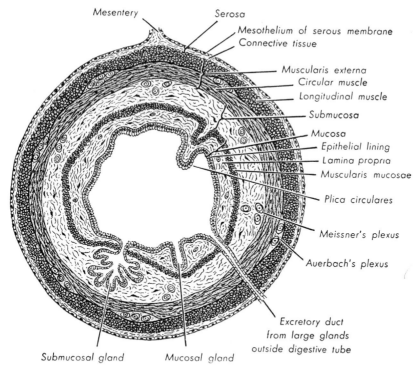

Mesentery
Serosa
Mesothelium of serous membrane
Connective tissue
Muscularis externa
Circular muscle
Longitudinal muscle
Submucosa
Mucosa
Epithelial lining
Lamina propria
Muscularis mucosae
Plica circulares
Meissner's plexus
Auerbach's plexus
Excretory duct from large glands outside digestive tube
Submucosal gland
Mucosal gland

Fig. 16-22. Diagrammatic cross section to illustrate the structure of the wall of the alimentary tract

muscularis mucosae, appears for the first time at the beginning of the esophagus. This is composed of smooth muscle, most of the fibers running in a longitudinal direction. The submucosa differs somewhat in successive segments of the alimentary tract, chiefly as regards the presence or absence of glands. The muscularis externa (so named in contradistinction to the muscularis mucosae) is formed of two very regularly arranged layers, an *inner circular* and an *outer longitudinal,* except in the stomach. As in other saccular organs, the muscle of the stomach is irregularly arranged, especially in the upper, more saccular part. Three rather indistinct layers have been distinguished, largely by exposing the muscle through dissection.

Two nerve plexuses from the autonomic nervous system are present, beginning with the esophagus. One of these, the *myenteric (Auerbach's) plexus,* is readily seen in most

sections of the tract. It is located between the two layers of the muscularis externa. The other, the *submucous (Meissner's)* plexus, is in the submucosa. It is more difficult to find.

A knowledge of these general features will be helpful in the more detailed descriptions which follow.

THE ESOPHAGUS

The *esophagus* begins at the level of the cricoid cartilage and extends to slightly below the diaphragm where it becomes continuous with the stomach, a distance of 10 to 12 inches.

There is no sharp structural demarcation between the esophagus and pharynx, although a greater regularity in the muscularis externa and also the beginning of the muscularis mucosae soon become evident. The esophagus is the most muscular segment of the alimentary tract. Except during the

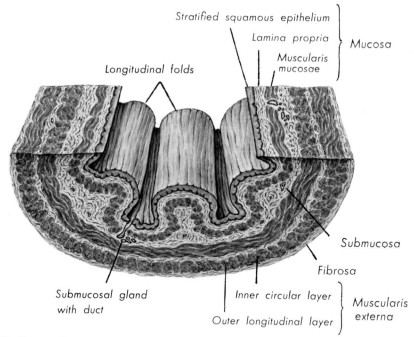

Fig. 16-23. Camera lucida drawing of a segment of the dorsal half of human esophagus. The entire esophagus had been in fixing solution before being cut open, thus preserving the internal longitudinal folds normally present. ×8.

passage of food or water, the lumen is small and irregular in shape as a result of the contraction of the inner layer of the muscularis externa, with a consequent formation of longitudinal folds (Fig. 16-23).

Mucosa. The *mucous membrane* (Figs. 16-23 to 16-25) is lined with a stratified squamous epithelium and, as in the pharynx, it is not cornified in man. The lamina propria is formed of fine interlacing connective tissue fibers with fibroblasts and histiocytes, and it may have areas of infiltration with lymphocytes (Fig. 16-24). The *muscularis mucosae* is formed of smooth muscle running in a longitudinal direction but with some inner circular fibers. It occupies a position corresponding to that of the elastic stratum of the pharynx, with which it is continuous. The muscularis mucosae is thicker in the esophagus than in any other segment of the digestive tube.

Submucosa. The *submucosa* is composed mainly of coarse, loosely interweaving collagenous fibers which permit the formation of extensive folds of the mucous membrane. It contains a plexus of the larger blood vessels, lymphatics and occasional autonomic (parasympathetic) ganglion cells and nerve fibers.

Muscularis. The *muscularis externa of the first quarter* or even less of the esophagus is composed of skeletal muscle and, from the juncture with the pharynx, it becomes progressively more regularly arranged into inner circular and outer longitudinal layers. Some smooth muscle soon appears in each of the layers (Fig. 16-24) and gradually increases in amount. Skeletal fibers extend for a variable distance, but they are rarely present below the juncture of the upper and lower halves of the organ and may be entirely replaced by smooth muscle at a higher level. Small groups of autonomic ganglion cells, part of Auerbach's

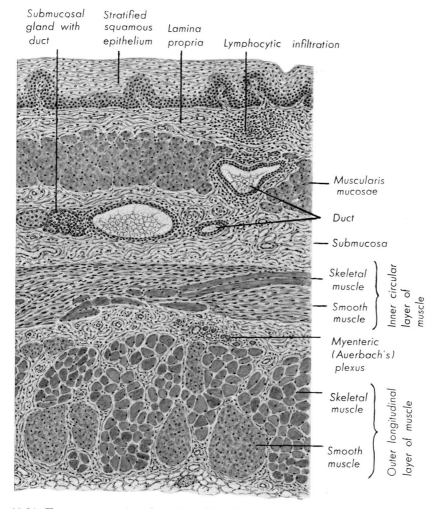

Submucosal gland with duct

Stratified squamous epithelium

Lamina propria

Lymphocytic infiltration

Muscularis mucosae

Duct

Submucosa

Skeletal muscle

Smooth muscle

} Inner circular layer of muscle

Myenteric (Auerbach's) plexus

Skeletal muscle

Smooth muscle

} Outer longitudinal layer of muscle

FIG. 16-24. Transverse section through wall of the upper third of human esophagus. ×65

plexus, are frequently found in the connective tissue between the inner and outer layers of muscle. *peined adventitia*

Fibrosa. The *fibrosa* is composed of loosely arranged connective tissue which binds the esophagus to surrounding structures. The short segment of esophagus that extends below the diaphragm lies in the peritoneal cavity and is covered by a *serosa*.

Glands of the Esophagus. Glands occur in the submucosa (*submucosal glands*) and in the mucosa (*mucosal* or *cardiac glands*). The number of *submucosal glands* is extremely variable in man. In some

animals, as the dog, they are very numerous. The submucosal glands are composed of typical mucous alveoli such as those in the tongue. Several alveoli open by short ducts into a main duct which, in its course through the submucosa and muscularis mucosae, is dilated, forming an ampulla. In the lamina propria, the walls of the duct change from a simple cuboidal to a stratified epithelium, the surface cells being either squamous or columnar. The duct opens between two adjacent connective tissue papillae. In the connective tissue near the duct, there is a lymphocytic infiltration (Fig. 16-24).

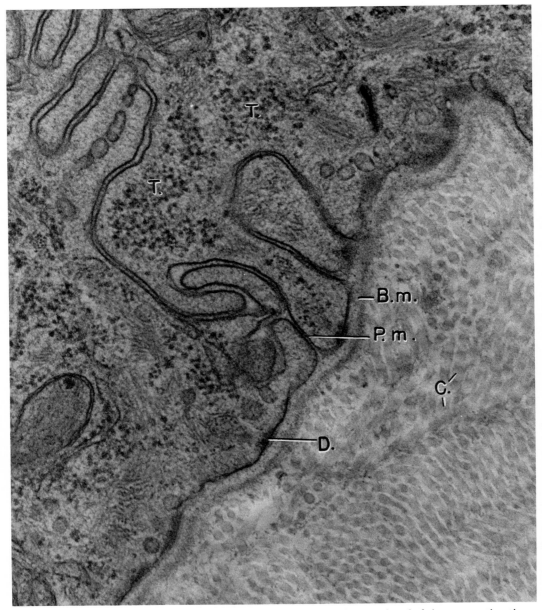

Fig. 16-25. Electron micrograph of junction of stratified epithelium and underlying connective tissue from the esophagus of a bat. The basal lamina (B.m.) beneath the epithelium is clearly shown, and numerous collagen fibers (C) are seen in the connective tissue. Half-desmosomes (D) are seen along the plasma membrane at the basal end of the cell. The plasma membranes (P.m.) of the epithelial cells follow an irregular course at intercellular junctions. Numerous aggregates of tonofilaments (T) are seen in the cytoplasm of the epithelial cells. ×65,000. (Courtesy of Dr. Keith Porter.)

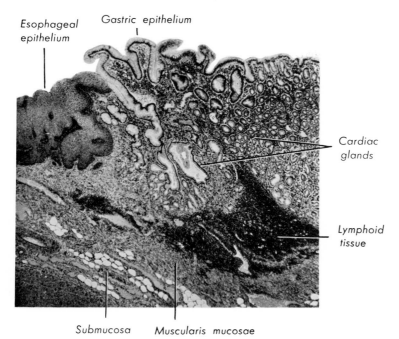

Esophageal epithelium

Gastric epithelium

Cardiac glands

Lymphoid tissue

Submucosa   Muscularis mucosae

FIG. 16-26. Longitudinal section through juncture of human esophagus and stomach. Photomicrograph. ×26.

The *cardiac glands* of the esophagus occur in its uppermost and lowermost regions and lie in the lamina propria. The upper group is frequently absent. The cardiac glands are structurally similar to the glands in the upper or cardiac region of the stomach (Figs. 16-26 and 16-27). They are branched tubular glands which secrete a mucous substance.

THE STOMACH

The stomach extends from the esophagus to the duodenum. In the empty state, it is almost tubular in shape except for the upper part, which has a pear-shaped bulge superiorly and to the left. A frequently assumed shape when the organ is moderately distended is shown in Figure 16-28. As regards motor activity, the stomach is divisible into upper and lower halves. The upper half acts as a reservoir and has no—or only slight—peristaltic contractions. The lower half has peristaltic contractions

which increase in intensity towards the pylorus. It is in this part that the various constituents of the food are thoroughly mixed with each other and with the secretions of the glands of the stomach. Associated with this motor activity is an increase in musculature, especially in the pyloric canal.

At the junction of the esophagus and stomach, the epithelium changes abruptly from stratified squamous to simple columnar. The transition is seen strikingly in fresh specimens where the smooth, whitish mucosa of the esophagus gives way to the more irregular, pinkish mucosa of the stomach. The pink color of the stomach mucosa is due to the thinness of the epithelium and the proximity of the richly vascular connective tissue to the surface.

In the deeper structures, the line of demarcation is not as clear, the muscularis mucosae of the esophagus being continuous with that of the stomach, and glands

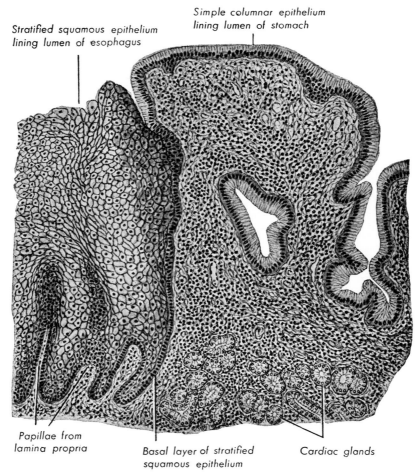

Stratified squamous epithelium lining lumen of esophagus

Simple columnar epithelium lining lumen of stomach

Papillae from lamina propria

Basal layer of stratified squamous epithelium

Cardiac glands

FIG. 16-27. A longitudinal section through the juncture of the esophagus and stomach in man. ×110.

of the stomach type extending up under the stratified epithelium of the esophagus (Fig. 16-26).

Mucosa. The *mucous membrane* of the stomach has numerous ridges or *folds*, also known as *rugae* (Fig. 16-28), which vary in height and number with the degree of distention of the organ. When the stomach is fully distended, they almost disappear. The epithelial surface is also divided by grooves into small irregular areas, 1 to 5 mm. in diameter, the *mamillated* or *gastric areas* (Fig. 16-29).

The entire surface of the mamillated or gastric areas is studded with minute depressions, the *gastric pits* or foveolae (Fig. 16-29). In the fundus, they are comparatively shallow, extending through about one-fifth the thickness of the mucosa; in the pyloric region, the pits are much deeper, extending through one-half or more of the thickness of the mucous membrane. The glands open into the bottoms of the gastric pits.

THE SURFACE EPITHELIUM. The epithelium that lines the inner surface of the stomach and gastric pits is made up of columnar cells which differ structurally and functionally from the cells of the gastric glands. The characteristics of the stomach lining cells also differentiate them from the lining cells of all other parts of the digestive tract. The

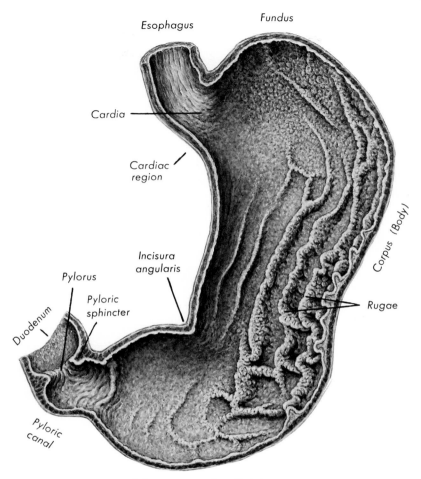

Esophagus

Fundus

Cardia

Cardiac region

Incisura angularis

Pylorus

Pyloric sphincter

Duodenum

Corpus (Body)

Rugae

Pyloric canal

Pyloric antrum (vestibule)

FIG. 16-28. Drawing of a cast of human stomach. The organ had been moderately distended *in situ* with formalin. Preparation and drawing made by Mr. Kellner. ×4/9.

apical end of every surface cell has a deep, cup-shaped zone filled with mucigen. Since the mucigen is not preserved and stained in ordinary histological preparations, the cells show a deep, clear distal zone characteristic of this cell type (Fig. 16-30). The nucleus is oval or spheroidal, depending on the shape of the cell and the amount of mucigen in the cytoplasm. These mucous lining cells differ from goblet cells in shape and in the chemical constitution of their mucigen. Electron micrographs show that the mucinogen droplets of the stomach lining cells are smaller, more dis-

crete and more electron-dense than are those of the goblet cells.

The epithelium lining the stomach, in contrast with that of the intestine, has no striated free border as seen with the light microscope. However, electron micrographs do show microvilli on the free surface of these cells. The absence of an obvious striated border aids in delimiting the epithelium of the stomach from that of the intestine at the stomach-duodenal junction.

As the epithelium extends progressively deeper into the gastric pits, the cells be-

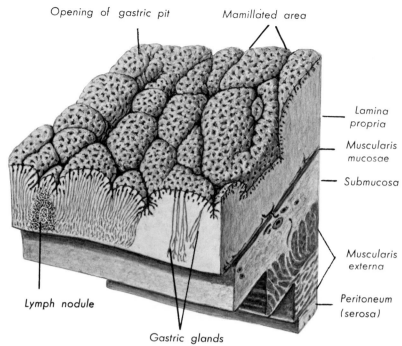

Opening of gastric pit   Mamillated area

Lamina propria

Muscularis mucosae

Submucosa

Muscularis externa

Lymph nodule

Peritoneum (serosa)

Gastric glands

Fig. 16-29. Reconstruction of a portion of wall of stomach, semidiagrammatic. (Slightly modified after Braus.) ×17.

come progressively shorter and have a narrower apical zone of mucigen. This gradual transition correlates with evidence that desquamated cells of the surface of the stomach are replaced by a migration of cells up the walls of the foveolae. Radioautographic studies using tritium-labeled thymidine, which is incorporated into nuclei only during DNA replication, show that the surface cells arise by differentiation from cells which multiply in the isthmus or neck region of the glands. From the latter regions some cells move upward to replace the worn-out surface cells, whereas others may move downward to differentiate into parietal and zymogenic cells in the gastric glands (Hunt and Hunt, 1962).

LAMINA PROPRIA. The lamina propria (Figs. 16-30 and 16-31), in which the glands are located, consists of delicate, interweaving connective tissue fibers plus connective tissue cells and occasional smooth muscle cells. In most regions the glands are so numerous that connective tissue fibers

are reduced to thin strands. There is a diffuse infiltration of lymphocytes throughout the lamina propria; in addition, there are scattered lymphatic nodules, or "solitary follicles," which occur most frequently in the pyloric region (Fig. 16-33).

MUSCULARIS MUCOSAE. The muscularis mucosae consists of a thin layer of smooth muscle in which the fibers usually course in both the circular and longitudinal directions. Strands of smooth muscle extend into the lamina propria between the glands.

Glands of the Stomach. The glands extend from the bottoms of the gastric pits, and their epithelium is continuous with that of the pits (Fig. 16-30). There are three types of glands: (1) *gastric* or *fundic glands*, distributed through the greater part of the gastric mucosa, (2) *pyloric glands*, confined to the region immediately above the pylorus, and (3) *cardiac glands*, found in the cardiac region of the stomach near its junction with the esophagus.

The gastric glands produce the essen-

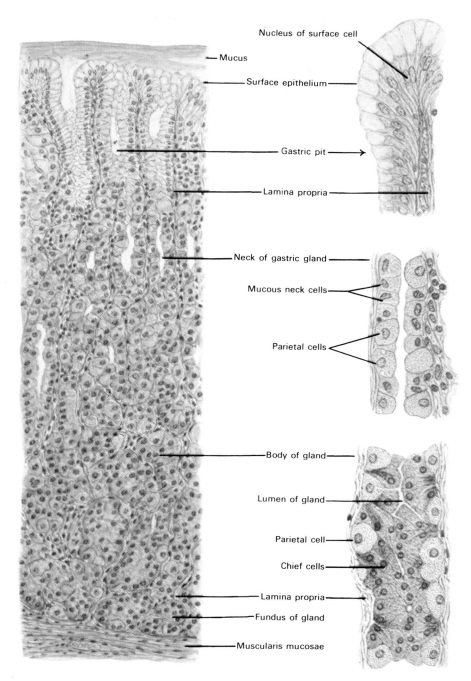

Nucleus of surface cell

Mucus

Surface epithelium

Gastric pit

Lamina propria

Neck of gastric gland

Mucous neck cells

Parietal cells

Body of gland

Lumen of gland

Parietal cell

Chief cells

Lamina propria

Fundus of gland

Muscularis mucosae

FIG. 16-30. Vertical section through mucous membrane of body of human stomach, showing surface epithelium, gastric pits and gastric glands. Hematoxylin-eosin strain. Figure at *left*, ×250; figures at *right*, ×500.

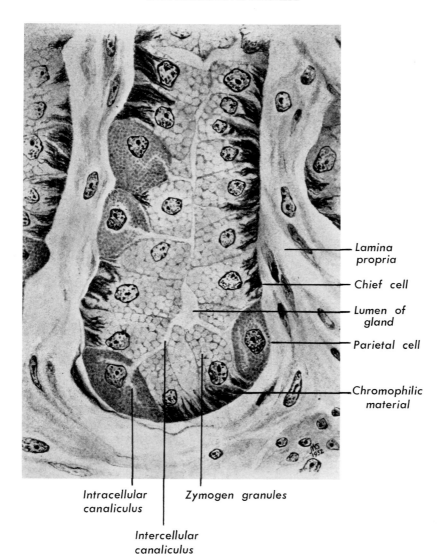

Lamina propria

Chief cell

Lumen of gland

Parietal cell

Chromophilic material

Intracellular canaliculus

Zymogen granules

Intercellular canaliculus

Fig. 16-31. Vertical section through the fundus of a gastric gland of monkey stomach. Regaud fixation; Harris' hematoxylin-eosin stain. ×950.

tial digestive elements of the gastric juice, and the pyloric and cardiac glands function largely as mucous glands.

The terminology is not entirely satisfactory. For example, the term *gastric glands* might be thought to indicate that these glands occur throughout the stomach, whereas they are absent from a narrow zone around the cardia and from the lower part of the pyloric region. A synonym, *fundic glands*, is even more misleading for it indicates that these glands are limited to the fundic

region of the stomach, whereas they are much more widely distributed.

THE GASTRIC GLANDS. The gastric glands (Fig. 16-30) are simple, sometimes branched, tubular glands, of which from three to seven open into each gastric pit. They extend downward through the entire thickness of the lamina propria to the muscularis mucosae.

Each gland consists of (1) a *mouth*

opening into the pit, (2) a constricted portion, the *neck*, (3) the *body* or main portion of the tubule and (4) a slightly dilated and bent blind extremity, the *fundus* (Fig. 16-30).

In the glands proper, one can distinguish three types of cells in most preparations. These are: (a) *chief cells*, (b) *parietal cells* and (c) *mucous neck cells* (Figs. 16-30, and 16-31). A fourth type, the *argentaffin cell*, is present but usually can be demonstrated only by special techniques.

Chief Cells. The chief cells (zymogenic cells), as the name indicates, are the most numerous cells of the gastric glands.

They are large squarish or pyramidal shaped cells (Fig. 16-31) whose bases lie against the (basal lamina) and whose apical borders face the lumen of the gland. The nucleus lies in the basal half of the cell. In the usual histological preparations, the apical region appears as a delicate cytoplasmic meshwork enclosing clear, vacuolated spaces, which represent the position of the unpreserved zymogen granules. With proper fixatives and stains, these zymogen granules can be preserved and stained in situ.

In the base of the cell, below and lateral to the nucleus, is a substance that stains with basic dyes. It has been shown that this material (*chromophilic* or *chromidial substance, ergastoplasm*) is composed largely of ribonucleic acid. In routine preparations, the chromophilic substance frequently appears striated or filamentous (Fig. 16-31). From electron micrographs it can be seen that this appearance is due to the arrangement of the endoplasmic reticulum with its adherent ribosomes. In the basal portions of these cells, the granular endoplasmic reticulum is abundant and arranged in closely packed, parallel lamellae, similar in appearance to pancreatic acinar cells (Fig. 16-63). As with the pancreatic acinar cell, the high concentration of rough surfaced endoplasmic reticulum in the gastric chief cell is correlated with the function of the cell in synthesizing the proteins of the zymogen granules, in this case, the pepsinogen containing granules.

Mitochondria and a *Golgi apparatus* may be demonstrated by special methods. The mitochondria tend to be concentrated in the basal region of the cell and they are largest and most numerous when the cell is active in replenishing its secretory granules. The Golgi complex occupies a position between the nucleus and the apical border of the cell and it has an important role in secretion.

The stages in the formation of secretions by exocrine glands have been outlined in Chapter 15 and described in some detail in Chapter 1 (see sections on the endoplasmic reticulum and the Golgi complex). It will be recalled that the proteins are synthesized from amino acids in the region of the polyribosomes of the rough surfaced endoplasmic reticulum, that polysaccharides are synthesized from simple sugars in the endoplasmic reticulum and the Golgi complex, that the molecules of proteins are combined to form membrane-bounded secretory droplets in the Golgi region, and that the secretory materials are released from the apical end of the cell by a merocrine mode of secretion. The pepsinogen becomes activated after release and is converted into *pepsin*.

In addition to forming pepsinogen, the chief cells appear to be responsible for forming a *glandular mucoprotein* which enhances the absorption of vitamin B_{12} by the lower portion of the small intestine. It was discovered several decades ago that normal gastric mucosa contains a substance (the intrinsic factor of Castle) which facilitates the absorption of vitamin B_{12} (the extrinsic factor, antipernicious anemia factor) that is essential for the normal development of erythrocytes (Chapter 7). Although there has been some controversy about the origin of the intrinsic factor, labeled antibody studies indicate that the chief cells form this factor in rats whereas the parietal cells appear to have a role in the process in the human.

Parietal Cells. The parietal cells were

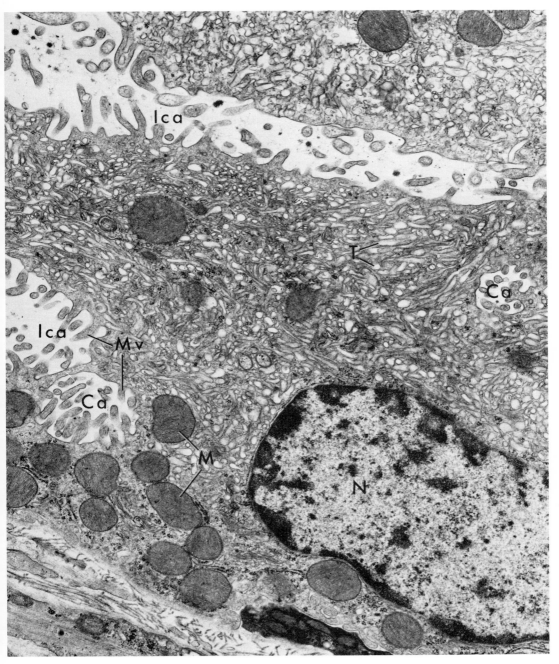

Fig. 16-32. Electron micrograph of a gastric parietal cell. Intercellular canaliculi (*Ica*) extend between adjacent cells from the lumen of the gastric gland (at upper left). Intracellular canaliculi (*Ca*) are surface invaginations that penetrate into the cytoplasm, above and lateral to the nucleus (N). The surface area of the cell is increased by the invaginated canaliculi and by the microvilli (*Mv*). The cytoplasm contains a network of smooth surfaced tubules (*T*) that are so numerous that they displace most of the mitochondria (*M*) laterally in the cell. Electron microscopic studies have shown that electron opaque markers that do not enter the cisternae of the endoplasmic reticulum from the environment of the cell do penetrate into the smooth-surfaced tubules. The extensive system of intracellular membranes is apparently the site where ion concentration occurs during the process of acid secretion. From the stomach of a mouse. ×15,120. (Courtesy of Drs. K. R. Porter and M. A. Bonneville.)

the earliest described cells of the gastric glands and have retained their nondistinctive name. They are often spoken of as the HCl cells because they secrete the hydrochloric acid of the gastric juice. The cells are often larger than the chief cells and are oval or polygonal in shape (Figs. 16-30 and 16-31). The nuclei are spherical and centrally located. Binucleate or multinucleate cells are occasionally seen. Unlike the chief cells, the parietal cells have frequently been reported to divide. The cytoplasm of the parietal cells is finely granular throughout. It stains intensely with acid aniline dyes, with the result that, in stained specimens, these cells contrast sharply with the chief cells. In fresh, unstained preparations, the cytoplasm appears clearer than that of the chief cells. In electron micrographs, it is seen that the cytoplasm contains an abundance of large mitochondria with numerous cristae. These are apparently responsible for the acidophilia and granular appearance of the cytoplasm seen with the light microscope. Electron micrographs also show an abundance of smooth surfaced endoplasmic reticulum.

The parietal cells are very numerous in the neck region of the gland, where they are interspersed among the neck mucous cells. Here their inner margins reach the glandular lumen. In the body and especially in the fundus of the gland, the parietal cells are pushed away from the lumen by the crowding chief cells, so that they come to lie peripherally against the basement membrane. However, they maintain a connection with the lumen of the gland by means of *intercellular canaliculi*, channels between the chief cells (Fig. 16-32). In some preparations, and particularly after the silver impregnation method of Golgi, one can see that the intercellular canaliculi become continuous with so-called *intracellular canaliculi*. Electron micrographs show that the latter are not actually within

the cytoplasm but are only complex channels formed by involution of the cell membrane. The plasmalemma lining the intracellular canals and that covering the remainder of the apical (luminal) surface of the cell have numerous microvilli which increase the area of the membrane.

The mechanism of acid secretion in the stomach remains somewhat obscure. Since free acid is not found within the parietal cells, investigators have presumed that it must either be present in the form of bound acid or be formed in the vicinity of the cell membrane. In microdissection studies of living gastric mucosa, using a variety of indicator dyes including neutral red, it has been found that, although the cytoplasm of the parietal cell gives a somewhat alkaline reaction, the canaliculi, both intra- and intercellular, and the lumen of the gland contain free acid. It appears, therefore, that the membrane of these cells is a highly selective structure which plays an important part in segregating and secreting the constituents of the acid.

There is considerable evidence that the total chemical change between the blood of the underlying connective tissue and the constituents of the parietal cell concerned with HCl secretion may be expressed by an equation in which sodium chloride and carbonic acid are converted into bicarbonate and hydrochloric acid. In this proposed equation of the changes involved in secretion of HCl, the reaction will go spontaneously toward sodium chloride and carbonic acid, whereas energy will be needed to reverse the reaction in the direction toward bicarbonate and hydrochloric acid. In support of this equation of the changes concerned with secretion, it has been found that the secretion of HCl into the lumen of the stomach is accompanied by an equivalent release of bicarbonate into the blood draining from the stomach. *Carbonic anhydrase*, an enzyme present in the parietal cell, apparently plays an

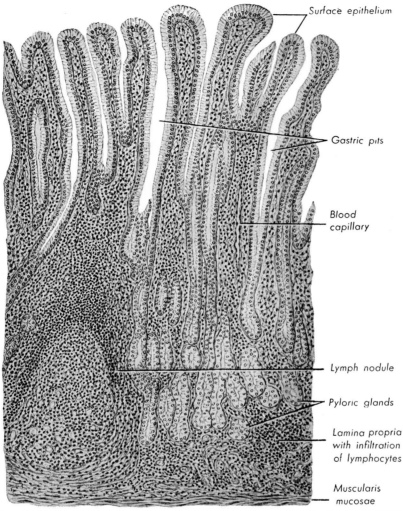

Surface epithelium

Gastric pits

Blood capillary

Lymph nodule

Pyloric glands

Lamina propria with infiltration of lymphocytes

Muscularis mucosae

FIG. 16-33. Vertical section through mucous membrane of pyloric canal. ×110

important role by bringing about the formation of carbonic acid from water and carbon dioxide.

Mucous Neck Cells. The mucous neck cells were not identified until many years after the chief and parietal cells had been described. Certain cells which differ from the pepsinogen cells are found mainly in the neck region of the gland, where they occur in groups interspersed among the parietal cells. The mucous neck cells are cuboidal or low columnar in shape, with a finely granular cytoplasm which, in routine preparations, is paler than that of the chief cells but not as pale as the mucous surface cells. With special fixation and staining, it may be seen that the cells contain many small mucigen granules. The nucleus is situated basally and is frequently oval, with its long axis perpendicular to the long axis of the cell. The upper surface of the nucleus is sometimes indented (Figs. 16-30).

The mucus of the neck cells differs in

several respects from that of the surface cells. Histochemical staining reactions indicate that the mucigen in the neck cells is an acid mucopolysaccharide, whereas that in the surface cells is a neutral polysaccharide. The droplets of mucigen are distributed differently, being dispersed throughout the cytoplasm in the neck cells and confined to the apical region of the surface cell. The mucus produced by the two types differs in consistency, that of the neck cells being less viscous. The mucus secreted by the neck cells, however, is apparently similar to that formed by the cardiac and pyloric glands. It has been suggested that the secretion of the mucous neck cell has a role in protecting the gastric gland itself from attack by HCl and proteolytic enzymes released from the other cell types.

The *argentaffin cells* (enterochromaffin cells) are not recognizable in routine histological preparations, but they can be identified by their cytoplasmic granules which stain black with silver ammonium oxide. Their granules also give a reaction with chromates, becoming brownish yellow. Some authors divide the cells into two types on the basis of their reactions with silver: argentaffin cells which have granules that stain with silver without prior treatment with a reducing agent, and argyrophilic cells which have granules that react with silver only after treatment with a reducing agent. Electron microscopic studies give morphological evidence for five different types of gastrointestinal endocrine cells (Forssmann et al., 1967), and most, if not all, of these types are enterochromaffin cells. The type I gastrointestinal endocrine cell is found in all parts of the gastrointestinal tract and is particularly abundant in the duodenum. The cell has a pyramidal shape and it differs from most of the other gastrointestinal endocrine cells in that its apex extends to the lumen and has microvilli, even when present in the stomach. It is worthy of note that the secretory granules

are located chiefly in the basal part of the cell and toward the blood vessels. This type is an enterochromaffin cell that secretes serotonin, a stimulant of smooth muscle contraction. Serotonin-producing carcinoid tumors probably develop from this cell type.

The type II gastrointestinal endocrine cell has ultrastructural characteristics of the pancreatic islet A cells. It is found particularly in the stomach and is also present in Brunner's glands of the duodenum and the crypts of Lieberkühn of the small intestine. It is a rounded cell which does not reach the lumen. The Golgi complex and most of the cytoplasmic granules (about 500 to 700 mμ in diameter) are located in the basal part of the cell. It is a modified enterochromaffin cell and there is considerable evidence that it secretes enteroglucagon. The type III cell has structural characteristics like those of the pancreatic islet D cell. Its granules are variable in size, usually about 150 to 250 mμ in diameter. The function of this cell, like that of the D cell of the pancreas, is unclear. Some authors suggest that it is a different functional state of the A cell. The type IV cell is similar in structure to chromaffin cells of the sympathetic trunk and it is found chiefly in the gastric mucosa near the pylorus. The type V cell is present in the pyloric region of the stomach and occasionally in the upper part of the duodenum.

THE PYLORIC GLANDS. These are simple, branched, tubular glands, several of which open into each of the deep *pyloric pits*. These pits occupy a much greater proportion of the thickness of the mucous membrane than do the pits of the gastric glands (compare Figs. 16-30 and 16-33), and the proportionate depth occupied by the glands themselves is correspondingly less. The pyloric glands, though short, are quite tortuous, so that in section the tubules are seen cut mainly transversely or obliquely. Most of the pyloric gland cells resemble the mucous neck cells of the gastric glands in that their secretion protects against auto-digestion. They differ morphologically from the neck cells in that they are taller and their ovoid nuclei are generally oriented parallel with the long axes of the cells. Parietal cells are found only occasionally in the pyloric glands.

The transition from the gastric to the pyloric type of stomach gland is not abrupt but is marked by a "transitional border zone" in which gastric and pyloric glands are intermingled and in which are also found single glands which combine the characteristics of both types.

CARDIAC GLANDS. The transition zone between esophagus and stomach contains glands that resemble those in the lamina propria of the lower end of the esophagus (Figs. 16-26 and 16-27). Because of their location they have been designated *cardiac glands*. Those nearest the esophagus are lined with clear cells which resemble closely the cells of the pyloric glands and the mucous neck cells of the gastric glands. As one passes farther from the stomach-esophageal junction, parietal cells and chief cells make their appearance and become more and

more numerous. The glands thus pass over by gradual transition into typical gastric glands.

Submucosa. The *submucosa* consists of coarse, loosely arranged connective tissue. It contains the larger blood vessels and nerves, including the plexus of Meissner.

Muscularis. The *muscular coat* of the stomach is usually described as consisting of three layers, an inner oblique, a middle circular and an outer longitudinal. In the fundus, however, the muscle bundles run in various directions, so that a separation of the muscular coat into layers having definite directions is difficult. The inner and middle layers of the pylorus are thickened to form the sphincter pylori. In the connective tissue which separates the longitudinal and circular muscles, there are groups of parasympathetic nerve cells and fibers which, while much less distinct, are homologous to Auerbach's plexus of the intestine.

Serosa. The *serous coat* consists of a layer of loosely arranged connective tissue which is covered by mesothelium.

Blood vessels, lymphatics and nerves are so similar throughout the stomach and

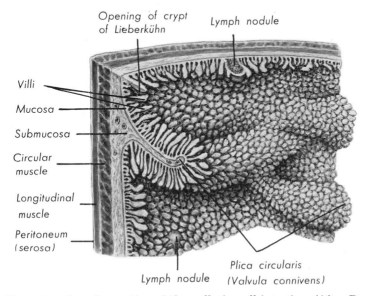

FIG. 16-34. Reconstruction of a portion of the wall of small intestine. (After Braus.) ×17

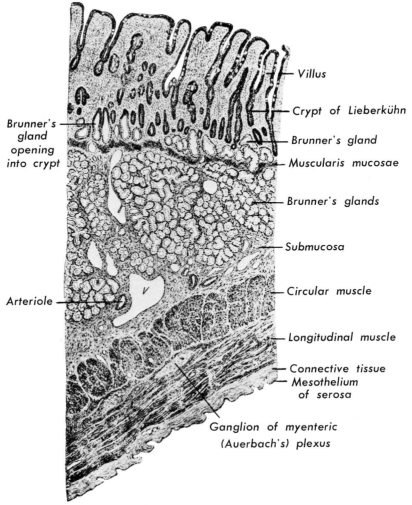

Brunner's
gland
opening
into crypt

Arteriole

Villus

Crypt of Lieberkühn

Brunner's gland

Muscularis mucosae

Brunner's glands

Submucosa

Circular muscle

Longitudinal muscle

Connective tissue
Mesothelium
of serosa

Ganglion of myenteric
(Auerbach's) plexus

FIG. 16-35. Longitudinal section through upper duodenum of man. (After Schaffer.) ×30

intestines that they are described together at the close of the sections on the intestines.

THE SMALL INTESTINE

The small intestine, which extends from the pylorus of the stomach to the colon, is commonly divided into three regions, an upper, the *duodenum;* a middle, the *jejunum;* and a lower, the *ileum.* The subdivisions of the small intestine are not demarcated by abrupt structural changes as is the case where the duodenum joins the stomach and where the ileum joins the colon. Changes

occur gradually along the small intestine and the differences between different divisions are not as obvious as are the similarities. Therefore the divisions will be described together, pointing out the general characteristics first, and directing attention to certain distinctive features as they occur. However, it may be helpful to understand at the outset that some areas are readily differentiated in routine histological preparations. For example, the first part of the duodenum is easily identified by the presence of Brunner's glands in the submucosa, and the lower part of the ileum is characterized by aggregates of lymphatic tissue known as Peyer's patches. Structural changes along the remainder of the tract (lower duodenum, jejunum, and upper ileum) occur gradually and are more obscure.

If the small intestine is opened by a longitudinal incision through its wall, a series of definite folds will be seen on its inner surface. They are in general parallel to one another and pass in a circular or oblique manner partly around the lumen of the tube. These folds are known as *plicae circulares* or *valves of Kerckring*. They are absent in the upper region of the duodenum, tallest in the jejunum and much

less prominent in the ileum as it nears the colon. These folds involve the entire mucosa, and also carry into them a portion of the submucosa (Fig. 16-34). Unlike the folds of the stomach, the plicae cannot be completely flattened out by distention of the intestine.

The mucosa is further carried up into finger-like projections, the *villi*, which cover not only the surface of the plicae but the entire surface of the small intestine (Fig. 16-34). The villi differ in shape in the different parts of the small intestine, being leaf-shaped in the duodenum, rounded in the jejunum and club-shaped in the ileum. The plicae and the villi are characteristic of

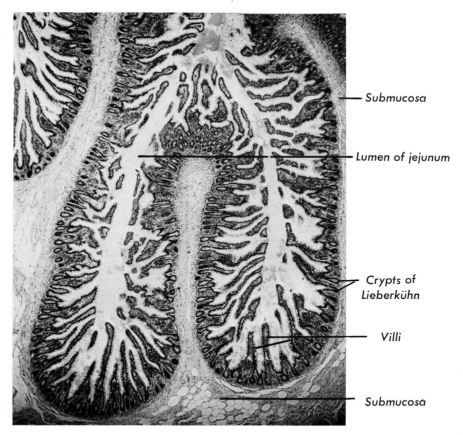

Submucosa

Lumen of jejunum

Crypts of Lieberkühn

Villi

Submucosa

FIG. 16-36. Longitudinal section of mucosa of jejunum. The section shows a short plica circularis in the *center* of the field, and on either side of it part of a taller plica. The entire lumen surface is covered with villi; submucosal connective tissue forms the core of each plica. Human. Hematoxylin-eosin stain. Photomicrograph. ×32.

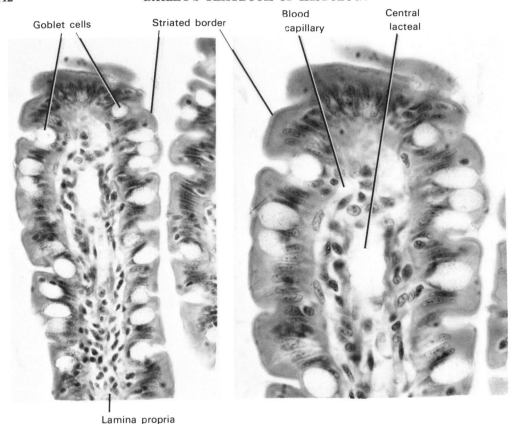

Goblet cells   Striated border   Blood capillary   Central lacteal

Lamina propria

FIG. 16-37. Photomicrographs of a longitudinal section of the upper portion of a villus of the jejunum of a cat. The double border appearance at the tip of the villus is caused by the relationship between the plane of the section and irregularities in the contour of the surface of the villus. The central lacteal is dilated somewhat because the animal was actively absorbing fat prior to the time of autopsy. *Left,* ×390; *right,* a portion of the same field at ×650.

the small intestine. It is important to note that, while the pits of the stomach are *depressions in* the mucous membrane, the intestinal villi are *projections above* the general intestinal surface. By means of its folds and projections, the absorbing and secreting surface of the intestinal mucosa is enormously increased. Opening between the villi and extending into the mucosa as far as the muscularis mucosae are simple glandular pits, the *crypts of Lieberkühn* (glandulae intestinales). All of the above modifications are treated in detail in a discussion of the mucosa.

The wall of the intestine consists of the same four coats that constituted the wall of the stomach: *mucosa, submucosa, muscularis externa* and *serosa.*

The Mucosa. The mucosa is composed of its lining *epithelium,* a *lamina propria* with its glands, and a limiting *muscularis mucosae* below. The most characteristic feature of the small intestinal mucosa is the *villus* (Figs. 16-34 to 16-38).

The villi are mucosal projections barely visible to the naked eye. Situated close together and covering the entire mucosal surface, they give the interior of the intestine a soft, velvety appearance grossly.

Each villus consists of a core of delicate, loose connective tissue and an epithelial covering. The connective tissue, the lamina propria of the mucous membrane, is infiltrated with lymphocytes to a variable extent. In addition to these and the cells of the connective tissue, occasional isolated smooth muscle cells from the muscularis mucosae are present.

A single small lymphatic vessel (lacteal) with definite endothelial lining traverses the center of each villus, beginning at the tip in a slightly dilated, blind extremity. Since this *central lacteal* is usually collapsed in ordinary preparations, it is often difficult to see. It appears most frequently as two closely approximated rows of flat cells with bulging nuclei. During absorption of fat from the intestinal lumen, the lacteals become distended with fat droplets and are then clearly visible (Fig. 16-43). The blood capillaries of the villus form a network which lies, for the most part, away from the lacteal, just beneath the basement membrane of the intestinal epithelium.

Observations of the villi in the living condition have revealed that they continually change in length and undergo waving motions. This is possible because of the presence of smooth muscle in them. These movements bring the villi into contact with new material to be absorbed and aid in the circulation of the villus, particularly in the movement of fluid in the lymph vessels (lacteals).

EPITHELIUM. The *epithelium* covering the villi is a single layer of columnar cells attached to a delicate basement membrane (i.e., basal lamina plus lamina reticularis). The epithelium consists of two quite different kinds of cells, *columnar absorbing cells* and *goblet cells*. The columnar absorbing cells are quite plastic and, although generally long and narrow, they vary as to length and breadth as they adapt themselves to movements of the intestine. Their various shapes can best be studied in dissociated (macerated) epithelium. The cytoplasm is finely granular, its appearance changing somewhat in different phases of absorption. It frequently contains fat droplets. The nucleus is ovoid and is usually situated in the lower half of the cell (Fig. 16-38).

One of the most striking and distinguishing features of the columnar absorbing cells is their *striated free border* (brush border).

With low magnification, this is seen as a nearly homogeneous, refractile layer (Figs. 1-9, *C*, and 16-38) covering the apical surface of the cell but, with greater magnification, it appears finely striated. By means of phase contrast and electron microscopy, it is seen that the striated free border is actually composed of a great many very fine, closely packed microvilli (Figs. 16-39 and 16-40). The length of the microvilli varies in cells of different regions, being greatest (1 to 1.5 μ) on cells at the tips of the villi. High resolution electron micrographs show that the outer leaflet of the plasmalemma over the microvilli has very slender branching filaments which form a coat of fuzzy appearance. This surface coat gives staining reactions of protein polysaccharides and ranges in thickness from 0.1 to 0.5 μ. The central portion of each microvillus contains fine filaments oriented longitudinally and anchored in a feltwork of filaments, the *terminal web*, in the cytoplasm just beneath the level of the microvilli. The terminal web zone is free of cell organelles and is rich in filaments which course chiefly in a direction perpendicular to the long axis of the cell. In addition to providing structural support to the central core of filaments of each microvillus, the filaments of the web connect laterally with electron-dense material in the subplasmalemmal region of the intercellular attachments.

The striated border region contains a number of enzymes, including alkaline phosphatase, maltase, adenosine triphosphatase and aminopeptidase. Thus, the border not only provides an increase in the luminal surface of the cell for absorption but also contains enzymes of importance for the final stages of the digestive process.

The *mitochondria* (Fig. 1-9, *C*) are distributed above and below the nucleus. In both regions they are rod-shaped or filamentous. Those in the basal portion of the cell are particularly numerous.

The *Golgi apparatus* lies between the nucleus and the free surface of the cell. Its possible significance in the absorption of

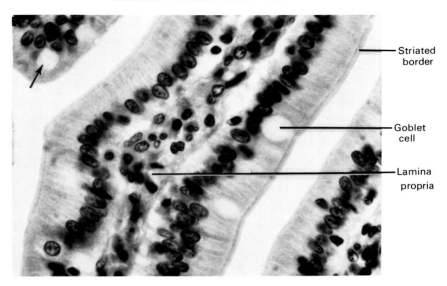

Striated border

Goblet cell

Lamina propria

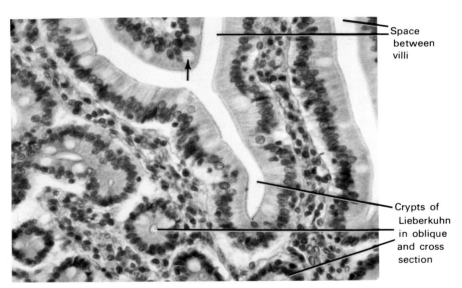

Space between villi

Crypts of Lieberkuhn in oblique and cross section

FIG. 16-38. Photomicrographs of basal portions of villi and subjacent portions of crypts of Lieberkuhn from a section of human jejunum. Some of the crypts are seen in transverse section. The *upper* figure is a higher magnification micrograph that includes the upper portion of the field shown in the *lower* figure. As an aid in orientation, an *arrow* is directed to the same goblet cell in each photograph. *Upper,* ×650; *lower,* ×390.

foodstuffs is discussed below under the section on cytological changes in absorption.

The *endoplasmic reticulum* is chiefly of the smooth variety in the apical part of the cell and mostly of the rough surfaced variety in the deeper portion of the cell. Free ribosomes are also fairly numerous in the basal part of the cell.

The *intercellular junctions* at the adluminal ends of the. cells are typical junctional

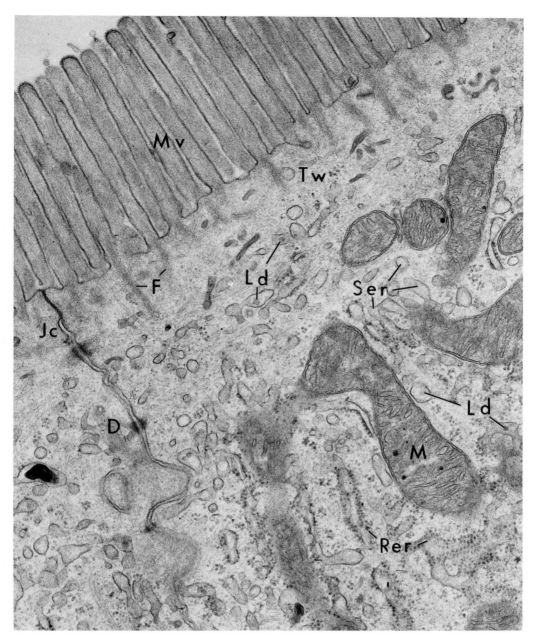

FIG. 16-39. Electron micrograph of a portion of the apical region of a columnar absorptive cell from the jejunum of a rat. The area of the adluminal surface of the cell is increased by microvilli (*Mv*). Fine filaments in the core of each microvillus are continuous with filaments (*F*) in the subjacent cytoplasm, in a region known as the terminal web (*Tw*). Filaments of the terminal web also loop into portions of the junctional complex (*Jc*). The complex consists, from above downward, of a zonula occludens, a zonula adherens, and a macula adherens (desmosome) as described in Chapter 4. Other desmosomes (*D*) are seen at irregular intervals along the course of apposing membranes of adjacent cells. Tubules of smooth-surfaced endoplasmic reticulum (*Ser*) become continuous with rough surfaced endoplasmic reticulum (*Rer*). Some small lipid droplets (*Ld*) are seen within tubules of the *Ser*. This is explained by the fact that the animal was given fat by stomach tube 45 min prior to autopsy. *M*, mitochondrion. ×35,000. (Courtesy of Drs. R. R. Cardell, Jr., S. Badenhausen, and K. R. Porter, J. Cell Biol., vol. 34, 1967.)

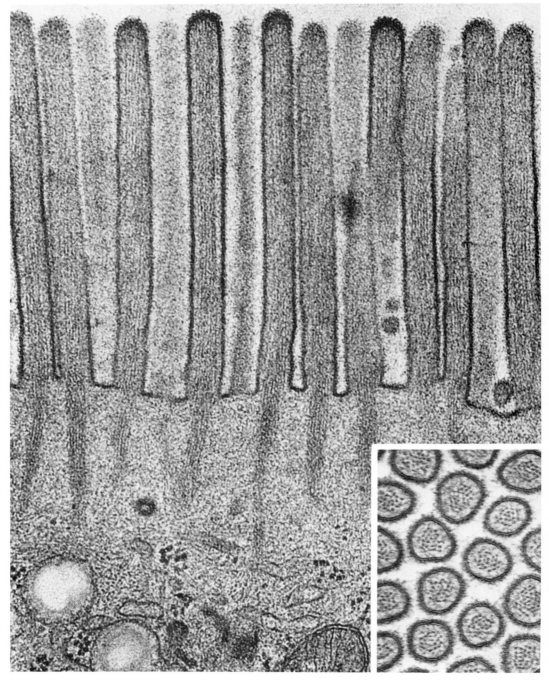

FIG. 16-40. Electron micrograph of the apical region of a columnar absorbing cell, showing the micro-villi and the terminal web region of the cytoplasm at higher magnification than in the preceding figure. Note the prominent core of filaments in each microvillus. The adluminal surface of the plasmalemma of each microvillus is covered with a fuzzy coat (see Chapter 1, Fig. 1-34). The *insert at lower right* shows the microvilli in transverse section. Small intestine of a rat. ×75,000. (Courtesy of Drs. Mary Bonne-ville and Keith Porter.)

complexes as described in Chapter 4 (Fig. 4-6). Maculae adherens, or desmosomes, are found at deeper levels. It will be recalled that potential intercellular space is sealed around the adluminal ends of the cells by zonulae occludentes and that the width of the intercellular space in most other regions is about 100 to 200 A. In the deeper regions nearer the basal lamina, however, the intercellular space may reach a width of 2000 A.

Goblet cells, unicellular mucous glands, are dispersed among the columnar absorbing cells. In the early stages of the secretory process, only a few mucigen droplets are present in the cytoplasm adjacent to the Golgi region. As more droplets form, the apical portion of the cell becomes distended to the typical goblet shape, and the nucleus, together with most of the remaining cytoplasm, is displaced into the narrow basal region or stem. These cells differ from the absorbing cells in a number of respects, including shape and staining. The mucigen droplets are dissolved by routine methods of preparing sections for light microscopy; thus, the upper portion of the goblet cell appears relatively empty. When the mucigen droplets are preserved by special methods, they are found to be basophilic, metachromatic and periodic acid-Schiff-positive. Electron micrographs show that microvilli are short and sparse on goblet cells. More details on the goblet cells are given in Chapters 4 and 15.

The number of goblet cells is small in the duodenum and becomes progressively greater in the jejunum, ileum and colon.

Crypts of Lieberkühn or *intestinal glands* occur throughout the small intestine. They are simple tubular glands located in the mucous membrane. They open between the villi and extend down through the lamina propria as far as the muscularis mucosae. The epithelium of the crypt is continuous at its opening with the surface epithelium of the villi. In general, the columnar cells which lie near the fundus of the gland are less differentiated and somewhat shorter than the columnar absorbing cells of the villi. The striated border of the cells deep in the glands is poorly developed (with microvilli of less than 0.5 μ in length). There is a gradual increase in the height of the microvilli of the striated border on the columnar cells from the fundus to the mouth of the crypt. This fact, together with the presence of numerous mitoses in the crypts, correlates well with the results obtained by thymidine labeling studies which show conclusively that the intestinal surface cells arise from undifferentiated cells in the crypts (Leblond and Messier, 1958). The undifferentiated cells multiply and differentiate as they move up the crypts to the sides of the villi. They seldom divide after they reach the villi but they continue to migrate upward and eventually slough from the tips of the villi into the intestinal lumen at the end of their relatively short life cycle.

Goblet cells are also found in the crypt epithelium. They are more numerous in the upper portion but may be found even in the region just above the base of the gland. Goblet cells also most probably arise from the undifferentiated type of columnar cell.

In addition, there are also found in the depths of the crypts of Lieberkühn groups of coarsely granular cells, the *cells of Paneth* (Fig. 16-46). These cells appear to be serozymogenic in that they have characteristic chromophilic material basally and acidophilic granules apically. The zymogenic function of these cells, however, is not well established. Their cytoplasm contains lysosomes and there is some evidence that they are phagocytic. Paneth cells occur mainly in the crypts of the small intestine but may occasionally be present in the large intestine also.

Argentaffin or *enterochromaffin cells* are present in small numbers among the epithelial cells lining the crypts and occasionally among the epithelial cells covering the villi (see section on the stomach). They are fairly common in the duodenum, sparse in the jejunum and ileum, and relatively numerous in the appendix. They have fine granules that are stained by silver and chromium salts, and the granules are located in the part of the cell that faces the basal lamina. One of these cell types, like the same type in the gastric mucosa, secretes serotonin, a vasoconstrictor.

Cytological Changes in Absorption. The epithelium of the gastrointestinal tract must be considered as having two main functions: (1) The *secretion* of substances necessary in digestion, and (2) the *absorption* of the products of digestion. The first of these functions has been dealt with in connection with the description of the various secretory cells. The matter of absorption of digestive products deserves some further elaboration. The epithelium of the intestines must absorb, in addition to water, salts and mineral substances, the three classes of food—carbohydrates, proteins and fats.

The absorption of fats has been studied extensively by biochemical methods and by electron microscopy. Breakdown of dietary fats in the intestine is effected by pancreatic lipase with the aid of bile salts. There have been some questions concerning the amount of hydrolysis which is prerequisite for fat absorption. Biochemical studies indicate that about one-fourth of the ingested fat is hydrolyzed completely to fatty acids and glycerol, and that the remainder is hydrolyzed to monoglycerides and diglycerides. It seems clear that most of the fat is absorbed in the form of fatty acids and monoglycerides and that these are recombined to form triglycerides within the intestinal mucosa.

In order to follow absorption cytologically, the substance being studied must be marked for identification. This is readily achieved for fat, since lipids are blackened by the osmium tetroxide generally used for tissue fixation in electron microscopy. The pathway of fat can be deduced from electron microscope studies of tissue fixed at different time intervals subsequent to introduction of fat into the digestive tube. Within relatively short periods after introduction of fat into the digestive tube, small lipid droplets are present within the tubules of the smooth

surfaced endoplasmic reticulum (SER) of the apical portions of the absorbing cells (Fig. 16-39). Lipid droplets are also found within bulbous expansions of the SER and within isolated vesicles of the SER (Fig. 16-41). The vesicles are apparently derived from the SER and some of them may be derived from the Golgi complex with which they are often associated. By this stage of fat absorption, the lipid droplets range up to 500 A in diameter and aggregates of them are visible under the light microscope (Fig. 16-43). The vesicles, containing the lipid droplets, migrate to the lateral surface of the cell where the droplets are released, free of enveloping membranes, into extracellular space (Fig. 16-42). The droplets pass through the basal lamina and into the intercellular connective tissue spaces and thence to lymphatic capillaries. Diagrammatic summaries of the sequence of events in fat absorption, as revealed by electron microscopic and histochemical studies, are shown in Figure 16-44. It is thought that monoglycerides and fatty acids pass from the intestinal lumen into the cytoplasm of the columnar absorbing cell by diffusion through the cell membrane. The monoglycerides and fatty acids then pass into the tubules of the SER where they are resynthesized to triglycerides that are released into the intercellular spaces.

The pathway from the epithelial cells to the vascular system proceeds primarily by the lymphatics. Neutral fats (triglycerides) pass from the connective tissue underlying the epithelial cells into lymphatic capillaries and eventually reach the blood vessels via the thoracic ducts. Most of the absorbed fatty acids which are more than 10 carbon chains in length are resynthesized with glycerol to form triglycerides and enter the lymphatics. Fatty acids with short carbon chains (less than 10 or 12 carbons) pass directly into the blood capillaries of the intestine and thence to the portal vein. The bile salts which were combined with the fatty acids during the absorptive process become free and they are absorbed directly into the blood to return by the portal vein

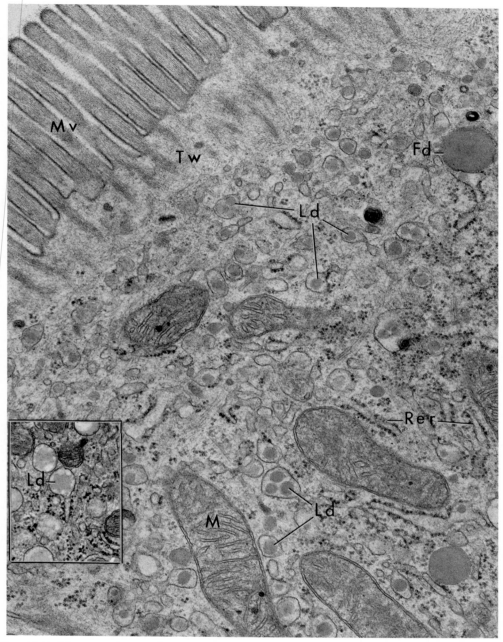

Fig. 16-41. Electron micrograph of the apical portion of an intestinal absorptive cell fixed during active fat absorption. Numerous lipid droplets (*Ld*) are present within tubules of the smooth-surfaced endoplasmic reticulum. The latter is hypertrophied and is often seen in continuity with the rough surfaced endoplasmic reticulum (*Rer*). Lipid droplets are often seen in bulbous expansions of the reticulum (*Ld* of *inset*). Free lipid droplets (*Fd*) within the cell can be distinguished from the droplets in stages of absorption by their large diameter and by the absence of an enveloping membrane. *M*, mitochondrion; *Mv*, microvilli; *Tw*, terminal web area. From rat jejunum fixed 40 min after intubation of corn oil; *inset*, from rat jejunum fixed at 60 min after intubation of corn oil. ×31,500. (Courtesy of Drs. R. R. Cardell, Jr., S. Badenhausen, and K. R. Porter, J. Cell Biol., vol. 34, 1967.)

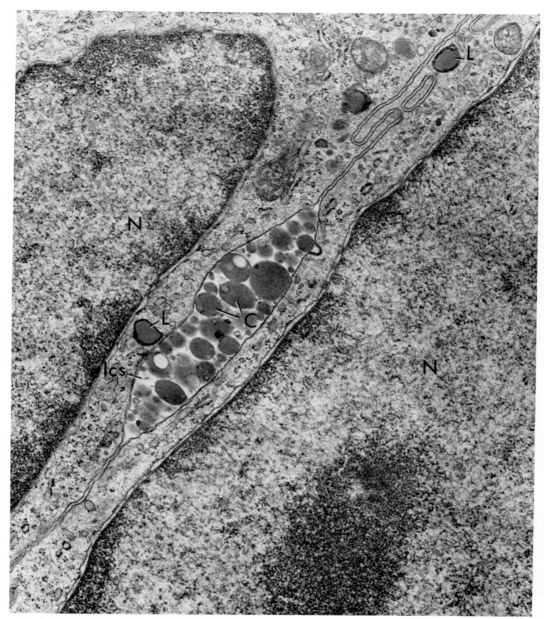

FIG. 16-42. Electron micrograph of portions of two columnar absorbing cells of rat intestine subsequent to the intubation of corn oil. Intercellular spaces (*Ics*) are generally enlarged during fat absorption and they contain chylomicra (*C*) which are similar to the largest lipid droplets (*L*) in the cytoplasm except that the latter are membrane-bounded whereas the former are not. The chylomicra pass downward through the intercellular spaces and through the basal lamina of the epithelium to reach the subepithelial connective tissue where they enter lymphatic capillaries. *N*, nuclei. ×23,225. (Courtesy of Drs. R. R. Cardell, Jr., S. Badenhausen, and K. R. Porter, J. Cell Biol. vol. 34, 1967.)

Fat droplets in columnar absorbing cell   Central lacteal   Lamina propria of villus

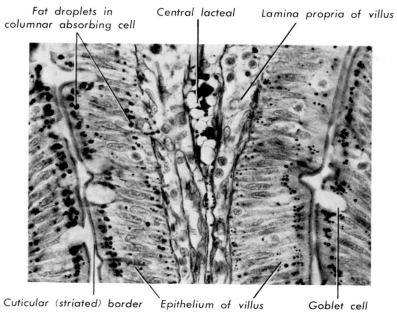

Cuticular (striated) border   Epithelium of villus   Goblet cell

FIG. 16-43. Fat absorption in small intestine of rhesus monkey given fat by stomach tube 4 hours prior to autopsy. Parts of three villi and two intervillous (luminal) spaces are shown. Fat droplets are seen in the cytoplasm of the apical regions of the columnar cells and also within the central lacteal. On the basis of electron microscopic studies, it can be concluded that the droplets which appear to be in the basal part of the cell, as seen here in a 10μ thick section under the light microscope, are actually within relatively narrow intercellular spaces. Osmic acid fixation; azocarmine stain. ×480.

to the liver where they are excreted into the bile for a role in another cycle of fat absorption.

LAMINA PROPRIA. The *stroma*, besides forming the centers of the villi, fills in the spaces between the crypts of Lieberkühn and between the latter and the muscularis mucosae. It is composed of interweaving reticular and delicate collagenous fibers, with a considerable number of elastic fibrils. It also contains connective tissue cells: fibroblasts, eosinophils, plasma cells, mast cells, etc. Lymphocytes are abundant everywhere and in many places they are so numerous as to give the appearance of diffuse lymphatic tissue. Here and there the lymphatic cells are more closely packed together to form distinct lymph follicles. These are known as *solitary nodules* (follicles) to distinguish them from groups of lymph nodules which occur in the lower sections of the small intestine

and are known as Peyer's patches (see below). Solitary nodules are much more numerous in the small intestine than in the stomach. They are identical in structure with those of the stomach.

PEYER'S PATCHES (aggregated follicles). These are aggregations of solitary follicles or groups of lymph nodules found mainly in the ileum, especially near its junction with the colon. They always occur on the side of the gut opposite the attachment of the mesentery. Each patch consists of from 10 to 70 nodules, which lie side by side and are so arranged that the entire patch has a generally oval shape, its long diameter lying lengthwise of the intestine. The pear-shaped apices of the follicles are directed toward the lumen and project almost through the mucosa. They are not covered by villi, a single layer of columnar epithelium alone separating them from the lumen of the gut,

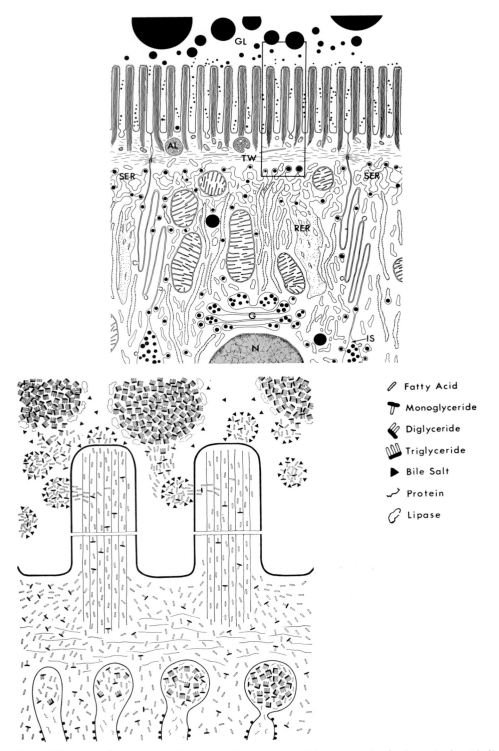

Legend:

- ∅ Fatty Acid
- ⊤ Monoglyceride
- ✦ Diglyceride
- ▥ Triglyceride
- ▶ Bile Salt
- ∿ Protein
- ℰ Lipase

Fig. 16-44. The *upper* figure gives a diagrammatic summary of fat absorption by intestinal epithelial cells as interpreted from results of electron microscopic and biochemical studies. Fat in the gut lumen

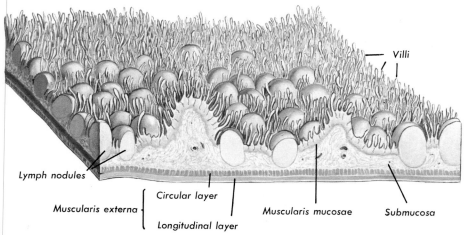

Villi

Lymph nodules

Circular layer

Muscularis externa

Longitudinal layer

Muscularis mucosae   Submucosa

FIG. 16-45. Low power, three dimensional view of a segment of human ileum, showing part of a Peyer's patch. ×15.

where their smooth surfaces can readily be seen in gross dissection (Fig. 16-45).

The bases of the nodules are not confined to the lamina propria but extend into the submucosa. The relation of the patch to the mucosa and submucosa can be best appreciated by following the course of the muscularis mucosae. This is seen to stop abruptly at the circumference of the patch, appearing throughout the patch as isolated groups of smooth muscle cells. Sometimes the individual nodules that make up a Peyer's patch are quite discrete and well defined. More frequently, however, the nodules tend to coalesce except at their apices, so that the individual nodules can be definitely outlined only at their apices and identified to some extent by their germinal centers. Peyer's

patches are most prominent in children. In the adult and in old age, the lymphatic tissue gradually undergoes regression and involution.

MUSCULARIS MUCOSAE. The muscularis mucosae is thin, consisting of an inner circular and an outer longitudinal layer of smooth muscle. Small groups of muscle fibers extend from the muscularis mucosae into the stroma of the villi.

Submucosa. The *submucosa* (Figs. 16-35 and 16-45) consists, as in the stomach, of loosely arranged connective tissue, and it contains the larger blood vessels and lymphatics. The submucosa is free from glands except in the duodenum, where it contains the *glands of Brunner* (Fig. 16-35). *Brunner's glands* are the most distinguish-

(GL) is broken down to small lipid droplets seen above and between the microvilli. Fat diffuses through the cell membrane in the form of monoglycerides and fatty acids. These enter the tubules of the smooth-surfaced endoplasmic reticulum (SER) where they are resynthesized to form droplets of triglycerides. The membrane-bound droplets are transported either directly or via the Golgi complex (G) to intercellular spaces (IS) at the level of the nucleus (N). Al, apical lysosomes; RER, rough surfaced endoplasmic reticulum; TW, terminal web. The enclosed area is enlarged in the *lower* figure to show the biochemical events in the initial phases of fat absorption. Triglycerides and diglycerides, in the presence of bile salts in the gut lumen, are hydrolyzed by pancreatic lipase to form micelles of monoglycerides and fatty acids. The monoglycerides and fatty acids diffuse from the micelles into and through the cell membrane to enter the cell cytoplasm where they encounter a network of smooth-surfaced endoplasmic reticulum. Within the tubules of SER, they are resynthesized to triglycerides that form droplets, along with phospholipids and cholesterol, in a protein solution. By the synthesis and sequestration of triglycerides within the cell, an inward diffusion gradient of monoglycerides and fatty acids is maintained. (Both figures, courtesy of Drs. R. R. Cardell, Jr., S. Badenhausen, and K. R. Porter, J. Cell Biol., vol. 34, 1967.)

ing characteristic of the upper duodenum, and they are often spoken of as the duodenal glands. Whereas their presence is an identifying feature of the duodenum, it must be remembered that these glands are absent in its inferior part. Brunner's glands are generally classified as branched and compound tubular glands, although the lumen of the terminal portion of the tubule is frequently enlarged to approach a tubulo-alveolar form (Fig. 16-35). They are lined with a columnar epithelium similar to that of the pyloric glands. The ducts are also lined with simple columnar epithelium. From the glands they pass up through the muscularis mucosae and lamina propria and empty usually into a crypt of Lieberkühn, although occasionally they empty on the surface between the villi. In the region of the juncture between the pylorus and duodenum, there is a zone in which the glands of the two segments merge imperceptibly. Glands of similar structure lie partly in the lamina propria and partly in the submucosa, with strands of the muscularis mucosae present among the alveoli. The juncture of the stomach and duodenum thus is not sharply demarcated by the position of the glands. Brunner's glands, like the pyloric glands, secrete an alkaline mucoid substance.

Muscularis. The *muscular coat* (Figs. 16-35 and 16-45) consists of two well defined layers of smooth muscle, an inner circular and an outer longitudinal. Connective tissue septa divide the muscle cells into groups or bundles, while between the two layers of muscle is a connective tissue septum which varies greatly in thickness at different places and contains a plexus of nerve fibers and parasympathetic ganglion cells known as the plexus of Auerbach.

Serosa. The *serous coat*, as in the stomach, consists of loose connective tissue covered by a layer of mesothelium.

THE LARGE INTESTINE

The large intestine is divided topographically and to some extent structurally into three main segments: colon, rectum and anal canal. Throughout the length of the large intestine, the wall consists of the same four coats that have been described for the stomach and small intestine, viz., mucosa, submucosa, muscularis and serosa (or fibrosa).

Colon

There is an abrupt change at the ileocecal juncture from the small intestine to the *colon*. The greater diameter of the colon is perhaps the most striking difference grossly. Other differences of structure are noted in the description of the various coats.

Mucosa. The *mucous membrane* of the colon has a comparatively smooth surface, for *there are no plicae or villi* as in the small intestine. Long, straight, tubular glands extend from the surface down through the entire thickness of the mucosa. These glands are *crypts of Lieberkühn*.

The surface *epithelium* is tall columnar. The absorbing cells have a striated border which is thinner than that on the cells of the small intestine. Goblet cells are interspersed among the columnar absorbing cells. As the epithelium continues down into the tubular glands, the columnar cells become lower and goblet cells become exceedingly numerous. In fact, the walls of the glands frequently appear to be composed almost entirely of goblet cells. The cells at the base of the tubes are believed to be the more undifferentiated ones which, by division, push new cells toward the surface to replace those which are being lost. Paneth and argentaffine cells are very rarely found.

The mucous membrane of the colon has two chief functions which are attributed to the columnar absorbing and goblet cells, respectively: namely, the absorption of water and the copious production of mucus. This mucous secretion lubricates the surface of the colon and facilitates the forwarding of the gradually dehydrated feces.

The connective tissue of the *lamina propria* extends up between the glands but is re-

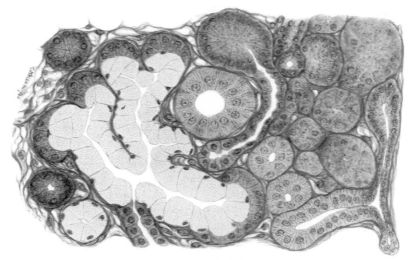

Submandibular gland

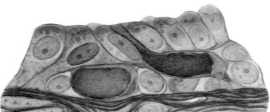

Epithelium of a parotid interlobar duct

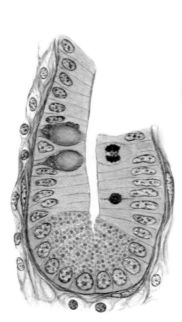

Crypt of Lieberkühn

Neck of a gastric gland

Fig. 16-46. Camera lucida drawings of human tissues (except epithelium of interlobar duct, which is from the parotid gland of a rhesus monkey). Stains: hematoxylin, Altmann's acid fuchsin and aniline blue.

Submandibular Gland. At the left of the gland, three mucous alveoli (light blue), capped with serous demilunes, empty into the intercalated duct below. At lower left are cross sections through serous and mucous alveoli respectively. At lower right, two intercalated ducts join a secretory (salivary) duct, whose cells have a reddish stained (fuchsin) granular cytoplasm with blue (aniline blue) basal striations. An intercalated duct from a serous alveolus curves around the right side of the large central salivary duct.

Epithelium of Parotid Interlobar Duct. Note that the blue goblet cell at the right, although greatly distorted, reaches the surface. The one to the left does so also, but it is cut off in this section. The large surface epithelial cell (second from left) stretches around the goblet cell to reach the basement membrane at separate places. Adjacent sections show that the four cells at upper right likewise reach the basement membrane. Thus the epithelium, stratified in appearance, is actually pseudostratified.

Crypt of Lieberkühn. The basal cells, full of large, red secretory granules, are Paneth cells. At upper left are two blue goblet cells. One of the columnar epithelial cells on the right is dividing by mitosis. The dark round nucleus of a lymphocyte, migrating between two columnar cells, is also shown.

Neck of Gastric Gland. This cross section shows two large red parietal (HCl) cells with their clear intracellular canals. The light blue cells with indented basal nuclei are mucous neck cells. The darker blue cells are chief cells.

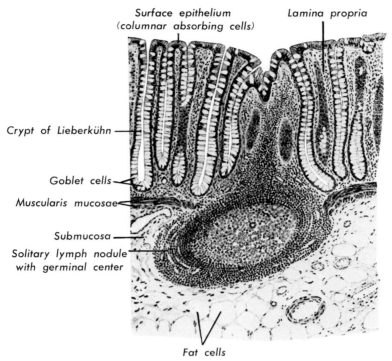

Surface epithelium
(columnar absorbing cells)   Lamina propria

Crypt of Lieberkühn

Goblet cells

Muscularis mucosae

Submucosa

Solitary lymph nodule
with germinal center

Fat cells

FIG. 16-47. Transverse section through mucosa and submucosa of colon of man. ×70. (After Braus)

duced to a minimum because the tubules are close together. Solitary lymph nodules are present in the mucosa and push through the muscularis mucosae into the submucosa (Fig. 16-47).

The *muscularis mucosae* consists of an inner circular and an outer longitudinal layer of smooth muscle.

Submucosa. The *submucosa* is composed of loosely arranged connective tissue. It contains large blood vessels and the nerve plexus of Meissner. Solitary lymph follicles, although properly considered as structures of the lamina propria from which they originate, lie mainly in the submucosa.

Muscularis. The *muscularis externa* in the colon shows some variation from its usual structure. The inner circular layer is complete and prominent, but the longitudinal muscles become arranged into three strong, flat, equidistant, longitudinal bands, the *lineae coli* (taenia coli). Between these thick strands the longitudinal muscle coat be-

comes thinned but is rarely entirely absent. Nerve cell and fiber components of the plexus of Auerbach lie as usual in the connective issue just external to the circular muscle layer.

Serosa. The *serous coat* is composed of a thin connective tissue layer covered by mesothelium. In certain regions, the mesothelial covering is absent. Here the connective tissue *fibrosa* binds the colon firmly to adjacent structures.

VERMIFORM APPENDIX

The vermiform appendix is a diverticulum from the cecum. Its walls are continuous with those of the latter and closely resemble them in general structure. There are the same four coats: mucous, submucous, muscular and serous.

The *mucous membrane* has its usual characteristic structures: the epithelium, glands, lamina propria and the muscularis mucosae. The surface epithelium is simple columnar with a striated apical border. It continues into the glands or crypts of Lieberkühn where the border gradually becomes thinner. The glands frequently have many goblet cells, some Paneth cells and a number of argentaffine cells. In the embryo, the mucosal surface is lined with villi, but these disappear early in life. The lumen is often thrown into deep, pocketed folds, and in many adults it is nearly or completely obliterated.

The most characteristic histological feature of the appendix is the lymphatic tissue. Not only is the lamina propria infiltrated with lymphocytes, but it is often conspicuously occupied by a complete ring of solitary lymphatic follicles. These closely resemble the follicles that surround the crypts of the palatine tonsils. The follicles do not remain confined to the mucosa but push through the muscularis mucosae and invade the submucosa. In fact, the lymphatic development frequently makes it difficult to follow the muscularis mucosae and to separate the mucosa from the submucosa (Fig. 16-48). The *submucosa* contains numerous fat cells. It should be mentioned that, in some instances, more commonly after middle age, the mucosa and portions of the submucosa are largely replaced by fibrous connective tissue.

The *muscularis externa* varies greatly, both in thickness and in the amount of admixture of fibrous tissue. The inner circular layer is usually thick and well developed. The outer longitudinal layer differs from that of the

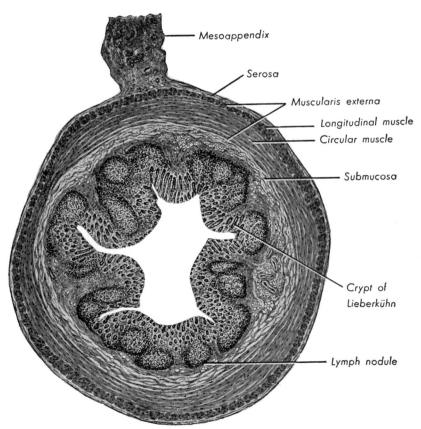

FIG. 16-48. Transverse section of human vermiform appendix. ×14

large intestine in having no arrangement into lineae, the muscle tissue forming a continuous layer. The muscular layers are covered as usual by the *serosa*.

RECTUM

The *rectum* is usually divided into two parts. The *upper part* (the rectum proper), measuring 5 to 7 inches in length, is structurally similar to the colon. The crypts of Lieberkühn are longer than in the colon, however, and are lined almost entirely by goblet cells. The longitudinal layer of the muscularis externa is thicker on the front and back than it is on the sides. This segment of the gut has no mesentery, and the serous coat is incomplete.

The *lower part* (*anal canal*) is 1 to 1½ inches in length. It pierces the pelvic floor and is closed except during defecation. Its mucous membrane has a number of permanent longitudinal folds, the *rectal columns* (*anal columns, columns of Morgagni*) which terminate distally about ½ inch from the anal orifice. These contain strands of smooth muscle and usually an artery and a vein.

The bases (distal ends) of these columns are connected by transverse folds of the mucosa, the *anal valves* (Fig. 16-49).

Above the anal valves, the mucosa is lined by simple columnar epithelium like that of the rectum proper, composed of columnar absorbing cells, interspersed with many goblet cells. Crypts of Lieberkühn are present (Fig. 16-50).

At the level of the anal valves, the epithelium becomes a stratified squamous type, the surface cells of which are not cornified. No crypts of Lieberkühn are present below the juncture. The noncornified stratified squamous epithelium extends nearly to the anal orifice, where it changes to epidermis. Hairs, sebaceous glands and sweat glands appear at the anal orifice.

The sweat glands are of two types. One type has the characteristic structure of the general body sweat glands (Chapter 14, "Sweat Glands," and Figs. 14-5 and 14-6). The other type (*circumanal glands*) are very large and are structurally similar to the axillary sweat glands. Their secretory cells contain granules, and inside the basement

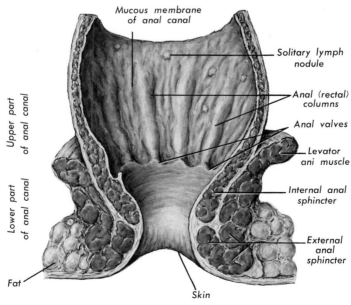

FIG. 16-49. Mucous surface of anal canal. Redrawn. (Courtesy of Wyeth Laboratories, Philadelphia, Pa).

Crypts of   Juncture of simple columnar and
Lieberkühn   stratified squamous epithelium
                                                              Lamina
                                                              propria

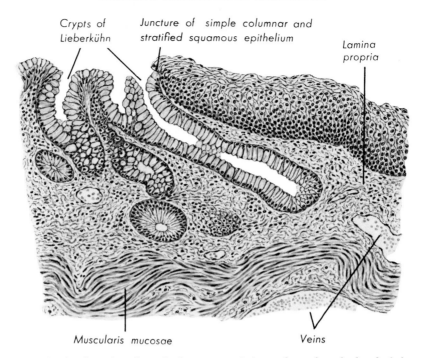

Muscularis mucosae   Veins

Fig. 16-50. Longitudinal section through the mucosa of the anal canal at the level of the anal valves. ×190.

membrane are prominent myoepithelial cells (Figs. 14-7 and 14-8).

At about the level of the anal valves, the muscularis mucosae subdivides into diverging strands which soon disappear.

The submucous coat of the anal canal has a rich plexus of blood vessels. The veins are often tortuous. Their size and arrangement and the absence of valves are conducive to the formation of hemorrhoids.

The circular layer of smooth muscle of the anal canal is thick and forms the *internal anal sphincter*. The longitudinal layer of smooth muscle continues over the sphincter and attaches to connective tissue. The *external anal sphincter* is formed of skeletal muscle. It lies just inside the levator ani muscles which also act as a sphincter (Fig. 16–49).

THE PERITONEUM

The *peritoneum* is a serous membrane which lines the walls of the abdomen (parietal peritoneum) and is reflected over the contained viscera (visceral peritoneum). It consists of two layers, a connective tissue stroma and mesothelium. The stroma consists of loosely arranged connective tissue bundles which interlace in a plane parallel to the surface. There are numerous elastic fibers, especially in the deeper layer of the parietal peritoneum. There are comparatively few connective tissue cells. The mesothelium consists of a single layer of flat, polygonal cells with bulging nuclei. The cells have irregular, wavy outlines which are easily demonstrated with silver preparations. The shapes of the cells vary considerably according to the direction in which the tissues are stretched.

Over some parts, e.g., the liver and intestine, the peritoneum or serosa is thin and very closely attached. In places where the peritoneum is freely movable, a considerable amount of loose connective tissue, rich in elastic fibers and containing varying numbers of fat cells, connects the peritoneum with the underlying tissue. This is known as the "subserous tissue." The peritoneum is well supplied with blood vessels and lymphatics. The former give rise to a rich capillary network.

The *mesentery* is a sheet of loosely arranged connective tissue covered with peritoneum. It attaches the visceral organs to the posterior abdominal wall and it carries to these organs their blood vessels, lymphatics and nerves. Parts of the mesentery are comparatively short, and certain organs are, therefore, quite firmly fixed to the abdominal wall. In other regions it is longer, allowing greater freedom of movement. The mesentery contains numerous lymph nodes and also considerable fat. From the mesentery, the peritoneum continues onto and envelops the viscera.

The *omenta* and the visceral ligaments are similar in general structure to the mesentery. The greater omentum usually contains large deposits of fat. Its connective tissue bundles are arranged in networks, the strands and meshes of which vary greatly in size and shape. The strands are covered by mesothelium.

BLOOD VESSELS OF THE STOMACH AND INTESTINES

The arteries reach the gastrointestinal canal through the mesentery, give off small branches to the serosa and pass through the muscular coats to the submucosa, where they form an extensive plexus of large vessels (Heller's plexus). Within the muscular coats, the main arteries give off small branches to the muscle tissue. From the plexus of the submucosa, two main sets of vessels arise, one passing outward to form the main supply of the muscular coats, the other inward to supply the mucous membrane (Fig. 16-51). Of the former, the larger vessels pass directly to the intermuscular septum, where they form a plexus from which branches are given off to the two muscular tunics. Of the branches of the submucous plexus which pass

to the mucous membrane, the shorter supply the muscularis mucosae, while the longer branches pierce the latter to form a capillary plexus among the glands of the stroma. These capillaries are most numerous around the bodies and necks of the glands. They pass over into a dense network of capillaries just beneath the surface epithelium. From the capillaries, small veins take origin which pierce the muscularis mucosae and form a close-meshed venous plexus in the submucosa. These in turn give rise to larger veins, which accompany the arteries into the mesentery.

In the small intestine, the distribution of the blood vessels is modified by the presence of villi (Fig. 16-52). Each villus receives one small artery or, in the case of the larger villi, two or three small arteries. The artery passes through the long axis of the villus close under the epithelium to its summit, giving off a network of fine capillaries which for the most part lie just beneath the epithelium. From these, one or two small veins arise which usually lie on the opposite side of the villus from the artery.

LYMPHATICS OF THE STOMACH AND INTESTINES

Small lymph or chyle capillaries begin as blind canals in the stroma of the mucous membrane among the tubular glands (Fig. 16-51). In the small intestine, a lymph capillary (lacteal) occupies the center of the long axis of each villus, ending in a blind extremity beneath the epithelium of its summit (Fig. 16-52). The walls of the lymph capillaries are made up of a single layer of large endothelial cells. Although the lymph capillaries are considerably larger than the blood capillaries, they are usually collapsed and inconspicuous. These vessels unite to form a narrow-meshed plexus of lymph capillaries in the deeper part of the stroma, lying parallel to the muscularis mucosae. Vessels from this plexus pass through the muscularis mucosae and form a wider meshed plexus of larger lymph vessels in

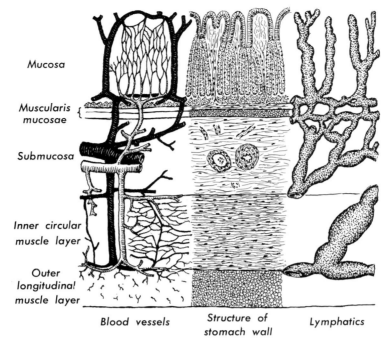

FIG. 16-51. Three sections of stomach wall placed side by side to show relationship of blood vessels and lymphatics to the different layers. (Redrawn after Mall.)

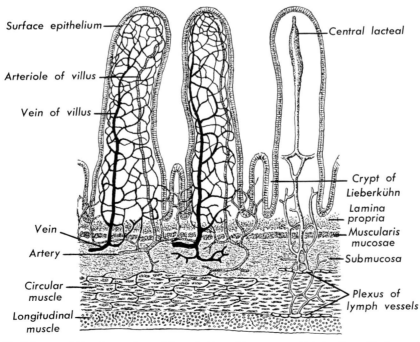

FIG. 16-52. Scheme of blood vessels and lymphatics of human small intestine. (Redrawn from Böhm and von Davidoff, after Mall.)

the submucosa. In this region they often expand into sinuses surrounding the lymphatic follicles. A third lymphatic plexus lies in the connective tissue which separates the two layers of muscle. From the plexus in the submucosa, branches pass through the inner muscular layer, receive vessels from the intermuscular plexus and then pierce the outer muscular layer to pass into the mesentery in company with the arteries and veins. The larger lymph vessels are provided with definite valves, and their walls are also supported by a thin tunic of smooth muscle cells. In their course through the mesenteries, they are associated with numerous mesenteric lymph nodes. These relations are well demonstrated in the cat by the injection of 1% Berlin blue into the intestinal wall.

Although ·the primary function of the lymphatic system is the return of tissue fluids to the blood stream, the vessels of the small intestine form channels through which absorbed fats are drained. During digestion, the lymph fluid, carrying a rich emulsion of fat (chyle), gives to the vessels a white appearance and renders them clearly visible.

NERVES OF THE STOMACH AND INTESTINES

The nerves to the stomach consist of preganglionic parasympathetic fibers (branches of the vagus nerve) and postganglionic sympathetic fibers. They reach the intestinal walls through the mesentery. In the connective tissue between the two layers of muscle, these fibers are associated with groups of parasympathetic ganglion cells to form the *plexus myentericus* or *plexus of Auerbach*. Within this plexus, the preganglionic parasympathetic fibers synapse with the ganglion cells. The axons are grouped together in small bundles of nonmyelinated fibers which pass, together with the sympathetic fibers, into the muscular coats where they form intricate plexuses, from which are given off club-shaped terminals to the smooth muscle cells. From Auerbach's plexus, fibers pass to

the submucosa, where they form a similar but finer meshed and more delicate plexus which is also associated with other groups of parasympathetic ganglion cells, the *plexus of Meissner*. Both fibers and cells are smaller than those of Auerbach's plexus. From Meissner's plexus, delicate fibrils pass to their terminations in submucosa, muscularis mucosae and mucous membrane.

THE SALIVARY GLANDS

The smaller tubular and tubuloalveolar glands which form a part of the mucous membrane and submucosa of the alimentary tract have been described. There remain to be considered certain larger compound tubuloalveolar glands, the development of which is similar to that of the smaller glands but which come to lie wholly outside the alimentary tract, connected with it by their main excretory ducts. Functionally, they are an important part of the digestive system.

These structures are: (1) the *salivary glands*, (2) the *pancreas* and (3) the *liver*.

The salivary glands include a number of glandular structures which secrete a liquid, the *saliva*. The smaller of these glands are situated in the oral mucous membrane, which their secretions serve constantly to lubricate and moisten. The larger of the glands are some distance removed from the oral cavity, to which their products are conveyed through excretory ducts. These glands, which are paired structures and may be spoken of as the salivary glands proper, are the *parotid*, *submandibular* and the *sublingual glands*. Their secretions contain enzymes which aid in preparing the food for the digestive processes that ensue in the stomach and intestines. Their secretions, together with those from the numerous smaller glands of the oral cavity, are very important in moistening and softening the bolus.

In the following account, only the salivary glands proper—the parotid, submandibular and sublingual—are considered. These three are compound tubuloalveolar glands. In man, the parotid has only serous alveoli; the submandibular and sublingual have serous and mucous alveoli. Hence the latter are known as mixed glands, in contradistinction to the purely serous glands (parotid, von Ebner's glands) and the purely mucous (palatine) glands.

Structure of the Salivary Glands. Each gland consists of gland tissue proper (*parenchyma*) and a supporting connective tissue framework (*interstitial tissue, stroma*). In the parotid and submandibular, there is a definite connective tissue capsule which encloses the gland and blends with the connective tissue of surrounding structures. The sublingual has no distinct capsule. Connective tissue septa divide each gland into *lobes* and *lobules*. In these septa are found the larger ducts, the blood vessels and occasional ganglion cells. For a description of the development of the duct system, see Chapter 15 under "Architecture of Compound Glands."

Some of the larger divisions of the intralobular ducts are lined by simple columnar epithelium similar to that of the interlobular ducts, into which they open. Most of the intralobular ducts of the salivary glands, however, are lined with columnar cells which have a contributory role in the secretory process. They are known as *striated ducts* (salivary ducts). In the parotid and submandibular glands, these ducts arise from tubules which have a narrow lumen and are lined with low or flat epithelium. Since they lie between the salivary ducts and the terminal alveoli (Figs. 16-53 and 16-54), they are known as *intercalated ducts* (intermediate tubules, necks, isthmuses).

The Serous Alveoli. The serous alveoli are lined with pyramidal epithelial cells which rest upon a basement membrane and surround a narrow lumen. The cell boundaries are likely to be indistinct. The appearance of these cells varies according to their particular phase of activity (see Fig. 15-8). In a "resting" condition, the cytoplasm is filled with a number of small, highly refrac-

tile droplets, which may be demonstrated clearly after formalin fixation. These droplets occupy the distal portion of the cell, toward the lumen, and, as they increase in number, the nucleus is pushed toward the base of the cell, the cell becomes slightly swollen and the lumen of the alveolus becomes decreased in diameter. Following active secretion, there is a diminution in the number of droplets, so that they occupy only the more apical portion of the cell. These droplets are known as *zymogen granules* and must be looked upon as the intracellular representatives of the enzymes secreted by the cell.

There is an abundance of basophilic or *chromophilic material* (ribosomes of rough surfaced endoplasmic reticulum) in the basal portion of the cell. This region has a striated appearance in the light microscope, as a result of the parallel arrangement of rod-shaped mitochondria and the configuration of the endoplasmic reticulum. The ribosomes are sites for synthesis of the protein molecules of the enzymes. The protein is combined with polysaccharides in the Gogli region to form membrane-bound secretory droplets. The latter move into the apical region of the cell for storage as zymogen granules until the time of secretion.

By employing the Golgi silver technique, one can demonstrate fine *intercellular secretory canaliculi* between adjacent cells of the serous alveoli.

Although not apparent in routine histological preparations, peculiar stellate-shaped cells may be demonstrated by special techniques in the region between the secreting cells and the basal lamina. They lie in close contact with the secreting cells, and their processes form a sort of basketwork around the alveolus. These are the *basal* or *basket cells* (Fig. 16-55), and they are similar to the *myoepithelial cells* of sweat glands and circumanal glands (Figs. 14-6 and 14-8). By their contraction, they assist in the discharge of the secretion products into the excretory ducts.

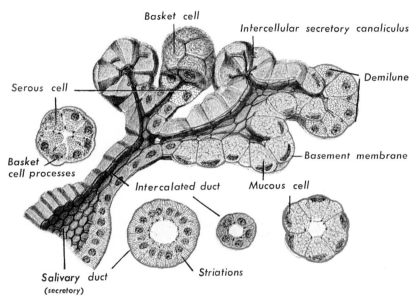

Basket cell

Intercellular secretory canaliculus

Serous cell

Demilune

Basket
cell processes

Basement membrane

Intercalated duct

Mucous cell

Salivary duct
(secretory)

Striations

Fig. 16-53. Reconstruction of terminal ramification of human submandibular gland, showing salivary and intercalated ducts and several alveoli. (From Braus, after a reconstruction by A. Vierling.)

The Mucous Alveoli. In the ordinary hematoxylin-eosin preparations, the purely mucous alveoli present a light bluish purple appearance, in contrast with the deep reddish purple of the serous alveoli (Fig. 16-53). Usually the lumen is fairly large and may contain masses of mucin. The mucous cells rest on a basal lamina, and their boundaries are usually quite distinct. When the cell becomes filled with secretory droplets, the nucleus becomes flattened in the basal part of the cell. Most of the cell is occupied by a network of cytoplasm with spaces that, in the living state, were occupied by secretory droplets. The mucigen droplets are dissolved out by most of the routine methods used in preparing sections for light microscopy, leaving only a network of cytoplasm and remnants of some of the precipitated secretory droplets. After the cell discharges its secretion, the nucleus resumes a spherical or oval shape. Mitochondria are present, but the chromophilic substance (rough surfaced endoplasmic reticulum), which is so abundant in sero-zymogenic cells, is so sparse that it is revealed only by microchemical methods or by electron microscopy. Intercellular canaliculi are not seen in the mucous alveoli.

In the mixed glands, several types of terminal alveoli may be seen. Some alveoli may be composed entirely of serous cells, others entirely of mucous cells. An alveolus may contain both kinds of cells, in which case the serous cells are more likely to occupy the blind end of the alveolus, with the mucous cells nearer the exit (Fig. 16-53). In many instances, at the base of the mucous alveolus or along its sides, there occur crescent-shaped groups of serous cells, the *demilunes of Heidenhain* or *crescents of Giannuzzi* (Fig. 16-53). These may have direct access to the lumen of the alveolus, but more often they communicate with it by means of intercellular secretory canaliculi which pass between the mucous cells and branch among the serous cells of the demilune.

Consideration is now given to the more important characteristics of the particular glands.

Parotid Gland. The *parotid gland* is the largest of the salivary glands and, in man, dog, cat and rabbit, it is entirely *serous* (Figs. 16-56 and 16-57). Its duct system is complex. The main excretory duct (Stenson's) opens into the oral cavity opposite the second upper molar tooth. It is lined with pseudostratified columnar epithelium, with occasional goblet cells. The main duct divides into interlobar ducts which, in turn, divide to form interlobular ducts, the various branches following the connective tissue septa. Except in the larger of these ducts (Fig. 16-46), the epithelium becomes reduced to a simple columnar type. From the interlobular ducts, branches are given off which penetrate the lobules.

Most of the large intralobular ducts are of the striated variety (*salivary* or *secretory ducts*). They are lined by a single layer of columnar cells in which the nucleus is spheroidal and centrally located. The cytoplasm is finely granular and acidophilic. In the basal portion of the cell, it presents a characteristic striated appearance (Figs. 16-53 and 16-57). The rodlike mitochondria in this part of the cell are oriented perpendicular to the base of the cell. Also, electron micrographs show deep infoldings of the basal plasma membrane up into the cytoplasm. The configuration of mitochondria and plasmalemmal infoldings at the basal ends of the cells is somewhat like that in the proximal convoluted tubules of the kidney and is characteristic of regions active in transport of sodium and fluids. The *intercalated ducts*, connecting the salivary ducts and the terminal alveoli, are of small diameter (Figs. 16-53 and 16-54) and are lined by low cuboidal epithelium. In the parotid, they are fairly long elements.

The gland is covered by a thick connective tissue capsule, from which branches extend inward around subdivisions of glandular tissue known as lobes and lobules. Fine

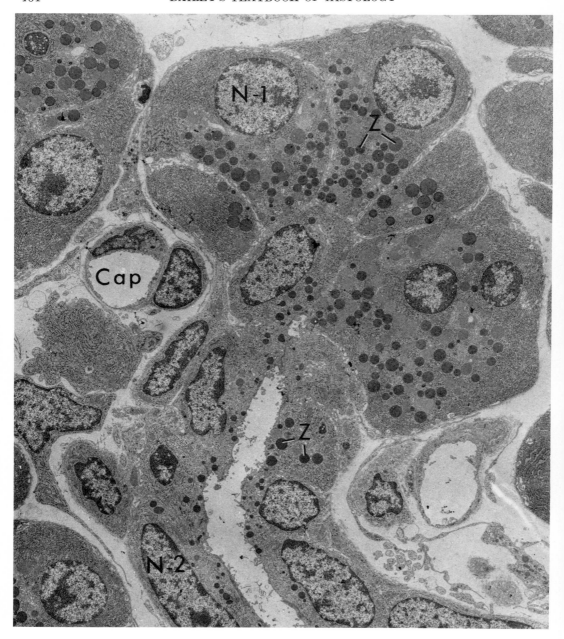

Fig. 16-54. Electron micrograph of a rat parotid gland showing the junction of an intralobular inter-calated duct with an acinus composed of parenchymal cells. The cells lining the junctional region of the duct have ultrastructural characteristics that are intermediate between those of acinar and duct cells. They have some zymogen granules and they also have more rough surfaced endoplasmic reticulum than do typical duct cells. *Cap*, capillary; *N-1*, nucleus of acinar parenchymal cell; *N-2*, nucleus of duct cell; *Z*, zymogen granules. ×2250. (Courtesy of Dr. I. Joel Leeb.)

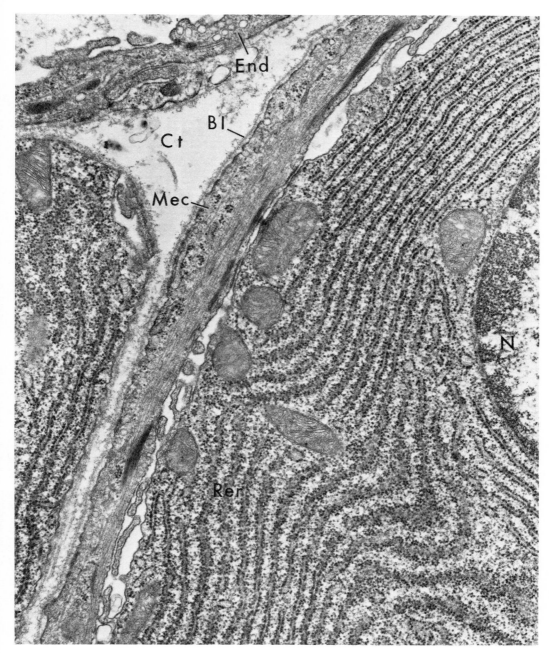

FIG. 16-55. Electron micrograph of portions of two cells of adjacent acini of the rat parotid gland. A portion of a myoepithelial cell (*Mec*) is seen between the basal end of an acinar cell and the basal lamina (*Bl*) of the acinar cells. The myoepithelial cells resemble the smooth muscle cells of other parts of the body in that they have a number of fine filaments and are contractile. *Ct*, connective tissue space; *End*, endothelium lining a small blood vessel; *N*, nucleus of acinar cell; *Rer*, rough surfaced endoplasmic reticulum. ×22,500. (Courtesy of Drs. R. L. Wood and I. Joel Leeb.)

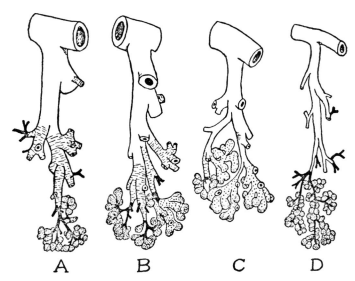

FIG. 16-56. Schematic drawing to illustrate the structure of the salivary glands and pancreas. *A*, parotid; *B*, submandibular; *C*, sublingual; *D*, pancreas. Excretory ducts, white; salivary ducts, cross striped; intercalated ducts, black; mucous alveoli, coarse stipple; serous alveoli, fine stipple. (Redrawn, slightly modified, after Braus.)

connective tissue fibers also envelop each alveolus. Fat cells are a frequent occurrence in the connective tissue of the parotid, and they tend to increase in number with age.

Submandibular Gland. The *submandibular* (submaxillary) in man and most other mammals is a *mixed gland*, but the proportion of serous and mucous alveoli is not the same in all species. In man, it is preponderantly serous (Fig. 16-58). The main duct (Wharton's) opens into the mouth beneath the tongue. It is lined by pseudostratified columnar epithelium and has, in addition, a richly cellular stroma and longitudinally disposed smooth muscle cells. The main duct branches in the manner described for the parotid, the pseudostratified epithelium continuing into the larger interlobular ducts. The intralobular ducts are of the same types as in the parotid gland. The salivary ducts are longer and more numerous than in the parotid; the intercalated ducts are short and narrow.

The serous alveoli greatly outnumber the mucous ones. The latter frequently are capped by serous demilunes. Some mucous alveoli have serous cells lining their terminal portions. The connective tissue stroma and capsule are well developed.

Sublingual Gland. The *sublingual gland* is also a *mixed gland* in man, dog, cat, rabbit and sheep. It is the smallest of the large salivary glands and in man is preponderantly mucous. A series of ducts opens into the mouth at the side of the frenulum of the tongue, near the opening of Wharton's duct. The pseudostratified epithelium that lines the larger ducts is replaced by simple columnar in the smaller ones. There are relatively few intralobular ducts. Typical salivary ducts are rare. However, patches of striated cells may occur in the walls of intralobular ducts with an otherwise unmodified simple columnar epithelial lining. Intercalated ducts are likewise reduced in number so that most of the terminal alveoli, which are often quite elongated, either open directly into the larger intralobular ducts (Fig. 16-59) or into the interlobular ducts at the periphery of the lobule. Some investigators believe that typical intercalated ducts are entirely lacking.

Salivary (striated) duct   Serous alveoli

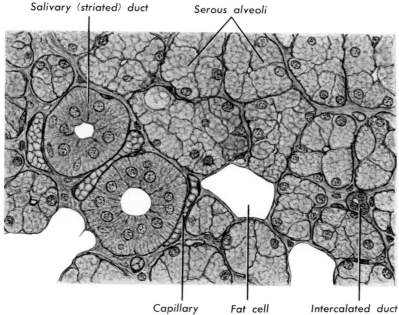

Capillary   Fat cell   Intercalated duct

FIG. 16-57. Section of human parotid gland. Surgical specimen. ×465

The terminal alveoli are mostly of the mucous type. Very few purely serous alveoli are seen. Serous cells occur in the form of demilunes around mucous alveoli. Such demilunes are numerous and large (Fig. 16-59).

The connective tissue septa are well developed in the sublingual, but the gland does not have a distinct capsule, as do the parotid and submandibular.

Blood Supply. The salivary glands have a relatively rich blood supply. The larger arteries run in the connective tissue septa with the ducts, giving off branches which accompany the divisions of the ducts to the lobules, where they break up into capillary networks surrounding the alveoli. These give rise to veins which follow the course of the arteries.

Lymphatics. Relatively few in number, the lymphatics begin as minute vessels in the smaller connective tissue septa and empty into lymph vessels which accompany the arteries.

Nerve Supply. The sensory innervation

of the salivary glands is by the trigeminal nerve. The motor innervation is derived both from the sympathetic and from the parasympathetic systems. Preganglionic sympathetic fibers run in the thoracocervical trunk to terminate in the superior cervical ganglion. Here they form synapses with postganglionic fibers which course in the walls of the branches of the carotid artery to the respective glands.

The parasympathetic supply to the parotid is by way of preganglionic fibers of the ninth cranial nerve to the otic ganglion, from which postganglionic fibers pass to the gland. The parasympathetic innervation of the mandibular and sublingual glands is by way of preganglionic fibers in the chorda tympani nerve to the mandibular ganglion, which usually lies within the glands. Short postganglionic fibers pass to the elements of the gland.

THE PANCREAS

The pancreas is a compound tubuloacinar gland, lying behind the stomach and extend-

Interlobular
connective tissue   Salivary duct   Serous demilune   Mixed alveolus

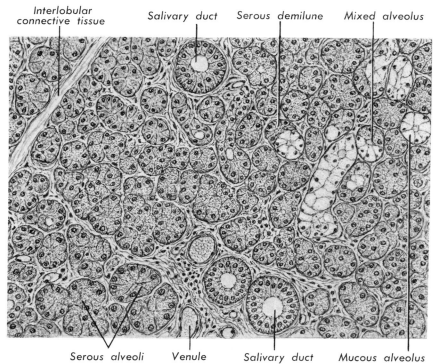

Serous alveoli   Venule   Salivary duct   Mucous alveolus

FIG. 16-58. Section of human submandibular gland. ×216

Serous demilune   Serous alveolus   Mucous alveolus   Venule

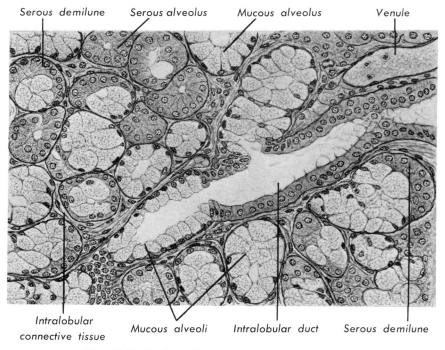

Intralobular
connective tissue   Mucous alveoli   Intralobular duct   Serous demilune

FIG. 16-59. Section of human sublingual gland. ×315

ing transversely from the spleen to the loop of the duodenum. The broader portion of it, the *head*, lies in the concavity of the latter organ. The head is joined to the *body* of the gland by a slightly constricted portion, the *neck*. The body tapers gradually into an extremity, the *tail*.

The pancreas is both a gland of *external secretion*, furnishing the pancreatic juice which is conveyed to the duodenum and which contains several digestive enzymes, and a gland of *internal secretion*, elaborating substances which, circulating in the blood, play an essential role in the regulation of the carbohydrate metabolism of the body. Serving the former function, it has a system of excretory ducts and terminal secreting acini, the arrangement of which somewhat resembles that of the parotid gland. For the performance of its endocrine function, there are highly vascular aggregations of secreting cells, the *islands* (or *islets*) *of Langerhans* (Fig. 16-60).

The pancreas has no distinct connective tissue capsule but is covered with a thin layer of loose tissue from which septa pass into the gland, subdividing it into many small lobules. In some of the lower animals (as, for instance, the cat), these lobules are well defined, being completely separated from one another by connective tissue. A number of these *primary lobules* are grouped together and surrounded by connective tissue which is considerably broader and looser in structure than that separating the primary lobules. These constitute a *lobule group* or secondary lobule. It is difficult to distinguish lobes and lobules in sections of human pancreas because the connective tissue septa are very incomplete.

The main excretory duct of the pancreas, the *pancreatic duct* or *duct of Wirsung*, extends almost the entire length of the gland, giving off short lateral branches, one of which courses to each lobule. As the ducts enter the lobules, their epithelium becomes

(lobe)

Island of Langerhans — Interlobular connective tissue septa

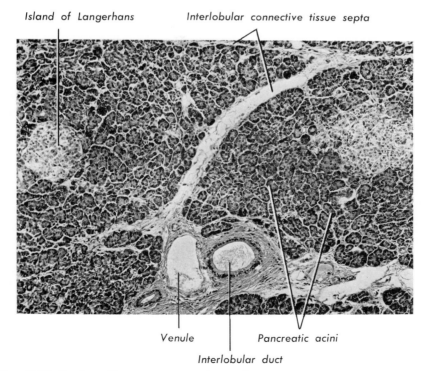

Venule — Pancreatic acini

Interlobular duct

FIG. 16-60. Section of human pancreas. Surgical specimen. Photomicrograph. ×100

intralobular ducts

low cuboidal. They have all of the characteristics of the intercalated ducts of other glands, and it should be noted that these ducts of narrow caliber are the only intralobular ducts present in the pancreas; there are no striated ducts as in the salivary glands. The intralobular intercalated ducts are long, and they branch many times before terminating in the serous acini.

In addition to the main excretory duct, there is also a secondary excretory duct, the *accessory pancreatic duct* or *duct of Santorini*. It may have an independent opening into the duodenum; otherwise, it communicates with the duct of Wirsung.

The interlobular and main ducts are lined with a simple high columnar epithelium which rests upon a basement membrane. Outside of this is a connective tissue coat, the thickness of which is directly proportional to the size of the duct. Goblet cells are present in the lining epithelium; in the accompanying connective tissue of the main duct and its larger branches, there are small mucous glands. As the ducts decrease in size, the epithelium becomes lower until, in the intercalated ducts, it is low cuboidal.

The *acini* are all of the serous (serozymogenic) type. They are lined by an irregularly pyramidal epithelium resting on a basal lamina. Intercellular secretory canaliculi extend between the acinar cells. In each cell, there may be distinguished an inner zone toward the lumen and an intensely staining basal zone toward the basal lamina. The inner zone contains numerous *zymogen granules* (Figs. 16-61 to 16-63). These granules vary in number with the functional activity of the cell, and they are the intracellular antecedents of the enzymes.

The nucleus lies in the basal zone of the cell. It is spherical and characteristically contains one or more distinct nucleoli. Binucleate cells may occur, but this condition is infrequently met with in man; in the white rat, it is said to occur in about half the acinar cells.

The basal zone also contains the *basophilic* or *chromophilic substance* (see above under "Serous Alveoli") which in routine preparations usually appears as longitudinal striations or fine filaments (Fig. 16-62). Electron micrographs show the endoplasmic reticulum in this region to be highly developed and arranged in parallel or concentric lamellae (Fig. 16-63). The surfaces of its membranes are studded with ribosome granules, which accounts for the basophilic staining. The striated appearance in the basal region of the cell is accentuated by the presence of

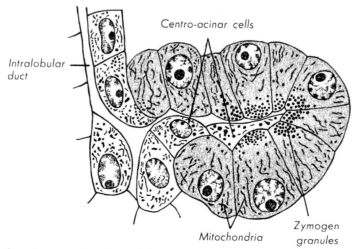

Centro-acinar cells

Intralobular duct

Mitochondria

Zymogen granules

Fig. 16-61. Section of pancreatic acinus of the guinea pig, showing intercalated duct and centroacinar cells. In the acinar cells may be seen zymogen granules and long mitochondrial filaments. (After Bensley.)

Island of Langerhans

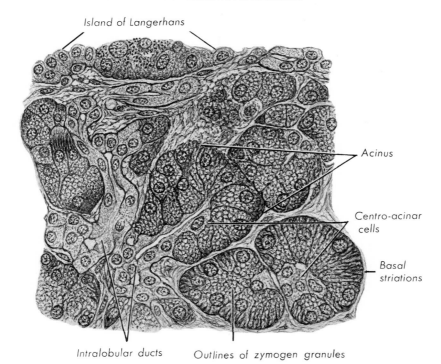

Acinus

Centro-acinar cells

Basal striations

Intralobular ducts   Outlines of zymogen granules

FIG. 16-62. Camera lucida drawing of a section of human pancrease removed surgically. The zymogen granules are not well preserved but the spaces which they occupied are outlined. Chrome hematoxylin-phloxine stain of 4 μ section. ×600.

numerous elongated mitochondria which remain unstained except by special methods.

In sections of the pancreas, there are seen within the lumina of many of the acini one or more small epithelial cells, lying in contact with the apices of the secreting cells. These are the *centroacinar cells* of Langerhans. These cells represent a continuation of duct epithelium with the acinar cells but the course of the junctional region is somewhat irregular (Fig. 16-61). The centroacinar cells often appear to be isolated within the acinus (Fig. 16-62) as a result of the plane of section.

The Islands of Langerhans. As mentioned earlier in this discussion, the pancreas also has an *endocrine* function, which is carried on by cellular aggregations interspersed irregularly among the acini or along the ducts. These cell groups are the *islands of Langerhans;* their secretion is poured directly into the blood stream, and they

have no functional communication with the duct system of the gland.

In ordinary hematoxylin-eosin preparations, the islands appear as more or less spheroidal masses of pale staining cells, arranged in the form of irregular anastomosing cords (Fig. 16-64). Between the cords, closely applied to the epithelial cells, are numerous blood capillaries. Only a few fine connective tissue fibers are present within the islets. The islands may be more or less closely surrounded by pancreatic acini (Fig. 16-64), or they may lie in the interlobular connective tissue septa.

The size of the islands varies from those having only a few cells to islands which are macroscopically visible. Isolated islet cells are also found occasionally among the cells lining the ducts of the exocrine pancreas. The number of islands varies in different portions of the gland as well as in different

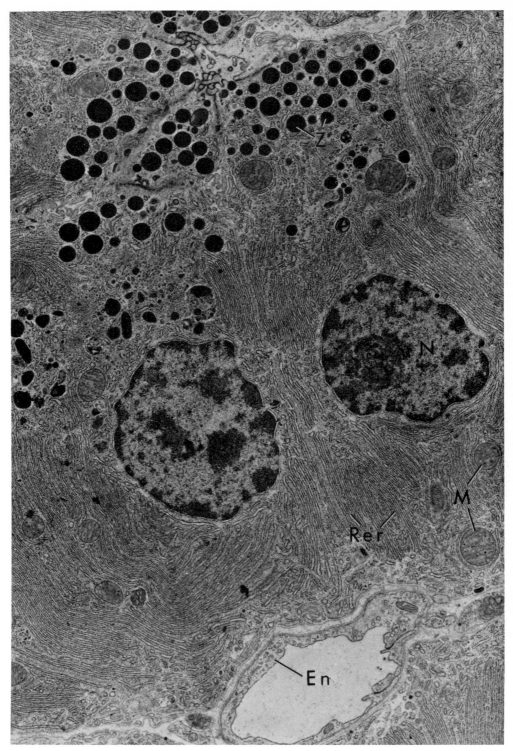

FIG. 16-63. Electron micrograph of pancreatic exocrine cells. The cytoplasm contains an abundance of rough surfaced endoplasmic reticulum (*Rer*) in which the cisternae are flattened and oriented parallel to one another and to the long axis of the cell. Above the nucleus (*N*), and around and apical to the Golgi complex, there are numerous zymogen granules (*z*). *M*, mitochondria; *En*, endothelium of a capillary in the lamina propria. From the pancreas of a bat. ×10,125. (Courtesy of Drs. K. R. Porter and M. A. Bonneville.)

472

individuals. They are more abundant in the tail of the pancreas than in the head.

In routine histological preparations, all of the islet cells appear to be similar (Fig. 16-64); by special methods, however, three types of cells have been distinguished in the human pancreas, namely, A or *alpha* cells, B or *beta* cells and D cells. The A and B cells are by far the most numerous, the D cells being relatively few in number.

The granules of the A and B cells differ from each other in solubility and in staining reactions. The A cell granules are preserved by alcohol, whereas those of the B cells are soluble in alcohol. Of the various staining methods used for differentiating the cells (e.g., Masson's trichrome, chrome hematoxylin-phloxine, aldehyde fuchsin), the chrome hematoxylin and phloxine method is the one most commonly used. With this

technique (Fig. 16-65) the A cells are seen to contain numerous fine, red-staining granules in contrast with blue-staining granules of B cells. Electron micrographs show that the granules are enclosed by membranes. The A cell granules are highly opaque (electron-dense), relatively uniform in size, and distributed evenly in the cytoplasm. The granules of the B cells are less opaque than those of the A cell, they are more variable in cytoplasmic distribution, and each granule is characteristically separated from its enclosing membrane by a prominent clear space. The B cell granules vary in shape in different species; in man, dog, and cat, they appear as crystalloids.

Although the relative numbers of A and B cells vary in different islands, the B cells are generally more numerous. B cells may also occur outside the islets, either singly or

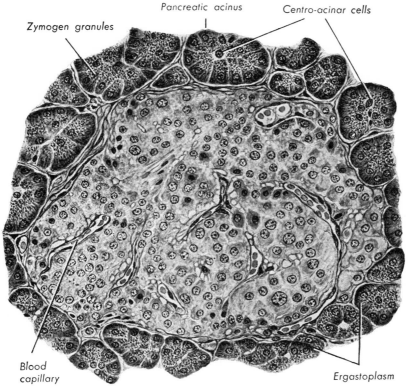

FIG. 16-64. A section through an island of Langerhans and surrounding acini. Human pancreas. Hematoxylin-eosin. ×450.

as small groups, in association with fully developed ducts or with acini. Estimates of the percentages of the various cell types indicate that the B cells comprise 60 to 90 % of all of the islet cells in the human pancreas.

The D cells are differentiated by Masson's triple stain (Fig. 1-9, *B*), which also selectively colors the A cells. There are few D cells in the human, and their significance is not clearly understood.

Another type of cell has also been described by Bensley in the pancreas of the guinea pig. Its cytoplasm contains no granules. It has been suggested that this type, the C cell, represents the progenitor of the A cells.

The question of the source of new islet cells in the adult, particularly whether acinar cells may be transformed into islet cells, has frequently been raised. In a study of the pancreas of the guinea pig, Bensley described a system of fine, anastomosing tubules which originate from the intralobular ducts and branch freely in the connective tissue surrounding these ducts. Smaller or larger islands of Langerhans are found attached to this system of tubules. Also attached to these tubules, but less frequently, are small pancreatic lobules, varying in size from a single acinus to a group of acini. Bensley regarded these branching tubules as tissue of a low order of differentiation, capable, under proper conditions, of producing by differentiation and mitotic division new islands of Langerhans or pancreatic acini. It must be remembered that this system of tubules does not comprise a duct system for the islands of Langerhans.

Secretions of the Pancreas. The *external secretion* of the pancreas is an alkaline liquid, the pancreatic juice, the important constituents of which are certain enzymes. Among these are *trypsin*, a powerful proteolytic enzyme which breaks down proteins into amino acids, *amylase*, which converts starches into maltose, and *lipase*, which splits fats into glycerol and fatty acids.

It is interesting to note that, although these several chemically dissimilar enzymes are elaborated by the pancreatic acini, the acinar cells are apparently cytologically similar.

Secretory pathways have been studied extensively in pancreatic acinar cells. These are described in some detail in the sections on "Granular Endoplasmic Reticulum" and the "Golgi Apparatus" in Chapter 1 and they are reviewed in Chapter 15.

The pancreas may be stimulated to activity either by nervous impulses from the vagus or by the action of a hormone, *secretin*, which is formed in the duodenal mucosa and carried to the pancreas in the blood stream. Secretin appears to be formed whenever acid substances, such as the acid contents of the stomach or acid bile, come in contact with the duodenal mucosa.

The *internal secretion* of the pancreas includes two hormones. One of these, *insulin*, is known to play an important role in carbohydrate metabolism. Without this hormone, the cells of the body are unable to utilize the available glucose and allow formation of glycogen stores. The clinical condition resulting from a deficiency of insulin, *diabetes mellitus*, is thus marked by hyperglycemia and glycosuria of variable severity.

Insulin is produced in the islands of Langerhans, specifically by the B cells of the islets. Evidence for this is available from various sources, both clinical and experimental. Impaired sugar assimilation results from removal of the entire pancreas but not from ligation of the pancreatic duct, which destroys the acinar tissue but leaves the islands intact. Furthermore, it has been amply demonstrated, as in the first successful extractions of insulin by Banting and Best, that insulin is present in such a duct-ligated pancreas. In man, functional tumors of the B cells produce hypoglycemia, the effect being comparable to that caused by the administration of insulin. Removal of the tumor restores the patient to a normal condition. Experimentally, diabetes can be

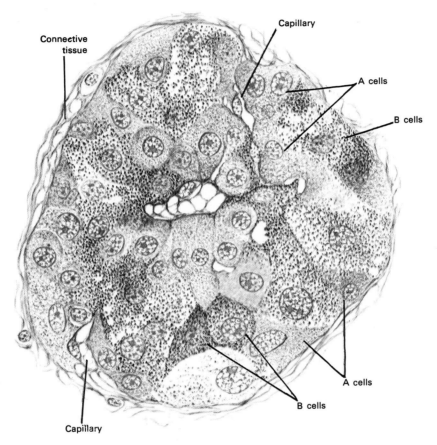

Fig. 16-65. A section of an island of Langerhans of human pancreas showing A and B cells. A 3 μ section of a surgical specimen. The relative proportions and distributions of the A and B cells are unusual in the particular section illustrated. The B cells are generally about 3 times as numerous as the A cells and the latter are usually found toward the periphery of the island.

produced in many animals by the selective destruction of the B cells by injection of the drug alloxan. Also, in certain species the repeated injection of crude extracts of the anterior pituitary gland results in B cell injury and diabetes.

The pancreatic islets also secrete another hormone known as *glucagon*, a hyperglycemic-glycogenolytic factor. This hormone is formed by the A cells and it has an effect which is, in some respects, antagonistic to that of insulin. It causes an elevation of blood sugar. Like insulin, it is present in pancreatic tissue following duct ligation. Unlike insulin, it is present in the pancreas of a duct-ligated, alloxan-treated animal.

Blood Supply. The pancreas receives its blood supply from the superior and inferior pancreaticoduodenal arteries and from pancreatic rami of the splenic artery. The vessels course in the interlobular connective tissue and give off branches which enter the lobules. These form capillary networks among the acini and in the islands. The islands have an extremely rich vascular network, a characteristic which they share with other endocrine tissues. Also in common with other endocrine tissues, the capillaries have a fenestrated endothelium with diaphragms spanning the pores. The extensiveness of the capillary network within the islets is not usually appreciated in sections but can be demonstrated in injected specimens. The blood leaves the pancreas by the pancreaticoduodenal veins to the superior mesenteric and portal veins and by several small pancreatic veins to the splenic vein.

Lymphatics. The lymph vessels lie mainly in the interlobular connective tissue. They drain chiefly into the celiac lymph nodes.

Nerve Supply. The nerves to the pancreas are from the splanchnic (sympathetic) and the vagus (parasympathetic). The former are nonmyelinated. The latter are myelinated preganglionic fibers; the cell bodies of their postganglionic fibers lie within the substance of the gland. The terminal fibers of the nerves are distributed about the secreting acini and on the walls of blood vessels. Pacinian corpuscles are occasionally found in the interlobular connective tissue of the gland.

THE LIVER

The liver is the largest gland of the body. It has an exocrine function, the secretion of bile, which is conveyed to the intestine by a system of ducts. It also produces prothrombin, serum albumin, and serum lipoproteins. It performs the important function of storing carbohydrate foods and releasing them into the blood at such times as they are needed by the body—a function which was first described as one of internal secretion, although it is not now designated as such. Fats, proteins and vitamins are also stored in the liver cells. The liver is also an organ of excretion, essential in the removal of waste products from the blood. Despite the multiplicity and diversity of its functions, the liver has no groups of cells cytologically specialized for the performance of one function or the other, as is the case, for example, in the pancreas. It also presents several other structural features in which it differs from other glands.

The liver is situated in the upper and right part of the abdominal cavity, immediately below the diaphragm. Several fissures partially divide it into four *lobes*. It is incompletely invested by an outer *tunica serosa*, derived from the peritoneum, within which is a delicate connective tissue capsule, the *capsule of Glisson*. This capsule, which contains a fair abundance of elastic fibers, covers the entire surface of the organ. At the *porta hepatis* (transverse fissure, hilum), it surrounds the entering blood vessels and follows into the gland, forming a framework and dividing it into innumerable small *lobules*. In some animals, e.g., the pig and camel, each lobule is completely invested by connective tissue. In man, the connective tissue is sparse and the lobular investment is incomplete. It is apparent mainly at points

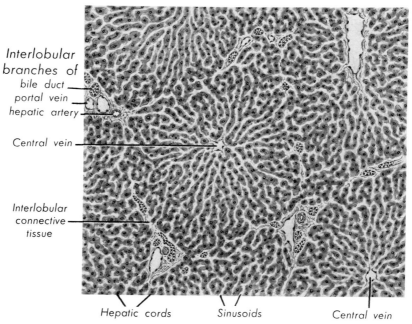

Interlobular
branches of
bile duct
portal vein
hepatic artery

Central vein

Interlobular
connective
tissue

Hepatic cords *Sinusoids* *Central vein*

FIG. 16-66. Low power view of a portion of a section of human liver, showing one complete lobule and portions of adjacent lobules. ×60.

where three or more lobules meet (Fig. 16-66). The lobules are cylindrical or irregularly prismatic in shape and approximately 1 mm. in breadth and 2 mm. in length. Except just beneath the capsule, where they are frequently arranged with their apices directed toward the surface, the lobules are irregularly arranged.

The *hepatic lobule*, which may be considered the anatomical unit of structure of the liver, has two main constituents: an epithelial parenchyma and a system of anastomosing blood channels. The parenchyma is made up of hepatic cells arranged in irregular, branching, interconnected plates. Since in sections the sheets of cells often give the appearance of cell cords (Fig. 16-66), they have frequently been called the *hepatic cords*. However, reconstructions which portray the interrelationships of the cells in three dimensions clearly show that the cells are aligned in broad plates or sheets (Fig. 16-68). The plates tend to be arranged in a radiating manner around the central blood vessel of the lobule.

The hepatic plates or laminae form the secretory portions of the gland and are thus analogous to the secretory tubules of other glands. The hepatic plates are arranged in a definite manner relative to the blood channels, forming partitions between them. The blood vessels may therefore conveniently be considered first.

Blood Supply. The blood supply of the liver is peculiar in that, in addition to the ordinary arterial supply and venous return which all organs possess, the liver receives venous blood in large quantities through the portal vein. There are thus *two afferent vessels*, the *hepatic artery* and the *portal vein*, the former carrying arterial blood, the latter venous blood from the intestines and spleen. Both vessels enter the liver at the porta and divide into large *interlobar branches* which follow the connective tissue septa between the lobes. From these are given off *interlobular branches* which run in the smaller connective tissue septa between the lobules.

From the interlobular branches of the portal vein arise veins which are still inter-

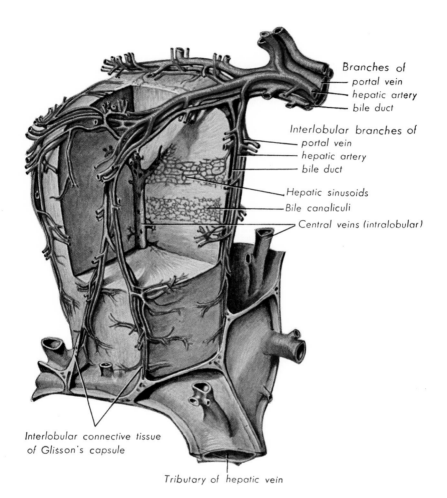

Branches of
— portal vein
— hepatic artery
— bile duct

Interlobular branches of
— portal vein
— hepatic artery
— bile duct

Hepatic sinusoids
Bile canaliculi
Central veins (intralobular)

Interlobular connective tissue
of Glisson's capsule

Tributary of hepatic vein

Fig. 16-67. Reconstruction of a lobule from the liver of a pig. A portion of the lobule is cut away to show the hepatic sinusoids and bile canaliculi. (Redrawn and slightly modified from Braus, after a reconstruction by A. Vierling.)

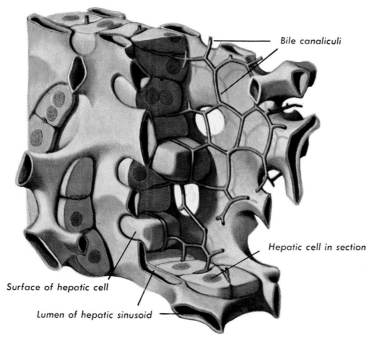

Bile canaliculi

Hepatic cell in section

Surface of hepatic cell

Lumen of hepatic sinusoid

Fig. 16-68. Diagrammatic reconstruction of a small portion of human liver to show the relationship of the anastomosing plates of hepatic cells to the blood sinusoids and to the network of bile canaliculi. For the purposes of the diagram, both the sinusoids and the bile canaliculi are shown as independent structures, particularly at *right*, where the hepatic cells have been "dissected away." It should be recalled, however that the bile canaliculi, being formed by the modified cell membranes of adjacent hepatic cells, are always surrounded by hepatic cells and that the lining of the sinusoids is not smooth and homogeneous as shown, but is made up of Kupffer cells and fine reticular fibers. (Redrawn and modified from Braus.)

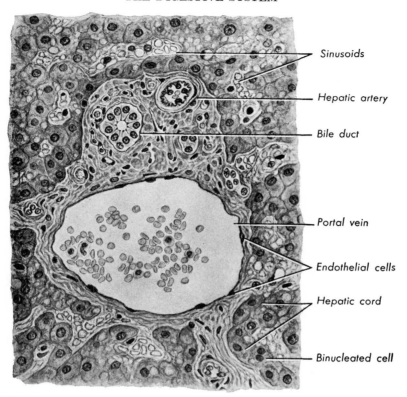

Sinusoids

Hepatic artery

Bile duct

Portal vein

Endothelial cells

Hepatic cord

Binucleated cell

FIG. 16-69. The juncture of three lobules of the human liver, showing interlobular branches of the portal vein, hepatic artery and bile duct. The region occupied by this aggregation of structures is frequently designated as a portal canal. Hematoxylin-eosin. ×455.

lobular and encircle the lobules. These send branches into the lobule, where they subdivide to form a rich network of intralobular vessels known as the hepatic _sinusoids_ (Figs. 16-67 to 16-69). They all converge toward the center of the lobule, where they empty into the _central vein_. The central veins are the smallest radicles of the _hepatic veins_, which are the efferent vessels of the liver. As it passes through the center of the long axis of the lobule, the central vein constantly receives sinusoids from all sides and, increasing in size, leaves the lobule at its base. Here it unites with the central veins of other lobules to form a _sublobular vein_, which is a branch of the hepatic vein.

The hepatic artery accompanies the portal vein, following the branchings of the latter through the interlobar and interlobular connective tissue. Some of the interlobular

arterioles break up into capillary networks which supply the interlobular structures and then empty into the smaller branches of the portal veins. Other arterioles empty into the hepatic sinusoids.

Duct System. The duct system of the liver serves to convey the external secretion, the _bile_, to the duodenum. The smallest branches of the duct system are the narrow, intralobular _bile canaliculi_ which form a ramifying network of channels between the cells of the hepatic plates (Figs. 16-68 and 16-71). Like the plates in which they lie, the canaliculi radiate outward from the central axis of the lobule. Most of the canaliculi drain from the network in the outer limiting plate of the lobule into small _interlobular bile ducts (terminal bile ducts, cholangioles)_ found at the periphery of a lobule. The short connnections between the hepatic cells and the interlobular bile ducts are sometimes called the canals of Hering. They are lined by cuboidal cells which are smaller and paler staining than the hepatic cells. The lumen is little if at all larger than that of a bile canaliculus (Fig. 16-72). A few of the canaliculi empty into small intralobular bile ducts which extend to variable depths within the lobule.

Each interlobular duct joins with others,

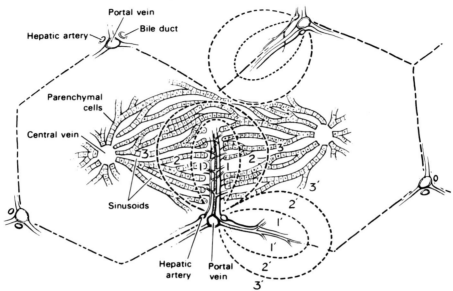

FIG. 16-70. Diagram of the arrangement of liver parenchymal cells in functional units (acinar units) around terminal afferent blood vessels and terminal bile ductules. The oxygen tension and nutrient level of the blood is highest in zone 1 and lowest in zone 3. Zones labeled as 1', 2', and 3' represent corresponding regions of the adjacent portion of the acinar unit. (Adapted from A. M. Rappaport, Z. J. Borowy, W. M. Lougheed, and W. N. Lotto, Anat. Rec., vol. 119, 1954.)

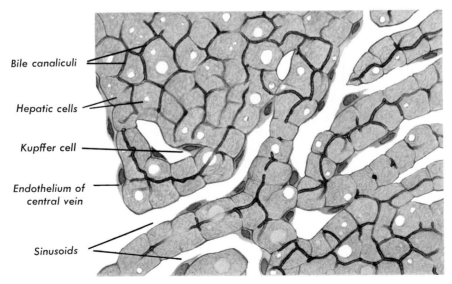

FIG. 16-71. Section of liver impregnated by Golgi silver technique to show bile canaliculi. Human. ×720.

forming progressively larger ducts lined by cuboidal or columnar epithelium. As the ducts increase in size toward the porta of the liver, the epithelium becomes high columnar and the connective tissue layer becomes thicker, with many elastic fibers and a few scattered smooth muscle cells.

In their ramifications through the connective tissue septa, the interlobular bile ducts always accompany the branches of the portal vein and the hepatic artery. These structures, together with the interlobular connective tissue which marks the point of separation of three or more lobules, occupy the *portal canal* or *portal area* (Fig. 16-69). A network of lymphatic vessels accompanies the branches of the portal vein in the portal area and in the interlobular connective tissue. However, the lymphatic vessels tend to collapse and do not form a very obvious component of the portal area in sections prepared by routine methods.

Extrahepatic Ducts. The right and left hepatic ducts join to form the *hepatic duct* which, after its juncture with the cystic duct, becomes the *common bile duct* (ductus choledochus) and conveys the bile to the duodenum. The hepatic ducts, the cystic duct and the common bile duct may be referred to as the *extrahepatic ducts* of the liver, in contrast with the intrahepatic system of ducts within the gland.

The extrahepatic ducts are lined by high columnar epithelium which rests on a connective tissue lamina propria containing smooth muscle and elastic fibers. The epithelium and underlying lamina propria are thrown into numerous folds. Goblet cells occur in the epithelium, more abundantly in the lower portion of the common bile duct. Small multicellular glands may be seen extending into the lamina propria. In the cystic duct, the smooth muscle fibers are disposed in transverse, longitudinal and diagonal directions. They are less abundant in the hepatic ducts and the common duct, except in the duodenal end of the latter, where they form a sphincter.

It is apparent that the hepatic lobule, the *anatomical unit* of structure of the liver, differs markedly from the lobules of glands such as the pancreas or salivary glands. In the latter, the lobule is surrounded by interlobular connective tissue and comprises a group of secreting tubules drained by the terminal branch of an interlobular duct. Thus, the unit of structure and the unit of function are identical.

In the liver, the parenchyma comprising one hepatic lobule is drained of its secretion by several interlobular bile ducts lying in the adjacent portal canals. As a result, a single interlobular bile duct carries off the secretions of portions of several adjacent hepatic lobules. This area of hepatic tissue, drained by a single interlobular bile duct lying in the axis of the area, has been designated a *portal lobule*. According to another interpretation, a *functional unit* of liver tissue is defined as a small parenchymal mass (*acinar unit*) that surrounds a terminal branch of a portal vein, accompanied by an hepatic arteriole and a bile ductule (Rapport et al., 1954). A diagrammatic representation of this unit is shown in Figure 16-70. It can be seen that this interpretation differs from the portal lobule in that it includes only the parenchymal tissue around a terminal branch of a portal vein rather than all of the parenchyma around all branches of a portal vein located at an axis. The diagram of acinar units also calls attention to the fact that triads, (composed of portal veins, hepatic arteries and bile ducts), are present in only two or three of the portal canal areas of hexagonal shaped lobules. The hexagonal lobule is readily identified in the liver of the pig and a few other mammals, but this is not the case in man and in most other mammals. Acinar units are of particular interest in relation to pathological lesions. The latter frequently occur in areas corresponding to the units of parenchyma around terminal branches of the portal venules.

The Hepatic Plates or Laminae. The parenchymal cells of the liver were described in the older literature as being arranged in elongated, anastomosing cords made up of two rows of cells, with the main channel of the bile canaliculus extending throughout the length of the cord and its branches. This interpretation was based largely on studies of the liver of lower vertebrates. In sections of liver of man and other mammals, the cord appears to be either one cell thick or two or more cells thick, depending on the plane of the section. Since the cords radiate from the periphery of the lobule to the center with the cells of a row frequently arranged in a vertical relationship to each other (i.e., in a plane parallel to the course of the central vein), cross sections of a lobule often show the cord as a single row of cells. Cords of two rows of cells, as outlined above, are found in some embryonic livers and in livers of some of the lower vertebrates. However, a modified arrangement is present in man and other mammals where the cells are arranged in sheets known as *hepatic plates* or *hepatic laminae.* This understanding of the cell arrangement resulted from a study of reconstructions showing the structure of the liver lobule in three dimensions (Elias, 1949). One might postulate that a plate represents

the fusion of a number of cords, each made up of two rows of cells, but this would give only one canaliculus for each paired row of cells. In a plate, there is a canaliculus at each margin where two cells adjoin (Fig. 16-68). The plates probably arise by progressive widening (or heightening) of cords by cell proliferation and accompanying formation of new canaliculi during development. At any rate, the hepatic plates of the adult liver differ considerably from the secretory tubules of other glands.

Bile Canaliculi. Between the hepatic cells are minute channels, the *bile canaliculi.* These branch and have a very irregular course (Figs. 16-71 and 16-72). Short side branches of the canaliculi frequently extend

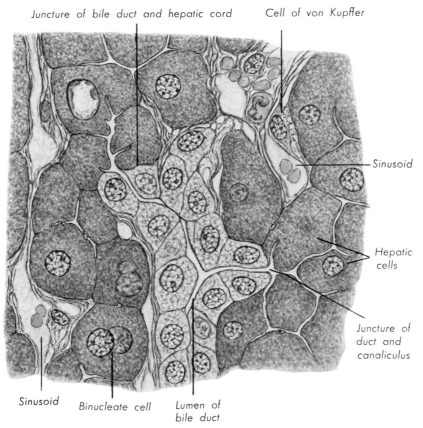

Juncture of bile duct and hepatic cord   *Cell of von Kupffer*

Sinusoid

Hepatic cells

Juncture of duct and canaliculus

Sinusoid   *Binucleate cell*   *Lumen of bile duct*

FIG. 16-72. Section through the margin of a human liver lobule, showing the juncture of termina bile duct with hepatic cords. The lumens of two of the terminal branches of the duct are directly continuous with bile canaliculi. A 5 μ section stained with phosphotungstic acid-hematoxylin-phloxine. ×1070.

between the liver cells toward the surface of a plate. They ramify throughout the hepatic parenchyma, anastomosing with the canaliculi of adjacent anastomosing plates (Fig. 16-66), but they seldom approach the surface of a plate.

Each canaliculus lies midway along the interface between adjacent hepatic cells and is formed by the somewhat modified cell membranes of the two opposing cells. They can be demonstrated in light microscope preparations particularly well by the Golgi silver impregnation method (Fig. 16-71). They are difficult to distinguish in ordinary preparations. Electron micrographs show that the membranes of the hepatic cells which form the canaliculi have short microvilli projecting into the canaliculi (Fig. 16-73).

Hepatic Cells. The hepatic cells which make up the hepatic plates are polyhedral in form and, under normal conditions, their boundaries are quite sharply defined. Each cell has a central nucleus with a distinct nuclear membrane and one or more prominent nucleoli. Multinucleate hepatic cells are occasionally seen, the usual variation being the binucleate condition.

Binucleate cells result from mitotic division of the nucleus of a mononucleate cell without accompanying division of the cytoplasm (Beams and King, 1942). Each of the two nuclei is of approximately normal size and possesses the normal (diploid) number of chromosomes; the cytoplasmic portion of the cell may be large. Large hepatic cells with either one or two unusually large nuclei also occur. These result from mitotic division of the above mentioned binucleate cells in which all of the chromosomes merge on one spindle, with the formation of either (1) two large mononucleate cells, each with an unusually large nucleus containing a tetraploid number of chromosomes, or (2) one large cell with two large tetraploid nuclei. Further divisions of this type may produce mononucleate cells with still larger

nuclei having a further increase in chromosome number.

The mitochondria of the hepatic cells are spherical, rod-shaped, or filamentous, depending on the location of the cell within the lobule and on the functional state. The Golgi apparatus lies either near the edge of the cell beneath the bile canaliculus, or close to the nucleus. The cytoplasm contains angular clumps of *basophilic material* which is found by histochemical methods to consist chiefly of nucleoproteins. Electron micrographs show that this material is in the form of clusters of free ribosomes plus ribosomes attached to the cisternae of the endoplasmic reticulum (rough surfaced endoplasmic reticulum). Electron micrographs show that there are also numerous areas of smooth surfaced endoplasmic reticulum which becomes continuous in places with the rough surfaced reticulum. Lysosomes are present, and another organelle known as a *microbody* or *peroxisome* is present. The peroxisomes vary somewhat in morphology in different species. In most species, but not in man, they have a dense core or nucleoid (Fig. 16-74). They contain oxidative enzymes, including urate oxidase and catalase. The urate oxidase is localized to the nucleoid and the absence of this component of the peroxisome in man is correlated with a lack of liver urate oxidase. The origin and function of peroxisomes are not clearly understood.

Scattered throughout the cytoplasm in ordinary preparations are small clear areas. These represent areas of *glycogen* which can be seen with the light microscope only after appropriate methods of fixation and staining. *Fat droplets* may also appear as inclusions in the cytoplasm, particularly after fasting or after ingestion of an excess of fats. The amount of fat which may be demonstrated in the hepatic cells varies inversely with the amount of glycogen. Pigment granules (bile pigments) are occasionally seen in the cytoplasm.

As in other gland cells, the appearance of

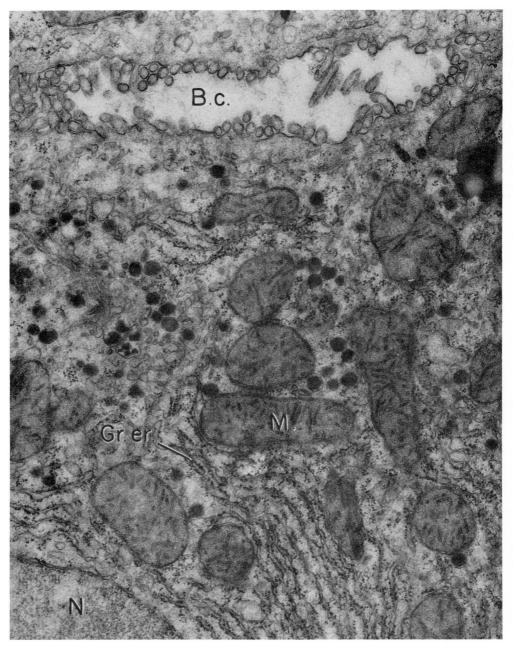

Fig. 16-73. Electron micrograph of a portion of two adjacent liver cells, showing a bile canaliculus. Note that the bile canaliculus (*B.c.*) has fine microvilli projecting into it. The photograph includes a portion of a nucleus (*N*) of one of hepatic cells, mitochondria (*M*), granular endoplasmic reticulum (*Gr.er.*), cisternae of some nongranular endoplasmic reticulum, and a number of small, electron-dense, tipid bodies. The section is from a regenerating mouse liver 7 hours following partial hepatectomy. A temporary increase in small lipid granules of this type is one of the changes which follows partial hepalectomy. ×30,500. (Courtesy of Dr. Nancy L. Trotter.)

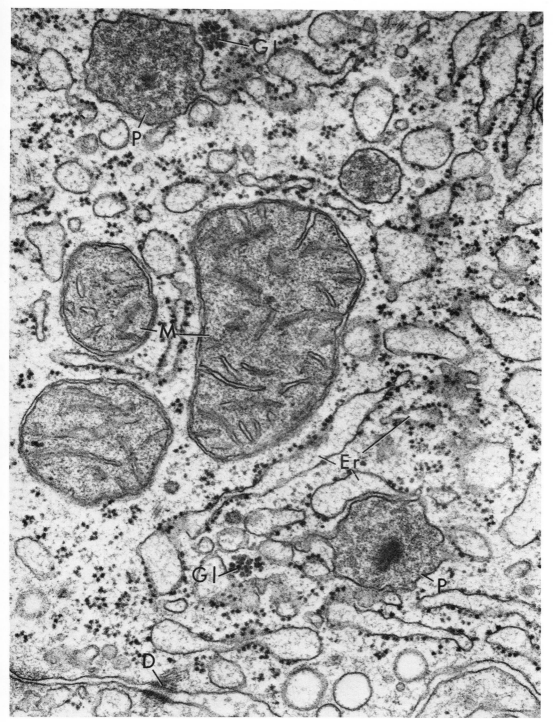

Fig. 16-74. Electron micrograph showing peroxisomes (microbodies) in a liver parenchymal cell of a fetal rat. The peroxisomes (*P*) of the rat liver (and of most mammals other than man) contain electron dense cores (nucleoids) in which liver urate oxidase is localized. Outpouchings are seen at the surface of 2 of the peroxisomes present in the field illustrated. This suggests that new peroxisomes form either as buds from other peroxisomes or as vesicles derived from the smooth-surfaced endoplasmic reticulum, consisting of a mixture of smooth-surfaced and rough-surfaced varieties. *Gl*, glycogen; *M*, mitochondria. ×10,275. (Courtesy of Dr. R. L. Wood.)

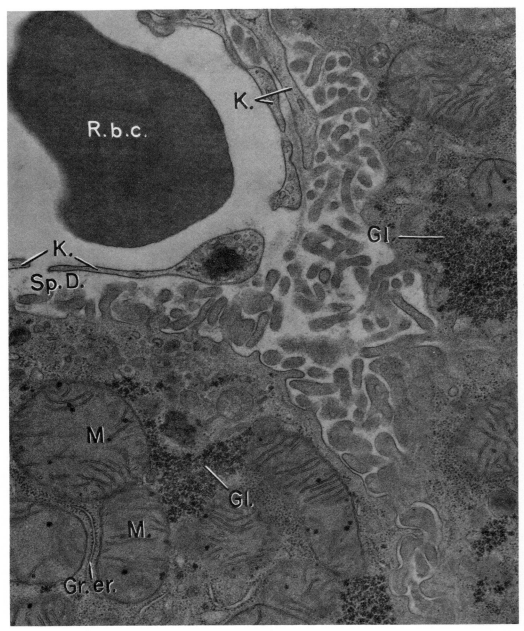

FIG. 16-75. Electron micrograph of a portion of the liver from a bat, showing a part of a sinusoid. A red blood cell (*R.b.c.*) is seen within the lumen of a sinusoid. Parts of overlapping Kupffer cells (*K*) are seen. Note that they do not form a complete lining of the sinusoid. The space of Disse (*Sp.D.*) is seen between the Kupffer cells and the liver parenchymal cells; the latter have numerous microvilli. The parenchymal cells contain numerous mitochondria (*M*) and many ribosomes, some attached to cisternae of endoplasmic reticulum (*Gr.er.*) and some dispersed at random. Cisternae of smooth endoplasmic reticulum are sparse in this particular field. Aggregates of stored glycogen (*Gl.*) are present. ×22,700. (Courtesy of Dr. Keith Porter.)

the cytoplasm varies with the functional state of the cell. Both glycogen and the basophilic material are markedly reduced after a prolonged period of fasting, and they reaccumulate in the cytoplasm with refeeding. Glycogen is more abundant in the hepatic cells after digestion of a carbohydrate meal. It represents stored carbohydrate, which is returned to the blood as glucose when the needs of the body demand it.

The liver lobule may be divided into three zones on the basis of structural and functional differences: an inner, hepatic zone around the central vein, an outer, portal zone at the periphery of the lobule and an intermediate zone between the central and peripheral regions. The mitochondria differ in appearance in the different zones, probably in relation to functional activity. The basophilic substance also differs in the different zones. The zones differ, particularly in relation to their storage and release of glycogen. According to Eckman and Holmgren (1949), when the livers of rats and mice are depleted of glycogen by prolonged fasting, feeding results in the deposition of glycogen in the peripheral region first, progressing centrally until the lobule is filled. Following completion of the period of digestion, glycogen is usually given up from the peripheral region of the lobule first, leaving a central region with stored glycogen.

The membranes of the hepatic cells which border on the sinusoids show a surface modification similar to that on the free surfaces of cells in many other locations. Short, irregular microvilli which can be seen only with the electron microscope project from the cells (Fig. 16-73); in most areas the processes are covered by the lining cells of the sinusoids.

Hepatic Sinusoids. The hepatic sinusoids make up the intralobular system of blood capillaries which course centripetally through the lobule and convey the blood from the interlobular branches of the portal vein to the central vein. They have relatively wide lumina, they anastomose irregularly and everywhere they separate the hepatic plates one from another. It thus follows that the hepatic cells have one or more surfaces abutting on bile canaliculi and one or more surfaces always adjacent to blood sinusoids (Fig. 16-69).

In the lining of the sinusoids, there may ordinarily be distinguished two types of cells (or more likely, two modifications of the same cell type). One is a cell with a dark nucleus and sparse cytoplasm lying flattened against the hepatic cells. The other is a larger cell with larger, more vesicular nucleus and branching pseudopodial processes. Although the former resembles an endothelial cell, all gradations between it and the enlarged form may be seen, and the two should probably be considered variations of the same type of cell, the stellate cells of von Kupffer, usually referred to as *Kupffer cells* (Figs. 16-72, 16-75 and 16-76). They are phagocytic cells and are a part of the reticuloendothelial system (see Chapter 5, under section on reticuloendothelial system). Because of their intimate relation to the function of the liver, however, they must be considered an integral part of that organ.

If a substance such as trypan blue or India ink is repeatedly injected into an animal, it will be found that the Kupffer cells readily ingest the foreign substance and store it in large amounts in their cytoplasm (Figs. 16-76 and 16-77). Thus they act to free the blood stream of foreign particles. They are also said to be active in fat metabolism and in the formation of bile pigments. The flattened lining cells are somewhat less phagocytic but, after continual overloading, all of the lining cells are apparently capable of mobilizing into phagocytic cells. The structure of the sinusoidal lining cells as seen in electron micrographs (except for the phagocytized material in those which were actively phagocytic at the time of fixation) does not differ sufficiently to distinguish two types.

There has also been some doubt in the past in regard to the completeness of the sinusoidal lining. In histological sections it often appears that there are spaces between the processes of adjacent Kupffer cells. Electron micrographs of normal liver tissue have confirmed this impression. Such an incomplete or fenestrated sinusoidal lining and the absence of a complete basal lamina leaves the hepatic cells in some areas exposed to the blood stream. The mobile, nonendothelial character of the lining cells is further accentuated by their lack of firm attachment to the parenchymal cells of the hepatic plates.

Connective Tissue. Ordinary sections of the human liver reveal scant amounts of connective tissue. The interlobular connective tissue concentrated in the portal areas has already been described. Special methods show that there is, in addition, a framework of reticular (argyrophilic) fibers within each lobule (Fig. 16-78). This consists of extremely delicate fibrils lying between the

Kupffer cells and the hepatic cells, forming a network which envelops each sinusoid, and a small number of coarser fibers which radiate outward from the region of the central vein.

Lymphatics. The lymph vessels of the liver form a rich plexus in the capsule of Glisson and in its connective tissue septa within the gland. Lymph vessels enmesh the larger blood vessels and ducts, and there are anastomoses between lymphatics which surround the portal veins and those which surround hepatic veins. Anastomoses between lymphatics of neighboring portal canals enclose the hepatic lobules in a network of small lymph vessels but, so far as can be determined, no lymphatic vessels penetrate the lobules themselves. Since the lobules comprise the bulk of the liver tissue, it is puzzling to explain the fact that more lymph

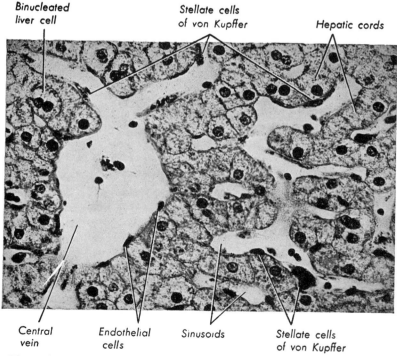

Binucleated liver cell — Stellate cells of von Kupffer — Hepatic cords

Central vein — Endothelial cells — Sinusoids — Stellate cells of von Kupffer

FIG. 16-76. Photomicrograph of a section of the liver of a monkey which had received several injections of trypan blue. All lining cells of the sinusoids contain some of the dye. They vary greatly, however, in the amount which has been ingested. At *lower right* is a very heavily laden cell. The trypan blue granules photograph black, as do also the nuclei of all of the cells. Azocarmine.

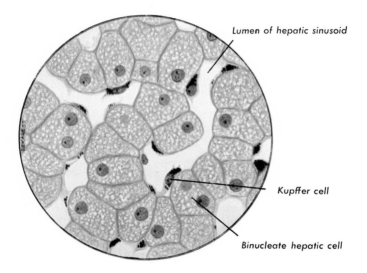

Lumen of hepatic sinusoid

Kupffer cell

Binucleate hepatic cell

FIG. 16-77. Section of liver from a monkey which had received several intraperitoneal injections of trypan blue. Most of the sinusoidal lining (Kupffer) cells have taken in some of the dye by phagocytosis. Azocarmine and metanil yellow stain. ×720.

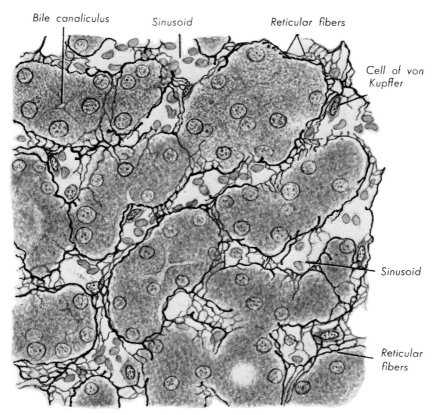

Bile canaliculus   Sinusoid   Reticular fibers

Cell of von Kupffer

Sinusoid

Reticular fibers

FIG. 16-78. Human liver, showing reticular tissue in a lobule. Reticular fibers do not extend through the lumen of the sinusoid, although tangential sections through the wall of the sinusoid may give this impression. Foot's silver technique. ×700.

flows from the liver than from any other organ of the body.

There is a potential tissue space between the Kupffer cells lining the sinusoids and the hepatic cells. This is the so-called *space of Disse* (Fig. 16-75), which is traversed by the reticular fiber network. In view of the large volume of lymph arising in the liver and the absence of any lymphatic capillaries within the liver lobule, it has been postulated that the lymph is formed in the perisinusoidal space. The space of Disse should not, however, be confused with a lymphatic vessel.

Nerve Supply. The nerves of the liver are mainly nonmyelinated fibers of the sympathetic system. They accompany the blood vessels and bile ducts, around which they form plexuses. These plexuses give off fibers

which terminate on the blood vessels and bile ducts.

Functions of the Liver. The exocrine function of the liver is concerned with the production of bile, which is carried by the system of bile ducts into the duodenum.

Bile is a product of the hepatic cells and is partly a secretion important in the absorption of fats and partly an excretion carrying off waste products which are eliminated with the feces. Among the constituents of bile are the following: bile acids, bile pigments, cholesterol, lecithin, neutral fats and soaps, traces of urea, and water and bile salts. The bile salts, as emulsifying agents, facilitate the absorption of fats in the intestine. They are themselves reabsorbed in part from the intestine and are again secreted by the hepatic cells. The bile pigments are derived from the breaking down of hemoglobin; this apparently takes place elsewhere in the body than in the liver, although the Kupffer cells may play a part. The bile pigments are removed from the blood by the liver and excreted in the bile as a waste product. Cholesterol is also excreted in the bile.

Claude Bernard was the first to show that the liver stored glycogen and gave it up as glucose. The liver not only stores reserve sugars but it is essential for the transformations which are necessary before some of the sugars can be utilized by the body. Conversion of fats and perhaps also of proteins to carbohydrates is accomplished in the liver (gluconeogenesis). Through its diversified chemical processes, the liver is able to maintain a constant blood sugar level under widely different dietary conditions.

The liver has other important functions. It is involved in protein metabolism and is the chief site of deaminization of amino acids, with the production of urea as a by-product. Fats are likewise metabolized and stored in the liver. Some of the plasma proteins (fibrinogen, prothrombin, albumin) are synthesized in the liver. The liver is also an important place of storage for many vitamins, chiefly A, D, B_2, B_3, B_4, B_{12} and K, which are essential to the body. The liver also plays an important role in the detoxification of a number of lipid soluble drugs, e.g., barbiturates.

Regeneration of Liver. When a part of the liver is removed by operation or when there is partial destruction by toxic agents (chloroform, etc.), the organ regains its normal weight within a relatively short time. In the rat, surgical removal of as much as 75% of the gland is followed by complete weight restitution within 1 month (Higgins and Anderson, 1931). The repair is accomplished by mitotic multiplication of parenchymal cells throughout the remaining portion of the organ and by cell enlargement. Differentiation of new liver cells from budding interlobular bile ducts may also

play a part. In restored liver tissue, there is an increased number of the mononucleated cells which have large nuclei containing a multiple number of chromosomes (Sulkin, 1943). These are produced by division of binucleated cells. There is also a general increase in nuclear size of all of the parenchyma cells.

THE GALL BLADDER

The gall bladder is a hollow, pear-shaped organ lying obliquely on the inferior surface of the liver. It may be regarded as a diverticulum of the bile duct. It consists of a *fundus*, which is the blind end, a *body* and a *neck* which passes into the cystic duct. In the neck, folds of the mucosa form the *spiral valve of Heister*.

The wall of the gall bladder is composed of three layers: *mucosa*, *muscularis* and an *adventitia* or *serosa*. The mucosa is thrown into numerous folds which divide the surface roughly into irregular polygonal areas (Fig. 16-79). The epithelium is composed of tall columnar cells with oval nuclei situated in the basal zone (Figs. 16-80 and 4-10, *B*). A thin, striated border has been demonstrated on the apical surface of the cells. It is less prominent than that of the intestinal cells, so that it is seen well only with phase contrast and electron microscopes (Figs. 16-81 and 16-82). The tunica propria consists of connective tissue containing extensive vascular plexuses and a few scattered smooth muscle cells derived from the muscularis. Near the neck of the gall bladder, small tubuloalveolar glands occur in the mucosa.

Small diverticula of the mucosa which extend down into the muscular and perimuscular layers are known as the *Rokitansky-Aschoff sinuses*. Their epithelium is a continuation of the surface epithelium.

The muscular layer of the gall bladder is formed of interlacing bundles of smooth muscle fibers. Bundles of longitudinal fibers occur nearer the lamina propria, coursing the length of the bladder and curving over the fundus. The remainder of the muscle

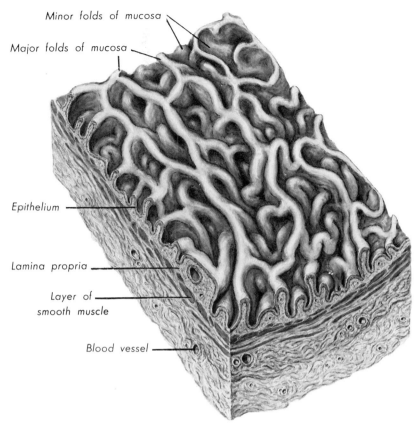

Minor folds of mucosa

Major folds of mucosa

Epithelium

Lamina propria

Layer of
smooth muscle

Blood vessel

FIG. 16-79. Low power, three dimensional view of a portion of the wall of a human gall bladder. ×24.

bundles, which form the greater part of the muscularis, are circularly disposed. Connective tissue, with an abundance of elastic fibers, occurs between the muscle bundles.

The external connective tissue layer is usually thick but shows wide individual differences. Just external to the muscularis, it consists of fibrous connective tissue sufficiently distinct to be designated the *perimuscular layer*. Outside this is a subserous layer of connective tissue containing blood and lymph vessels and nerves. On its free surface, the gall bladder is covered by the peritoneum; the connective tissue of its attached surface merges with that of the liver.

Lymph nodules occur in the wall of the gall bladder. One may also find ductlike structures, lined with epithelium, which have no connection with the lumen of the bladder, although they have occasionally been described as having connections with the bile ducts. These are known as *Luschka ducts*. They are interpreted as aberrant embryonic bile ducts.

The gall bladder functions as a reservoir for the bile produced by the liver. By the reabsorption of large quantities of water and mineral salts through its mucosal layer, it also serves to concentrate the bile.

THE BILE DUCTS

There are three main ducts associated with the gall bladder. These are (1) the cystic duct, (2) the hepatic duct and (3) the common bile duct (*ductus choledochus*). The

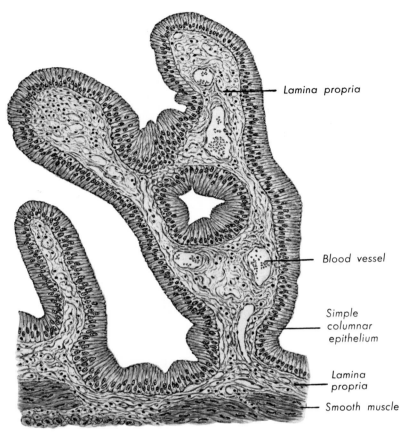

                                       — *Lamina propria*

                                       — *Blood vessel*

                                     Simple columnar epithelium

                                     Lamina propria

                                     — *Smooth muscle*

Fig. 16-80. A section through the wall of the human gall bladder which is shown in perspective in Figure 16-79. ×175.

hepatic duct conducts bile from the liver to a point where the cystic duct from the gall bladder meets the common bile duct leading to the duodenum. The bile then passes through the cystic duct into the gall bladder for concentration and storage. Contraction of the gall bladder forces the bile back through the cystic duct and thence through the common bile duct to the intestine. As the ductus choledochus passes obliquely through the wall of the duodenum, it lies side by side with the ductus pancreaticus. In their course through the submucosa of the duodenum, the associated pancreatic and bile ducts are surrounded by layers of smooth muscle which form the *sphincter of Oddi*. A portion of this muscular sheath which encircles only the bile duct is known as the *sphincter choledochus*. While this sphincter remains contracted (as for example during fasting), pressure is maintained in the duct system, and bile from the liver is forced into the gall bladder for storage. Upon the ingestion of food, especially fats or proteins, the sphincter of Oddi relaxes, the gall bladder is stimulated to contract and bile traverses the cystic duct and common bile duct to the duodenum.

The ducts are lined with a columnar epithelium similar to that of the gall bladder. Most of the bile ducts have epithelial-lined outpouchings which simulate irregularly distributed glands. Mitosis of epithelial cells occurs chiefly in these outpouchings, and the cells move upward to replace worn-out cells of the luminal surface much like the replace-

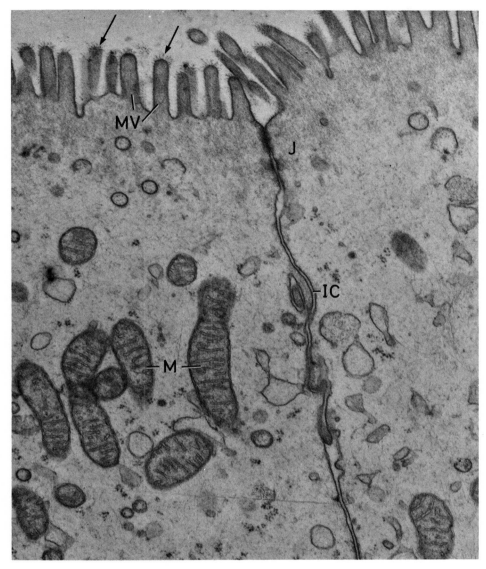

FIG. 16-81. Electron micrograph of the apical portion of two epithelial cells from the gall bladder of a rabbit. The microvilli (MV) are covered by hairlike projections or "fuzz." A typical junctional complex (J) is present at the adluminal end of the intercellular space (IC). M, mitochondria. ×27,000. (Courtesy of Drs. G. I. Kaye, H. O. Wheeler, R. T. Whitlock, and N. Lane. J. Cell Biol., vol. 30, 1966.)

ment cells in the intestine by mitosis of cells in the crypts of Lieberkühn. Near the neck of the gall bladder, the mucosa of the cystic duct has a series of relatively high folds which are continuous with those of the spiral valve of Heister. After removal of the gall bladder surgically, the common bile duct expands and assumes some of the storage functions of the gall bladder. The muscularis of the ducts is not as prominent as in the gall bladder. The arrangement of muscle fibers into layers is not definite, but they tend to be circularly arranged in the hepatic duct and longitudinally disposed in the cystic and in the common bile duct preceding its entry into the duodenum.

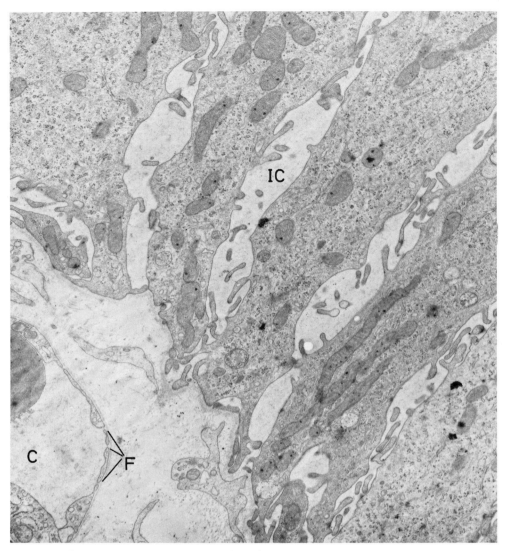

Fig. 16-82. Electron micrograph of the basal portion of several epithelial cells from a gall bladder that has been stimulated to absorb water at an accelerated rate. The contents of a surgically exposed gall bladder from an anesthetized rabbit were aspirated and replaced with a Krebs-Henseleit bicarbonate solution for a period of one hour prior to fixation of the tissue. Note that the width of the intercellular space (*IC*) in the basal portion of the epithelium is increased in correlation with increased absorption. A capillary (*C*) with fenestrated endothelium (*Fe*) is seen within the connective tissue lamina propria. *F*, fibroblasts. ×15,000. (Courtesy of Drs. G. I. Kaye, H. O. Wheeler, R. T. Whitlock, and N. Lane. J. Cell Biol., vol. 30, 1966.)

DEVELOPMENT OF THE DIGESTIVE SYSTEM

In the development of the digestive system, all of the layers of the blastoderm are involved. Mesoderm and entoderm are the layers most involved, however, as the ectoderm forms only a part of the mouth and a part of the anal canal.

An embryo of about 2 weeks consists of a relatively flat embryonic disc with its inner layer or entoderm forming the roof of the yolk sac. By differential growth rates, the embryonic area buckles upward and then folds into a cylindrical embryo. In this process, the two sides of the originally flattened gut-entoderm are folded together to produce an internal tube known as the *foregut* in the head end of the embryo, and a similar process produces the *hindgut* in the caudal end. The intermediate region remains open to the yolk sac for a short time and is known as the *midgut*. This closes off relatively soon, however; the yolk stalk detaches from the gut in most cases by the end of the fifth week.

A portion of the mesoderm accompanies the entoderm as it folds into foregut and hindgut. This is known as the *visceral layer* of mesoderm. The primary gut, composed of entoderm and its surrounding mesoderm, is at first a *blind tube*, except for its temporary opening to the yolk stalk. Connections to the exterior occur later by oral and anal invaginations of ectoderm which extend inward and open into the ends of the hitherto imperforate gut. The ends of the alimentary tract, including the oral cavity and all of the glands and other structures connected with it, are of ectodermal origin. The epithelial lining of the gut and the parenchyma of all glands connected with it are derived from entoderm. The muscle, the connective tissue and the mesothelium of the serosa are developed from mesoderm.

The mesodermal elements show little variation throughout the gut, the peculiarities of the several anatomical divisions being dependent mainly on special differentiation of the entoderm (epithelium). Beneath the entodermal cells is a narrow layer of loosely arranged tissue which later separates into lamina propria, muscularis mucosae and submucosa. Outside this, a broader mesodermal band of firmer structure represents the future muscularis.

The *stomach* first appears as a spindle-shaped dilation about the end of the first month. Its entodermal cells, which had consisted of a single layer, increase in number and arrange themselves in short, cylin-drical groups. These are the first traces of tubular glands. They increase in length and extend downward into the mesodermal tissue. For a time the cells lining the gastric glands are all apparently alike, but at about the fourth month the differentiation into chief cells and parietal cells takes place.

In the *intestines* a proliferation of the epithelium and of the underlying stroma results in the formation of *villi*. These appear about the 10th week, in both small and large intestines. In the former they increase in size, while in the latter they atrophy and ultimately disappear. The simple tubular glands of the intestines develop in a manner similar to those of the stomach.

The mesothelium of the serosa is derived from the mesodermal cells of the primitive body cavity.

The *development of the larger glands* connected with the digestive tract takes place in a manner similar to the formation of the simple tubular glands. All originate as extensions of entodermal cords into the underlying mesodermal tissue. From the lower ends of these cords, branches extend in all directions to form the complex systems of tubules found in the compound glands.

The *salivary glands*, being developed from the oral cavity, originate as similar invaginations of ectodermal tissue.

The *pancreas* arises as two separate outgrowths from the embryonic duodenum. The dorsal outgrowth forms a part of the head and all of the body and tail of the adult pancreas. The ventral outgrowth forms the remainder of the head of the pancreas. The entodermal evaginations grow into the underlying mesenchyme which forms the connective framework of the organ. The entodermal outgrowths are solid at first but they soon become hollowed out and differentiate into ducts and acini. The duct of the ventral outgrowth enlarges to form the main pancreatic duct (duct of Wirsung) which drains the acini derived from both outgrowths. A small accessory duct often persists at the site of the dorsal outgrowth. The islands of

Langerhans develop as buds from a system of fine tubules which are derived from the ducts and which form a network around the ducts Many of the islands become secondarily detached, but some of them retain their attachment to the tubules in the adult.

The *liver* originates as an outgrowth of entoderm of the ventral wall of the future duodenum into the mesoderm of the transverse septum. At its cephalic end, the outgrowth is solid and gives rise to the liver; at the caudal end, it is hollow and gives rise to the gall bladder. As the evagination increases in size, it becomes almost completely separated from the intestine, the slender connection which does remain becoming the ductus choledochus. Between the latter and the gall bladder anlage, a slender connection also remains, the cystic duct. The mesenchyme surrounding these structures develops their connective tissue framework.

As the liver bud grows, it comes into intimate relation with the growing vitelline veins. The veins break up into a network of anastomosing vessels, the future hepatic sinusoids, which tunnel through the growing liver tissue, dividing it into irregular, anastomosing trabeculae, the future hepatic plates. This relationship is maintained in the adult.

REFERENCES

Beams, H. W., and King, R. L. 1942 The origin of binucleate and large mononucleate cells in the liver of the rat. Anat. Rec., vol. 83, pp. 281–297.

Bensley, R. R. 1932 The gastric glands. Special Cytology (Cowdry, editor), vol. 1, pp. 199–320. Paul B. Hoeber, New York.

Boas, A., and Wilson, T. H. 1963 Cellular localization of gastric intrinsic factor in the rat. Amer. J. Physiol., vol. 206, pp. 783–786.

Cardell, R. R., Jr., Badenhausen, S., and Porter, K. R. 1967 Intestinal triglyceride absorption in the rat. An electron microscopical study. J. Cell Biol., vol. 34, pp. 123–155.

Caro, L. G., and Palade, G. E. 1964 Protein synthesis, storage and discharge in the pancreatic exocrine cell. J. Cell Biol., vol. 20, pp. 473–495.

Clara, M. 1934 Der Gallenkapillaren unter physiologischen und experimentellen Bedingungen; morphologische und experimentalle Untersuchungen an der Kaninchenleber. Z. Mikr. Anat. Forsch., vol. 35, pp. 1–56.

Clark, S. L., Jr. 1959 The ingestion of proteins and colloidal materials by columnar absorptive cells of the small intestine in rats and mice. J. Biophys. Biochem. Cytol., vol. 5, pp. 41–49.

Cohen, P. J. 1964 The renewal areas of the common bile duct epithelium. Anat. Rec., vol. 150, pp. 237–242.

de Duve, C. 1953 Glucagon. The hyperglycemic-glycogenolytic factor of the pancreas. Lancet, vol. 2, pp. 99–104.

Dukes, H. H. 1955 The Physiology of Domestic Animals. Comstock Publishing Associates, Cornell University Press, Ithaca.

Eckman, C. A., and Holmgren, H. 1949 The effect of alimentary factors on liver glycogen rhythm and the distribution of glycogen in the liver lobule. Anat. Rec., vol. 104, pp. 189–216.

Eicholtz, A., and Crane, R. K. 1965 Studies on the organization of the brush border in intestinal cells. J. Cell Biol., vol. 26, pp. 687–697.

Elias, H. 1949 A re-examination of the structure of the mammalian liver. I. Parenchymal architecture. Amer. J. Anat., vol. 84, pp. 311–333; II. The hepatic lobule and its relation to the vascular and biliary systems. Amer. J. Anat., vol. 85, pp. 379–456.

Forsmann, W. G., Orci, L., Pictet, R., Renold, A. E., and Rouiller, C. 1969 The endocrine cells in the epithelium of the gastrointestinal mucosa of the rat. An electron microscope study. J. Cell Biol., vol. 40, pp. 692–715.

Frazer, A. C. 1946 The absorption of triglyceride fat from the intestine. Physiol. Rev., vol. 26, pp. 104–120.

Friend, D. S. 1965 The fine structure of Brunner's glands in the mouse. J. Cell Biol., vol. 25, pp. 563–576.

Higgins, G. M., and Anderson, R. M. 1931 Experimental pathology of the liver. I. Restoration of the liver of the white rat following partial surgical removal. Arch. Path. (Chicago), vol. 12, pp. 186–202.

Hoedemaker, P. J., Abels, J., Wachters, J. J., Arends, A., and Nieweg, H. O. 1964 Investigations about the site of production of Castle's gastric intrinsic factor. Lab. Invest., vol. 13, pp. 1394–1399.

Hoedemaker, P. J., and Ito, S. 1970 Ultrastructural localization of gastric parietal cell antigen with peroxidase-coupled antibody. Lab. Invest., vol. 22, pp. 184–188.

HUNT, T. E., AND HUNT, E. A. 1962. Radioautographic study of proliferation in the stomach of the rat using thymidine-H[3] and compound 48/80[1,2]. Anat. Rec., vol. 142, pp. 505–517.

ITO, S. 1965 The enteric surface coat on intestinal microvilli. J. Cell Biol., vol. 27, pp. 475–491.

JONES, A. L., AND FAWCETT, D. W. 1966 Hypertrophy of the agranular endoplasmic reticulum in hamster liver induced by phenobarbital (with a review of the functions of this organelle in liver). J. Histochem. Cytochem., vol. 14, pp. 215–232.

KAYE, G. I., MAENZA, R. M., AND LANE, N. 1966 Cell replication in rabbit gall bladder. Gastroenterology, vol. 51, pp. 670–680.

KAYE, G. I., WHEELER, H. O., WHITLOCK, R. T., AND LANE, N. 1966 Fluid transport in rabbit gall bladder. A combined physiological and electron microscope study. J. Cell Biol., vol. 30, pp. 237–268.

KRAEHENBUHL, J. P., AND CAMPICHE, M. A. 1969 Early stages of intestinal absorption of specific antibodies in the newborn. J. Cell Biol., vol. 42, pp. 345–365.

LACY, D., AND TAYLOR, A. B. 1962 Fat absorption by epithelial cells of the small intestine of the rat. Amer. J. Anat., vol. 110, pp. 155–185.

LADMAN, A. J., PADYKULA, H. A., AND STRAUSS, E. W. 1963 A morphological study of fat transport in the normal human jejunum. Amer. J. Anat., vol. 112, pp. 389–419.

LEGG, P. G., AND WOOD, R. L. 1970 New observations on microbodies. A cytochemical study on CPIB-treated rat liver. J. Cell Biol., vol. 45, pp. 118–129.

LINDERSTRØM-LANG, K. 1939 Distribution of enzymes in tissues and cells. Harvey Lectures, Ser. 34, pp. 214–245.

MALL, F. 1896 The vessels and walls of the dog's stomach. Johns Hopkins Hosp. Rep., vol. 1, pp. 1–36.

MUKHERJE, T. M., AND WILLIAMS, A. W. 1967 A comparative study of the ultrastructure of microvilli in the epithelium of small and large intestine of mice. J. Cell Biol., vol. 34, pp. 447–461.

ORBAN, B. 1960 Atlas of Oral Histology and Embryology. The C. V. Mosby Company, St. Louis.

PALADE, G. E. 1956 The endoplasmic reticulum. J. Biophys. Biochem. Cytol., vol. 2, no. 4, suppl., pp. 85–97.

PALADE, G. E., AND SIEKEVITZ, P. 1958 Pancreatic microsomes. J. Biophys. Biochem. Cytol., vol. 2, pp. 671–690.

PALAY, S., AND KARLIN, L. 1956 Absorption of fat by jejunal epithelium in the rat. Anat. Rec., vol. 124, p. 343.

PALAY, S. L., AND KARLIN, L. 1959 An electron microscope study of the intestinal villus. I. The fasting animal. J. Biophys. Biochem. Cytol., vol. 5, pp. 363–384.

PALAY, S. L., AND REVEL, J. P. 1964 The morphology of fat absorption. In Lipid Transport (Meng, H. C., editor). Charles C Thomas, Publisher, Springfield, Ill.

PORTER, K. R., AND BRUNI, C. 1959 An electron microscope study of the early effects of 3-Me-DAB on rat liver cells. Cancer Res., vol. 19, pp. 997–1009.

RALPH, P. H. 1950 The surface structure of the gall bladder and intestinal epithelium of man and monkey. Anat. Rec., vol. 108, pp. 217–225.

RAPPAPORT, A. M., BOROWY, Z. J., LOUGHEED, W. M., AND LOTTI, W. N. 1954 Subdivision of hexagonal liver lobules into a structural and functional unit. Role in hepatic physiology and pathology. Anat. Rec., vol. 119, pp. 11–34.

RAPPAPORT, A. M. 1963 Acinar units and the pathophysiology of liver. In: The Liver; Morphology, Biochemistry, Physiology, (Rouiller, Ch. editor), vol. 1, pp. 265–328. Academic Press, New York.

REISER, R., BRYSON, M. J., CARR, M. J., AND KUIKER, K. A. 1952 The intestinal absorption of triglycerides. J. Biol. Chem., vol. 194, pp. 131–138.

SCOTT, D. B. 1953 Recent contributions in dental histology by use of the electron microscope. Int. Dent. J., vol. 4, pp. 64–95.

SELZMAN, H. M., AND LIEBELT, R. A. 1962 Paneth cell granules of mouse intestine. J. Cell Biol., vol. 15, pp. 136–139.

SENIOR, J. R. 1964 Intestinal absorption of fats. J. Lipid Res., vol. 5, pp. 495–521.

SINGH, I. 1964 On argyrophile and argentaffin reactions in individual granules of enterochromaffin cells of the human gastro-intestinal tract. J. Anat., vol. 98, pp. 497–500.

SPICER, S. S., STALEY, M. W., WETZEL, M. G., AND WETZEL, B. K. 1967 Acid mucosubstance and basic protein in mouse Paneth cells. J. Histochem. Cytochem., vol. 15, pp. 225–242.

STRAUSS, E. W. 1966 Electron microscopic study of intestinal fat absorption in vitro from mixed micelles containing monoolein, and bile salt. J. Lipid Res., vol. 7, pp. 307–323.

SULKIN, N. M. 1943 A study of the nucleus in

the normal and hyperplastic liver of the rat. Amer. J. Anat., vol. 73, pp. 107–125.

TROTTER, N. 1965 Electron opaque, lipid-containing bodies in mouse liver at early intervals after partial hepatectomy and sham operation. J. Cell Biol., vol. 25, No. 3, pt. 2, pp. 41–55.

WALKER, D. G. 1963 A survey of dehydrogenases in various epithelial cells in the rat. J. Cell Biol., vol. 17, pp. 255–277.

WILSON, J. W., AND LEDUC, E. H. 1958 Role of cholangioles in restoration of the liver of the mouse after dietary injury. J. Path. Bact., vol. 76, pp. 441–450.

WILSON, J. W., AND LEDUC, E. H. 1963 Mitochondrial changes in the liver of essential fatty acid-deficient mice. J. Cell Biol., vol. 16, pp. 281–313.

WOOD, R. L. 1970 Peroxidase activity in rat liver microbodies after aminotriazole inhibition. J. Cell Biol., vol. 45, pp. 576–585.

YAMADA, E. 1955 The fine structure of the gall bladder epithelium of the mouse. J. Biophys. Biochem. Cytol., vol. 1, pp. 445–458.

ZETTERQVIST, H. 1956 The ultrastructural organization of the columnar absorbing cells of the mouse jejunum. Aktïebolage Godvil, Karolinska Institutet, Stockholm.

17

The Respiratory System

The respiratory system consists of the lungs and a series of passages leading to them. On the basis of their primary functions, the different parts of the system can be classified in two categories: (1) an *air conducting division* composed, in sequence, of the nasal cavity, nasopharynx, oropharynx (which serves for conduction of air as well as food), larynx, trachea, bronchi and bronchioles, and (2) a *respiratory division* specialized for the exchanges of gases between air and blood. The latter is composed of respiratory bronchioles, alveolar ducts, alveolar sacs and alveoli. These divisions of the respiratory system perform their functions with the aid of a ventilation mechanism that includes the rib cage, the intercostal muscles, the diaphragm and the elastic tissue of the lungs.

NASAL CAVITY AND NASOPHARYNX

Nasal Cavity

The nasal cavity extends from the nares (nostrils) to the choanae, through which it opens into the nasopharynx. The cavity of the nose is divided into lateral halves or *fossae* by a median cartilaginous and bony septum. The inferior region of each fossa is somewhat expanded and is named the *vestibule* (Fig. 17-1). This leads into the major cavity, which is named the respiratory region in contrast with the olfactory region in the upper part of each fossa, which has receptor cells for the sense of smell.

The medial wall of each fossa (the septum) is smooth, but the lateral wall has an irregular contour because of the presence of horizontal scroll-shaped structures, the *conchae* (Figs. 17-1 and 17-2). Each concha is attached along its upper margin to the lateral wall, and the space beneath each concha is known as a *meatus*. The lacrimal duct and some of the nasal sinuses open into the meatuses.

The main current of air passing through the nose comes in contact with the mucosa of the septum and the medial surfaces of the conchae. Therefore, these surfaces are subjected to more cooling and drying than are the less exposed surfaces of the meatuses and the even less exposed mucous membranes of the sinuses. The mucous membranes of different parts of the nasal cavity have histological differences that appear to be correlated with differences in exposure.

The nasal passages function for the conduction of air and also as efficient air conditioning and filtering units. By the numerous blood vessels beneath the epithelium of some areas, the inhaled air is warmed before being transmitted to the lungs. By the mucous and serous glands, the moisture content of the air is maintained at a proper value and the epithelium itself is protected from excessive drying. The mucous coat over the epithelium, combined with ciliary action, traps a portion of the particulate matter of the inspired air and moves it to

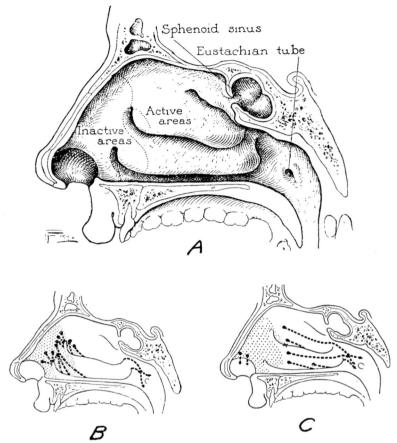

Fig. 17-1. Lateral wall of right nasal fossa and nasal pharynx. The superior, middle and inferior nasal conchae are seen, together with the opening of the sphenoid sinus into the sphenoethmoidal recess above the superior nasal concha. The right frontal sinus opening, which opens usually into the middle meatus in back of the middle concha, is not seen. *A*, the areas of the lateral wall where ciliary movements are active and relatively inactive. *B*, the course of mucous drainage of the inactive area. *C*, the course of mucous drainage of the active area. (After Hilding.)

the oropharynx to be expectorated or swallowed into the digestive tract.

The lining of the anterior part of the vestibule is quite similar to the epidermis of the nose. However, it has long thick hairs or vibrissae and associated sebaceous glands. Sweat glands are also present. The junction of the anterior part of the vestibule with the major or respiratory region of the nasal cavity is known as a transitional zone. The latter has stratified squamous epithelium like that of the anterior part of the vestibule, but it lacks sweat glands, sebaceous glands and hair follicles. It has mixed mucous and

serous glands like those of the respiratory region.

The *respiratory region* is lined by a ciliated pseudostratified columnar epithelium which is the characteristic type of the conducting division of the respiratory system. In the more exposed areas, the epithelium is thick, goblet cells are numerous and the basement membrane (basal lamina plus lamina reticularis) is very prominent (Fig. 17-3) by reason of a relatively thick lamina reticularis. In the meatuses, the epithelium is thinner, goblet cells are fewer and the basement membrane is not prominent. Intraepithelial

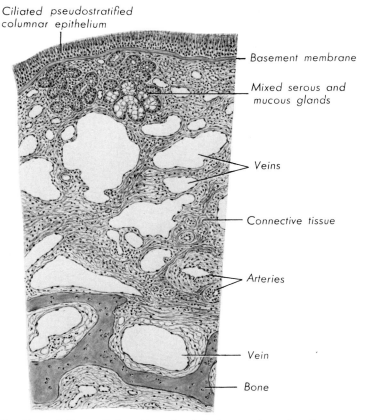

Ciliated pseudostratified columnar epithelium

Basement membrane

Mixed serous and mucous glands

Veins

Connective tissue

Arteries

Vein

Bone

FIG. 17-2. Section through the medial portion of an inferior nasal concha of a woman 47 years of age. Blood which filled the veins is not shown. ×67.

glands (mucous crypts) are present in a few individuals. These glands are depressions in the epithelium and are lined by a continuous layer of goblet cells.

The *olfactory mucosa* occupies a small area in the upper part of the respiratory region. For details of the structure of the olfactory region, see Chapter 22.

Experimental work shows that the nasal epithelium will change its character with increased ventilation. If all of the air is made to pass through one side of the nose by occluding the other nostril, the epithelium of the side subjected to the increased ventilation at first hypertrophies and then changes to a stratified squamous type (metaplasia).

The lamina propria contains numerous mucous and serous glands, particularly in the more exposed regions. Lymphocytes are usually present in both the epithelium and the lamina propria (Fig. 17-3).

The lamina propria of the nasal mucosa is quite vascular everywhere, but on the medial surfaces of the middle and inferior conchae, and to a degree on the apposed surface of the septum, it is so vascular as to be distinctive. There are many large veins (Fig. 17-2) which may become engorged with surprising rapidity. With their engorgement, the mucosa becomes swollen and turgid, obstructing the flow of air through the nasal cavities, e.g., in allergic reactions.

The *paranasal sinuses*—maxillary, ethmoid, frontal, sphenoid—are lined by an epithelium which is continuous with that of the nasal passages. It is a pseudostratified columnar ciliated epithelium (Fig. 17-4), but

Ciliated pseudostratified columnar epithelium   Goblet cells

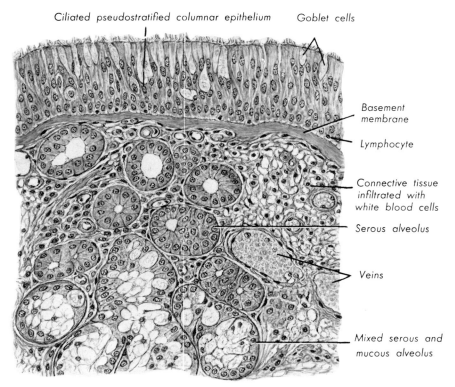

Basement membrane

Lymphocyte

Connective tissue infiltrated with white blood cells

Serous alveolus

Veins

Mixed serous and mucous alveolus

FIG. 17-3. Section through the epithelium and subjacent part of the lamina propria of inferior nasal concha. Human, 49 years old, with no history of nasal inflammation. ×286.

is only about half as thick as that which lines the nose, having two or three rows of nuclei instead of four or five as in the nasal epithelium. Goblet cells and glands are also less numerous. In contrast with the nasal and tracheal epithelium, the basement membrane is very thin. The lamina propria is thin and is attached to the periosteum.

NASOPHARYNX

In the *nasopharynx*, both stratified squamous and pseudostratified ciliated columnar epithelia are found. The distribution of these two types here and in the other respiratory passages is correlated with the attrition to which the surface is subjected. When surfaces are frequently brought in contact with each other, they are lined by stratified squamous epithelium. Those passages which usually remain open are lined by pseudostratified epithelium. Since, in the occlusion

of the upper part of the naso- from the oropharynx, the soft palate and its appendage (the uvula) are brought in contact with the posterior wall of the nasopharynx, these surfaces are lined by stratified squamous epithelium. Other areas of the nasopharynx are lined by pseudostratified columnar epithelium.

In the deeper stratum of the subepithelial connective tissue of the posterior and lateral walls of the pharynx, there is a layer of elastic tissue whose fibers course largely in a longitudinal direction. It is closely applied to the subjacent muscle layer, into which it sends fibers. Near the juncture with the esophagus, the elastic layer disappears. In the superior lateral region, but not elsewhere in the pharynx, a submucosa which lies beneath the elastic stratum can be distinguished.

Glands are present throughout the naso-

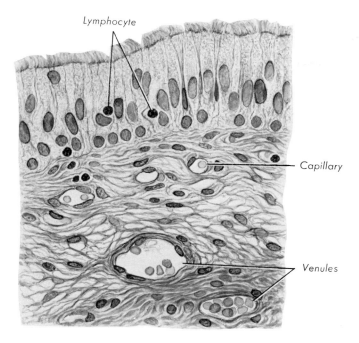

Lymphocyte

Capillary

Venules

FIG. 17-4. Section through the mucous membrane of maxillary sinus of man. ×665

pharynx. In the regions covered by stratified squamous epithelium, they are mucous and lie beneath the elastic layer. In the other areas, they are mixed serous and mucous, as in the other parts of the respiratory passages, and they lie more superficially.

Lymphatic tissue is especially abundant in the superior part of the nasopharynx. In addition to the general lymphatic infiltration of the connective tissue, there are, in the posterior wall, aggregations of lymph nodules known as the pharyngeal tonsils. Lymphatic aggregations also occur behind the openings of the Eustachian tubes, forming the tubal tonsils.

The *muscle* of the pharynx, which is striated, is deficient near the base of the skull. External to it there is a fibrosa.

Ciliary Action. The epithelium lining the paranasal sinuses, nasal passages and nasopharynx is coated with a mucous film. Since the cilia of the paranasal sinuses beat toward the openings of these cavities into the nose, and since the cilia on the epithelium lining the nose and nasopharynx beat toward

the oropharynx, there is a continuous movement of this mucous coat toward the oropharynx. The surfaces are thus freed of particulate matter that has impinged on and adhered to the mucous covering. In the posterior three-fourths of the nose, the movement is more rapid than it is in the anterior part, which has led to the characterization of these two portions as active and inactive parts. The path of movement of the mucus is shown in Figure 17-1, taken from the work of Hilding.

THE LARYNX

The wall of the larynx consists essentially of a mucosa, a poorly defined submucosa, a series of irregularly shaped cartilages connected by joints or fibroelastic membranes, and a group of intrinsic skeletal muscles which act upon the cartilages.

Each lateral wall of the larynx has two prominent folds, between which is a deep recess or *ventricle*. The superior pair of folds, the *ventricular folds*, are also known as the false vocal cords; the inferior pair, the *vocal folds*, are the true vocal cords. The *epiglottis* is a broad, flat structure projecting upward from the anterior wall of the larynx. During swallowing, there is active constriction of the pharyngeal wall, with a depression of the epiglottis and an upward movement of the larynx, trachea and pharynx. The latter movement plays an important role in closure of the glottis, preventing food from entering the larynx and trachea. The lidlike action of the epiglottis appears relatively unimportant, inasmuch as surgical removal of the tip of the epiglottis does not interfere with swallowing.

Two types of epithelium line the walls of the larynx, pseudostratified ciliated co-lumnar and stratified squamous. These are distributed in accordance with the principle discussed in connection with the nasophar-ynx. At the juncture of these two types of epithelium, a third type—ciliated stratified columnar—is frequently present (Fig. 17-5). The wall of the aperture of the larynx, including the epiglottis down nearly as far as its tubercle or cushion, is lined by strati-fied squamous epithelium. This is succeeded by the ciliated pseudostratified type that lines the remainder of the laryngeal wall, except for the vocal folds, which have the stratified squamous variety.

The lamina propria is rich in elastic fibers. It is infiltrated with lymphocytes, and

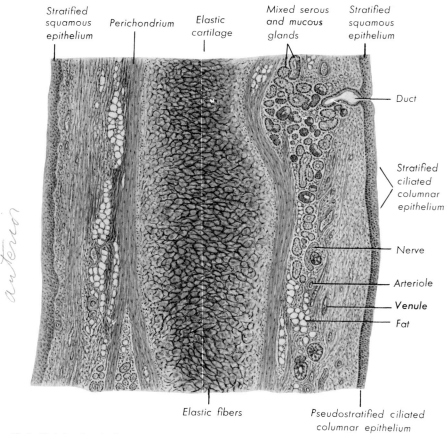

FIG. 17-5. Epiglottis of a boy 13 years old. The middle part of the free portion, cut in a saggital plane is illustrated. The lingual surface is at *left*. Stained with elastin H, Delafield's hematoxylin and eosin. ×45.

lymphatic nodules occur in the stroma of the ventricles. There is no sharp demarcation between the mucosa and the submucosa. The latter is structurally less dense and more cellular than the lamina propria. Over the vocal folds and epiglottis, the mucosa is more closely adherent to the underlying framework than it is in the other parts of the larynx. Mixed glands are present except in the vocal folds and are especially numerous in the ventricular folds (false vocal cords).

Most of the cartilages composing the framework of the larynx are hyaline. The epiglottic, the corniculate and the cuneiform cartilages are elastic, and this variety of cartilage is said also to occur inconstantly in the apex and vocal process of each arytenoid cartilage. Calcification in the thryoid and cricoid cartilages begins in males during the second decade of life and at a somewhat later period in females.

THE TRACHEA AND CHIEF BRONCHI

The layers composing the larynx continue, with certain modifications, into the trachea and bronchi. The chief changes are in the cartilaginous framework and musculature (Fig. 17-6).

The trachea and chief bronchi are lined by pseudostratified columnar ciliated epithelium which rests on a distinct basement membrane (Figs. 4-11, and 17-7). Several types of cells can be identified. The tall *ciliated columnar* cells are the most numerous. *Goblet cells* are fairly numerous and exhibit the characteristics already described in Chapter 15 (Fig. 15-1). There are nonciliated columnar cells (brush cells) which have microvilli as seen under the electron microscope. It has been suggested that they represent an inactive stage of the goblet cell. There are a number of *short cells*, more or less pyramidal in shape, which rest on

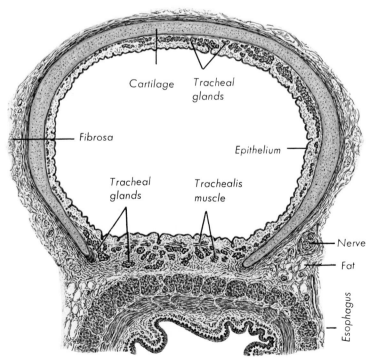

FIG. 17-6. Transverse section through midregion of trachea and adjacent part of esophagus. The section is through a cartilage ring. Woman, 35 years old. ×5.

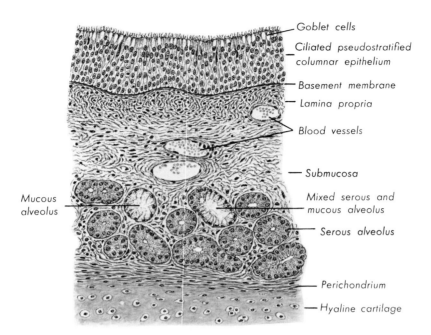

FIG. 17-7. Transverse section through anterior wall of trachea. Woman, 39 years old. ×165

the basal lamina but do not extend to the lumen as the other cell types do. The lamina propria contains many elastic fibers, which are especially numerous in the deeper zone of the lamina (membrana elastica interna). The submucosa consists of loose connective tissue and contains fat and mixed glands, the latter often penetrating into or even through the muscle layer (Fig. 17-6).

The framework of the trachea and chief bronchi consists of a series of regularly spaced, C-shaped hyaline cartilages. The open segment points posteriorly. The cartilages vary in width and thickness; their ends may bifurcate, and they may have bars that fuse with an adjoining cartilage. The lowest tracheal cartilage (carinal cartilage) especially varies in shape.

A fibroelastic membrane, which blends with the perichondrium of the cartilages, extends across their open segments and connects adjacent cartilages to each other, thus forming a tube. Posteriorly, in the cartilage-free zone, smooth muscle is imbedded in the fibroelastic membrane. Most

of these muscle fibers run transversely. Some, however, run longitudinally and obliquely. The transverse fibers attach largely to the inner surface of the ends of the cartilage rings and to a lesser extent to the intervening membrane. This is often called the "trachealis" muscle.

Localized areas of stratified squamous epithelium have been described in the trachea and bronchi of individuals suffering from chronic coughs. This change to a stratified squamous type of epithelium is possible because of the capacity of the pseudostratified epithelium of the respiratory passages to undergo metaplasia and to change to the more resistant type when subjected to attrition, as has been pointed out in the description of the nasopharynx.

THE LUNGS

The lungs are paired structures which, together with the mediastinum, fill the thoracic cavity. On the right side, the lung is divided by two deep clefts into three lobes; on the left side, it is divided by a

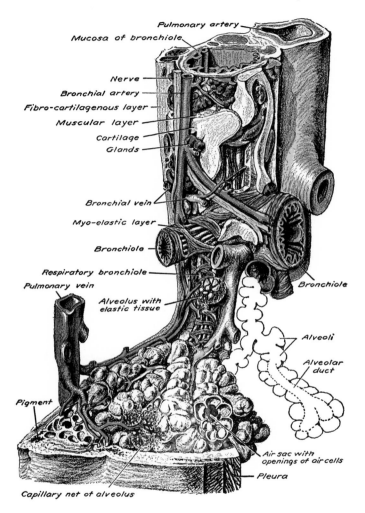

FIG. 17-8. A portion of a lung lobule. (After Braus, from a reconstruction by A. Vierling)

single deep cleft into two lobes. Entering the hilum, and forming the root of each lung, are a bronchus, a pulmonary artery and vein, bronchial arteries and veins, lymphatics and nerves. These structures are imbedded in connective tissue.

The surface of the lungs is covered by a serous membrane, the visceral pleura, which dips into the interlobar fissures and covers the interlobar surfaces. At the hilum, the visceral pleura becomes continuous with the parietal pleura.

The surface of the lungs is pinkish in early life but later becomes grayish in color as a result of the inspired particulate matter which is in the pulmonary tissue. On the surface of the lungs, small, irregularly shaped areas (1 to 2 cm.) are delineated by dark lines. Each of these areas is the base of a lobule (Fig. 17-8), the apex of which points toward the hilum of the lung. The dark lines are due to deposits of inspired particulate matter in the delicate interlobular connective tissue. Each of these units is designated a *secondary lobule*, to distinguish it from smaller *primary lobules*. Each of the latter is made up of a respiratory bronchiole and its branches.

PLAN OF THE LUNGS

A main bronchus, the primary division from the trachea, enters the root of each lung. There it divides, one secondary bronchus going to each lobe. Thus there are three branches to the right and two to the left lung. Each lobar (secondary) bronchus divides, the number of branches varying from two to five in the different lobes. Each of these bronchi supplies a portion of a lobe known as a *segment* or bronchopulmonary segment. There are 10 segments in the right lung and eight in the left lung. These segments are of considerable importance from a surgical standpoint. The segmental bronchi divide a number of times within the lung, with a progressive reduction in diameter and a gradual decrease in cartilage (Fig. 17-9). When the tubes reach a caliber of about 1 mm., the cartilage disappears completely and the tubes are known as *bronchioles*. The bronchioles continue to divide and, when their branches have been reduced to a caliber of about 0.5 mm. (or less), they become devoid of glands and goblet cells and are known as *terminal bronchioles* (Figs. 17-10 to 17-12). There are a number of terminal bronchioles within a secondary lung lobule. The terminal bronchioles, as their name implies, are the terminal segments of the purely conducting division of the respiratory system. Each of them terminates by branching into two or more *respiratory bronchioles* (Figs. 17-10 and 17-11). As noted earlier, each respiratory bronchiole and its subsidiary divisions make up a functional unit known as the *primary lobule*. Each respiratory bronchiole undergoes further divisions, each of which branches into *alveolar ducts* (ductuli alveolares). These in turn may further branch, terminating after a relatively long course in *alveolar sacs* (sacculi alveolares, air sacs). The smallest units or subdivisions are the *pulmonary alveoli* (air cells), small outpocketings that form the lining of the alveolar ducts and alveolar sacs and in whose walls the interchange of gases between air and blood takes place.

Pulmonary alveoli are confined to the respiratory division of the lung. They first appear, in the branching system outlined above, in the respiratory bronchioles, which have characteristics of both the conducting and respiratory divisions. The alveolar ducts and alveolar sacs have continuous pulmonary alveoli forming their walls. The pulmonary alveoli of one system interdigitate with those of neighboring systems, so that two adjacent alveoli have a common capillary bed, an arrangement which gives a maximal surface area for the exchange of gases.

CHANGES IN THE LUNGS DURING RESPIRATION

An understanding of the changes that occur during respiration gives a better ap-

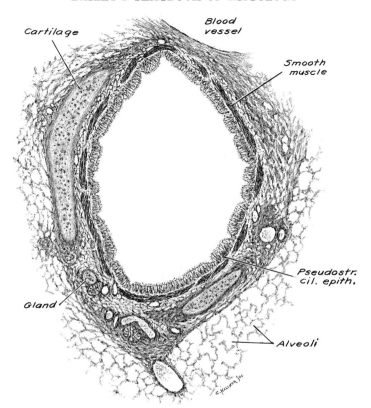

Fig. 17-9. Section through a bronchus approximately 2 mm. in diameter

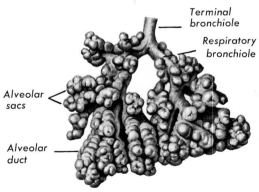

FIG. 17-10. Cast (Wood's metal) of a terminal bronchiole and its branches. (Braus, after Loeschcke).

preciation of the distribution of elastic tissue, smooth muscle and cartilage within different parts of the respiratory system. Since the existence of a negative (subatmospheric) pressure within the pleural cavities is an important factor in respiration, it is one of the first items to consider. It should be noted that the lungs fill the pleural cavities in early embryos and that a negative pressure is not present at first. However, as the pleural cavities enlarge and as elastic tissue and smooth muscle develop within each lung, tending to contract each toward its hilus, a negative intrathoracic pressure develops. This exerts an expanding or stretching action on the lungs. The presence of an elastic recoil mechanism is clearly demonstrated by the fact that the lung collapses and retracts toward its hilus when air is allowed to enter the pleural cavity through a hole in the chest wall, producing *pneumothorax*, and when fluid increases in the cavity, producing *hydrothorax*. The retraction of the lung tissue is brought about by the recoil of the stretched elastic tissue and by contraction of the spirally arranged smooth muscle fibers in the walls of the conducting divisions and parts of the respiratory divisions of the lungs.

In respiration, the volume of the lung changes in correlation with changes in intrathoracic pressure, and the latter in turn varies in association with changes in intrathoracic volume. In inspiration, the volume of the thoracic cavity is increased by muscular movements which elevate the ribs to increase the cross sectional area of the thoracic cavity and by contraction of the diaphragm to increase the cephalocaudal dimension. This increases the negative pressure, and the lungs expand. In expiration, the elastic forces of the lungs are usually sufficient to expel the air and allow the chest to return passively from its expanded state in a person at rest. Muscular movements play a greater part in expiration during strenuous exercise, when there is an increase in rate and amplitude of respiration.

We can now outline some of the ways in which the microscopic structures of the several parts of the conducting and respiratory divisions of the lungs are adapted to perform particular functions. The presence of hyaline cartilage in the form of separate plates in the walls of the bronchi (Fig. 17-9) gives strength to these divisions without hindering changes in their length and diameter. The presence of smooth muscle, coursing in a spiral direction around the bronchi and bronchioles and onto the alveolar ducts, provides for reducing the length and breadth of these passages by muscular contraction. Elastic tissue is present in the form of a dense feltwork of longitudinally oriented fibers in the lamina propria of the conducting divisions and as a network around all of the respiratory divisions. This permits expansion of lung tissue when the negative intrathoracic pressure is increased during inspiration. The elastic recoil plays an important part in the contraction of the lung tissue during expiration. The epithelium lining the conducting and respiratory divisions shows particularly important functional adaptations. These can best be considered in connection with a more detailed description of structure.

STRUCTURE OF THE LUNGS

The Conducting Division. Modifications in the structure of the bronchi appear with the first branching in the root of the lungs and continue to take place with each subsequent branching. A comparison of a terminal segment (terminal bronchiole) with a main bronchus reveals how great these changes have been. The series of changes, however, is gradual, and therefore our discussion bears on the nature of the modifications that occur, rather than describing bronchi of different diameters.

The epithelium, although continuing as a pseudostratified columnar type through most of the conducting division, nevertheless decreases in height as the tubes become progressively smaller. In the terminal bronchiole, it becomes a single layer of columnar or cuboidal cells which, however, still bear cilia (Fig. 17-12). Both goblet cells and glands (seromucous) become fewer, and both cease to be present before the terminal bronchioles are reached.

The lamina propria also decreases in thickness as the conducting divisions decrease in caliber, and elastic fibers become relatively more numerous. The elastic fibers form a feltwork, with the majority of them coursing in a longitudinal direction. Smooth muscle increases in relative amounts along the conducting divisions and is arranged in bundles that follow a spiral course around the bronchi, interior to the cartilage plates (Fig. 17-9). This contrasts with the trachea, in which the smooth muscle is found primarily in the posterior wall, in the region between the ends of the C-shaped cartilages. The smooth muscle is relatively most abundant in the terminal bronchioles, where it forms a prominent component of the wall (Fig. 17-12).

The outer layer of the bronchi and bronchioles also shows pronounced changes. With the first branching of the primary bronchi,

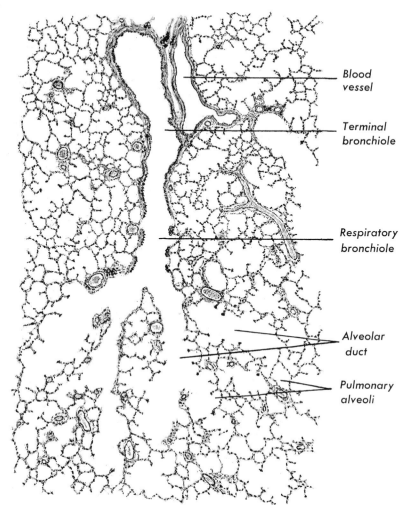

Blood
vessel

Terminal
bronchiole

Respiratory
bronchiole

Alveolar
duct

Pulmonary
alveoli

FIG. 17-11. Section through a terminal bronchiole, together with part of the system arising from it. Camera lucida drawing. Human lung. ×19.

the cartilage ceases to occur as C-shaped rings and becomes distributed in irregularly shaped plates. As the bronchi continue to branch and decrease in diameter, the cartilaginous plates are replaced by islands of cartilage (insulae cartilagineae). As noted earlier, cartilage disappears completely when the bronchioles are reached, at a diameter of about 1 mm. The mucosa of the bronchioles usually has longitudinal folds as a result of the absence of cartilage and the proportional increase in muscle and elastic tissue.

Terminal bronchioles (0.5 mm. or less in

caliber) are lined by simple columnar or cuboidal ciliated epithelium. There are no goblet cells or glands. Elastic tissue and smooth muscle are closely associated, and the amount of muscle in proportion to the diameter of the tubule is proportionally higher than in the other divisions of the system.

It is significant that the cilia extend farther down the tubes than do the mucous secreting elements. If the reverse were the case, accumulations of mucus might occlude the tubules.

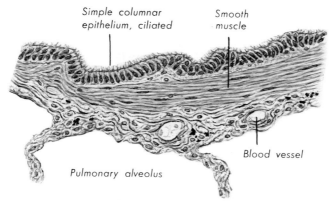

Simple columnar
epithelium, ciliated

Smooth
muscle

Blood vessel

Pulmonary alveolus

FIG. 17-12. Transverse section through a portion of the wall of a terminal bronchiole and adjacent pulmonary alveoli. Human lung. ×320.

The Respiratory Division. Each terminal bronchiole divides into two or more respiratory bronchioles (Fig. 17-10) which may further branch so that respiratory bronchioles of the first (I) and second (II) order are formed. The *respiratory bronchioles* bear pulmonary alveoli on those portions of their walls which are not in contact with the accompanying pulmonary artery (Fig. 17-13). The alveoli are few in number proximally but become more numerous distally. Between the alveoli, the wall of the respiratory bronchiole is lined in the proximal part by ciliated cuboidal epithelium. In the distal part, cilia are absent. Smooth muscle and elastic fibers are very well developed in the respiratory bronchiole, although they do not form as thick a layer as in the terminal bronchiole. Collagenous and reticular fibers are also present. The smooth muscle bundles and the elastic fibers course obliquely, i.e., in a spiral direction, but they branch and anastomose, thus forming a loose elastic and contractile network. In sections through the opening of an alveolus into a respiratory bronchiole, the muscle fibers are seen to be cut obliquely or transversely (Fig. 17-13). The walls of the alveolar ducts are formed by pulmonary sacs and alveoli without intervening patches of cuboidal epithelium. Small smooth muscle bundles which branch and anastomose are present. They are con-

centrated around the openings of the alveoli so that, in a transverse section through an alveolar duct, the muscle bundles mark the circular extent of the lumen (Fig. 17-14). Reticular, elastic and delicate collagenous fibers are also present (Figs. 17-15 and 17-16). The alveolar ducts terminate in a variable number of alveolar sacs.

The *alveolar sacs* are extremely thin walled structures which are closely studded with pulmonary alveoli. The walls of the alveolar sacs contain no smooth muscle but have elastic and reticular fibers. As in the alveolar ducts, there is no epithelial lining other than that of the alveoli (see below under pulmonary alveoli).

THE PULMONARY ALVEOLI

Pulmonary alveoli (air cells) are cup-shaped structures through whose thin walls the interchange of gas between the blood and air takes place. The open end or mouth of each alveolus opens into the lumen of a respiratory bronchile, an alveolar duct or an alveolar sac (Figs. 17-8 and 17-11). Because of the interdigitating arrangement of the alveoli, a single wall, or *interalveolar septum*, is usually formed between adjacent alveoli (Figs. 17-14 to 17-16).

An *interalveolar septum* is composed of the lining cells of adjacent alveoli and the structures interposed between the alveoli.

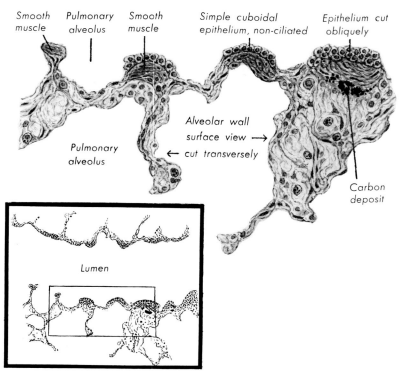

FIG. 17-13. Longitudinal section through wall of respiratory bronchiole near juncture with alveolar duct. Human lung. ×335. *Inset*, the orientation of illustrated part of the wall.

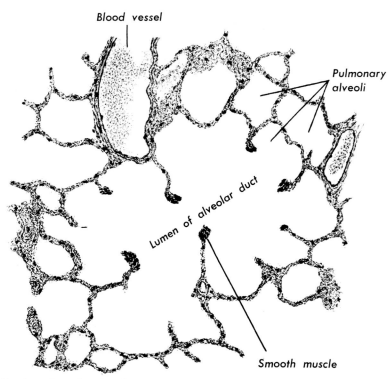

FIG. 17-14. Section of an alveolar duct, showing especially the smooth muscle. Human lung. ×78

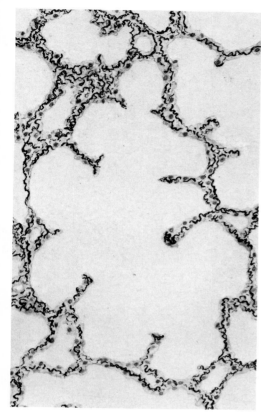

FIG. 17-15. Section through an alveolar duct, showing the reticular fibers (black). Lung of rhesus monkey. Foot-Hortega silver carbonate method and Orth's carmine. ×240.

Capillaries occupy a major portion of the septum, and they are shared by the lining cells of the adjacent alveoli (Fig. 17-17). It should be noted that the capillaries have wide lumina and that they anastomose so freely that the total area of the vascular network exceeds that of the intervening spaces (Fig. 17-18). The meshes of the capillary network contain reticular and elastic fibers arranged in a manner to permit expansion and contraction of the alveolar wall. The intercapillary spaces also contain a few fibroblasts, some wandering leukocytes, histiocytes and occasional smooth muscle cells.

The interalveolar septa are interrupted in places where adjacent alveoli not only make contact but open to each other to form *alveolar pores* (Fig. 17-19). They are about

10 to 15 μ in diameter in the expanded lung. In certain pathological conditions, they become more prominent and contain strands of fibrin extending from one alveolus to another. With regard to their functional significance, it has been suggested that, by providing intercommunication, they prevent the overdistention of some alveoli and the collapse of others when small bronchioles of a functional unit are occluded.

The alveolar lining cells have been studied very extensively. Prior to the advent of electron microscopy, there was considerable controversy as to whether the alveoli are completely lined by epithelium. It was known from light microscope studies that the entire pulmonary system is lined by epithelium in early stages of fetal development, but this was questionable as applied to late fetal life and postnatal life when the walls of the alveoli are extremely thin. The problem was clarified by electron microscope studies

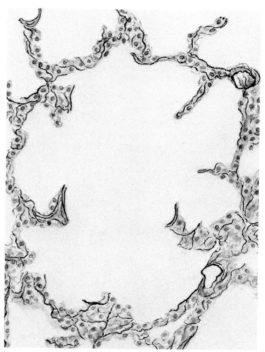

FIG. 17-16. Sections through an alveolar duct, showing elastic tissue (black). Lung of rhesus monkey. Weigert's elastic tissue stain and Orth's carmine. ×240.

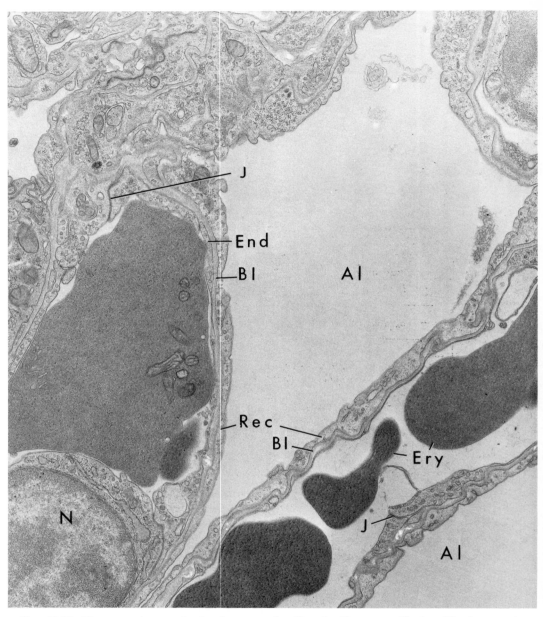

Fig. 17-17. Electron micrograph of pulmonary alveoli and adjancet capillaries. The lumen of an alveolus (*Al*) is separated from the lumen of the capillaries by a thin layer of tissue composed of: 1) respiratory epithelial cells (*Rec*) that line the alveolus; 2) a basal lamina (or laminae, *Bl*); and 3) endothelial cells (*End*) that line the capillaries. The basal lamina of the endothelium appears to be fused with that of the squamous respiratory cells along a considerable portion of the interalveolar septum. The respiratory cells are very attenuated in regions where they are apposed to the endothelial cells, but they form a continuous layer. Likewise, the endothelial cell is attenuated except in the region around the nucleus (*N*). *Ery*, erythrocytes in the capillaries; *J*, intercellular junctions of endothelial cells. From the lung of a mouse. ×16,000. (Courtesy of Drs. K. R. Porter and M. A. Bonneville).

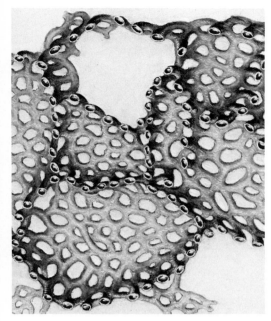

FIG. 17-18. Injected lung, showing capillaries in walls of pulmonary alveoli. Dog. Preparation by Mr. Kellner. ×400.

which showed that the alveoli are completely lined by epithelium but that the cells have regions which are so attenuated that they lie at the limits of resolution provided by the light microscope.

The alveolar lining consists of *squamous epithelial cells* (also known as respiratory epithelial cells or low alveolar cells) and *great alveolar cells* (septal cells).

The *respiratory* or *squamous cells* have low or flat nuclei, much like those of the cells of mesothelium. The cytoplasm becomes very thin or attenuated beyond the perinuclear region (Fig. 17-17). The squamous cells have junctional attachments laterally with each other and with the great alveolar cells.

The great *alveolar cells* (septal cells) have an irregular, cuboidal shape. They are fairly numerous, they are taller than the squamous cells, and they can be seen more readily with the light microscope. They have characteristic cytoplasmic structures which look like vacuoles under the light microscope but

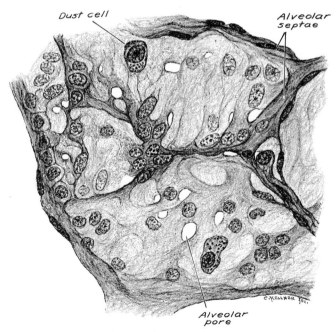

FIG. 17-19. Surface view of the walls of pulmonary alveoli, showing alveolar pores. From a thick (50 μ) section of lung of a rhesus monkey.

which are seen in electron micrographs as osmiophilic bodies with internal concentric lamellae. These bodies, which are 0.2 to 1.0 μ in diameter, are known as *cytosomes*. They are periodic acid-Schiff-positive, and they also stain with Sudan black. Electron micrographs show transitional stages between multivesicular bodies and the cytosomes, indicating that the latter arise from multivesicular bodies (Sorokin, 1966). The cytosomes are ultimately secreted onto the alveolar surface, and it has been proposed that they contribute to the pulmonary surfactant that coats alveolar cells and lowers surface tension. Electron micrographs show that the alveolar cells rest on the basal lamina and that they have a well developed granular endoplasmic reticulum, free ribosomes and an extensive Golgi complex. In other words, they have the cytological characteristics of secretory cells.

The *alveolar membrane* may be defined as the barrier through which gases must pass in exchange between air and blood. This membrane consists of the *respiratory epithelial cell* (squamous cell) together with its underlying *basal lamina* and the capillary endothelial cell with its *basal lamina*. The basal laminae of epithelium and endothelium are in contact in some areas and are separated in many other areas only by thin strands of connective tissue. The endothelium of the capillaries is relatively thin but is not fenestrated, i.e., it does not have endothelial pores.

Alveolar phagocytes or *dust cells* are found within the alveolar wall and also in the alveoli, resting on the alveolar surface. They are phagocytic cells and therefore belong to the reticuloendothelial system. They received the name dust cells because they remove inspired particles that reach the alveoli. In clinical disorders in which the pulmonary vessels become congested with blood, the phagocytes ingest some of the erythrocytes and become filled with brownish granules of hemosiderin.

Dust cells may arise from several sources,

according to the literature on this subject. Some may develop from mononuclear leukocytes which migrate into the alveolar lining, and some may arise from connective tissue cells of the septa. It has been suggested that they may also arise from great alveolar (septal) cells because cells with cytological characteristics intermediate between these types have been observed in electron micrographs.

INSPIRED PARTICULATE MATTER

Many particles of dust are present in the air which is inspired, and the number of particles is greatly increased in smoky regions and in industries or regions in which the air is laden with dust. Many of the inspired particles are removed by their adherence to the vibrissae in the nasal vestibule and by lodging on the mucous film of the respiratory portion of the nose, nasopharynx, larynx and trachea. The mucous film and adherent particles are constantly being moved by ciliary action to the oropharynx, from which they are either expectorated or swallowed. These structures thus serve not only to humidify and warm the air but also to remove particulate matter.

The bronchi and bronchioles in the lung also play a very important role in the removal of particulate matter. As repeated branchings take place, with only a slight increase in cross section area (volume), the surface of the walls is greatly increased. Because of the increased area, particles would be more likely to impinge on the mucous coat than in the upper, larger passages. For this lower part of the conducting system, Hilding has proposed the name "bronchiolar filter." As in the trachea and nasal passages, ciliary action carries the particles lodged on the mucous film to the oropharynx.

Many of the smaller particles, however, reach the alveoli of the lungs, and their removal by ciliary action is not possible. A different mechanism operates to dispose

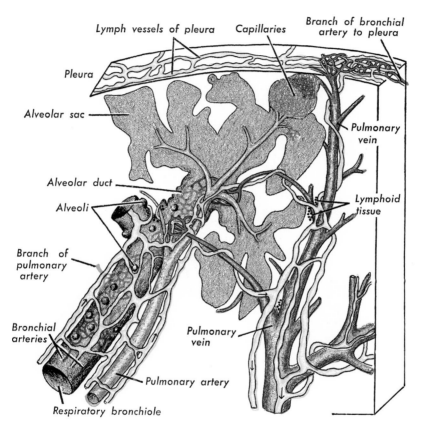

Lymph vessels of pleura

Capillaries

Branch of bronchial
artery to pleura

Pleura

Alveolar sac

Pulmonary
vein

Alveolar duct

Alveoli

Lymphoid
tissue

Branch of
pulmonary
artery

Bronchial
arteries

Pulmonary
vein

Pulmonary artery

Respiratory bronchiole

FIG. 17-20. The blood supply and lymph drainage of a portion of a lung lobule and the pleura. (From Miller, The Lung. Charles C Thomas.)

of them. The particles are removed by alveolar phagocytes, called *dust cells*.

The dust cells phagocytize the particles on the alveolar walls and deposit them, perhaps after passage through several cells, in the connective tissue of the lungs or in the lymphatic tissue. In this transport of the particles, the lymph vessels play an important role. The connective tissue may increase greatly in amount (fibrosis) and may encapsulate masses of the particles. The degree of connective tissue overgrowth is influenced by the type of the inhaled dust. Siliceous dust and asbestos, for instance, cause a marked fibrosis, whereas coal dust, even when present in large amounts, induces a very slight reaction, or none at all, of the connective tissue. The condition which results from the dust is termed pneumo-coniosis, special names (anthracosis, silicosis, asbestosis, etc.) being used to designate the reactions to the various types of dust.

THE PLEURA

The pleura is a serous membrane which completely lines the pleural cavity. The visceral portion invests and is closely adherent to the lungs. It is continuous with the parietal pleura at the root of the lungs. Beneath the mesothelial lining of the pleura is a fibroelastic stroma which contains smooth muscle. In the stroma are blood capillaries and a rich plexus of lymph vessels.

Continuous with the stroma of the pleura are delicate septa that extend between the lobules, anastomosing with each other and with the peribronchial connective tissue. They are composed of fibrous and elastic connective tissue, and they contain smooth muscle, lymph and blood vessels and histio-cytes.

THE BLOOD AND LYMPH CIRCULATION OF THE LUNGS

Blood Vessels. The lungs receive blood from two sources: venous blood, to be purified, through the *pulmonary arteries*, and arterial blood, for the nutrition of the walls of the conducting system and blood vessels, through the *bronchial arteries*. This blood is returned to the systemic circulation through the pulmonary and bronchial veins. The former, in contrast with the latter, are devoid of valves.

The pulmonary artery enters the lung with the corresponding chief bronchus. It branches with and follows the bronchial tree to the termination of the respiratory bronchioles. As the alveolar duct is reached, the artery gives rise to the capillary plexus in the walls of the alveoli (Figs. 17-18 and 17-20). Veins arise from these capillaries. They do not immediately join the bronchioles but course in the septa. Later they join the bronchioles and course along them to the root of the lung.

The bronchial arteries likewise accompany the bronchi. Along their course they give origin to capillaries which supply the walls of the bronchi, arteries, veins and the peri-bronchial and septal connective tissue. The bronchial arteries do not extend beyond the respiratory bronchioles. The capillaries aris-ing from them in that segment anastomose with the pulmonary capillary plexus. Part of the blood carried by the bronchial arteries passes into the pulmonary veins through this anastomosis. The remainder returns through the bronchial veins.

The pleura, in man, is supplied by the bronchial arteries. This blood returns through the pulmonary veins.

Lymphatics. There are two sets of lymphatic vessels in the lung: a superficial set in the pleura and a deep set in the sub-stance of the lung. The superficial (pleural) lymph vessels are particularly numerous near the juncture of the interlobular septa with the pleura, and thus they outline the lobules (Fig. 17-21). There are numerous anastomoses between the vessels of the superficial and deep plexuses at the surface of the lung. These serve as afferents to the superficial vessels; numerous valves in the latter prevent the backflow of lymph. The efferents of the superficial plexus course

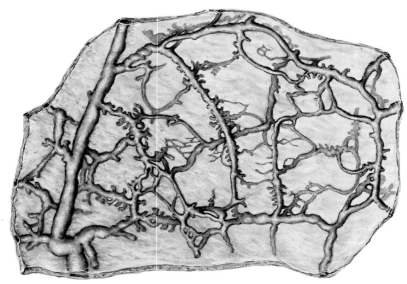

Fig. 17-21. Lymphatics of pleura; the area outlined by the large (peripheral) vessel is the base of a lung lobule. ×8. (Miller.)

first in the pleura and then in the connective tissue along the larger bronchi to the root of the lung.

The vessels of the deep plexus are found chiefly in the following locations: around the bronchi and bronchioles, around the branches of the pulmonary artery and in the interlobular connective tissue associated with the branches of the pulmonary veins. There are no lymphatics in the interalveolar septa; they begin in the connective tissue around the respiratory bronchioles and blood vessels. Although some of the lymph from the deep plexus enters the superficial vessels by channels of anastomosis over the lung surface, a considerable portion of the lymph of the deep plexus is carried by larger vessels which follow the bronchi and blood vessels to the hilum, where the main vessels of the two sets of lymphatics join. There are no valves in the deep lymphatics, except in a few of the larger trunks.

Lymphatic tissue in the form of lymph nodes or solitary nodules with germinal centers occurs along the larger bronchial branches. The amount of lymphatic tissue is said to increase with age. It becomes infiltrated with the inspired particulate matter. There is also a lymphocytic infiltration of the walls of the bronchi.

Nerves. The bronchi are accompanied by sympathetic and parasympathetic nerves. The latter come from the vagus. Ganglion cells are present in the walls of the bronchi. The vagus fibers cause constriction of the air tubes; the sympathetic fibers cause dilation.

DEVELOPMENT OF THE RESPIRATORY SYSTEM

The epithelium of the respiratory system develops from entoderm. The rudiment of the larynx, trachea and lungs appears as a ventral, groove-like evagination in the floor of the primitive pharynx. This evagination grows caudally and becomes cut off by constriction from the digestive tube except in its superior part, and its apex bifurcates. The portion which does not bifurcate, together with the surrounding mesenchyme, forms the larynx and trachea. The bifuracted part is the anlage of the epithelium and epithelial derivatives of the bronchial system and lungs, the mesenchyme forming the other portions of the walls. The right branch subdivides into three branches corresponding to the three lobes of the future right lung, and the left divides into two branches corresponding to two lobes of the left lung. By repeated branching of these tubules, the entire bronchial system of the lungs is formed. This process is similar to the development of a compound gland. The last to develop are the respiratory bronchioles and the alveolar ducts and sacs, structures that are characteristic of the lung. During fetal life, the alveoli are lined by a cuboidal epithelium. At the time of birth, these cells become extremely thin, so thin in fact that filmlike peripheral portions of the cells are masked by the underlying denser tissue.

Following birth, as well as during gestation, there is a continued growth of the lung. The bronchioles increase in length, and new respiratory units are formed. The increase in the length of the bronchioles, while to a small degree caused by an interstitial growth of the existing bronchioles, is mainly due to the transformation of the repiratory bronchioles, alveolar ducts and alveolar sacs into bronchioles. The lengthening of the respiratory division takes place by a terminal budding and growth of the air sacs. Their growth is thus much like that which occurs in a tree.

REFERENCES

ADAMS, F. H. 1965 Fetal and neonatal cardiovascular and pulmonary function. Ann. Rev. Physiol., vol. 27, pp. 257–284.

AVERY, M. E. 1962 The alveolar lining layer. A review of studies of its role in pulmonary mechanisms and in pathogenesis of atelectasis. Pediatrics, vol. 30, pp. 324–330.

BERTALANFFY, F. D., AND LEBLOND, C. P. 1953 The continuous renewal of the two types of alveolar cells in the lung of the rat. Anat. Rec. vol., 115, pp. 515–542.

BOYDEN, E. A. 1955. Segmental Anatomy of the Lungs. A study of the patterns of the segmental bronchi and related pulmonary vessels. The Blakiston Division, McGraw-Hill Book Company, New York.

BOYDEN, E. A., AND TOMPSETT, D. H. 1965 The changing patterns in the developing lungs of infants. Acta Anat., vol. 61, pp. 164–192.

DEREUCK, A. V. S., AND O'CONNOR (editors) 1961 Ciba Foundation Symposium on Pulmonary Structure and Function. Little, Brown and Company, Boston.

ELEFTMAN, A. G. 1943 The afferent and parasympathetic innervation of the lungs and trachea of the dog. Amer. J. Anat., vol. 72, pp. 1–27.

ENGEL, S. 1962 Lung Structure. Charles C Thomas, Publisher, Springfield, Ill.

HAYEK, HEINRICH VON (translated by V. E. Krahl) 1960 The Human Lung. Hafner Publishing Company, New York.

HILDING, A. C. 1932 The physiology of drainage of nasal mucus. Arch. Otolaryng. (Chicago), vol. 15, pp. 92–100; vol. 16, pp. 9–17.

HILDING, A. C., AND HILDING, D. 1948 The volume of the bronchial three at various levels and its possible physiological significance. Ann. Otol., vol. 57, pp. 324–342.

JACKSON, C. L., AND HUBER, J. F. 1943 Correlated applied anatomy of the bronchial tree and lungs with a system of nomenclature. Dis. Chest, vol. 9, pp. 319–326.

KRAHL, V. E. 1964 Anatomy of the mammalian lung. In American Physiological Society Handbook of Physiology. Section 3, vol. 1, p. 213. The Williams & Wilkins Company, Baltimore.

LARSEL, O. AND DOW, R. S. 1933 The innervation of the human lung. Amer. J. Anat., vol. 52, pp. 125–146.

LATTA, J. S. AND SCHALL, R. F. 1934 The histology of the epithelium of the paranasal sinuses under various conditions. Ann. Otol., vol. 43, pp. 945–972.

LOOSLI, C. G. 1937 Interalveolar communications in normal and pathological mammalian lungs. Arch. Path. (Chicago), vol. 24, pp. 743–776. See also: Amer. J. Anat., vol. 62, pp. 375–425, 1938.

LOW, F. N. 1953 The pulmonary alveolar epithelium of laboratory mammals and man. Anat. Rec., vol. 117, pp. 241–264.

LOW, F. N. 1961 The extracellular portion of the blood-air barrier and its relation to tissue space. Anat. Rec., vol. 139, pp. 105–123.

MACKLIN, C. C. 1929 The musculature of the bronchi and lungs. Physiol. Rev., vol. 9, pp. 1–60.

MACKLIN, C. C. 1935 Alveolar pores and their significance in the human lung. Arch. Path. (Chicago), vol. 21, pp. 202–216.

MILLER, W. S. 1947 The Lung. Charles C Thomas, Publisher, Springfield, Ill.

PRATT, S. A., FINLEY, T. N., SMITH, M. H., AND LADMAN, A. J. 1969 A comparison of alveolar macrophages and pulmonary surfactant (?) obtained from the lungs of human smokers and nonsmokers by endobronchial lavage. Anat. Rec., vol. 163, pp. 497–508.

ROBERTSON, O. H. 1941 Phagocytosis of foreign material in the lung. Physiol. Rev., vol. 21, pp. 112–139.

SOROKIN, S. P. 1966 A morphologic and cytochemical study of the great alveolar cell. J. Histochem. Cytochem., vol. 14, pp. 884–897.

TOBIN, C. E. 1954 Lymphatics of the pulmonary alveoli. Anat. Rec. Rec., vol. 120, pp. 625–636.

WEIBEL, E. R. 1964 Morphogenetics of the lung. In American Physiological Society Handbook of Physiology. The Williams & Wilkins Company, Baltimore.

18

The Urinary System

THE KIDNEY

The kidney is a compound tubular gland which separates urea and other nitrogenous waste products from the blood. It also maintains the constituents of blood plasma at proper levels, and, in so doing, it has an important role in regulating the chemical composition of the extracellular fluid which bathes the cells and tissues of the body. It is enclosed by a firm connective tissue capsule composed of collagenous fibers and a few elastic fibers. In many of the lower animals and in the human fetus, septa extend from the capsule into the gland, dividing it into a number of lobes or *renculi*. In human adults, the lobated character is obliterated by the great reduction of the interstitial connective tissue and the apparent blending of the peripheral parts of the different lobes. Rarely, the fetal divisions persist in adult life, such a kidney being known as a "lobated kidney." In some animals, such as the guinea pig and rabbit, the entire kidney consists of a single lobe.

On the mesially directed border of the kidney is a depression known as the *hilum*. This serves as the point of entrance for the *renal artery* and of exit for the *renal vein* and *ureter*.

On section, the kidney shows a parenchyma of *cortex* and *medulla* partially surrounding a cavity—the *renal sinus*—which opens at the hilum (Fig. 18-1). The renal sinus contains: (1) the upper, expanded portion of the ureter which is known as the *renal pelvis*, (2) subdivisions of the pelvis that form two or three *major calyces* and about eight *minor calyces*, (3) branches of the renal arteries, veins and nerves, and (4) loose connective tissue and fat. In fresh, unfixed kidneys, the outer or cortical zone of the parenchyma is dark brown in color and granular in appearance. It contains many convoluted tubules and numerous round, reddish bodies, the *renal* or *Malpighian corpuscles*, which are barely visible to the unaided eye. The inner, medullary zone of the parenchyma is radially striated in appearance because its tubular and vascular elements run in parallel radial lines.

The cortex not only forms the outer zone of the kidney but, at intervals, plugs of cortical tissue, the *columns of Bertini* or *renal columns*, penetrate the whole depth of the medulla. The main medullary mass consists of eight to 18 *medullary* or *Malpighian pyramids*, the number corresponding to the number of lobes in the fetal kidney. The broad base of each pyramid is in contact with the cortex, and the rounded apex projects into a minor calyx (Fig. 18-1). As a rule, two or sometimes three pyramids unite to form a single *papilla;* hence, the number of papillae is less than that of the pyramids. The tip of the papillary surface presents a sieve-like appearance, *area cribrosa*, as a result of the presence of 10 to 25 pores or *foramina papillaria*, which are

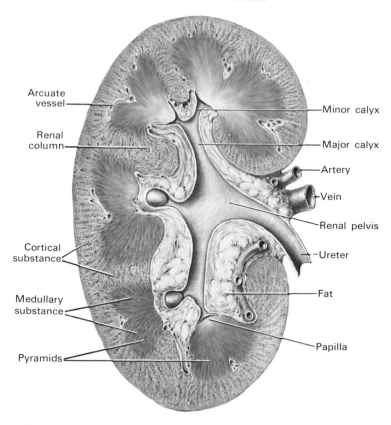

Arcuate vessel

Renal column

Cortical substance

Medullary substance

Pyramids

Minor calyx

Major calyx

Artery

Vein

Renal pelvis

Ureter

Fat

Papilla

FIG. 18-1. Longitudinal section of a human kidney. Natural size

the openings of the uriniferous ducts. Even in gross preparations, two zones may be distinguished in the medulla: an outer, more deeply colored zone in contact with the cortex, and an inner, somewhat paler papillary zone.

The cortical region is subdivided into many radiating, slender columns composed of straight tubules alternating with regions containing glomeruli and convoluted tubules (Figs 18-2 and 18-3). The columns of straight tubules radiate outward from the medulla and hence are named *pars radiata* or *medullary rays*. They are also known as the *processes of Ferrein*. The regions between the rays contain glomeruli and convoluted tubules and are called *pars convoluta* or *cortical labyrinths*. A medullary ray and the portions of the adjacent labyrinths whose tubules drain into the collecting tubules constitute a *lobule*.

THE URINIFEROUS TUBULES

The parenchyma of the kidney consists of closely packed uriniferous tubules, between which are blood vessels and a scanty amount of interstitial connective tissue. As in any other gland, two types of tubules are distinguished: the terminal or "secretory" tubules, which function in the formation of the urine, and the collecting tubules, which are the ducts conveying the urine to the pelvis and ureter. The terminal tubule constitutes a structural and functional unit known as the *nephron*. Each nephron is long (30 to 40 mm.) and unbranched and, for the greater part of its course, it is highly tortuous, forming compact convoluted masses (Fig. 18-4). Each nephron begins

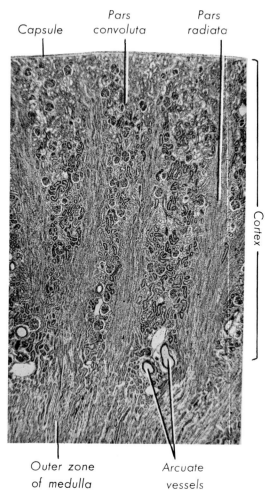

Capsule — Pars convoluta — Pars radiata — Cortex — Outer zone of medulla — Arcuate vessels

FIG. 18-2. Low power photomicrograph of a section of a kidney from an infant of 8 months, showing topography of the cortex and a part of the outer zone of the medulla. ×28.

As a rule, the larger ones are found near the border of the medulla. Their structure is best understood by a brief reference to their development (Chapter 20 and Fig. 20-44). During development, the rounded, blind end of a tubule grows around a blood vessel, giving the impression that the tubule is being invaginated by the blood vessel. By this growth and differentiation, the end of the tubule becomes transformed into a two-layered capsule, the capsule of Bowman, which encloses the glomerulus.

The glomerulus consists of a number of separate capillaries connecting an afferent arteriole with an efferent arteriole; in other words, *the entire vascular system of the glomerulus is arterial.* The afferent vessel is named the *afferent glomerular arteriole;* the efferent vessel is known as the *efferent glomerular arteriole.* These vessels usually lie close together at the point where they enter and leave the glomerulus (Fig. 18-6), and the region where they enter and exit is spoken of as the vascular pole of the renal corpuscle.

As it enters the glomerulus, the afferent arteriole divides into four or five relatively large capillaries. Each of the latter vessels subdivides into a number of smaller capillaries that follow an irregularly looped course in their pathway from the afferent to the efferent arteriole. The looped capillaries arising from each main branch of the afferent arteriole tend to be grouped together, giving the glomerulus a lobulated appearance. Carefully injected preparations show that there are numerous anastomoses between the capillaries within each lobule, as well as occasional anastomoses between those of different lobules. All of the capillaries of the different lobules eventually reunite to form the efferent arteriole, which is always smaller in caliber than is the afferent arteriole. The difference in size correlates with a functional condition: the efferent vessel carries less fluid than the afferent vessel because a considerable quantity of fluid is filtered from the blood while it flows through the glomeru-

as a double walled, cup-shaped expansion known as *Bowman's capsule,* which encloses a tuft of capillaries, the *glomerulus.* Bowman's capsule and the glomerulus together form the *renal* or *Malpighian corpuscle* (Fig. 18-5).

The Renal Corpuscle. The renal corpuscles are spheroidal, slightly flattened bodies that occur in large numbers in the cortical labyrinths (Fig. 18-2). Their diameter in the adult is about 200 μ, although there are considerable variations in size.

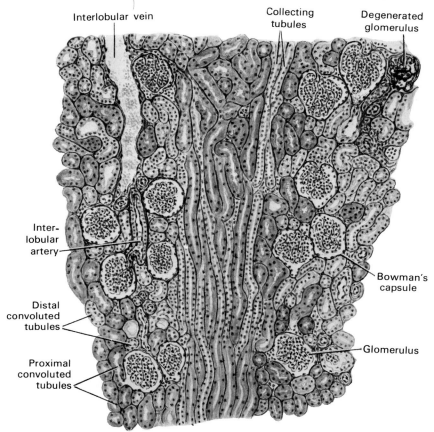

Interlobular vein   Collecting tubules   Degenerated glomerulus

Inter-lobular artery

Distal convoluted tubules

Proximal convoluted tubules

Bowman's capsule

Glomerulus

Fig. 18-3. Section through a part of the cortex of a human kidney, showing the structure of a pars radiata (*central part of figure*) and of adjacent cortical labyrinths (*lateral parts of figure*). ×55.

lar capillaries. A small amount of connective tissue accompanies the arterioles into the renal corpuscle for a short distance at the vascular pole, but connective tissue fibers and the different types of connective tissue cells do not follow the capillaries throughout their course as they do in most other parts of the body. Electron micrographs, however, show a third type of cell (i.e., in addition to endothelium and epithelium) deep within the renal corpuscle (Farquhar and Palade, 1962). These are known as *mesangial cells* (Gr. *mesos*, between, and *angeion*, vessel). They are associated with the basal lamina of glomerular capillaries in a manner similar to that of pericytes on vessels in other locations (Chapter 12).

Bowman's capsule consists of an inner or "visceral" layer covering the glomerulus and an outer or "parietal" layer (Figs. 18-5 and 18-6). The visceral layer follows an irregular course as it closely invests the glomerulus and dips down between the lobules of glomerular capillaries. It is composed of a single layer of epithelial cells resting on a basal lamina which is fused with the basal lamina beneath the endothelium of the capillaries; i.e., visceral epithelium and endothelium are separated merely by a single thin layer. This layer between endothelium and visceral epithelium is often referred to as a basement membrane, but it lacks the lamina reticularis component of basement membranes of most other types of epithelium (Chapter 4). It is more correctly designated *basal lamina* or *basement lamina.* It is also known as a *lamina densa* because it is relatively electron-dense in electron micrographs. The lamina varies in thickness from 0.08 to 0.12 μ, and is observable under the light microscope in sections stained with the periodic acid-Schiff (PAS) technique. It is difficult to identify in hematoxylin-eosin preparations.

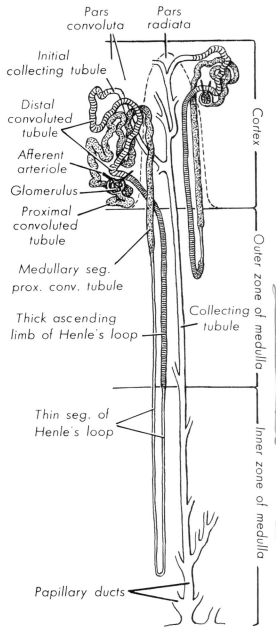

The *endothelial cells of the glomerular capillaries* are extremely thin, with the exception of the regions where the nuclei are located. Most of the endothelial cell cytoplasm extends along the basal lamina in the form of a cribriform plate (lamina fenestra), with pores that measure 0.04 to 0.10 μ in diameter (Fig. 18-7). Most investigators believe that these pores lack diaphragms and that they differ in this respect from those of fenestrated capillaries in other parts of the body. Regardless of whether diaphragms are present, as held by some investigators, it is known from studies in which tracers are used that large molecules (e.g., ferritin) can readily pass through the pores.

The cells of the *visceral layer of Bowman's capsule* are relatively large, and their nuclei bulge into the capsular space. Their cytoplasm is in the form of trabecular processes that subdivide into many small footlike processes (pedicels) which are in contact with the basal lamina (Figs. 18-7 and 18-8). The entire glomerular epithelial cell with its little feet is known as a *podocyte*. The pedicels of different podocytes interdigitate along the basal lamina. The spaces between the pedicels vary in width from about 0.02 to 0.04 μ. There is general agreement, based on studies of high resolution electron micrographs, that the spaces between the pedicels of the podocyte are spanned by a thin, electron-dense line, the *slit membrane.*

As outlined above, the layer of tissue through which substances must pass in moving from blood to provisional urine consists of an endothelium with pores, a relatively thick basal lamina and a visceral epithelium with slits spanned by membranes. Since ferritin, a very large molecule, readily passes through the endothelial pores and enters the basal lamina only very slowly,

FIG. 18-4. Diagram of the subdivisions of the uriniferous tubules to show their relations and locations in a section extending from the capsule to the tip of a renal pyramid. (Redrawn and modified from Peter.)

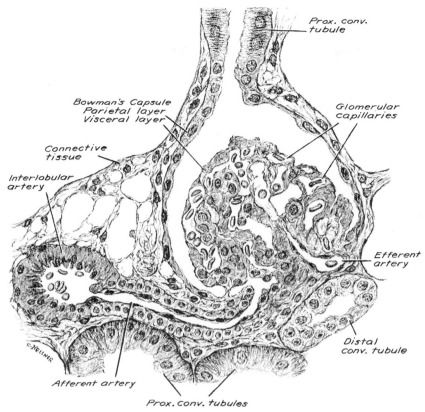

Fig. 18-5. Renal corpuscle from kidney of mouse. ×1320

it was thought that the basal lamina is the chief barrier to the filtration of proteins. Further studies with substances of different molecular weights show that some substances (e.g. myeloperoxidase which has a molecular weight of 160,000) pass through the basal lamina and pile up at the level of the membranes which cover the clefts between the pedicels of the podocytes. Substances of low molecular weight readily pass through all the layers to enter the capsular space. From these results, it appears that the slit membranes act as the ultimate filtration barrier which controls the permeability to proteins on the basis of molecular size.

The *parietal layer of Bowman's capsule* begins where the visceral layer is reflected at the vascular pole (Fig. 18-6). At the urinary pole, usually opposite the vascular

pole, the parietal layer becomes continuous with the wall of the proximal segment of the renal tubule through a short transitional zone which is called the "neck." At this point, the capsular space (Bowman's space) becomes continuous with the lumen of the proximal tubule. The wall of the parietal layer is composed of simple squamous epithelium resting on a thin basal lamina, but the epithelial cells are somewhat thicker than those of the visceral layer. The cells increase in height and become cuboidal in the neck region.

Terminal Uriniferous Tubule. The terminal tubule or nephron consists of an expanded portion, described above as Bowman's capsule, and an elongated tubular portion composed of a proximal thick segment, an intermediate thin segment and a distal thick segment. The proximal thick

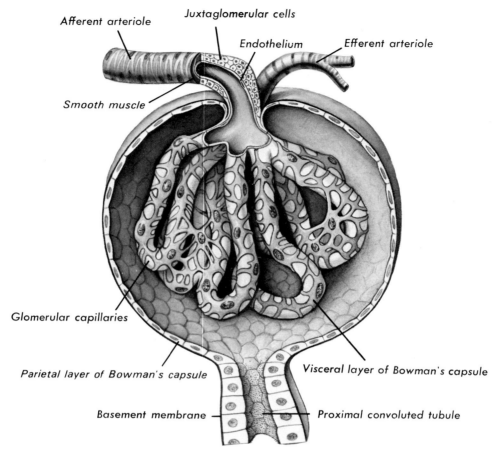

Afferent arteriole

Juxtaglomerular cells

Endothelium

Efferent arteriole

Smooth muscle

Glomerular capillaries

Parietal layer of Bowman's capsule

Visceral layer of Bowman's capsule

Basement membrane

Proximal convoluted tubule

Fig. 18-6. Diagram of structure of renal corpuscle, showing relationship of Bowman's capsule to glomerular capillaries. (Redrawn and modified from Bargmann.)

and distal thick segments can both be subdivided into convoluted and straight portions. Hence, the tubular portion of the nephron is composed of the following segments: (1) the proximal convoluted tubule, (2) the straight or medullary segment of the proximal tubule (this part forms the thick proximal segment of Henle's loop), (3) the thin segment of Henle's loop, (4) the thick distal (ascending) segment of Henle's loop, and (5) the distal convoluted tubule. The latter joins the arched (initial) collecting tubule which begins the system of ducts or collecting tubules.

(1) *The proximal convoluted tubule* is the longest and most convoluted segment

of the nephron, and it forms a major portion of the cortical substance. It has a length of about 14 mm. and a diameter of 57 to 60 μ. It takes a winding, looped course in the vicinity of the glomerulus and eventually turns toward the nearest medullary ray (pars radiata of cortex), where it continues as the straight segment of the proximal tubule.

The proximal convoluted tubule is lined by a single layer of low columnar or pyramidal cells with round nuclei and granular cytoplasm which stains deeply with eosin (Fig. 18-9). The cell boundaries are difficult to make out in ordinary preparations. In silver impregnations, they appear irregularly serrated, with processes which interdigitate with those of adjacent cells.

An important characteristic of the proximal convoluted tubule is the *brush border* at the apical surface of the cells (Fig. 18-9). This region undergoes rapid postmortem change and has a ragged appearance in many histological preparations. Electron micro-

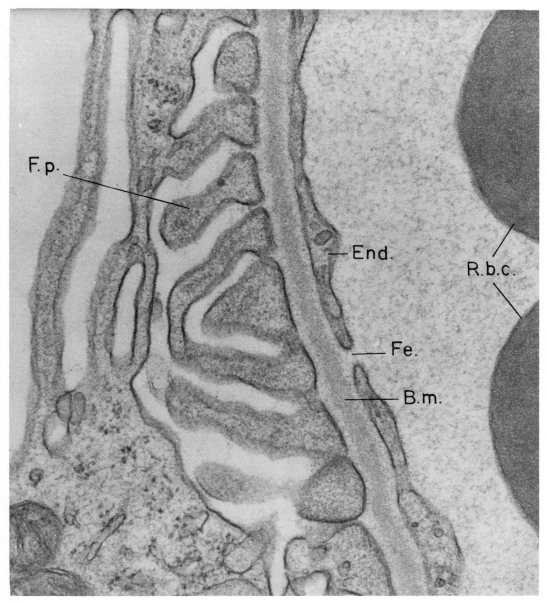

FIG. 18-7. Electron micrograph of a portion of a renal corpuscle of a bat. The glomerular capillary is at *right*, the lumen of Bowman's capsule is at *left*. Portions of two red blood cells (*R.b.c.*) are seen in the capillary, and fenestrae (*Fe.*) are present in the thin endothelial layer of cytoplasm. A continuous basal lamina (*B.m.*) separates the endothelium of the capillary from the epithelium of the visceral layer of Bowman's capsule. The epithelial cells have cytoplasmic processes applied as foot plates (*F.p.*) against the basal lamina. ×57,000. (Courtesy of Dr. Keith Porter.)

graphs of well fixed material show that the brush border is composed of microvilli about 1.2 μ in length and about 0.03 μ in width (Fig. 18-10). The cell surface availa-

ble for resorption is thus greatly increased. Histochemical studies show that the border has a high concentration of alkaline phosphatase and oxidative enzymes. The border

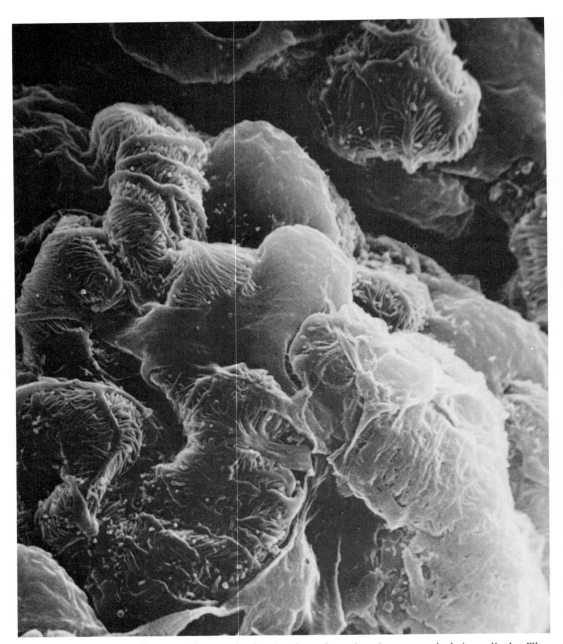

FIG. 18-8. Scanning electron micrograph showing branches of podocytes and their pedicels. The micrograph gives a three dimensional view and shows the interdigitations of pedicels from different branches of different podocytes. ×4,900. (Courtesy of Mr. Edward H. Finke and Dr. Charles Kuhn.)

Distal convoluted tubule   Proximal convoluted tubule

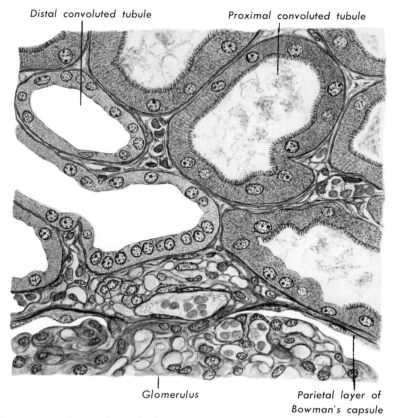

Glomerulus   Parietal layer of
Bowman's capsule

FIG. 18-9. Portion of a glomerulus and adjacent tubules from the cortex of a human kidney. One of the segments of a distal convoluted tubule shows a modification, known as the macula densa, where it borders on the vascular pole of the glomerulus. In this region, there is an increase in the height and number of cells with a concentration of nuclei. ×635. (The slide from which this drawing was made was kindly supplied by Dr. T. E. Hunt.)

also contains mucopolysaccharides, as indicated by its intense staining with the PAS reagent. In electron micrographs, invaginations are often seen between the bases of the microvilli, and vesicles are present in the apical cytoplasm. There is an increase in the number of vesicles and vacuoles during diuresis, and it seems likely that micropinocytosis has a part in tubular resorption. The cytoplasm also contains lysosomes and peroxisomes.

The subnuclear portion of the cell appears striated as a result of involutions of the plasmalemma and the arrangement of mitochondria. Electron micrographs show deep infoldings of the plasmalemma at the base of the cell (Figs. 18-11) and irregular

contours and involutions of the lateral borders. The presence of complex interdigitations of neighboring cells explains why the intercellular boundaries cannot be followed in ordinary preparations under the light microscope. The plasmalemmal infoldings partially subdivide the cell into compartments. The mitochondria are numerous, rod-shaped and oriented within the compartments parallel to the long axis of the cell. It is to be noted that the cell interdigitations are extensive and that processes of different cells alternate along the basal lamina in a manner somewhat like that described above for the pedicels of podocytes.

(2) *The straight or medullary portion*

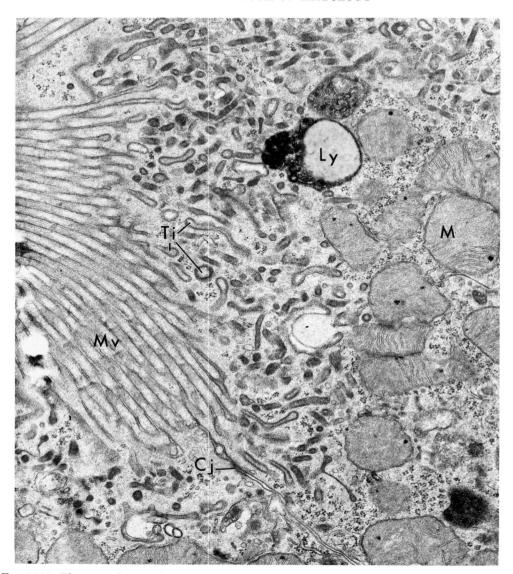

Fig. 18-10. Electron micrograph of adluminal portions of two epithelial cells of a proximal convoluted tubule of a mouse kidney. The adluminal surface of each cell is increased in area by numerous microvilli (*Mv*). Invaginations, arising from clefts between the basal portions of the microvilli, penetrate downward into the cell to form tubular invaginations (*Ti*) that are also known as apical canaliculi. The invaginations become continuous with vesicles in the cytoplasm and they apparently function in the resorption of large molecules, such as proteins. *Cj*, junction of apposing cells; *Ly*, lysosomes; and *M*, mitochondrion. ×23,250. (Courtesy of Drs. K. R. Porter and M. A. Bonneville).

of the proximal tubule is a direct continuation of the convoluted portion of the proximal tubule and is not sharply delimited from it. As the proximal tubule leaves the cortical labyrinth and enters the medullary ray, it assumes first a spiral and then a straight course. This segment is known as the *straight portion* of the proximal tubule because of its course, and it is also named the *medullary segment* of the proximal tubule because it is located in the medullary ray and in the outer, subcortical zone of the medulla (Fig. 18-4). It is lined by cells that appear structurally similar with those of the convoluted portion of the proximal tubule as seen in preparations stained with hematoxylin and eosin; that is, the cells have a brush border, an acidophilic granular

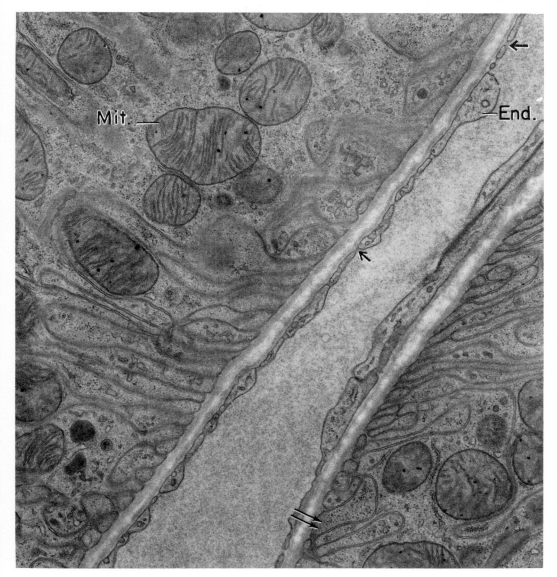

FIG. 18-11. Electron micrograph of the basal portions of epithelial cells of two proximal convoluted tubules and a blood capillary within the connective tissue between the tubules. The plasmalemma of the basal surface of each proximal tubule cell has numerous infoldings which partially partition the cytoplasm of the basal region into cylindrical columns around the mitochondria (*Mit*). Isolated cell processes (*double arrows*) are seen along the basal lamina of each tubule. Processes of different epithelial cells apparently interdigitate along the basal lamina in a manner somewhat like that of podocytes of glomerular epithelium. The endothelial cells (*End*) of the capillaries around the tubules are attenuated and have "pores" or fenestrae (*arrows*). The basal lamina of the endothelium is separated from the basal lamina of the proximal tubule by only a narrow space. Section of a kidney of a bat. ×27,000. (Courtesy of Dr. Keith Porter).

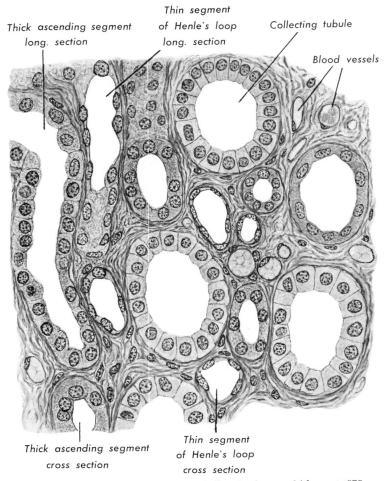

Fig. 18-12. Section from the medulla of a human kidney. ×575

cytoplasm and the other characteristics described for the convoluted segment. By means of special technique, differences have been demonstrated for some laboratory mammals (see Foote and Grafflin, 1942). Electron micrographs also show differences: there is a decrease in the number of microvilli that form the brush border and there are fewer mitochondria.

The straight segment of the proximal tubule forms the proximal portion of the descending arm of Henle's loop (Fig. 18-4). It should be noted that this loop is composed of three parts: a proximal thick segment, a thin segment and a distal thick segment.

(3) *The thin segment of Henle's loop* is about 15 μ in diameter and is lined by a single layer of flattened epithelial cells with nuclei that bulge into the lumen (Fig. 18-12). In the human kidney, the cells of the thin segment are somewhat less flattened than are the endothelial cells of the adjacent blood vessels (Fig. 18-12). The nuclei also differ from those of the endothelium in shape and they stain less intensely in routine hematoxylin and eosin preparations. Electron micrographs show the presence of a few very short microvilli. They also show an abundance of cytoplasm around the nuclei and extremely attenuated regions elsewhere (Fig. 18-13). The cells have fewer

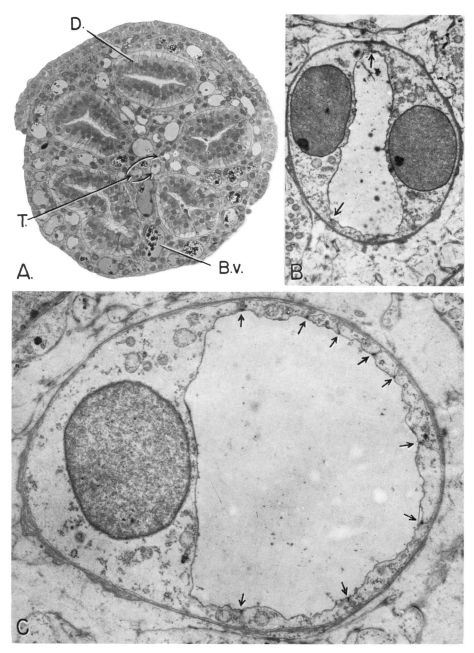

Fig. 18-13. A series of photographs to illustrate the relationships of tubules and blood vessels in the papillary region of the hamster kidney. *A*, photomicrograph of a cross section of a renal papilla with five papillary ducts (*D*), several thin segments of Henle's loop (*T*), and numerous blood vessels (*B.v.*). ×190. *B*, electron micrograph of a cross section of a thin segment from the descending portion of Henle's loop. Contacts between the squamous epithelial cells designated by *arrows*. ×3,700. *C*, electron micrograph of a cross section of a thin segment from the axcending limb. The squamous cells branch extensively, somewhat like the arms of a starfish. The branches interdigitate and are attached to one another by terminal bars at points designated by *arrows*. In some species, including the hamster, the ascending thin segment differs from the descending thin segment. ×5,800. (Figures by courtesy of Dr. Johannes Rhodin.)

mitochondria than those of other segments of the nephron. Electron micrographs of thin sections cut approximately parallel with the basement membrane show that the cells have an irregular starfish outline, with processes of one cell interdigitating with those of another. The change from the columnar cells of the proximal thick segment to the simple squamous epithelial cells of the thin segment is rather abrupt. The change usually occurs in the outer, subcortical zone of the medulla but may occur in a higher level in some of the short loops.

The extent of the thin segment, as well as the length of the entire loop, varies greatly in different tubules (Fig. 18-4). As a rule, the tubules whose Malpighian corpuscles lie near the junction of cortex and medulla have long loops, and their thin segments extend nearly to the apex of the medullary pyramid. In them, the thin segment forms the entire crest of the loop and continues a considerable distance up the ascending limb (Fig. 18-4). On the other hand, tubules associated with glomeruli of the outer part of the cortex have relatively short loops, and their thin segments are limited to a small part of the descending arm (1 to 2 mm. or even less). There are many intermediate types between the two extremes described. The shorter loops with short, thin segments outnumber the longer ones by about seven to one.

(4) *The thick distal (ascending) segment of Henle's loop* is about 9 mm. long and 30 μ in diameter. In the short loops, it may begin in the lower part of the proximal limb (Fig. 18-4). It ascends to the cortex and closely approaches the vascular pole of the glomerulus from which the nephron began. At this point, it becomes continuous with the distal convoluted tubule. It is lined by cuboidal cells which are lower than are those of the thick segment of the proximal limb of the loop. In comparison with the proximal segment, the cells of the distal segment are narrower and therefore their

nuclei appear closer to each other in sections. No brush border is observable under the light microscope, although a few short microvilli can be seen in electron micrographs. There are numerous infoldings of the plasma membrane at the basal part of the cell and the mitochondria are more numerous in the cells of the distal limb than in those of the proximal limb. These are characteristics of cells which function in pumping sodium and they also account for the basal striations seen with the light microscope. Electron micrographs also show numerous infoldings of cell membranes and complex interdigitations along the lower portions of the lateral borders of the cells. This correlates with the fact that the basal portions of the intercellular boundaries are not as apparent under the light microscope as are the apical (adluminal) portions.

(5) The *distal convoluted tubule* begins near the vascular pole of the glomerulus and terminates by becoming continuous with the arched collecting tubule (Fig. 18-4). At one point, it comes in direct contact with the afferent glomerular arteriole (Fig. 18-5). It is much less convoluted than the proximal tubule and is only 4½ to 5 mm. in length. It has an irregular outline, and its diameter varies from 22 to 50 μ. It is lined by cuboidal cells containing a granular cytoplasm which stains less intensely with acid dyes than does the cytoplasm of the proximal convoluted tubules. The basal striations are less pronounced than those of the distal ascending limb, and no brush border is observable under the light microscope. Electron micrographs show fewer mitochondria and less basal infoldings in the cells of the distal convoluted tubule than in the distal ascending limb. The distal convoluted segment resembles the distal ascending limb in that its cells are not as broad as those which line the proximal convoluted tubules, and therefore the nuclei are closer together and more numerous in sections of distal tubules than they are in sections of proximal tubules (Fig. 18-9).

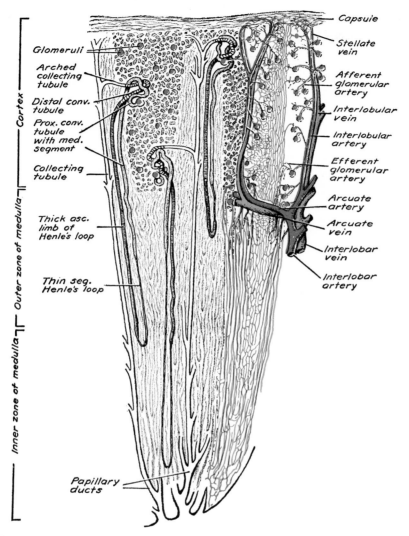

Labels on the figure:

Cortex

Outer zone of medulla

Inner zone of medulla

Glomeruli

Arched collecting tubule

Distal conv. tubule

Prox. conv. tubule with med. segment

Collecting tubule

Thick asc. limb of Henle's loop

Thin seg. Henle's loop

Papillary ducts

Capsule

Stellate vein

Afferent glomerular artery

Interlobular vein

Interlobular artery

Efferent glomerular artery

Arcuate artery

Arcuate vein

Interlobar vein

Interlobar artery

Fig. 18-14. Diagram of the structure of the human kidney. The cortical labyrinth is indicated by the presence of convoluted tubules and glomeruli, and the medullary ray is marked by the parallel arrangement of tubules. The medullary ray with adjacent regions of cortical labyrinths represents the lobule. Note that the straight medullary (*med.*) segment of the proximal tubule forms the upper part of Henle's loop and that these loops extend varying distances into the medulla. The thick ascending (*asc.*) limb of the loop is sometimes subdivided into a proximal opaque portion (stippled) and a distal more clear portion (closely cross-lined). Electron microscope studies show that the portion described by light microscopists as opaque has more mitochondria and more basal infoldings. For clearer illustration, the convoluted tubules are simplified and all segments of the tubules are magnified more in width than in length. (Blood vessels are redrawn and modified from Braus and tubules are modified from Peter.)

The cells of the distal tubules show special cytological characteristics where the tubule comes in contact with the glomerular arterioles. This is also the approximate point at which the distal ascending segment becomes continuous with the distal convoluted portion. In this region, the cells on the side of the tubule adjacent to the afferent arteriole and a portion of the efferent arteriole are taller and more slender than elsewhere in the distal tubules. The nuclei are closer together and the region appears darker under the light microscope; hence, it is named the *macula densa* (Fig. 18-9). The Golgi complex of these cells is in a subnuclear position, in contrast with its supranuclear position in other portions of the tubules. A thin basement membrane is the only structure separating the macula densa cells from the *juxtaglomerular cells* of the afferent arteriole (Fig. 18-15).

The Collecting Tubules. The *arched* (initial) *collecting tubules* are still in the cortical labyrinth and empty into the *straight collecting tubules*. The straight tubules receive a number of arched tubules (seven to 10) as they pass down through the medullary rays of the cortex, but they receive no branches in the outer zone of the medulla (Fig. 18-4). In the inner zone of the medulla, they unite with other straight tubules, and after a number of fusions the *papillary ducts* or *ducts of Bellini* are formed, which open on the area cribrosa of the papilla. According to Peter, seven successive fusions occur before the papillary ducts are formed.

The caliber of the collecting tubule while it is still in the medullary ray is about 40 μ. In the papillary ducts the diameter may exceed 200 μ. The lining of the collecting tubules consists of a single layer of cuboidal or columnar cells with round, darkly staining nuclei and clear, faintly staining cytoplasm (Fig. 18-12). The cell borders are distinct and more obvious than in any of the other portions of the uriniferous tubules. The cytoplasm stains lightly and is less acido-philic than in other segments of the tubules. The cells of the collecting tubule vary in height according to the caliber of the tubule and range from cuboidal in the arched tubules to tall columnar in the papillary ducts.

Light microscope studies of well stained preparations often show dark staining cells interspersed with the more numerous light staining ones, particularly in the upper part of the collecting tubule. The dark staining cells of light microscopy are electron-dense in electron micrographs and they have numerous spherical mitochondria. The light cells have relatively few mitochondria and their basal surfaces are relatively flat in contrast with the invaginations seen in many portions of the nephrons.

The length of the collecting tubule from its beginning in the medullary ray to its opening on the papilla is 20 to 22 mm.; that of the terminal tubule (nephron) is 30 to 38 mm. The entire uriniferous tubule thus measures from 50 to 60 mm., the variations depending mainly on the length of Henle's loop.

A summary of the locations of the various portions of the uriniferous tubules is given in Table 18-1.

The epithelium of all parts of the uriniferous tubule rests on a basement membrane The interstitial connective tissue is scanty in the cortical region but more developed in the medulla (Figs. 18-9 and 18-12). It consists of a fine network of fibers, together with the usual connective tissue cells, chiefly fibroblasts and histiocytes.

BLOOD VESSELS (FIG. 18-14)

The *renal* artery enters the kidney at the hilum and splits into a number of large branches, the *interlobar arteries*. These give off fine twigs to the pelvis and to the capsule; then without further branching they pass between the pyramids to the boundary zone of medulla and cortex. Here they bend sharply and form short arches, the *arcuate* or *arciform arteries*, which run parallel to the surface. The arches do not

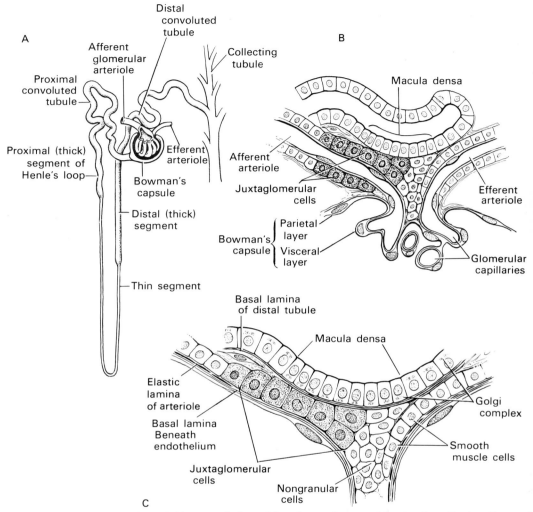

FIG. 18-15. Diagrams of a uriniferous tubule and its glomerular arterioles to show the location and structure of the juxtaglomerular cells and macula densa. *A*, a diagram of the relationship between the glomerular arterioles and the uriniferous tubule at the point where the distal segment of Henle's loop continues into the distal convoluted tubule. *B*, a portion of the region at higher magnification. The *macula densa* in the wall of the distal tubule is apposed to portions of the afferent and efferent glomerular arterioles and is particularly close to the *granular juxtaglomerular cells*. *C*, an enlargement of a portion of *B* showing that the internal elastic membrane of the arteriole and most other connective tissue elements are absent from the region where the macula densa cells and granular juxtaglomerular cells are apposed.

communicate with one another as was formerly believed, each representing merely the curved terminal portion of an interlobar artery. The arcuate arteries break up into a large number of finer branches, the *inter-lobular arteries*, which ascend perpendicularly through the cortical labyrinths to the surface, about midway between adjacent medullary rays. From the interlobular arteries are given off numerous short lateral branches, each of which enters a renal corpuscle as the afferent glomerular vessel

TABLE 18-1

LOCATIONS OF PORTIONS OF URINIFEROUS TUBULES

Location of kidney	Portion of tubule
CORTEX	
Cortical labyrinth	Malpighian corpuscles Proximal convoluted tubules Distal convoluted tubules Arched collecting tubules
Medullary ray	Straight portions (medullary segments) of proximal tubules Thick segments of ascending arms of Henle's loops Straight collecting tubules
MEDULLA	
Outer zone	Straight portions (medullary segments) of proximal tubules Thick segments of ascending arms of Henle's loops Thin segments of Henle's loops Crests of shorter loops Straight collecting tubules
Inner zone	Thin segments of Henle's loops Crests of long loops Straight collecting tubules Fusions of straight collecting tubules Papillary ducts

and subdivides as described above under "The Renal Corpuscle." Often the short branches subdivide and supply a cluster of glomeruli. On reaching the periphery of the cortex, the terminal portions of most interlobular arteries themselves become afferent glomerular vessels.

As the afferent glomerular arteriole approaches the glomerulus, some of its muscle cells are overlaid with or partly replaced by *myoepithelioid* cells that form part of a juxtaglomerular complex. The *juxtaglomerular complex* consists of *juxtaglomerular* (JG) *cells* (granular and nongranular) in the wall of the afferent arteriole, a group of so-called *polkissen cells*, between the afferent and efferent arterioles at the vascular pole of the renal corpuscle, and the *macula densa* of the distal tubule. The polkissen cells have an agranular, pale staining cytoplasm. They resemble the *nongranular juxtaglomerular cells* in the wall of the arteriole. The function of the polkissen

and nongranular JG cells and their functional relationship to the granular JG cells are obscure. The *granular juxtaglomerular cells*, together with a few nongranular cells, form a collar or *juxtaglomerular cushion* on the afferent arteriole. They replace the smooth muscle cells of the tunica media in this part of the vessel (Fig. 18-15). They are separated from the blood in the afferent arteriole only by endothelium and a basal lamina. Their opposite poles are separated from macula densa cells of the distal tubule only by a thin basal lamina. The close anatomical relationship of the JG and macula densa cells lends support to the view that they are in functional intercommunication. The granular JG cells have cytoplasmic granules which are readily seen under the light microscope in preparations treated with PAS or with Bowie's ethyl violet. Electron micrographs show the granules as electron-dense and membrane-bound. There is evidence that they contain acid phosphatase and that they qualify as lysosomes. It has been known for many years that the kidney secretes a proteolytic enzyme known as *renin,* and more recent evidence indicates that renin is secreted by the JG granular cells. Renin acts on a specific substrate in the blood stream that leads to the formation of *angiotensin,* which produces a general vasoconstriction. The elevated blood pressure produced by this substance is known as renal *hypertension.*

The efferent glomerular arteriole, immediately after leaving the corpuscle, divides into a *second* system of capillaries, the *peritubular plexus,* which forms a dense network around the tubules of the cortex (Fig. 18-14). So densely are the capillaries arranged that the tubules seem bathed in blood.

Nonglomerular arterioles may be found extending directly from an afferent arteriole to the peritubular plexus. Known as Ludwig's arterioles, they are infrequent in normal kidneys and are said to arise from a continuity of afferent and efferent vessels following glomerular degeneration (Mac-Callum).

The arterial supply of the medulla is furnished by the efferent glomerular vessels of those renal corpuscles which lie close to the medulla (Fig. 18-14). These vessels, the *arteriolae rectae spuriae,* pursue a straight course into the outer layer of the medulla and give rise to long-meshed capillary nets that extend to the apex of the pyramids. The *arteriolae rectae* and *venae rectae* together with their capillary loops are known as the *vasae rectae.* Although the vessels which form the loops have a wider lumen than that of ordinary capillaries, they have very thin walls. The hairpin loops of vessels are closely associated with the loops of Henle, and the endothelium of many of these vessels is of the attenuated (fenestrated) type. Numerous investigations have shown that the blood supply of the medulla comes mainly from the efferent glomerular vessels. The so-called arteriolae rectae verae, which

extend directly from the arcuate arteries into the medulla, are few in number and probably arise following the degeneration of glomeruli that previously existed along their course.

The blood from the peripheral portion of the cortex is collected into small venules that unite beneath the capsule to form the *stellate veins of Verheyen.* From these arise the *interlobular veins,* which accompany the corresponding arteries and empty into the arcuate veins. The latter also receive short interlobular veins from the deeper portions of the cortex. Straight veins, the *venae rectae,* collect the blood from the capillary nets of the medulla and accompany the straight arteries, to terminate in the *arcuate veins.* The venous arches, unlike the arterial ones, combine with one another to form venous arcades. From the arcuate veins the large *interlobar veins* pass down between the medullary pyramids and unite to form the renal vein.

In addition to the distribution just described, some interlobular arteries on reaching the periphery of the cortex break up into capillaries that supply the fibrous capsule of the kidney. These anastomose with capillaries from the suprarenal, lumbar and phrenic arteries and with those of the capsular twigs which arise directly from the renal artery or its interlobar branches.

Arteriovenous anastomoses have been described at various levels: between interlobar arteries and veins, between arcuate arteries and veins and between interlobular arteries and veins.

LYMPHATICS

The lymph capillaries are arranged in two systems: a superficial system which ramifies in the capsule, and a deeper system which lies in the glandular tissue. The capsular lymph is collected by superficial lymph vessels that communicate with the lymphatics of adjacent organs. The lymph from the parenchyma is collected by a number of lymphatic trunks which accompany the blood vessels. They leave the kidney at the hilum to enter lymph nodes that are situated on both sides of the aorta.

NERVES

The kidneys are richly supplied with nerves, the majority of which are unmyelinated. They are derived from the celiac plexus and from the 10th to the 12th thoracic nerves. It is probable that branches from the vagus also supply the kidney. The non-myelinated fibers follow the blood vessels and terminate by numerous endings in the vascular wall, particularly in the glomerular arterioles. Delicate terminals have been described as ramifying in the basement membrane of the tubules or even between the epithelial cells. Sensory myelinated fibers go to the capsule, the smooth muscle of the pelvis and the adventitia of the renal vessels.

THE EXCRETION OF URINE

The kidney has several important functions. It excretes urea and other nitrogenous waste products, it eliminates substances foreign to the body and it maintains the constant volume of the blood by the elimination of excess water. It is important to note that water and other substances needed by the body are eliminated only to the extent that they exceed the needs; in other words, the kidneys conserve the proper amounts of water, electrolytes and other chemicals of value to the body.

By maintaining the constituents of blood plasma at normal values, the kidneys play an important role in regulating the chemical composition of the extracellular fluid which is the internal environment for the cells and tissues of the body. The kidneys share the regulation of the internal environment with the lungs, which control the levels of oxygen and carbon dioxide.

The kidneys perform their functions by (1) filtration of blood plasma in the glomeruli, (2) selective reabsorption by the tubules of substances which the body needs to retain, (3) active excretion by the tubules of certain substances to be added to the urine, and (4) exchange of hydrogen ions and formation of ammonia as part of the process of acid base regulation.

The renal corpuscles have a number of structural features that facilitate filtration. The presence of glomerular capillaries between afferent and efferent arterioles rather than between arterioles and venules provides for a glomerular capillary blood pressure of about 75 mm. Hg. This is higher than the pressure in other capillaries, and it is more than sufficient to overcome the factors which oppose filtration (osmotic pressure of the blood plasma, renal interstitial pressure and resistance to flow in the tubule). A large surface area for filtration is provided by the number of tortuous capillary loops in each glomerulus and by the large number of glomeruli (over 2,000,000 for the two kidneys). The filtration surface has been estimated as 5200 to 5860 sq. mm. per gram of human kidney (Kirkman and Stowell, 1942). The layer of tissue between the blood and the lumen of the upper, expanded end of the nephron consists of a fenestrated endothelium, a basal lamina and the processes of the podocytes (Fig. 18-7). Filtration through this layer is a physical process and depends on the pressure within the glomerular capillaries, the condition of the filtering membrane and the nature of the blood plasma.

The *capsular* or *provisional* urine is an ultrafiltrate of plasma and contains unchanged all of the constituents of plasma with the exception of all but a trace of the plasma proteins, fat droplets and blood cells, which are unable to pass through the normal filtration barrier because of their molecular weight or size. Direct evidence that the provisional urine is a filtrate of plasma was established by chemical analysis of capsular urine withdrawn by micropipette from the renal corpuscles of amphibians (Richards, 1935). Although it is more difficult to apply the micropipette method to the mammalian kidney, studies of this type have been made, with results essentially similar to those obtained on amphibians (Walker et al., 1941).

Procedures for determining the rates at which different substances are "cleared" from the blood by excretion into the urine have contributed greatly to our knowledge of the function of the human kidney (Smith, 1951). Para-aminohippuric acid (PAH) and the polysaccharide inulin are particularly useful chemicals for clearance studies. PAH is filtered in the glomeruli and is eliminated in addition by tubular excretion. It is cleared completely from the plasma in one passage through the kidney when injected in low concentrations. Therefore, by measuring the amount of PAH in the urine in a unit of time and knowing the initial concentration in the plasma, one can readily calculate the renal blood flow. By this method, it has been found that the average normal flow through the two kidneys is about 1200 cc. per minute, or about 1700 liters of whole blood in a 24-hour period.

Inulin is eliminated solely by glomerular filtration, and none is reabsorbed in the tubules. Therefore, by simultaneous measurements of the plasma level of inulin and the amount of inulin excreted in the urine in a unit of time, one can calculate the glomerular filtration rate. Studies of this type show that about 170 liters of fluid are filtered daily through the two kidneys under normal conditions.

The 170 liters of capsular or provisional urine become concentrated to 1 liter or less of actual urine and become altered in composition by the resorption of water and other constituents during passage through the uriniferous tubule. In the process of resorption, substances pass through the tubular epithelium to the surrounding connective tissue and thence to the peritubular capillaries and venules. The proximal tubules and their capillaries come into close association at many points where only a minimal amount of connective tissue separates the basal lamina of the tubular epithelium from that of the capillary endothelium (Fig. 18-11). Although some resorption occurs by diffusion through the tubular epithelium, the resorption of most substances is dependent upon work done by the cells.

Resorption has been studied by a variety of methods. Samples of tubular urine have been withdrawn by micropipette in amphibians (Richards, 1935) and in mammals (Walker et al., 1941; Wirz, 1956; and Gottschalk and Myle, 1959). Knowing that the excretion of inulin is a measure of glomerular filtration, one can also gain information on tubular function by comparing the clearance rate of any given substance with that of inulin; for example, the clearance of a substance at a rate higher than that for inulin indicates tubular excretion in addition to glomerular filtration, whereas clearance at a lower rate indicates tubular resorption. Another method consists of stop-flow experiments (Malvin, Wilde and Sullivan, 1958; and Pitts et al., 1958). In this case, the ureter is blocked for several minutes and then opened for the collection of urine samples in series. It is assumed that the first samples come from the more distal portions of the nephron and the later samples from more proximal portions. The study of the functional activity of thin slices from different regions of the kidney in solutions of known composition has been a valuable method for analyzing factors involved in active transport (Forster and Taggart, 1950; and Taggart, 1958).

Resorption in the proximal convoluted tubules is facilitated by the extensive surface area provided by the convolutions of the tubule and by the multitude of closely packed, slender processes that form the brush border. Surface area is only one of many factors affecting resorption, however. A partial list of other factors includes the types of enzymes at the cell borders as well as within the cells, the complexity and arrangement of mitochondria, infoldings at the basal ends of the cells, the relations of the resorbing cells to the capillaries, the osmotic pressures within the peritubular connective tissue, the presence of certain hormones within the blood and the concentration of the substance in question within the blood plasma. For example, glucose is completely resorbed in the proximal tubule under normal conditions and is maintained in the blood plasma at a definite level which is known as its threshold value. When the plasma glucose level exceeds its threshold value, as in diabetes mellitus, the amount of glucose filtered by the renal corpuscle exceeds the resorptive capacity of the tubule, and glucose appears in the urine. A comparison of the resorption of glucose with that of urea illustrates the selectivity involved. Urea and other protein wastes are destined to be completely eliminated. They have no threshold values in the blood and are resorbed only passively or not at all.

About 80 % of the sodium and water filtered from the blood in the renal corpuscle is resorbed in the proximal tubule. Sodium, like glucose, is moved from the lumen of the tubule to the peritubular capillaries by an active process, i.e., by work on the part of the cells. This establishes an osmotic force favoring the passive diffusion of water, chlorides and bicarbonates in the same direction. Since salts and water are resorbed together in the proximal convoluted tubules, the provisional urine is reduced in volume in this segment of the nephron without any change in osmolality. The urine entering the descending limb of Henle's loop is isosmotic with the surrounding connective tissue and with blood plasma.

The appearance of thin segments in birds and mammals during phylogenesis allows these forms to secrete hypertonic urine and conserve water. In the process of conserving water, there are marked changes in the osmolality of the provisional urine along the course of Henle's loops in correlation with differences in the osmolality of the interstitial connective tissue at different levels of the medulla. There is a progressive increase in the hypertonicity of the urine as it passes down the thin segment of the descending limb, and a progressive decrease in hypertonicity as it passes up the ascending limb, becoming hypotonic in the upper part of the ascending limb and hypertonic again in the collecting tubules. The intertubular connective tissue of the medulla also becomes progressively more hypertonic toward the papilla of the pyramids, in contrast with renal cortical tissue, which is isosmotic. Likewise, blood collected from capillaries of the papillary regions of the medulla is hypertonic to systemic blood. The progressive loss of hypertonicity as the urine passes up the ascending limb results from the active pumping of sodium out of the thick ascending segment through an epithelium impermeable to water. By the pumping of sodium without water, the intertubular tissue becomes hypertonic. Some of the sodium reenters the thin descending limb of Henle's loop, probably by diffusion, and recirculates through the loop, to be pumped out again without water in the ascending limb. This provides a countercurrent multiplier effect. The increased osmolality of the connective tissue also provides for resorption of water by diffusion from the collecting tubules when the epithelium of these segments becomes water-permeable under the influence of the antidiuretic hormone (ADH) from the neurohypophysis. Although solutes and fluids pass from the connective tissue to the blood vessels, the hypertonic state of the connective tissue is maintained by the countercurrent multiplier effect in Henle's loops as noted above and also by a countercurrent exchange between the ascending and descending limbs of the neighboring capillary loops of the vasae rectae.

In the distal convoluted tubule there is further resorption of sodium, accompanied in this case by water. The permeability of the epithelium of the distal convoluted tubule and of the collecting tubule is controlled by ADH. A deficiency or lack of ADH produces a type of diuresis known as *diabetes insipidus*. In this condition, water cannot diffuse from the collecting tubules into the hypertonic connective tissue of the medulla. This differs from diabetes mellitus, in which diuresis may occur as an accompaniment to an increase of solute (glucose) in the urine. Resorption of sodium from the distal convoluted tubule is under the influence of the mineralocorticoid, aldosterone, which is formed in the adrenal cortex.

For further details on countercurrent factors in kidney function, reference may be made to textbooks of physiology and to an excellent account by Pitts (1968).

THE RENAL PELVIS AND URETER

The renal pelvis with its subdivisions (the calyces) and the ureter constitute the *main excretory duct* of the kidney. The walls of the renal pelvis and ureter consist of three coats: an inner mucous, a middle muscular and an outer fibrous.

The *mucosa* of the ureter is lined by transitional epithelium which varies in thickness, depending on the state of distension of the ureter (Fig. 4-14). In the collapsed state, the cells of the basal layers are cuboidal, almost columnar. The superficial layer consists of large cuboidal cells with lighter cytoplasm, often containing two or more nuclei. A basement membrane is not discernible with the light microscope, but a basal lamina and a thin lamina reticularis can be seen in electron micrographs. Diffuse lymphatic tissue frequently occurs in the lamina propria, especially of the pelvis. Occasionally the lymphatic tissue takes the form of small nodules. There is no distinct submucosa, although the outer part of the stroma is sometimes referred to as such.

The *muscularis* consists of an inner longitudinal and an outer circular layer (Fig. 18-16). In the lower part of the ureter,

a discontinuous outer longitudinal layer is added.

The *fibrosa* consists of loosely arranged connective tissue and contains many large blood vessels. It is not sharply limited externally but blends with the connective tissue of surrounding structures and serves to attach the ureter to the latter.

The larger *blood vessels* run in the fibrous coat. From these, branches pierce the muscular layer, give rise to a capillary network among the muscle cells and then pass to the mucosa, in the stroma of which they break up into a rich network of capillaries. The veins follow the arteries.

The *lymphatics* follow the blood vessels, being especially numerous in the stroma of the mucosa.

Plexuses of both myelinated and nonmyelinated *nerve fibers* occur in the walls of the ureter and pelvis. The nonmyelinated fibers pass mainly to the cells of the muscularis. Myelinated fibers enter the mucosa, where they lose their myelin sheaths. Terminals of these fibers have been traced to the lining epithelium.

THE URINARY BLADDER

Except for the increased thickness of the muscular coat, the walls of the bladder are similar in structure to those of the ureter. The mucous membrane is thrown up into folds or is comparatively smooth, according to the degree of distention of the organ. The epithelium is of the same general type—transitional—as that of the ureter and, as already described for the ureter, the surface cells may have two or more nuclei. The ultrastructural characteristics of transitional epithelium are shown in Fig. 18-18 and they are discussed in some detail in the Section on "Transitional Epithelium" in Chapter 4. The number of layers of cells and the shapes of the cells depend largely upon whether the bladder is full or empty. In the moderately distended bladder, the superficial cells become flatter and the entire epithelium thinner than in the contracted

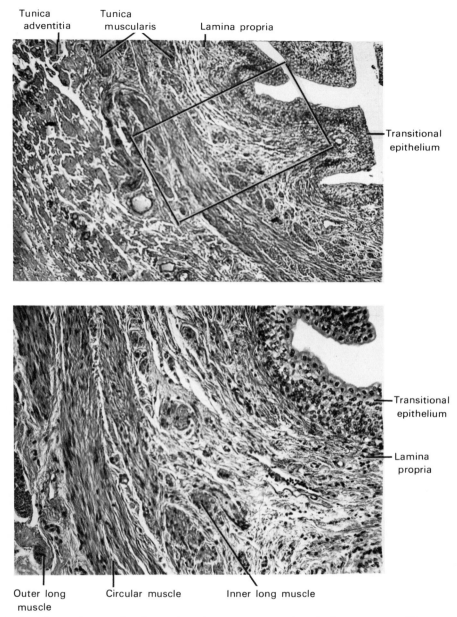

Tunica adventitia

Tunica muscularis

Lamina propria

Transitional epithelium

Transitional epithelium

Lamina propria

Outer long muscle

Circular muscle

Inner long muscle

FIG. 18-16. Photomicrographs of a portion of a transverse section of a human ureter. The area outlined in the *upper* figure is shown at higher magnification in the *lower* figure. The inner and outer longitudinally (long) oriented smooth muscle fibers do not form continuous layers. Upper figure, ×60; *lower* ×145.

organ. In the distended organ, there is still further flattening of the superficial cells, and the entire epithelium may have a thickness of only two or three cells. The stroma consists of fine, loosely arranged connective

tissue containing many lymphocytes and sometimes small lymph nodules. There is no distinct submucosa and, as in the ureter, there are no glands.

The three muscular layers of the lower

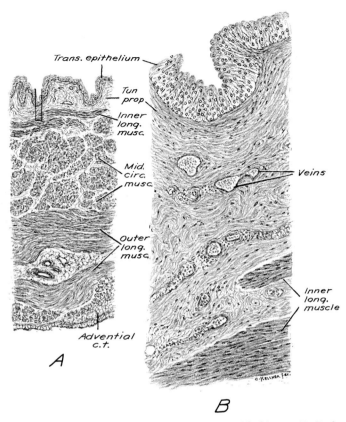

FIG. 18-17. *A*, section through the wall of a contracted human bladder. ×12. *B*, drawing of the region outlined by solid line in *A*. ×100. *Inner long. musc*, inner longitudinal muscle; *Mid. circ. musc*, middle layer of circular muscle; *Outer long. musc.* outer layer of longitudinal muscle; *Tun. prop*, tunica propria; *Trans.*, transitional; *c.t.*, connective tissue.

part of the ureter continue onto the bladder, where the muscle bundles of the different layers interlace and anastomose but can still be indistinctly differentiated into an inner longitudinal, a middle circular and an outer longitudinal layer (Fig. 18-17).

The fibrous layer, which is similar to that of the ureter, attaches the organ to the surrounding structures.

The blood and lymph vessels have a distribution similar to that in the ureter.

Sensory myelinated nerve fibers pierce the muscularis, branch repeatedly in the stroma, lose their myelin sheaths and terminate among the cells of the lining epithelium. Sympathetic fibers form plexuses in the fibrous coat, where they are inter-

spersed with numerous small groups of ganglion cells. Axons of these sympathetic neurons penetrate the muscularis. Here they form plexuses, from which terminals are given off to the individual muscle cells.

THE URETHRA

The male and female urethrae differ from each other in many respects. The short female urethra is merely the terminal urinary passage conducting urine from the bladder to the vestibule. The relatively long male urethra constitutes a urogenital duct conducting both urine and seminal fluid to the exterior.

The Male Urethra. The male urethra has a length of about 20 cm. and is divisible into three portions, prostatic, membranous and cavernous. The *prostatic portion*, about 3 to 4 cm. in length, is surrounded by the prostate gland. From the dorsal wall of this portion a conical elevation, the *colliculus seminalis*, extends into the lumen. On the apex of the colliculus is the small opening of a blind tubule, the *utriculus prostaticus* or

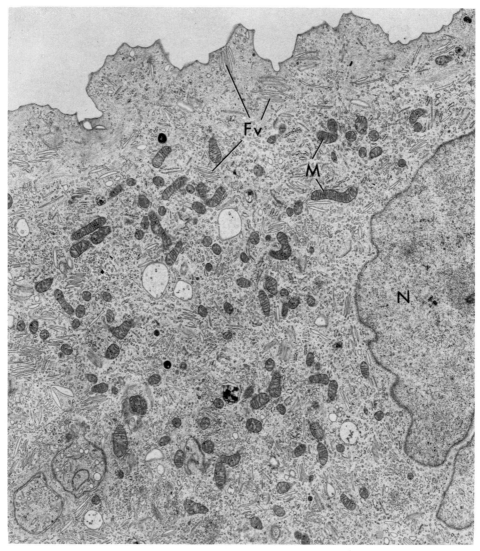

Fig. 18-18. Electron micrograph of a portion of a surface cell of transitional epithelium of the urinary bladder. The inner surface has an irregular contour, showing a number of crests and hollows. The cytoplasm just beneath the adluminal surface contains a meshwork of fine filaments but is generally free of mitochondria (*M*). Fusiform vesicles (*Fv*) are found throughout the cytoplasm of the surface cells. They are lined by trilaminar membranes similar to the plasmalemma. Electron micrographs of sections of bladders fixed after intraluminal injection of marker substances (e.g. ferritin) show the marker within the fusiform vesicles. The latter apparently form by a pinching off of trough-like depressions from the surface into the underlying cytoplasm. *N*, nucleus. From a section of the urinary bladder of a mouse. ×8,650. (Courtesy of Drs. K. R. Porter and M. A. Bonneville).

uterus masculinus, a remnant of the Müllerian duct. On either side of the utricle are the slitlike openings of the ejaculatory ducts, the terminal portions of the ductus deferens (see Chapter 19 on the male reproductive system). Also in this part of the urethra are the numerous small openings of the ducts of the prostate gland.

The *membranous* portion is the narrowest and shortest, measuring about 1 cm. in length.

The *cavernous* portion is about 15 cm. long and extends through the penis to open on the end of the glans. At its beginning, the lumen is enlarged to form the *bulb* of the urethra. Then it continues with a uniform diameter to the glans penis, where the lumen is again enlarged in a dorsoventral direction and is known as the *fossa navicu-*

laris. Throughout its course this portion is surrounded by a cylindrical mass of erectile tissue, the *corpus spongiosum* or *corpus cavernosum urethrae* (Figs. 18-19 and 19-28).

The structure of the mucous membrane varies in the different portions. The prostatic urethra is lined by a transitional epithelium similar to that of the bladder. In the membranous and cavernous portions, the epithelium is stratified columnar or pseudostratified, up to the fossa navicularis. There it changes to stratified squamous which, at the external urethral opening, becomes continuous with the epidermis of the skin. More or less extensive areas of stratified squamous epithelium are often seen throughout the whole course of the urethra.

The epithelium rests on a thin basement

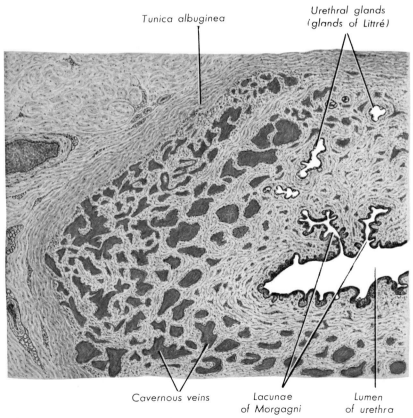

Tunica albuginea

Urethral glands
(glands of Littré)

Cavernous veins

Lacunae
of Morgagni

Lumen
of urethra

FIG. 18-19. Transverse section of a part of the cavernous portion of the urethra. See Figure 19-28 for lower magnification, showing complete section of penis. ×19.

membrane, beneath which is a stroma of loose connective tissue rich in elastic fibers and containing in its deeper portion a plexus of capillaries and thin walled veins. Smooth muscle fibers, both longitudinally and circularly disposed, are found in the prostatic and membranous portions. A definite submucosa cannot be distinguished.

The prostatic urethra is surrounded by the fibromuscular tissue of the prostate which, under ordinary conditions, keeps the urethral lumen closed. The membranous portion is encircled by a sphincter of skeletal muscle fibers from the deep transverse perineal muscle.

The mucosa of the cavernous portion contains very little muscle and is surrounded by a cylindrical mass of erectile tissue, the corpus spongiosum. The latter consists of a network of large, irregular, venous spaces, or lacunae, which are lined by endothelium and are separated from each other by trabeculae of fibroelastic tissue containing numerous smooth muscle fibers running both longitudinally and circularly. These lacunae connect with the plexus of veins in the mucosal stroma. The corpus spongiosum is enclosed in a connective tissue capsule containing numerous elastic fibers and, on its inner surface, smooth muscle cells.

The lumen of the urethra shows a number of deep, irregular outpocketings, the *lacunae of Morgagni*. The lacunae continue into branched tubular glands, the *glands of Littré*, which extend deep into the stroma and may even penetrate into the corpus

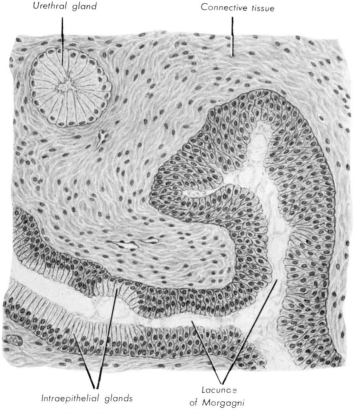

FIG. 18-20. Section through the dorsal portion of the corpus cavernosum urethrae, showing clear, mucous-secreting cells in a tubule of the urethral glands (glands of Littré) and groups of similar cells (intraepithelial glands) in the lacunae of Morgagni. ×294.

spongiosum. They are most numerous in the dorsal part of the cavernous portion of the urethra (Figs. 18-19 and 18-20). Most of the cells lining the gland tubules are clear staining, mucous secreting cells. Isolated mucous cells or groups of them (intraepithelial glands) are likewise found interspersed in the epithelium lining the lacunae of Morgagni.

The Female Urethra. The female urethra is a short tube 3 to 5 cm. long. The epithelium varies considerably in different individuals. Near the bladder it is usually transitional. The remainder of the urethra is lined mainly by stratified squamous epithelium, with areas of stratified columnar or pseudostratified epithelium. The mucosa is thrown into longitudinal folds. Glands of Littré, although fewer in number than in the male, open into the lacunae between the folds.

The abundant stroma is rich in elastic fibers and contains a plexus of numerous thin walled veins.

The rather indefinite muscularis contains both longitudinal and circular smooth muscle fibers, many of which penetrate into the stroma between the veins. An outer layer of skeletal muscle fibers forms a urethral sphincter.

A definite fibrosa is absent, the outer connective tissue fusing with that of the vagina.

DEVELOPMENT OF THE URINARY SYSTEM

The development of the urinary system is closely associated with that of the reproductive system. The formation of these systems is given at the end of Chapter 20.

REFERENCES

AJZEN, H., SIMMONS, J. L., AND WOODS, J. W. 1965 Renal vein renin and juxtaglomerular activity in sodium-depleted subjects. Circl. Res., vol. 17, pp. 130–134.

BARAJAS, L., AND LATTA, H. 1967 Structure of the juxtaglomerular apparatus. Circ. Res., vol. 21, suppl. 2, pp. 15–28.

BULGER, R. G. 1965 The shape of rat kidney tubular cells. Amer. J. Anat., vol. 116, pp. 237–255.

EDWARDS, J. G. 1928 Studies of aglomerular and glomerular kidneys. Amer. J. Anat., Vol. 42, pp. 75–108.

ELIAS, H. 1956 The renal glomerulus by light and electron microscopy. In Research in the Service of Medicine, vol. 46, pp. 3–29. G. D. Searle and Company, Chicago.

FARQUHAR, M. G., AND PALADE, G. E. 1962 Functional evidence for the existence of a third cell type in the renal glomerulus. Phagocytosis of filtration residues by a distinctive "third" cell type. J. Cell Biol., vol. 13, pp. 55–87.

FARQUHAR, M. S., WISSIG, S. L., AND PALADE G. E. 1961 Glomerular permeability I. Ferritin transfer across the normal glomerular capillary wall. J. Exp. Med., vol. 113, pt. 1, pp. 47–66.

FISHER, E. R. 1966 Lysosomal nature of juxtaglomerular granules. Science, vol. 152, pp. 1752–1753.

FOOTE, J. J., AND GRAFFLIN, A. L. 1942 Cell contours in the two segments of the proximal tubule in the cat and dog nephron. Amer. J. Anat., vol. 70, pp. 1–20.

FORSTER, R. P. 1961 Kidney cells. In The Cell; Biochemistry, Physiology, Morphology (Brachet, J. and Mirsky, A. E., editors), vol. 5, pp. 89–161. Academic Press, New York.

FORSTER, R. P., AND TAGGART, J. V. 1950 Use of isolated renal tubules for the examination of metabolic processes associated with active cellular transport. J. Cell. Comp. Physiol., vol. 36, pp. 251–270.

GERSH, I. 1934 Histochemical studies on the mammalian kidney. II. The glomerular elimination of uric acid in the rabbit. Anat. Rec., vol. 58, pp. 369–385.

GOTTSCHALK, C. W., AND MYLLE, M. 1959 Micropuncture study on the mammalian urinary concentrating mechanism: evidence for the countercurrent hypothesis. Amer. J. Physiol., vol. 196, pp. 927–936.

GRAHAM, R. C., AND KARNOVSKY, M. J. 1966 The early stage of absorption of injected horseradish peroxidase in the proximal convoluted tubules of mouse kidney: ultrastructural cytochemistry by a new technique. J. Histochem. Cytochem., vol. 14, pp. 291–302.

HALL, V. 1955 Further studies of the normal structure of the renal glomerulus. Proc. of Sixth Ann. Conf. on Nephrotic Syndrome, National Nephrosis Foundation, New York.

HATT, P.-Y. 1967 The juxtaglomerular apparatus. In Ultrastructure of the Kidney (Dalton,

A. J., and Haguenau, F., editors), pp. 101–141. Academic Press, New York.

HICKS, R. M. 1965 The fine structure of the transitional epithelium of rat ureter. J. Cell Biol., vol. 26, pp. 25–48.

HUBER, G. C. 1932 Renal tubules. In Special Cytology (Cowdry, E., editor), vol. 2, pp. 933–976.

KIRKMAN, H., AND STOWELL, R. E. 1942 Renal filtration surface in the albino rat. Anat. Rec., vol. 82, pp. 373–392.

LATTA, H., MAUNSBACH, A. B., AND OSVALDO, L. 1967 The fine structure of renal tubules in cortex and medulla. In Ultrastructure of the Kidney (Dalton, A. J., and Haguenau, F., editors), pp. 2–56. Academic Press, New York.

MACCALLUM, D. B. 1939 The bearing of degenerating glomeruli on the problem of the vascular supply of the mammalian kidney. Amer. J. Anat., vol. 65, pp. 69–93.

MALVIN, R. L., WILDE, W. S., AND SULLIVAN, L. P. 1958 Localization of nephron transport by stop flow analysis. Amer. J. Physiol., vol. 194, pp. 135–142.

MÖLLENDORFF, W. V. 1930 Der Exkretionsapparat. Handb. mikr. Anat. Menschen. (v. Möllendorff, editor), vol. 7, pt. 1, pp. 1–328. Springer-Verlag, Berlin.

MONIS, B., AND DORFMAN, H. D. 1967 Some histochemical observations on transitional epithelium of man. J. Histochem. Cytochem., vol. 15, pp. 475–481.

MONIS, B., AND ZAMBRANO, D. 1968 Ultrastructure of transitional epithelium of man. Z. Zellforsch., vol. 87, pp. 101–117.

OLIVER, J. 1944 New directions in renal morphology: a method, its results and its future. Harvey Lectures, Ser. 40, pp. 102–155.

PEASE, D. C. 1955 Fine structure of the kidney seen by electron microscopy. J. Histochem., vol. 3, pp. 295–308.

PETER, K. 1927 Untersuchungen über Bau und Entwicklung der Niere. Fischer, Jena.

PITTS, R. F. 1968 Physiology of the kidney and body fluids; an introductory text. Year Book Medical Publishers, Chicago.

RHODIN, J. 1958 Electron microscopy of the kidney. Amer. J. Med., vol. 24, pp. 661–675.

RHODIN, J. A. G. 1962 Electron microscopy of the kidney. In Renal Disease (Black, D. A. K., editor). Blackwell Scientific Publications, Ltd. Oxford.

RHODIN, J. A. G. 1962 The diaphragm of capillary endothelial fenestrations. J. Ultrastruct. Res., vol. 6, pp. 171–185.

RICHARDS, A. N. 1935 Urine formation in the amphibian kidney. Harvey Lectures, Ser. 30, pp. 93–118.

SMITH, H. W. 1951 The Kidney: Structure and Function in Health and Disease. Oxford University Press, New York.

SMITH, H. W. 1956 Principles of Renal Physiology. Oxford University Press, New York.

STRAUS, W. 1964 Cytochemical observations on the relationship between lysosomes and phagosomes in kidney and liver by combined staining for acid phosphatase and intravenously injected horseradish peroxidase. J. Cell Biol., vol. 20, pp. 497–507.

TAGGART, J. V. 1958 Mechanisms of renal tubular transport. Amer. J. Med., vol. 24, pp. 774–784.

TRUETA, R. J. 1948 Studies of the Renal Circulation. Charles C Thomas, Publisher, Springfield, Ill.

TRUMP, B. F., AND BULGER, R. E. 1968 Morphology of the Kidney. In Structural Basis of Renal Disease (Becker, E. L., editor), pp. 1–92. Hoeber Medical Division, Harper & Row, New York.

WAGERMARK, J., UNGERSTEDT, U., AND LJUNGGVIST, A. 1968 Sympathetic innervation of the juxtaglomerular cells of the kidney. Circ. Res., vol. 22, pp. 149–153.

WALKER, A. M., BOTT, P. A., OLIVER, J., AND MACDOWELL, M. C. 1941 The collection and analysis of fluid from nephrons of the mammalian kidney. Amer. J. Physiol., vol. 134, pp. 580–595.

WIRZ, H. 1956 Der osmotische Druck in den corticalen Tubuli der Rattenniere. Helv. Physiol. Acta, vol. 14, pp. 353–362.

WIRZ, H., AND BOTT, P. A. 1954 Potassium and reducing substances in proximal tubule fluid of the rat kidney. Proc. Soc. Exp. Biol. Med., vol. 87, pp. 405–407.

19

The Male Reproductive System

The reproductive system of the male consists of the testes, the various excretory ducts, the accessory reproductive glands—seminal vesicles, prostate and bulbourethral glands—and the penis (Fig. 19-1).

The essential constituents of the seminal fluid, the spermatozoa, are not products of cellular secretion but are themselves cellular elements that are formed in the tubules of the testis and leave the body through the genital ducts. For this reason, the testes, and the ovaries as well, are known as *cytogenic* organs. The other constituents of the semen are not formed in the testis but are secreted by the genital ducts, seminal vesicles, prostate and bulbourethral glands. Besides forming the cellular sex elements, the testes and ovaries secrete physiologically important substances directly into the blood, and hence they are endocrine glands.

The *testes* are ovoid or walnut-shaped bodies that have the organization of compound tubular glands. Each testis is enclosed in a dense fibrous capsule, the *tunica albuginea*, underneath which there is a looser layer of connective tissue rich in blood vessels, the *tunica vasculosa*. A closed serous sac, the *tunica vaginalis*, surrounds the anterior and lateral surfaces of the testis. This cleftlike sac is a detached diverticulum from the peritoneal cavity. The testes have approximately the same relationship with this sac as they had with the peritoneal cavity before their descent into the scrotum.

The visceral layer of the tunica vaginalis adheres as a smooth, glistening membrane to the tunica albuginea; the parietal layer lines the inner surface of the scrotum. Both layers are lined by mesothelial cells. Posteriorly the serous sac is lacking, the testis lying behind and outside the tunica vaginalis.

The tunica albuginea of the posterior portion of the testis is greatly thickened to form the *mediastinum testis* or *corpus Highmori*, from which connective tissue septa, the *septula testis*, radiate into the organ and blend with the tunica albuginea at various points (Fig. 19-1). In this way, the interior of the testis is subdivided into a number of pyramidal lobules, with bases directed toward the periphery and apices at the mediastinum. The septula do not form complete partitions, the lobules anastomosing with each other in numerous places.

Behind the testis and outside of its tunica albuginea is an elongated body, the *epididymis*. Three regions may be distinguished in it: (1) an upper expanded portion, the *head* or *globus major*, which projects above the upper pole of the testis, (2) a narrower middle portion or *body*, and (3) a somewhat thickened lower portion, the *tail* or *globus minor*. At the lower pole of the testis, the tail of the epididymis turns sharply upon itself and becomes continuous with the main excretory duct, the *ductus deferens*.

Each lobule of the testis contains several

intricately coiled tubules, the *convoluted seminiferous tubules*, surrounded and supported by intertubular connective tissue. They have a length of 30 to 70 cm. and a caliber varying in different individuals from 150 to 300 μ. In the same individual, the diameter is relatively constant.

The tubules do not end blindly but form single, double or even triple arches. Both limbs of an arch are not always in the same lobule. Communication between the tubules of adjacent lobules is established by lateral branches that pass through the incomplete interlobular septa. The course of the seminiferous tubules, which has been determined in laboratory mammals by teasing out the tubules after maceration and by reconstructions, forms the basis of the description given here. Toward the apex of a lobule, the convoluted tubules unite with the narrow *straight tubules*, which are about 30 μ in diameter. The straight tubules pass into the mediastinum and there empty into an irregular network of thin walled channels, the *rete testis* (Fig. 19-14). The straight tubules and rete testis form the beginning of the genital duct system.

From the rete testis arise eight to 15 tubules, the *ductuli efferentes*, which pass into the head of the epididymis and there converge to form the *duct of the epididymis* (Fig. 19-1). The efferent ductules start as straight tubules but, soon after leaving the mediastinum, they pursue a tortuous spiral course, each tubule with its surrounding connective tissue forming a conical lobule or *conus vasculosus* of the head of the epididymis. The length of the efferent tubules is about 6 to 10 cm. The most anterior ductule becomes directly continuous with the duct of the epididymis, which then receives the remaining efferent ductules at shorter or longer intervals.

The duct of the epididymis is an enormously convoluted tubule having a length of about 4 meters. It begins in the head, where it receives the ductuli efferentes, and winds in a most intricate manner through

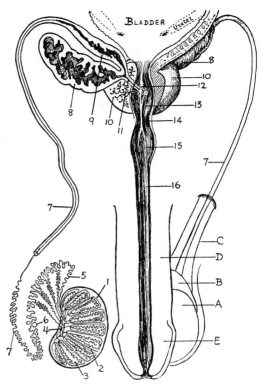

FIG. 19-1. Sketch of male genital organs. *A*, testis; *B*, head of epididymis; *C*, spermatic cord; *D*, penis, *E*, glans penis; *1*, tunica albuginea; *2*, septum of testis; *3*, seminiferous tubule; *4*, mediastinum with rete testis; *5*, ductulus efferens; *6*, ductus epididymidis; *7*, ductus deferens; *8*, seminal vesicle; *9*, ampulla of ductus deferens; *10*, prostate gland; *11*, ejaculatory duct; *12*, colliculus seminalis with opening of utriculus prostaticus; *13, 14, 16*, prostatic, membranous, and penile portions of urethra; *15*, bulb of urethra. (After Dickinson.)

the body and tail of the epididymis. At the caudal pole, it turns sharply upon itself and passes without any definite demarcation into the *ductus deferens*.

THE TESTIS

The Convoluted Seminiferous Tubule. The wall of a convoluted tubule consists of (a) an outer capsule or tunica propria of fibroelastic connective tissue and flattened fibroblasts, which closely invests the tubule; (b) a basement membrane; and

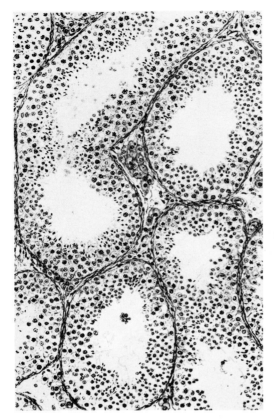

Fig. 19-2. Section through the right testis of a healthy man, 34 years of age. ×150. (After Stieve.)

(c) a lining of a complex stratified epithelium (Fig. 19-2).

The epithelium consists of two kinds of cells, the supporting cells or cells of Sertoli and the spermatogenic cells.

(1) The *cells of Sertoli* (Fig. 19-3) are tall, irregularly columnar cells that extend from the basal lamina to the lumen. Their sides are markedly uneven, showing pits and depressions into which fit the adjoining germ cells. The nucleus is ovoid and pale staining with finely dispersed chromatin, and it usually contains one or more prominent nucleoli. The nuclear membrane often shows a characteristic longitudinal groove. The location of the nucleus varies in different Sertoli cells from the basal position to positions located at a considerable distance from the basal lamina. Electron micrographs

show that the mitochondria, described as filamentous from light microscope studies, are unusually long and slender. In addition to the usual organelles, the cytoplasm contains lipid droplets, glycogen and, in man, a spindle-shaped crystalloid. The cell border is difficult to distinguish in routinely stained preparations, but the entire cell and its borders can be defined by silver methods (Elftman, 1950).

The Sertoli cells are the only ones that extend from the basement membrane to the lumen, and thus they give structural organization to the tubule. They rest on the basement membrane in a patterned array that is readily seen in silver preparations of tangential sections of the tubule. Following the Sertoli cell from the basal lamina to the lumen, one finds that it is surrounded first by spermatogonia and then by different stages of spermatocytes and spermatids. The pattern of arrangement is seen best at the level of the primary spermatocytes, which are arranged in rings around the Sertoli cell.

Electron micrographs show the presence of occluding junctions between the basal portions of apposing Sertoli cells (Dym and Fawcett, 1970). Studies with tracers indicate that these junctions are mainly responsible for a blood-brain barrier at the level of the preleptotene primary spermatocytes. Passage of substances from the interstitial spaces to germinal elements beyond the preleptotene spermatocytes is via the cytoplasm of the Sertoli cells.

Special staining methods show that the cytoplasmic processes of the Sertoli cells increase in number and size when the spermatids are maturing. Thus, the Sertoli cells exhibit a cyclic activity that is correlated with the stage of spermatogenesis in any given region of the seminiferous tubule.

(2) The *spermatogenic cells* lie between the cells of Sertoli in an orderly manner, with four to eight layers occupying the space between the basal lamina and the lumen. In the undeveloped testis, only the

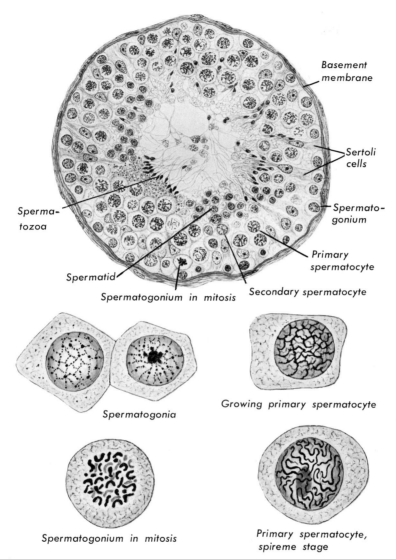

Basement
membrane

Sertoli
cells

Spermato-
gonium

Primary
spermatocyte

Secondary spermatocyte

Sperma-
tozoa

Spermatid

Spermatogonium in mitosis

Spermatogonia

Growing primary spermatocyte

Spermatogonium in mitosis

Primary spermatocyte,
spireme stage

FIG. 19-3. The *top figure* illustrates a seminiferous tubule of a man 19 years old. ✕360. (After Stieve.) The *lower figures* illustrate cells from seminiferous tubules of a man 21 years old. ✕1200. (After Stieve.) (See Fig. 19-4 for later stages.)

primitive germ cells or spermatogonia are present. With the onset of sexual maturity, the spermatogenic cells are represented in all stages of differentiation and are arranged in several more or less distinct layers (Fig. 19-3).

The primitive germ cells, or *spermatogonia*, from which all of the spermatozoa are ultimately derived, are located directly inside the basal lamina. They are spherical or cuboidal in shape, with a diameter of about 12 μ. They have a spherical nucleus with granular chromatin. They divide to maintain their own number and to provide the cells that differentiate into spermatocytes. Two types of spermatogonia can be identified by special stains, namely, the *A* or *stem cells* and the *B* or *derivative cells*.

They differ in the intensity of cytoplasmic staining, and the A cells usually have one or two nucleoli at the inner surface of the nuclear envelope, whereas the B cells usually have a centrally located nucleolus. An A cell may divide either into two new stem cells or into two derivatives. The latter divide further before differentiating into spermatocytes. Electron micrographs show that the last division of the spermatogonium is often incomplete regarding the cytoplasm, and that the two primary spermatocytes may be connected by a protoplasmic bridge.

The *primary spermatocytes* lie next to the spermatogonia on their inner side. They are large cells with a diameter of 17 to 19 μ and are formed from the innermost layer of the spermatogonia. The chromatin of the large vesicular nuclei has a variable appearance, depending on the functional state of the cells. It may be in the form of either elongated spiremes or condensed chromosomes preparatory to cell division (Figs. 19-3 and 19-4).

Each primary spermatocyte gives rise by division to two *secondary spermatocytes* or *prespermatids*. They are smaller cells than the primary spermatocytes and lie internally to them (Fig. 19-3). Almost as soon as it is formed, each secondary spermatocyte divides to form two spermatids. Electron micrographs show that the cytoplasm of the daughter cells often remains connected by protoplasmic bridges after the division of secondary spermatocytes, similar to the condition observed at the last spermatogonial division and at the primary spermatocyte division. Consequently, the spermatids are often grouped in clusters of eight interconnected cells. When bridges persist from earlier stages of multiplication, the clusters consists of 16 or more interconnected cells. The connections normally disappear during sperm maturation.

The *spermatids* adjoin the lumen of the tubule. They are easily recognized by their small size (about 9 μ) and location. These cells form the last generation in the spermatogenic process. They undergo no further division but, by profound changes in their structure, they become directly transformed into the mature *spermatozoa*. Groups of maturing spermatids can be seen in close relationship with the Sertoli cells.

Thus, in the mature testis, the following cell types are distinguished, passing from the periphery of the tubule toward the lumen: spermatogonia, primary spermatocytes, secondary spermatocytes and spermatids, the latter often in process of transformation into spermatozoa.

Mature or nearly mature spermatozoa are frequently observed with their heads in close association with the cytoplasmic processes of the Sertoli cells and their tails extending out into the lumen. Free spermatozoa in the lumen of the tubule are relatively rare, for as soon as they are detached from the Sertoli cells they pass into the tubules of the epididymis, where they are stored.

In animals with periodic rutting seasons, transverse sections through several seminiferous tubules will show clearly all stages of spermatogenesis. During the long intermissions between breeding seasons, the tubules revert to a prepubertal condition and contain only spermatogonia and cells of Sertoli. In man and other animals in which spermatogenesis is a continuous process, the histological picture varies in different sections, since all of the stages of sperm formation do not occur simultaneously in all portions of the seminiferous tubule. As a rule, those stages that last a considerable time are easily seen in most sections, such as spermatogonia, primary spermatocytes and spermatids. Secondary spermatocytes that divide almost as soon as formed are usually few in number and more difficult to find.

In rodents, there is a definite wave of spermatogenetic activity along the seminiferous tubule, and a clear correlation is seen between the several developmental

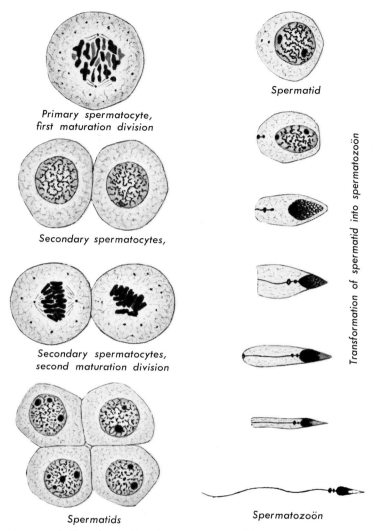

Primary spermatocyte,
first maturation division

Secondary spermatocytes,

Secondary spermatocytes,
second maturation division

Spermatids

Spermatid

Transformation of spermatid into spermatozoön

Spermatozoön

FIG. 19-4. Cells from seminiferous tubules of a man 21 years old. ×1200. (After Stieve.) (See Fig. 19-3 for earlier stages.)

stages of the spermatogonia and the other generations of spermatogenic cells. In man, the picture is complicated by the fact that active areas of seminiferous epithelium are intermingled with inactive areas. Studies by Clermont, 1963, have shown, however, that typical cellular associations can be identified in man and that they can be classified in six stages. These stages are not all visible together; on the average, three can be seen in a single cross section of a tubule. Radioautographic studies on testicular tissue,

taken by biopsy at different intervals following injection of tritiated thymidine, indicate that spermatogenesis (from spermatogonial stem cells to spermatozoa) occupies a total of about 64 days (Heller and Clermont, 1963).

In many testes secured at autopsy, there are regions in which spermatogenesis is greatly reduced or entirely absent, the seminiferous epithelium either reverting to a prepubertal condition or occasionally showing an entire absence of germ cells. After prolonged sickness and in senility, the degenerative changes may be very pronounced. Fairly extensive degenerative changes in the testes may also occur in medically normal men during the reproductive period of life. In studies of medically normal men ranging in age from 20 to 50 years, Sand and Okkels (1938) found that only 17 of their 72 cases showed a structural condition of the testes that is usually depicted in textbooks as normal. In the remainder, the basement membrane and capsule of the seminiferous tubules and often the intertubular connective tissue were thickened either diffusely or in localized areas. Hyalinization of the connective tissue was not infrequent. In about one-third of their cases, spermatogenesis was severely reduced. They noted that the illustrations of seminiferous tubules in textbooks of histology must have been obtained from carefully selected material. Figure 19-5 illustrates pronounced degenerative changes in the testes of a healthy middle aged individual.

The mechanism causing the sperm to pass from the seminiferous tubules into the rete and hence into the efferent ductules, a very considerable journey, is of particular interest. The sperm do not become motile until they leave the testes and the duct system of the reproductive tract and, consequently, their migration cannot be caused by an intrinsic movement. Experimental studies on laboratory animals show that a considerable quantity of fluid is "secreted" by the seminiferous tubules and resorbed by the rete tubules, efferent tubules and the duct of the epididymis (Mason and Shaver, 1952). The current thus produced may be an important factor in moving the sperm from the seminiferous tubules. It has also been shown by recent electron microscope studies that some of the cells in the connective tissue of the seminiferous tubule have fine cytoplasmic filaments resembling those of smooth muscle. Consequently, earlier views that there are no smooth muscle cells in the walls of the semi-niferous tubules are probably incorrect, and the movement of sperm out of the tubules may be aided by contraction of the walls of the tubules. Beginning with the efferent tubules, the walls of the ducts have appreciable amounts of smooth muscle readily seen under the light microscope.

The testes of sexually mature mammals are rich in hyaluronidase. This enzyme is present elsewhere (Chapter 1), but the testes of slaughterhouse animals are the main source of the hyaluronidase used experimentally and clinically. There is more than one hyaluronidase, that derived from testes being designated as "testicular hyaluronidase."

Spermatozoa are the source (or carriers) of testicular hyaluronidase. The latter is not present in the testes before sexual maturity or in those devoid of sperm. It is still present in sperm that have been washed several times. If sperm are autolyzed, a large amount of the enzyme is found. Hyaluronidase is present in semen, being localized chiefly in the sperm.

Spermatogenesis. The cytological details and genetic significance of spermatogenesis are fully discussed in textbooks of genetics. Only a brief sketch can be given here of the various changes through which the primitive germ cells are transformed into mature sperm (Fig. 19-6).

It is convenient to distinguish several successive periods or stages in spermatogenesis as outlined above, even though the stages merge into one another as parts of a continuous process.

The nucleus of each spermatogonium, the stem cell from which all sperm are eventually derived, contains the somatic or diploid number of chromosomes. This number in man is 46, consisting of 23 pairs, one member of each pair being of maternal and the other of paternal origin. After a number of ordinary mitotic divisions, by which each daughter cell receives the diploid number of chromosomes, the last generation of spermatogonia enters an intermitotic period

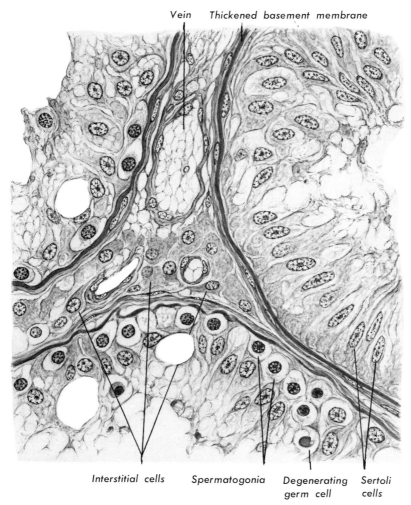

Vein   Thickened basement membrane

Interstitial cells   Spermatogonia   Degenerating   Sertoli
germ cell   cells

FIG. 19-5. Parts of three seminiferous tubules, showing pronounced degeneration. The tissue was from a healthy middle aged man. Camera lucida drawing. ×565.

characterized by growth and by nuclear change leading to differentiation of the cells to primary spermatocytes.

At the close of the growth period of the primary spermatocyte, long thread-like chromosomes can be seen in the nucleus that seem to be like those present in early prophase stages of spermatogonia. As the threads shorten and thicken, however, it can be seen that they are not single as in mitotic prophase, but double as the result of synapsis (pairing) of homologous chromosomes. Instead of 46 single chromosomes, there are 23 double threads. Next, each member of the pair, having replicated DNA prior to prophase, divides and a tetrad is formed. The tetrads have individual differences in size and form by which they may be identified. Even after they thicken and go on to the spindle, they retain individual characteristics.

In the *first maturation division*, the chromosomes that paired during synapsis become separated, one member from each pair going to each of the resulting two secondary spermatocytes. This division

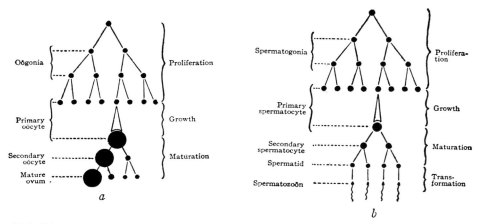

Fig. 19-6. Diagrams comparing stages of (a) oogenesis and (b) spermatogenesis. (Modified from Boveri.)

differs from ordinary mitosis in that it does not consist of the longitudinal splitting of individual chromosomes following DNA replication, but whole, previously paired chromosomes are separated from each other, the daughter cells actually receiving only half the somatic number. It is a *reductional* or *heterotypic* division, in contrast to the ordinary *equational* or *homeotypic* division. It is the first nuclear division in the process known as *meiosis*, in contrast to *mitosis*. Each tetrad separates into two dyads, each dyad representing an original single chromosome replicated precociously for the second maturation division.

Another difference between meiosis and mitosis is that the first maturation division of the former is characterized by a long prophase required for the exact pairing of homologous chromosomes. Successive stages in meiotic prophase may be identified as follows: *leptotene, zygotene, pachytene,* and *diplotene.* Leptotene is the term used to describe the stage in which the chromosomes are seen as long thin threads; zygotene applies to the stage when homologous chromosomes begin to pair; pachytene describes the stage when pairing is completed and the chromosomes become shorter and thicker; and, diplotene is applied to the stage when the paired chromosomes begin to repel each

other, but remain joined at numerous places of interchange known as *chiasmata*. This is the stage when some segments of homologous chromosomes are exchanged by a process known as *crossing over.*

The two secondary spermatocytes, which are smaller than the primary spermatocyte, pass through a short interphase period and then enter the second maturation division to form four spermatids. The dyads are separated into single elements or monads, and one monad from each dyad goes to each daughter cell. Each spermatid is about half the size of the secondary spermatocytes.

By spermatogenesis, every primary spermatocyte, the tetrad spermatocyte, gives rise to four spermatids, each containing the haploid number of chromosomes. Likewise, each spermatid nucleus contains only half as much deoxyribonucleic acid (DNA) as those of the spermatogonia.

A similar reduction in number of chromosomes and in DNA content occurs during the maturation of the oocytes. Fertilization restores the diploid number of chromosomes with the characteristic amount of DNA.

The members of one pair of chromosomes (the sex chromosomes) are dissimilar in the male. One is known as the X chromosome and is of maternal origin. The other is the Y chromosome, of paternal origin. When the members of homologous pairs of chromosomes separate during the meiotic division of the primary spermatocytes, one half of the secondary spermatocytes receives an X chromosome, whereas the other half receives a Y chromosome. This differs from the condition in the female, in which each ovum contains an X chromosome. Consequently, when a sperm carrying an X chromosome fertilizes an ovum, an XX combination is established and a female develops. On the other hand, when a sperm bearing a Y chromosome fertilizes an ovum, an XY combination is produced and the embryo develops as a male.

Spermiogenesis. The spermatids do not divide but mature to form the spermatozoa by a process known as spermiogenesis. During most of their maturation, the spermatids are enveloped by the cytoplasmic processes of the Sertoli cells, from which they apparently receive nourishment.

The spermatids are small cells, about half the size of the secondary spermatocytes. They have round and rather dark staining nuclei. The stages of their transformation into mature sperm have been clarified by the use of electron microscopy.

One of the earliest changes is in the Golgi complex where small granules, known as *proacrosomal granules*, appear in some of the Golgi vacuoles. Fusion of these leads to the formation of a larger vacuole with a relatively large granule, the *acrosomal granule*, visible with the light microscope. Continued growth of the acrosomal complex occurs by incorporation of other newly formed vesicles and granules. In the meantime, the acrosomal system of the Golgi complex moves closer to the nucleus, thereby marking the anterior pole of the cell (Figs. 19-7 and 19-8). The acrosomal vesicle increases its zone of contact with the nucleus, and then the vesicle, with its enclosed acrosomal material, forms a caplike structure over the anterior two-thirds of the nucleus that is known as the *acrosomal cap*, or head cap. The cap can be identified as a distinct

structure in the mature sperm of many species, but in man it becomes closely flattened against the nucleus.

Concurrently with the changes outlined above, the centrioles move toward the caudal portion of the cell, where the distal centriole functions as a basal body for the development of the flagellum. Then the centrioles and the base of the flagellum move back toward the nucleus. The proximal centriole becomes closely applied to the caudal pole of the nucleus and maintains its ultrastructural characteristics in the mature sperm. The distal centriole is not identifiable in the mature sperm, and its fate is obscure. While these changes have been occurring, a ring appears around the nucleus at about the level of the caudal end of the acrosomal cap. Microtubules project caudally from the ring, forming a cylindrical *caudal sheath* or *manchette*. This is followed by a rapid elongation of the cell, accompanied by a redistribution of cytoplasm caudally, and the mitochondria move to a position in the proximal portion of the developing tail of the sperm.

While the changes in centrioles are occurring, another structure known as an *annulus* arises in a region near the distal centriole. It was once named a ring centriole, although it has none of the structural features of a centriole. The annulus eventually moves to a position at the caudal end of the middle piece of the tail (Fig. 19-9).

In summary, spermiogenesis produces a slender motile cell retaining only the essentials for fertilization and for transmitting hereditary material. It retains its nucleus, the Golgi-derived acrosomal cap, a proximal centriole and mitochondria; the remainder of the cytoplasm is extruded.

The Mature Spermatozoa. The spermatozoa are slender, motile, flagellate bodies having a total length of 55 to 65 μ. They are formed in enormous numbers. It has been estimated that about 60,000 spermatozoa are contained in 1 cubic millimeter of seminal fluid, or 200 to 600 million in a

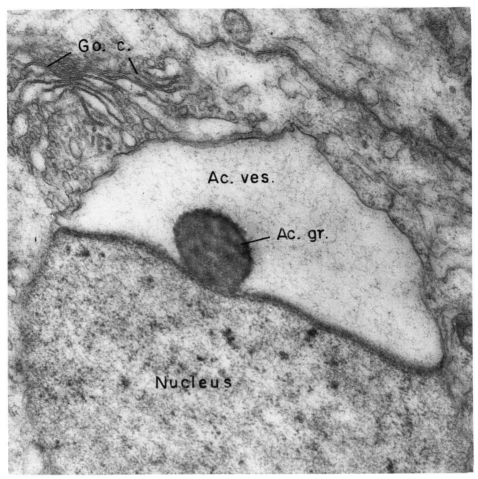

Fig. 19-7. Electron micrograph of cat spermatid, showing nucleus, acrosomal granule (*Ac. gr.*), acrosomal vesicle (*Ac. ves.*), and the Golgi complex (*Go. c.*). (Courtesy of Dr. D. W. Fawcett.)

single ejaculation. By the undulatory motion of the tail, they swim about freely, capable when fully active of covering a distance of 1 to 3 mm. per minute. In the seminiferous tubules and ducts of the testis, they are sluggish or entirely quiescent. When expelled by the peristaltic action of the ductus deferens and duct of the epididymis, they are activated into movement by the secretion of the accessory genital glands, especially the prostate. In the favorable environment of the male genital tract, the spermatozoa remain alive for some time after leaving the testis. Living spermatozoa have been found in the epididymis several weeks after

the experimental ligation of the ductuli efferentes. In the female reproductive tract, their life is very short.

The mature spermatozoan consists of a *head* and a *tail*. The latter is composed of the following parts in sequence: *middle piece*, *principal piece* and *end piece*. The junction between the head and tail is known as the *neck*.

The *head* of the human spermatozoan is a flattened, oval body with a length of 4 to 5 μ and a maximal width of about 3 μ. The anterior portion is thinner than the posterior so that in profile it is pear-shaped (Fig. 19-9). It consists chiefly of a nucleus with

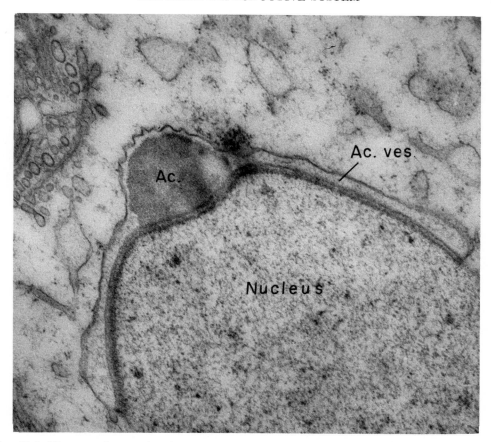

FIG. 19-8. Electron micrograph of human spermatid, showing stage of maturation in which the acrosomal vesicle (*Ac. ves.*) has collapsed to form a membrane-bounded narrow cavity containing the acrosome (*Ac.*). (Courtesy of Dr. D. W. Fawcett.)

compact, deep staining chromatin enclosed within the nuclear envelope. The anterior two-thirds of the nuclear envelope is covered by the acrosomal cap, and the entire cell is covered by the cell membrane or plasmalemma. The different membranes cannot be identified by light microscopy. An understanding of their structure and arrangement has evolved from electron microscope studies of developing sperm.

The *neck* is a short region connecting the head of the sperm with the middle piece. The proximal centriole is located against the basal end of the nucleus (or head) at an angle of about 45° to the axis of the tail. The peripheral portion of the neck region contains coarse fibers that are continuous with the longitudinally oriented fibers of the middle piece. Electron micrographs show that some of the coarse fibers are fused in the neck region, and they also appear cross banded due to electron-lucent segments. The central pair of fibrils of the flagellum continues farther into the neck and closer to the proximal centriole than do the nine outer doublets.

The *middle piece* is about 5 to 9 μ in length and about 1 μ in width. It has a core with the typical structure of a flagellum or elongated cilium, i.e., a central pair of single fibrils surrounded by nine doublets (Figs. 19-9 and 19-10). Peripheral to the axial filament complex, there is a ring of nine longitudinally oriented, dense fibers. These

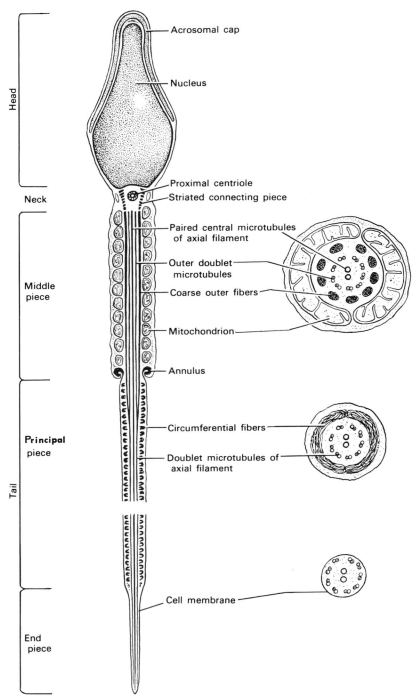

FIG. 19-9. Diagrammatic representation of the structure of a mature spermatozoon as determined by light and electron microscopic studies. At the *left*, a longitudinal section; at the *right*, transverse sections of the tail at levels of the middle piece, principal piece, and end piece respectively. (Diagrams based on descriptions and electron micrographs by Dr. Don W. Fawcett).

are large and well defined in the proximal part of the middle piece, but they gradually taper and become more irregular during their course caudally in the middle piece. A sheath of longitudinally oriented mitochondria is a characteristic feature of the middle piece.

The *principal piece* is the longest portion of the tail, being 40 to 45 μ in length. It lacks the mitochondrial sheath of the middle piece, and the outer coarse fibers continue only a short distance into this segment in human sperm. A characteristic feature of the principal piece is a fibrous sheath shown by electron micrographs to consist of a large number of circumferentially oriented, rib-like bundles that pass halfway around the axial filament complex to fuse with two longitudinal columns of fibers (Fig. 19-10).

The *tail piece* is relatively short and slender, being about 5 to 10 μ in length. It has the typical appearance of a flagellum, with two single fibrils surrounded by nine doublets.

The significance of the different parts of the spermatozoon has been brought out in the description of its development. It is seen that the spermatozoon, like the mature ovum, is a sex cell containing half the somatic number of chromosomes. In spite of its small size and modified form, it contains all of the elements important for fertilization and heredity. The head carries the genetic material, a Golgi-derived acrosomal cap important in penetrating the ovum, and a centriole. The tail is a temporary accessory that enables the spermatozoon to reach the ovum by active movement.

Tunica Albuginea. The *tunica albuginea testis* is a tough, fibrous membrane that

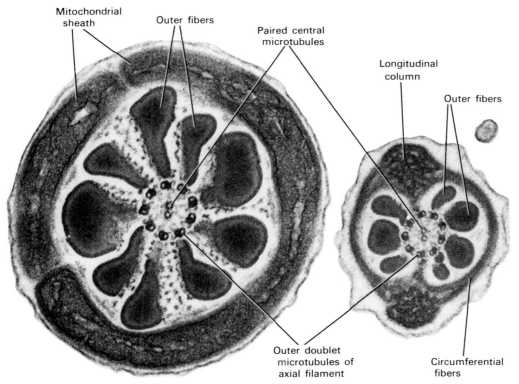

FIG. 19-10. Electron micrographs of transverse sections of the tail of a mature spermatozoon of a Chinese hamster. At the *left*, micrograph of a section through the middle piece; at the *right*, through the principal piece. (Courtesy of Dr. Don W. Fawcett).

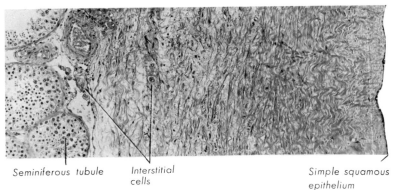

Seminiferous tubule   Interstitial
cells

Simple squamous
epithelium

FIG. 19-11. Cross section through the anterior wall of a testis, showing the tunics of the organ and subjacent seminiferous tubules. Masson's trichrome stain. Photomicrograph. ×104.

encapsulates the testis (Fig. 19-11). It is about 0.5 mm. in thickness. Externally it is covered by mesothelium. During the early development of the testis, this covering layer of epithelium is cuboidal and is the germinal epithelium.

Beneath the basal lamina of the simple squamous epithelium, there is a layer of rather fine, closely woven collagenous fibers that blends with a deeper layer of interweaving, coarse collagenous fibers. This deeper layer forms the main component of the tunica albuginea. The inner part of the tunic is composed of looser connective tissue, the innermost part of which is highly vascular and is called the *tunica vasculosa.* Just beneath the tunica vasculosa is the parenchyma of the testis. The delicate connective tissue forming the interlobular septa of the testis attaches to and is continuous with the tissue of the tunica vasculosa.

The surface epithelium of the testis and the subjacent connective tissue is often called the *visceral layer* of the *tunica vaginalis.* At the posterior part of the testis, this layer is continuous with the parietal layer of the tunica vaginalis. Between the visceral and parietal layers is a cavity which is a remnant of the peritoneal cavity.

The tunica vasculosa contains numerous quite large blood vessels. Branches of these penetrate the denser part of the tunica albuginea.

Interstitial Cells. Besides the usual connective tissue elements, the stroma contains characteristic cells known as the *interstitial cells* or *cells of Leydig.* These cells form the internal secretion known as testosterone (see below under "Internal Secretion of the Testis").

The interstitial cells occur in groups of various sizes and are quite distinct in the human testis (Figs. 19-11 and 19-12). Small blood vessels are usually present in the groups. The interstitial cells are large and are ovoid or polygonal in shape. They have a large nucleus which is frequently eccentrically located. The cytoplasm of the interstitial cells is granular and fairly dense near the nucleus but peripherally it is vacuolated, and in usual preparations it stains quite lightly. This is largely due to the dissolving out of lipid granules and droplets. Most of the endoplasmic reticulum is of the smooth surfaced type, and the mitochondria have tubular rather than shelflike cristae. These are characteristic features of cells that secrete steroid hormones. The interstitial cells also contain lipochrome pigment granules and crystalloids. The pigment granules increase in number in older men, and ultrastructural studies indicate that they may represent autophagic vacuoles (Christensen, 1965). The crystalloids are rod-shaped structures and in cross section are oval or round. Their number and size vary greatly.

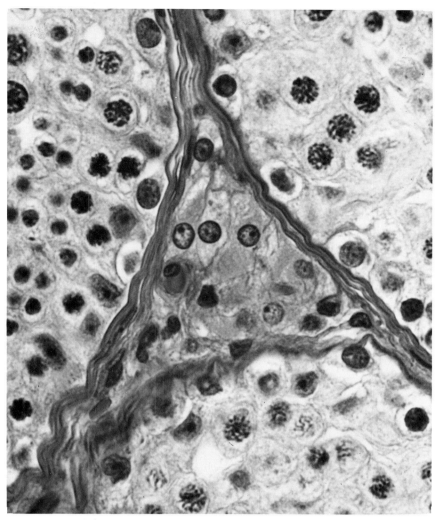

FIG. 19-12. Photomicrograph of a group of human interstitial (Leydig) cells between three contiguous seminiferous tubules. (Courtesy of Dr. D. W. Fawcett.)

They are formed of an albuminous substance and are quite resistant to solvents. Fixation soon after death is necessary to preserve them.

Electron micrographs show two types of Leydig cells: fusiform cells with relatively few organelles, and large cells that have the usual organelles plus many small membrane-bound vesicles, granules, lipid droplets, osmiophilic pigment and large protein crystals. The presence of cells with intermediate characteristics indicates that the fusiform cell is a precursor stage of the mature interstitial cell.

The Leydig cells arise from fibroblasts and may revert to cells that are indistinguishable from fibroblasts.

Blood Vessels. Branches of the spermatic artery ramify in the mediastinum and tunica vasculosa. These send branches into the septa of the testis which give rise to a capillary network around the seminiferous tubules. The blood is collected by veins that accompany the arteries.

Lymphatics. In the intertubular tissue are numerous lymphatics, appearing as clefts lined by endothelium. These connect with lymph vessels in the mediastinum. Relatively few lymphatics are found in the tunica albuginea.

Nerves. Nerve fibers accompany the blood vessels and enter the interior of the testes through the mediastinum. Some fibers go to blood vessels; the termination of other fibers is not known.

GENITAL DUCTS

Straight Tubules and Rete Testis. At the juncture of a seminiferous tubule with a straight tubule, there is an abrupt change in structure. The junctures occur at varying distances from the rete, the straight tubules thus varying in length. Close to a juncture, the developing sex cells

of a seminiferous tubule decrease in number and then finally disappear. The Sertoli cells change somewhat in structure, their cytoplasm becoming more vacuolated and their nuclei more dense. They increase in number and finally form a continuous epithelial layer. This protrudes into the enlarged end of the straight tubule (Figs. 19-14 and 19-15). The epithelial lining then changes abruptly into the cuboidal or columnar type characteristic of the straight tubules and rete.

The rete testis is composed of wide, anastomosing channels, the general course of which is upward toward the ductuli efferentes. The spaces of the rete are lined by a simple epithelium that varies in height from a low cuboidal to a columnar (Fig. 19-14). Some of the cells have a single cilium (flagellum) that is connected to the distal

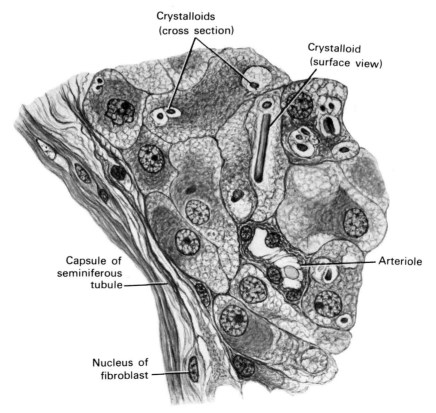

Crystalloids (cross section)

Crystalloid (surface view)

Capsule of seminiferous tubule

Arteriole

Nucleus of fibroblast

FIG. 19-13. A group of interstitial cells (cells of Leydig) of a normal adult man. Surgical specimen fixed in Worcester's fluid and stained with iron hematoxylin and erythrosin. ×990.

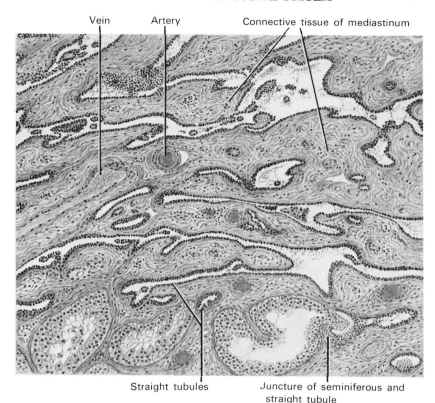

Vein   Artery   Connective tissue of mediastinum

Straight tubules   Juncture of seminiferous and straight tubule

Fig. 19-14. From a longitudinal section through a testis, showing a part of the mediastinum and rete testis and the adjacent seminiferous tubules. The juncture of a seminiferous with a straight tubule is shown in the *lower right quadrant* of the figure. The separation between the rete and the straight tubules is topographical, not structural. The upper pole of the testis is to the *right*. Human, accident case, 54 years old. ×65.

centriole. No secretion droplets are present. In contrast with Sertoli cells, the nuclei stain deeply and the cell wall is well defined. The tubules of the rete have no definite lamina propria that is distinct from the connective tissue comprising the mediastinum. No smooth muscle is present around the straight tubules or rete testis.

Ductuli Efferentes. The epithelium of the efferent ductules consists mainly of groups of high columnar cells alternating with groups of cuboidal cells. This gives the inner surface of the tubule a characteristic irregular contour, with the low cells lining cryptlike depressions or pockets (Fig. 19-16). The basal border of the tubule is not affected by the alternating height of the cells and has a relatively smooth contour. In

addition to the columnar and cuboidal cells, rounded cells that do not extend to the lumen occasionally occur at intervals along the basal lamina; hence, the epithelium, strictly speaking, belongs to the pseudostratified type.

Cilia are present on many of the tall cells and generally absent from the cuboidal cells, but the distribution is variable. Most of the low cells have microvilli. Bleblike apical projections, generally interpreted as secretory material, are seen on some cells of both types. In addition to the usual organelles, the cytoplasm often contains fat droplets and pigment granules. The cytoplasm of the cells with the higher content of lipid takes a lighter stain in routine preparations.

The epithelial cells of the efferent ductules

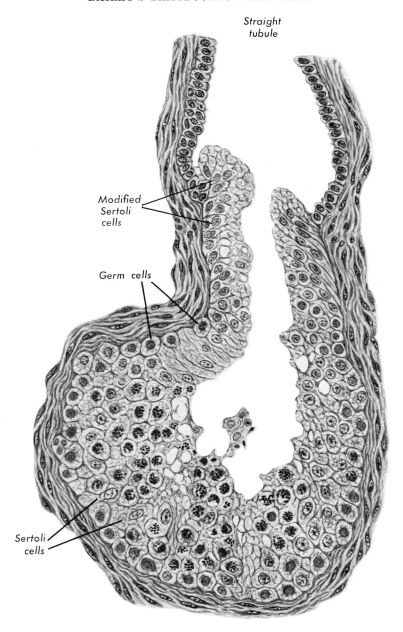

Straight
tubule

Modified
Sertoli
cells

Germ cells

Sertoli
cells

Seminiferous tubule

FIG. 19-15. A juncture of a seminiferous tubule and a straight tubule. The seminiferous tubule is cut somewhat obliquely. From the same testis shown in Fig. 19-14. ×445.

are generally described as secretory, but studies of the pathway of injected dyes show that the tubules also absorb some substances. Beating of cilia, chiefly of the tall columnar cells, aids in the transport of sperm.

The epithelium rests on a distinct basement membrane, surrounded by a lamina propria of connective tissue containing many capillaries and some circular smooth muscle fibers.

Ductus Epididymidis (Duct of the Epididymis). This duct has an even contour, not only externally but internally as well, for the epithelial cells all end at the same level and the smooth muscle in fixed preparations has not undergone a contraction sufficient to cause a folding of the mucosa as is the case with the ductus deferens. The lining epithelium of the epididymis is composed of two types of cells: very narrow, tall columnar cells and rounded or angular basal cells (Figs. 19-17 and 19-18). Although it cannot be determined with certainty, even in very thin sections, that all of the columnar cells overlying the basal ones reach the basement membrane, nevertheless many of them certainly do by curving around the basal cells. Presumably all of them reach the basement membrane. The epithelium is thus pseudostratified.

The columnar cells bear nonmotile processes originally called stereocilia. Electron micrographs show that these structures lack the cytological characteristics of cilia and that they are merely long, branching cell processes. They differ from microvilli by their greater length and by their branching. The cytoplasm contains fairly numerous droplets described as secretory in nature and some pigment granules. Electron micrographs show that there are numerous multivesicular bodies which give a reaction for acid phosphatase, and many of the droplets are apparently lysosomal in nature. From ultrastructural studies and from studies of the course of injected dyes, it seems likely that the epididymis functions more for resorption than for secretion. The nuclei of the columnar cells are elongate and lie at somewhat different levels. The basal cells are similar to those in the efferent tubules but are much more numerous (Fig. 19-18).

There is a basement membrane and lamina propria. The smooth muscle is circular but is small in amount. As the juncture with the ductus deferens is approached, the muscle increases in amount and longitudinal bundles appear.

Ductus Deferens. The main genital duct

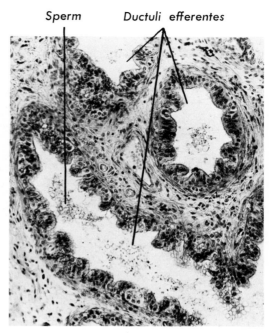

FIG. 19-16. Sections of ductuli efferentes from the head of the epididymis. Adult man. Photomicrograph. ×130.

is a direct continuation of the duct of the epididymis. Its proximal portion, which runs along the epididymis, is coiled. Then it straightens out and, as part of the spermatic cord, passes into the abdominal cavity to terminate in the prostatic portion of the urethra. Shortly before reaching the prostate, the ductus deferens shows a spindle-shaped dilation, the *ampulla*, which gradually narrows to form the thin *ejaculatory duct*. The two ejaculatory ducts penetrate the prostate gland and empty into the urethra on either side of the prostatic utricle. When fully straightened, the duct is about half a meter in length.

The wall of the ductus deferens consists of three coats: mucosa, muscularis, and fibrosa (Fig. 19-19).

The *mucosa* is lined by a pseudostratified columnar epithelium somewhat similar to that of the duct of the epididymis. The surface cells are lower, however, and the stereocilia show a variable distribution, being absent on some cells and present on

Sections through ductus epididymis

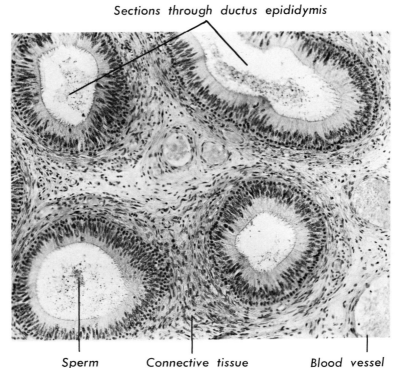

Sperm   Connective tissue   Blood vessel

FIG. 19-17. Sections through the duct of the epididymis. Adult man. Photomicrograph. ×105.

others. Cytoplasmic granules are not as numerous as they are in the epithelium of the epididymis. The epithelium is surrounded by a stroma exceedingly rich in elastic fibers which forms a compact lamina propria around the basal lamina. In the deeper portion of the stroma are numerous blood vessels. Owing to the abundant elastic tissue and strong muscularis, the mucosa is thrown into four or five longitudinal folds, so that in transverse section the lumen appears star-shaped.

The *muscularis* is by far the thickest coat (1 to 1½ mm.) and consists of three smooth muscular layers: an inner longitudinal, a middle circular and an outer longitudinal. The middle and outer coats are strongly developed layers. The inner longitudinal layer is relatively thin.

The *fibrosa* consists of fibroelastic tissue containing numerous blood vessels, nerves and often scattered bundles of smooth muscle fibers. It merges without definite demarcation with the surrounding connective tissue.

In the *ampulla*, the mucosa shows numerous folds forming crypts or recesses, many of which extend as tubular structures into the stroma (Fig. 19-20). These are glandular structures lined by a cuboidal or columnar epithelium of a secretory character, the cells frequently containing yellow pigment granules.

The *ejaculatory ducts* have a thin mucous membrane thrown into numerous fine folds, with glandular recesses like those of the ampulla. The epithelium is simple columnar or pseudostratified and becomes transitional near the urethral opening. Beneath the epithelium is a rich network of elastic fibers. A distinct muscularis is present only at the beginning. In the prostatic portion, the muscularis disappears and is replaced by the fibromuscular tissue of the prostate gland.

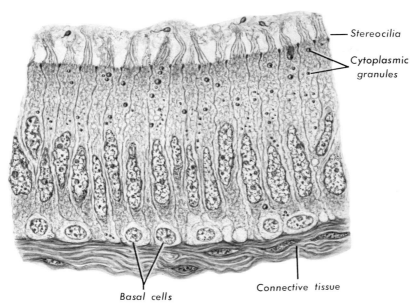

FIG. 19-18. A section through the duct of the epididymis showing the epithelium and subjacent connective tissue. Most of the granules seen in the cytoplasm are apparently related to absorption of substances from the lumen rather than to secretion. Human accident case, 54 years old. Mallory-ozan stain, 3 μ section. ×945.

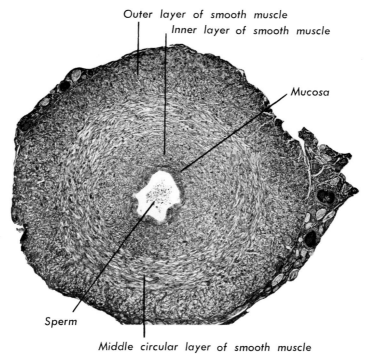

FIG. 19-19. Transverse section through ductus deferens. Adult man. Photomicrograph. ×38.

STORAGE OF SPERM

The ductuli efferentes, epididymis and the first part of the ductus deferens are the storehouse for the sperm. The passage of the sperm through the straight tubules and rete testis must be relatively rapid, for they are rarely seen in these ducts, although they are numerous in the ductuli efferentes and the duct of the epididymis. The storage place of the sperm is thus correlated with the secretory capacity of the epithelial cells of the different segments of the duct system. It has been pointed out that, in the straight tubules and rete, the epithelial cells show no evidence of secretion, whereas in the efferent ductules and epididymis, secretory granules (glycogen, etc.) are numerous. Ligation experiments in animals have shown that, when the testes are left intact, the sperm retain their capacity of becoming motile for 40 to 60 days, although the period during which they retain the capacity to fertilize the egg is somewhat shorter. During at least a part of their sojourn in these ducts, they are probably undergoing further maturation. It is certain that their survival is aided by a secretion from the epithelium. If the testes are removed, thus depriving the animal of testosterone, and the ducts are left intact, the epithelium involutes and the life of the sperm is reduced by about one-half.

VESTIGIAL STRUCTURES IN TESTIS AND EPIDIDYMIS

Connected with the testis and its ducts are remains of certain fetal structures associated with the development of the genital system.

(1) The *paradidymis* or *organ of Giraldés* is situated between the vessels of the spermatic cord near the testis. It consists of several blind tubules lined with a simple columnar epithelium, part of which is ciliated. The cells may vary in height and the tubule may have the appearance of an efferent duct.

(2) The *ductus aberrans Halleri* or inferior aberrant duct arises from the lower portion of the ductus epididymidis and extends toward the head, where it ends blindly. It is lined with simple columnar, ciliated epithelium.

A smaller *superior aberrant duct* is often present. It arises from the rete testis and ends blindly in the epididymis.

(3) The *appendix testis* (hydatid of Morgagni) is situated on the cranial pole of the testis near the epididymis. It is a vesicular structure lined by simple columnar epithelium surrounded by vascular connective tissue.

(4) The *appendix epididymidis* (stalked hydatid) is found occasionally on the head of the epididymis near the appendix testis. Its lumen is lined with a single layer of cuboidal or columnar cells.

The paradidymis, aberrant tubules and appendix epididymidis represent vestiges of the fetal mesonephros, while the appendix testis is derived from the Müllerian duct.

ACCESSORY GENITAL GLANDS

The Seminal Vesicles. The seminal vesicles are elongated, convoluted sacs which lie closely apposed to the ampullae and open into the ductus deferens at the junction of ampulla and ejaculatory duct. The mucosa is folded in a complicated manner, forming numerous irregular chambers or crypts (Fig. 19-21). The epithelium varies somewhat but is usually pseudostratified, being composed of cuboidal or columnar cells that reach the surface, and irregularly shaped basal cells similar to those described in the genital ducts. The walls of the surface cells are very distinct. The cytoplasm of these cells contains secretion granules and a yellowish lipochrome pigment (Fig. 19-22). The pigment makes its appearance at sexual maturity and increases with age.

The lamina propria is rich in elastic fibers and forms a continuous layer around the vesicle. The stroma of the folds is likewise rich in elastic fibers and contains some smooth muscle cells. Outside of the lamina propria is smooth muscle, which can be

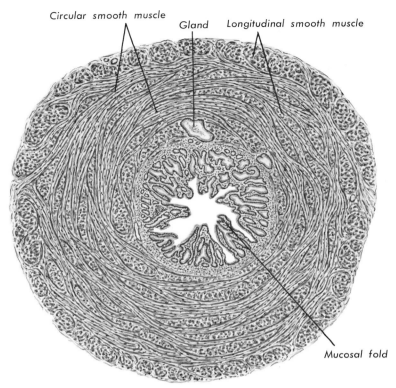

Circular smooth muscle   Gland   Longitudinal smooth muscle

Mucosal fold

Fig. 19-20. Section through the ampulla of the ductus deferens. Man, 21 years of age. ×30. (After Stieve.)

rather indefinitely divided into inner circular and outer longitudinal layers, both layers being thinner than in the ductus deferens.

Spermatozoa in varying numbers are often seen in the seminal vesicles. Their presence there is accidental, however. The seminal vesicles are not storehouses for sperm but are glandular structures contributing a slightly alkaline, viscid secretion to the seminal fluid. The secretion is rich in fructose which serves as an energy source for the sperm.

The Prostate Gland. (Figs. 19-23 to 19-25). The prostate is in reality an aggregation of many branched tubuloalveolar glands with wide ducts and terminal tubules. The glands number from 30 to 50, and their ducts converge to form 20 or more terminal ducts which open into the urethra.

The gland is surrounded by a vascular capsule of fibroelastic tissue containing numerous smooth muscle fibers in its inner layer. From the capsule, broad septa penetrate into the interior to form the unusually abundant stroma, which separates the scattered tubules or alveoli. As in the capsule, the stroma is rich in elastic fibers and contains numerous smooth muscle fibers that course in various directions (Fig. 19-26). This fibromuscular tissue may constitute one-third or even more of the whole mass of the prostate.

The epithelium shows a great variation in different glands and alveoli and even in a single alveolus. It is usually a simple cuboidal or columnar type. Basal cells may be present. The walls of the epithelial cells are usually distinct. Certain cells show bleblike protrusions. The cytoplasm contains secretion granules and lipid droplets. The epithelium

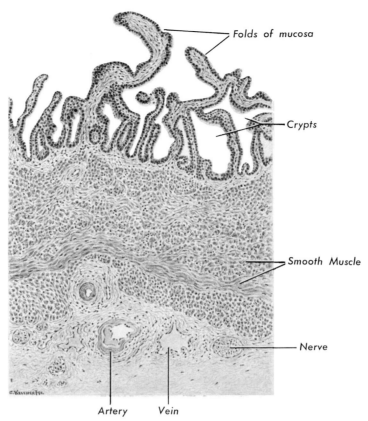

FIG. 19-21. From a section through wall of seminal vesicle. Human, 34 years old. Mallory-azan stain. ×65.

and subjacent stroma form folds that project into the cavities of the glands. The ducts are lined by a simple columnar epithelium that changes, near the terminations of the ducts, to the transitional epithelium of the urethra.

Corpora amylacea occur normally in some of the alveoli of most prostate glands (Fig. 19-24). Typically, they are spherical bodies about 250 μ in diameter, but there is considerable variation in size. In the fresh condition, they are fairly soft and light yellowish brown in color. In sections, concentric layers that stain with different intensities are evident. They are composed of protein and carbohydrates. Corpora increase in number with age. They may become calcified and then are known as *calculi*, some of which reach a very large size.

Prostatic secretion is rich in citric acid and contains lipids. "Lipid bodies" that stain with eosin are frequent. Prostatic secretion also contains large amounts of acid phosphatase which, because of a normal daily discharge of prostatic secretion (0.5 to 2 cc. per day), is present also in urine. Normal blood serum also contains acid phosphatase in small amounts. In prostatic carcinoma, however, there is frequently a pronounced discharge of the enzyme from the prostate into the blood stream. The acid phosphatase content of the blood may be increased sufficiently to make its determination of clinical significance in judging whether metastasis has occurred. It may also be useful in indicating the response to therapy.

Within the prostate is found the *vesicula*

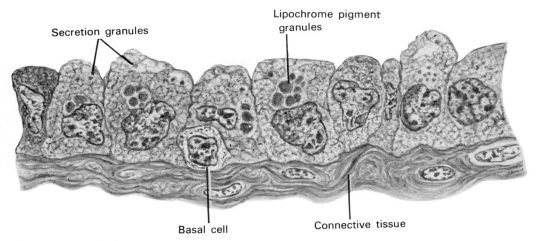

Secretion granules

Lipochrome pigment granules

Basal cell

Connective tissue

FIG. 19-22. Epithelium of seminal vesicle. Human, 34 years old. Mallory-azan stain, 3-μ section. ×1900.

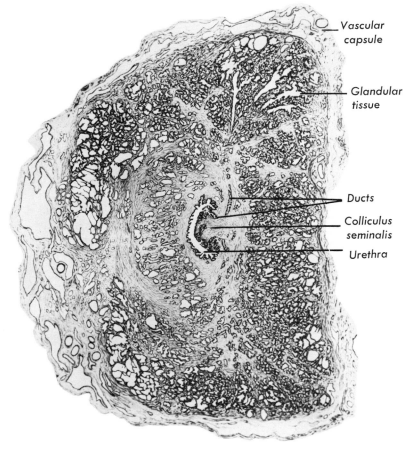

Vascular capsule

Glandular tissue

Ducts

Colliculus seminalis

Urethra

FIG. 19-23. Transverse section through the prostate at the level of the colliculus seminalis. Man, 19 years old. ×4. (After Stieve.)

Concretions   Alveolus

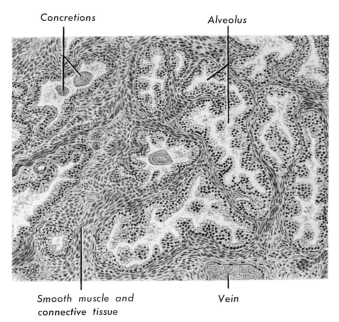

Smooth muscle and   Vein
connective tissue

FIG. 19-24. Section of prostate gland. Human, accident case, 54 years old. Hematoxylin-eosin. ×65

Secretion granules

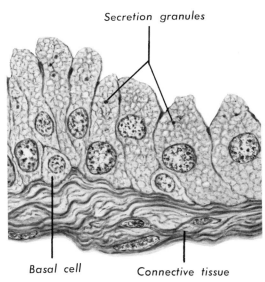

Basal cell   Connective tissue

FIG. 19-25. Epithelium of prostate gland. Human, 54 years old. Accident case. Mallory-azan stain, 3-μ section. ×1660.

prostatica (*utriculus prostaticus, uterus masculinus*), the remains of the fetal *Müllerian duct*. It consists of a blind tubule with a folded mucous membrane lined by a simple

or pseudostratified columnar epithelium that dips down to form short tubular glands.

The *blood vessels* of the prostate ramify in the capsule and trabeculae. The small arteries give rise to a capillary network that surrounds the tubules. From these arise small veins that accompany the arteries in the septa and form venous plexuses in the capsule.

The *lymphatics* begin as clefts in the trabeculae and follow the general course of the blood vessels.

The *nerves* of the prostate are both motor and sensory; the majority is unmyelinated. Many of them come from groups of autonomic ganglion cells which are found underneath the capsule and in the larger trabeculae. Axons of these cells pass to the smooth muscle of the trabeculae and blood vessels and probably also to the epithelium of the tubules.

The Bulbourethral Glands (Fig. 19-27). The bulbourethral glands or *glands of Cowper* are two small glandular structures placed close to the bulb of the urethra. They are compound tubuloalveolar glands whose tubules and ducts have a very irregular diameter. The terminal portions may be tubular or alveolar or in the form of cyst-like dilations. They are lined by a simple epithelium whose height varies from co-lumnar to low cuboidal and which may even be flat in distended alveoli. Most of the columnar cells are of the mucous type, with the nuclei basally placed, and the cytoplasm containing mucinogen droplets. Other cells stain darker with eosin and have a granular appearance, often containing fibrillar or spindle-shaped inclusions. During erotic stimulation, the gland secretes a glairy sub-stance resembling mucus into the urethra. This probably serves as a lubricant for the epithelium.

The smaller ducts are lined by a simple epithelium and seem to be secretory in character. They unite to form two main ducts that run parallel to the urethra for a variable distance and then open into the latter. The main ducts have a stratified columnar epithelium.

The stroma between the tubules consists of fibroelastic tissue with few muscle fibers.

FIG. 19-26. Prostate of a man 34 years old. The large number of smooth muscle fibers in the stroma is shown. ×190. (After Stieve.)

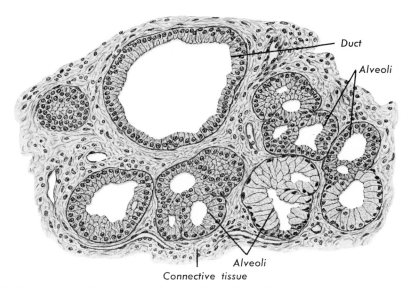

FIG. 19-27. Section through a lobule of the bulbourethral (Cowper's) gland. Human, 23 years old. ×200.

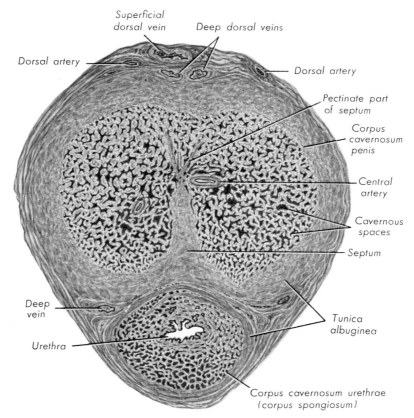

FIG. 19–28. Cross section of penis of adult man. The section is at the juncture of the proximal two-thirds and the distal one-third of the organ. The skin has been removed. ✕4.5.

Smooth and skeletal muscle fibers are, however, quite numerous in the septa between the lobules. Externally, the glands are enclosed by a layer of skeletal muscle fibers from the deep perineal and bulbocavernosus muscles.

THE PENIS

The penis (Fig. 19-28) consists largely of three cylindrical masses of erectile tissue, the paired, dorsally placed *corpora cavernosa* and, lying underneath them, the unpaired *corpus spongiosum (corpus cavernosum urethrae)*. The latter surrounds the urethra and terminates distally in a conical enlargement, the *glans penis*. The three cylindrical bodies are enclosed in a common fascia of loose, irregularly arranged connective tissue rich in elastic fibers, to which the covering skin is

loosely attached. In the glans, the loose connective tissue is lacking and the skin adheres firmly to the underlying erectile tissue.

Each corpus cavernosum is surrounded by a dense capsule or *tunica albuginea* composed of collagenous fibers, the inner ones running circularly, the outer ones longitudinally. Elastic fibers are quite numerous. Between the cavernosa, the capsules fuse to form a median septum which is thickest and most complete near the root of the penis. Farther forward it becomes thinner and contains numerous slitlike spaces that permit a communication between the two bodies (Fig. 19-28). Directly underneath the albuginea is an irregular plexus of small veins.

The interior of each body consists of a network of large spaces or lacunae lined by endothelium (cavernous veins). These are separated by fibrous trabeculae rich in smooth muscle fibers which are disposed both circularly and longitudinally. The lacunae are large and trabeculae are thin in the central portion. At the periphery is a layer of narrower spaces which communicate with the venous plexus on the inner surface of the albuginea. In the flaccid organ, the lacunae are kept closed by the tonus of the trabecular muscle and appear as mere slits.

The corpus spongiosum has a similar structure, but the albuginea is thin and contains many elastic fibers, so that the organ is not highly resistant to expansion. The trabeculae are thin, the lacunae are quite uniform in size and a peripheral layer of smaller lacunae is absent. Toward the urethra the lacunae become continuous with the mucosal plexus of veins; at the periphery they communicate with the venous network of the albuginea.

In the glans, the erectile tissue has the character of a dense, venous plexus. An albuginea is lacking, the skin being firmly attached to the erectile tissue.

The skin of the penis is characterized by tall dermal papillae and a thin epidermis containing considerable pigment in the basal layer. Coarse hairs are found only at the root, but fine lanugo hairs are distributed over all of the shaft. Only the glans and inner surface of the prepuce are entirely hairless.

The *prepuce* is a fold of skin that overlies the glans. It consists of fibroelastic tissue containing bundles of muscle fibers and is covered by a very thin epidermis. On its inner surface, and on the glans as well, are found a number of modified sebaceous glands, the *glands of Tyson*.

Blood Vessels. The penis has a complicated blood supply that can respond to its varying functional states. The organ is chiefly supplied by the *arteria dorsalis* and the *arteria profunda*, which are branches of the *arteria penis*. The dorsal artery sends twigs to the albuginea and the larger

cavernous trabeculae, where they break up into capillaries. Leaving the capillaries, the blood enters the lacunae and is drained by the plexus of albugineal veins. This is the course of most of the blood during the flaccid state.

The principal vessels for filling the lacunae during erection are the deep arteries (*arteriae profundae*), one of which runs lengthwise in each corpus cavernosum. They give off numerous branches that are supported by the trabecular tissue and end in minute arteries that open directly into the cavernous spaces. In the flaccid organ, many of the arterial branches project into the lacunae as looped or spiral vessels, the *helicine arteries*. Similar vessels are found in the corpus spongiosum.

The helicine arteries have an unusually thick media of circular muscle fibers, and in many of them the intima shows valve-like structures in the form of marked longitudinal thickenings or cushions. When the muscle of the arteries contracts, these thickenings plug up the lumen and shut off the blood supply.

During erection, the muscle of the helicine arteries and of the cavernous trabeculae relaxes, and the lacunae are flooded with arterial blood from the helicine vessels, which empty mainly in the central spaces of the cavernous bodies. The sudden filling of the large central spaces tends to compress the narrower peripheral ones, which communicate with the venous plexus of the albuginea. Egress of blood is blocked or at least greatly reduced, and the organ becomes swollen and rigid. At the end of the erectile state, the muscle of the helicine arteries contracts and the inflow of blood is shut off. The trabecular muscle regains its tonus and the blood is slowly driven out into the venous plexus. There are special provisions for emptying the corpora cavernosa. One or perhaps several veins originate directly from the central lacunae. These are equipped with funnel-shaped valves whose small openings permit the passage of only a small stream of blood. When the blood supply of the helicine arteries is cut off, these veins begin to empty the central lacunae. The internal pressure is reduced, the peripheral lacunae open and then the blood is pressed out more rapidly into the peripheral veins, the organ gradually returning to the flaccid condition. Most of the blood from the corpora cavernosa is drained by the *vena profundis penis*.

The corpus spongiosum is filled in a similar manner. However, the albuginea is more elastic, the lacunae are more uniform in size and the outflow of blood is not blocked to the same extent. The spongiosum naturally swells during erection, owing to the increased blood supply, but it always remains compressible and does not assume the rigidity of the paired cavernous bodies.

Lymphatics. Numerous lymphatics are found in the skin of the shaft, prepuce and glans (superficial plexus) and in the mucosal stroma of the urethra. A deeper lymphatic network in the erectile tissue has also been described. The lymphatics drain chiefly into the inguinal lymph nodes.

Nerves. The penis is abundantly supplied with spinal, sympathetic and parasympathetic nerve fibers. The sensory spinal fibers terminate in a variety of end organs: free sensory endings, Meissner's corpuscles in the papillae, and Pacinian corpuscles and end bulbs of Krause in the connective tissue.

Sympathetic and parasympathetic motor fibers form extensive networks in the walls of the blood vessels and the smooth muscle of the cavernous trabeculae.

INTERNAL SECRETION OF THE TESTES

It has been known for a long time that the testes are in some way responsible for the appearance of the secondary sex characters. When the testes are removed before puberty, these characters remain in an infantile condition or are entirely suppressed. The penis and prostate gland are small, the male type of chest and pelvis fails to develop, the face, chest and limbs are hairless, the larynx remains small and, as a result, the voice maintains its infantile pitch. The bones grow beyond their normal length but are not robust. Sometimes there is considerable deposition of fat, its distribution characteristic of the feminine type.

When castration is performed after puberty, the effects are less pronounced, for the sex characters are already established and the changes are retrogressive.

The most profound and constant effects of castration in mammals, as shown experimentally, are upon the genital ducts and accessory glands. The epithelium of these structures fails to develop to the normal height and does not show secretory activity if the testes are removed before puberty or, if they are removed after maturity, the epithelium of these structures will involute. The effect of the testes on these accessory reproductive structures appears to be due solely to a hormone secreted by the testes called *testosterone*. There are other male sex hormones that are found in the urine, but presumably they are not secreted by the testes but are transformation products of the testis hormone or are secreted by other organs (adrenals), although not in sufficient amounts to substitute for the testis hormone. The response of the various accessory reproductive organs and of the comb of the capon have been used in assays of the male hormone content of extracts.

The evidence is quite conclusive that the interstial cells of the testes secrete the male sex hormone. In undescended or partially descended testes (cryptorchid), the epithelium of the seminiferous tubules, but not the interstitial tissue, atrophies from continued exposure to the temperature of the body cavity. Extensive degeneration of the spermatogenic cells is likewise produced by treatment with X-rays, the interstitial cells being uninjured when the correct dosage is used. In both cases, the secondary sex characters remain normal. Histochemical studies have shown that compounds with the chemical properties of testosterone are present in the interstitial cells but not elsewhere in the testis (Pollock). There is a correlation between the testosterone content and amount of interstitial tissue (Hooker).

Estrogen, the female sex hormone, also occurs in the male. It has been shown that about 80% of the estrogen arises from the Leydig cells and about 20% from the adrenal gland.

Hormones secreted by cells of the anterior hypophysis are essential for the endocrine and spermatogenic function of the testis. The activity of the interstitial cells of Leydig is dependent on the interstitial cell-stimulating hormone (luteinizing hormone), and the development of germ cells is dependent on the follicle-stimulating hormone (Chapter 21). The anterior hypophysis has an indirect influence on the accessory reproductive organs through its action on the testis.

SEMEN

Semen consists of seminal plasma, spermatozoa and usually some cells cast off from the lining of the reproductive ducts and glands. Seminal plasma consists of the secretion of the prostate, seminal vesicles, bulbourethral glands and epididymis, the chief contribution being from the prostate and seminal vesicles. The seminal plasma serves as a food source and vehicle for the spermatozoa.

The volume of semen from a normal ejaculation varies greatly among different individuals and in the same individual, as does also the number of sperm. The usual range in volume is from 2 to 5 or 6 cc. The total number of sperm ranges from a high of 500,000,000, or even more, to a low of a few million or to complete azoospermia. A variable percentage of sperm is malformed or inactive.

Testicular or epididymal sperm are inactive but quickly become active in seminal plasma (or saline). They carry little of the foodstuff for metabolism but acquire this from the carbohydrate, chiefly fructose, in the seminal plasma. The sugar is reduced to lactic acid, glycolysis being best carried out under nearly anaerobic conditions.

The role of the high content of hyaluronidase in sperm is not entirely understood, but histochemical studies indicate that it breaks down the egg coating and aids the sperm in penetrating the egg.

REFERENCES

ALBERT, A. 1961 The mammalian testis. *In* Sex and Internal Secretion (Young, W. C., editor), vol. 1, pp. 305–366. The Williams & Wilkins Company, Baltimore.

AUSTIN, C. R., AND PERRY, J. S. (Editors) 1965 Symposium on Agents Affecting Fertility. Little, Brown and Co. Boston.

BAWA, S. R. 1963 The fine structure of the Sertoli cell of the human testis. J. Ultrastruct. Res., vol. 9, pp. 459–474.

BURGOS, M. H. 1964 Uptake of colloidal particles by cells of the caput epididymis. Anat. Rec., vol. 148, pp. 517–525.

BURGOS, M. H., AND FAWCETT, D. W. 1955 Studies on the fine structure of the mammalian testis. J. Biophys. Biochem. Cytol., vol. 1, pp. 287–300.

CHANG, M. C., AND PINCUS, G. 1951 Physiology of fertilization in mammals. Physiol. Rev., vol. 31, pp. 1–26.

CHRISTENSEN, A. K. 1965 The fine structure of testicular interstitial cells in the guinea pig. J. Cell Biol., vol. 26, pp. 911–935.

CLERMONT, Y. 1963 The cycle of the seminiferous epithelium in man. Amer. J. Anat., vol. 112, pp. 35–52.

DEANE, H. W., AND PORTER, K. R. 1960 A comparative study of cytoplasmic basophilia and the population density of ribosomes in the secretory cells of mouse seminal vesicle. Z. Zellforsch., vol. 52, pp. 697–711.

DYM, M., AND FAWCETT, D. W. 1970 The blood-testis barrier in the rat and the physiological compartmentation of the seminiferous epithelium. Biol. Reprod., vol. 3, pp. 308–326.

ELFTMAN, H. 1950 The Sertoli cell cycle in the mouse. Anat. Rec., vol. 106, pp. 381–393.

ELFTMAN, H. 1963 Sertoli cells and testis structure. Amer. J. Anat., vol. 113, pp. 25–34.

FAWCETT, D. W., AND BURGOS, M. H. 1960 Studies on the fine structure of the mammalian testis. II. The human interstitial tissue. Amer. J. Anat., vol. 107, pp. 245–270.

FAWCETT, D. W., AND ITO, S. 1965 The fine structure of bat spermatozoa. Amer. J. Anat., vol. 116, pp. 567–610.

FRANK, A. L., AND CHRISTENSEN, A. K. 1968 Localization of acid phosphatase in lipofuscin granules and possible autophagic vacuoles in interstitial cells of guinea pig testis. J. Cell Biol., vol. 36, pp. 1–13.

GOMORI, G. 1941 Distribution of acid phosphatase in the tissues under normal and under pathological conditions. Arch. Path. (Chicago), vol. 32, pp. 189–199.

HELLER, C. G., AND CLERMONT, Y. 1963 Spermatogenesis in man: an estimate of its duration. Science, vol. 140, pp. 184–185.

HELLER, C. G., AND CLERMONT, Y. 1964 Kinetics of the germinal epithelium in man. In Recent Progress in Hormone Research (Pincus, G., editor), vol. 20, pp. 545–575. Academic Press, New York.

HOOKER, C. W. 1944 The postnatal history and function of the interstitial cells of the testis of the bull. Amer. J. Anat., vol. 74, pp. 1–37.

HUGGINS, C. 1947 The prostatic secretion. Harvey Lectures, Ser. 42, pp. 148–193.

LEBLOND, C. P., AND CLERMONT, Y. 1952 Definition of the stages of the cycle of the seminiferous epithelium in the rat. Ann. N. Y. Acad. Sci., vol. 55, pp. 548–573.

MANN, T. 1964 Biochemistry of semen and of the male reproductive tract. John Wiley & Sons, Inc., New York.

MASON, K. E., AND SHAVER, S. L. 1952 Some functions of the caput epididymis. Ann. N. Y. Acad. Sci., vol. 55, pp. 585–593.

MOORE, R. A. 1936 The evolution and involution of the prostate gland. Amer. J. Path., vol. 12, pp. 599–624.

MOORE, R. A. 1936 Morphology of prostatic corpora amylacea and calculi. Arch. Path. (Chicago), vol. 22, pp. 24–40.

MORITA, I. 1966 Some observations on the fine structure of the human ductuli efferentes testis. Arch. Histol. Jap., vol. 26, pp. 341–365.

POLLOCK, W. F. 1942 Histochemical studies of the interstitial cells of the testis. Anat. Rec., vol. 84, pp. 23–31.

ROOSEN-RUNGE, E. C. 1962 The process of spermatogenesis in mammals. Biol. Rev., vol. 37, pp. 343–377.

ROOSEN-RUNGE, E. C., AND BARLOW, F. D. 1953 Quantitative studies on human spermatogenesis. Amer. J. Anat., vol. 93, pp. 143–169.

ROSS, M. H. 1966 Contractile cells in human seminiferous tubules. Science, vol. 153, pp. 1271–1273.

SAND, K., AND OKKELS, H. 1938 The histological variability of the testis from normal and sexual-abnormal, castrated men. Endokrinologie, vol. 19, pp. 369–374.

SCHMIDT, F. C. 1964 Licht- und elektronemikroskopische Untersuchungen am menschlichen Hoden und Nebenhoden. Z. Zellforsch., vol. 63, pp. 707–729.

STIEVE, H. 1930 Männlichen Genitalorgane. Handb. mikr. Anat. Menschen (v. Möllendorff, editor), vol. 2, pt. 2, pp. 1–399.

YAMADA, E. 1967 Some observations on the fine structure of the interstitial cell in the human testis. In Fifth International Conference on Electron Microscopy (Breese, S. S., Jr., editor), vol. 2, pp. LL–1. Academic Press, New York.

20

The Female Reproductive System

The female genital organs comprise the ovaries in which the egg cells are formed, a system of genital ducts—the Fallopian tubes, uterus and vagina—and the external genitalia, including the labia majora, labia minora and clitoris. The mammary glands, although not one of the genital organs, are important glands of the female reproductive system. The ovaries, like the testes, are also important glands of internal secretion.

THE OVARY

The ovaries are somewhat flattened, ovoid bodies, measuring about 4 cm. in length, 2 cm. in width and 1 cm. in thickness. One lies on each side of the uterus in relation to the lateral wall of the pelvis (Fig. 20-1). Each is attached at its hilum to the back of the broad ligament by a peritoneal fold, the mesovarium, and by the ligament of the ovary. The ovary is pinkish gray and does not have the glistening or shiny appearance characteristic of the peritoneum. Its surface is uneven and becomes puckered to an increasing degree with aging.

At the hilum, the connective tissue of the mesovarium and ovarian ligament passes into the ovary and becomes continuous with the ovarian stroma. The mesothelial covering of the mesovarium changes at the hilum to a low cuboidal *surface epithelium* which covers the ovary. This is also known as germinal epithelium, although there is no convincing evidence that it is the site of formation of the germ cells.

In sections of the ovary, two zones may be distinguished, a central deeper portion, the *medulla* or *zona vasculosa*, and a broad outer layer, the *cortex* (Fig. 20-2). The two zones blend into each other without any distinct demarcation.

The medulla is composed of a stroma of loose connective tissue rich in elastic fibers and containing numerous large blood vessels, lymphatics and nerves. Bundles of smooth muscle fibers are found near the hilum. In some individuals, vestiges of certain fetal structures, the *rete ovarii*, occur as epithelial strands or tubules in the region of the hilum.

The cortex is a broad peripheral layer interrupted at the hilum where the medulla becomes continuous with the tissues of the mesovarium. It consists of a compact, richly cellular stroma in which are scattered the characteristic glandular structures of the ovary, the *ovarian follicles* (Fig. 20-2). The connective tissue cells are fusiform or spindle-shaped, with elongated vesicular nuclei. They are placed in a feltwork of delicate collagenous fibrils. Elastic tissue, except in the walls of the blood vessels, is practically absent. Directly underneath the germinal epithelium, the stroma forms a denser fibrous layer, the *tunica albuginea*, composed of fewer cells and more closely packed fibers.

The Follicles. Each ovarian follicle consists of an ovum surrounded by epithelial

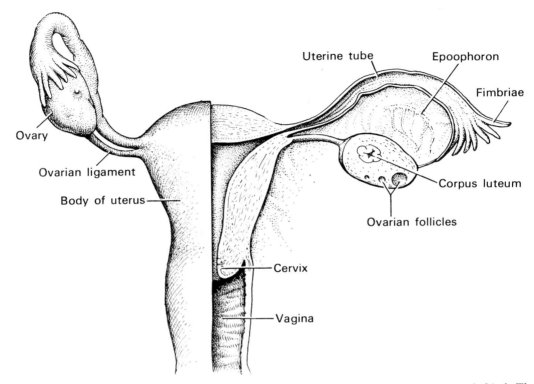

FIG. 20-1. Diagram of the internal organs of the female reproductive system seen from behind. The ovary and uterine tube are shown in approximately normal position at the left and they are drawn apart and away from the uterus at the right.

cells. A brief outline of the embryonic origin of the follicles is given to facilitate an understanding of their nature in pre- and postnatal stages.

Primordial germ cells appear in the wall of the yolk sac during the third week of human development, and they migrate to the germinal ridges (embryonic gonads) by the fifth week. The primordial germ cells become intermingled with the surface epithelial cells, and cordlike projections of cells extend from the surface into the underlying ovarian stroma during the second and third months. These masses of cells proliferate actively and become subdivided into clusters, each composed of several primordial germ cells and numerous follicular cells. It was once thought that the germ cells as well as the follicular cells arise by differentiation of ovarian surface cells. Most of the evidence

indicates, however, that the germ cells form from entoderm in the wall of the yolk sac and then migrate to the embryonic gonads, where they divide and differentiate.

After a relatively short period, the clusters of cells that have invaded the ovarian stroma become subdivided into smaller bodies known as *primordial* and *primary follicles*, each consisting of an oocyte surrounded by a single layer of follicular cells (Fig. 20-3, *A*). A primordial follicle is defined as one in which the ovum is inconstantly and incompletely surrounded by a very low epithelium (Simkins, 1932), whereas the ovum of a primary follicle is completely surrounded by a cuboidal epithelium. In late fetal life, the tunica albuginea is formed, and the surface epithelium is reduced to a single layer of cells which are columnar in early life and cuboidal in the adult.

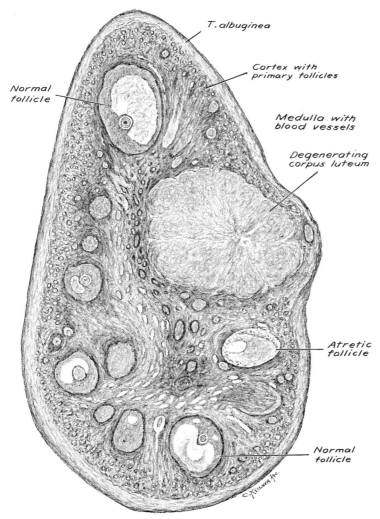

T. albuginea

Cortex with primary follicles

Medulla with blood vessels

Degenerating corpus luteum

Normal follicle

Atretic follicle

Normal follicle

FIG. 20-2. Longitudinal section through the ovary of a normal adult rhesus monkey. The corpus luteum is probably degenerating.

There is considerable evidence that multiplication of oogonia in the human generally ceases by about the sixth fetal month. In fact, the most marked proliferation occurs even earlier, and the majority of the cells differentiate to the primary oocyte stage by the fifth fetal month (see reviews by Witschi, 1963, and Franchi, Mandl and Zuckerman, 1962). The primary oocytes spend a long time prior to completing their differentiation to the first meiotic (chromosomal reduction) division.

Most of the follicles in the ovary of the newborn are of the primordial and primary types, with the former predominating. A few follicles with small antra (vesicular stage) may be present in the ovary at birth for a brief period, apparently through stimulation by maternal hormones during the latter part of fetal life. Estimates of the total number of oocytes present at birth vary within wide limits. Counts made on serial sections show that at least 400,000 primordial and primary follicles are present in the ovaries of the newborn infant.

Of this large number, relatively few are

destined to reach full maturity. The reproductive life of a woman, from puberty to menopause, lasts about 30 to 35 years. During this period, even if no disturbing factors appear, one ovum matures normally each month, so that only about 400 eggs actually reach maturity. All of the others ultimately degenerate and, from birth on, the follicles progressively diminish in number. Follicular degeneration occurs most intensely in early life but continues actively throughout the period of sexual maturity. After the menopause, the remaining follicles degenerate within a few years.

In the mature ovary, the follicles are found in all stages of growth. Most numerous are the primary follicles found mainly in the peripheral layer of the cortex. As a follicle grows, it occupies progressively deeper positions.

The primary follicles (Fig. 20-3) are spheroidal bodies measuring 30 to 40 μ. The central ovum, about 20 μ in diameter, has a large, vesicular nucleus with a deeply staining chromatin reticulum and a rather indistinct nucleolus. The cytoplasm is finely granular. The follicular cells are either flattened or low cuboidal. A definite connective tissue capsule is lacking.

Growth and Maturation of the Follicles. The further growth of the primary follicles is characterized by the proliferation of the follicular cells, the increase in size of the ovum and the formation of a connective tissue capsule. The follicular cells become cuboidal, divide actively and soon form a stratified layer around the ovum (Fig. 20-3). Irregular small spaces appear in the follicular mass and fuse to form a crescent-shaped cavity, the *antrum* or follicular cavity, filled with a serous fluid, the *liquor folliculi*. Subsequent to the formation of a definite antrum, the structure is known as a *vesicular follicle*.

While the follicle is increasing in size, it assumes an ovoid shape and moves to a deeper position in the stroma. By continual division of follicular cells and by an expansion of the antrum, the ovum is pressed to one side of the follicle, where it is surrounded by a mound of follicular cells forming the *cumulus oophorous* or germ hill (Fig. 20-4, *A*). The follicular cells immediately adjacent to the ovum form a *corona radiata* around the ovum.

Concurrently with the growth of the ovum and the multiplication of the follicular cells, the stroma around the follicle develops into a follicular sheath, the *theca folliculi*, composed of an inner vascular region, the *theca interna*, and an outer fibrous layer, the *theca externa* (Figs. 20-3 and 20-4). Although the cells of both layers of the theca folliculi are connective tissue derivatives, those of the *theca interna* have epithelioid characteristics. They are ovoid or polyhedral, have ovoid or rounded nuclei and have lipid droplets in their cytoplasm. Electron micrographs show that the cristae of their mitochondria are tubular rather than shelf like and that they resemble those of cells known to be active in the secretion of steroid hormones. It seems likely that the theca interna cells form the estrogen secreted by the follicle. The theca externa is composed of connective tissue fibers and spindle-shaped cells. The interna is separated from the membrana granulosa by the basement membrane beneath the granulosa cells which is known as the *follicular basement membrane*. There is no distinct boundary between the theca interna and the theca externa, and the junction of the latter with the surrounding stroma is very poorly defined.

The ovum grows rapidly during the early stages of follicular growth and is already approaching its maximal size by the time the antrum appears in the follicle (Fig. 20-3, *C*). The nucleus of the ovum becomes large and vesicular (germinal vesicle), with a sparse chromatin reticulum and a large, deeply staining nucleolus (germinal spot). Yolk accumulates in the cytoplasm, particularly in the interior, which becomes coarsely granular in contrast with the finely granular, clearer zone at the periphery. A relatively

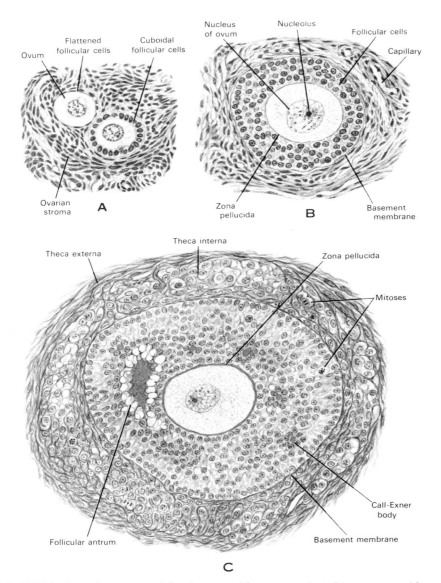

FIG. 20-3. Follicles in various states of development. These were selected from a normal human ovary removed surgically on the 14th day of the cycle and fixed by injection with Bouin's fluid. The patient was 36 years of age. The illustrations are drawn at a uniform magnification, ×289. Sections illustrated in A and B were stained in hematoxylin and eosin, C in Masson's trichrome strain without a preliminary application of hematoxylin. A, two follicles in early stages of development: primordial (left) and primary (right). B, an early stage of a growing follicle. C, a follicle, showing the beginning of the formation of the antrum.

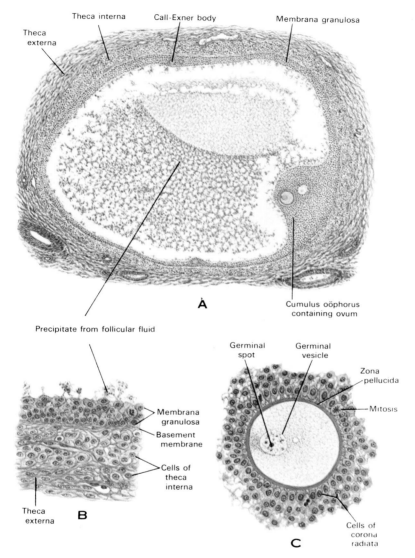

FIG. 20-4. On this plate is illustrated a follicle with a maximal dimension of 4.5 mm. From the same ovary as Figure 20-3. Masson's trichrome stain. *A*, low power view, ×53. *B*, a portion of the wall of this follicle, ×287. *C*, the ovum of this follicle drawn at the same magnification as the illustrations in Figure 20-3, ×287.

thick membrane known as the *zona pellucida* is formed around the outer surface of the ovum (Figs. 20-4 to 20-6). It is rich in polysaccharides, and apparently it is formed partly by the ovum and partly by the granulosa cells. It is a resistant membrane which persists during atresia longer than the ovum. Phase and electron microscope studies show that processes from the corona radiata cells extend through the zona pellucida to make contact with the plasma membrane of the ovum (Fig. 20-5). It is thought that the processes facilitate the transport of substances to the ovum. Other processes (microvilli) extend from the ovum into the zona pellucida.

The *mature vesicular follicle* (Graafian follicle) attains a diameter of 10 to 12 mm. It extends through the whole thickness of the cortex and encroaches peripherally upon the tunica albuginea, producing a bulge which is visible on the surface of the ovary. In the latter part of follicular maturation, fluid continues to accumulate in the antrum, and fluid-filled spaces also appear among the cells of the cumulus oophorous, thereby weakening the attachment of the ovum and its associated cells to the follicular wall.

Ovulation. Just prior to ovulation, there is a marked increase of fluid in the antrum, producing greater pressure on the wall of the follicle and on the thin layer of ovarian tissue at the surface. In laboratory animals in which the events of ovulation can be observed, it is seen that blood flow stops in a small area near the center of the translucent bulge on the ovarian surface just prior to ovulation. A small conical projection appears at this spot, known as the *stigma*, and the follicle ruptures. Fluid escapes, and the ovum, together with its corona radiata and a number of cells of the germ hill, also passes through the opening. This process of rupture of the follicle and discharge of the ovum is known as *ovulation*. The egg and its associated cells enter the peritoneal cavity briefly, then pass into the fimbriated funnel

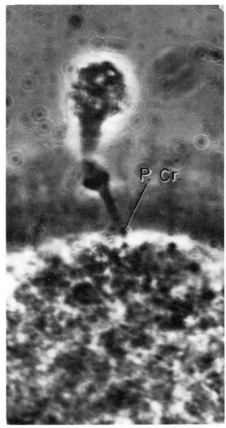

FIG. 20-5. Photomicrograph of a corona radiata cell with a process extending through the zona pellucida. The end of the process (*P. Cr.*) is seen in the perivitelline space around the ovum. It is thought that nutritive material is supplied to the ovum in this manner. (Courtesy of Dr. L. B. Shettles.)

of the oviduct. The fimbriae of the duct are close to the surface of the ovary at this time.

The ovum must be fertilized soon after ovulation or it will degenerate, fragment and disappear. Although no data are available for the human, studies on animals show that the ovum does not retain the capacity to be fertilized much longer than 24 hours. In some species fertilization must occur within 4 to 6 hours after ovulation. The union of ovum and sperm takes place either before or immediately after the ovum enters the fimbriated extremity of the tube. Following

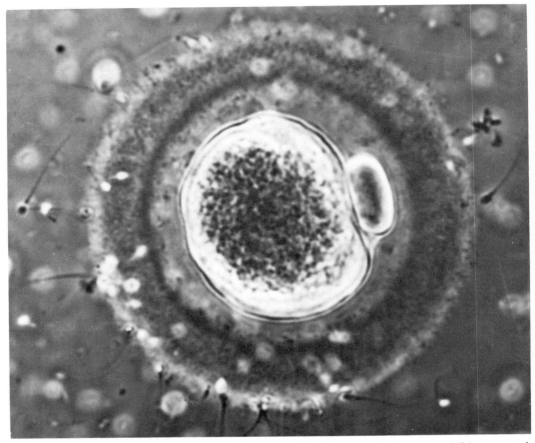

FIG. 20-6. Photomicrograph of living human ovum and its first polar body surrounded by zona pellucida and by cumulus cells. Sperm, which are attempting to reach the ovum, are seen at the periphery of the cumulus cells. (Courtesy of Dr. L. B. Shettles.)

fertilization, the journey of the egg down the tube to the uterus is a leisurely one. Data from early human embryos secured by Hertig and Rock show that the ovum reaches the uterus about 3 days after ovulation. It is implanted in the endometrium about 6 days after ovulation.

Atresia. Of the numerous follicles, only a few reach full maturity and discharge the ovum. The vast majority undergo degeneration either as primary follicles or after a varying period of growth. The degeneration of follicles is known as *atresia*.

In atresia of the *primary follicles*, the ovum undergoes degeneration accompanied by chromatolysis and fragmentation of the nucleus, and this is followed by similar changes in the follicular cells. The follicle is resorbed and disappears, and the space that it occupied is filled with stroma.

Atresia of the *growing* and *maturing follicles* is a more complicated process which varies in details, depending on the size of the follicle and the behavior of the theca interna. Here too the disintegrative changes start in the ovum and spread to the follicular cells. These changes are in the nature of fatty degeneration, evidenced by the accumulation of fatty granules in the cytoplasm, chromatolysis of the nuclei and ultimate liquefaction. The zona pellucida swells, becomes folded and may persist for some time after the disappearance of the ovum and follicular cells.

The theca interna cells persist for a longer

Zona pellucida   Loose connective tissue filling follicular antrum

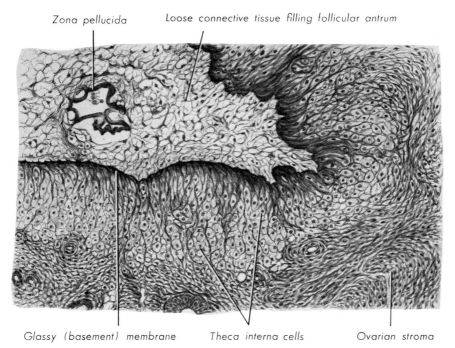

Glassy (basement) membrane   Theca interna cells   Ovarian stroma

Fig. 20-7. A moderately early stage in follicular atresia. The ovum and the granulosa cells have been resorbed. The glassy (basement) membrane is much thickened and the theca interna cells have reached their maximal development. Normal ovary of a woman 36 years old. Surgical specimen removed at the midcycle. Masson's trichrome stain. ×193.

period than do the granulosa cells (Figs. 20-7 to 20-9). The former enlarge and show an increase in cytoplasmic lipid droplets, thereby resembling lutein cells. These cells persist for long periods in some animals and form the *ovarian interstitial cells.* They disappear more rapidly in humans, and cells of interstitial type cannot be identified with certainty in the adult human ovary. They can be recognized during childhood when large numbers of follicles are continually undergoing atresia.

In the mature ovary, there are always several antrum-containing follicles of various sizes. Most of these are destined to undergo atresia at some stage in their growth. As a rule, only one follicle matures each month, and the process of transformation from a growing to a mature follicle is accomplished in about 2 weeks. In rare instances, two or even several follicles may ripen at the same time.

Oogenesis. In preparation for the union with the spermatozoon, the ovum passes through a series of changes similar to that described for the sperm cells (see under "spermatogenesis," Chapter 19) and with the same end result, namely, the reduction of its chromosomes to one-half the somatic number. The changes differ, however, in one important respect. In the male, each primary spermatocyte gives rise to four functioning spermatozoa. In the female, one primary oocyte gives rise to but one mature ovum, the other three being discarded as abortive minute bodies, the *polar bodies.*

The *oogonia,* or primitive ova which contain the somatic (*diploid*) number of chromosomes, divide mitotically as do the spermatogonia, the daughter cells likewise containing the full number of chromosomes. The mitotic period for oogonia differs, however, from that for spermatogonia, ending at about the sixth month of fetal life for

Invading blood vessels   Ovarian stroma

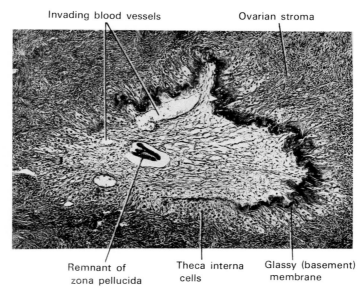

Remnant of   Theca interna   Glassy (basement)
zona pellucida   cells   membrane

FIG. 20-8. Medium stage of follicular atresia. Normal ovary of a woman 36 years old. The ovary was surgically removed at the midcycle. Masson's trichrome strain. Photomicrograph. ×95.

Vein   Arteriole

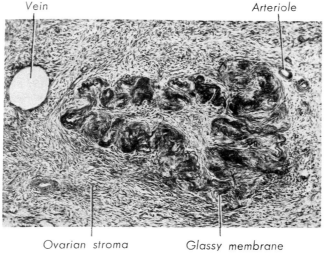

Ovarian stroma   Glassy membrane

FIG. 20-9. Late stage of follicular atresia. Normal ovary of a woman 36 years old. The ovary was surgically removed at the midcycle. Masson's trichrome strain. Photomicrograph. ×95.

oogonia and continuing to old age for spermatogonia. Replication of DNA in the chromosomes of the primary oocytes is completed during fetal life. During the growth of the primary oocytes, homologous chromosomes become paired (undergo synapsis) as in primary spermatocytes. The primary oocyte then passes through the two *matura-* *tion divisions, meiosis,* as a result of which the chromosomes are reduced to the *haploid* number. In these divisions, the chromatin is divided equally between the daughter cells, but the division of the cytoplasm is extremely unequal. The spindle of the first maturation division forms near the periphery of the cell (Fig. 20-10) and, when cleavage occurs, one of the *secondary oocytes* receives most of the cytoplasm, while the other, the *first polar body*, receives practically none and soon degenerates.

The second maturation division is similar to the first. Once more the spindle forms at the periphery, and again two cells of unequal size are formed. One, the *mature ovum*, retains most of the cytoplasm; the other is cast off as the *second polar body*. In some lower forms, the first polar body may also divide, so that altogether three polar bodies are formed, all of which ultimately degenerate. Thus, of the four cells formed from the primary oocyte, only one reaches functional maturity, retaining practically all of the cytoplasm with its nutritive contents. The volume of the mature ovum is about 250,000 times greater than that of the spermatozoon.

The egg cells of the primary follicles are often described as oogonia. DNA replication is completed during fetal life, however, and the oogonia differentiate to early stage oocytes (diplotene stage of the first meiotic

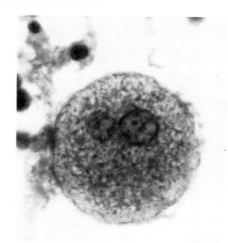

FIG. 20-11. Photomicrograph showing male and female pronuclei in an ovum shortly after sperm penetration. Ovum was located by sectioning the Fallopian tube. ×700. (From a preparation by Dr. T. E. Hunt.)

prophase) before birth. Thus, the egg cells of the primary follicles are early stage primary oocytes that have entered a long period of rest. The majority of these degenerate before much growth occurs, but degeneration may occur at any stage of follicular growth. The exact time of occurrence of the maturation divisions is not definitely known for the human ovum. In most mammals, the first polar body is formed in the ovary, whereas the second is cast off after ovulation and after fertilization. The appearance of the ovum shortly after sperm penetration is shown in Figure 20-11.

The Corpus Luteum (Figs. 20-12 and 20-13). After ovulation, the ruptured follicle does not degenerate at once but is transformed temporarily into a glandular structure, the *yellow body* or *corpus luteum*. The follicular cavity closes over by healing of the wound and becomes filled with a serous, fibrin-containing fluid which usually contains some blood. The granulosa cells of the follicle do not proliferate but increase greatly in size. Both granulosa and theca interna cells enlarge and become epithelioid in their characteristics. They can be distinguished from each other, however, on the basis of

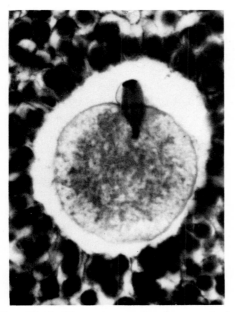

FIG. 20-10. Photomicrograph of ovum during first maturation division. Corona radiata cells are seen encircling the ovum. ×700. (From a preparation by Dr. T. E. Hunt.)

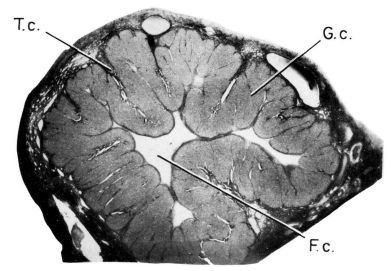

FIG. 20-12. Photomicrograph of a section of a human ovary, showing a fully formed corpus luteum of pregnancy. Granulosa-lutein cells (*G.c.*) form the major portion of the corpus; theca-lutein cells (*T.c.*) surround it and penetrate between folds of granulosa-lutein cells; a remnant of the follicular cavity (*F.c.*) contains loose connective tissue. ×5.

their location, size and staining reactions. In comparison with the *granulosa lutein cells*, the *theca lutein cells* are peripheral in position, they are smaller and their nuclei stain darker (Fig. 20-13).

The cytoplasm of the lutein cells contains yellowish lipochrome pigment droplets and lipid droplets. Removal of lipids by the routine methods in preparing sections generally gives a finely vacuolated appearance to the cytoplasm as seen under the light microscope. Electron micrographs show that the cytoplasm contains considerable smooth surfaced endoplasmic reticulum, some free ribosomes and mitochondria with tubular cristae. Thus, the cells which are known to secrete progesterone have the cytological characteristics of other steroid hormone-secreting cells.

Connective tissue from the theca externa penetrates the lutein mass and forms delicate interlacing septa, in which are numerous capillaries. The connective tissue finally penetrates the entire layer and spreads to form a continuous covering on the inner surface of the lutein cells. In the center, the follicular cavity remains as a greatly reduced space of irregular outline, still filled with a serous fluid or, more rarely, with the disintegrating remains of the blood clot (Figs. 20-12 and 20-14).

If the discharged ovum is not fertilized and dies on its way to the uterus, the corpus luteum reaches its greatest development about 1 week after ovulation and then begins to degenerate. This is the *corpus luteum menstruationis (spurium)*. The cells of such a corpus luteum gradually decrease in size, show increasing vacuolization and are finally resorbed. The connective tissue between the lutein cells increases in amount, and a loose, gelatinous type of connective tissue, often containing brownish pigment of the extravasated blood, fills the central cavity. The gland becomes progressively smaller and, several weeks after beginning of involution, is transformed into a whitish scar of microscopic size, the *corpus albicans*.

If the ovum is fertilized, the corpus increases in size for a time and is known as the *corpus luteum graviditatis*. It attains a size of 20 to 30 mm., and persists until the later

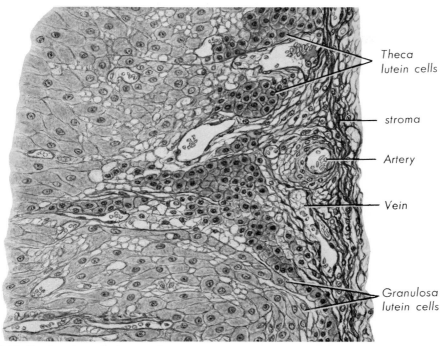

Theca lutein cells

stroma

Artery

Vein

Granulosa lutein cells

FIG. 20-13. Section through the peripheral part of corpus luteum removed during the progravid stage of the sexual cycle. Masson's trichrome stain. ×200.

months of pregnancy, when it likewise undergoes a slow involution.

Although human corpora lutea are bright yellow, this is not true for all mammals. The corpora lutea of cows have an orange hue. In some animals (dog, cat and some rodents) they contain no pigment and consequently are pale in color.

Interstitial Cells. In many mammals, the cortical stroma contains clusters or strands of epithelioid connective tissue cells whose cytoplasm contains fine lipid granules. These form from the theca interna and are known as *interstitial cells*. In the mature human ovary, the theca interna cells of degenerating follicles form radiating cords which persist for only a short time (Figs. 20-7 and 20-8). There are relatively few cells in the mature human ovum that resemble the interstitial cells of rodents and their origin is questionable.

Hormones of the Ovary. The ovary is under the direct influence of hormones of the anterior hypophysis. These hormones, the gonadotropins, control the maturation of follicles and the formation of corpora lutea. The ovary in turn produces hormones of its own, which affect the accessory reproductive organs such as the uterus, Fallopian tubes and mammary glands, and which also exert a regulatory effect upon the anterior hypophysis.

The ovarian hormones are steroids. One of them, *estrogen* (principally *estradiol*), is secreted by the growing follicles and to a lesser degree by the corpus luteum. The other, *progesterone*, is produced mainly by the corpus luteum but also to some extent by the mature follicle just prior to ovulation. Since there is a wave of follicular maturation during the first half of each month, followed by formation of a corpus luteum immediately after ovulation, the levels of the two hormones normally show regular cyclic fluctuations. Estrogen secretion is high during the preovulatory period and reaches a peak at about the time of ovulation; progesterone secretion increases rapidly as the ruptured follicle becomes luteinized, and it remains at a high level until regression of the corpus luteum. The fluctuations in ovarian hormone levels are reflected, as discussed later, in cyclic variations in other structures, notably in the mucous membrane of the uterus.

Blood Vessels. Branches of the ovarian and uterine arteries enter the medulla at the hilum and divide into a number of spirally coursing vessels. These vessels run to the boundary zone of cortex and medulla, where they ramify and anastomose into plexuses. From these are given off branches that enter the cortex radially and break up into extensive capillary networks in the thecae of the growing and mature follicles. From the capillaries, veins arise that accompany the arteries, form an extensive plexus in the medulla and leave the ovary at the hilum.

Lymphatics. Lymph capillaries begin in the theca externa of the follicles, and unite into somewhat larger vessels which pass radially through the medulla and leave at the hilum. There they are collected in a number of lymphatic trunks that drain into the lumbar lymph nodes.

Nerves. Nerve fibers, mostly unmyelinated, enter at the hilum and follow the course of the blood vessels. Many terminate in the muscle fibers of the medullary blood vessels. Others enter the cortex and form delicate plexuses in the thecae of the follicles but apparently do not penetrate the granulosa. According to some authors, groups of sympathetic ganglion cells are found in the medulla.

Vestigial Structures. As is the case with the testis, certain rudimentary organs, the remains of fetal structures, are connected with the ovary.

The *epoophoron* consists of a number of blind tubules situated in the folds of the broad ligament between the ovary and the oviduct. The tubules open into a longitudinal duct, the canal of Gärtner, which passes along the lateral wall of the uterus and reaches the vagina. The duct is often interrupted and may be altogether absent in some cases.

The *paroophoron* is situated in the connective tissue of the hilum and consists of a few blind tubules or cords. It is rarely found in the adult.

Both epoophoron and paroophoron are remains of the embryonal mesonephros, while Gärtner's canal represents a vestige of the Wolffian (mesonephric) duct.

THE FALLOPIAN TUBES

The Fallopian (uterine) tubes are paired structures, each of which is about 15 cm. long and 6 to 8 mm. in diameter. One end of a tube opens into the peritoneal cavity near the ovary; the other end opens into the superior lateral part of the uterine cavity. The tubes conduct the ova that are discharged at ovulation to the uterine cavity.

Four regions of the tubes are usually distinguished. Beginning with the ovarian end, these are: (a) infundibulum, (b) ampulla, (c) isthmus, (d) uterine or interstitial segment. The *infundibulum* is funnel-shaped and is formed of a number of processes or fimbriae (Fig. 20-1). The *ampulla* is the longest of the segments and, like the fimbriae, is thin walled. It terminates in a relatively short segment which extends to the uterus, the *isthmus*. This segment is smaller in diameter and thicker walled than the ampulla. The last portion, *pars uterina*, is embedded in the wall of the uterus. The mucosa of the infundibulum and ampulla is thrown into many tall folds with correspondingly deep grooves. The lumen thus is very irregular in shape (Fig. 20-15). The folds progressively decrease in height toward the uterus and are low in the isthmus (Fig. 20-16). In the pars uterina, there are only slight folds, and the cavity reaches its smallest diameter, about 1 mm.

The wall of the Fallopian tube consists of three coats: mucosa, muscularis, and serosa.

The *epithelium* lining the Fallopian tubes is a simple columnar type, some cells of which are ciliated, whereas others are narrow, peg-shaped and nonciliated (Figs. 20-17 and 20-18). The height of the epithelium and the proportion of ciliated to nonciliated secretory cells, although varying considerably even in neighboring regions of a tube, show changes that correlate with the stages of the menstrual cycle. The epithelium during the first half (follicular phase) of the cycle is taller than it is in the second half, which is under the influence of the corpus luteum. The relative number of nonciliated, peg-shaped cells also increases in the corpus luteum phase of the cycle. During pregnancy, the epithelium is quite low and there is an increased number of "peg" cells (Fig. 20-18). The epithelium secretes mucus and probably other substances necessary for the maintenance of the ovum during its journey down the tube.

The cilia beat toward the uterus. The beating of the cilia and the waves of muscular contraction transport the ovum through the tubes. No glands are present in the Fallopian tubes.

The stroma of the lamina propria is composed of a richly cellular connective tissue, quite compact in the isthmus, more loosely arranged in the high folds of the ampulla.

The *muscularis* is thickest in the isthmus and gradually thins out toward the fimbriated end. It consists of a well developed inner circular layer and a rather thin outer longitudinal layer. The latter is complete only in the isthmus. In the ampulla, the longitudinal muscle bundles are discontinuous and may be absent altogether in the fimbria.

The *serosa* has the usual structure of peritoneum.

The larger *blood vessels* run in the stroma along the bases of the folds. They send off branches that give rise to a dense capillary network in the stroma.

The *lymphatics* arise as relatively large lacunae in the stroma of the mucosal folds. These empty into narrower channels that pass through the muscularis and form a rich

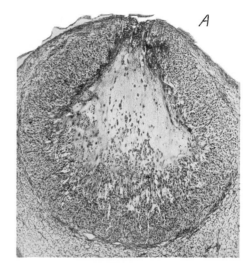

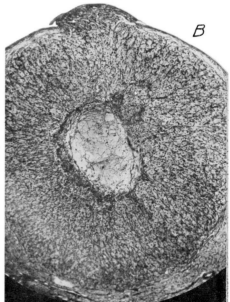

FIG. 20-14. Stages in the formation of the corpus luteum in the rabbit. *A*, corpus luteum from an ovary removed 48 hours after mating (about 36 hours after ovulation). *B*, corpus luteum from the other ovary of the same animal. This ovary was removed 4 days after mating (about 84 hours after ovulation).

subserous net. The lymphatics drain into the upper lumbar lymph nodes.

The *nerves* form a rich plexus in the stroma, from which fibers pass to the blood

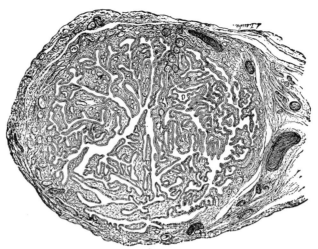

FIG. 20-15. Cross section of Fallopian tube near fimbriated extremity, showing complicated foldings of mucous membrane (Orthmann).

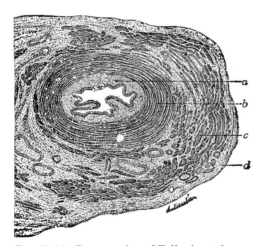

FIG. 20-16. Cross section of Fallopian tube near uterine end. *a*, mucous membrane; *b*, circular muscle coat; *c*, longitudinal muscle coat; *d*, connective tissue of serous coat (Orthmann).

vessels and muscular tissue and to the epithelial lining.

THE UTERUS

The uterus is a thick walled, pear-shaped organ, somewhat flattened dorsoventrally in its upper two-thirds. It varies considerably in size, averaging some 7 cm. in length, 5 cm. in width at its upper (broadest) part and 2.5 cm. in thickness. Its cavity conforms to the general shape of the organ, being very narrow dorsoventrally in the body of the organ and more circular in the lower portion. The uterine tubes open into the superior lateral part of the uterine cavity, one on either side. The lower part of the cavity (the cervical canal) opens into the vagina.

Anatomically, two main regions of the uterus are distinguished: (a) an upper *body* or *corpus* with its rounded, dome-shaped top, the *fundus*, and (b) a narrower, cylindrical

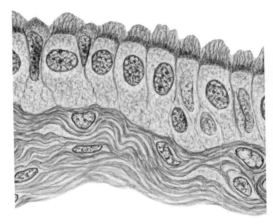

FIG. 20-17. Section of Fallopian tube removed at the middle of the menstrual cycle, showing the characteristic type of epithelium present at that stage. ×1200.

neck or *cervix* whose terminal portion projects into the vagina as the *portio vaginalis*. The narrow zone of transition between corpus and cervix is known as the *isthmus*.

The wall of the uterus consists of three coats which, from the outermost inward, are the serosa or *perimetrium*, the muscularis or *myometrium* and the mucosa or *endometrium*.

The *perimetrium* is the peritoneal layer of the broad ligament, which covers the corpus and a portion of the cervix. It is firmly attached to the underlying muscularis and has the usual structure of a serous membrane.

Myometrium. The myometrium is a massive muscular coat, about 15 mm. in thickness, consisting of bundles of smooth muscle fibers held together by connective tissue. The disposition of the muscle fibers is quite complicated but, in a general way, three layers may be distinguished. The inner, muscular layer, the *stratum subvasculare*, consists of fibers running longitudinally, i.e., parallel to the long axis of the organ. The middle layer, *stratum vasculare*, forms the bulk of the muscularis and is composed mainly of fibers running circularly or spirally. In the interstitial tissue are numerous large blood vessels, especially veins. The outer layer, *stratum supravasculare*, is relatively thin and is composed of both circular and longitudinal fibers. The latter predominate and form a fairly distinct subserous layer which becomes continuous with the longitudinal muscle coat of the vagina. In the cervix, the inner longitudinal layer is absent.

The muscle cells of the virgin uterus have a length of 40 to 90 μ, the variations conforming to definite phases of the menstrual cycle. The fibers are shortest in the first week after menstruation and reach their greatest length in the fourth week of the cycle. During pregnancy, the muscle tissue of the uterus is greatly increased. This is due partly to an increase in the number but mainly to the tremendous increase in the size of the muscle fibers, which in the later stages of pregnancy may have a length of over 500 μ.

The interstitial tissue contains numerous blood vessels and consists of loosely arranged collagenous fibers and relatively few connective tissue cells. Elastic fibers are found in considerable amounts in the outer layer of the muscularis and in the subserous connective tissue. The inner portions of the myometrium are relatively poor in elastic tissue. In the cervix, elastic tissue is abundant.

Endometrium. The endometrium is lined by simple columnar epithelium composed of small patches of ciliated cells interspersed with nonciliated cells. Numerous tubular glands are present, and they are lined by columnar cells which resemble those at the surface except that there are fewer ciliated cells. There is no submucosa, and the mucosa is closely attached to the myometrium, the juncture between them being very irregular.

During the childbearing period, the mucosa of the corpus and fundus passes through cyclic changes, each cycle closely related to the maturation of an ovarian follicle, the discharge of the contained ovum and the subsequent formation of a corpus luteum. In general, these changes are in the nature of a preparation for pregnancy, and they consist of a hypertrophy of the glandular, vascular and interstitial elements of the mucosa. If the egg is fertilized and implantation occurs, the hypertrophy continues. If the egg is not implanted, the hypertrophied layer breaks down, and the tissue debris, together with a certain amount of blood, is discharged as the *menstrual fluid*. With cessation of the flow, regeneration occurs rapidly and a new cycle sets in, determined as before by a new ovarian cycle. A uterine bleeding or *menstruation* occurs typically at intervals of about 28 days and lasts for 3 to 5 days, but there is great variability among different individuals and often in any one individual. The first day of menstruation is

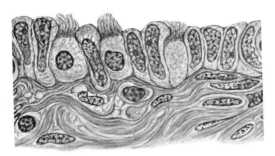

FIG. 20-18. Section of Fallopian tube of a woman 2½ months pregnant, showing the type of epithelium characteristic of pregnancy and of the progravid stage of the menstrual cycle. ×1200.

counted as the first day of the uterine or menstrual cycle.

Four stages, each of which has characteristic structural features, are distinguishable in the endometrium during an ovulatory menstrual cycle. It should be kept in mind, however, that the endometrium undergoes a continuous change, and that in each stage the structural features change somewhat, so that one stage does not abruptly pass into the next. The indicated duration of each stage is based on a 28-day cycle. (1) The *menstrual* stage occupies the first 3 to 5 days of the cycle, during which time there is an external menstrual discharge. (2) The *proliferative* (estrogenic) stage begins with the termination of menstruation and extends to about the middle of the cycle, namely, to the 13th or 14th day. (3) The *progravid* or *secretory* (luteal or progestational) stage extends from the middle of the cycle to the 26th or 27th day. (4) The *premenstrual* stage is 1 or 2 days in length and is terminated by the appearance of visible external bleeding. The length of the proliferative stage is less constant than that of the others, and variations in its duration are chiefly responsible for the varying lengths of the menstrual cycles.

A description of the changes occurring during the *proliferative* stage of the cycle is given first (Fig. 20-19 A). This stage is characterized by rapid regeneration of the endo-metrium from the narrow basal zone remaining after menstruation (Fig. 20-20 B). Epithelial cells from the remaining portions of the glands migrate and cover the raw surface of the mucosa. Numerous mitoses occur in cells of the glands and of the stroma. As the gland cells increase in number, they become tall and closely packed together (Fig. 20-21), and the glands increase in length. Although forked terminations of the glands are frequent, the glands remain relatively straight and uniform in diameter (Fig. 20-19, A). Near the close of the proliferative stage, some secretion appears in the basal ends of the gland cells. The stroma is formed of branching cells, among which are reticular fibers. Blood vessels (coiled arteries) grow into the regenerating tissue and, toward the end of the proliferative stage, a considerable degree of edema develops, although it is not as pronounced as in the secretory stage. During the proliferative stage, the endometrium increases from a postmenstrual thickness of 0.5 mm. or less to 2 or 3 mm.

In the *secretory* stage of the cycle, the endometrium hypertrophies, reaching a thickness of 4 to 5 mm. The increase is due not to mitotic activity but to hypertrophy of the gland cells and to an increase in edema and vascularity. The gland cells remain about the same in height but become broader (Figs. 20-21 and 20-22). The glands assume a corkscrew shape, and their lumina become large and irregular in diameter, giving them a characteristic appearance (Fig. 20-19). The edema increases, and the coiled arteries grow nearly to the surface.

With the development of the secretory stage, several layers can be distinguished in the endometrium (Fig. 20-19). The *basalis* is the deepest layer and is relatively narrow. Its glands undergo little or no change. This layer is not lost at menstruation or at parturition. The *functionalis* comprises all of the endometrium lying above (superficial to) the basalis. It undergoes periodic changes in the menstrual cycle and is lost at menstruation and at parturition. The functionalis is

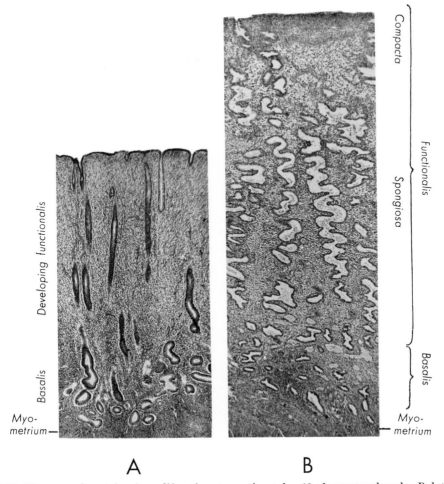

A   B

FIG. 20-19. Human endometria. *A*, proliferative stage, about day 10 of menstrual cycle; *B*, late secretory stage, day 25 of cycle. Photomicrographs. ×30. The tissue of the secretory stage illustrated in this figure and the stages illustrated in Figures 20-20 through 20-23 were supplied by Dr. Arthur Hertig.

divided into two layers, a superficial layer, the *compacta*, and a deep layer, the *spongiosa* (Fig. 20-19). The *compacta* is relatively narrow. It has little edema, and the portions of the glands that lie in it are quite straight. The *spongiosa* comprises the bulk of the endometrium. It is edematous, and the glands are tortuous and have large lumina, giving the zone a spongy appearance. It is emphasized that these zones become evident only with the development of the secretory stage.

During the secretory stage, the gland cells undergo certain progressive secretory changes. With the onset of this stage, both glycogen and mucigen increase rapidly in the gland cells of the functionalis, and these secretions are localized at first in the basal portions of the cells. With the usual technical procedures, the secretion is dissolved (Fig. 20-22). During the latter half of the secretory stage, the secretion moves to the apical zone of the gland cells, and the nuclei consequently become basally located (Fig. 20-23). The secretion, composed of glycogen, mucin and some fat, then appears in the lumina of the glands, thus terminating the secretory cycle of the cells of the glands.

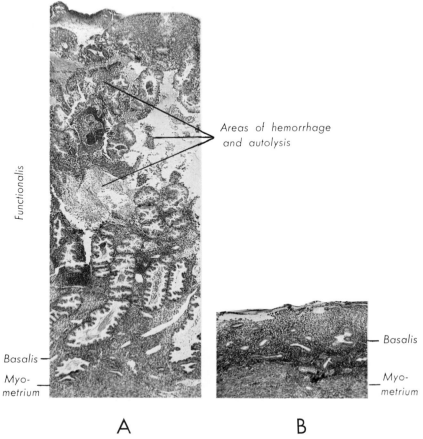

Fig. 20-20. Human endometria. *A*, early menstrual phase; *B*, termination of menstruation. Photomicrographs. ×30.

In the *premenstrual* phase of the cycle, important changes occur in the coiled arteries, leading to a breakdown of the functionalis. In studies made on living endometrial transplants in the anterior chamber of the eye in monkeys, Markee observed that a constriction of the coiled arteries and vascular stasis occurred during the premenstrual period, producing a condition of anemia and anoxia. Finally, blood escaped from the vessels. These observations assist in explaining the immediate factor responsible for the areas of hemorrhage and autolysis seen in sections of fixed tissue (Fig. 20-20, *A*). In the premenstrual stage there is also a decrease in edema and an infiltration of the stroma with leukocytes. The glands fragment, the surface of the endometrium breaks down and blood and tissue debris appear in the uterine lumen.

During *menstruation*, the functionalis is lost, although there may be considerable variation in the amount of endometrial destruction. The coiled arteries undergo necrosis and some blood may spurt from them, although most of the menstrual blood comes from veins. To this blood are added the secretion of the glands and the broken down tissue of the functionalis.

Thus, in each uterine cycle a period of growth and proliferation is followed by one of secretory activity. In the first period, a new functional layer is built up, with its glands and interstitial tissue. In the second,

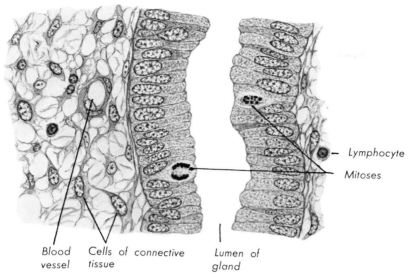

Fig. 20-21. A section of human endometrium in the proliferative stage (about day 11), showing a part of a gland tubule and adjacent stroma. ×650.

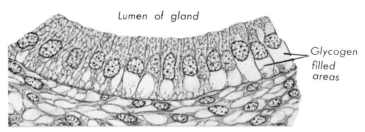

Fig. 20-22. A section of human endometrium in the early secretory stage. Day 19 of menstrual cycle. ×650.

the functional layer is transformed into a swollen nutritive compartment ready for the implantation of the ovum. If the egg is not implanted, desquamation of the functionalis occurs, rapidly followed by regeneration of the epithelial surface. Menstruation thus indicates a "biological failure," a failure of the egg to be fertilized and implanted.

The mucosa of the *cervix* (Fig. 20-24) is somewhat thicker than that of the body and fundus of the uterus and shows numerous folds, the *plicae palmatae*. The stroma also is firmer and less cellular.

The lining epithelium consists mainly of high columnar mucous secreting cells, although a few ciliated cells may also be present. The numerous forked glands are much larger than those of the body of the uterus and are lined by tall mucous secreting cells. Closure of the mouths of some of the glands frequently occurs, leading to the formation of cysts of considerable size, the so-called *ovula Nabothi*. Near the external opening of the cervix, the simple columnar epithelium changes abruptly to a stratified squamous epithelium, which likewise covers the external surface of the portio vaginalis. The cervix does not exhibit distinct menstrual changes.

Relation of Menstruation to Ovulation. As already stated, the cyclic uterine changes are closely related to the ovarian cycles associated with ovulation. From the available evidence, it is possible to relate, temporally, the specific phases of the two

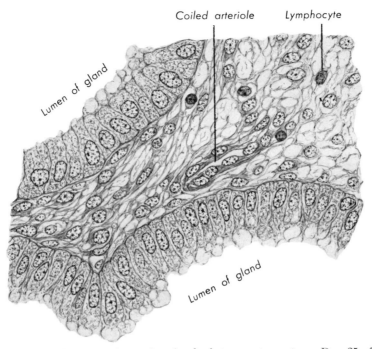

FIG. 20-23. A section of human endometrium in the late secretory stage. Day 25 of cycle. ×650

cycles. The postmenstrual proliferative changes correspond to the preovulatory period of maturation of the follicle. The secretory stage is always associated with the formation and growth of the corpus luteum, and it lasts as long as the latter retains its full function. The beginning involution of the corpus luteum always marks the onset of menstruation. Ovulation occurs normally at the end of the proliferative period, although the estimates of different investigators vary within relatively wide limits (from the eighth to the 20th day of the cycle). Very precise and extensive data have been collected by Hartman on rhesus monkeys. Their sex cycles and reproductive processes are very similar to those of the human. In some 300 observations, Hartman found that ovulation occurred most frequently on days 11, 12 and 13 (dated from the first day of the preceding menstruation), although occasional instances of ovulation were found between the eighth and 23rd day of the cycle.

A schema of the temporal relations of two cycles is given in Figure 20-25.

Evidence secured from the human as well as from rhesus monkeys has revealed that the cyclical uterine changes are induced by estrogen, a product of the follicle and perhaps of other parts of the ovary, and of progesterone, a product of the corpus luteum. The endometrium involutes after ovariectomy but can be caused to undergo the proliferative changes by estrogen injections. Continued injections of this hormone will not cause a development of the secretory phases, progesterone administration being necessary to induce the development of this phase, but injection of progesterone must be preceded by estrogen treatments in order for it to act. It is established that the corpora lutea in women secrete estrogen as well as progesterone and that, in the latter half of the cycle, the uterus is under the influence of both of these hormones. A more highly developed secretory type of endometrium can be produced experimentally if the proges-

Epithelium lining lumen of cervix

Vein

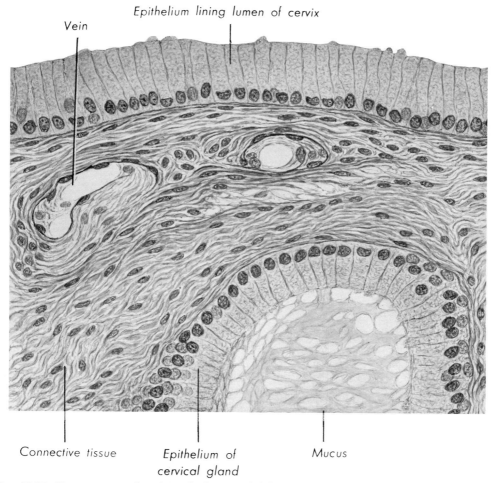

Connective tissue   Epithelium of   Mucus
                           cervical gland

FIG. 20-24. Transverse section through the superficial portion of the cervical mucosa of a woman 31 years old. End of the second month of pregancy. Therapeutic abortion. Stained with iron hematoxylin. ×625.

terone injections are supplemented by estrogen administration. By the use of these two hormones, the endometrial changes characteristic of the normal cycle can be secured in ovariectomized women, as well as in monkeys. The changes thus induced obviously correlate with the follicular and lutein phases through which the ovary passes in the complete ovulatory cycle.

Experimental work has revealed the role of the hormones in menstruation, although it was confused for a time by the fact that, during the summer months, rhesus monkeys in captivity do not ovulate or form corpora lutea but still exhibit periodic menstruation. Such cycles are known as *anovulatory cycles.* It has been demonstrated that bleeding will occur from a proliferative endometrium if the estrogen administration that induced this phase is stopped. If progesterone injections are commenced at the time that the estrogen injections are stopped, however, menstruation does not occur but will take place a few days after the progesterone treatment is terminated. The institution of estrogen injections when the progesterone treat-

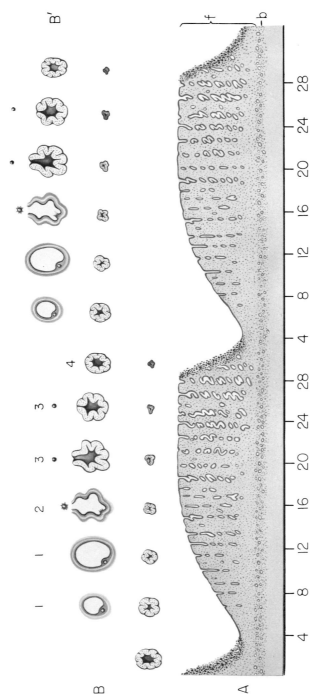

FIG. 20-25. Diagram illustrating relation of menstruation to ovulation. *A*, cyclic changes in uterine mucosa; *B*, ovarian cycles; *b*, basal layer; and *f*, functional layer of mucosa; *1, 1*, maturing follicle; *2*, rupture of follicle and discharge of ovum (ovulation); *3, 3*, corpus luteum in full function; *4* and remaining figures, degenerating corpus luteum. Numbers at *base* indicate days of menstrual cycle. (Redrawn after Schroeder.)

ment is withdrawn, however, will not inhibit the expected menstruation that results from progesterone withdrawal.

Blood Vessels. Branches from each uterine artery penetrate to the middle (vascular) layer of the uterine muscle and then continue both ventrally and dorsally in this layer to the midline, forming the arcuate arteries. They anastomose with the branches from the other uterine artery. Two sets of branches arise from these arched arteries: (1) small branches that course peripherally and supply the supravascular (outer) part of the uterus, and (2) larger branches that course centrally. Branches from the latter in turn form two systems. One set, which penetrates the endometrium for a variable distance, depending on the stage of the cycle, is extremely coiled (coiled arteries) and terminates in a tuft of arterioles (Fig. 20-26). The other set supplies the inner layer of the uterine muscle and the basal part of the endometrium, where branches from it anastomose with the branches of the coiled arteries. The endometrium is thus supplied by a basal and a superficial set of vessels. The basal set, as would be expected, does not undergo modifications with the stages of the cycle, but the coiled arteries show pronounced changes. During the proliferative stage of the cycle, they penetrate only one-half or two-thirds through the thickness of the endometrium, but during the secretory stage they increase in extent, approach the surface and, with the tissue loss at menstruation, may protrude into the uterine lumen. Their peripheral part then undergoes necrosis. With the reparative postmenstrual

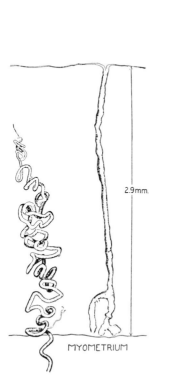

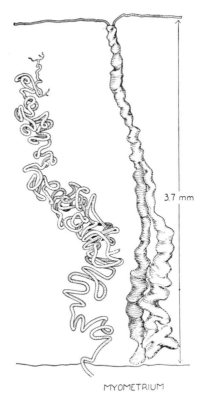

FIG. 20-26. Projection reconstructions of the coiled arteries and the glands in the endometrium of rhesus monkey (Old World monkey). *Left*, early proliferative stage (early postmenstrual); *Right*, late progravid stage. (After Daron.)

process, the vessels again grow. The menstrual blood, however, does not come mainly from the arteries but from the veins. Two mechanisms appear to operate to prevent the bleeding of the coiled arteries. One of these is the tortuosity of the vessels, which would slow the flow. The other and more effective mechanism is arterial constriction, a constriction that is aided by localized thickenings or cushions, composed of longitudinal smooth muscle, on one side of the arterial lumen.

Menstrual fluid is composed of extravasated blood, desquamated tissue and the secretion of the uterine glands. The discharge does not clot, for it is markedly fibrinolytic. It is also toxic, as shown by injection into experimental animals.

Lymphatics. The lymph vessels are larger and more abundant in the uterus than in most other organs of the body. They are enlarged during pregnancy. All layers of the uterine wall have lymph vessels except the superficial part of the endometrium (compacta), which is devoid of them. During its cyclical changes, the endometrium exhibits pronounced changes in its water content, and these changes are probably responsible for the unusually extensive lymph drainage.

Nerves. Both myelinated and unmyelinated nerve fibers occur in the uterus. The latter predominate and are connected with minute ganglia found in the upper vaginal wall near its junction with the cervix. These fibers supply the walls of the blood vessels and the muscle tissue of the myometrium. The myelinated fibers apparently run to the mucosa and form a scanty plexus beneath the epithelium. The distribution and endings of the mucosal nerve fibers have not been fully investigated.

The Uterus during Pregnancy

The ovum, if fertilized, becomes implanted in the endometrium at about the sixth day after ovulation. At this time, the endometrium has reached a highly developed secretory or progravid condition. It is thick and edematous, and the lumina and cells of the glands are large and contain glycogen, mucigen and some lipid. Implantation may take place in any region of the uterine mucosa and even in the tubal epithelium. The uterine changes and correlated events in the ovary and ovum during the early phases of pregnancy in women are shown in Figure 20-27.

From the extensive studies of Hertig, Rock and Adams on a considerable series of ova and later stages, secured from timed hysterectomies, it appears that the following events occur subsequent to ovulation. Fertilization takes place before or soon after the ovum enters the uterine tube. The migration down the uterine tube is leisurely, the ovum undergoing cellular division during its migration and arriving in the uterus on the third day after ovulation. An ovum having two normal blastomeres was recovered from the middle third of the uterine tube 2 to $2\frac{1}{2}$ days after the estimated time of ovulation, and one in an eight-cell stage was recovered from the uterus on the third day. A blastula, also lying free in the uterine cavity, was recovered on the fourth day. It was found to consist of a thin epithelial membrane and a small inner cell mass, destined to form the embryo. A blastocyst secured 7 to $7\frac{1}{2}$ days after ovulation was implanted just beneath the surface of the endometrium, and the eroded epithelium had not, as yet, undergone sufficient repair to cover it. The chorionic membrane had proliferated; it is now known, because of its nutritive role, as the *trophoblast*. From the evidence summarized above, together with evidence from other fertilized but abnormal ova that have been recovered, it has been concluded that implantation occurs about the sixth day after ovulation.

At somewhat later stages, when the developing ovum is imbedded entirely within the endometrium, the trophoblast over the entire surface is found to have undergone growth (Fig. 20-28). The outer surface of the trophoblast shows irregular processes, between which are irregular spaces or lacunae.

Formation and growth of corpus luteum of pregnancy

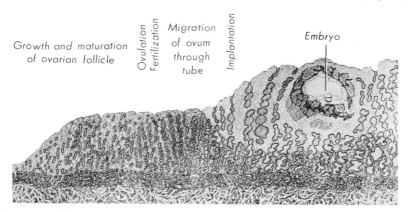

Fɪɢ. 20-27. A semidiagrammatic figure depicting the uterine changes and correlated events in the ovary and ovum. (That part of the diagram showing the uterine changes has been taken from Schroeder's monograph.)

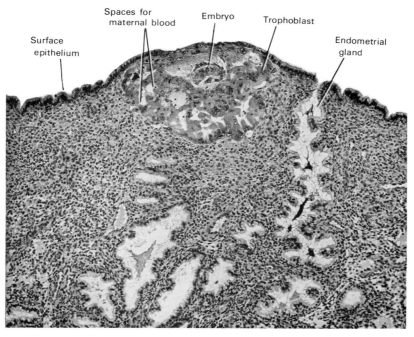

Fɪɢ. 20-28. Section through a human embryo 9½ days old. The embryo lies just beneath the epithelial surface of a 26-day secretory endometrium. ×100. (Courtesty of Drs. Rock and Hertig.)

In these spaces, maternal blood which comes from the eroded coiled arteries of the endometrium will later flow. This is returned by the maternal veins.

Some of the trophoblast cells differentiate into a syncytial layer very early, and two layers can be distinguished in the trophoblast by the 11th day (Hertig, Rock, and Adams, 1956). These are: an inner layer, the *cytotrophoblast,* and an outer layer, the *syncytial trophoblast.* Beneath these is a stratum of mesenchyme which is destined to form the connective tissue component of the chorion (fetal portion of the placenta). From the irregularities on the outer surface of the trophoblast, finger-like sprouts or *villi* grow into the surrounding space. These at first are composed only of epithelial cords (primitive villi). Later, a core of embryonal connective tissue, which is connected with the inner stratum of mesenchyme mentioned above, forms within them. They are then designated as secondary (chorionic) villi. In the core of embryonal connective tissue, branches of the fetal blood vessels soon develop.

On the surface of the chorion facing the uterine lumen, the villi do not grow as rapidly as on the deeply embedded surface. They disappear from the luminal surface at about the end of the first third of pregnancy, leaving that surface smooth. It is named the *chorion laeve*. On the deep-lying surface of the chorion, i.e., the surface facing the myometrium, the villi continue to increase and form the fetal component of the placenta. This portion of the chorion is designated the *chorion frondosum*. That part of the chorion to which the villi of this deep surface are attached forms a fairly firm plate-like structure and is called the *chorionic plate*.

The *endometrium* also undergoes important changes in pregnancy. It is called the *decidua graviditatis* because, except for the deepest layer, it is destined to be cast off at parturition. Thus, the process at birth is not unlike menstruation except that it is much more cataclysmic and involves the loss of much more tissue.

In relation to the developing embryo, three regions of the decidua are distinguished: (a) the *decidua basalis* or *serotina*, that part of the mucosa lying beneath the embryo, i.e., between the embryo and the myometrium, (b) the *decidua capsularis*, or *reflexa*, that part of the mucosa which lies between the embryo and the lumen of the uterus, and (c) the *decidua parietalis* or *vera*, which consists of all of the remaining mucosa

of the body and fundus of the uterus (Fig. 20-29).

In the early part of pregnancy, the endometrium increases in thickness. The glands enlarge and become more tortuous, and the cells of the endometrial stroma become large and rounded, forming characteristic cellular elements, the *decidual cells*. These are described later. In the latter half or two-thirds of pregnancy, the parietal decidua gradually becomes thinner and the glands become reduced to slitlike spaces. As the lumen of the uterus is obliterated by the growth of the fetus, the decidua parietalis and capsularis come in contact with each other. The capsularis degenerates, and the parietalis, denuded of epithelium, fuses with the external fetal membrane, the chorion.

The Placenta. The human placenta at term measures about 7 inches in diameter and 1 inch in thickness. It is usually circular but may vary a good deal in shape. The placenta reaches nearly its maximal diameter during the first half of pregnancy but continues to increase in thickness throughout most of the gestational period as a result of the growth of the villi.

The placenta consists of two components, a *fetal* and a *maternal*, which develop as described in the preceding section. The *fetal component* consists of a chorionic plate and branching processes or villi which arise from chorionic plate and lie in the spaces through which the maternal blood circulates.

The *chorionic villi* are usually classified into two types, *anchoring* and *free* or *floating* villi, the structure of the two being similar. The anchoring villi pass from the chorionic plate to the decidua basalis; thus, one of their functions is the anchoring of the chorionic plate to the decidua (Fig. 20-30). They give origin throughout their length to branches that float in the blood-filled lacunar spaces between the fetal portion of the placenta and the decidua basalis, and these are known as free or floating villi. As development proceeds, the villi become very numerous. They also become increasingly ir-

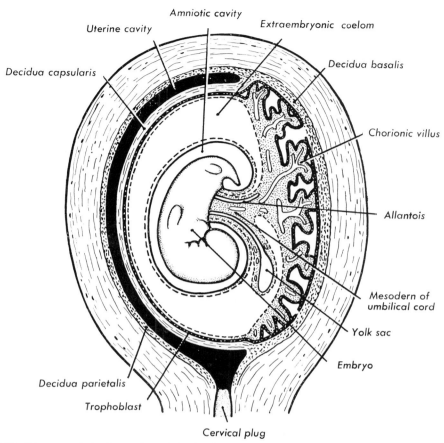

Uterine cavity

Amniotic cavity

Extraembryonic coelom

Decidua capsularis

Decidua basalis

Chorionic villus

Allantois

Mesodern of umbilical cord

Yolk sac

Embryo

Decidua parietalis

Trophoblast

Cervical plug

FIG. 20-29. Diagram of the formation of the fetal membranes in relation to the decidual membranes. (Redrawn after Hamilton, Boyd and Mossman.)

regular in shape, with many protuberances which correspond with the loops and coils of the capillaries that they contain. Their complex pattern is seen particularly well in pictures made by use of the scanning electron microscope which gives considerable depth of field and a three-dimensional effect (Figs. 20-31 and 20-32). Their total surface area has been estimated to be 6 to 7 square meters. Each villus has a central core of mesenchymal tissue and contains branches of fetal blood vessels. These receive their blood from the umbilical arteries and drain into the umbilical vein. They are covered by trophoblast, as are also the chorionic plate and the chorionic surface of the decidua basalis (Fig. 20-30). The outer (maternal)

border of the villus often has adherent fibrin and fibrinoid material, particularly in the later months of pregnancy.

The structure of the trophoblast differs somewhat according to the age of the embryo. A syncytial layer differentiates from some of the trophoblast cells very early, and two layers then become distinguishable, an inner cellular and an outer syncytial layer (Figs. 20-33 to 20-34). Since the cells of the inner layer are discrete and well defined, this layer is named the *cellular trophoblast* or *cytotrophoblast*. The cells composing it are frequently called *Langhans cells*. The outer layer of the trophoblast, i.e., the layer next to the spaces filled with maternal blood, is plasmodial in nature and is named, there-

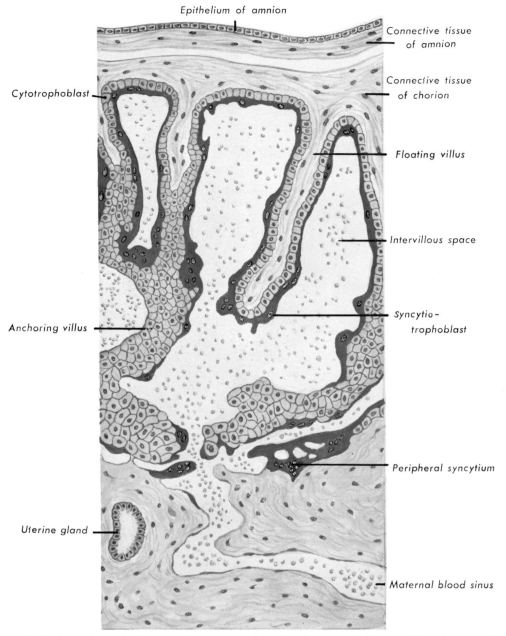

Fig. 20-30. Semischematic diagram of structure of fetal and maternal tissues of the placenta. (Redrawn and modified after Hamilton, Boyd and Mossman.)

fore, the *syncytial trophoblast*. These two cell layers persist for approximately the first half of pregnancy. The cells of the cytotrophoblast then gradually decrease in number and, at term, they are very inconspicuous.

The cells of the *cytotrophoblast* are irregularly ovoid in shape and vary considerably in size (Figs. 20-33). Their cytoplasm stains very lightly and contains some glycogen. Their nuclei are distinct and have a

Microvilli on surface of
terminal chorionic villus

Maternal red blood cells
and fibrin on surface of villus

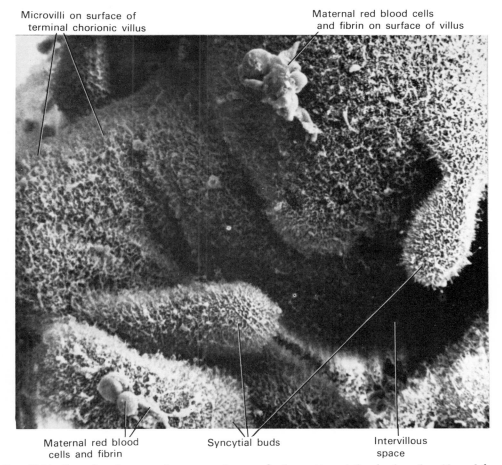

Maternal red blood
cells and fibrin

Syncytial buds

Intervillous
space

FIG. 20-31. Scanning electron microscope micrograph of a portion of the chorion of an 11-week human fetus. The micrograph shows the chorionic surface facing the intervillous spaces and gives a three-dimensional effect. ×3,000. (Courtesy of Dr. Edward W. Dempsey).

small amount of chromatin and distinct nucleoli. Beneath the cellular trophoblast is a delicate basement membrane composed of a basal lamina and a lamina reticularis of argyrophilic fibers. It is generally accepted that the cytotrophoblastic cells divide and give rise to the syncytial cells.

The *syncytial trophoblast* persists throughout pregnancy. It forms a narrow lamina in which dark staining nuclei are fairly regularly spaced in young placentae (Figs. 20-33, 20-34, and 20-35); in older placentae, knots or clumps of nuclei are of frequent occurrence (Fig. 20-34). No intercellular boundaries can be distinguished. As seen under the

light microscope, the syncytial trophoblast has an irregular brush border at its surface and scattered vacuoles and granules in its cytoplasm. Electron micrographs reveal that the surface is quite irregular in contour and that it has numerous microvilli (Fig. 20-36). Invaginations of the plasmalemma connect with canaliculi and with vacuoles within the cytoplasm of the apical region, indicating that this zone functions in absorption. The middle zone of the cytoplasm contains an extensive network of rough surfaced endoplasmic reticulum, indicating that this region is secretory in function. The ultrastructure of the basal part of the syncytial

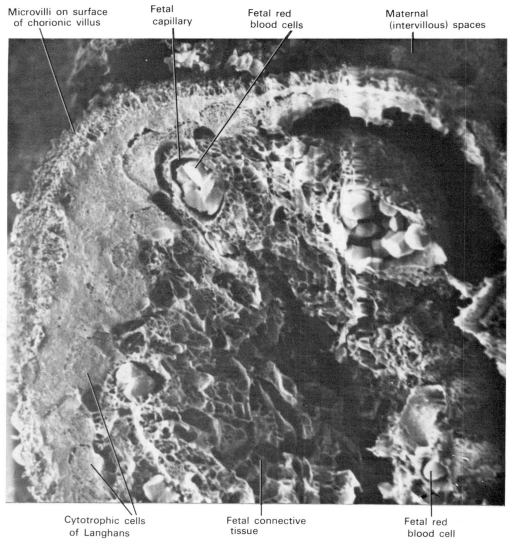

Microvilli on surface of chorionic villus   Fetal capillary   Fetal red blood cells   Maternal (intervillous) spaces

Cytotrophic cells of Langhans   Fetal connective tissue   Fetal red blood cell

FIG. 20-32. Micrograph made with a scanning electron microscope showing a portion of a chorionic villus that is broken in a manner that gives a "sectional" view of the wall of the villus. The micrograph shows the interior of the villus in a three-dimensional view. Chorion of an 11-week human fetus. ×3,000. (Courtesy of Dr. Edward W. Dempsey).

trophoblast has many of the characteristics of the cytoplasm of the cytotrophoblast. This correlates with the evidence derived from radioautographic studies that the syncytial trophoblast is derived from the cytotrophoblast. Many of the blood vessels (fetal) of the villi, especially in the latter two-thirds of pregnancy, lie very close to the surface of the villus (Fig. 20-35), the syn-

cytial trophoblast over them being attenuated and thin.

The *maternal component of the placenta* is formed by the decidua basalis. This comprises all of the endometrium beneath the fetal portion of the placenta except the deepest part, which is destined to remain after parturition as in normal menstruation. In the decidua basalis, and also in the decidua

Blood vessels   Cells of cytotrophoblast

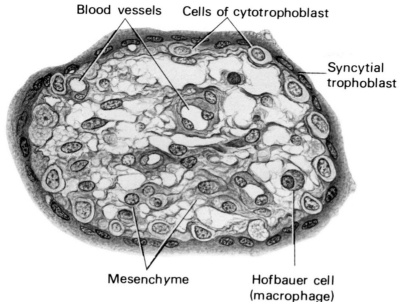

Syncytial
trophoblast

Mesenchyme   Hofbauer cell
(macrophage)

Fig. 20-33. Transverse section of a secondary (free) villus of a human placenta. From a pregnancy of 4½ months duration. Therapeutic abortion. Masson's trichrome stain. ×775.

Group of nuclei of syncytial trophoblast

Blood vessels

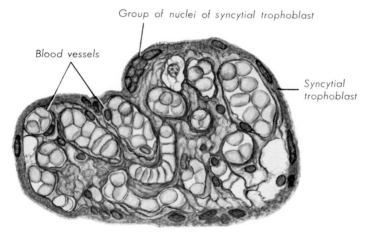

Syncytial
trophoblast

Fig. 20-34. Transverse section of a secondary villus of a human placenta at term. The blood vessels are engorged. Masson's trichrome stain. ×775.

parietalis, many of the connective tissue cells undergo a pronounced change. They hypertrophy, forming large, ovoid cells of somewhat irregular shape, and are named *decidual cells*. They are one of the most striking features of the endometrium in the first half of pregnancy, for they are very numerous and some become relatively very large (Fig. 20-37). Some of them contain two or more nuclei. The nuclei are large and the chromatin appears sparse. Nucleoli are present. The cytoplasm is vesicular or finely granular. Especially the smaller decidual cells contain large amounts of glycogen.

Some indication of decidual cell formation may be seen even in the terminal phase of a nonfertile menstrual cycle (predecidual reaction). With the onset of pregnancy, these cells rapidly develop and form a large component of the decidua in early pregnancy, as stated above. They then regress and by the end of pregnancy are rarely present. Their function is obscure.

Function of the Placenta. An obvious

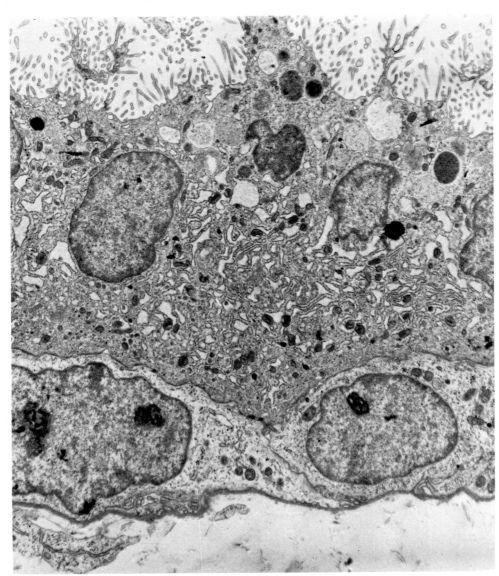

Fig. 20-36. Section through the trophoblast from a 20 mm. human embryo. The upper region, facing the intervillous space, has several protrusions and many branched and unbranched microvilli. Indenting the surface, invaginations connect with a canalicular system probably terminating in the small and large apical vacuoles. These structures, and small mitochondria, characterize the apical, *absorptive* zone. Beneath it, occupying approximately the middle third of the figure, is a region rich in rough endoplasmic reticulum. The cisternae are filled with an amorphous substance. The cisternae and the sparse but medium-sized mitochondria distinguish the middle, *secretory* zone. It contains granular cytoplasm, moderately-sized mitochondria and other organelles resembling those of the cytotrophoblast. Dalton's fixation. ×8500. (Figure and legend, Courtesy of Dr. Edward W. Dempsey).

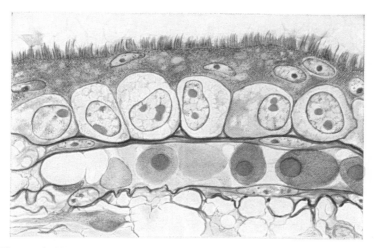

Fig. 20-35. The trophoblast of a secondary villus of a 30-day human placenta. The syncytial layer is faintly vacuolated and has a distinct brush border. The cytotrophoblastic cells form a continuous layer. Subjacent to the basement membrane is a capillary which contains nucleated erythrocytes. Mallory's connective tissue stain. ×1600. (Courtesy of Drs. Wislocki and Bennett.)

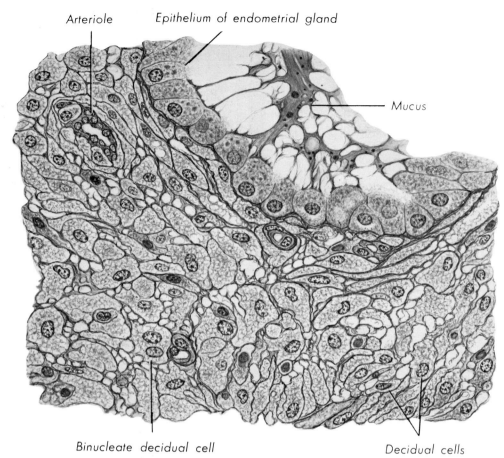

FIG. 20-37. Section through the decidua of a 6-week human pregnancy. The numerous decidual cells and a part of an endometrial gland are illustrated. Therapeutic abortion. Masson's trichrome stain. ×500.

function of the placenta is to transfer from the maternal to the fetal circulation the nutritive and other substances necessary for the development of the embryo. It also transfers waste products of fetal metabolism to the maternal circulation. Although the circulations of the mother and child are entirely separate, nevertheless, they are in close contiguity. The maternal blood circulates through the intervillous spaces, and thus it is separated from the fetal circulation only by the syncytial trophoblast, the cytotrophoblast (in the first part of pregnancy), a delicate basement membrane and the struc-

tures forming the walls of the fetal blood vessels.

The placenta also acts as a selective barrier against the transmission of certain substances from the maternal to the fetal circulation.

Another function of the placenta is the elaboration of hormones. It is known to secrete the steroids *estrogen* and *progesterone*. If the ovaries are removed in women, even early in pregnancy, abortion does not occur and the urinary excretion of estrogen and a degradation product of progesterone—pregnandiol—show only a temporary decrease.

Estrogen and progesterone can be extracted from the placenta. The fetal part of the placenta also forms a hormone called *chorionic gonadotrophin*, which differs physiologically from gonadotrophin of hypophyseal origin. This hormone begins to be formed, as judged by urinary assays, shortly after implantation and reaches a maximum in about 2 months, after which it gradually decreases in amount. There is evidence from histochemical and immunochemical studies that the syncytial trophoblast forms chorionic gonadotrophin, estrogen and progesterone. The cytotrophoblastic cells appear to function chiefly in the formation of the syncytial trophoblast.

Other Uterine Changes During Pregnancy. The changes described above involve the endometrium of the body and fundus of the uterus. A very pronounced hypertrophy of the smooth muscle of these regions of the uterus also takes place. The muscle fibers increase both in diameter and length. They may reach a length of half a millimeter. An increase in the number (hyperplasia) of the muscle fibers also takes place. Although the major uterine changes during pregnancy involve the body and fundus, some changes in the cervix also occur. The glands become more extensive and secrete copious amounts of mucus which forms a plug that occludes the cervical canal.

THE VAGINA

The wall of the vagina consists of three coats: mucosa, muscularis and fibrosa (Fig. 20-38).

The *mucosa* shows transverse folds or

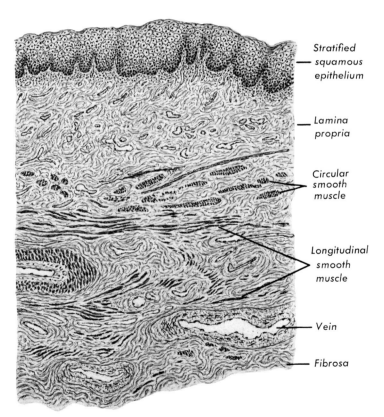

Stratified squamous epithelium

Lamina propria

Circular smooth muscle

Longitudinal smooth muscle

Vein

Fibrosa

FIG. 20-38. Longitudinal section through the posterior wall of vagina. Human, age 50 years. Camera lucida drawing. ×35.

rugae. It is lined by stratified squamous epithelium which rests on a basement membrane and an underlying lamina propria. Many studies have been made from biopsy specimens in attempts to correlate changes in the epithelium with the menstrual cycle. The findings described, however, are not entirely harmonious, because of the fact that there are variations in the structure of the epithelium in different parts of the vagina which make it difficult to establish the presence or absence of cyclical changes.

The vaginal epithelium is rich in glycogen which, in the primates, increases with the administration of estrogen. This has also been established in women, and it has been fairly well determined that, in the estrogen phase of the cycle, the vaginal fluid has a lower pH than at other times. This is attributed to the action of the lactic acid-forming bacteria on the carbohydrate from the vaginal epithelium. The effect of estrogen on the formation of glycogen, and the consequent increase of acidity of the vagina, is used clinically in the treatment of gonorrheal vaginitis in children.

In the tissue beneath the epithelium, lymphocytes and polymorphonuclear leukocytes are common. These invade the epithelium especially just before, during and just after menstruation, and they appear as free cells in the lumen of the vagina.

In some lower mammals (e.g., rat), the different types of free cells in the vagina show periodic changes in their proportions which are correlated with the ovarian cycle. The free cells consist of desquamated epithelial cells and leukocytes. The stage of the cycle is thus readily diagnosed by smears. This finding, first established by Stockard and Papanicolaou in 1917, has been of the greatest value in experimental work on reproduction. Although the cyclical changes are not as clear in the human as in some other species, the vaginal smear techniques developed by Papanicolaou are extremely valuable in detecting malignancy at an early stage.

The lamina propria consists of loose connective tissue especially rich in elastic fibers. It also contains polymorphonuclear leukocytes and lymphocytes, as noted above, and it occasionally has aggregations of lymphocytes resembling solitary nodules. A few isolated glands resembling those of the cervix may be found in the uppermost portion of the vagina. Elsewhere the vaginal wall is entirely devoid of glands, and the mucus found in the lumen is derived from the glands of the cervix. In the posterior wall of the vagina, the connective tissue papillae are especially high.

The *muscularis* consists mainly of bundles of longitudinally disposed smooth muscle fibers that become continuous with the myometrium of the uterus. In the inner portion of the muscularis, circular bundles interlace with the longitudinal ones. The muscle bundles are separated by connective tissue rich in elastic fibers. At the entrance there are skeletal muscle fibers in the vaginal wall.

The *fibrosa* consists of dense connective tissue with many coarse elastic fibers. It serves to connect the vagina with the surrounding structures.

The *hymen* is a thin, transverse semilunar fold at the opening of the vagina into the vestibule. It has the same structure as the vaginal mucosa.

The larger *blood vessels* run in the deeper portion of the mucosa, giving off branches that break up into capillary networks in the stroma and muscularis. These networks have a general direction parallel to the surface. The capillaries empty into the veins that form a plexus of broad venous channels in the muscularis. In the rugae, there are large veins which give the rugae somewhat the character of erectile tissue.

An unusually well developed system of *lymph vessels* is present in the wall of the vagina.

The vagina receives both myelinated and unmyelinated *nerve fibers*. The latter, which are connected with scattered groups of sympathetic ganglion cells, innervate the muscle tissue and walls of the blood vessels. Sensory myelinated fibers arborize in the mucosa. Their terminals are not fully known.

EXTERNAL GENITALIA

The *vestibule*, into which the vagina and urethra open, is lined by a typical stratified squamous epithelium whose superficial layers are cornified. It contains numerous small mucous glands, the *glandulae vestibulares minores*, placed chiefly near the clitoris and opening of the urethra. They are similar in structure to the glands of Littré of the male reproductive system. The larger *glandulae vestibulares majores* or *glands of Bartholin*, analogous to the bulbourethral glands of the male, are placed in the lateral wall of the vestibule, their ducts opening close to the base of the hymen.

The *clitoris* consists mainly of erectile tissue similar to that of the corpora cavernosa of the penis. It is covered with a thin stratified squamous epithelium, underneath which is a papillated stroma rich in blood vessels and containing numerous sensory nerve fibers with highly specialized terminations, such as Meissner's corpuscles and Pacinian corpuscles.

The *labia minora*, which flank the vestibule, are covered with a stratified squamous epithelium whose basal layer contains considerable pigment. The underlying, richly vascular connective tissue contains numerous elastic fibers and sends tall slender papillae into the epithelium. In the stroma are found large sebaceous glands, not associated with hairs, and nerve endings similar to those of the clitoris.

The *labia majora* are folds of skin which cover the labia minora. They have the general structure of skin and consist of a stratified squamous epidermis and an underlying corium of fibroelastic tissue. On the outer side there are numerous hairs, sweat glands and sebaceous glands. On the inner side the epidermis is thinner and hairs are absent. The interior of the labia is filled with fatty tissue.

THE MAMMARY GLANDS

The mammary glands are cutaneous in origin, developing within the superficial fascia (tela subcutanea). Each gland consists of 15 to 20 lobes, each of which is a compound gland with a separate lobar duct opening at the apex of the nipple.

Stroma. The stroma is both fibrous and fatty in nature. Surrounding or encasing the gland both on the superficial (except at the areola) and deep surface is a layer of fat. Fat is also present within the gland, the amount varying with the functional state. Extending from the dermis into the gland are rather dense fibrous strands (Cooper's ligaments) serving a suspensory function. The interlobar and interlobular connective tissue is also a dense type and forms septa between the subdivisions of the gland. The intralobular connective tissue, on the other hand, is fine and cellular (Fig. 20-39). The amount of connective tissue varies considerably with the functional state of the glands, being reduced in the lactating gland.

Ducts. There is one main duct for each lobe. These lobar ducts course through the nipple and open on the surface. Just beneath the nipple there is a local enlargement (sinus lactiferous). The ducts branch as in any compound gland, a terminal duct finally entering each lobule as an intralobular duct. The epithelium lining an intralobular duct is simple cuboidal. It increases in height as the ducts increase in size, and it becomes stratified squamous near the opening onto the surface. Lying between the epithelium and basement membrane are myoepithelial cells which are more readily observed in the larger ducts.

Nipple and Areola. The skin of the nipple is pigmented and somewhat wrinkled, and it has tall connective tissue papillae. It has many sebaceous but no sweat glands or hairs. The areola, an area extending outward from the nipple for 1 to 2 cm., is also pigmented and has modified mammary glands (glands of Montgomery) whose ducts open through the skin of the areola. These glands, which have some of the features of sweat glands, produce small elevations on the surface. Sweat and sebaceous glands and a variable number of coarse hairs are also present. The subcutaneous tissue of the nipple and areola contains both radially and circularly coursing smooth muscle fibers.

Parenchyma. The parenchyma of the mammary gland has extreme variations in structure associated with its functional state. Variations are evident also among individuals in similar functional states.

The Inactive Mammary Gland. The glandular tissue in a nonlactating mammary gland of a sexually mature, nonpregnant woman is sparse and consists of tubules that have the appearance of ducts. These are grouped together in lobules (Figs. 20-39 and 20-40). Many inactive glands show deviations from this normal structure, however,

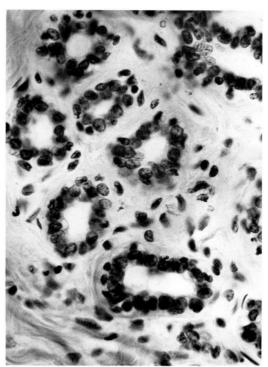

Fig. 20-40. Inactive mammary gland. Woman, 20 years of age. Photomicrograph. ×720.

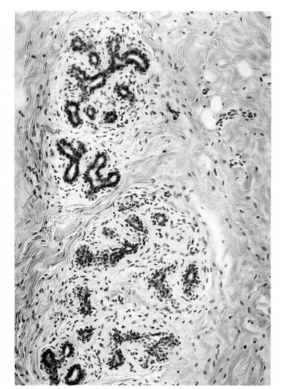

Fig. 20-39. Section through two lobules of an inactive mammary gland. Woman, 20 years of age. Photomicrograph. ×140.

and a considerable percentage has, without any clinical symptoms, some degree of gross or microscopic cystic disease or other abnormalities, as for instance, groups of secretory cells. The examination of many autopsy and surgical specimens is necessary in order to secure normal mammary gland tissue.

The Mammary Gland During Lactation. Throughout pregnancy, the mammary gland undergoes extensive changes in preparation for lactation. The tubules characteristic of the inactive gland form buds that enlarge into alveoli. As this growth of glandular tissue proceeds, the fat and the intralobular and interlobular connective tissue decrease in amount, the latter forming septa in which the ducts are embedded (Figs. 20-41 and 20-42). The alveoli at the termination of pregnancy are large and irregular in shape, although there is frequently great variation in the degree of development

Inactive lobule   Active lobule

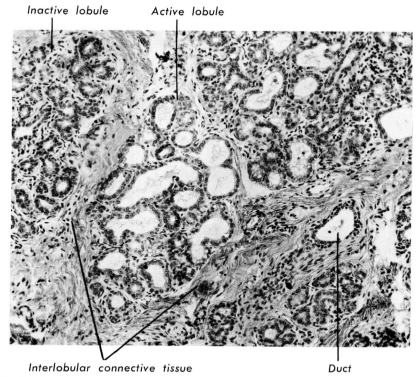

Interlobular connective tissue   Duct

FIG. 20-41. Section of mammary gland showing active and inactive glandular tissue. Fourth day post-partum. Woman, 29 years of age. Surgical specimen. Photomicrograph. ×140.

among the lobules or even within a lobule (Fig. 20-41). The alveoli are lined by a simple cuboidal epithelium that rests on a delicate basement membrane. Electron micrographs show that the cells have randomly distributed microvilli, relatively large mitochondria, a Golgi complex that enlarges during secretory activity and granular endoplasmic reticulum that increases during cell activity. The secretory process for protein constituents of milk resembles that of other cells which synthesize proteins for export.

The proteins are synthesized in association with polyribosomes, packaged in the Golgi complex, and then transported in membrane-bound vesicles to the apical surface, where they are discharged by a merocrine mode of secretion. Lipid droplets appear to arise in the cytoplasm outside the Golgi complex and pass to the apical end of the cell. They project outward and are pinched off into the

lumen enclosed by a membrane derived from the cell plasmalemma, along with an ultra-microscopic portion of cytoplasm. The amount of cytoplasm lost is so small that it is questionable whether the process should be classified as an apocrine mode of secretion. With the usual preserving techniques, the fat droplets are dissolved and the spaces that they occupied appear as vacuoles (Figs. 20-42 and 20-43), but they can be preserved with proper reagents.

After cessation of lactation, the parenchyma of the mammary glands involutes, the alveoli decreasing in size until they become no longer recognizable. The connective tissue and fat again become abundant as the structure of an inactive gland is reassumed.

The mammary glands undergo progressive atrophy following the *menopause*. Some of the lobules and ducts may be obliterated;

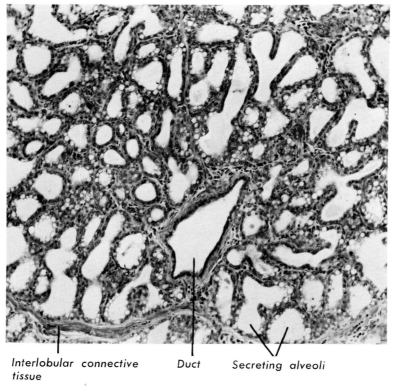

Interlobular connective tissue   Duct   Secreting alveoli

Fig. 20-42. Section of mammary gland, showing marked secretory activity. Photomicrograph. ×140.

the connective tissue becomes increasingly dense and frequently hyalinized. Cystic dilation of the ducts frequently occurs.

Milk consists of an albuminous fluid containing casein, milk sugar (lactose) and salts in which fat droplets are suspended. Milk is rich in calcium needed by the growing infant. Some cellular debris is also present.

Colostrum is the secretion formed during the first few days after parturition. It contains colostrum corpuscles, which are large spherical or oval cells filled with fat droplets of varying sizes. They are probably leukocytes or other wandering cells that have migrated into the alveoli and have taken up fat droplets by phagocytosis.

The Mammary Gland of the Male. There is little agreement as to the constitution of the male breast. Some mammary tissue always is present, but it attains its maximal development during early adolescence and then undergoes involution. The gland consists of ducts with usually no alveoli or lobulation. Under conditions of abnormal hormonal stimulation, as in some testicular tumors, the male mammary gland may enlarge and develop extensively, a condition designated as gynecomastia.

Hormonal Control of the Mammary Gland. Although some development of the mammary gland occurs during childhood, growth characteristically is greatly accentuated during adolescence. At this time the gland comes under the influence of estrogen and progesterone secreted cyclically by the ovaries, a secretory process which in turn is dependent on hormones from the anterior hypophysis. During gestation, when there is a continuous and prolonged production of both estrogen and progesterone by the ovaries and placenta, the greatest de-

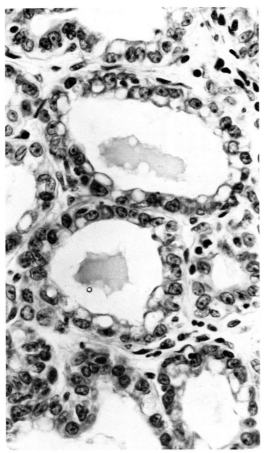

Fig. 20-43. Section of a few of the alveoli of a mammary gland in active secretion. Photomicrograph. ×720.

velopment of the mammary glands takes place, alveoli and a presecretory condition being established.

The role of estrogen and progesterone in the development of a secretory condition of the mammary gland has been extensively investigated experimentally. Both of these hormones are essential, but the degree of response to each is subject to some species variation. In general, estrogen causes duct growth, which is followed by the development of alveoli when progesterone is subsequently administered.

The influence of the anterior hypophysis on the hyperplasia of the mammary gland,

aside from its indirect effect through the ovarian hormones, has not been fully clarified. In those animals that do not abort following hypophysectomy during gestation (rats, mice, guinea pigs, rhesus monkeys) the mammary glands will attain a nearly complete gestational development in the absence of the anterior hypophysis and will briefly lactate. Lactation is not maintained in the absence of the hypophysis, however. Although some fat droplets form in the secretory cells of the mammary gland during the latter part of pregnancy, there is a tremendous increase in secretory activity following parturition. This is brought about by the action of an increased amount of lactogenic (luteotrophic, LTH) hormone from the anterior hypophysis. The effects attributed to LTH seem well established for rodents and for some other species. It is reported, however, that growth hormone will produce the results ascribed to LTH in some species, including humans (see Chapter 21).

The maintenance of lactation, following its initiation by LTH, appears to depend on a number of hormones. Crude extracts from the anterior hypophysis have an effect, and the adrenal cortex is essential.

One of the neurohypophyseal hormones, oxytocin, has a definite and pronounced effect on the lactating mammary gland, causing the contraction of the myoepithelial cells that surround the alveoli. This is the "milk ejection" or "milk let-down" effect. The secretion of oxytocin is initiated by nerve impulses reaching the hypothalamus, the most effective stimulus being suckling or similar stimulation of the nipple area. Some investigators also favor the possibility that oxytocin, reaching the anterior hypophysis by way of the blood stream, may be responsible for the release of anterior pituitary factors necessary for milk secretion.

It is difficult to secure material to determine whether structural changes occur in the human breast during the menstrual cycle. Material must be secured either at autopsy, usually after a debilitating illness, or by surgical removal because of pathological conditions. In an extensive study of rhesus monkeys, which have menstrual cycles similar to humans, it has been found that there is lobular enlargement and dilation of mammary alveoli during the corpus luteum phase of the menstrual cycle (Speert, 1948). This supplies presumptive evidence that similar changes occur in women.

Blood Vessels. The blood supply of the mammary gland comes from several neighboring vessels: the intercostals, internal mammary and thoracic branches of the axillary arteries. These vessels subdivide and form a rich capillary plexus around the ducts and alveoli. The richness of the blood supply fluctuates with activity, being much greater in the active than in the inactive or the involuted gland. From the capillaries, veins arise which accompany the arteries.

Lymphatics. The lymph vessels of mammary glands are numerous. An understanding of the course of these vessels is facilitated by keeping in mind the fact that the gland arises from the ectoderm and grows into the underlying mesoderm and that in this underlying tissue there is, over the whole body, a plexus of lymph vessels. Thus, as the developing ducts grow deeply into the connective tissue, lymph vessels accompany them and drain toward the surface into the subcutaneous lymph plexus. This plexus is particularly well formed beneath the areola. From the subcutaneous plexus, vessels pass to the axillary lymphatics and nodes along the pectoral muscles. There are accessory paths of drainage. Some vessels cross the midline, others follow the branches of the internal mammary artery and drain through the sternal nodes, and still others may drain into the abdominal lymph nodes. Because of the frequency of mammary carcinoma, the lymph drainage of this gland is of great importance.

Nerves. Both cerebrospinal and sympathetic nerves supply the gland, the larger trunks following the interlobar and inter-

lobular connective tissue septa. The nerve terminals break up into plexuses that surround the alveoli just outside their basement membranes. From these plexuses, delicate fibrils have been described passing through the basement membrane and ending between the secreting cells.

DEVELOPMENT OF THE URINARY AND REPRODUCTIVE SYSTEMS

During development, three generations of urinary structures make their appearance. These in order of their succession are known as the *pronephros, mesonephros* and *metanephros*. The first two, which are present only in the embryo in higher animals, are important in furnishing the efferent duct system of the male reproductive organs. The metanephros, generally known as the kidney, forms the adult urinary organ in all of the higher vertebrates (reptiles, birds and mammals).

All three kidney generations arise from the intermediate cell mass or nephrotome, a mesodermal mass which connects the primitive somites with the lateral coelomic plates. In man, only the cranial portion of the intermediate cell mass shows a definite segmentation corresponding to that of the primitive somites, and it is in this region that the pronephros develops. Below the 10th somite, the segments of the nephrotome are so close together as to form a continuous cord of mesoderm, the nephrogenic strand, extending to the sacral region of the body. The upper, longer portion of the strand (mesonephric strand) furnishes the mesonephros. The uriniferous tubules of the permanent kidneys are formed from the lower portion (metanephric strand).

The *pronephros* in man is a variable and rudimentary structure which has no urinary function whatever. In some embryos it may be entirely missing. It arises in the cranial segments of the nephrotome in the form of ridge-like condensations which may or may not acquire a lumen. The most anterior ridges or tubules are the most rudimentary and soon undergo involution. The caudal ones become somewhat longer and fuse at their lateral ends to form a duct, the pronephric duct, which grows caudally beyond the territory of the pronephros and ultimately empties into the cloacal portion of the intestine. The pronephric duct is placed lateral to the nephrotome, directly underneath the ectoderm. The greatest extent of the pronephros is seen in embryos of about 2.5 mm., while in embryos of 5 mm. involution of the tubules has definitely begun. All of the tubules gradually disappear, leaving only the pronephric duct.

The *mesonephros* or Wolffian body begins its

development in embryos of 2.5 mm., just caudal to the pronephros. Cellular condensations appear in the mesonephric strand and soon become vesicular by developing lumina. The vesicles elongate and are transformed into S-shaped tubules, which then connect at one end with the pronephric duct. The latter is now called the mesonephric or Wolffian duct. The distal end of each tubule becomes invaginated to form a two-layered capsule which encloses a tuft of blood vessels, the glomerulus, derived from a branch of the aorta. The capsule, together with the enclosed glomerulus, constitutes a Malpighian corpuscle.

The mesonephric tubules develop progressively from the front backward and finally form a series extending from the cervical to the pelvic region of the embryo. By increase in number and length of the tubules, each mesonephros comes to form a large structure projecting into the dorsal part of the body cavity. The greatest extent is reached during the fifth or sixth week.

From the sixth week on, the mesonephros gradually atrophies, leaving finally only certain parts which differ in the two sexes. In the male, eight to 15 tubules in the cephalic portion persist as the ductuli efferentes, while a few in the caudal portion remain as the paradidymis and aberrant ducts. The mesonephric duct is transformed into the ductus epididymidis, ductus deferens and ejaculatory duct. In the female, the mesonephric tubules disappear for the most part, only a few remaining to form the epoophoron and paroophoron, while the duct persists in part as Gärtner's canal.

Each *metanephros* or kidney begins in embryos of about 5 mm. as a hollow bud from the dorsal side of the mesonephric duct near its opening into the cloaca. This bud, the anlage of the ureter, grows dorsally and cranially into the metanephric blastema, where it ends in a terminal dilation or ampulla, the primitive pelvis. The pelvis elongates in a cranioventral direction and forms four to six branches that likewise terminate in ampullae. These branches are the primordia of the primary calyces. Each ampulla then divides into two to four secondary ampullae, and this process is repeated again and again until the whole system of collecting tubules is formed.

The nephrons, or uriniferous tubules proper, have an independent origin from the metanephric tissue which forms caplike condensations around the growing ampullae of the collecting tubules (Fig. 20-44). Portions of the condensations acquire a lumen and detach themselves from the nephrogenic cap. Each vesicle elongates into an S-shaped tubule which secondarily establishes a communication with the collecting tubule. The place of junction becomes the arched or junctional collecting tubule. By further growth and histological

differentiation, the S-shaped tubule gives rise to the convoluted tubules and loop of Henle, while the enlarged blind end becomes invaginated as Bowman's capsule to enclose a glomerulus (Fig. 20-44). Thus, the two types of tubules found in the adult kidney have separate origins. The nephrons are derived from the metanephric blastema (metanephric strand). The ureter, pelvis, calyces and all of the collecting tubules are formed from the ureteric bud, an outgrowth from the mesonephric duct.

The *gonads* or sex glands make their first appearance on the mesial surface of the mesonephros as ridge-like thickenings of the celomic epithelium, the *genital ridges*, which at first extend from the mid-thoracic to the sacral levels. As development proceeds, the anterior portion retrogresses and the gonads become restricted to the lumbar region. The cells of the ridge proliferate and form a band composed of two types of cells: a large number of small cuboidal cells which stain rather intensely and, scattered between them, larger spherical cells with vesicular nuclei and clearer cytoplasm, the primitive sex cells. The whole epithelial band is known as the *germinal epithelium*.

As the germinal epithelium continues to proliferate, irregular plugs or strands of epithelial cells, the *medullary* or *sex cords*, extend into the underlying connective tissue. These are likewise composed of the two types of cells. The deepest portions of the cords, which lie closest to the mesonephric tubules, anastomose with one another to form the anlage of the *rete*.

Up to about the sixth week, development proceeds similarly in both sexes. This is the so-called "indifferent" period. Although sex is determined at a much earlier time by the constitution of the fertilized egg, histological differences between the male and female cannot be observed during this period.

From the sixth week on, histological changes occur that lead to a definite differentiation of the gonads. In the *testis*, a layer of embryonal connective tissue, the future *tunica albuginea*, grows in between the medullary cords and the germinal epithelium, and the latter becomes gradually reduced to a single layer of flat cells, the visceral layer of the tunica vaginalis. The medullary cords become more distinct and elongate to form the convoluted *seminiferous tubules*. The deeper anastomosing portions of the cords unite with a number of mesonephric tubules to form the *rete testis* of the adult. As already stated, the mesonephric tubules with which such union is established become the *ductuli efferentes*, while the mesonephric duct is transformed into the *ductus epididymidis* and *ductus deferens*. The larger sex cells of the cord either become smaller temporarily or, according

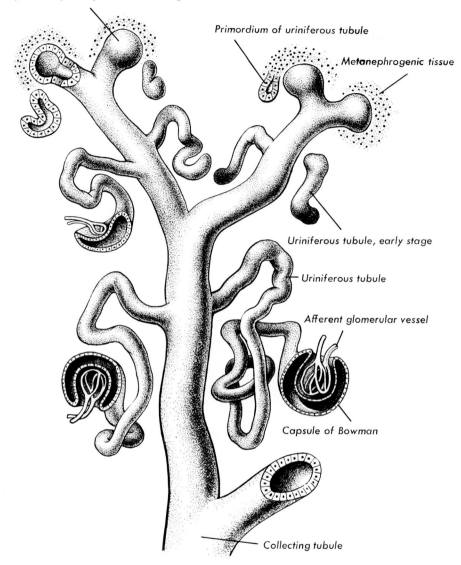

Expanded, growing end of collecting tubule

Primordium of uriniferous tubule

Metanephrogenic tissue

Uriniferous tubule, early stage

Uriniferous tubule

Afferent glomerular vessel

Capsule of Bowman

Collecting tubule

Fig. 20-44. Diagram of development of kidney tubules. Early differentiation of uriniferous tubules from metanephrogenic tissue is shown in the *upper part* of figure; later stages are shown in the *lower portion* of the diagram. (Redrawn and modified from Corning.)

to some authors, disappear entirely, and the semi-niferous tubules consist for a time of only the smaller cuboidal cells. From these are differentiated both the spermatogenic cells and the cells of Sertoli.

Differentiation of the *ovary* begins at a later period and differs considerably from the process in the male. The medullary cords and rete formed during the indifferent period gradually disappear,

though vestiges of the rete may remain in the stroma of the adult ovary. On the other hand, the cells at the surface continue to proliferate and form a layered epithelial mass. The masses of cells are subdivided by strands of connective tissue into clusters containing oogonia, probably derived from primordial germ cells that migrated from the yolk sac by the sixth week and follicular cells derived from the germinal epithelium. At first, the clusters consist of several larger egg cells scattered in a mass of small (follicular) cells. Later, each cluster is broken up by invading connective tissue into several primary follicles, each containing a single egg cell surrounded by a layer of flattened follicular cells.

Proliferation of oogonia continues until about the sixth fetal month. By the time of birth, the connective tissue of the ovary forms a dense tunica albuginea beneath the germinal epithelium, separating the latter from the ovarian cortical tissue. The germinal epithelium persists as a layer of cuboidal or columnar cells.

The primordia of the female genital ducts are the *Müllerian ducts* of the embryo. These begin in both sexes as celomic invaginations into the cranial portions of the mesonephric ridge which then grow backward, running parallel and close to the mesonephric duct. Caudally, the two Müllerian ducts approach each other and fuse to form a terminal unpaired tube which ends in the urogenital sinus (cloaca) between the openings of the mesonephric ducts. In the male, the Müllerian duct degenerates, leaving as vestiges the *appendix testis* and the *colliculus seminalis* (utriculus prostaticus, uterus masculinus). In the female, the paired upper portions become the *Fallopian tubes* or *oviducts*, while the unpaired terminal portion forms the *uterus* and *vagina*.

Development of Mammary Glands. In animals with numerous glands, the beginnings of the mammary glands are represented by two ridges of thickened epithelium, the mammary lines, which extend from the axillary to the inguinal regions. At various points on these ridges, epithelial proliferations form the primordia of future glands, while the intermediate portions of the milk lines ultimately disappear. In the human, the mammary line (ridge) is poorly defined and of brief duration, and normally only one pair of glands develops. Each gland appears in the second month as a broad epidermal thickening in the region of the future nipple, produced by a proliferation and downgrowth of the germinative layer. The thickening spreads laterally to form a hemispherical mass whose convex surface is directed towards the derma. Externally, the circular patch of skin, or mammary area, corresponding to the thickening sinks below the surface as the mammary pit.

Around the fifth month, a varying number of secondary sprouts, the future lactiferous ducts and sinuses, grow down into the derma and there branch repeatedly, the branches ending in terminal swellings. At first the sprouts are solid but, from the seventh month on, lumina appear in various places and finally become confluent. This process of branching and canalization continues until birth, the histological picture being that of a prepubertal gland. The formation of the glandular alveoli does not take place until adolescence.

Soon after birth, the shallow mammary pit is raised above the surface by the proliferation of connective tissue. The central portion develops into the nipple, which contains the openings of the lactiferous ducts. The remainder of the mammary area forms the areola, which is distinguished from the surrounding skin by its hairlessness, pigmentation and thinness of epidermis.

REFERENCES

ADAMS, E. C., AND HERTIG, A. T. 1969 Studies on the human corpus luteum. I. Observations on the ultrastructure of development and regression of the luteal cells during the menstrual cycle. J. Cell Biol., vol. 41, pp. 696–715.

AGATE, F. J., JR. 1952 The growth and secretory activity of the mammary glands of the pregnant rhesus monkey (Macaca mulatta) following hypophysectomy. Amer. J. Anat., vol. 90, pp. 257–284.

BAKER, B. L., HOOK, S., AND SEVERINGHAUS, A. E. 1944 The cytological structure of the human chorionic villus and decidua parietalis. Amer. J. Anat., vol. 74, pp. 297–327.

BARGMAN, W., AND KNOOP, A. 1959 Über die Morphologie der Milchsekretion: Licht- und Elektronen-mikroskopische Studien ab der Milchdrüse der Ratte. Z. Zellforsch., vol. 49, pp. 344.

CORNER, G. W., JR. 1956 The histological dating of the human corpus luteum of menstruation. Amer. J. Anat., vol. 98, pp. 377–402.

CRAWFORD, J. M. 1956 The foetal placental circulation. J. Obstet. Gynaec. Brit. Emp., vol. 63, pp. 542–547.

DARON, G. H. 1936 The arterial pattern of the tunica mucosa of the uterus in Macacus rhesus. Amer. J. Anat., vol. 58, pp. 349–419.

DEMPSEY, E. W., AND LUSE, S. A. 1970 Electron microscopic observations on fibrinoid and histiotroph in the junctional zone and villi of the human placenta. Amer. J. Anat., vol. 128, pp. 463–484.

ENDERS, A. C. 1970 Fertilization, cleavage and implantation. *In* Reproduction and Breeding Techniques for Laboratory Animals. (Hafez, E. S. E., editor), pp. 137–156. Lea & Febiger, Philadelphia.

ENDERS, A. C. 1971 The fine structure of the blastocyst. *In* The Biology of the Blastocyst (Blandau, R. J., editor), pp. 71–94. The University of Chicago Press, Chicago.

FRANCHI, L. L., MANDL, A. M., AND ZUCKERMAN, S. 1962 The development of the ovary and the process of oogenesis. *In* The Ovary (Zuckerman, S., editor), vol. 1, pp. 1–88. Academic Press, New York.

GRANDY, H. G., AND SMITH, D. E. (editors) 1963 The Ovary. The Williams & Wilkins Company, Baltimore.

GREEP, R. O. 1962 Histology, histochemistry, and ultrastructure of adult ovary. *In* The Ovary (Grandy, H. G., and Smith, D. E., editors). The Williams & Wilkins Company, Baltimore.

HERTIG, A. T. 1968 Human Trophoblast. Charles C Thomas, Publisher, Springfield, Ill.

HERTIG, A. T., AND ADAMS, E. C. 1967 Studies on the human oocyte and its follicle. I. Ultrastructural and histochemical observations on the primordial follicle stage. J. Cell Biol., vol. 34, pp. 647–675.

HERTIG, A. T., ROCK, J., AND ADAMS, E. C. 1956 A description of 34 human ova within the first 17 days of development. Amer. J. Anat., vol. 98, pp. 435–494.

KEENAN, T. W., MORRÉ, D. J., OLSON, D. E., YUNGHANS, W. N., AND PATTON, S. 1970 Biochemical and morphological comparison of plasma membrane and fat globule membrane from bovine mammary gland. J. Cell Biol., vol. 44, pp. 80–93.

LUCKETT, W. P. 1970 The fine structure of the flattened villi of the rhesus monkey. Anat. Rec., vol. 167, pp. 141–164.

MARKEE, J. E. 1940 Menstruation in endometrial transplants in the rhesus monkey. Carnegie Inst. Wash., Contrib. Embryology, vol. 28, no. 177, pp. 221–308.

MIDGLEY, A. R., JR., AND PIERCE, G. B., JR. 1962 Immunohistochemical localization of hyman chorionic gonadotropin. J. Exp. Med., vol. 115, pp. 289–294.

MILLS, E. S., AND TOPPER, Y. J. 1970 Some ultrastructural effects of insulin, hydrocortisone, and prolactin on mammary gland explants. J. Cell Biol., vol. 44, pp. 310–328.

NOYES, R. W., HERTIG, A. T., AND ROCK, J. 1950 Dating the endometrial biopsy. Fertil. Steril., vol. 1, pp. 3–25.

PAPANICOLAOU, G. N. 1933 The sexual cycle in the human female as revealed by vaginal smears. Amer. J. Anat., vol. 53, pp. 519–637.

PAPANICOLAOU, G. N., TRAUT, H. F., AND MARCHETTI, A. A. 1948 The Epithelia of Woman's Reproductive Tract. Commonwealth Fund, New York.

RAMSEY, E. M. 1956 Circulation in the maternal placenta of the Rhesus monkey and man, with observations on the marginal lakes. Amer. J. Anat., vol. 98, pp. 159–190.

REECE, R. P. 1958 Mammary gland development and function. *In* The Endocrinology of Reproduction (Velardo, J. T., editor), pp. 213–240. Oxford University Press, New York.

RICHARDSON, G. S. 1966 Ovarian Physiology. New Eng. J. Med., vol. 274, pp. 1008–1015, 1064–1075, 1121–1134, 1184–1194.

ROCK, J., AND HERTIG, A. T. 1942 Some aspects of early human development. Amer. J. Obstet. Gynec., vol. 44, pp. 973–982.

ROCK, J., AND HERTIG, A. T. 1948 The human conceptus during the first two weeks of gestation. Amer. J. Obstet. Gynec., vol. 55, pp. 6–14.

SHETTLES, L. B. 1954 Studies on living human ova. Ann. N. Y. Acad. Sci., vol. 17, pp. 99–102.

SHETTLES, L. B. 1958 The nourishment of the human ovum. Bull. Sloane Hosp. Women, vol. 4, pp. 34–38.

SIMKINS, C. S. 1932 Development of the human ovary from birth to sexual maturity. Amer. J. Anat., vol. 51, pp. 465–505.

SMITH, O. W., AND SMITH, G. VAN S. 1946 Studies concernig the cause and purpose of menstruation. J. Clin. Endocr., vol. 6, pp. 483–492.

SPEERT, H. 1948 The normal and experimental development of the mammary gland of the rhesus monkey, with some pathological correlations. Carnegie Inst. Wash., Contrib. Embryology, vol. 32, pp. 9–65.

TRAUT, H. F., BLOCH, P. W., AND KUDER, A. 1936 Cyclical changes in the human vaginal mucosa. Surg. Gynec. Obstet., vol. 63, pp. 7–15.

VELARDO, J. T. (editor) 1958 The Endocrinology of Reproduction. Oxford University Press, New York.

VILLEE, D. B. 1969 Development of endocrine function in the human placenta and fetus. New Eng. J. Med., vol. 281, pp. 473–484, 533–542.

WISLOCKI, G. B., AND BENNETT, H. S. 1943 The histology and cytology of the human and monkey placenta, with special reference to the trophoblast. Amer. J. Anat., vol. 73, pp. 335–451.

WISLOCKI, G. B., AND DEMPSEY, E. W. 1939 Remarks on the lymphatics of the reproductive tract of the female rhesus monkey. Anat. Rec., vol. 75, pp. 341–364.

WISLOCKI, G. B., AND DEMPSEY, E. W. 1955 Electron microscopy of the human placenta. Anat. Rec., vol. 123, pp. 133–168.

WITSCHI, E. 1963 Embryology of the Ovary. *In* The Ovary (Grady, H. G., and Smith, D. E., editors). The Williams & Wilkins Company, Baltimore.

YOUNG, W. C. (editor) 1961 Sex and Internal Secretions, vols. 1 and 2. The Williams & Wilkins Company, Baltimore.

21

The Endocrine Glands

The endocrine glands, or glands of internal secretion, include a diverse group of tissues and organs widely scattered in the body. Although physiological criteria are of primary importance in deciding whether any given tissue or organ belongs to the endocrine system, all tissues and organs of this system do have certain anatomical features in common. They have no ducts and they secrete directly into the vascular channels: therefore, they are known as ductless glands. They have a rich supply of blood vessels to provide not only for their own metabolic needs but also for the transport of their secretions to other parts of the body. The parenchyma of the endocrine organs is usually, although not invariably, composed of cells of epithelial or epithelioid characteristics. In other anatomical features, such as arrangement of cells and cytological characteristics, the various endocrine glands differ widely from each other.

Physiologically, the endocrine glands have certain similarities. Each endocrine gland secretes one or more specific substances, called *hormones*, and each hormone has a specific effect upon a particular tissue or organ or on the body as a whole. Since the hormones are secreted into the blood or lymph, they all reach all parts of the body. Only a limited part of the organism may respond, however, as for example, a particular organ. The responsive structure, designated the "target" organ or tissue, selec-

tively utilizes the circulating hormone. This is in contrast with the transmission of nerve impulses, which cause a response in a limited part of the organism because they are carried over definite, discrete pathways to a limited area.

In some cases, it can readily be determined whether or not an organ has an endocrine function. Experimental ablation of the thyroid gland, for example, produces certain effects which are reversed by thyroid administration. Such is also the case, as can be shown both experimentally and clinically, with the anterior hypophysis, neurohypophysis, adrenal cortex, the parathyroids, the testes and ovaries (their endocrine portions only) and the islets of the pancreas. The specific hormones of some of the glands have been chemically isolated, analyzed and synthesized; the secretions of others have been extracted in a more or less highly purified state.

Whereas severe disabilities or even death may result from ablation of certain endocrine glands, this is not true of all endocrines. For example, removal of the adrenal medulla, whose hormone was the first one to be chemically analyzed and synthesized, does not produce severe disabilities.

Hormone, the term applied to the specific product of an endocrine gland, is used in a somewhat limited sense. By derivation it means a chemical excitant. In this sense, carbon dioxide would be a hormone since it is an excitant of the respiratory center. Since carbon dioxide is a general product of tissue metabolism, however, it is usually not spoken of as a true internal secretion or hormone.

There are some tissues which have an endocrine function but which are not organized into definite glandular organs. The mucosa of the gastrointestinal tract, for instance, secretes hormones that have effects on other structures, such as the exocrine portion of the pancreas and the muscle of the gall bladder.

Although the follicles and corpora lutea of the ovary, the fetal placenta, the interstitial tissue of the testis and the islets of the pancreas elaborate hormones, it has seemed wise to include a description of them under the organs to which they belong.

THE HYPOPHYSIS CEREBRI

MACROSCOPIC STRUCTURE

The *hypophysis* (pituitary gland) structurally and functionally is the most complex of the endocrine glands. It is derived in part from oral ectoderm and in part from the brain, with which it maintains its connections in the adult (Fig. 21-1). The major part of the gland (anterior and posterior lobes) in most forms lies in a bony fossa, the sella turcica. This part is ensheathed by the dura, an extension of which, the *diaphragma sellae*, roofs over the sella turcica. There is a small aperture in the diaphragma through which the pituitary stalk passes. The suprasellar portion of the gland includes the pituitary stalk and that portion of the hypothalamus known as the median eminence of the tuber cinereum. The infundibular stem forms the bulk of the pituitary stalk. The smaller component, the pars tuberalis, surrounds the infundibular stem and flares out onto the median eminence.

Table 21-1 gives the various parts of the gland, their embryological derivation and the more common synonyms.

The pars nervosa and pars intermedia are intimately fused, forming a single main division, the posterior lobe. Except at the circumferential portion of the junctional region, the posterior lobe in most species is separated from the anterior lobe by a cleft-like cavity, the vestigial lumen (Fig. 21-2). In man, only remnants of this cleft are present. In the cetacea (whale, porpoise), in birds and in the armadillo, a pars inter-

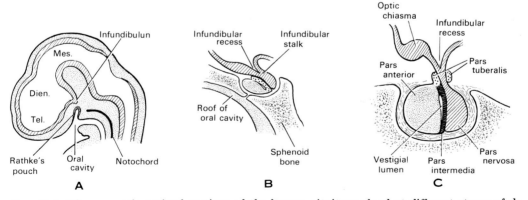

FIG. 21-1. Diagrammatic sagittal sections of the human pituitary gland at different stages of development. *A*, cephalic region of a 6-week embryo showing Rathke's pouch as an outgrowth from the dorsal wall of the oral cavity. The infundibulum is seen as a thickening in the floor of the diencephalon (*Dien.*). *Tel.*, telencephalon, and *Mes.*, mesencephalon. *B*, and *C*, stages of pituitary development at the end of the third and fourth months, respectively. The interrelationships of the major subdivisions of the gland in the 4-month fetus approximate those of the adult. (Redrawn and modified after Langman.)

TABLE 21-1

Components of Hypophysis and Their Derivation

Derivations	Divisions	Components		Lobes of pituitary gland within sella turcica
Oral ectoderm	Adenohypophysis	Pars tuberalis		
		Pars anterior—pars distalis		Anterior lobe
		Pars intermedia		
		Pars nervosa—infundibular process (neural lobe)		Posterior lobe
Neural ectoderm	Neurohypophysis	Infundibulum (neural stalk)	Infundibular stem	
			Median eminence of tuber cinereum	

media is not present and there is no vestigial lumen. In these species, the neural lobe is encapsulated by the meninges and consequently is entirely separated from the anterior lobe.

The human pituitary gland measures about 1.2 to 1.5 cm. in the transverse plane, about 1 cm. in the sagittal plane and about 0.5 cm. in height. Its weight varies considerably but correlates better with stature than with body weight. In the human, the weight of the anterior lobe increases with pregnancy and decreases slightly in old age. The average weight of the hypophysis in the male is about 0.6 gram. In multipara it may weigh more than 1 gram.

Blood and Nerve Supply

The *blood supply* of the hypophysis has unusual features, and it plays such an important role in pituitary gland function that it seems appropriate to describe it in advance of the microscopic structure.

The hypophysis is supplied by *superior hypophyseal arteries*, which arise from the internal carotids and circle of Willis, and by a pair of *inferior hypophyseal arteries* from the internal carotids. The superior hypophyseal vessels supply the infundibulum and thence the anterior lobe by way of a portal system. The inferior hypophyseal vessels serve mainly for the blood supply of the

neural lobe, although their interlobar branches do give off some vessels that anastomose with branches from the superior hypophyseal vessels to supply the lower portion of the infundibulum and thence, by a portal system, the anterior lobe. It is to be noted that the anterior lobe usually receives no direct arterial supply and it is dependent upon the portal system from the infundibulum.

Although there are several superior hypophyseal arteries and their pattern is complex because of numerous variations and anastomoses, two main vessels can usually be identified on each side. These are known as the *anterior superior hypophyseal artery*, which enters the anterior portion of the infundibulum, and the *lateral* or *posterior superior hypophyseal artery*, which continues around the stalk to enter the posterior portion of the infundibulum (Fig. 21-2). Within the infundibulum, some branches from both the anterior and posterior hypophyseal arteries ascend to supply the median eminence of the tuber cinereum, while other branches descend to anastomose with vessels projecting upward from the lower part of the stalk. The latter are derivatives from a pair of vessels (loral arteries, trabecular arteries) that arise from the anterior superior hypophyseal arteries, descend in front of the neural stalk to enter the anterior lobe, and

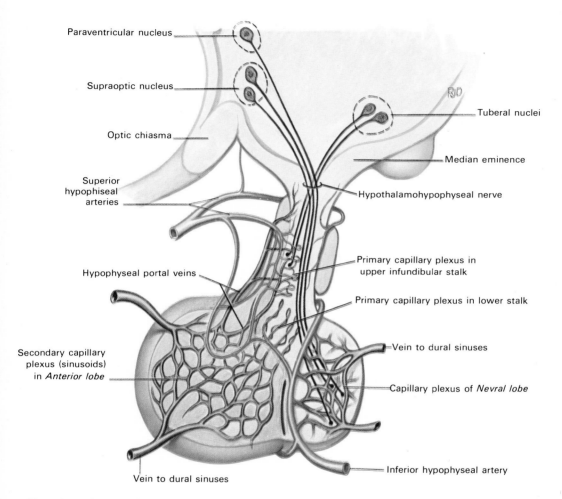

Paraventricular nucleus

Supraoptic nucleus

Optic chiasma

Superior
hypophiseal
arteries

Hypophyseal portal veins

Secondary capillary
plexus (sinusoids)
in *Anterior lobe*

Vein to dural sinuses

Tuberal nuclei

Median eminence

Hypothalamohypophyseal nerve

Primary capillary plexus in
upper infundibular stalk

Primary capillary plexus in lower stalk

Vein to dural sinuses

Capillary plexus of *Nevral lobe*

Inferior hypophyseal artery

FIG. 21-2. Diagram of the blood supply of the pituitary gland as seen from the left side. The infundibular stalk is shown in sagittal section and portions of the left sides of the anterior and neural lobes have been removed in order to show the vessels that penetrate deeply into the glandular tissue. The left inferior hypophyseal artery is shown in its course at the exterior of the gland, above the cut surface of the glandular tissue. The inferior hypophyseal artery joins with its corresponding vessel of the opposite side (not visible from the left) to form an arterial circle around the junction of the neural lobe with the anterior lobe. Branches from the circle penetrate inward, as shown, to supply the neural lobe and the lower portion of the infundibular stalk. (Based on descriptions and diagrams by Greep, 1963; Xureb, Prichard, and Daniel, 1954; Stanfield, 1960; and others.)

then swing backward and upward into the stalk (Fig. 21-2). A branch of each loral artery also continues caudally toward the lower portion of the infundibular stem, where it anastomoses with branches from the inferior hypophyseal arteries in supplying parallel arteries to the lower infundibulum. A small, inconstant branch of the loral artery also enters the interlobar fibrous connective tissue core.

The arterioles in the median eminence and upper part of the stalk terminate in characteristic patterns of looped sinusoidal capillaries, (primary set of capillaries), which join to form venules that in turn unite to form long descending veins which course downward in the peripheral portion of the stalk to supply sinusoids in the pars distalis (secondary set of capillaries). A characteristic pattern of short venous trunks draining from the sinusoidal capillaries in the upper and lower portions of the infundibulum and ending in the sinusoids of the pars distalis constitutes the *hypophyseal portal system.* Thus, a pathway is established by which neurosecretory material released from nerves in the median eminence can pass to the pars distalis.

The pars nervosa (neural lobe) receives its blood supply from the *inferior hypophyseal arteries,* which form an arterial circle near the junction of the anterior and posterior lobes. Numerous arterial branches pass into the neural lobe tissue to enter sinusoidal capillaries. Interlobar arteries from the arterial circle also contribute branches which anastomose with vessels from the superior hypophyseal arteries, as outlined above, to supply the lower (intraglandular) portion of the infundibulum and thence to the sinusoids of the pars distalis (Fig. 21-2). The sinusoidal capillaries of the neural lobe have an important function in receiving neurosecretory material conveyed to the neural lobe by nerve fibers from the hypothalamus.

The sinusoidal capillaries of the pars distalis form an elaborate plexus of channels which are wider than the sinusoidal capillaries of the neural lobe. Electron micrographs show a fenestrated type of endothelium in the sinusoidal vessels of both locations with diaphragms spanning the fenestrae.

The *innervation* of the hypophysis consists chiefly of the hypothalamico-hypophyseal tracts of nonmyelinated nerve fibers that extend into the neural lobe from their cells of origin in the supraoptic and paraventricular nuclei and of tracts to the upper part of the stalk (Fig. 21-2). They serve to carry neurosecretory substances. There are no nerves to the anterior lobe, other than some vasomotor fibers with blood vessels. Although the parenchymal cells of the pars distalis have no nerve supply, there is substantial evidence that they are under nervous control.

Section of the pituitary stalk in rabbits prevents ovulation after mating. In this species, as in the cat and ferret, ovulation occurs only after copulation. The inhibition of ovulation after stalk section is attributed to the interruption of the *neurohumoral pathway* from the hypothalamus to the anterior lobe. Coitus in the rabbit normally causes the release of certain anterior lobe hormones, the stimulation for this release being a substance produced in the brain and transmitted to the anterior lobe by way of the *hypophyseal portal system.* Other functions of the anterior hypophysis are apparently regulated by the brain through such a neurohumoral pathway.

Microscopic Structure and Function

Pars Anterior. About 75 % of the hypophysis is anterior lobe. The parenchyma of this lobe is formed of anastomosing cords of cells separated from sinusoidal capillaries by only a meager amount of irregularly arranged connective tissue. Small masses of colloid occur within the cell cords only occasionally (Fig. 21-3).

The parenchymal cells fall into two main categories: chromophobes and chromophils.

The latter were subdivided into acidophils and basophils by the early pituitary cytologists on the basis of some of the staining reactions in routine preparations. In hematoxylin and eosin preparations, the cytoplasmic granules of the acidophils stain well with eosin, although the granules of the so-called basophils do not stain well with hematoxylin. Moreover, the granules of the basophils stain very well with the aniline blue of the Mallory's and modified Masson's trichrome stains, reacting in this sense like collagen which is acidophilic (Fig. 21-15, *A*). It is obvious that the terms acidophils and basophils are not particularly appropriate for pituitary cells, but the terms are well established in the literature. The three types of cells identified in trichrome-stained preparations are known as: *chromophobes* (about 50%), *acidophils* (35%) and *basophils* (15%). Additional types within the acidophil and basophil groups can be identified by special staining and by histochemical methods. Electron micrographs also show differential characteristics, such as granules of different sizes in different cells. By the various available techniques, as many as six different types of cells have been identified in the pars distalis.

The *chromophobes* (reserve or chief cells) tend to appear in groups near the centers of the cords. Thus grouped, they were earlier described as nuclear heaps (Kernhaufen). Their nuclei are surrounded by a small amount of diffuse, light staining cytoplasm. The cell boundaries are not distinguishable in ordinary preparations. Secretory granules of specific types are usually not seen by light microscopy in cells classified as chromophobes. However, electron microscope studies show relatively few nongranular cells, and it seems likely that many of the cells counted as chromophobes in routine preparations are acidophils and basophils that have become degranulated following a secretory cycle.

The *acidophils* (*alpha cells*) stain readily and are easily identified in ordinary preparations (Figs. 21-3 and 21-15). These cells are usually larger than the chromophobes, and their cytoplasm contains secretion granules which take the acid dyes such as eosin, acid fuchsin and orange G. They also take certain basic dyes such as safranin. Therefore, some investigators use the name alpha cell in preference to acidophil.

The acidophils can be divided into two groups by the use of special staining methods, using either a modified Heidenhain azan stain or a tetrachrome stain (Herlant, 1960). In the tetrachrome method, the granules of some acidophils stain with orange G, while the granules of other acidophils stain with erythrosin. It seems well established that the former are *somatotrophs*, or growth hormone-secreting cells, while the latter are *prolactin cells*, also known as *luteotrophs*. Strong support for this has been obtained from immunohistochemical studies utilizing labeled antibodies. The method and its results are well illustrated by recent studies in which an enzyme, horseradish peroxidase, is conjugated to an antibody for growth hormone. After a section of the anterior pituitary gland is reacted with the enzyme-labeled antibody, it is chemically treated to visualize the peroxidase at the site where the labeled antibody reacted with its hormone. Next, the immunochemically stained section is photographed and then destained, in order to restain by a trichrome method to identify immunochemically reacting cells in terms of acidophils and basophils (Fig. 21-4; Baker, 1970). The findings confirm that the somatotroph is a relatively large acidophil, ovoid in shape, with relatively fine cytoplasmic granules.

The cells that give immunochemical reactions for prolactin are acidophils of polyhedral shape with relatively coarse cytoplasmic granules. Evidence for two types of acidophils is also derived from electron microscope studies. In one type of acidophil, now established as a somatotroph, the cytoplasmic granules measure up to about 350 mμ, whereas in the prolactin cell the granules

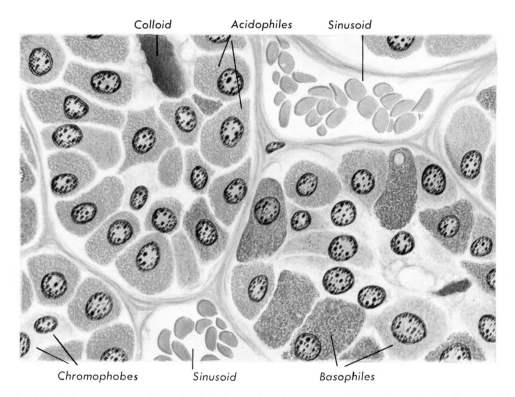

Colloid   Acidophiles   Sinusoid

Chromophobes   Sinusoid   Basophiles

FIG. 21-3. Human anterior hypophysis. The section shows parts of several cords of cells containing acidophils (orange), two types of basophils (purple and green) and chromophobes. Fine connective tissue and sinusoids separate the cords. Masses of colloid are seen in the centers of two of the cords. A 4-μ section stained with aldehyde fuchsin-fast green-orange G. Woman, age 26. Camera lucida drawing. ×1200.

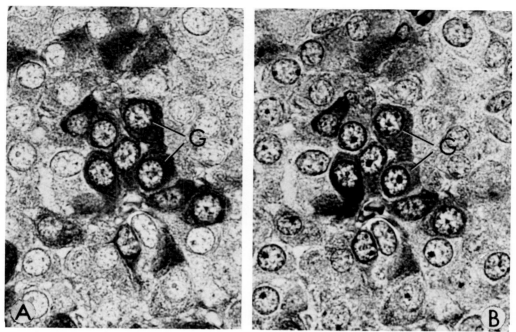

FIG. 21-4. Photomicrographs of a section of rat anterior hypophysis. In A, the section has been stained (immunochemically after application of a rabbit antiserum to human growth hormone. This selectively demonstrates the cells (G) whose cytoplasm contains growth hormone. In B, the section shown in A has been destained and subsequently restained by the Masson's trichrome procedure. The growth hormone cells shown in A, have given the characteristic reaction of cells that are identified as acidophils by routine histological methods. Immunochemical methods for demonstrating prolactin secreting cells, show that the prolactin cells are acidophils of a type that differs from the growth hormone acidophils in the rat hypophysis. Both figures, $\times 1000$ (Courtesy of Dr. Burton L. Baker, J. Histochem. Cytochem., vol. 18, 1970).

measure up to about 700 mμ (Heidinger and Farquhar, 1957). The more recent findings on a special type of acidophil for prolactin elucidate the observations of earlier workers that acidophils of a particular type increase in numbers during pregnancy.

The *basophils (beta cells)* show considerable variation in their staining properties, both within an individual gland and from one species to another. The cytoplasmic granules also vary in size in a given cell and in different species. Electron micrographs show that they measure up to about 200 mμ in the rat (Figs. 21-5 and 21-6). Thus, the granules are definitely smaller than in the acidophils. The granules stain poorly with hematoxylin, well with the aniline blue of the trichrome methods (Fig. 21-15) and

excellently with the periodic acid-Schiff (PAS) technique. It is to be noted that the granules of all of the basophils of the pars distalis stain by the PAS method because of their content of glycoproteins, and that none of the acidophils stain with PAS.

The aldehyde fuchsin technique enables one to distinguish two types of basophils: an aldehyde fuchsin-positive type (beta basophil) and an aldehyde fuchsin-negative type (delta basophil). The *beta basophils* are polyhedral or angular in shape, and they tend to be located centrally in the gland. They show pronounced changes following thyroidectomy, and they apparently secrete thyrotrophic hormone, as shown by immunohistochemical methods using peroxidase-labeled antibody for thyrotrophic hormone.

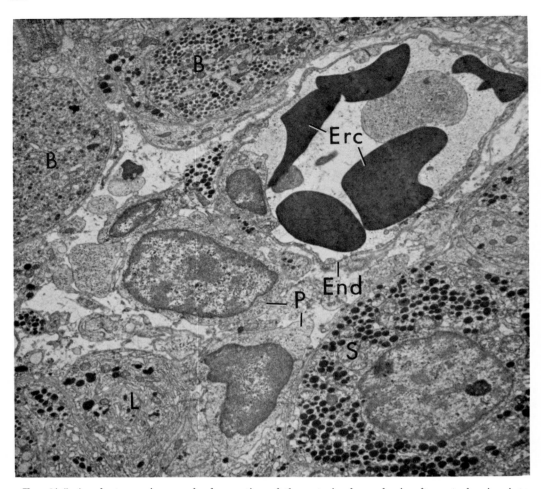

FIG. 21-5. An electron micrograph of a portion of the anterior hypophysis of a rat showing inter-relationships of blood capillaries, perivascular spaces, and parenchymal cells. Two types of acidophilic parenchymal cells are seen: somatrophs (*S*) with cytoplasmic granules ranging up to 350 mμ, and luteo-traphs (*L*) with granules ranging up to 700 mμ. The basophils (*B*) have relatively small cytoplasmic granules. The cytoplasm of the capillary endothelium (*End*) is thin except in the perinuclear region. The basal lamina beneath the endothelium is separated from that around the parenchymal cells by peri-vascular space that contains collagen and connective tissue cells. The perivascular connective tissue cells (*P*) included in this particular field resemble macrophages. *Erc*, erythrocytes. $\times$16,000. (Courtesy of Dr. M. G. Farquhar, Angiology, vol. 12, 1961.)

The *delta basophils* are more rounded in shape than are the beta basophils (thyro-trophs). There is substantial evidence that they secrete the gonadotrophic hormones, i.e., *follicle-stimulating hormone* (FSH) and *luteinizing hormone* (LH). By special stain-ing techniques and experimental procedures, some evidence has been obtained that the delta basophils can be divided into two types, one for FSH and one for LH. When

separately labeled antibodies, one for FSH and one for LH, are applied to the same sections, however, some of the basophils located peripherally in the gland are seen to have FSH and LH in the same cell, whereas some other basophils located cen-trally contain only LH (Nakane, 1970). Thus, in this instance, the same cell often contains both FSH and LH.

The proportion of each of the cell types

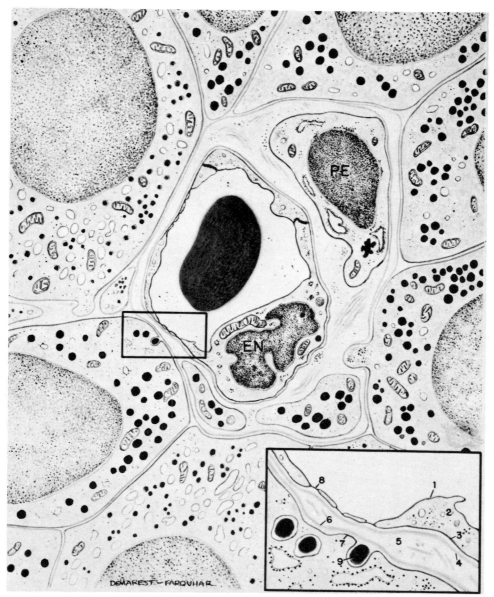

FIG. 21-6. A composite diagram of some of the details observable in electron micrographs of the anterior hypophysis. The cytoplasm of the capillary endothelial cell is generally attenuated except in the region around the nucleus (*EN*). The perivascular space may be narrow as seen at the *left* of the capillary or it may be relatively broad as shown at the *right*. It contains collagen and connective tissue cells; a perivascular macrophage (*PE*) is included in the diagram. The parenchymal cells also rest on a basal lamina. The area enclosed by the rectangle is enlarged at the *lower right*. Structures between the lumen of the capillary and the cytoplasm of a parenchymal cell are numbered in sequence. *1*, plasma membrane of luminal surface of endothelial cell; *2*, endothelial cell cytoplasm; *3*, membrane of basal surface of endothelial cell; *4*, basal lamina of endothelial cell; *5*, perivascular space; *6*, basal lamina of parenchymal cell; and *7*, the plasma membrane of a parenchymal cell. In some areas, *8*, the endothelial cells have fenestrae closed only by thin diaphragms. At *9*, the membrane around a secretion granule is shown in continuity with the parenchymal cell membrane. ×12,000; Insert, ×40,000. (Courtesy of Dr. M. G. Farquhar, Angiology, vol. 12, 1961.)

present in the cell cords varies greatly, not only in different regions of the anterior lobe but even in adjacent cords. In the human hypophysis, the basophils are most numerous in the region of the midsagittal plane and anterolateral margin of the gland. The acidophils are most numerous in the central and posterior part of each lateral half of the gland. A survey of much of the gland is necessary in order to determine the percentages of the various cell types.

The *lineage* of the cells of the anterior lobe is important in the interpretation of experimental work and tumor formation. Since mitoses are rare, it is certain that few if any of the cells are destroyed when their secretion is liberated; thus the cells must pass through secretory cycles. It also seems certain that the chromophobes represent the nonsecretory stage of the cycle. They form true reserve cells. As they pass into an active stage, granules begin to form in them. These granules are specific for the different cell types, acidophilic in some cells, basophilic in others. When a cell becomes engorged with secretory granules, it takes on the characteristics of a typical acidophil or basophil. The secretion is then liberated, and the cell returns to the chromophobe type.

Investigations on the appearance of the Golgi complexes in cells of the rat hypophysis have provided strong support for such a secretory cycle. In this species, the Golgi bodies of the acidophils and of the basophils differ from each other in their morphology and position, and these two types are present in the chromophobes (Severinghaus). This has made it possible to differentiate between the chromophobes that will develop into each type of chromophil cell and to detect the various stages of granule formation and granule discharge. It seems certain, in this species, that the basophils and the acidophils have separate lineages and that neither transforms into the other type of cell subsequent to differentiation from a common stem cell during histogenesis.

In other species studied, including man,

there are not constant differences in the Golgi apparatus of the acidophils and basophils. Nevertheless, there is presumptive evidence for secretory cycles similar to those in the rat. Detailed cytological studies, including those with the electron microscope, have shown progressive stages in granule formation and depletion in the different cell types.

Functions of the Anterior Hypophysis. The multiplicity of the functions of the anterior hypophysis is shown by the disabilities that result from its surgical removal or destruction by disease.

Following hypophysectomy, there is a cessation of general body growth and an involution of the gonads, the thyroid and the cortex of the adrenal glands. Numerous secondary effects also result. For instance, the inactivation of the gonads with loss of their endocrine function is followed by involution of the accessory reproductive organs. Involution of the thyroid brings about a lowering of the basal metabolic rate. The involution of the adrenal cortex results in a lowering of resistance to stress and a disturbance in carbohydrate metabolism. The anterior hypophysis is well named the master gland of the endocrine system.

The anterior hypophysis secretes at least six different hormones. They are proteins of complex chemical structure, and the amino acid composition has been worked out for only a few of them. However, six have been prepared from the anterior hypophysis in quite pure form, as judged by their physiological activity and by their molecular homogeneity as shown by electrophoresis and ultracentrifugation.

The hormones receive their names, in most cases, from the name of the target organ plus the suffix *trophic* or *tropic*. The two suffixes are often used interchangeably, although their literal meanings are different. Trophic (to nourish) implies the nourishment of the target organ by the anterior pituitary, whereas tropic (to turn toward) implies that the hormone is "aimed at" the target organ. Used in a broad sense, either suffix can be interpreted to mean that the hypophysis influences the activities of the target organ. The names and chief characteristics of the hormones are as follows.

(1) *Somatotrophin (somatotrophic hormone, STH; growth hormone, GH).* Somatotrophin stimulates body growth, particularly growth of long bones by promoting the proliferation of cartilage cells in the epiphyses. Hypophysectomy of growing animals brings about a cessation of growth, which can be restored by administration of the hormone. In the human, anterior lobe tumors produce gigantism when they occur before closure of the epiphyses; when they occur after epiphyseal closure, they produce acromegaly, i.e., an increase in thickness of the mandible and of the bones of the calvaria, hands and feet.

The growth hormone was obtained originally from pituitary glands of cattle. More recently, it has been isolated from human and monkey pituitary glands by Li and Chung (1956), and it has been synthesized recently. Its molecular weight and amino acid composition differ for different species. In humans, the growth hormone has a molecular weight of about 21,000 and consists of amino acid residues, arranged in a straight chain structure.

(2) *Lactogenic Hormone (prolactin; luteotrophic hormone, LTH).* This hormone initiates the secretion of milk following parturition. Its action is on mammary glands that have hypertrophied during pregnancy under the influence of estrogen and progesterone. The lactogenic hormone also initiates and maintains the secretion of progesterone from the cells of the corpus luteum; hence, it also bears the name luteotrophic hormone (LTH).

(3) *Adrenocorticotrophin (adrenocorticotrophic hormone, ACTH; corticotrophin).* The atrophy of the adrenal cortex which follows hypophysectomy can be prevented by injections of ACTH. Administration of ACTH to normal animals produces hypertrophy and hyperplasia of the adrenal cortex, par-

ticularly of the zona fasciculata and zona reticularis. Hypertrophy and hyperplasia of the cortex also result from hyperfunction of the hypophysis. ACTH has been prepared in a highly purified state from sheep and pig pituitaries, and the hormone has also been synthesized.

(4) *Thyrotrophin (thyrotrophic hormone; thyroid-stimulating hormone, TSH).* Thyrotrophin has not been prepared in a chemically pure form, but preparations made from the anterior lobe give a specific activation of the thyroid. Injections of TSH to normal animals produce all of the symptoms of hyperthyroidism. Injections of TSH into hypophysectomized animals restore the involuted thyroids and relieve the hypothyroid symptoms resulting from hypophysectomy. That the effect is through thyroid stimulation is demonstrated by the fact that it is not produced when TSH is administered to thyroidectomized animals.

(5) *Follicle-stimulating Hormone, FSH.* This stimulates growth of the follicles in the ovaries and spermatogenesis in the seminiferous tubules of the testes. Atrophy of the gonads following hypophysectomy can be partially prevented by administration of FSH, but complete maintenance requires some luteinizing hormone in addition to FSH.

(6) *Luteinizing Hormone, LH (interstitial cell-stimulating hormone, ICSH).* LH in the female does the following: (a) stimulates the theca interna cells to secrete estrogen following their prior stimulation by FSH, (b) contributes to the maturation of the ovarian follicle after follicular growth has been stimulated by FSH, (c) brings about ovulation following follicular maturation, and (d) produces luteinization of the granulosa and theca interna cells following ovulation. In the male, LH (ICSH) stimulates the interstitial cells of Leydig to produce testosterone which, in turn, maintains the accessory reproductive organs and the secondary sex characteristics. LH also has an indirect effect on spermatogenesis through testos-

abnormal cell multiplication

terone which, in proper amounts, will augment the action of FSH. In excess amounts, testosterone depresses spermatogenic activity through an inhibition of formation of FSH by the hypophysis.

The rate of hormone production by the target organ influences the rate of secretion by the hypophysis itself. For example, administration of the thyroid hormone (or iodide) decreases the output of thyrotrophic hormone by the hypophysis. On the other hand, the administration of an antithyroid drug such as propylthiouracil inhibits the formation of hormone by the thyroid, and the decreased level of circulating thyroid hormone causes an increase in thyrotrophic hormone secreted by the hypophysis. Similarly, administration of adrenal cortical hormones or of sex hormones (estrogen, androgen) decreases the hypophyseal output of adrenocorticotrophic or of gonadotrophic hormones. This is a feedback type of regulation in which the hormones from the end organs modify the secretion of the specific trophic hormones from the controlling organ. There is evidence that the circulating end organ hormone acts on certain hypothalamic centers and that a factor (or factors) from these centers reaches the anterior lobe by way of the hypophyseal portal system.

Several lines of evidence associate the secretion of growth hormone with the acidophils. In acromegaly and gigantism, tumors of acidophils are almost invariably present. In a strain of mice showing hereditary dwarfism in a mendelian ratio, the hypophyses of the dwarfs lack acidophils and no growth hormone is shown by the most sensitive tests (Smith and MacDowell, 1931).

There is good evidence that the acidophils also secrete luteotrophin (prolactin). The acidophils increase in number and size during pregnancy and, at the same time, there is a comparable increase in the luteotrophin content of the hypophysis. As noted above, immunochemical studies with labeled antibodies show the presence of a special type of acidophil for luteotrophin.

A number of facts indicate that the basophils secrete FSH, TSH and LH (ICSH). Chemical analyses show that these hormones are rich in glycoproteins, and cytochemical studies reveal that the granules of the basophils, but not of the acidophils, contain glycoprotein.

After castration, there is an increase in the number of uniformly dispersed delta basophils, and many of these cells become so vacuolated that they have a signet ring appearance (castration cells); these represent a type of delta basophil that secretes LH (ICSH). In the human anterior hypophysis, two types of basophils can be distinguished by their staining reactions under the light microscope and by the size of their granules in electron micrographs; presumably, they are thyrotrophs and gonadotrophs.

Attempts to associate the secretion of ACTH with a particular cell type have given controversial results. Most of the recent evidence, however, including results of immunohistochemical studies, indicates that the adrenocorticotroph is a type of basophil.

Pars Intermedia. In most of the mammals, the pars intermedia forms a well developed epithelial stratum lining the vestigial lumen dorsally. It is formed of several layers of polygonal cells which take the basic dyes and in which secretory granules have been described. In the human, a distinct cleft is present during fetal life and is still present in infancy. Most of the cleft eventually disappears, however, and the intermediate lobe becomes rudimentary. The remnant of the lobe consists of a thin stratum of cells and small vesicles which often contain colloid. The zone blends with the pars distalis anteriorly and some of its cells migrate posteriorly into the contiguous neural lobe (Fig. 21-7). Some of the cells stain deeply with basic dyes, whereas others are small and pale staining. The colloid

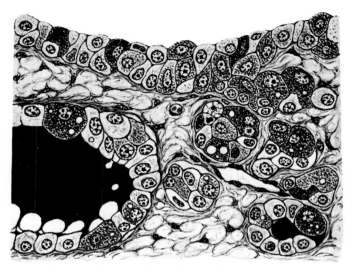

FIG. 21-7. Pars intermedia of adult human hypophysis, showing the growth of cords of cells up into the neural lobe. The formation of vesicles with colloid (black) is shown in two of the ingrowths. The basophilic cells are dark. (Rasmussen.)

present in the vestigial spaces contains only a small amount of iodine and differs from that of the thyroid.

A melanocyte - stimulating hormone (MSH) is produced by the pituitary gland, and the evidence has established that it is present in the intermediate lobe in animals in which this lobe is well demarcated. The hormone is found both in the pars distalis and pars nervosa in man. The cell of origin is controversial, but it is apparently a type of basophil.

In amphibians, MSH controls the dispersal of melanin granules within the cytoplasmic branches of the melanocytes and thus alters skin color. The normal function of this hormone in mammals is obscure, but its injection does increase pigmentation, probably by stimulating melanin synthesis.

Neurohypophysis. The neural lobe of the hypophysis or infundibular process is, as indicated above, a downgrowth from the hypothalamic region of the brain. Both anatomically and functionally, it forms a part of a larger unit, the *neurohypophysis*. The neurohypophysis includes the infundibular process (neural lobe) and the infundibulum

which, in turn, includes the infundibular stem and the median eminence of the tuber cinereum (Figs. 21-2 and 21-8). These regions are similar in that they possess the same type of cell and the same nerve and blood supply, and they yield the same active substances upon extraction.

The cells of the neural lobe are known as *pituicytes*. In some respects, the pituicytes resemble the neuroglia cells found elsewhere in the central nervous system: i.e., they are small cells with ramifying processes but without the distinctive features of nerve cells. Unlike neuroglia cells, many of the pituicytes contain variable numbers of refractile droplets or granules in their cytoplasm. Some of the pituicytes also contain yellow-brown pigment granules, the number of which increases with age.

The nuclei of the pituicytes (Fig. 21-10) are round or oval with a fine chromatin network. The cytoplasm is drawn out into a variable number of processes which often end either on the walls of blood vessels or on connective tissue septa of the gland. In routine preparations, the cytoplasm surrounding the nucleus is barely discernible, and

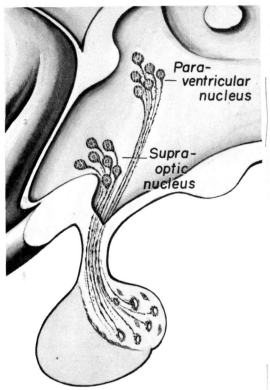

FIG. 21-8. Diagram of the hypothalamico-hypophyseal tract in the human. Nerve fibers from the supraoptic and paraventricular nuclei of the hypothalamus carry the neurosecretion to the blood vessels of the pars nervosa by way of the infundibular stem.

the processes cannot be followed at all. Between the cell bodies, the meshwork of interweaving processes stains faintly. The pituicytes may be blackened by special silver techniques and their form may thus be determined. Romeis, who has made a thorough study of the cytology of the human neural lobe, distinguished several types of pituicytes according to their morphological characteristics in silvered preparations.

The secretory substances released into the blood vessels of the neurohypophysis are formed in cell bodies of the nerve cells of the supraoptic and paraventricular nuclei located in the hypothalamus of the brain, and they pass by way of the unmyelinated fibers of the cell bodies to the neural lobe.

After sectioning of the pituitary stalk in experimental animals, the stainable neurosecretory material accumulates in large masses in relation to the severed nerve fibers proximal to the cut. Normally, accumulations of stainable neurosecretory material are found also within the nerve fiber terminals of the human posterior lobe; these are known as the Herring bodies (Fig. 21-9).

The neurosecretory material, both in the nerve cells of the supraoptic and paraventricular nuclei and in the nerve fibers of the hypothalamico-hypophyseal tract, is stained by a number of methods, among them chrome hematoxylin (Figs. 21-9 and 21-10). This stainable material of the neurohypophysis is believed to be a protein associated with the actual hormones, perhaps as a carrier. The amount of stainable material corresponds to the amount of hormone that can be extracted from the tissue, although the purified hormones themselves are not stained.

Most of the fibers of the hypothalamico-hypophyseal tract terminate in various regions of the neural lobe, a few going to the pars tuberalis and the pars intermedia. They terminate in close association with the capillaries, often in a palisade arrangement along the wall of the blood vessel (Figs. 21-9 and 21-11). Electron micrographs show that the cell bodies and axon terminals contain membrane bounded electron-dense granules which represent the neurosecretory material. There is a marked increase in the number of granular vesicles in physiological conditions which stimulate secretion (Fig. 21-12). The nerve terminals also contain smaller agranular vesicles. The endothelium of the capillaries of the neurohypophysis is seen in electron micrographs to be fenestrated (Palay). This presumably facilitates the passage of the secretion into the lumina of the capillaries.

Extracts of the tissue components of the neurohypophysis yield two hormones, both polypeptides. Both substances have also been synthesized. One of these, *oxytocin*, stimu-

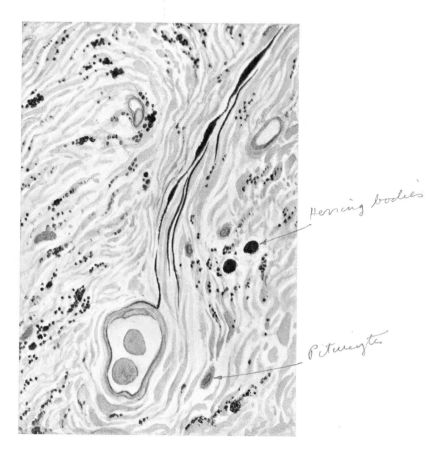

FIG. 21-9. Posterior hypophysis. A section from the para nervosa, human, age 26. Nerve fibers containing neurosecretory material (deep blue) are cut in both cross and longitudinal sections. One of the longitudinal sections shows three bulging masses of neurosecretory material; it appears to terminate on the surface of a small blood vessel (*lower center of field*). Larger accumulations of neurosecretion (Herring bodies) appear at *right*. Nuclei of pituicytes are stained red A 4-.μ section, stained with chrome hematoxylin and phloxine. $\times$1200.

lates the contraction of the uterine musculature during the latter part of pregnancy. It is used clinically in obstetrics for the induction of labor. Oxytocin also has a contractile action on the myoepithelial cells of the alveoli and ducts of the mammary gland and thus brings about the ejection of milk; hence it is also known as the milk let-down factor. The other fraction, *vasopressin (antidiuretic hormone, ADH)*, inhibits diuresis by increasing the permeability of the distal and collecting tubules of the kidney for water resorption. Vasopressin also raises blood pressure and, in large doses, causes contraction of the intestinal and bronchial musculature.

Pars Tuberalis. The pars tuberalis is a layer of cuboidal cells that covers the neural stalk and tuberal area of the brain. The cytoplasm of the cells is faintly basophilic. In contrast with the pars intermedia, the pars tuberalis is quite vascular. The cells frequently form vesicles which contain colloid. In the pars tuberalis, especially at its upper and lower poles, groups of squamous cells have been described which probably are "remnants" from the craniopharyngeal duct.

Pharyngeal Hypophysis. There occurs constantly in the vault of the nasopharynx, in man, a body of typical anterior lobe tissue. It has not been demonstrated in other species. This body lies in the midline and is elongated, its longitudinal axis being parallel to the sagittal plane of the body. It measures from 3.5 to 7 mm. in length by 1 mm. or less in diameter. The cells of the pharyngeal hypophysis are structurally identical to those of the anterior lobe and they parallel them in their differentiation and development, but experimental implantation of the pharyngeal hypophysis into animals has not revealed that it contains pituitary hormones.

THE THYROID

The thyroid consists of two lateral lobes and a connecting part, the isthmus. The lobes lie lateral to the superior part of the trachea and the inferior part of the larynx.

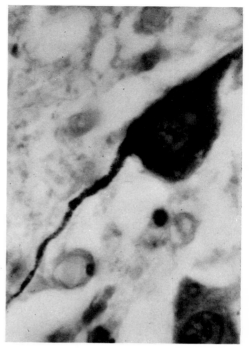

FIG. 21-10. Photomicrograph of a neuron from the human supraoptic nucleus. Both the nerve cell body and its axon contain granular neurosecretory material. Chrome hematoxylin stain. ×1200. (Courtesy of Dr. S. L. Palay.)

The isthmus crosses anterior to the trachea at the level of the second to fourth tracheal cartilages. A median process, the pyramidal lobe, is present in a number of individuals, extending upward from the left side of the isthmus. The thyroid has a connective tissue sheath formed by the deep cervical fascia. Beneath this is a delicate stratum of connective tissue, the true capsule of the gland. Delicate trabeculae and septa penetrate the gland substance, indistinctly dividing it into lobes and lobules.

The thyroid is an extremely labile gland and varies in size and structure in response to a large number of factors, among which are sex, nutrition, temperature, age, season and the iodine content of the food, the latter being of great importance.

The structural unit of the thyroid is the *follicle* or acinus (Fig. 20-13). These units

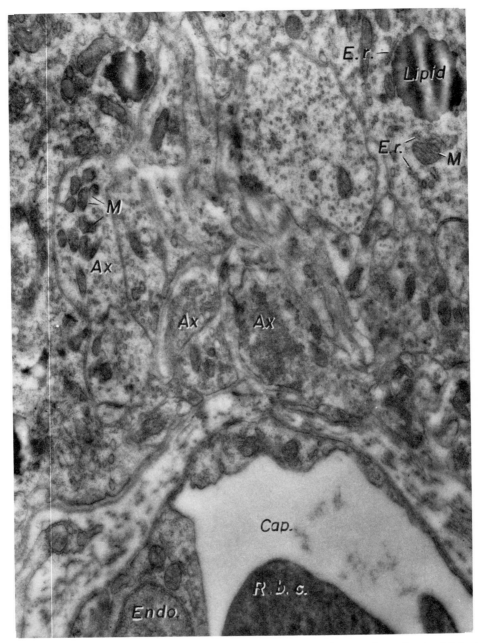

FIG. 21-11. Electron micrograph showing perivascular "palisade" in neurohypophysis of dehydrated rat. Nerve endings (terminal axons of hypothalamico-hypophyseal fibers) arrayed around capillary contain mitochondria and characteristic small vesicles. Neurosecretory material is lacking in the endings because of the dehydration of the animal. Pituicytes contain lipid droplets and endoplasmic reticulum. Separating the terminal axons from the capillary endothelium is a thin connective tissue space, and on either side of this is a thin basement membrane. Ax, terminal axon; M, mitochondria; $E.r.$, endoplasmic reticulum; $Cap.$, capillary; $Endo.$, endothelial cell nucleus; $R.b.c.$, red blood cell. $\times 23,900$. (Courtesy of Dr. S. L. Palay.)

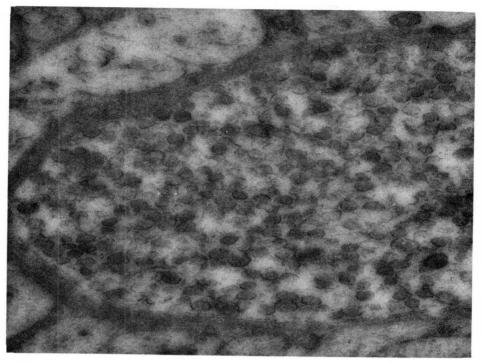

Fig. 21-12. Electron micrograph showing a portion of a nerve ending in the neurohypophysis of a hydrated rat. The terminal axon is filled with vesicles that contain a dense material, the neurosecretory substance. ×37,100. (Courtesy of Dr. S. L. Palay.)

are usually of microscopic dimensions but may become sufficiently large, as in colloid goiter, to be visible macroscopically. Follicles vary greatly in shape as well as in size, but they are usually irregularly spheroidal. In highly activated glands they become extremely irregular in shape (Fig. 21-14). A follicle consists of a layer of simple epithelium enclosing a cavity, the follicular cavity, which usually is filled with a gel-like material, colloid.

The principal thyroid cells, follicle cells, have their apical ends facing inward, i.e., toward the follicular cavity, and their basal ends resting on a thin basement membrane. In addition to the principal cells, there are parafollicular cells which are found singly or in small groups both within the follicle and within the interfollicular connective tissue. Those within the follicle are wedged between the principal cells and the basal

lamina; they generally do not extend to the colloid cavity. Those in an interfollicular position arise from epithelium and then migrate into the connective tissue. The parafollicular cells are generally larger than the principal cells, and they have a lighter staining cytoplasm. They apparently form thyrocalcitonin, a hormone that lowers blood calcium and thus exerts an effect opposite to that of the parathyroid hormone.

The principal cells are generally cuboidal in the normal gland (Fig. 21-13) but become low cuboidal or even squamous in the relatively inactive gland. They enlarge and become tall columnar cells during periods of increased activity (Figs. 21-14 and 21-15). The intercellular boundaries are distinct and fairly obvious under the light microscope. Electron micrographs show the presence of typical junctional complexes (Chapter 4).

The nuclei are generally rounded in shape,

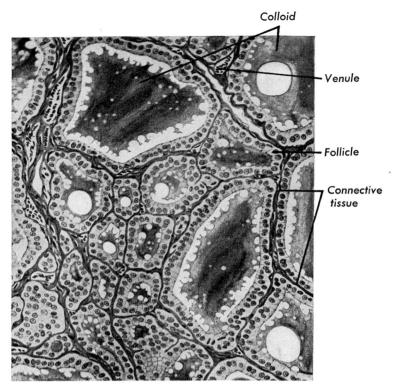

FIG. 21-13. Thyroid of human adult. (Stöhr.)

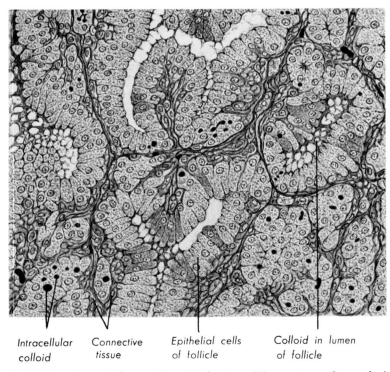

Intracellular colloid   Connective tissue   Epithelial cells of follicle   Colloid in lumen of follicle

FIG. 21-14. Surgical specimen of human thyroid showing diffuse extreme hyperplasia. The patient was a woman with toxic goiter who had been treated with thiouracil and then operated upon without pretreatment with iodine. A surgical specimen. Heidenhain's azan stain. ×320. (Aranow et al., Surg. Path., No. 88452. Ann. Surg., vol. 124, p. 167, 1946.)

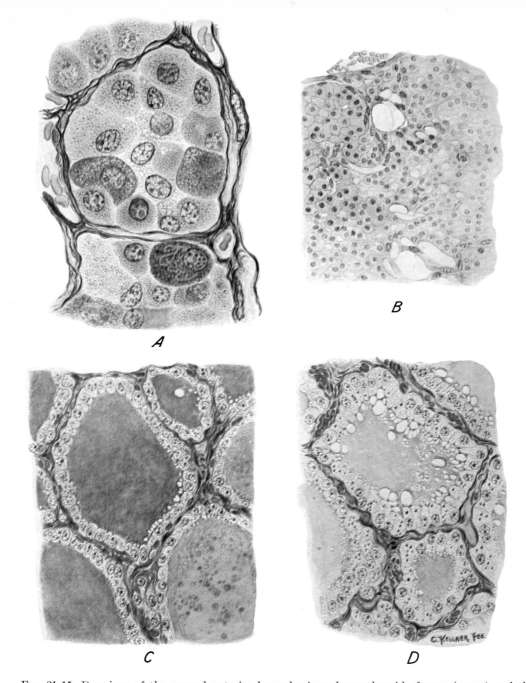

Fig. 21-15. Drawings of the normal anterior hypophysis and parathyroid of man (*upper*) and the normal and activated thyroid of the rhesus monkey (*lower*). *A*, anterior hypophysis of an executed man, 38 years old. Cords of cells are from the central part of the gland. In three of the acidophils (pink), the Golgi area is stained bluish. In the basophil in the lower cord, a negative picture of the Golgi apparatus is shown as clear canals. Chromophobes are present in the middle of the central cord. The rather large amount of connective tissue shown in the drawing is characteristic of the human anterior hypophysis. A colloid mass (blue) is shown at the lower part of the inferior cell cord. Modified Masson stain. ×1250. *B*, parathyroid of normal human adult. The oxyphils are pink and the chief cells are bluish purple. The spaces shown were filled with fat. Hematoxylin-eosin stain. ×350. *C*, thyroid of a normal adult rhesus monkey. A few peripheral and central colloid vacuoles are shown. Modified Masson stain. ×570. *D*, activated thyroid of a normal adult rhesus monkey. The thyroid was activated by injections of an anterior hypophysis extract. The epithelium is high and many absorption vacuoles are present. Colloid droplets and vacuoles are present in the thyroid epithelium. Modified Masson stain. ×570.

and the cytoplasm is lightly basophilic. The mitochondria are rod-shaped or filamentous and vary in number with the activity of the cell. The Golgi complex, which is located on the apical side of the nucleus, becomes enlarged during cell activity. The cytoplasm also contains lipid droplets and PAS-positive droplets (colloid resorption droplets). An additional type of cell is occasionally seen in the follicle, the colloid cells of Langendorff. They are slender cells with darkly staining cytoplasm that often appears to be filled with colloid, and they have pycnotic nuclei. They are degenerating cells.

Electron micrographs show that the apical end of the principal cell has short, irregularly distributed microvilli which are more numerous on the columnar (hyperactive) cells than on the lower, relatively inactive cells. Electron micrographs also show that there is an increase in rough surfaced endoplasmic reticulum in the activated cells. Lysosomes are present, predominantly in the apical region. The basal lamina of the follicle cells is often in close association with the basal lamina of the endothelium of the capillaries. The endothelial cells are of the fenestrated type, a characteristic of many regions in which there is rapid transport.

The cavity of the thyroid follicle is filled with a semifluid or gel-like substance, the thyroid *colloid*. In most preparations for light microscopy, a number of relatively large vacuoles may be seen in the colloid, particularly at the junction of the colloid with the apical ends of the cells. Most of these vacuoles apparently arise as a result of shrinkage of colloid and cells during the ordinary technical procedures used in preparing slides. Nevertheless, the vacuoles tend to occur more frequently in follicles with heightened activity in colloid resorption (Fig. 21-15, *C* and *D*). The colloid also becomes less dense during resorption and takes a lighter, more irregular stain.

Thyroid colloid varies in its chemical composition as well as in its physical properties. It is composed chiefly of nucleoproteins, thyroglobulin and proteolytic enzymes. It also occasionally contains desquamated cells. *Thyroglobulin* is an iodinated glycoprotein in which iodine and tyrosine are important constitutents of a macromolecular complex. Both the amount of thyroglobulin in the colloid and the degree of iodination may vary. For instance, in colloid goiter, which is associated with hypothyroidism, the iodine content is lower than in the colloid of a normal gland. The iodine content, however, generally does not vary to any significant extent in the follicles of the same individual at any given time (Robinson and Davis, 1969).

The *secretory process* of the thyroid involves the synthesis of the thyroid hormone, which is a component of the follicular colloid, and it also involves the transport of the thyroid hormone from the follicular cavity to the perifollicular capillaries. Both the formation of new secretion and the outward transport of the stored hormone may occur at the same time.

The synthesis of thyroid hormone has been studied by techniques of radioautography in combination with light and electron microscopy. By fixing tissues from experimental animals at different intervals following injection of labeled precursors of hormones, one can follow the events in hormone synthesis. Leucine, one of the essential amino acids, has been used in labeled form to trace the formation of proteins. H^3-labeled leucine appears over the basal portion of thyroid cells in about 10 minutes following intraperitoneal injection (Fig. 21-16). It is seen first over the cisternae of the rough surfaced endoplasmic reticulum, later in the Golgi complex and still later in the colloid. It seems clear that the proteins are synthesized from amino acids in association with the polyribosomes, that they are then transported via the cisternae of the reticulum to the Golgi complex, where they are combined with polysaccharides to form tyrosyl groups, and that they are secreted later into the lumen of the thyroid follicle. In other studies utilizing radioactive iodide (I^{125}), it is found that iodide begins to appear in the thyroid cells about 5 minutes after an intraperitoneal injection. It appears first at the basal end of the cell, which has a remarkable capacity for taking iodide from the blood and concentrating it. The iodide is oxidized within the cell to form active iodine, presumably by the action of a peroxidase. Then, the tyrosol groups are iodinated to form monoiodotyrosine and diiodotyrosine. Although the exact location of this step is obscure, it is generally assumed to occur near the apical end of the cell, either at or just outside the plasmalemma. Triiodothyronine and tetraiodothyronine (thyroxin) are derived from mono- and diiodotyrosine precursors. Only the thyronines have hormonal activity and they constitute only a small portion of the macromolecular complex known as thyroglobulin. The thyroglobulin is stored for variable periods, depending on the functional activity of the gland. In hyperactive thyroids, the hormone is released into the capillaries almost as soon as it is formed.

The reabsorption of the colloid and release of hormone into the vessels involves hydrolysis of thyroglobulin. Although the exact site of hydrolysis is somewhat controversial, there is considerable evidence that droplets of colloid are taken up by a process resembling pinocytosis (Nadler, Sarkar and Leblond, 1962) and that hydrolysis occurs within the cell through lysosomal action (Fig. 21-17). The active principles of the hormone are released into the capillaries as triiodothyronine and tetraiodothyronine (thyroxin), with the latter in much greater proportion. Only a small percentage of the iodine in the thyroid colloid is in the form of tetraiodothyronine. When thyroglobulin is hydrolyzed, the mono- and diiodo-components are liberated, as well as the tri- and tetraiodo-components. The former are deiodinated, and thus their iodine becomes available for use in the formation of new thyroglobulin.

Thyroxin circulating in the blood is carried almost entirely in association with thyroxin-binding hormones. Triiodothyronine, which has several times the hormonal potency of thyroxin (tetraiodothyronine), is not as firmly bound. Only a small percentage of the hormone is entirely unbound or "free" as a metabolically active substance within the plasma. The level of the binding proteins in the plasma has an important role in regulating the level of free hormone.

The use of *tracer doses* of radioactive iodine has found clinical application, especially in two ways. The rapidity with which the radio-iodine is taken up by the thyroid (as determined by a Geiger counter) is an indication of the activity of the gland of a patient. In thyroid carcinoma, the site of metastases can frequently be determined by their radioactivity. Radioiodine is also extensively used as a therapeutic agent in hyperthyroidism. As a result of the radiation from the I^{131} taken up, part of the overactive gland tissue is destroyed. This reduction in functioning tissue thus substitutes for surgical removal.

BLOOD VESSELS

The thyroid has a rich plexus of blood and lymph capillaries, which are in intimate relation to the follicular epithelium. The arteries, at the places where they branch, frequently have localized padlike thickenings beneath the intima. These do not encircle the vessels. They probably assist in shunting the blood to different parts of the gland as the arteries contract, and they may also serve to reduce the pulse wave. Arteriovenous anastomoses are common. The architecture of the blood vessels, as well as the fact that all of the follicles do not show the same degree of activity at any one time, indicates that there are fluctuations in the amount of blood received by different parts of the gland.

NERVES

A large number of nonmyelinated nerve fibers are present in the walls of the thyroid

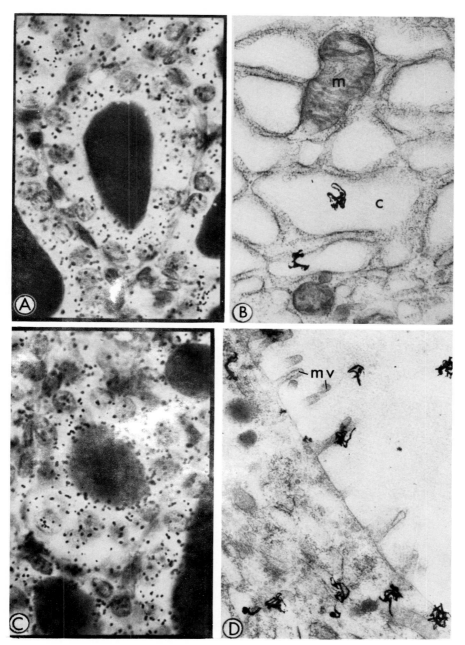

Fig. 21-16. Light and electron micrographs of radioautographic preparations of thyroids from rats sacrificed at different intervals of time after injection of leucine-³H. A, radioautograph of a periodic acid-Schiff and hematoxylin stained preparation from an animal sacrificed at 30 minutes after injection of labeled leucine. Radioactivity is seen rather diffusely over the cytoplasm in the light micrograph. B, electron micrograph of a radioautographic preparation from an animal sacrificed at one hour after injection. Irregularly shaped silver grains, indicating the location of the incorporated leucine, are seen over the cisternae (c) of the endoplasmic reticulum. m, mitochondrion. C, radioautograph of tissue fixed at four hours after injection of labeled leucine. The labeled material is present chiefly in the adluminal ends of the cell. D, Electron micrograph of a radioautograph at 3½ hours after injection of labeled leucine. Silver grains are seen in the adluminal cytoplasm and also in the colloid. mv, microvilli. A and B, ×1200; C, and D, ×30,000. (Courtesy of Drs. N. J. Nadler, B. Young, C. P. Leblond, and B. O. Mitmaker, Endocrinology, vol. 74, 1964.)

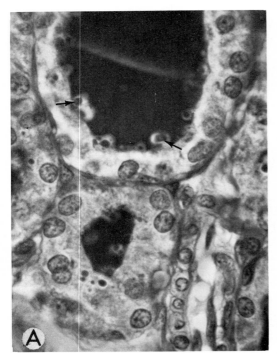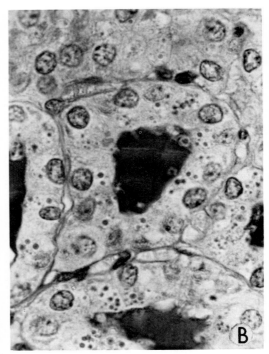

FIG. 21-17. Photomicrographs of periodic acid-Schiff and hematoxylin stained sections of rat thyroid fixed at different intervals of time after an injection of thyroid stimulating hormone (TSH). *A*, from tissue fixed at eight minutes after TSH. Colloid droplets in contact with the adluminal ends of the cells are apparently being surrounded by cytoplasmic processes of the cells. (Two of the several droplets in the field are indicated by *arrows*). *B*, from tissue fixed at 30 minutes after TSH. Droplets are present chiefly in the adluminal cytoplasm but a few are still being formed at the adluminal surfaces and some have migrated to the basal ends of the cells. The sequence of events indicates that the colloid is taken into the cells by a process resembling pinocytosis and that the doplets are hydrolysed by lysosomal activity to release the hormone that enters the blood vessels which are closely associated with the basal laminae of the thyroid cells. ×900. (Courtesy of Drs. N. J. Nadler, S. K. Sarkar, and C. P. Leblond, Endocrinology, vol. 71, 1962.)

arteries. Most of these terminate in plexuses around the blood vessels.

FUNCTION

The main effect of the thyroid hormone is on the rate of metabolism of tissues in general. The ramifications of this effect are very extensive, however, extending to activities as diverse as the rate of absorption in the intestine, carbohydrate metabolism, the rate of the heart beat, mental activity, general body growth and many other effects. Hypothyroidism in the infant causes cretinism; in the adult, it causes myxedema.

The symptoms in both conditions are attributable to a lowered metabolic rate not only in the general body tissues but in other endocrine glands. Administration of thyroid hormone has a striking therapeutic effect. The opposite condition, hyperthyroidism, leads to overactivity and sometimes is followed by exophthalmic goiter (Grave's disease). Surgical removal of a part of the thyroid, or the use of antithyroid drugs or radioiodine, reduces the metabolic rate but does not alleviate the exophthalmos when this is once established. The thyroid is not essential to life, although in early work the close topographical association of the parathyroids with it caused confusion on this point.

THE PARATHYROIDS

STRUCTURE

There are normally two pairs of parathyroids in mammals. Because of their origin from the third and fourth pharyngeal pouches, respectively, they are designated as parathyroids III and IV. In man, a member of each pair lies on the posterior surface of each lateral lobe of the thyroid, near the arterial anastomosis of the inferior and superior thyroid arteries. These glands, which are somewhat flattened, measure some 6 mm. in length and about half this in width. In man they are brown, but in some species they are white or only faintly colored. A connective tissue capsule separates them from the thyroid. Delicate connective tissue septa partially divide the gland into poorly defined lobules, and still finer septa tend to separate the parenchymal cells into anastomosing cords and groups. The separation of parenchymal cell groups by connective tissue becomes particularly obvious in the adult as a result of a marked increase in fat cells.

The parenchyma is composed of two types of cells: the *principal* or *chief cells* and the *oxyphil cells* (Fig. 21-15 B). The chief cells are of constant occurrence, while the oxyphil cells do not appear in man until near the end of the first decade of life. They have not been observed in many other species, except in monkeys and cattle.

The chief cells are polyhedral in shape and have round nuclei with a loosely arranged chromatin giving a vesicular appearance. They have been subdivided into *light cells* and *dark cells*, primarily on differences in staining of the cytoplasm. The light chief cells are more numerous than the dark ones, and they are usually slightly larger. Their cytoplasm appears nongranular in routine preparations, but PAS-positive granules and a few argyrophilic granules can be demonstrated by appropriate techniques. The dark chief cells have numerous fine cytoplasmic granules which are mostly argyrophilic. Electron micrographs show that the dark cells contain membrane-bound secretory granules, a relatively large Golgi complex, enlarged filamentous mitochondria and very little glycogen (Munger and Roth, 1963). The membrane-bound granules apparently correspond to the argyrophilic granules seen with the light microscope. The light cells have a smaller Golgi complex, few or no secretory granules and considerable glycogen. It seems obvious that the dark cells represent an active secretory stage and that the light cells represent a resting or less active stage of the same cell type.

The oxyphil cells are larger than the chief cells, but they usually have smaller and darker staining nuclei. Their cytoplasm stains well with eosin and contains fine granules. Electron micrographs show that the cytoplasm of the oxyphil contains an abundance of mitochondria, a factor that is apparently responsible for their acidophilic staining in light microscopy. The function of these cells is unknown.

Small colloid follicles are of frequent occurrence in the parathyroid. This colloid has no relation functionally to that of the thyroid. In contrast with the thyroid, the parathyroid contains no more iodine than do other tissues of the body.

BLOOD VESSELS AND NERVES

The parathyroids have an abundant blood supply, but in vascular injections the capillaries do not appear to be as numerous as in the thyroid. In man there is said to be a plexus of veins at the periphery of the gland.

Unmyelinated nerves in small numbers occur in the parathyroid. They are probably vasomotor.

FUNCTION

The parathyroid glands regulate calcium concentration in bone and in body fluids.

Removal of the parathyroids causes a fall in blood calcium, nervous hyperexcitability and spasms, leading to death. Calcium administration relieves these symptoms, and the injection of parathyroid extract, parathyroid hormone, maintains the animals in good health. Such injections in normal animals raise the blood calcium, and excessive doses will cause death.

Removal of one or more of the parathyroids does not cause a compensatory hypertrophy of those which remain. In rickets the parathyroids enlarge. The parathyroids readily "take" in autotransplantation.

THE ADRENAL GLANDS

The adrenal glands are paired organs, one being situated close to the cranial pole of each kidney in the retroperitoneal tissue. Both are somewhat flattened, the left adrenal gland being crescentic, the right one more triangular in shape. The combined weight of the two glands is some 10 to 12 grams, the left usually being somewhat heavier than the right one. In most mammals they are more regular in shape than in the human, being ovoid or spheroid.

The adrenal glands are composite organs consisting both functionally and structurally of two distinct parts, the cortex (interrenal tissue) and the medulla (chromaffin tissue). In lower vertebrates, these two tissues are not united into a common organ but are topographically separated. Correlated with the evolution of the higher vertebrates is a progressively closer association of the cortical and medullary components. In mammals, the chromaffin tissue is surrounded by the interrenal tissue.

Grossly, in a section of the fresh human gland, an outer and broader yellowish zone of the cortex can be distinguished from a brownish yellow inner zone. The medulla when unstained is white or gray.

The adrenal gland has a tough connective tissue capsule in which small blood vessels course. From the capsule, delicate trabeculae penetrate the cortex, although the main supporting tissue of the cortex is reticular fibers. From the capsule, capillaries and arterioles also penetrate the gland.

The hilum is situated ventromedially (toward the vena cava) and is chiefly marked by the emerging thick walled adrenal vein.

The arrangement and distribution of the cortex and medulla in the human do not have the uniformity characteristically found in laboratory animals. This lack of uniformity may be due in part to the irregularity in shape of the human adrenal. The line of separation between the cortex and medulla is frequently very irregular and, in single sections, clumps of cortical cells may appear to be surrounded by medulla, although a study of serial sections will reveal that these clumps are connected with the cortical zone. The distribution of the medulla also varies among different adrenal glands. It very often is absent in the "wings" of the glands, the cortical zones of the two sides abutting against each other, separated only by some connective tissue and small veins (Fig. 21-18). A study of sections through the gland near the emergence of the adrenal vein may reveal cortical tissue adjacent to the vein. This cortical tissue may be, at least in part, enclosed by medulla, outside of which are the peripheral cortical zones (Fig. 21-18). The cortex surrounding the vein appears to have been inverted into the gland, with the outermost zone of the cortex lying next to the wall of the vein.

In the zonation of the cortex, there is not as much uniformity in the human as in laboratory animals, although the zones are always readily recognizable.

Cortex. The cortex is classically divided into three zones according to differences in the cordlike arrangement of the cells composing it: an outer zone, the *zona glomerulosa*; a middle zone, the *zona fasciculata*; and an inner zone, the *zona reticularis* (Fig. 21-19). The zona fasciculata is by far the broadest of the three but is not uniform in structure throughout its full

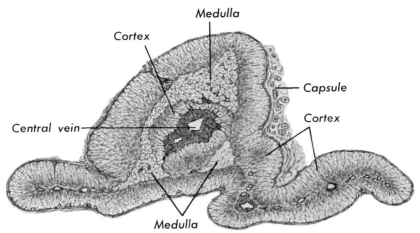

FIG. 21-18. A transverse section through the left adrenal of a man 72 years old. The adrenal was surgically removed in an attempt to give relief in prostatic carcinoma with metastases. Camera lucida drawing. ×6.

extent. Primarily because of differences in the lipid content of its cells and the consequent differences in staining, the fasciculata may be divided into outer and inner zones (Fig. 21-19). There is no sharp demarcation between the cortical zones, each blending with the adjacent one.

The *zona glomerulosa* is a relatively narrow zone in which the arrangement of the cords is such that the cells are in ovoid groups. There is no central cavity within a cell group as in exocrine glands, but there is a rich network of blood vessels just outside the basement membrane of the cells. The cells tend to be columnar, and they have spherical nuclei that stain rather heavily. A few lipid droplets may be found in the cytoplasm, but they are sparse in comparison with the droplets in the zona fasciculata. Electron micrographs show that the cytoplasm has a well developed smooth surfaced endoplasmic reticulum and that the Golgi complex is often on the side of the nucleus facing toward the blood vessel. The mitochondria of this region generally have shelflike cristae similar to those of most other organs.

The *zona fasciculata*, the broadest zone, is composed of cell cords coursing parallel to one another in a radial direction toward the medulla. As seen in sections, the cords are usually only one or two cells in width. In three-dimensional reconstructions, it is seen that each cord is enclosed by a longitudinally oriented meshwork of sinusoidal capillaries. The parenchymal cells are generally cuboidal or polyhedral in shape, and they are often binucleate. The nuclei appear more vesicular than those of the glomerulosa, with less dense chromatin. The cells are relatively large, and their cytoplasm contains an abundance of lipid droplets composed of cholesterol, fatty acids and neutral fat. Cholesterol is concentrated chiefly in this zone. Since the lipids are dissolved by the usual technical procedures, the cytoplasm has a spongy appearance, and the cells are often called spongiocytes. Electron micrographs confirm the presence of numerous lipid droplets and show that most of the endoplasmic reticulum is of the smooth surfaced type (Fig. 21-20). Mitochondria are numerous and are characterized by having tubular rather than shelflike cristae. In the rat adrenal, which has been studied extensively, the cristae are vesicular-like invaginations from the inner limiting membrane, practically filling the matrix of the mitochondrion. It has been noted that the mitochondria have a close relationship with the lipid droplets.

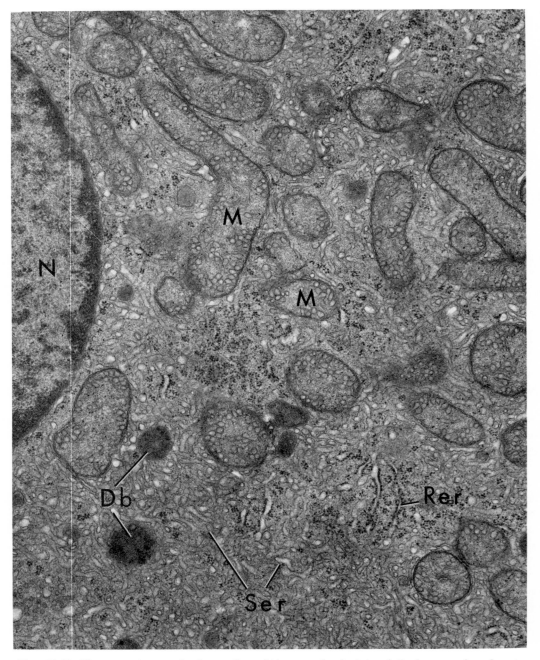

FIG. 21-20. Electron micrograph of a section of the zona fasciculata of the human adrenal cortex. Note that the mitochondria (*M*) have tubular rather than shelf-like cristae. Smooth-surfaced endoplasmic reticulum (*Ser*) is abundant, although some rough surfaced endoplasmic reticulum (*Rer*) is present. *Db*, dense bodies, probably lysosomes; *N*, nucleus. ×22,000. (Courtesy of Drs. J. A. Long and A. L. Jones.)

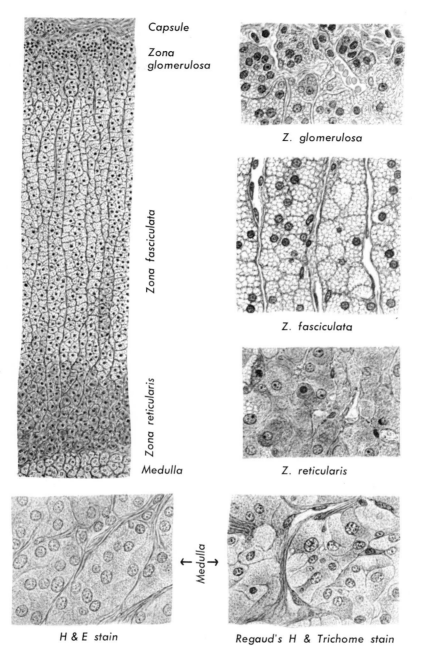

Capsule

Zona
glomerulosa

Z. glomerulosa

Zona fasciculata

Z. fasciculata

Zona reticularis

Z. reticularis

Medulla

Medulla

H & E stain

Regaud's H & Trichome stain

FIG. 21-19. Sections through the right adrenal of a man 35 years old. The adrenal was removed in an attempt to give relief from a testicular tumor with metastases. The tissue was fixed in Helly's fluid (formol Zenker). The section used for all of the drawings, except the *lower left one*, was stained with Regaud's hematoxylin and Masson's trichrome. The low power (*upper left*) is ×205, the others, ×535.

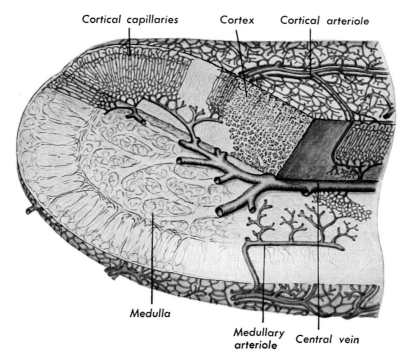

Cortical capillaries   Cortex   Cortical arteriole

Medulla

Medullary arteriole   Central vein

Fig. 21-21. Blood supply of adrenal of dog. One end only of the adrenal is shown. (After Flint.)

The *zona reticularis* is composed of a network of cell cords. The cells are generally smaller than those of the fasciculata, and they frequently have deeply staining nuclei. The cytoplasm has relatively few lipid droplets in comparison with the fasciculata, and the cytoplasm takes a darker stain in routine preparations. Toward the inner part of the reticular zone, some of the cells stain particularly darker than others, and "dark" and "light" cells have been described. The former have pycnotic nuclei and often have more lipofuscin pigment in their cytoplasm. The cells of the reticularis, like those of the fasciculata, have a smooth surfaced endoplasmic reticulum.

It should be noted that the parenchymal cells form continuous cords through the zones and that the change in cytology from one zone to the next is gradual rather than abrupt. According to one theory, new cells arise in the glomerulosa, move inward through the fasciculata in correlation with changes in their secretory activity and finally degenerate in the reticularis. This view is based partly on the fact that a complete cortex can regenerate in the rat after removal of all of the cortex except the outer part of the glomerulosa. On the other hand, it is clearly established that mitoses occur in the fasciculata and to some extent in the reticularis. The latter is not merely a zone of degenerating cells. Furthermore, the different zones have functional differences, and they respond differently to hormones from the anterior hypophysis. The fact that the glomerulosa serves as a regenerative zone after the extirpation of the rest of the cortex does not conflict with the view that the glomerulosa also serves for the secretion of particular hormones. Neither does it conflict with the fact that mitoses normally occur in the fasciculata and that the latter serves for secretion of different hormones.

Medulla. The parenchymal cells of the medulla are found in anastomosing groups in close association with blood vessels. When the tissue is fixed by vascular perfusion, which prevents collapse of blood vessels, it is seen that the cells are arranged as a collar or sleeve around the vessels, each cell with one end in contact with a small venule and the opposite end in contact with a capillary. The cells tend to be columnar in shape, and the Golgi complex and most of the secretory granules are in the advenous end of the cell. The cells contain fine cytoplasmic granules which become brown when oxidized by potassium bichromate, and they are therefore known as *chromaffin cells* or *pheochrome cells*. The granules also "stain" by other oxidizing agents. Thus, they become green with ferric chloride, yellow with iodine and brown with osmium tetroxide. The chromaffin reaction of the granules is due to their content of *catecholamines*, derivatives of tyrosine. Two types of catecholamines are present in the medulla: *epinephrine* and *norepinephrine*. Two types of cells can be identified by histochemical methods with light microscopy and by electron microscopy. Histochemical studies show that the cytoplasmic granules in norepinephrine cells are autofluorescent, and they stain darkly with silver and iodine. On the other hand, the granules of the epinephrine cells are not fluorescent and they react only lightly, or not at all, with silver and iodine. Electron micrographs show that the granules of both types range in size from about 50 to 350 mμ, with a mean of about 200 mμ. The granules of the norepinephrine cells are much more electron-dense than those of the epinephrine cells. Electron micrographs also show a well developed Golgi complex, an average number of mitochondria, granular endoplasmic reticulum and some polyribosomes.

BLOOD SUPPLY

The adrenal glands are highly vascular organs. The arterial supply is subject to great individual variation in the human, but there is always a number, sometimes large, of small arteries to each gland. These commonly arise from the inferior phrenic, celiac and renal arteries. The adrenal arteries usually branch before entering the gland so that there are small branches entering the capsule at intervals over most of its surface. From arteries that enter and course in the capsule, three sets of branches arise (Fig. 21-21). One of these sets gives rise to capillaries that supply the capsule. Blood from these is collected in the veins of the capsule. The second set supplies the sinusoids of the cortex, which then empty into veins within the medulla. The third set sends arterial branches through the cortex which empty into the capillary plexus of the medulla (Fig. 21-21). The venules arising from the second and third sets drain into the vena cava through the medullary vein, which is unusually thick walled for a vein with many longitudinally directed smooth muscle fibers. In both the cortex and medulla, the terminal network from the arterioles is in close relationship to the parenchyma. Electron micrographs show that the sinusoidal capillaries have a fenestrated type of endothelium. Lymph vessels have not been described in the adrenal gland except in relation to the larger blood vessels.

NERVES

The adrenals are abundantly supplied with nerves. Most of these are derived from the sympathetic division of the autonomic nervous system and course through the splanchnic nerves. Some of the fibers are distributed to the cortex. The majority, however, pass to the medulla; these have been described as being preganglionic. A few ganglion cells are present in the medulla.

Stimulation of the splanchnic nerves causes an outpouring of epinephrine. Cutting the splanchnics (denervation) inhibits the secretory activity of the medulla.

FUNCTIONS

Attention was first attracted to the physiological importance of the adrenal glands by Addison in 1855. He described a fatal syndrome, since named Addison's disease, which resulted from a destruction of the adrenals by some disease process. Experimentally, work beginning with that of Brown-Séquard in 1856 has shown that the adrenal cortex, but not the medulla, is essential for life. Destruction of the *cortex* causes a loss of sodium and an accumulation of potassium, so that diets high in sodium and low in potassium are helpful. There is a concentration of the blood, a sluggish circulation and an increase in urea resulting from impaired kidney function. Carbohydrate stores are depleted, and there is hypoglycemia with lowered resistance to insulin. There is a decreased resistance to stress (heat, cold, trauma, fatigue, etc.). Cortical extracts, first successfully prepared in 1930, are assayed on the basis of their ability to prolong life or to alleviate the other disabilities resulting from adrenalectomy.

Thus far, more than 40 crystalline compounds (steroids) have been isolated from the adrenal cortex. A number of these have been shown to have physiologic effects as evidenced by their substitutive action in survival tests on adrenalectomized animals. In general, the active compounds can be divided into two categories as judged by their type of activity. Those in one category have an effect on electrolyte and water balance (mineralocorticoids); those in the other category have their greatest effect on carbohydrate metabolism (glucocorticoids). In addition, there is a third group of steroids which includes the female sex hormones (estrone and progesterone) and several androgenic steroids. Certain adrenal tumors have a feminizing or a masculinizing influence. The cortical hormones (except possibly the estrogens) may be synthesized from cholesterol, in which the adrenal cortex is very rich.

There is some evidence that the mineralocorticoids are produced primarily in the zona glomerulosa, the glucocorticoids in the zona fasciculata, and the sex hormones in the zona reticularis.

The normal activity of the adrenal cortex

is at least partially under the control of a hormone of the anterior hypophysis, the adrenocorticotrophic hormone. Injection of ACTH causes a drop in the cholesterol and ascorbic acid content of the adrenal. This response is commonly used (with hypophysectomized rats) in determining the potency of ACTH extracts. The zona glomerulosa is less under pituitary control than are the other cortical zones. After hypophysectomy the zona glomerulosa shows less atrophy than the remainder of the cortex, and electrolyte metabolism is less affected after hypophysectomy than after adrenalectomy. This is interpreted as evidence for the continued secretion of some mineralocorticoids by the zona glomerulosa after hypophysectomy.

Clinical use of one of the adrenal steroids (cortisone) and also of ACTH is quite extensive in some of the "collagen" diseases, e.g., rheumatoid arthritis and rheumatic fever.

The *adrenal medulla* or chromaffin tissue is not essential to life. From it an extract epinephrine is prepared which has an effect on organs similar to that produced by stimulation of the sympathetic nervous system. It provides a quick response to emergencies through combined action of the adrenal and the sympathetic nervous system. It also has metabolic effects.

The hormone of the adrenal medulla was the first hormone obtained in crystalline form (1901). It has since been discovered that what appeared to be a pure compound is in reality two closely related substances, epinephrine and norepinephrine. They are secreted by different cells in the medulla, and they have somewhat different physiological effects. For example, epinephrine brings about an increase in heart rate without any significant increase in blood pressure, whereas norepinephrine has little effect on heart rate but markedly increases blood pressure by producing vasoconstriction. Norepinephrine is readily converted to epinephrine, and it may serve as a precursor for epinephrine in the synthetic process in the cells.

Norepinephrine is also found in the brain and in endings of sympathetic nerves. As a *neurohumor* released by nerve endings, it acts locally and for only a short time prior to inactivation. It contrasts in this respect with the norepinephrine released into blood vessels by the adrenal medulla.

THE POSTNATAL INVOLUTION OF HUMAN ADRENAL GLANDS

The adrenal glands at birth in the human are relatively large bodies about one-third the size of the kidneys, whereas in the adult they are about one twenty-eighth the size of the latter organs. Immediately following birth, the adrenals undergo a pronounced involution. In the first 14 days of postnatal life, this decrease amounts to one-third their birth weight, and in the first 4 months it amounts to one-half. The loss in weight is due to the degeneration of the inner part of the cortex. At birth the cortex consists of a narrow, outer zone, which will proliferate and form the cortex of the adult, and a massive inner zone which is destined to degenerate, the so-called "fetal cortex."

The adrenal glands attain their large prenatal size by a steady growth throughout intrauterine life. Their growth in this period is proportionate to general body growth.

THE PARAGANGLIA

Under the head of *paraganglia* are included groups of cells that are closely associated both anatomically and embryologically with the sympathetic nervous system. They are largely retroperitoneal, occurring in association with sympathetic ganglia. In shape and staining reaction, the cells are similar to those composing the adrenal medulla. They are clear when unstained, become yellow with chromic acid and its salts and turn dark with osmic acid. The cells are oval or polyhedral and have a cord-like arrangement. They lie in close contact with capillaries. Because they are embryo-

Interlobular trabecula   Blood vessels

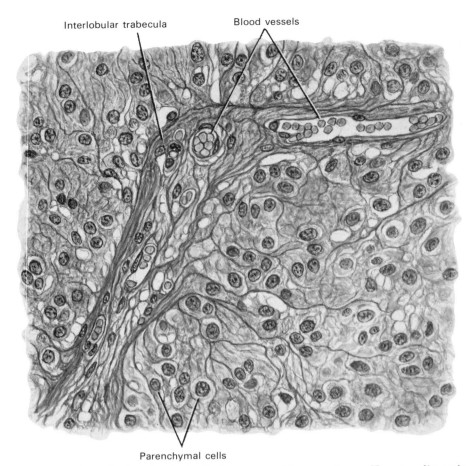

Parenchymal cells

FIG. 21-22. Section through the pineal gland of a woman 37 years of age. Hematoxylin-eosin. ×535

logically and structurally similar to the chromaffin cells composing the medulla of the adrenal and have the same staining reaction, it is assumed that they secrete epinephrine.

The *aortic chromaffin bodies* (lumbar paraganglia, organs of Zuckerkandl) are relatively large, irregularly paired masses formed by a fusion of paraganglia. They are located retroperitoneally and lie ventrolaterally to the aorta at about the level of the origin of the inferior mesenteric artery.

THE PINEAL BODY

The pineal body or pineal gland (epiphysis cerebri) in man is a slightly flattened, coneshaped structure measuring 8 to 12 mm. in length and 5 to 8 mm. in width. Its base is constricted to form a peduncle by which it is attached to the roof of the third ventricle. The peduncle or stalk is hollow, with a narrow prolongation of the third ventricle extending up into it. Pia mater covers the pineal body except at its attachment and forms a capsule from which connective tissue trabeculae penetrate the organ, partially dividing it into poorly defined lobules. The capsule and trabeculae carry numerous blood vessels and nerves (Fig. 21-22).

In all vertebrates that have pineal systems, a saccular organ is present during embryonic stages as the primordium evaginates from the roof of the diencephalon. However, in all mammals, in some reptiles

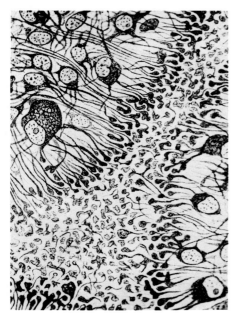

FIG. 21-23. Section of a pineal gland of a boy. The parenchymal cells and their processes were impregnated with silver. The processes are shown extending into an interlobular septum. Collagenous tissue and glia are not shown with this technique. Semidiagrammatic. (After del Rio-Hortega.)

(snakes and turtles) and in some birds, there is a rapid proliferation of secondary, tertiary and subsequent evaginations which converts the sac into cords and follicles of *pinealocytes* (principal pineal cells) interwoven with *glial cells*, connective tissue and vessels.

The *pinealocytes* have relatively large nuclei with prominent nucleoli, and their nuclei often have an irregular contour because of infoldings of the nuclear envelope. The cytoplasm usually stains lightly in hematoxylin and eosin preparations. The cells have an irregular shape which can be seen best after the del Rio-Hortega silver method (Fig. 21-23). They have cytoplasmic processes with club-shaped terminations near other principal cells and in the vicinity of perivascular spaces.

Electron micrographs show that the endoplasmic reticulum of the pinealocytes is mostly of the smooth surfaced type and that ribosomes and polysomes are randomly dispersed. The Golgi complex consists of flattened sacs and rounded vesicles of the usual pattern. The mitochondria are fairly large and have the usual shelflike cristae. The cytoplasm is characterized particularly by numerous microtubules of about 220 to 300 A in diameter and indefinite length. The cytoplasm also has lipochrome pigment and lysosomes.

The *glial cells* provide a network surrounding and pervading the cords and follicles (Figs. 21-24 and 21-25). They are less numerous than the principal cells, and their nuclei are smaller and darker staining. Their cytoplasm is also more basophilic. The cells are usually elongated, and they have long cytoplasmic processes seen best after special silver techniques. They are often described as a type of astrocyte. Electron micrographs show that microtubules are scarce and that those which may be present lack the beaded appearance seen on microtubules of pinealocytes. The glial cells are characterized by

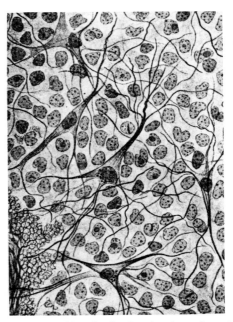

FIG. 21-24. Pineal gland, showing the glial cells and their processes. The nuclei of the parenchymal cells are also shown. Silver preparation. (After del Rio-Hortega.)

Glia   Parenchyma

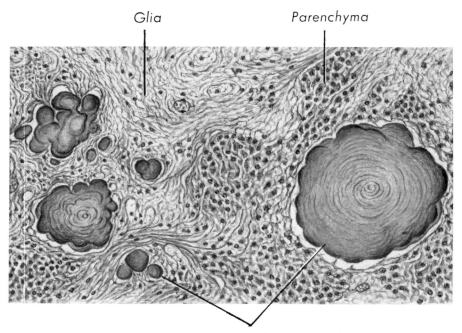

Calcareous granules (acervuli)

FIG. 21-25. Section through a region of the pineal gland of a woman 37 years old, showing calcareous granules (acervuli, brain sand). Hematoxylin-eosin. ×240.

numerous fine filaments, 50 to 60 A in diameter, that are not nearly so abundant in pinealocytes, and their mitochondria have unusually electron-dense matrices. The cristae also have a different arrangement, with some oriented longitudinally and some transversely. The endoplasmic reticulum is of the rough surfaced variety and is unevenly distributed in compact masses. The cytoplasm also has numerous single-membrane-bounded bodies of varying diameter, which are probably responsible for the fine granulation seen under the light microscope; these are probably lysosomes.

Sand granules (corpora arenacea) are generally present in the human pineal body and, according to some authors, they tend to increase with age. They are mulberry-shaped concretions which show concentric zones in sections (Fig. 21-25). They are found in the capsule and also within the organ. In the latter case, they are usually surrounded by or adjacent to areas rich in glia. They are not present in many species, and their significance is not understood.

The pineal body reaches its maximal development in man by the middle of the first decade or shortly thereafter. It shows regressive changes later in life, but these are quite variable in time of appearance.

The mammalian pineal body is supplied by *postganglionic sympathetic nerve fibers* which have their cells of origin in the superior cervical ganglion. This is one of the rare instances in which a portion of the central nervous system receives a sympathetic supply. The pineal also has a *rich vascular supply*. Studies on the rat show that substances such as intravital colloidal dyes diffuse into the pineal body. This is not true of brain tissue in general, in which there is a hematoencephalic or blood-brain barrier. However, the lack of a pineal blood-brain barrier should not be assumed for other mammals until further study.

The pineal system of some of the *lower*

vertebrates (e.g., many lizards) consists of two bodies: a parietal (or *parapineal*) *organ*, which is placed in or above an opening in the roof of the skull as a "third eye," and a deeper lying intracranial *epiphysis*. Cytological studies show that many of the cells lining the lumina of these structures have characteristics similar to the cones of the retinae. The pineal organs of mammals, birds and some reptiles lack such photoreceptor elements and differ markedly from the pineals of the lower vertebrates.

Although there have been a number of divergent opinions regarding the *functions of the pineal body* in mammals, it is generally agreed that it is an endocrine or neuroendocrine organ and not a useless vestige. There is considerable evidence that it has an inhibitory action on the development and maturation of the gonads. This was suggested first by clinical observations that boys having tumors of pineal-supporting elements (which presumably crowd out the parenchymal cells) show precocious development of the gonads. This view has been supported by experimental studies which show that pinealectomy of young rats results in early maturation of the gonads in both sexes.

Biochemical and histochemical studies have shown that the pineal organ of the rat has a high phosphate turnover, high amino acid formation and a high level of serotonin. The pineal also contains melatonin (5-hydroxyindole) and an enzyme (hydroxyindole-*O*-methyl transferase, or HIOMT) that has a role in the synthesis of melatonin from serotonin. It is known that melatonin produces blanching of melanophores in amphibians, having an effect opposite to that of the melanocyte-stimulating hormone of the pituitary gland. Although the functional significance of melatonin in man remains obscure, it is known that it partially counteracts the effects of pinealectomy when injected into experimental animals, and that it is one of the pineal hormones but not the only one (see review by Reiter and Fraschini, 1969). Furthermore, there is a reduction in the content of serotonin and HIOMT (the specific enzyme for melatonin formation) in the pineals of rats following prolonged exposure to light. There is also evidence for a diurnal rhythm in these substances. These responses to light are abolished by extirpation of the superior cervical ganglion, the source of the postganglionic nerve fibers to the pineal. On the basis of the various findings, it has been proposed that the pineal is part of a neuroendocrine mechanism regulating the gonads, and perhaps other organs, in response to light. Whereas in many lower vertebrates the pineal itself seems to be a photoreceptor, in higher forms the photic input to the organ seems to have been assumed by the lateral eyes. The sensory input is relayed to the pineal via fibers that course in the optic nerves and the median forebrain bundle to make apparent connection with the sympathetic fibers supplying the gland. Pineal function is a subject of active investigation, and additional information is anticipated with further utilization of newer techniques.

REFERENCES

Hypophysis

BAKER, B. L. 1970 Studies on hormone localization with emphasis on the hypophysis. J. Histochem. Cytochem., vol. 18, pp. 1–8.

BARGMANN, W. 1957 Relationship between neurohypophysial structure and function. *In* Proc. 8th Symp. Colston Res. Soc. (H. Heller, editor), pp. 11–22. Academic Press, New York.

BARGMANN, W., HILD, W., ORTMANN, R., AND SCHIEBLER, T. H. 1950 Morphologische und experimentelle Untersuchungen über das hypothalamischhypophysäre System. Acta Neuroveg. (Wien), vol. 1, pp. 233–275.

BARRNETT, R. J., LADMAN, A. J., McALLASTER, N. J., AND SIPERSTEIN, E. R. 1956 The localization of glycoprotein hormones in the anterior pituitary glands of rats investigated by differential protein solubilities, histological stains and bio-assays. Endocrinology, vol. 59, pp. 398–418.

COSTOFF, A., AND McSHAN, W. H. 1969 Isolation and biological properties of secretory granules from rat anterior pituitary glands. J. Cell Biol., vol. 43, pp. 564–574.

DORFMAN, R. I., AND UNGAR, F. 1965 Metabolism of Steroid Hormones. Academic Pres New York.

DU VIGNEAUD, V. 1954 Hormones of the posterior pituitary gland: oxytocin and vasopressin. Harvey Lectures, Ser. 50, pp. 1–26.

ELFTMAN, H. 1959 Combined aldehyde-fuchsin and periodic acid-Schiff staining of the pituitary. Stain Techn., vol. 34, pp. 77–80.

ELFTMAN, H., AND WEGELIUS, O. 1959 Anterior pituitary cytology of the dwarf mouse. Anat. Rec., vol. 135, pp. 43–49.

FARQUHAR, M. G. 1961 Fine structure and function in capillaries of the anterior pituitary gland. Angiology, vol. 12, pp. 270–292.

FARQUHAR, M. G., AND RINEHART, J. F. 1954 Electron microscopic studies of the anterior pituitary gland of castrate rats. Endocrinology, vol. 54, pp. 516–541.

FARQUHAR, M. G., AND WELLINGS, S. R. 1957 Electron microscopic evidence suggesting secretory granule formation within the Golgi apparatus. J. Biophys. Biochem. Cytol., vol. 3, pp. 319–322.

FRIEDGOOD, H. B., AND DAWSON, A. B. 1940 Physiological significance and morphology of the carmine cell in the cat's anterior pituitary. Endocrinology, vol. 26, pp. 1022–1031.

GREEN, J. D. 1966 Electron microscopy of the anterior pituitary. In The Pituitary Gland (Harris, G. W., and Donovan, B. T., editors), vol. 1, pp. 233–241. University of California Press, Berkeley.

GREEP, R. O. 1963 Architecture of the final common pathway of the adenohypophysis. Fertil. Steril., vol. 14, pp. 153–179.

HALMI, N. S. 1952 Two types of basophils in the rat pituitary: "thyrotrophs" and "gonadotrophs" vs. beta and delta cells. Endocrinology, vol. 50, pp. 140–142.

HARRIS, G. W., AND DONOVAN, B. T. (editors) 1966 The Pituitary Gland. University of California Press, Berkeley.

HEIDINGER, C. E., AND FARQUHAR, M. G. 1957 Elektronenmikrospische Untersuchungen von zwei Typen acidophiler Hypophysenvorderlappenzellen bei der Ratte. Schweiz. Z. Allg. Path., vol. 20, pp. 766–768.

HELLER, H. C. (editor) 1957 The Neurohypophysis. Academic Press, New York.

HERLANT, M. 1960 Étude critique de deux techniques nouvelles destinées à mettre en évidence les différentes catégories cellulaires présentes dans la glande pituitaire. Bull. Micr. Appl., Ser. 2, vol. 10, pp. 37–44.

HYMER, W. C., AND McSHAN, W. H. 1963 Isolation of rat pituitary granules and the study of their biochemical properties and hormonal activities. J. Cell Biol., vol. 17, pp. 67–86.

NAKANE, P. K. 1970 Classification of anterior pituitary cell types with immunoenzyme histochemistry. J. Histochem. Cytochem., vol. 18, pp. 9–20.

PALAY, S. L. 1957 Fine structure of the neurohypophysis. Progr. Neurobiol., vol. 2, pp. 31–44.

PURVES, H. D. 1961 Morphology of the hypophysis related to its function. In Sex and Internal Secretion (Young, W. C., editor), vol. 1, pp. 161–239. The Williams & Wilkins Company, Baltimore.

PURVES, H. D. 1966 Cytology of the adenohypophysis. In The Pituitary Gland (Harris, G. W., and Donovan, B. T., editors), vol. 1, pp. 147–232. University of California Press, Berkeley.

RINEHART, J. F., AND FARQUHAR, M. 1953 Electron microscope studies of the anterior pituitary gland. J. Histochem. Cytochem., vol. 1, pp. 93–113.

ROMEIS, B. 1940 Hypophyse. In Handb. mikr. Anat. Menschen (v. Möllendorff, editor), vol. 6, pt. 3. Springer-Verlag, Berlin.

SCHARRER, E., AND SCHARRER, B. 1954 Neurosekretion. In Handb. mikr. Anat. Menschen (v. Möllendorff, editor), vol. 6, pt. 5, pp. 953–1066. Springer-Verlag, Berlin.

SEVERINGHAUS, A. E. 1938 The cytology of the pituitary gland. In The Pituitary Gland, pp. 69–117. The Williams & Wilkins Company, Baltimore.

SIPERSTEIN, E. R. 1963 Identification of the adrenocorticotrophin-producing cells in the rat hypophysis by autoradiography. J. Cell Biol., vol. 17, pp. 521–546.

SMITH, P. E. 1930 Hypophysectomy and a replacement therapy in the rat. Amer. J. Anat., vol. 45, pp. 205–273.

SMITH, P. E., AND MacDOWELL, E. C. 1931 The differential effect of hereditary mouse dwarfism on the anterior-pituitary hormones. Anat. Rec., vol. 50, pp. 85–93.

STANFIELD, J. P. 1960 The blood supply of the human pituitary gland. J. Anat. (London), vol. 94, pp. 259–273.

TESAR, J. T., KOENIG, H., AND HUGHES, C. 1969 Hormone storage granules in the beef anterior pituitary. I. Isolation, ultrastructure and some biochemical properties. J. Cell Biol., vol. 40, pp. 225–235.

WISLOCKI, G. B. 1938 The vascular supply of the hypophysis cerbri of the rhesus monkey and man. In The Pituitary Gland, pp. 48–68. The Williams & Wilkins Company, Baltimore.

XUEREB, G. P., PRICHARD, M. M. L., AND DANIEL, P. M. 1954 The hypophyseal portal system of vessels in man. Quart. J. Exp. Physiol., vol. 39, pp. 219–229.

Thyroid

ANDROS, G., AND WOLLMAN, S. H. 1964 Autoradiographic localization of iodine[125] in the thyroid epithelial cell. Proc. Soc. Exp. Biol. Med., vol. 115, pp. 775–777.

DeGROOT, L. J. 1965 Current views on formation of thyroid hormones. New Eng. J. Med., vol. 272, pp. 243–250, 297–303, and 355–362.

DEMPSEY, E. W. 1949 The chemical cytology of the thyroid gland. Ann. N. Y. Acad. Sci., vol. 50, pp. 336–357.

DeROBERTIS, E. 1949 Cytological and cytochemical basis of thyroid function. Ann. N. Y. Acad. Sci., vol. 50, pp. 317–333.

GROSS, J., AND PITT-RIVERS, R. 1954 Triiodothyronine in relation to thyroid physiology. Recent Progr. Hormone Res., vol. 9, pp. 109–128.

KLINCK, G. H., OERTEL, J. E., AND WINSHIP, I. 1970 Ultrastructure of normal hyman thyroid. Lab. Invest., vol. 22, pp. 2–22.

NADLER, N. J., SARKAR, S. K., AND LEBLOND, C. P. 1962 Origin of intracellular colloid droplets in the rat thyroid. Endocrinology, vol. 71, pp. 120–129.

NADLER, N. J., YOUNG, B. A., LEBLOND, C. P., AND MITMAKER, B. 1964 Elaboration of thyroglobulin in the thyroid follicle. Endocrinology, vol. 74, pp. 333–354.

PEARSE, A. G. E., AND CARVALHEIRA, A. F. 1967 Cytochemical evidence for an ultimobranchial origin of rodent thyroid cell. Nature (London), vol. 214, pp. 929–930.

PITT-RIVERS, R., AND TROTTER, W. R. (editors) 1964 The Thyroid Gland. Butterworth and Company, Ltd., London.

ROBINSON, W. L., AND DAVIS, D. 1969 Determination of iodine concentration and distribution in rat thyroid follicles by electron-probe analysis. J. Cell Biol., vol. 43, pp. 115–121.

TURNER, C. D. 1966 General Endocrinology, ed. 4. W. B. Saunders Company, Philadelphia.

WISSIG, S. L. 1964 Morphology and cytology. In The Thyroid Gland (Pitt-Rivers, R., and Trotter, W. R., editors), pp. 32–70. Butterworth and Company, Ltd., London.

Parathyroids

BAKER, B. L. 1942 A study of the parathyroid glands of the normal and hypophysectomized monkey (Macaca mulatta). Anat. Rec., vol. 83, pp. 47–73.

GAILLARD, P. J., TALMAGE, R. V., AND BUDY, A. M. (editors) 1965 The Parathyroid Glands. University of Chicago Press, Chicago.

GREEP, R. O. 1963 Parathyroid glands. In, Comparative Endocrinology (von Euler, U. S., and Heller, H., editors), vol. 1, pp. 325–370. Academic Press, New York.

MUNGER, B. L., AND ROTH, S. I. 1963 The cytology of the normal parathyroid glands of man and Virginia deer. A light and electron microscopic study with morphologic evidence of secretory activity. J. Cell Biol., vol. 16, pp. 379–400.

Adrenal Glands

BENNETT, H. S. 1941 Cytological manifestations of secretion in the adrenal medulla of the cat. Amer. J. Anat., vol. 69, pp. 333–383.

COUPLAND, R. E. 1965 The Natural History of the Chromaffin Cell. Longmans, Green and Company, London.

DeROBERTIS, E. D. P., AND VAZ FERREIRA, A. 1958 Electron microscopic study of the excretion of catechol-containing droplets in the adrenal medulla. Exp. Cell Res., vol. 12, pp. 568–574.

GREEP, R. O., AND DEANE, H. W. 1949 Histological, cytochemical and physiological observations on the regeneration of the rat's adrenal gland following enucleation. Endocrinology, vol. 45, pp. 42–67.

INGLE, D. J., AND BAKER, B. L. 1953 Physiological and Therapeutic Effects of Corticotrophin (ACTH) and Cortisone. American Lecture Series, no. 179. Charles C Thomas, Publisher, Springfield, Ill.

JONES, C. I. 1957 The Adrenal Cortex. Cambridge University Press, London.

LEVER, J. D. 1955 Electron microscopic observations on the adrenal cortex. Amer. J. Anat., vol. 97, pp. 409–430.

LONG, J. A., AND JONES, A. L. 1970 Alterations in fine structure of the opossum adrenal cortex following sodium deprivation. Anat. Rec., Anat. Rec., vol. 166, pp. 1–26.

MERKLIN, R. J. 1966 Suprarenal gland lymphatic drainage. Amer. J. Anat., vol. 119, pp. 359–374.

SABATINI, D. D., AND DeROBERTIS, E. D. P. 1961 Ultrastructural zonation of adrenal cortex in the rat. J. Biophys. Biochem. Cytol., vol. 9, pp. 105–119.

WASSERMANN, G., AND TRAMEZZANI, J. H. 1963 Separate distribution of adrenaline- and noradrenaline-secretory cells in the adrenal of snakes. Gen. Comp. Endocr., vol. 3, pp. 480–489.

WOOD, J. G., 1963 Identification of and observations on epinephrine and norepinephrine containing cells in the adrenal medulla. Amer. J. Anat., vol. 112, pp. 285–303.

WOOD, J. G., AND BARRNETT, R. J. 1964 Histochemical demonstration of norepinephrine at a fine structural level. J. Histochem. Cytochem., vol. 12, pp. 197–209.

Pineal Body

ANDERSON, E. 1965 The anatomy of bovine and ovine pineals: light and electron microscope studies. J. Ultrastruct. Res., suppl. 8, pp. 1–80.

KELLY, D. E. 1962 Pineal organs: photoreception, secretion, and development. Amer. Sci., vol. 50, pp. 597–625.

KELLY, D. E., AND SMITH, S. W. 1964 Fine structure of the pineal organs of the adult frog, *Rana pipiens*. J. Cell Biol., vol. 22, pp. 653–674.

KITAY, J. I., AND ALTSCHULE, M. D. 1954 The Pineal Gland. Harvard University Press, Cambridge.

QUAY, W. B., AND HALVEY, A. 1962 Experimental modification of the rat pineal's content of serotonin and related indole amines. Physiol. Zool., vol. 35, pp. 1–7.

REITER, R. J., AND FRASCHINI, F. 1969 Endocrine aspects of the mammalian pineal gland: a review. Neuroendocrinology, vol. 5, 219–255.

ROTH, W. D., WURTMAN, R. J., AND ALTSCHULE, M. D. 1962 Morphologic changes in the pineal parenchymal cells of rats exposed to continuous light or darkness. Endocrinology, vol. 71, pp. 888–892.

WURTMAN, R. J., AXELROD, J., AND KELLY, D. E. 1968 The Pineal. Academic Press, New York.

22

*The Organs of Special Senses**

THE EYE*

The eyeball (*bulbus oculi*) constitutes the organ of vision. It is essentially a spherical structure, lightproof except for its transparent anterior surface (the cornea), and contains a system of refracting media with convex surfaces, which transmit light rays reflected from an object and bring them to a focus on a photosensitive surface (the neural retina) in the form of a small inverted image. The photosensitive elements (rods and cones) on which the image falls are thereby stimulated to nervous activity and send impulses over fibers of the optic nerve to the brain, where the sensation of vision is experienced. Correct focus is accomplished by changing the curvature of one of the refracting bodies (the lens) through alteration of the tension exerted on it by the mechanism from which it is suspended (the ciliary body). Placed perpendicularly in front of the lens is an adjustable diaphragm (the iris), the aperture of which (the pupil) can

be changed in diameter to regulate the amount of light admitted to the eye.

The eye is suspended by a series of ligaments in the bony orbit, which also contains the following structures: the extrinsic ocular muscles, which control movements of the eyeball; the lacrimal gland, which keeps moist its anterior surface; the nerves and blood vessels supplying the eye and orbital structures; and a considerable amount of connective tissue and fat, which fills in all otherwise unoccupied orbital space. Also associated with the eye are the lids and a duct system which drains the tears from the eye into the nasal cavity.

In form, the eyeball (Fig. 22-1) departs slightly from that of a ball; it is more accurately described as consisting of the segments of two spheres, unequal in size. The larger sphere forms the posterior five-sixths of the eyeball. The anterior one-sixth, which is the cornea, constitutes a segment of the smaller sphere and hence is more curved than the posterior part. The two segments are structurally continuous.

The wall of the eyeball consists of two epithelial layers (derived from the ectodermal optic cup) and two mesodermally derived connective tissue tunics which taken together enclose the transparent media through which light is transmitted to the sensitive retina.

The outermost component is the *tunica fibrosa*, comprising the stroma of the *cornea*

---

* A number of the illustrations of the eye that have been retained from earlier editions of this textbook were made from slides which were made available through the kindness of Dr. A. B. Reese of the Institute of Ophthalmology, Columbia-Presbyterian Medical Center, New York City. Figures 22-6, 22-7, 22-8, 22-10, 22-22 and 22-26 were made from slides in the personal collection of Dr. Reese. Figures 22-4 and 22-24, were made from slides in the collection of the Institute of Ophthalmology. Sections of the eye were also kindly loaned by Dr. R. Castroviejo of the Institute of Ophthalmology.

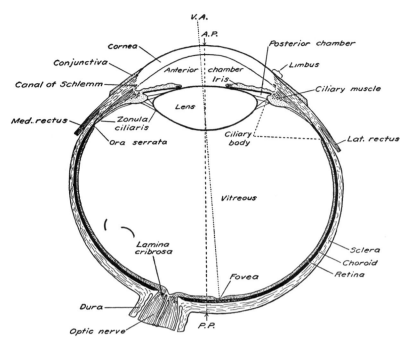

Fig. 22-1. Schematic horizontal meridional section of right eye. *A.P.*, anterior pole; *P.P.*, posterior pole; *V.A.*, visual axis. ×3. (Redrawn and modified from Salzmann.)

and *sclera*. The cornea forms the anterior portion of this tunic and is transparent. A fact not commonly appreciated is that most of the refraction of light takes place at the surface of the cornea rather than in the lens, the refractive power of the cornea being about two and one-half times that of the lens. The remainder of the outer tunic is the sclera, a grayish-white tough protective coat, a part of which is seen through the overlying transparent conjunctiva as the "white" of the eye. The tendons of the extrinsic ocular muscles insert into the sclera. Posteriorly, it is perforated where the fibers of the optic nerve leave the eye, this area being known as the *lamina cribrosa*.

The inner connective tissue tunic of the eye is the *tunica vasculosa*, or *uvea*, which includes the *choroid, ciliary body* and the stroma of the *iris*, the last named having a central circular opening, the *pupil*. All three regions of this tunic are characterized by extreme vascularity and the presence of con-

siderable amounts of pigment. In addition, the ciliary body and iridial stroma contain smooth muscle. That in the ciliary body serves as the muscle of accommodation; by its contraction, the tension on the suspensory ligament of the lens is relaxed and the lens assumes a greater curvature to bring the image of near objects into correct focus on the retina. The smooth muscle in the iris acts to regulate the diameter of the pupil.

The innermost component, the *tunica interna*, is represented chiefly by the photosensitive neural *retina* but also includes the *pigment epithelium layer* and the forward extension of elements of both of these layers to form the posterior layers of the ciliary body and iris. The nerve fibers of the retina converge about 3 mm medial to the posterior pole of the eye to form the *optic nerve;* consisting only of nerve fibers, this area constitutes a *blind spot.* Almost at the posterior pole is a small area of the retina known as the *macula lutea,* in the center of which is a depression—the *fovea centralis.* This is the region of most acute vision.

An understanding of certain commonly used descriptive terms facilitates discussion of the histology of the eyeball. Thus we speak of the anterior pole of the eye as being coincident with the midpoint of the cornea. A point diametrically opposite is the posterior pole. A line connecting the anterior and posterior poles is the geometric axis of the eye. This must be distinguished from the visual axis, which is a line joining the fovea centralis and the nodal point of the optic system. This latter point, which is the optical center, lies in the posterior part of the lens.

A section of the eyeball passing through the anterior and posterior poles is designated a meridional section. Most instructive of the various meridional sections is that which passes through the horizontal meridian. At an angle of 90° to this plane is the vertical meridian, which divides the eyeball into a medial, or nasal, half and a lateral, or temporal, half. The equator of the eye is a circle taken equidistant from the two poles; sections parallel to this plane are called equatorial sections.

The terms "outer" and "inner" are used as follows: "outer" (or external) refers to that which is nearer the surface of the eyeball; "inner" (or internal) refers to that which is nearer the midpoint of the bulb. The terms, anterior and posterior, refer to points which are nearer the anterior or posterior poles, whether such points be in a sagittal plane or along a meridian.

TUNICA FIBROSA

THE SCLERA

The sclera (Figs. 22-1 and 22-11), which forms the opaque posterior five-sixths of the protective outer tunic, is composed of dense fibrous connective tissue. It is thickest at the posterior pole (about 1 mm) and gradually becomes thinner until it is only 0.3-mm thick at the insertion of the recti muscles. It is pierced by three sets of apertures, or emissaria, through which pass nerves, blood vessels and lymphatics. At the point of attachment of the optic nerve, the sclera is sieve-like because its fibrous components have developed in such a way as to infiltrate the optic nerve fibers which leave the retina there. This region of infiltration is termed the *lamina cribrosa.*

Although the sclera and cornea are structurally continuous, their line of junction is marked externally by a slight circular furrow, the *external scleral sulcus.* On the inner surface of the sclera, close to its junction with the cornea, there is also a shallow furrow, the *internal scleral sulcus.* The posterior margin of this furrow projects slightly inward and forward to form the *scleral spur* (*scleral roll*), to which the ciliary body is attached (Figs. 22-1 and 22-6). The furrow itself is filled in by the *meshwork of the iris angle.* At the base of the furrow lies the *canal of Schlemm.*

Layers of the Sclera. For descriptive purposes, three layers of tissue may be designated in the sclera but they are in no sense sharply delimited from each other. From without inward, these layers are:

1. Episcleral tissue.
2. Sclera proper.
3. Lamina fusca.

The episcleral tissue is composed of loose collagenous and elastic fibers. Superficially, it is continuous with the loose tissue of *Tenon's space;* inwardly, it merges with the sclera proper; anteriorly, it attaches the conjunctiva to the sclera. It differs from the sclera in having a relatively large number of blood vessels.

The sclera proper is composed of a dense feltwork of collagenous fiber bundles running parallel to the surface. Near the cornea and around the optic nerve, the bundles of fibers are disposed chiefly in an equatorial direction; elsewhere, they cross and interlace with each other in a complicated fashion. Interspersed with the collagenous fibers, and particularly at the periphery of the bundle, are numerous delicate elastic fibers. The cellular component consists chiefly of flattened fibroblasts located between the fiber bundles.

The tendons of the ocular muscles resemble the sclera in structure except that the fiber bundles are all parallel and there are many thick elastic fibers. At their insertions, the tendons continue directly into the sclera, the tendon bundles spreading out and interweaving among those of the sclera.

The lamina fusca represents a zone of transition between the sclera and the choroid. Here the elastic fibers increase in number and thickness, the collagenous bundles become smaller and a number of branched pigment cells appear. These are characteristics common to the adjacent suprachoroid, which is the outer layer of the choroid coat.

THE CORNEA

As has been stated, the cornea constitutes the anterior one-sixth of the eye and is more curved than the remainder of the bulb. Viewed from in front, the cornea appears slightly elliptical, with a horizontal diameter of about 12 mm and a vertical diameter of about 11 mm. Viewed from behind, the cornea is circular, the difference in the two

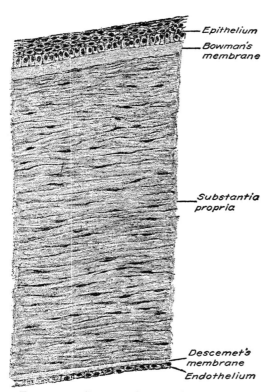

FIG. 22-2. Section through human cornea. (From a section by Dr. R. Castroviejo)

aspects being due to the fact that the sclera overlaps the anterior surface of the cornea above and below more than it does laterally and medially. The zone of transition between the cornea and sclera, known as the *limbus* of the cornea, is about 1 mm in width and has histological features differing from the remainder of the cornea.

Layers of the Cornea. Beginning at the front surface, the following five layers are seen in the cornea (Figs. 22-2 and 22-4):

1. Layer of epithelium.
2. Bowman's membrane.
3. Substantia propria.
4. Descemet's membrane.
5. Endothelium.

The corneal epithelium is of the stratified squamous variety, five or six cell layers in thickness (50 to 100 μ). The cells of the deepest layer are columnar in shape with the base of each cell resting on a periodic acid-Schiff positive basement membrane that is tenuously attached to the underlying Bowman's membrane. The nuclei of the basal cells are oval in shape, with their long axes at right angles to the surface of the cornea. The cells of the remaining layers range from polyhedral shapes in the intermediate strata to very flat plate-like shapes at the surface. Although the surface cells are somewhat thickened in the regions of their nuclei, the cell thickenings are directed toward the deeper cell layers, thus leaving the outer surface flat. This accounts for the smooth surface that is a characteristic feature of the cornea.

None of the corneal cells lose their nuclei and none of them ever normally undergo keratinization. They are attached to each other by desmosomes similar to those of epidermis.

Bowman's membrane consists of a thin layer of tissue which appears homogeneous and structureless under the light microscope. However, electron micrographs show that it contains a network of relatively fine collagenous fibers having an irregular arrangement in contrast with that of the pattern in the substantia propria. The anterior border of the membrane is sharply defined from the corneal epithelium and its basal lamina whereas the posterior border blends with the superficial lamellae of the corneal stroma.

The substantia propria (*corneal stroma*) forms about 90% of the thickness of the cornea and is composed of connective tissue fibers and cells. The characteristic transparency of the cornea is related, in part, to the pattern of its ultrastructural components. The predominant structural elements are collagenous fibrils arranged in layers, or lamellae, which course parallel with the surface of the cornea. Electron micrographs show that the fibrils within any one lamella are strictly parallel to one another but those of adjacent lamellae differ in direction (Fig. 22-3). Some fibrils also course from one lamella to another, thus helping to hold the lamellae together. The fibrils within each lamellae, as well as the different lamellae themselves, are also held together by mucopolysaccharides that consist of chondroitin sulfate A, keratosulfate and hyaluronic acid. The particular mucopolysaccharides present in the cornea apparently contribute to corneal transparency by maintaining the reversible swelling properties of the tissue. The continual loss of water from the corneal surface, thus preventing turgescence of the tissue, is an additional and important factor in maintaining corneal transparency.

Most of the connective tissue cells of the corneal stroma are modified fibroblasts. They are located between the lamellar bundles of collagenous fibers and are flat, with their greatest dimension parallel with that of the lamellae. In sections cut tangential to the corneal surface it can be seen that the cells have branching processes that often come into close apposition with neighboring cell processes.

Descemet's membrane appears homogeneous and highly refractile under the light microscope. It has resiliency and elasticity, and it stains, to some extent, with dyes commonly used for elastic tissue, e.g., with resorchin-fuchsin. Electron micrographs show, however, that Dsecemet's membrane does not contain elastic fibers. It appears to be a wide basement membrane consisting of a basal lamina and a reticular lamina of fibrous proteins of collagenous type that lack cross bands at typical 640-A intervals. Electron micrographs of cross sections of the membrane, particularly from older individuals, show a striated effect with bands of electron dense granules connected by filaments. Tangential sections show the granules and filaments in a hexagonal pattern (Jakus, 1956).

The endothelium. The posterior surface of the cornea is covered by a single layer of cells which extend over the inner surface of Descemet's membrane. In cross section, the cells appear rectangular in shape, with oval nuclei. They resemble a low cuboidal epithelium more than they do the typical endothelium of blood and lymph vessels. It should be noted that the term "endothelium" is used in this case to indicate the inner epithelial lining of the cornea in contrast to the epithelium which forms its outer covering. In accordance with the general classification of epithelial types the inner layer is mesenchymal epithelium or mesothelium rather than endothelium.

The cornea proper is entirely devoid of blood vessels, deriving its nutrition from the superficial marginal plexus of vessels, which is discussed below in the section on "The Limbus."

The cornea has a rich sensory nerve supply derived from the ophthalmic division of the trigeminal nerve. Small branches of this nerve enter at the periphery and branch extensively in the substantia propria as they course toward the surface and the center of the cornea. Near Bowman's membrane, this plexus proprius ends in a terminal net from which fibers, both individually and in bundles, pass as the corneal *rami perforantes* through pores in Bowman's membrane. Under the epithelium, they break up into finer

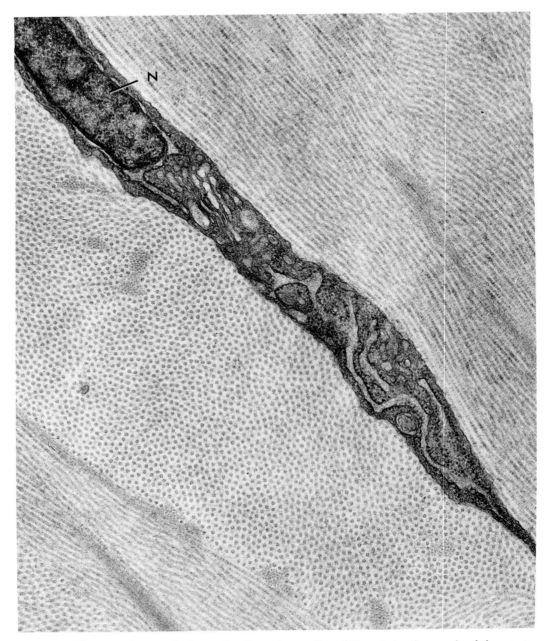

FIG. 22-3. Electron micrograph of a section through a portion of the substantia propria of the cornea. A portion of a stromal cell, with its nucleus (N), is seen between lamellae of collagenous fibrils. Note the precise alignment of collagenous fibrils at right angles to each other in adjacent lamellae. The endoplasmic reticulum of the stromal cell is not as prominent in the cornea of an adult as it is in the case illustrated, a chicken 5 days after hatching. ×34,000. (Courtesy of Drs. Elizabeth D. Hay and Jean-Paul Revel, Monographs in Developmental Biology, vol. 1, 1969.)

branches which extend forward and terminate between the epithelial cells. Other nerve endings are found in the stroma and just under the epithelium at the limbus.

THE LIMBUS

Transitional between the cornea and the adjacent sclera and conjunctiva is a zone about 1-mm wide known as the *limbus* (Fig. 22-4). The corneal epithelium, as it passes over into the limbus, increases in thickness up to 10 or more cells. The surface cells retain the characteristics of those of the cornea, but the basal cells become smaller, with scanty cytoplasm and small dark-staining nuclei. Furthermore, the basal border of the epithelium becomes irregular in contour. These are characteristics of the conjunctival epithelium with which the epithelium of the limbus is continuous.

The corneal stroma loses its regular lamellar arrangement, the fiber bundles assuming an irregular arrangement more like those of the sclera. Some elastic fibers are also found.

The only blood vessels which nourish the cornea are found in the limbus, where they form the superficial marginal plexus. These are in the superficial stroma and form a series of meridonally directed loops which extend to the border of Bowman's membrane. These vessels are derived from the anterior ciliary artery which is a derivative of the ophthalmic division of the internal carotid.

Descemet's membrane and the corneal epithelium become thinner as they approach the region over the scleral meshwork of the iris angle. The surface over the scleral meshwork has an irregular contour and numerous spaces extending inward toward the canal of Schlemm (see section on "The Iris Angle").

TUNICA VASCULOSA (UVEA)

The tunica vasculosa comprises the *choroid, ciliary body* and *iridial stroma* and is characterized by the presence of numerous blood vessels and pigment cells. If this deeply pigmented coat be viewed after removal of the overlying sclera and cornea, it greatly resembles a grape (uva); hence the name *uvea*, or *uveal tract*.

THE CHOROID

The term choroid (chorioid) is derived from the resemblance of this layer, in vas-

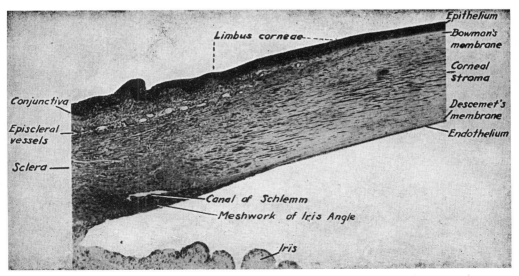

FIG. 22-4. Photomicrograph of a horizontal section through corneoscleral junction of human eye, showing the cornea, limbus corneae and structures of the iris angle.

cularity, to the chorion serving the fetus. It forms the posterior part of the uvea. Externally, it is separated from the sclera by a potential space, the *perichoroidal space*, across which delicate lamellae of the superficial layer of the choroid pass obliquely to blend with the lamina fusca of the sclera. The perichoroidal space, thus subdivided into numerous smaller but interconnected spaces, is limited anteriorly by the insertion of the ciliary muscle into the scleral spur. Posteriorly, it ends a short distance in front of the optic nerve. In life, this space is probably nonexistent; in the fixed specimen, it may appear as the result of shrinkage of tissues (Fig. 22-6).

Internally, the choroid is intimately related to the pigment epithelium layer of the retina. When the retina is detached, the pigment epithelium remains adherent to the choroid.

Layers of the Choroid. Histologically, the choroid (Figs. 22-1 and 22-11) may be divided into four layers, which from without inward are:

1. The suprachoroid.
2. The vessel layer.
3. The capillary layer.
4. The lamina vitrea.

Suprachoroid (*lamina suprachoroidea; epichoroid*). This, the superficial layer of the choroid, consists of loosely arranged collagenous and elastic fibers which course obliquely backward from choroid to sclera, bridging the perichoroidal space. Within the meshwork of fibers, there are occasional fibroblasts, some histiocytes and numerous chromatophores that contain black-brown melanin granules.

The vessel layer (*stratum vasculosa*). This layer is sometimes regarded as being subdivided into an outer layer of large vessels (*Haller's layer*) and an inner layer of medium-sized vessels (*Sattler's layer*). Only in the thicker portions of the choroid can such a division be discerned. In the region of the fovea, only the smaller vessels are present; anterior to the equator, the small vessels merge with the capillary layer, leaving as a distinct layer only the large vessels.

A characteristic of the veins of the vessel layer, is their confluence to form four whorl-like patterns—the *vortices*. In each vortex, the veins unite in an ampulla from which a single vortex vein arises. The vortex veins (*venae vorticossae*) leave the eye through emissaria in the sclera, two superiorly and two inferiorly.

The choroidal stroma occupies the spaces between the vessels. Its structure resembles that of the suprachoroid, but the stellate chromatophores have longer and more slender processes.

The capillary layer (*lamina choriocapillaris*), the only layer of the choroid which is not continued forward into the ciliary body, serves as the organ of nutrition for the outer layers of the retina. It consists of capillaries of wide bore arranged in a network disposed in one plane; i.e., the capillaries form a network in which the components are mostly in the same plane. The capillaries themselves are unique in having lumina of sufficient width to accommodate several red blood corpuscles side by side, whereas in most parts of the body, capillaries are so narrow that the blood cells must pass through them in single file. Structurally they are simple endothelial tubes (Fig. 22-11).

The interspaces of the capillary net are filled in by a stroma of delicate collagenous and elastic fibrillae. Toward the vessel layer, pigment cells are lacking, but connective tissue cells with vesicular nuclei are present and the stroma becomes continuous with that of the vessel layer. On the inner aspect of the capillary layer, a condensation of elastic fibrillae forms the outer lamella of the lamina vitrea.

Lamina vitrea (*Bruch's membrane, glassy membrane*). This constitutes the innermost layer of the choroid and borders directly on the retinal pigment epithelium, which, indeed, contributes to its formation (Fig.

22-11). It is a noncellular membrane with a thickness of about 2 to 2.5 μ, in which, under the most favorable conditions, two layers may be distinguished by light microscopy. The thin outer lamella is composed of slender collagenous fibers and a plexus of elastic fibers. The inner lamella is actually the basement membrane of the pigment epithelium of the retina. Electron micrographs show that this basement membrane is similar to that of other regions in that it consists of a basal lamina and a reticular lamina.

Nerves of the Choroid. The ciliary nerves course in the perichoroidal space and give off fine branches which form plexuses in the suprachoroid and the choroidal stroma. Multipolar ganglion cells associated with the plexuses are probably concerned with the sympathetic innervation of blood vessels.

Modifications of the Choroid. In certain of the teleost fishes a silvery layer of cells (*argentea*) is found between the suprachoroid and the vessel layer. It is formed by specialized cells containing crystals of guanine and extends into the iris, giving that membrane a characteristic silvery luster.

In most mammals, but not in man, a reflecting layer, the *tapetum lucidum*, is developed in the posterior region of the choroid. Lying between the choriocapillaris and the vessel layer, it consists either of several layers of flattened cells or several layers of fine fibers. The *cellular tapetum* is found in carnivores; the *fibrous tapetum*, in herbivores.

THE CILIARY BODY

The choroid extends anteriorly as far as the *ora serrata*, which is the anterior margin of the sensory portion of the retina (Fig. 22-1). In front of the ora serrata, the uveal tract is thickened to form the *ciliary body*. In its entirety, this forms a ring to which the suspensory ligament of the lens is attached and from which the iris takes origin. In meridional section, the ciliary body is triangular in shape, with its apex continuous

behind with the choroid (Fig. 22-6). Its outer surface is separated from the sclera by the perichoroidal space. Its inner surface faces the vitreous body and lens, and shows a modification into two zones, which may be identified macroscopically (Fig. 22-5). The posterior two-thirds appears darkly pigmented and is relatively smooth. This is the *orbiculus ciliaris*, or *pars plana*. The anterior third of the inner surface bears some 70 to 80 radially arranged ridges, the *ciliary processes;* this region is the *corona ciliaris* (*pars plicata*). The ciliary processes are pale in contrast to the darkly pigmented valleys between them.

The anterior surface or base of the ciliary body, from which the iris arises, faces toward the center of the cornea. Its outer edge is attached to the scleral spur. The greater part of the anterior surface is obscured by the overlying *meshwork of the iris angle*.

Layers of the Ciliary Body. In its histological structure, the ciliary body represents a forward continuation of all the elements of the choroid except the capillary layer, plus epithelial layers continued from the retina as the *pars ciliaris retinae*. Thus, from without inward, we find:

1. Suprachoroid and ciliary muscle.
2. Vessel layer.
3. Lamina vitrea.
4. Pigment epithelium⎱ Pars ciliaris
5. Ciliary epithelium ⎰ retinae.
6. Internal limiting membrane.

The suprachoroid and ciliary muscle. Reference has already been made to the presence of smooth muscle fibers in the suprachoroid. In the ciliary body, this smooth muscle increases in amount so that the bundles of fibers form a smooth muscle mass of very appreciable bulk (Fig. 22-6). According to the directions in which they are disposed, three sets of fibers are distinguished in the ciliary muscle:

a. The meridional fibers (longitudinal fibers, *Brücke's muscle*) are the outermost ones. They begin in the relatively sparse

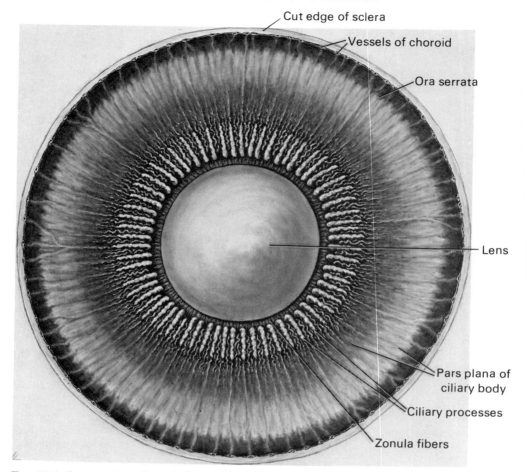

FIG. 22-5. Ora serrata, ciliary body, zonula ciliaris and lens viewed from behind after removal of the vitreous body. ×4.6. (Courtesy of Dr. S. R. Detwiler, labels added.)

star-shaped groups of muscle fibers of the suprachoroid in front of the equator and, increasing in amount, form bundles which run anteriorly to insert into the scleral spur (Fig. 22-10).

b. The radial fibers lie internal to the meridional fibers. They are intermingled with connective tissue elements which become continuous anteriorly with the meshwork of the iris angle.

c. The circular fibers (*Müller's muscle*) are continuous with the radial fibers and lie at the inner edge of the ciliary body. These fibers course in a circular direction around the ciliary body just posterior to the root of the iris. Immediately anterior

to them is the *circulus arteriosus iridis major,* from which comes the arterial supply of the iris and ciliary processes.

The blood vessels of the ciliary muscle run in the interstitial tissue and are of small caliber. The arteries are branches of the long posterior ciliary and anterior ciliary arteries.

The ciliary muscle is innervated by parasympathetic fibers of the oculomotor nerve. Preganglionic fibers reach the ciliary ganglion by way of the short motor root; the postganglionic fibers are the axons of ganglion cells in the ciliary ganglion and course to the ciliary muscle through the short ciliary nerves. These postganglionic

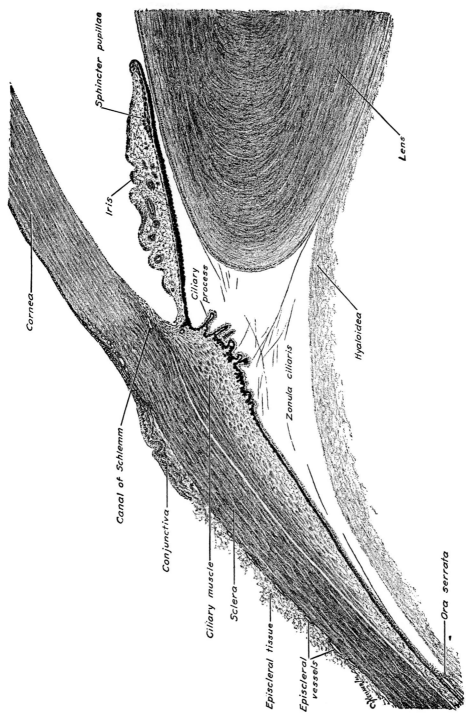

FIG. 22-6. Horizontal meridional section through anterior portion of human eye

fibers are unique in that they are myelinated, an exception to the general rule that
postganglionic fibers are nonmyelinated.

The action of the ciliary muscle is to
relax the tension on the suspensory ligament of the lens, thus allowing the lens
to assume a more convex form.

The vessel layer is similar in structure
to that of the choroid, with the exception
that there are fewer chromatophores and
more collagenous fibers. Unlike the choroid,
however, the vessels consist for the most
part of veins, a condition brought about by
the fact that the arteries supplying this
region enter through the perichoroidal space
and the ciliary muscle, leaving the vessel
layer as the almost exclusive avenue of the
returning veins.

In the orbiculus ciliaris, the vessels are
arranged almost in a single layer. Further
forward in the corona ciliaris, the vessels
are disposed in several layers. The ciliary
processes are formed by localized thickenings of the vessel layer (Fig. 22-7).

The lamina vitrea of the ciliary body
is a continuation of the vitreous lamina of
the choroid and it contains the same structures: an outer elastic lamella and an inner
lamella that is the basement membrane of
the pigment epithelium. In the ciliary region,
however, an added layer of connective
tissue is interposed between the two lamella.
The elastic lamella fades out at about the
middle of the corona ciliaris and the intermediate zone of collagenous fibers merges
with the stroma of the vascular layer. The
inner lamella, or basement membrane,
continues onto the iris.

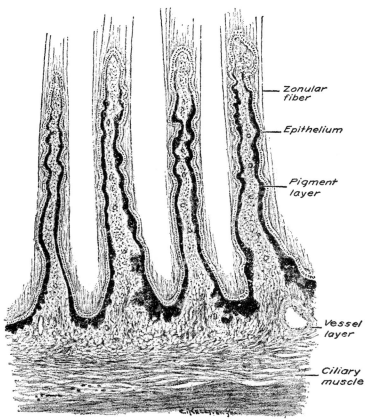

FIG. 22-7. Equatorial section through corona ciliaris of human eye

The pigment epithelium of the ciliary body is a forward continuation of the pigment epithelium layer of the retina. Its cells are so heavily filled with round melanin granules that cell borders are difficult to distinguish by light microscopy, except on the summits of the ciliary processes, where the cells are more cuboidal and have less pigment (Fig. 22-7). This accounts for the characteristic white appearance of the ciliary processes.

The ciliary epithelium represents a continuation from the sensory portion of the retina. Over the inner surface of the ciliary body, this becomes a single layer of columnar epithelial cells, unpigmented except in the region of the iris root, where they acquire increasing amounts of pigment and continue over the back surface of the iris as its pigment epithelium. Over the summits of the ciliary processes, the cells tend to become cuboidal in shape. Electron micrographs of ciliary epithelial cells show cytological characteristics commonly found in cells that are active in transport, such as numerous infoldings of the plasma membrane at the basal ends of the cells. Another characteristic of functional significance is the presence of a fenestrated type of endothelium in the capillaries of the ciliary processes (Chapter 12, Fig. 12-4).

It has been established that the aqueous humour is constantly formed in the posterior chamber and constantly drained at the angle of the anterior chamber. It seems clear that the formation of aqueous humour in the posterior chamber involves activity by the ciliary epithelium of the numerous ciliary processes. Although the details of aqueous humour formation are not fully understood, one hypothesis is that a filtrate from the blood capillaries passes between the epithelial cells where some substances are subtracted and other substances, such as ascorbic acid, sodium chloride and bicarbonate are added.

When different substances are injected into the blood, some reach the aqueous humour in amounts approaching that in plasma whereas many other substances such as protein, inulin and trypan blue do not usually enter the aqueous humour. The lack of passage of certain substances from the blood to the aqueous humour is referred to as the blood-aqueous barrier.

The internal limiting membrane is a thin structureless layer that is actually the basal lamina and reticular lamina of the optic cup on the inner side of the ciliary epithelium.

THE IRIS

The iris is a thin circular diaphragm placed directly in front of the lens and having a circular aperture, the pupil, located slightly to the nasal side of its center. Its peripheral border (*ciliary border, iris root*) is attached to the anterior surface of the ciliary body (Fig. 22-10); its *pupillary border* rests on the lens. The iris, therefore, does not have the shape of a flat curtain but inclines forward from the ciliary body. In meridional section, its shape is thus that of a low truncated cone. The iris divides the space between the cornea and the lens into two chambers which communicate through the pupil. In front of it is the *anterior chamber* of the eye; between it and the lens is the *posterior chamber*.

The anterior surface of the iris shows a division into two regions, an inner *pupillary zone* and an outer *ciliary zone*, which differ in structure and frequently also in color. The irregular circular line (about 1.5 mm from the pupillary margin) which forms the junction between these two zones is known variously as the *collarette, iris frill* or *angular line*. It marks the position of an underlying system of arteriovenous anastomoses, the *circulus vasculosus iridis minor*.

The pupillary zone is radially striated and near the collarette shows a number of depressions, the *pupillary crypts*, which may also occur in the neighboring part of the ciliary zone. At the pupillary margin is a dark border which represents the inner limit of the posterior pigmented epithelium.

The ciliary zone is marked by a series of fine radial striations formed by the blood vessels. In its outer half are a number of concentric circular furrows, the *contraction furrows*. Near the ciliary border, the *ciliary crypts* are seen. These are smaller than the pupillary ones.

Layers of the Iris. Like the ciliary body, the iris consists of structural continuations from both the tunica vasculosa and the tunica interna. The following five layers can be distinguished:

1. Endothelium.
2. Anterior border layer.
3. Vessel layer (stroma).
4. Dilator pupillae.
5. Pigment epithelium.

The first three layers form the uveal portion of the iris. The latter two represent a forward continuation of the tunica interna and constitute the *pars iridica retinae*.

The endothelium of the anterior surface of the iris is continuous with the endothelium of the iris angle and, in turn, with that of the cornea (Fig. 22-6). It is a thin and delicate layer that is difficult to demonstrate in sections prepared for light microscopy (Figs. 22-8 and 22-10).

The anterior border layer (Fig. 22-8) lies immediately under the endothelium and is the layer which determines the color of the iris. It is essentially a condensation of

the iris stroma but has fewer collagenous fibers and no blood vessels. It is formed principally of *chromatophores*—branched connective tissue cells containing granules of yellowish-brown pigment. This layer is lacking over the crypts and is thin on the contraction furrows.

The color of the iris depends upon the thickness of the anterior border layer and the degree of pigmentation of its cells. In the brown iris, the layer is thick and the cells heavily pigmented. In the blue iris, the layer is thin and there is a minimum amount of pigment. Light striking it, therefore, will pass through this layer and the underlying stroma and be reflected from the darkly pigmented posterior epithelium. The reflected light appears blue. Since the pigmentation of the border layer and stroma in the white races is acquired chiefly in the first few years of life, it follows that in these races, the ultimate color of the eyes is not apparent at the time of birth.

The vessel layer consists of a great number of blood vessels imbedded in a loose stroma of delicate collagenous fibrillae, with some elastic fibers and a number of stroma cells. Most of the latter are pigmented (chromatophores).

The arteries of the iris are branches of the greater arterial circle located at the root of the iris. The circle consists of vessels derived from the anterior and posterior ciliary arteries, all being derivatives of the ophthalmic division of the internal carotid

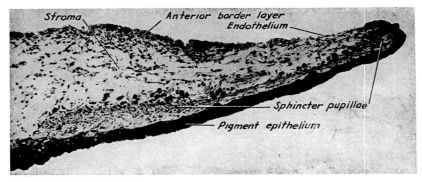

FIG. 22-8. Photomicrocrpah of a horizontal section through pupillary zone of human iris

arteries. Within the stroma of the iris, the arteries course radially and spirally. In comparison with arteries of most other parts of the body (see Chapter 12) the arteries in the iris have a poorly developed intima, a relatively thin muscular layer, and an unusually thick adventitia of collagenous connective tissue. The spiral patterns and firm connective tissue walls permit the vessels to either straighten or coil without either stretching or kinking; they appear to be structural modifications that are well-suited to the changes in the radial dimensions of the tissue in which they are located.

In the stroma of the pupillary zone there is a circular band of smooth muscle fibers, the *sphincter pupillae* (Fig. 22-8). This encircles the pupil and on contraction reduces the diameter of the opening. It is of ectodermal origin, derived from the pigment epithelium layer by a transformation of epithelial cells into smooth muscle fibers. This view, originally based on light microscopic studies, has been firmly established by electron microscopic studies (Tonosaki and Kelly, 1971). Stages in the differentiation of pigment epithelial cells into smooth muscle cells can be readily followed in electron micrographs from tissues fixed at different periods of development. Mesenchymal origin of the muscle cells can be ruled out because the pigment epithelial cells are clearly separated from mesenchyme by a basal lamina through all stages of differentiation.

The dilator pupillae muscle (Fig. 22-10) receives its name from the fact that its contraction produces dilation of the pupil. It is derived from pigment epithelial cells, being similar in this respect to the sphincter pupillae. The smooth muscle cells derived from the pigmented epithelial cells remain in close association with the ciliary epithelial cells which have become deeply pigmented over the posterior surface of the iris. The two layers can be distinguished best after bleaching (Fig. 22-9) or in tissues from albino animals. Since the smooth muscle

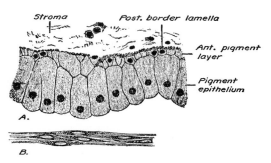

FIG. 22-9. *A*, transverse section, bleached, of the ectodermal layers of posterior surface of the iris; *B*, surface view of elements of dilator pupillae in middle of ciliary zone of the iris, (teased preparation) (Redrawn from Salzmann.)

cells retain some of the characteristics of epithelial cells they are sometimes described as "myoepithelial cells."

Together with the ciliary muscle, the sphincter and dilator pupillae comprise the intrinsic muscles of the eye. The sphincter is innervated by parasympathetic fibers of the oculomotor nerve. These follow the same course as those described for the ciliary muscle. The dilator pupillae is innervated by the sympathetic division of the autonomic nervous system. The preganglionic fibers arise from cell bodies located in the upper three thoracic segments of the spinal cord. These fibers course to the sympathetic chain by way of their respective white communicating rami and continue upward to terminate in the superior cervical ganglion. Here are located the cells of the nonmyelinated postganglionic fibers, which travel in the internal carotid nerve to the cavernous plexus, thence to the Gasserian ganglion and ophthalmic division of the trigeminal nerve, and finally by way of the nasociliary nerve and long ciliary nerves to reach the dilator muscle.

The pigment epithelium. It has already been mentioned that the ciliary epithelium as it nears the root of the iris acquires increasing amounts of pigment. From the ciliary body, it is continued over the posterior surface of the iris as its pigment epithelium (Figs. 22-8 and 22-10).

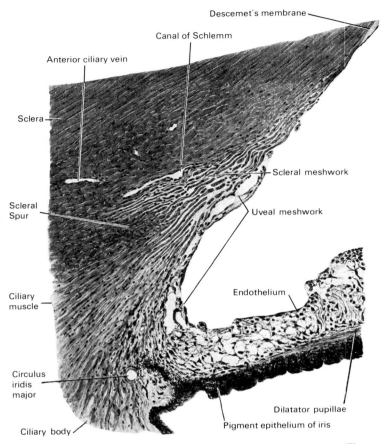

FIG. 22-10. Details of the iris angle. Drawn from the same section as Figure 22-6

So densely pigmented is this layer that neither cell boundaries nor nuclei can be distinguished in routine preparations for light microscopy. If the pigment be bleached out, however, the cells can be seen as columnar or prismatic elements with round nuclei (Fig. 22-9, *A*). At the pupil, this layer bends slightly forward around the pupillary border as the *pigment seam* and becomes continuous with the epithelial cells of the anterior pigment layer.

THE IRIS ANGLE

The lateral borders of the anterior chamber have, in meridional section, an angular shape. This angle, known as the iris angle or the angle of the anterior chamber, is occupied by a loose spongy tissue, the *mesh-work of the iris angle*. In section this tissue has the form of a triangle which fills in the scleral furrow and extends behind to the ciliary body (Figs. 22-4 and 22-10). The apex of the triangle is continuous with Descemet's membrane and the posterior lamellae of the cornea. Its base unites with the scleral spur and the anterior surface of the ciliary body; its outer border adjoins the tissues of the adjacent sclera and cornea; and, its inner border bounds the anterior chamber.

The major portion of the tissue is known as the *scleral meshwork*. The true nature of the meshwork is revealed by studies of tangential sections which show a series of perforated, flattened lamellae piled on top of one another. The fluid-filled channels between lamellae are connected with each other by the holes through the lamellae. The microscopic components of each lamella are as follows: a central core (or plate) of collagenous tissue, a layer of elastic fibers, a homogeneous glassy membrane and a covering of endothelium. The latter layer is continuous with the endothelium of the cornea. The spaces of the meshwork, known as the *spaces of Fontana*, are in direct communication with the anterior chamber.

Along the inner border of the scleral meshwork, there is a thin layer of trabeculae that lack elastic fibers and that are round instead of flat as described above for the lamella of the major portion of the uveal meshwork. In some species, the trabeculae along the inner border form a well-defined structure known as the *pectinate ligament*. This name is sometimes used for the similarly located, but poorly developed trabeculae in the human eye.

The *canal of Schlemm* also lies in the scleral furrow, close to its bottom. In meridional sections, it appears as one or more endothelial lined oval spaces, just in front of the scleral spur and adjacent to the meshwork of the iris angle (Figs. 22-4, 22-6 and 22-10). Actually, it encircles the eye as a canal which irregularly divides into two or more branches which recombine only to divide again. It communicates peripherally by means of 20 to 30 small branches with the anterior ciliary veins in the neighboring scleral tissue (Fig. 22-10). The outer borders of the endothelial cells of Schlemm's canal are in contact with the lining cells of some of the spaces of Fontana.

Together with the meshwork of the angle, Schlemm's canal forms a means of exit from the eye for the intraocular fluid. The aqueous humour passes readily through the spaces of Fontana and into the canal. Particulate matter is caught by the trabeculae of the meshwork. Under normal conditions, only aqueous humour is found in Schlemm's canal. It has been suggested

that the action of the ciliary muscle on the scleral spur provides a pumping mechanism for the canal.

The aqueous humour carries nutrients, substrates and metabolites. It also maintains an intraocular pressure which is higher than that in the surrounding tissues and thus, together with the fibrous tunics, it plays an important role in maintaining stability of optical dimensions. A normal intraocular pressure is present when the aqueous humour is formed and drained at normal rates. An increase in intraocular pressure, known as *glaucoma*, occurs when there is defective drainage by the outflow channels at the iris angle.

THE RETINA

The retina forms the *pars optica retinae* of the tunica interna and is the part of the eye which transforms the stimulus of light into nerve impulses, resulting in the sensation of vision. Thus it might be considered that all other parts of the eye serve the purpose of assisting the retina in the proper performance of its highly specialized function.

Embryologically, the retina arises from the two layers of ectoderm which form the optic cup. The outer layer gives rise to the pigment epithelium; the inner layer forms the remainder of the retina. In pathological detachment of the retina, or as often occurs in fixed and preserved specimens, the primary embryonic cavity between the two layers becomes reformed and the two parts of the retina separate, the pigment epithelium remaining adherent to the choroid. The strictly nervous portion is firmly attached to underlying structures at only two regions—at its scalloped anterior margin, the ora serrata (Fig. 22-6) and at the optic disc, where the nerve fibers pass through the wall of the bulb to form the optic nerve (Fig. 22-22). Detached from the pigment epithelium, it is a thin delicate layer which in life is transparent.

Layers of the Retina. Except at the

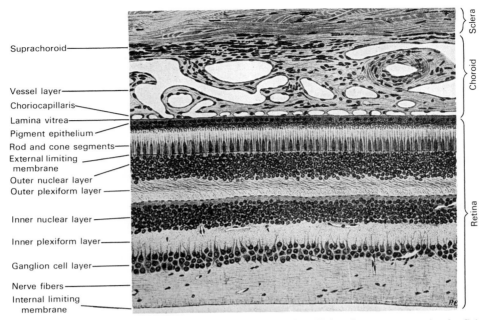

Suprachoroid

Vessel layer

Choriocapillaris

Lamina vitrea

Pigment epithelium

Rod and cone segments

External limiting
membrane

Outer nuclear layer

Outer plexiform layer

Inner nuclear layer

Inner plexiform layer

Ganglion cell layer

Nerve fibers

Internal limiting
membrane

Sclera

Choroid

Retina

FIG. 22-11. Section through retina, choroid and sclera. (After Eisler, from a preparation by Stieve.)

optic disc (optic papilla), the fovea centralis and the extreme periphery, the retina consists of 10 layers (Fig. 22-11), which, from without inward, are arranged as follows:

1. Pigment epithelium.
2. Layer of rod and cone outer and inner segments.
3. External limiting membrane (outer zone of intercellular attachments).
4. Outer nuclear layer.
5. Outer plexiform layer.
6. Inner nuclear layer.
7. Inner plexiform layer.
8. Ganglion cell layer.
9. Nerve fiber layer.
10. Internal limiting membrane (basal lamina).

The pigment epithelium consists of a layer of cuboidal cells that rest on a basal lamina that is continuous with the inner lamella of the lamina vitrea (Bruch's membrane) of the choroid (Fig. 22-12). The nuclei are spherical and are located in the outer (basal) portions of the cells. The inner portions of the cells contain a melanin pigment known as *fuscin*, and their cytoplasmic

processes interdigitate with rod and cone outer segments.

In certain animals (e.g., frog) the position of the pigment granules is determined by the illumination of the eye. In the dark or in low light intensities, the pigment is condensed in the cell body and the cell processes are devoid of it. In bright light, the pigment granules stream into the cell processes and form a dark curtain, as it were, around the rod outer segments. This phenomenon of pigment migration has not been demonstrated in mammals, including man.

The nature and significance of the remaining layers of the retina will be better understood if it is realized that the stratification depends upon the location and interrelationships of the photoreceptor cells and the intraretinal neurons of the afferent pathway. Considering them in the order of the conduction of an impulse, we find that the photoreceptors, the rod and cone cells, form the layer of that name plus the outer nuclear layer which consists of the nuclei and cell bodies of the photoreceptor cells.

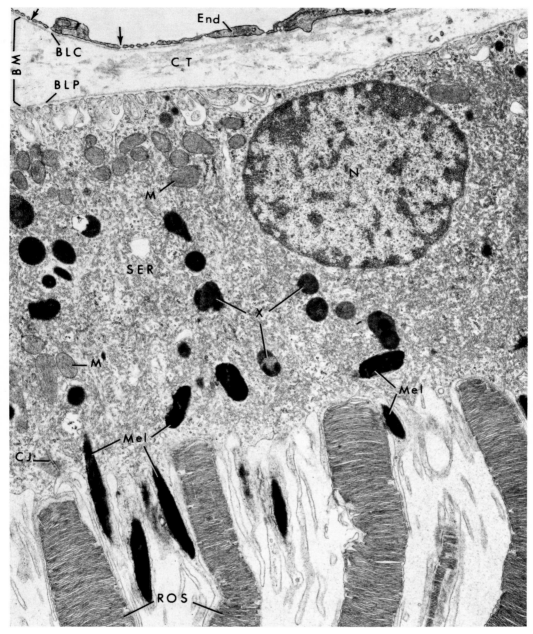

Fig. 22-12. Electron micrograph of pigment epithelium in relation to Brüch's membrane (*BM*) and to portions of rod cell outer segments (*ROS*). The endothelium of the choriocapillaris has fenestrae or pores (*arrows*) and rests on a basal lamina (*BLC*). Connective tissue (*CT*) is seen in the space between the basal lamina of the choriocapillaris and the basal lamina of the pigment epithelium (*BLP*). The field includes the nucleus (*N*) of a pigment epithelial cell, a region of specialized attachment (*CJ*) of adjacent pigment cells, mitochondria (*M*), melanin granules (*Mel*), smooth surfaced endoplasmic reticulum (*SER*), and granules (*X*) that are lysosomes and residual bodies. Numerous infoldings of the plasmalemma are seen in the basal portions of the pigment cells, i.e., adjacent to the basal lamina. From the retina of a rhesus monkey. ×11,000. (Courtesy of Dr. Richard W. Young.)

From the photoreceptor cells, processes that are homologous with axons extend into the outer plexiform layer where they make synaptic junctions with dendrites of bipolar neurons and with processes of horizontal cells. The nuclei of the bipolar cells lie in the inner nuclear layer; their axons pass into the inner plexiform layer, where they effect synapse with the dendrites of the ganglion cells. The relatively large cell bodies of the latter form the ganglion cell layer; their long axons course in the nerve fiber layer to the optic disk, where all the axons converge to form the optic nerve. These fibers are continuous to the brain, where the great majority end in the

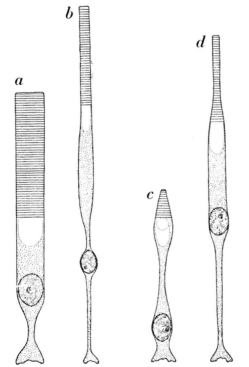

FIGS. 22-13. Diagrams of rod and cone cells. Although the retinal photoreceptors differ somewhat in different species, they have a similar general organization in all vertebrates. *Left,* typical rod cells from the frog retina (*a*) and the human retina (*b*); *right,* typical cone cells from the frog (*c*) and human (*d*). (After R. W. Young, Sci. Amer., vol. 223, 1970.)

lateral geniculate body, from which another neuron system carries the nerve impulse to the visual areas in the occipital cortex.

From the above description, it is evident that the true photoreceptive elements, the rods and cones, lie furthest removed and oriented away from the light stimulus, which to affect them must first pass through all the intervening layers (except at the fovea). Also, the nervous pathway at first travels directly toward the source of the stimulus before turning to course inward to the brain. Thus the retina is an upside-down sense organ. This *inverted* retina is characteristic of all vertebrates.

The layer of rod and cone outer and inner segments lies between the external limiting membrane and the pigment epithelium, facing the latter. The rod and cone outer segments are arranged in parallel fashion, perpendicular to the surface.

The Rod Cells. The *outer and inner segments* of these cells, known as the *rods proper,* are slender cylindrical elements, 40 to 60 μ in length and about 2 μ in diameter. Although the rod outer and inner segments vary in length and width in different species (Fig. 22-13), they are similarly organized in all vertebrates.

The outer segment is the receptor end of the cell that "traps" the light which reaches the retina. Electron micrographs show that the outer segment is made up of hundreds of membranous disks piled in a stack of uniform diameter (Figs. 22-14 to 22-16). These disks contain molecules of visual pigment which absorb the light and undergo chemical changes that lead to the production of a generator potential by the photoreceptor cell.

The outer segment is connected with the inner segment by a slender stalk or cilium (really a flagellum) which contains nine peripheral doublet microtubules that end in a centriole or basal body. Thus the outer segment is revealed to be a specialized cilium that differs from the cilia of most other types of epithelium (Chapter 4) in

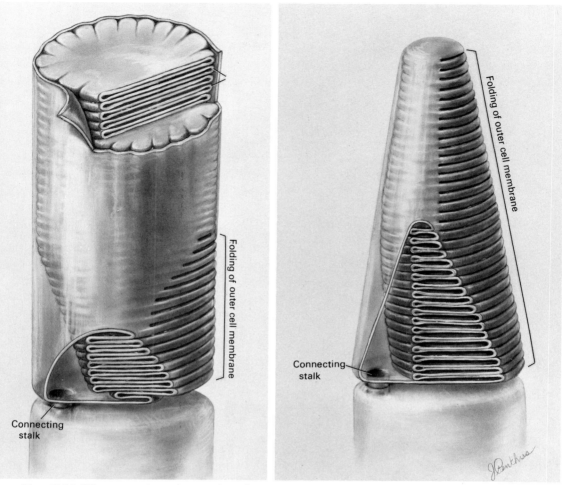

Folding of outer cell membrane

Connecting stalk

Folding of outer cell membrane

Connecting stalk

FIG. 22-14. Diagrammatic representation of the ultrastructure of rod and cone cell outer segments. In the rod, there is a continual formation of new disks by repeated infolding of the cell membrane. As the older disks are displaced away from the base of the outer segment, they lose their attachment to the cell membrane, and they are eventually cast off. The disks of the cone outer segment are not continually replaced, and they are generally not cast off. (Courtesy of Dr. Richard W. Young.)

that it lacks the central pair of microtubules. The outer portion of the inner segment, identified as an "ellipsoid" by light microscopists, contains closely packed mitochondria (Fig. 22-15). The inner portion of each inner segment contains the Golgi complex and granular and smooth endoplasmic reticulum.

Radioautographic studies of retinas from animals sacrificed at intervals after injection of radioactive amino acids show that rod cells synthesize new proteins in the inner segments and that these proteins are conducted by the ciliary stalks to the bases of the outer segments where new disks are built by infoldings of cell membranes. The older disks are displaced outward as new disks are built below, and they are eventually shed from the tips of the rods into the region of the pigment epithelium. Thus, the outer segments of the rod cells are continually renewed.

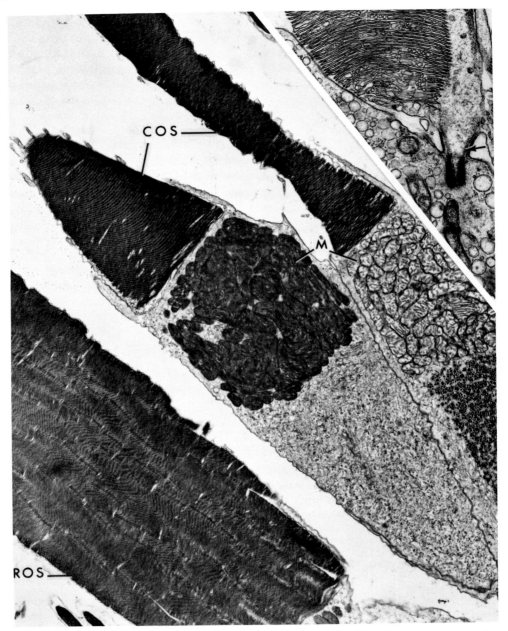

Fig. 22-15. Electron micrograph of portions of rod and cone cells. The field includes a portion of the outer segment of a rod (*ROS*) and the outer segments of a double cone (*COS*). The field also includes cone inner segments, showing closely packed mitochondria (*M*) in the outer portion of the inner segment. Endoplasmic reticulum is found chiefly in the inner portion of the inner segment. The electron-dense granules seen in the inner segment of one of the cones represent glycogen. *Insert, upper right,* junction of outer and inner segments of a photoreceptor cell at higher magnification. *Arrow,* connecting stalk. The electron-dense material subjacent to the stalk is the basal body. *Lower figure,* from a newt, *Taricha torosa,* ×7,200; *insert,* a photoreceptor cell from the same species at higher magnification, ×16,450. (Lower figure, courtesy of Dr. Anita Hendrickson; insert, courtesy of Dr. Douglas Kelly.)

When the retina is freshly removed from the eye of an animal which has been kept in the dark, it appears purplish-red in color when viewed in subdued light. The color fades rapidly when the preparation is exposed to light. Chemical studies have shown that rod visual purple consists of vitamin A aldehyde, now known as *retinald* (formerly called retinene) combined with a protein known as *rod opsin*. When a pigment molecule is exposed to light, there is a change in the form of the retinald and the relationship between retinald and its combined protein is broken. This leads to a change in electrical potential in the cell that results in the formation of a membrane generator potential (signal) which is released at the synaptic contact of the rod basal process to the dendrites of a biopolar ganglion cell. After light stimulation, the visual purple is rapidly reconstituted.

It was noted many years ago that animals that are particularly active at night (e.g.,

rats and mice) have many rods and few cones. On the other hand, animals active only in daytime have retinas composed almost entirely of cones (e.g., diurnal lizards and turtles). The respective roles of rods and cones in the human eye are well-established. The rods have a low threshold of stimulation by light and are particularly important in intensity (dark and light) discrimination and active in night vision. The cones have a higher threshold of stimulation and are particularly important in wavelength discrimination and in visual acuity. They are most active under daylight intensities.

The Cone Cells. Except in the region of the fovea centralis and its immediate vicinity, the cones are flask-shaped, having a relatively short and conical outer segment and a relatively broad and bulbous inner segment. The region that connects the cone inner segment to the cone body is short and it is not constricted as it is in the rods (Fig.

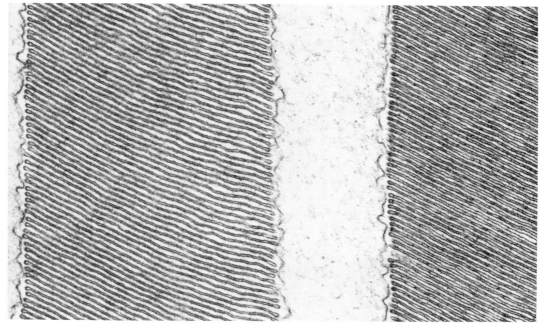

FIG. 22-16. Electron micrographs of portions of a cone outer segment (*left*) and a rod outer segment (*right*) from the retina of a monkey. Note that the rod disks are more closely packed than those of the cones. ✕53,000. (Courtesy of Dr. Richard W. Young.)

22-13). Variations in shapes of cones from different areas of the human retina are shown in Figure 22-18.

Electron microscopic studies of the retina show that the cone outer segments are composed of discs somewhat like those of the rods. The cone discs differ, however, in that they remain attached to the cell plasmalemma from which they arise. The cone disks also differ from the rod discs in that they become progressively smaller in diameter along the length of the cone (Fig. 22-14). The cone outer segment is attached to the cone inner segment by a ciliary stalk that is similar in structure to that in the rod.

The inner segment often contains a characteristic oil droplet just beneath the connecting cilium; otherwise it resembles the rod inner segment in having a region of closely packed mitochondria followed by a region containing the Golgi complex and smooth- and rough-surfaced endoplasmic reticulum.

Radioautographic studies of retinas taken from animals sacrificed at intervals subsequent to injection of labeled amino acids show that new proteins are also synthesized in the inner segments of the cones (i.e., in the region of the rough-surfaced endoplasmic reticulum and Golgi complex) just as in the rods. The new proteins, however, are distributed to the cone outer segments in a manner that differs from that in rods. The new proteins diffuse quickly into all of the cone discs and not only into the basal disk. In fact, the cone seems not to be renewed by the progressive formation of new disks throughout life. This finding correlates with the variation in the diameters of cone disks. When disks form during the early growth and differentiation of a cone, each newly formed disk at the base of the stack is larger than the preceding one and thus the cone becomes tapered or conical in shape.

The visual pigment of the cones is associated with the disks of the outer segment, as it is in the rods. In the cones, the pigment is known as *iodopsin* and it consists of retinald (retinene) combined with a cone opsin. The basic steps in light absorption and in the generation of an impulse are similar to those described above for the rods. It has also been noted above that the cones respond to light of relatively high intensity, and that they function for visual acuity and for color perception. Detection of different colors apparently depends upon the presence of different pigments in the cones, each apparently containing a pigment that absorbs light most efficiently at red, blue or green wavelengths. Rods, on the other hand, apparently have only one type of pigment.

The external limiting membrane is seen in electron micrographs as a region of junctional complexes between the outer ends of the supporting Müller cells and the adjoining photoreceptor cells. It is actually not a membrane.

The outer nuclear layer consists of rod and cone cell bodies containing rod cell and cone cell nuclei, respectively. The cone nuclei are located close to the so-called external limiting membrane, and with the exception of the region of the fovea, they are limited to a single row. The rod nuclei are more numerous than the cone nuclei, except in the fovea, and they are distributed in several layers. The rod nuclei are rounded and they stain intensely in most routine preparations for light microscopy.

The outer plexiform layer is composed chiefly of axons of rod and cone cells, dendrites of bipolar neurons and processes of the horizontal cells.

The inner nuclear layer is thinner than the outer nuclear layer but resembles it in general appearance. It contains the nuclei of the *bipolar neurons*, nuclei of association neurons known as *horizontal cells* and *amacrine cells* and nuclei of the supporting *Müller's cells*. In general, the nuclei of this layer are arranged in three zones: an outer one of horizontal cell nuclei; a middle one of bipolar cell nuclei; and, an inner one in which amacrine cell nuclei predominate. The

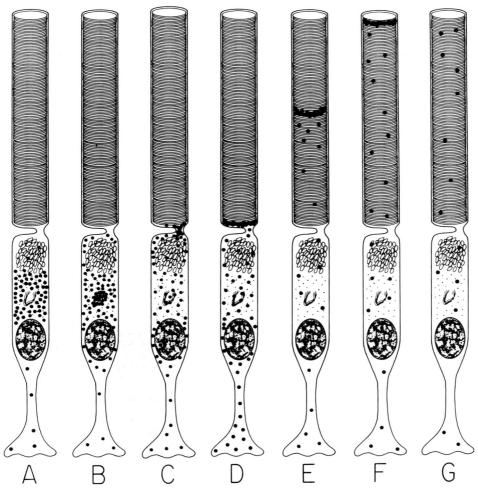

A B C D E F G

FIG. 22-17. Diagrammatic representation of the results of radioautographic studies of frog retinae fixed at different intervals of time after injection of labeled amino acids. Labeled material in newly synthesized protein (*dots*) is found in the region of the endoplasmic reticulum and the Golgi complex within 10 minutes after the injection (*A* and *B*). At later intervals, the newly formed protein passes around the mitochondria of the outer segment and reaches the connecting stalk (*C*). The synthesized protein is found in a newly formed basal disk of the outer segment in about 1 week (*D*), then moves outward (*E*), and reaches the end of the disk in about 8 weeks (*F* and *G*). (Courtesy of Dr. Richard W. Young.)

morphology and interrelationships of these cells are discussed below in the section on "Retinal Interneuronal Associations and Functions."

Inner plexiform layer. This consists of the processes of the amacrine cells, the axons of the bipolar cells and the profusely branched dendrites of the ganglion cells.

The ganglion cell layer is composed of multipolar ganglion cells, among which are scattered neuroglia cells. Branches of the retinal blood vessels are also present. The ganglion cells are variable in size (11 to 30 μ) with clear round nuclei containing one or more prominent nucleoli.

The nerve fiber layer consists of the axons of the ganglion cells. These nonmyelinated fibers are arranged in bundles which

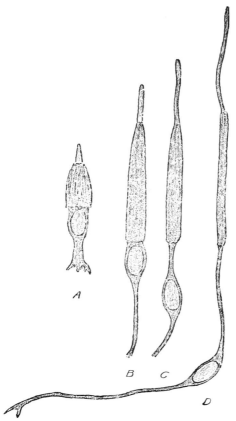

FIG. 22-18. Cones from different areas of the human retina. *A*, from near the ora serrata; *B*, from periphery of macula lutea; *C*, from the macula lutea; *D*, from the fovea centralis. (After Greeff.)

run parallel to the surface of the retina and converge at the optic disk to form the optic nerve. Between the bundles are numerous fibrous neuroglia cells (*spider cells*) and rows of Müller's fibers. Also present in this layer are the retinal blood vessels.

The "internal limiting membrane" is formed by the apposition of the expanded inner ends of processes of Müller's cells and by their basal lamina. As noted above, the nuclei of these cells are located in the inner nuclear layer and their processes (fibers) extend inward to the internal limiting membrane and outward to the outer ends of rods and cones. The Müller's cells are homologous with the glial cells of the central nervous system. They are the chief supporting cells of the retina although other cells of neuroglial type are also present.

Retinal Modifications in the Maculae Lutea and Fovea Centralis. Near the posterior pole of the eye, the retina undergoes a localized modification of its layers and shows a funnel-shaped depression. This region has a yellowish color when viewed in gross specimens; hence, it is named the *macula lutea*, or yellow spot. The inner layers of the retina spread apart and deviate from the center of the region, leaving a small pit known as the *fovea centralis* (Figs. 22-1 and 22-19). Here the photoreceptors consist only of cones. In the center of the fovea, in an area which is about 0.5 mm in diameter, the cones are only 2.5 μ in thickness. Their length is variously given as 60 to 85 μ. The fact that the cones are extremely slender and closely packed appears to partly explain the high visual acuity of the fovea.

Peripheral to the foveal region, rod receptors begin to appear among the cones and they gradually increase in numbers until three to four rods intervene between individual cones in areas peripheral to the macula. It has been estimated that there are about 7,000,000 cones in the retina; of this number, about 13,000 are said to be in the macular region and about 4,000 in the fovea centralis. Estimates of the number of rods range from 75,000,000 to 170,000,000.

Retinal Interneuronal Associations and Functions. The chief interneuronal relationships in the retina as currently described and interpreted from electron microscopic studies are shown schematically in Figure 22-20 and 22-21. It is seen that the terminal basal processes of rods and cones differ from each other in morphology: rod cell axons terminate as spherical-shaped end-bulbs whereas cone cell axons terminate as foot-shaped pedicles. The cone pedicles make separate synaptic contacts with dendrites of two types of bipolar cells: *midget bipolars* and *flat bipolars*. It seems function-

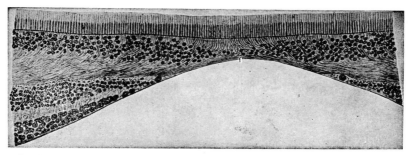

FIG. 22-19. Section through center of fovea centralis. The outer nuclear layer is represented in the fovea by only a few scattered cells. (After Eisler.)

ally significant that in the fovea of the retina, at least, a single midget bipolar cell is in synaptic contact with a single cone. This appears to be correlated with the high visual acuity of the central part of the fovea. The contact of the midget bipolar cell dendrite with the cone cell terminal forms a part of a triad synaptic complex, with the dendritic ending of the bipolar cell located between endings of two separate horizontal cells. It will be noted that contacts between rod and cone cell terminals are present also. The significance of some of these contacts is not fully understood.

Each rod bipolar ganglion cell synapses with several rod cells (only two are included in the simplified diagram, Fig. 22-21). This correlates with the findings that rods generally function as groups. The rod cell terminals are also in contact with processes of the horizontal cells.

The cell bodies of the amacrine cells, located in the inner cell layer of the retina, have processes that extend into the inner plexiform layer where they make contact with axon terminals of all types of bipolar cells and with the dendrites of both types of ganglion cells; they also make contact with each other, i.e., amacrine to amacrine contact.

Two types of ganglion cells have been identified: *midget ganglion cells*, with each cell dendrite in contact with the axon of a single midget bipolar cell, and *diffuse ganglion cells* which make contact with all types of bipolar cells. The synapses of the bipolar cells with the diffuse ganglion cells are both axodendritic and axosomatic in type.

The above retinal interneuronal relationships are significant in relation to the arrangement of retinal visual fields. The visual field of a particular ganglion cell is defined as that area of the retina which, upon stimulation, affects the ganglion cell. Each visual field consists functionally of a central region and a peripheral region; in light-adapted retinas, these two concentric fields function antagonistically. For example, if a given ganglion cell is excited when light is applied to the center of its visual field it will be inhibited when light is applied to the periphery of its field. When light is applied to the periphery and center of the particular ganglion's field at the same time, there is a summation of effects and the ganglion cell gives a weak response. In the case of color vision, it appears that the center of a field responds maximally to light of a particular wavelength and the periphery of the field responds maximally to light of another wavelength. In other words, the antagonistic central and peripheral zones of a field may be color coded.

The diameters of visual fields, particularly the diameters of the central portions of the fields, differ in different parts of the retina. In visual fields of the fovea, the diameter of the center of the field may be within the magnitude of the diameter of a single cone. This is one of the explanations for the greater visual acuity of the foveal region.

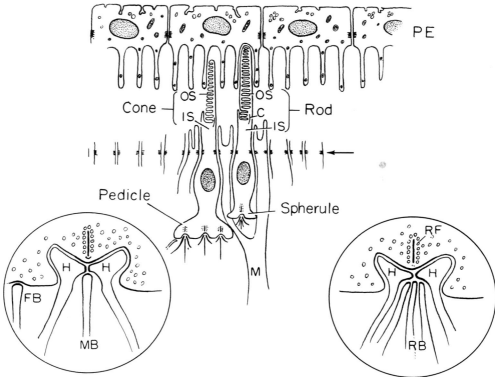

Fig. 22-20. Diagram of the ultrastructural organization of a portion of the retina showing the relationship of the rod and cone cells to the pigment epithelial cells and to the processes of Müller's cells. Desmosomes are seen at the lateral borders of apposing pigment epithelial cells (P). Processes of Müller's cells (M) project outward almost to the level of the connecting stalks (C) between the outer segments (OS) and inner segments (IS) of the photoreceptor cells. Arrow, the position of junctional complexes between the cell membranes of the processes of Müller's ependymal cells and membranes of rod and cone cells; this region is known as the outer limiting membrane of light microscope studies. The cone cell terminates in an expansion known as a pedicle, whereas the rod cell has a knoblike ending or spherule. Insert at lower left, the synaptic contacts of a cone cell pedicle with processes of midget bipolar cells (MB), flat bipolar cells (FB), and horizontal cells (H). Insert at lower right, synaptic contacts of a rod cell spherule with processes of rod bipolar cells (RB) and horizontal cells (H). An electron-dense line in the presynaptic terminal is known as a ribbon filament (RF). (Courtesy of Drs. Charles R. Noback and Lois K. Laemle, The Primate Brain, vol. 1, 1970.

The antagonistic responses to stimulation of "central" and "surround" regions of visual fields appear to correlate with the arrangement of neurons shown in Figures 22-20 and 22-21. A change in light intensity at the center of a field sets up a stimulus which is probably transmitted by direct receptor-bipolar-ganglion cell contacts. In the case of cone vision, this is by cone cell-midget bipolar cell-midget ganglion cell. On the other hand, a change in light intensity in the peripheral portion of the visual field of a ganglion cell sets up a stimulus which reaches the ganglion cell by a circuitous route that is apparently mediated by amacrine-amacrine cell contacts along the way.

Blood Vessels of the Retina. The layer of rod and cone outer and inner segments, the outer nuclear layer and the outer plexiform layer are devoid of blood vessels. Their nourishment comes from the choriocapillaris of the choroid. The remaining layers of the retina are supplied by a system of retinal vessels derived from the central retinal

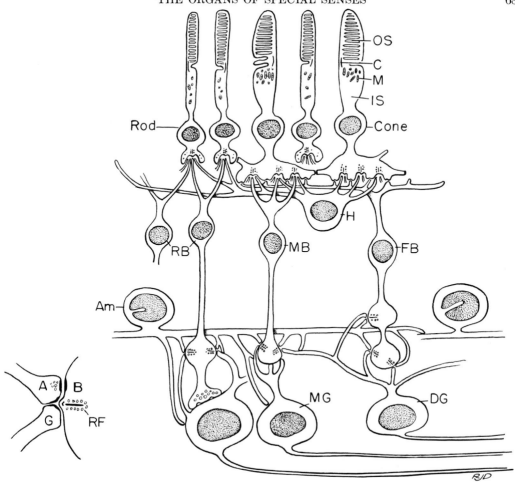

FIG. 22-21. Diagram of the ultrastructural organization of the retina showing the relationship of the photoreceptor cells and the intraretinal neurons. The rod cell terminals have synaptic contacts with rod bipolar cells (*RB*) and horizontal cells (*H*). Cone cell terminals have synaptic contacts with midget bipolar cells (*MB*), flat bipolar cells (*FB*), and horizontal cells. The amacrine cells (*Am*) have processes which have synaptic contacts with the processes of all types of bipolar cells and with the midget ganglion cells (*MG*) and diffuse ganglion cells (*DG*). *Insert, lower left*, a schematic representation of the synaptic contacts between an amacrine cell terminal (*A*), ganglion cell process (*G*) and bipolar cell process (*B*). *C*, connecting stalk; *IS*, inner segment; *M*, mitochondria; *OS* outer segment; *RF*, ribbon filament. (Courtesy of Drs. Charles R. Noback and Lois K. Laemle, The Primate Retina, vol. 1, 1970; adapted from Dowling and Boycott, 1966.)

artery, which enters the eye in the optic nerve. The larger arteries lie in the nerve fiber layer, with finer branches in the ganglion cell and inner plexiform layers. Two capillary networks are formed, one in the nerve fiber layer and another which extends as far as the outer border of the inner nuclear layer. The retinal veins follow the course of the arteries.

The Ora Serrata. The scalloped anterior border of the retina is known as the ora serrata (Fig. 22-1). Here the retina ends abruptly, its margin forming a step which may be rounded, angular or even overhanging. Approaching this region, the rods and cones become shorter and thicker (Fig. 22-18, *A*), the nuclear layers become thinner and the ganglion cell and nerve fiber layers cease altogether. There is a corresponding increase in the number of glial cells (Müller's fibers).

THE OPTIC NERVE

The nerve fibers of the retina converge at the optic disc and turn outward to pass through the sieve-like *lamina cribrosa* of the sclera as the optic nerve (Fig. 22-22). In this intraocular portion, the nerve has a structure similar to that of the nerve fiber layer; i.e., bundles of nonmedullated fibers surrounded by oligodendrocytes.

Immediately behind the lamina cribrosa, the nerve fibers acquire myelin sheaths, with a consequent increase in diameter of the entire nerve. Since the optic nerve actually is a tract of the brain rather than a true peripheral nerve, it is not surprising that it should resemble the brain in its coverings and its histological characteristics.

A cross section of the myelinated orbital portion of the optic nerve shows it surrounded by three connective tissue sheaths: an outer *dura*, an inner *pia* and an intermediate *arachnoid*, which divides the *intervaginal space* into a *subdural space* and a *subarachnoid space*. These sheaths are continuous with the corresponding meninges of the brain; at the bulb, they become continuous with the sclera.

From the pial sheath, connective tissue trabeculae pass into the nerve and together with the neuroglial elements form a system of septa which enclose groups of nerve fiber bundles. Between the bundles are glia cells whose processes and fibers penetrate between the individual nerve fibers.

In the anterior part of the nerve, for a distance of about a half inch behind the eye, the septa are united to a central core of connective tissue, the *central supporting tissue strand*. This carries the *central artery* and *central vein* of the retina. Small branches from these vessels course in the septal system to supply the nerve itself.

THE LENS

Structure of the Lens. The lens (Fig. 22-23) is a transparent and somewhat plastic biconvex body situated between the iris and the vitreous body. Its posterior surface has a greater convexity than the anterior surface (Fig. 22-1). Three structural components make up the lens:

1. The capsule.
2. The anterior epithelium.
3. The lens substance.

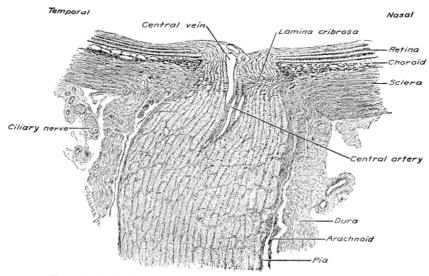

FIG. 22-22. Horizontal section of human optic nerve head

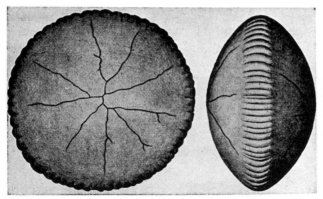

FIG. 22-23. The lens, viewed from behind and from the side. (From Eisler, after Rabl.)

The capsule consists of a basal lamina and reticular lamina ensheathing the lens. It is of varied thickness in different parts of the lens but is always thinnest at the posterior pole. On either surface a zone concentric with the equator serves for the insertion of the zonular fibers of the suspensory ligament (Fig. 22-24).

The anterior epithelium is a single layer of cuboidal cells on the anterior lens surface, just under the capsule (Fig. 22-24). There is no posterior epithelium, these cells having gone to form the primitive lens fibers during embryonic development. At the equator, or margin, the cells are elongated and arranged meridionally in rows (Fig. 22-25). This is the region where new lens fibers are constantly being formed and the cells themselves may be regarded as young lens fibers.

The lens substance consists of elongated prismatic elements, the *lens fibers*, which develop from lens cells. The first lens fibers that form during embryonic development arise by elongation and differentiation of the posterior epithelial cells of the lens and they course in an anteroposterior direction. Succeeding fibers are formed superficially by elongation and differention of epithelial cells at the equator of the lens. Consequently, these fibers are arranged meridionally in concentric layers. The older and deeper fibers lose their nuclei but the epithelial cells of the region of the equator continue to multiply and differentiate into new lens fibers. As a result, the concentric layers of fibers show varying degrees of differentiation. Individual fibers can be identified more readily in the outer part of the lens, known as the *cortex*, than in the inner part, sometimes called the *nucleus* of the lens. In the inner region the fibers are condensed and

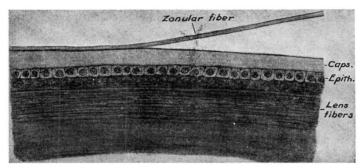

FIG. 22-24. Portion of anterior surface of equatorial zone of the lens, showing attachment of zonular fiber to the capsule. *Caps.*, anterior capsule of lens; *Epith.*, lens epithelium.

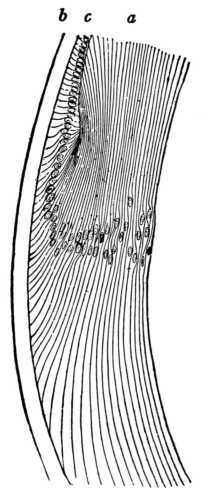

b c   a

FIG. 22-25. From section through margin of lens, showing longitudinal sections of lens fibers and transition from epithelium to lens fibers. *a*, lens fibers; *b*, capsule; *c*, epithelium. (Merkel-Henle.)

appear more homogeneous. The regions of the lens where cortical fibers from opposite sectors converge and make contact are known as lens *sutures.*

Electron micrographs show that the epithelial cells of the equatorial region have numerous interdigitations and occasional desmosomes. The lens fibers also show interdigitations, particularly in the so-called sutures. The intercellular spaces of epithelial cells and of lens fibers are very narrow, being similar in this respect to intercellular spaces of other types of epithelium.

THE ZONULA CILIARIS

The *zonula ciliaris (zonule of Zinn, suspensory ligament)* is a system of delicate collagenous fibers which form a fairly thick band radiating from the equatorial zone of the lens capsule to the inner surface of the ciliary body, thereby fixing the lens in place (Fig. 22-6). Many of the fibers arise from the orbiculus ciliaris and sweep forward over the surface of the ciliary body to the lens capsule. Others come from the corona ciliaris. They arise in the valleys between the ciliary processes (Fig. 22-7) and are closely applied to the sides of the latter as they course radially inward to the lens.

The zonular fibers are inserted on the lens capsule in two main zones—one in front of the equator and the other just behind it. The fibers which insert on the anterior capsule are the thicker ones.

Recalling the arrangement of the smooth muscle fibers of the ciliary muscle and its attachment anteriorly to the scleral spur, it becomes evident that contraction of this muscle will cause the ciliary body and choroid to be pulled forward, while the ciliary processes will at the same time be displaced toward the equator of the lens. The result of both actions will be to relax the tension normally maintained on the zonular fibers. The highly elastic lens capsule, in turn released from this tension, is thus enabled to mould the plastic lens cortex to a more spherical, or convex, form. This constitutes the process of accommodation, by which images of near objects are brought to correct focus on the retina. It should be noted that in a state of rest, the ciliary muscle is relaxed and the zonula ciliaris and lens are under tension.

THE VITREOUS BODY

The vitreous body occupies the space between the lens and the retina. (This space is not the posterior chamber.) In the fresh condition, the vitreous is a transparent firm jelly-like body (actually a form of connective tissue) which is particularly adherent to the retina in the region of the ora serrata and at the optic disc. On its anterior surface is a broad shallow depression, the *patellar fossa*, which accommodates the posterior convexity of the lens. Through its axis, from the optic disc to the patellar fossa, runs the *hyaloid canal*, which marks the site of the fetal hyaloid artery. In electron micrographs, the vitreous appears to have a dispersed collagenous fibrillar structure. The peripheral condensation of the vitreous seen in such sections is like a basement membrane.

THE EYELIDS

The eyelids are essentially movable folds of skin which protect the eye both from injury and from excessive light. Each lid is covered by a thin skin, which on the posterior surface is modified to form a transparent mucous membrane, the *conjunctiva*. This lines the lid as the *palpebral conjunctiva* and is reflected on to the anterior surface of the eye up to the cornea as the *bulbar conjunctiva*. The reflection forms a deep recess known as the *fornix*. The form of the lid is maintained by a tough fibrous *tarsal plate*. In the connective tissue between this and the anterior surface are the palpebral fibers of the *orbicularis oculi muscle*. Associated with the free margin of the lid are the *eyelashes* and certain small glands. The relation of these structures to each other is best seen in a vertical section of the upper lid as shown in Figure 22-26. The following description applies to the upper lid but the lower lid is similar in all main respects.

The skin is very thin. It is provided with many fine downy hairs, with which are associated small sebaceous glands. Numerous small sweat glands and pigment cells are also present. The subcutaneous layer is a loose connective tissue, rich in elastic fibers but containing no fat. It is loosely adherent to the underlying muscle.

The *orbicularis oculi* is a thin oval sheet of skeletal muscle which covers the lids. It is innervated by the facial nerve and its action is to close the eye by bringing the lids together. The muscle bundles are disposed concentrically and are loosely united to the underlying tarsal plate by the submuscular connective tissue. Tendon fibers of the superior levator palpebrae muscle pass through the latter tissue, either to insert on the lower anterior surface of the tarsal plate or to attach to the skin of the lid. This muscle acts to raise the lid.

The *tarsal plate*, or *tarsus*, is a curved plate of dense white fibrous connective tissue with some elastic fibers. Its lower free border extends to the lid margin and its upper border serves for attachment of the involuntary *superior palpebral muscle (muscle of Müller)*. Embedded in the tarsal plate are a number of simple branched alveolar glands, the tarsal or *Meibomian glands*. These sebaceous glands are arranged in a single row with their long axes perpendicular to the lid margin.

Each Meibomian gland consists of a long straight central duct surrounded by numerous alveoli which open into it. The ducts are lined by simple cuboidal epithelium and open on to the lid margin by a series of minute orifices. The fatty secretion of these glands lubricates the edges of the lids, preventing them from sticking together and also helping to form a water-tight seal when the lids are closed.

In the lid margin are the eyelashes, arranged in two or three irregular rows. They are short heavy curved hairs. Their follicles extend obliquely up to the tarsal plate and show the structure typical of hair follicles elsewhere in the body, with the exception that they lack erector muscles. The large sebaceous glands associated with them are known as the *glands of Zeis*. Between the follicles are large spiral sweat glands, the *glands of Moll*.

The conjunctiva consists of an epithelium and a connective tissue substantia propria.

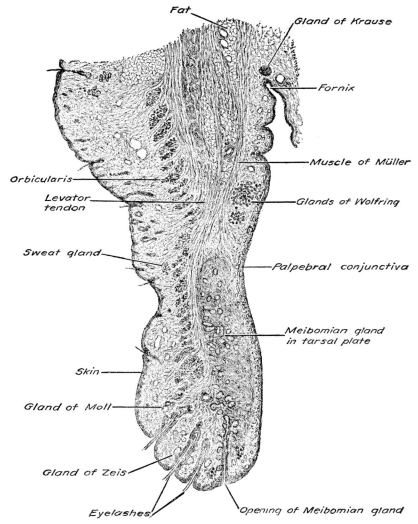

Fat

Gland of Krause

Fornix

Orbicularis

Levator tendon

Muscle of Müller

Glands of Wolfring

Sweat gland

Palpebral conjunctiva

Meibomian gland in tarsal plate

Skin

Gland of Moll

Gland of Zeis

Eyelashes

Opening of Meibomian gland

FIG. 22-26. Vertical section through human upper lid

At the lid margin, the epithelium has the stratified squamous character of the epidermis with which it is continuous. Over the tarsal plates (palpebral conjunctiva), it becomes reduced to two layers of cells; the surface cells are tall columnar and the deeper ones, low cuboidal. In the region of the fornix a third layer of cells appears. Toward the limbus, the epithelium of the bulbar conjunctiva gradually increases in thickness, the superficial cells becoming flatter and the deep cells more cuboidal. At the limbus it is again stratified squamous. Throughout the conjunctiva, but particularly in the fornix and bulbar region, goblet cells occur in the epithelium.

The substantia propria consists of a thin layer of fine connective tissue fibers in which a profuse infiltration of lymphocytes occurs. This is especially marked in the region between the upper border of the tarsal plate and the fornix. Over the tarsal plate, the substantia propria firmly ties down the epithelium; elsewhere, it merges with the richly elastic subconjunctival connective tissue.

In the subconjunctival tissue above the upper border of the tarsal plate are several small tubulo-alveolar glands, the *glands of Wolfring*. Their ducts open on the surface of the conjunctiva.

The *glands of Krause* are small accessory lacrimal glands which lie in the loose connective tissue beneath the fornix conjunctivae. Their ducts open into the margin of the fornix.

THE LACRIMAL GLANDS

The lacrimal gland lies in the superior temporal region of the orbit, just within the orbital margin. It is divided into a *superior* and an *inferior lobe,* which are continuous around the lateral horn of the aponeurosis of the levator muscle. It secretes the tears, which empty into the conjunctival sac through 10 or 12 ducts opening just in front of the superior fornix.

The lacrimal is a compound tubulo-alveolar gland of serous type. It bears considerable resemblance to the parotid gland, differing slightly in that the secretory cells of its terminal alveoli are more columnar in form. Between them and their basal lamina, there are numerous myoepithelial cells, (see Chapter 16, Fig. 16-55). The smaller excretory ducts are lined by a single layer of cuboidal cells; the larger ducts have a double-layered epithelium.

The stroma consists of loose connective tissue which blends peripherally with the surrounding structures. In the adult, considerable lymphatic tissue occurs in the stroma.

THE EAR

The organ commonly called the ear contains a series of receptors specialized not only for hearing but also for the perception of the position of the head and for head movement. The fact that the receptors for these seemingly diverse functions are housed within the same organ is less surprising when it is realized that each employs the same basic cytological mechanism—an epithelial cell surmounted by a group of projections called cell hairs. When these hairs are bent the hair-carrying cell signals nerve fibers contacting its base, and these convey signals to the brain. The simple hair cell may accomplish these diverse functions by three remarkable adaptations: (1) certain of the cells have minute weights positioned near the end of their projecting hairs; *gravity or linear movement* will variously bend these hairs and provide the basis for a series of nerve signals to the brain; (2) certain of the hair cells are surmounted by a gelatinous keel which is displaced by fluid flowing through a narrow channel; by placing such a device in each of three body planes the amount and direction of any *angular movement* of the head can be signaled by the subjacent nerve endings; (3) certain hair cells are mounted between two flexible membranes so that sound waves will cause their hairs to bend as one membrane vibrates; the signals sent to the brain from the nerve endings on these cells form the basis for *hearing*.

The special apparatus for each of these types of reception is mounted within fluid-filled spaces deep within the temporal bone (which forms part of the base of the skull). The complex of interconnecting channels containing these receptors is called the *inner ear*. The receptors for position and motion need no access to the external environment. But the mechanism for hearing requires a chamber in which sound waves in the air are converted into vibrations within the fluid spaces of the inner ear; this conversion chamber is called the *middle ear*. In addition a channel is required for the passage of sound waves from the external environment to the middle ear; this passageway is part of the *external ear*.

The whole of the external ear consists of the auricle, or pinna, and the external auditory meatus, a canal which leads into the temporal bone and ends at the *tympanic membrane* (the eardrum) (Fig. 22-27). The

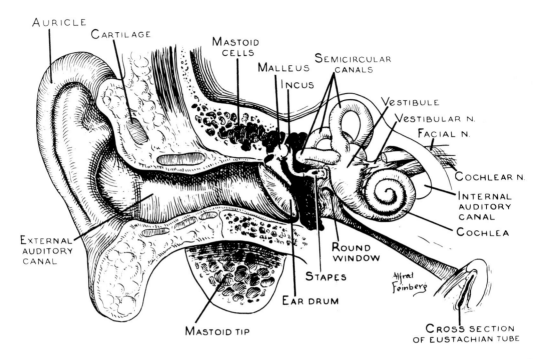

Fig. 22-27. Diagram of the external ear (extending from the auricle to the eardrum), the middle ear (containing the malleus, incus and stapes and communicating with the pharynx via the Eustachian tube) and the inner ear (formed by the three semicircular canals, the vestibule and the cochlea). The nerve signals arising from the inner ear travel to the brain via the cochlear and vestibular divisions of the eighth cranial nerve. (From Davis, H., editor 1947 Hearing and Deafness: A Guide for Laymen. Holt, Rinehart and Winston, Inc., New York.)

latter forms the lateral wall of the *tympanic cavity*, which, with the *auditory (Eustachian) tube*, comprises the middle ear. The tympanic cavity lies within the temporal bone and contains the chain of auditory ossicles, or ear bones, with which are associated two small muscles. The complex arrangement of fluid-filled membranous chambers and canals which forms the inner ear is called the *membranous labyrinth;* the membranous labyrinth lies within a similarly shaped shell of especially hard bone—the *osseous labyrinth*. The internal ear is related to the middle ear by means of two small apertures in the medial wall of the middle ear. One of these, the *oval window*, houses the base of the stapes, the smallest of the auditory ossicles. The other, the *round window*, is closed by a membrane, the *secondary tympanic mem-*

brane. Within the membranous labyrinth are the localized areas of neuroepithelium which comprise the sensory mechanisms discussed above. These areas are supplied by the 8th cranial nerve, variously termed the *statoacoustic*, and *vestibulocochlear* or simply (but less precisely) the *acoustic nerve*.

THE EXTERNAL EAR

The part of the ear we see, the *auricle* or *pinna*, consists of an irregularly shaped plate of elastic cartilage covered by connective tissue and skin. The cartilage is richly cellular; its perichondrium contains many elastic fibers. The skin covering the auricle is typical thin skin containing hairs and numerous large sebaceous glands. On its posterior surface, sweat glands also occur. The cartilage does not extend into the *lobule,* which is composed of connective tissue and fat.

The ear canal, or *external auditory meatus,* is a slightly S-shaped channel leading from the auricle to the middle ear and separated from the latter by the tympanic membrane. In the outer portion, its wall is formed by elastic cartilage, continuous with that of the auricle. The wall of the inner portion is formed by the temporal bone. In both parts, the wall of the meatus is lined by skin which is continuous with the skin of the auricle.

In the cartilaginous portion of the meatus, the skin is thicker and contains large stiff hairs, which guard against the entrance of foreign objects. Associated with them are large sebaceous glands. Another type of gland, the *ceruminous gland,* is peculiar to the skin of the meatus. These are simple coiled tubular glands which open upon the surface of the skin by long narrow ducts. The secretion of these glands, plus that of the sebaceous glands and desquamated epithelial cells, constitutes the ear wax, or *cerumen.* In the bony portion of the meatus, the skin is thinner and adheres closely to the periosteum. The hairs are small and fine and, together with the sebaceous glands, are found only along the superior wall of the canal.

THE MIDDLE EAR

The middle ear (Figs. 22-27 and 22-28) consists of an air-filled space called the *tympanic cavity.* This space is ventilated by means of the *auditory (Eustachian) tube* which leads from the front of the middle ear cavity to the pharynx. The tympanic cavity is a small narrow laterally compressed chamber lying within the temporal bone. It comprises the middle ear proper, or *atrium,* which is the part of the cavity medial to the tympanic membrane, and the *epitympanic recess,* or *attic,* which lies above the level of the tympanic membrane. Posteriorly, the tympanic cavity communicates, through the *tympanic antrum,* with the *mastoid cells,* which are air-filled cavities in the mastoid process of the temporal bone.

The lateral wall of the middle ear cavity is

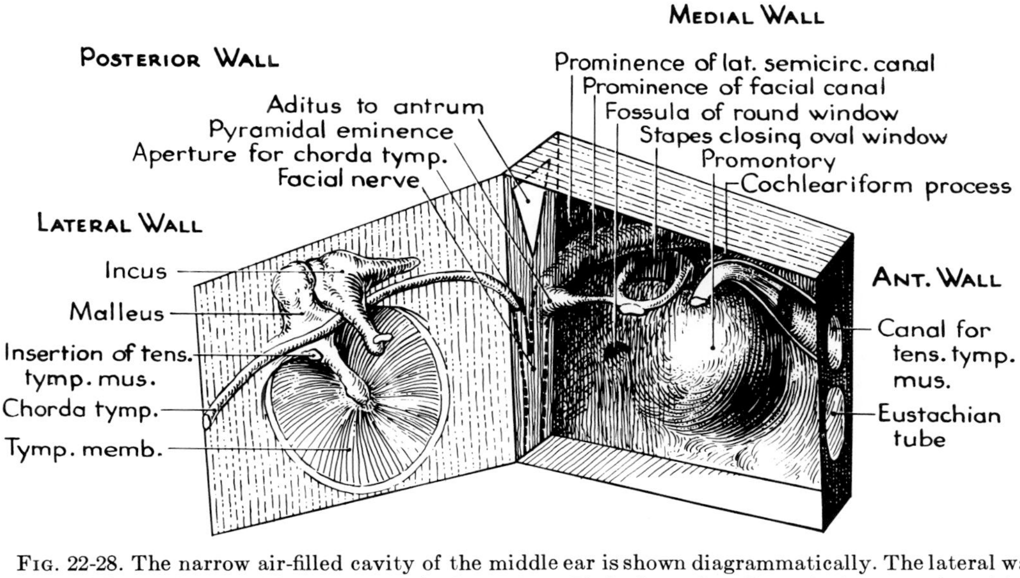

FIG. 22-28. The narrow air-filled cavity of the middle ear is shown diagrammatically. The lateral wall of the middle ear is turned back to show its inner face. If the lateral wall was in its normal position, the tensor tympani muscle would attach to the middle part of the malleus and the incus would articulate with the stapes. (From Boies, L. 1964 Fundamentals of Otolaryngology, ed. 4. W. B. Saunders Co., Philadelphia.)

formed almost entirely by the *tympanic membrane*. The periphery of the membrane is fixed firmly by fibrocartilage in a groove (the *tympanic sulcus*) in the surrounding bony ring. Superiorly, however, the bony ring is notched, so that a small area of the membrane remains lax. This is the *pars flaccida;* the remaining and greater part of the membrane is the *pars tensa*.

The bony inner wall of the middle ear cavity bears a rounded eminence, the *promontory*, which marks the position of the first, or basal, coil of the cochlea. Somewhat above and behind this is an oval aperture, the *oval window* (*fenestra vestibuli*), into which fits the base of the stapes. Behind and below the promontory is a funnel-shaped recess which leads to a second aperture in the bone, *the round window* (*fenestra cochleae*). This is closed by the thin *secondary tympanic membrane*.

Extending across the tympanic cavity is a chain of three small bones, the *auditory ossicles* (Fig. 22-28). These, from without inward, are the *malleus* (hammer), the *incus* (anvil) and the *stapes* (stirrup). The *manubrium* (handle) of the malleus is firmly attached to the tympanic membrane. The head of the malleus lies in the epitympanic recess, where it articulates with the head of the incus. The long process of the latter bends sharply near its end to articulate with the head of the stapes. The base of the stapes is firmly fixed to the border of the oval window by a ring of elastic fibers.

Associated with the auditory ossicles are several ligaments and two small muscles, the *tensor tympani* and *stapedius* muscles.

Lining the tympanic cavity, and investing all the structures contained within, is a mucous membrane, the *tympanic mucosa* (Fig. 22-28). This consists of a thin connective tissue tunica propria covered in part by simple squamous epithelium and in part by pseudostratified epithelium which is composed of ciliated columnar cells interspersed with secretory cells. The secretory portion of this epithelium is thought to be the source

of fluid in middle ear infections; the ciliated cells may play a part in removal of this fluid. This mucosa forms the linings of the tympanic antrum and the air filled spaces of the mastoid bone and covers the inner surface of the tympanic membrane.

The tympanic membrane. This is a thin, rather rigid, semitransparent structure in which three layers can be distinguished. The outer *cutaneous layer* is composed of very thin skin in which the epithelium is reduced to a stratum germinativum one or two cells thick, over which is a thin loose stratum corneum. The inner *mucous layer* of the tympanic membrane is composed of the tympanic mucosa. Here it is very thin and consists of a single layer of flat squamous epithelium on a sparse tunica propria. Between the two surface membranes is the *substantia propria*, which forms the main mass of the tympanic membrane. It consists of two layers of tendon-like collagenous fiber bundles. The fibers of the outer layer are disposed in a radial manner from the manubrium of the malleus outward to the fibrocartilaginous ring. The inner fibers course in a circular direction and are most numerous near the periphery. Both layers are lacking in the pars flaccida.

The auditory ossicles. The malleus, the incus and the stapes are composed of compact bone arranged in lamellae with scattered Haversian systems. Over their articular surfaces, they are covered by hyaline cartilage, which also occurs in patches on the base of the stapes and the manubrium of the malleus. The stapes alone contains a marrow cavity. The periosteum which covers the auditory ossicles is fused with the tunica propria of the overlying tympanic mucosa.

The muscles. The tensor tympani and the stapedius muscles consist of striated skeletal muscle fibers. The tensor tympani lies in a canal just above the auditory tube. It ends in a tendon which is inserted into the upper end of the malleus. When this muscle contracts, it draws the malleus inward and thus tenses the tympanic membrane.

The stapedius muscle lies within a small conical bony projection, the *pyramidal eminence*, on the posterior wall of the tympanic cavity. Its tendon passes through a minute aperture in the summit of the eminence and is inserted into the stapes.

Action of middle ear structures. The middle ear serves the important function of amplifying the weak forces of the sound waves that move the eardrum to provide larger force vibrations at the foot plate of the stapes in the oval window. This amplification can be accomplished even though no energy is added to the system in the middle ear because the eardrum is about 18 times as large as the opening in the oval window. This area difference means that the movements transmitted through the ossicle chain have enough force to move the stapes against the fluid of the inner ear. Thus the eardrum and the membrane covering the oval window move together, their impedance (the amount of resistance to movement) being well-matched.

In addition to allowing for this impedance matching, the middle ear provides (through its muscular components) an opportunity to adjust the responsiveness of the ossicle chain. It was previously thought that the primary function of the contraction of the tensor tympani and stapedius muscles was to dampen ossicle movement and thus to protect the delicate inner ear structures from excessive vibrations caused by very loud noises. Their contraction is now also thought to (a) play an important role in setting the degree of tension in the tympanic membrane so that transmission of sounds of moderate intensity through the middle ear is facilitated, (b) to improve hearing in a noisy environment and (c) to prevent us from hearing our own voices too loudly.

The auditory (Eustachian) tube. This is a flattened canal leading from the anterior wall of the tympanic cavity to the nasopharynx. In its upper extent, near the middle ear, it is surrounded by a bony wall. Below this osseous part, the wall is formed partly by a cartilaginous plate and partly by a fibrous membrane.

In cross section, the cartilage appears shaped like a hook, and forms the wall of the posterior surface, the upper margin and the superior portion of the anterior surface of the canal. The remainder of the wall is formed by the fibrous membrane. At its upper end, the cartilage is of the hyaline variety. In its lower portion, patches of elastic cartilage occur in the hyaline matrix.

The mucosa which lines the auditory tube consists of a connective tissue tunica propria covered by ciliated columnar epithelium. In the bony part, the mucosa is thin and firmly united to the underlying bony wall. The epithelium is a low ciliated columnar type. In the cartilaginous part of the tube, the mucosa is loose and the epithelium is of the pseudostratified ciliated variety. Goblet cells occur near the pharyngeal opening, as well as tubulo-acinar mucous glands.

The auditory tube serves as a means of ventilating the middle ear. Normally collapsed, the tube is opened during the acts of chewing and swallowing to allow pressure equilibration between the throat and the middle ear. Unfortunately it also serves as a route for the spread of infection between these two regions.

THE INTERNAL EAR

The internal ear is contained in the petrous part of the temporal bone and consists of an interconnected series of bony walled chambers and passages containing a similarly shaped series of membranous sacs and canals (Figs. 22-27 and 22-32). These are known as the *osseous labyrinth* and the *membranous labyrinth*, respectively. Intervening between the two is a space, the *perilymphatic space*, which contains the fluid *perilymph*. Within the membranous labyrinth there is also a fluid, the *endolymph*.

The osseous labyrinth. Although the osseous labyrinth does not occur as a separate entity, nevertheless the bone of its walls is of a harder texture than that surrounding it and with care the latter can be dissected away and the form of the osseous labyrinth revealed. Seen thus, it consists of an ovoid central chamber, the *vestibule*, from which are given off three *semicircular canals* and the *cochlea*. The vestibule is separated from the middle ear by a plate of bone which contains two openings—the oval window and the round window. A narrow canal extending from it to the posterior surface of the petrous part of the temporal bone is known as the *vestibular aqueduct*. The three semicircular canals are so arranged that their respective planes lie perpendicular to each other. Thus there are two vertical canals and one horizontal canal. The vertical ones comprise the *anterior* and the *posterior* canals; the horizontal canal is known as the *lateral*, or external, canal. The lateral canals of the two sides of the head lie in the same horizontal plane. The vertical canals are so oriented with respect to the sagittal plane of the head that the plane of the superior canal of one side is approximately parallel to the plane of the posterior canal of the opposite side. Just after leaving the vestibule, each canal presents a dilation, the *ampulla*.

Anteriorly, the vestibule opens into the bony cochlea, a conical structure consisting of an osseous axis around which winds a spiral canal. In man, the apex of the cochlea is directed forward, outward and downward.

The walls of the osseous labyrinth are composed of compact bone; the surface facing the perilymph has a periosteum covered by mesenchymal epithelium.

The membranous labyrinth. This consists of a connected series of sacs and canals whose walls are formed of a fibrous connective tissue lined internally by simple squamous epithelium of ectodermal origin. In general, the membranous labyrinth has the same form as the osseous labyrinth in which it is contained. However, that part enclosed within the osseous vestibule is divided into two sacs (compare Figs. 22-27 and 22-29). The larger of these, the *utricle*, is an elliptical sac lying in the upper posterior part of the vestibule. From it are given off the membranous semicircular canals. In front of the utricle is the smaller spherical *saccule*, from the lower part of which a short and narrow canal, the *ductus reuniens*, connects with the membranous cochlea, or *cochlear duct*. The utricle and the saccule are connected by the *utriculosaccular duct*, the two parts of which converge and continue backward through the

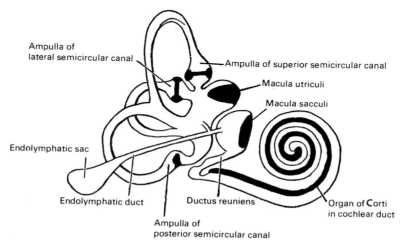

FIG. 22-29. This outline of cavities of the left membranous labyrinth viwed from the medial aspect shows the receptor regions of the neuroepithelium sketched in black. (Redrawn from Schaffer.)

vestibular aqueduct as the slender *endo-lymphatic duct.* Under the dura of the posterior surface of the temporal bone, this duct terminates in a blind enlargement, the *endolymphatic sac* (Fig. 22-29).

The membranous labyrinth only partially fills the space within the osseous labyrinth. At places, it lies close to the periosteum of the osseous wall, with which its connective tissue layer then blends. For the most part, however, it lies suspended in the perilymph by a number of connective tissue trabeculae which pass from the periosteum to the membranous wall (Fig. 22-32).

Except for the special neuroepithelial areas, the wall of the membranous labyrinth consists of an outer thin tunica propria and an inner lining epithelium composed of flat squamous cells resting on a basement membrane.

In certain definite regions, the wall of the membranous labyrinth is considerably modified to form the true sensory areas. In these areas, the epithelium takes on a special complexity and among its cells the fibers of the vestibulocochlear (8th cranial) nerve terminate. There are six such neuroepithelial areas in each labyrinth: one in each macula, the *macula utriculi* and the *macula sacculi;* one in each ampulla, the *cristae ampullares;* and one in the cochlear duct, the *organ of*

Corti (Fig. 22-29). The maculae and cristae ampullares (concerned with position and motion sense) are within the vestibule of the osseous labyrinth and are supplied by the vestibular portion of the 8th nerve; the organ of Corti (concerned with hearing) is located in the cochlea and is supplied by the cochlear division of the 8th nerve.

The maculae. The maculae represent local thickenings of the membranous walls, each covering an area about 3 mm by 2 mm in extent and forming an elevation into the endolymphatic space. The epithelium here is of the columnar type, in which two kinds of cells may be distinguished—the *sustentacular* or *supporting cells* and the *hair cells*.

The sustentacular cells are tall columnar elements resting on the basement membrane. Their basal portions, containing the oval granular nuclei, are broader than their upper portions, which pass between the hair cells. The free surface of each sustentacular cell bears a cuticular plate (Fig. 22-31). At the edge of the macula, the sustentacular cells show a gradual transition into the simple squamous epithelium characteristic of the remainder of the membranous labyrinth.

The hair cells occupy the outer part of the epithelium. Two types of hair cells have been described (Fig. 22-31). The first type is

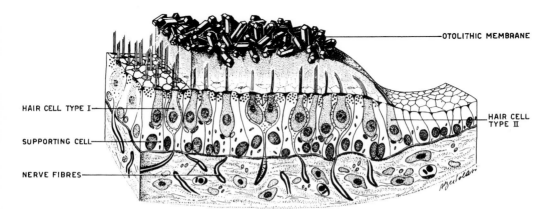

FIG. 22-30. Schematic drawing of the macula, as found either in the saccule or in the utricle of the vestibule. (From Iurato, S. 1967 Submicroscopic Structure of the Inner Ear, p. 18. Pergamon Press, New York.)

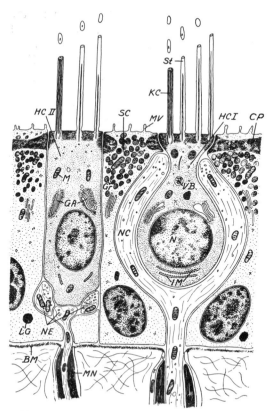

FIG. 22-31. This schematic drawing represents a section through the specialized sensory epithelium found in the maculae of the saccule and utricle and in the crista ampullaris of each semicircular canal. *HC I*, hair cell of type I; *HC II*, hair cell of type II; *SC*, supporting cell; *St*, stereocilia; *KC*, kinocilia; *N*, nucleus; *GA*, Golgi apparatus; *IM*, intracellular membranes; *VB*, multivesicular body; *NC*, nerve calyx; *CP*, cuticular plate; *M*, mitochondrion; *NE*, nerve endings; *BM*, basement membrane; *MN*, myelinated nerve fiber; *LG*, lipid granule; *MV*, microvilli. (From J. Wersall 1956 Acta Otolaryng. (Stockholm) (Suppl.), vol. 126, p. 1.)

a flask-shaped cell embraced over its entire inferior aspect by a single large nerve terminal. The second is a cylindrical cell contacted by a series of nerve endings only near its base. Some of these nerve endings are thought to receive signals from the hair cell while others deliver signals from the brain to the hair cell. Both these afferent and efferent nerve fibers are derived from the

vestibular portion of the 8th cranial nerve. The nerve fibers are myelinated as they pass through the osseous labyrinth. They lose their myelin in the tunica propria of the macula, and then pass through the basement membrane as naked axons prior to contacting the hair cells.

The free surface of each hair cell is covered by a cuticular plate, from which arises a long tapering process composed of a bundle of nonmotile projections (called stereocilia) and one conventional cilium (a kinocilium). These so-called hairs of the hair cells extend outward from the epithelium for 20 to 25 μ to penetrate a peculiar membrane which covers the surface of the macula.

This membrane, the *otolithic membrane*, consists of a gelatinous substance containing a great number of small bodies—the *otoconia* or *otoliths* (Fig. 22-30). The otoconia are minute crystals composed chiefly of calcium carbonate.

The hair cells are thought to alter their resting potential when their hairs are bent by the action of linear movement or of gravity on the overlying otolithic membrane. By an unknown mechanism this causes the generation of an action potential in the underlying nerve endings. It is not difficult to understand how this cytological mechanism provides the brain with information both on the position of the head in space and on linear head movements.

The semicircular canals. Each semicircular canal forms an arc which is slightly more than a semicircle. It does not occupy the center of the osseous canal but lies against the periosteum of the outer, or convex, border to which it is attached (Fig. 22-32). Connective tissue trabeculae from the wall of the osseous canal also serve to anchor it in the perilymphatic space.

The histological structure of the canals does not vary essentially from that described for the remainder of the membranous labyrinth. Certain special features are present, however, in the structure of the cristae

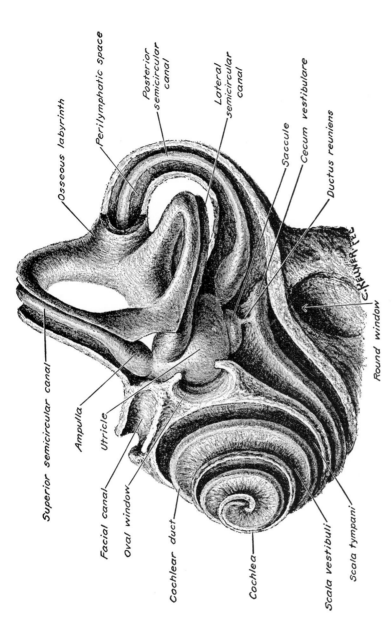

Superior semicircular canal

Osseous labyrinth

Perilymphatic space

Posterior semicircular canal

Lateral semicircular canal

Saccule

Cecum vestibulare

Ductus reuniens

Ampulla

Facial canal

Oval window

Cochlear duct

Cochlea

Scala vestibuli

Scala tympani

Utricle

Round window

C.REUVERPEC

FIG. 22-32. The membranous labyrinth (in yellow) is shown within the channels of the bony labyrinth. Perilymph fills the spaces around the membranous labyrinth; endolymph is within the cavities of the membranous labyrinth. Compare with Figure 22-29. (Based on a model by Tramond but considerably modified.)

ampullares, the sensory areas which are found in each ampulla.

In each crista ampullaris, the membranous wall is thickened to form a ridge, placed transversely to the long axis of the canal. This ridge consists of the connective tissue tunica propria, containing many nerve fibers and blood vessels and surmounted by a specialized columnar epithelium.

As in the maculae, the epithelium consists of two types of cells—the *sustentacular cells* and the *hair cells*. They are remarkably similar to those described above in the maculae.

In fixed preparations, the epithelium of the crista ampullaris is seen to be surmounted by a tall, rounded, longitudinally striated mass, the *cupula* (Fig. 22-33). This is a gelatinous structure which is separated from the epithelium by a narrow space containing endolymph. The long tapering hairs of the hair cells pass through this space and penetrate for some distance into the cupula, each hair occupying a narrow canal filled with endolymph. The hairs in the middle of the crista stand perpendicular to its surface. Those toward the border tend to be inclined in the direction of the median plane of the cupula.

Fibers of the vestibular nerve terminate in the epithelium of the crista in much the same manner as they do in the maculae. The naked axis cylinders pierce the basement membrane and form contacts around each of the two types of hair cells similar to those in the maculae.

Because the cupula has a flexible attachment to the crista ampullaris, it can be swayed by the flow of endolymph within the semicircular canals. A change in the speed of rotation of the head will cause a deflection of the cupula in two or more of the semicircular canals resulting in movement of the hairs embedded in its base. The underlying nerve endings are then signaled and the brain thus receives information regarding the speed and direction of rotation of the head.

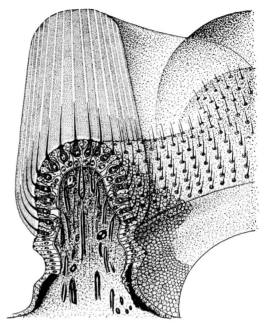

FIG. 22-33. Schematic drawing of one-half of a crista ampullaris, showing innervation of its epithelium. Thick nerve fibers form nerve calyces around type I hair cells at the summit of the crista, medium caliber fibers innervate type I hair cells on the slope of the crista, and medium caliber and fine nerve fibers form a nerve plexus which innervates hair cells of type II. The gelatinous mass surmounting the hair cells is the cupula, which is pushed to and fro by the flow of the endolymph in the semicircular canal. (From J. Wersall 1956 Acta Otolaryng. (Stockholm) (Suppl.), vol. 126, p. 1.)

The cochlea. The osseous cochlea consists of a conical axis of spongy bone, the *modiolus*, around which winds a spiral bony canal. This canal in man makes about two and one-half turns and ends at the rounded tip of the cochlea, which is known as the *cupula*. The base of the modiolus forms the bottom of the internal auditory meatus, through which the fibers of the cochlear nerve pass and enter the modiolus (Fig. 22-34). These fibers are processes of the bipolar ganglion cells of the spiral ganglion, which is lodged in the *spiral canal of the modiolus* (Fig. 22-35).

Projecting from the modiolus partly across

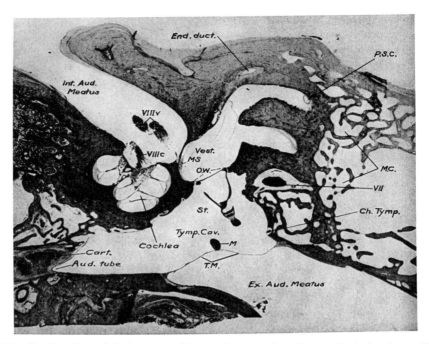

FIG. 22-34. Section through left temporal bone of a man (age 17 years). *Aud. tube*, auditory (Eustachian) tube; *Cart.*, cartilage of auditory tube; *Ch. tymp.*, chorda tympani nerve; *End. duct*, endolymphatic duct; *Ext. Aud. Meatus*, external auditory meatus; *Int. Aud. Meatus*, internal auditory meatus; *M*, manubrium of malleus; *M.C.*, mastoid air cells; *M.S.*, macula sacculi; *O.W.*, oval window; *St.*, stapes; *T.M.*, tympanic membrane; *Tymp. cav*,. tympanic cavity; *Vest.*, vestibule; *VII*, seventh cranial (facial) nerve; *VIIIc*, cochlear division of eighth cranial (auditory) nerve; *VIIIv*, vestibular division of eighth cranial nerve. (Photomicrograph of a section from the collection of Dr. E. P. Fowler, Jr.)

the osseous canal of the cochlea is a shelf of bone, the *osseous spiral lamina*, which follows the spiral turns of the cochlea and ends at the cupula. Along the outer wall of the canal, opposite the osseous spiral lamina, is a projection of thickened periosteum, the *spiral ligament*. A connective tissue membrane, the *membranous spiral lamina*, bridges the space intervening between the spiral ligament and the osseous spiral lamina. Thus the osseous canal of the cochlea is divided into two spirally parallel parts, an upper *scala vestibuli* and a lower *scala tympani*.*

From the thickened periosteum covering

* The terms "upper" and "lower" are here used arbitrarily as if the cochlea were oriented with its base downward and its apex upward. "Inner" and "outer" are used to designate directions with respect to the axis of the cochlea, the modiolus.

the upper surface of the osseous spiral lamina, there arises a thin membrane, the *vestibular membrane* (membrane of Reissner), which extends obliquely outward to the upper part of the spiral ligament. This membrane thus forms the roof of a canal, triangular in cross section and lying between the two scalae. This is the *cochlear duct*, or *scala media*. It is the cochlear extension of the channels of the membranous labyrinth.

The scalae (Fig. 22-36). The scala vestibuli arises in the vestibule and is in close relation to the oval window (fenestra vestibuli). It follows the spiral course of the osseous canal to its apex, where it communicates with the scala tympani through a small canal, the *helicotrema*. The scala tympani follows a course parallel to the scala vestibuli and ends at the round window (fenestra cochleae), which is closed by the secondary tympanic membrane. This is a thin but strong fibrous membrane, covered on its outer surface by the tympanic mucosa and on its inner surface by the lining epithelium of the scala tympani. Interposed between the scala vestibuli and scala tympani is the scala media or cochlear duct described below.

With the exception of the area covered by the spiral ligament, the bony walls of the scalae are lined by a thin periosteal connective tissue covered with mesenchymal epithelium.

The cochlear duct. This is a narrow tube in which the organ of hearing is located (Fig. 22-29). At the apex of the cochlea, its closed end is known as the *cecum cupulare*. The cochlear duct is triangular in transverse section, thus allowing a division of its walls into upper, outer and lower (Fig. 22-36).

The upper or vestibular wall is formed by the vestibular (Reissner's) membrane. This consists of a thin central lamina of connective tissue covered on either side by simple squamous epithelium. That on the upper surface is continuous with the mesenchymal epithelium of the scala vestibuli; on the lower surface, the epithelium is continuous with that of the cochlear duct and is of ectodermal origin.

The outer wall of the cochlear duct is formed by the *spiral ligament*, a thickening of the periosteum which appears triangular in cross section (Figs. 22-35 and 22-36). The outer part of the spiral ligament, nearer the osseous wall, consists of dense fibrous tissue. In its inner part, the connective tissue is more loosely arranged. The crest of the spiral ligament forms the *crista basilaris*, which serves for the attachment of the membranous spiral lamina. It contains dense converging fibers and relatively few cells.

Part of the spiral ligament lying between the crista basilis and the vestibular membrane is the *stria vascularis*. The epithelium of this region is relatively thick and is pseudostratified. The subepithelial connec-

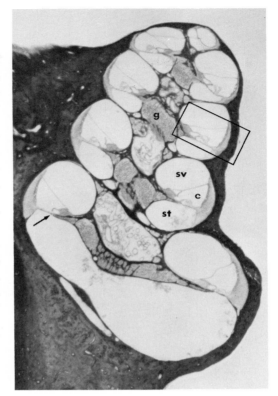

FIG. 22-35. Axial section through the cochlea of a guinea pig. In the spaces of the bony core are the ganglia (*g*), which contain sensory neurons supplying the hair cells of the organ of Corti. The cochlear duct (*c*), scala tympani (*st*) and scala vestibuli (*sv*) are marked in one turn of the cochlea. The area outlined in black is the region depicted in Figure 22-36. In this guinea pig, a portion of the hair cells in the basal turn was damaged before death by exposure to excessive sound. In this region, the hair cells are absent (*arrow*). Note the increasing length of the basilar membrane toward the apex of the cochlea. (Courtesy of Dr. W. Marovitz.)

tive tissue is richly supplied with capillaries which send loops into the epithelium, giving the unusual appearance of a vascular epithelium.

The stria vascularis is thought to be active in the production of the endolymph contained within the scala media, and in the regulation of its ion content. The regulation of ion content is of especial interest because the endolymph, unlike extracellular fluids

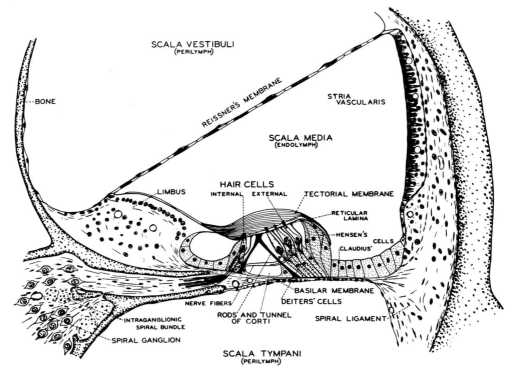

FIG. 22-36. This schematic diagram illustrates the membranous labyrinth as it is considerably modified in the region of the scala media. The drawing was prepared from a section through the lower part of the second turn of the guinea pig cochlea and illustrates the tectorial membrane in its normal position. (From Davis, H., et al. 1953 J. Acoust. Soc. Amer., vol. 25, p. 1180.)

in any other part of the body (and unlike perilymph), has a high potassium (144 meq/l) and a low sodium (15 meq/l) content. It thus resembles intracellular fluid. Reabsorption of endolymph may also take place in the stria vascularis (and perhaps also in the endolymphatic sac).

The lower or tympanic wall of the cochlear duct has an extremely complex structure. It is formed by the outer part of the osseous spiral lamina and the whole of the membranous spiral lamina, together with certain special modifications of their epithelial and connective tissue layers.

On the outer border of the osseous spiral lamina, a thickening of periosteal connective tissue forms an elevation known as the *limbus spiralis* (Figs. 22-35 and 22-36). Peripherally, the limbus terminates in an

upper and a lower projection, known respectively as the *vestibular lip* and the *tympanic lip*. They partially enclose a groove, the *internal spiral sulcus*. The connective tissue of the limbus is firm and unusually cellular.

The vestibular membrane attaches to the upper surface of the limbus. Lateral to this point of attachment, the limbus is covered by columnar epithelium, whose surface bears a cuticular formation which is continued into the *tectorial membrane* (Figs. 22-35 and 22-36).

The tympanic lip projects slightly farther outward than the vestibular lip. Its upper surface forms the floor of the internal spiral sulcus and is lined by a single layer of clear flat cuboidal cells, which continue to the vestibular lip as the lining of the sulcus. The lower surface of the tympanic lip is covered by a thin layer of epithelium continuous with that lining the scala tympani.

Continued directly from the tympanic lip is the *basilar membrane*, which extends outward to the crista basilaris of the spiral ligament. The basilar membrane consists of fine straight unbranched fibers, the *basilar fibers* or *auditory strings*, embedded in a sparse homogeneous ground substance.

The breadth of the basilar membrane varies in the different turns of the cochlea. It is greatest at the apex, gradually diminishing toward the base until its narrowest extent is reached in the proximal end of the basal coil.

Cells of the organ of Corti. On the upper surface of the basilar membrane, an arrangement of epithelial cells forms a complex structure which is the sensory part of the organ of hearing. This structure is the spirally disposed *organ of Corti*—the cochlear receptor. The cochlear receptor has three principal components: (1) a framework which supports the receptive hair cells and provides a mechanism for the transformation of acoustic energy into the proper stimulus for the hair cells, (2) the receptor cells themselves, the hair cells, which serve as the transducer of mechanical into electric energy and (3) the nerve endings which receive signals from the hair cells and provide signals to them.

The organ of Corti extends the entire length of the cochlear duct with the exception of a short distance at either end. The specialized cells which provide the components listed above are as follows (Figs. 22-37 and 22-38):

1. The border cells.
2. The inner hair cells.
3. The inner phalangeal cells.
4. The inner and outer pillar cells.
5. The outer phalangeal cells (cells of Deiters).
6. The outer hair cells.
7. The cells of Hensen.

The last named are continuous with the cells of Claudius, which extend over the remainder of the basilar membrane to the spiral ligament. All except the hair cells may be considered as sustentacular or supporting cells. The hair cells are intimately related to the endings of the cochlear division of the vestibulocochlear nerve.

The *border cells* are slender columnar elements which rest on the tympanic lip and form a single row along the inner side of the inner hair cells. Their surfaces are provided with a cuticle.

The *inner hair cells* are larger than the outer hair cells, being broader and slightly longer. They form a single row occupying only the upper part of the epithelial layer. The rounded base of each cell rests on the adjacent supporting cells. The cytoplasm is finely granular. The surface of the cell bears a cuticular plate and a number of stiff hairs which are in contact with the tectorial membrane. These are described below under outer hair cells.

The *inner phalangeal cells* are arranged in a row along the inner surface of the inner pillar cells. Their bases rest on the basilar membrane. The nucleus lies in the lower portion of the cell, which is continued as a slender process to the surface. Here it ends in a small cuticular plate. When viewed from above, this cuticular plate has a shape not unlike that of the phalanges, the finger bones.

The *inner and outer pillar cells* each consist of a broad curved protoplasmic base which contains the nucleus, and an elongated body or pillar which contains a stout bundle of closely packed microtubules. The thickened end of the pillar away from the base is known as the head and its free surface is covered by a cuticular plate to which the microtubules are attached. The head of the outer pillar presents a convexity on its inner side, which fits into a corresponding concavity on the head of the inner pillar, the heads of opposite pillars thus "articulating" with each other. From their articulation, the pillars diverge, so that their bases, which rest on the basilar membrane, are widely separated. There are

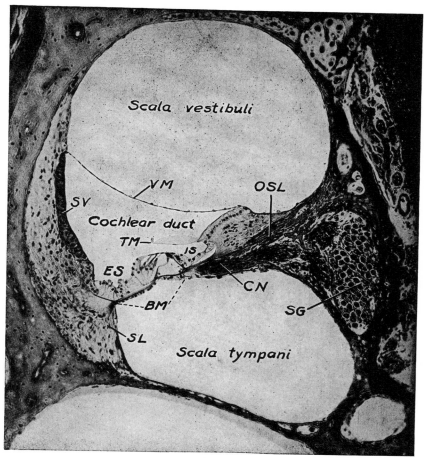

FIG. 22-37. Photomicrograph of a radial section through basal turn of cochlea of the guinea pig. *BM*, basilar membrane; *CN*, cochlear nerve; *ES*, external spiral sulcus; *IS*, internal spiral sulcus; *OSL*, osseous spiral lamina; *SG*, spiral ganglion; *SL*, spiral ligament; *SV*, stria vascularis; *TM*, tectorial membrane; *VM*, vestibular (Reissner's) membrane.

thus formed by the pillars a series of arches which enclose a triangular canal, the *inner tunnel* or Corti's tunnel (Fig. 22-38). This is crossed by delicate nerve fibers.

The *outer phalangeal cells (cells of Deiters)* are the supporting elements for the outer hair cells, one for each cell. Like the hair cells, therefore, their number varies in different regions of the cochlear duct. They form three rows in the basal coil, four in the middle coil and five in the apical coil. Between the innermost of the outer phalangeal cells and the outer pillar there is a space, the *space of Nuel.*

Each outer phalangeal cell is a long columnar element whose expanded base rests on the basilar membrane. At the level of the bases of the hair cells, each phalangeal cell bears a facet, or indented shelf, which receives the base of the hair cell whose support it furnishes. The cell is continued as a slender process which passes to the surface through the space between adjacent hair cells. The round nucleus lies in the broader part of the cell (Fig. 22-38).

Running through the cytoplasm of the phalangeal cell is a bundle of microtubules which stands out conspicuously in sections.

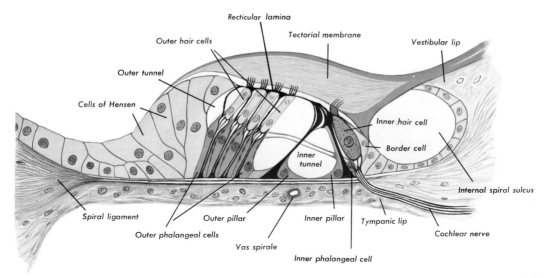

FIG. 22-38. Idealized diagram of a section through the human organ of Corti (from the upper end of the first coil). Note the position of the tectorial membrane; it is rarely preserved in this position in histological sections. (Redrawn and modified from Held, with assistance from Dr. E. P. Fowler, Jr.)

They are similar to those described in the pillar cells. The bundle is expanded at its base, and at the level of the hair cells the bundle of microtubules divides into two groups. One group terminates in a cup-shaped arrangement in the facet which lodges the hair cell. The other group of tubules continues on between the hair cells and spreads out at the surface into a flat cuticular plate. The cuticular plates of each row of cells interdigitate with those of the next row. Between them are the outer ends of the hair cells. In sections of the cochlear duct, these bundles of fibrils are seldom included in their whole extent but appear as a series of unconnected dark segments in the spaces between the hair cells.

The *outer hair cells* occupy the superficial third of the epithelium of the organ of Corti. They are columnar cells, the free surface of each bearing a number of short sensory hairs which are in contact with the tectorial membrane. The rounded bases of the cells are supported by the phalangeal cells. The nucleus occupies the lower portion of the hair cell and below it the granular cytoplasm stains more deeply than that of the re-

mainder of the cell. The terminal arborizations of the fibers of the cochlear nerve are closely applied around the bases of the hair cells (Fig. 22-40).

Electron microscopic studies have shown that the hairs are straight projecting rods surrounded by a typical unit membrane (Fig. 22-39). Internally the hair contains longitudinally arranged fibrillar material which continues into the fibrillar material of the cuticular plate as a rod-like structure. The hairs project from the surface in a regular pattern, with three rows forming a W-shape facing the modiolus (Fig. 22-41). The hairs are in contact with, but apparently not firmly embedded in, the tectorial membrane. The number of outer hair cells varies, there being three rows in the basal coil of the cochlea (Fig. 22-41), four rows in the upper end of the basal coil and in the middle coil and five rows in the apical coil.

The *cells of Hensen* are tall columnar elements which form the outer border cells of the organ of Corti. They are arranged in several rows on the basilar membrane lateral to the outer phalangeal cells. The base of each cell is narrower than its upper part,

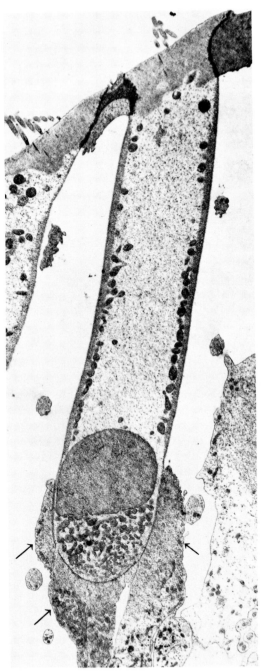

FIG. 22-39. Electron micrograph of parts of two of the outer hair cells from the organ of Corti of the chinchilla. One of the hair cells is shown in its entirety. At its base, this cell contains a nucleus and numerous mitochondria and receives several nerve endings (*lower arrows*). The middle portion

which contains the nucleus. The outer cells decrease in height and pass into the cells of Claudius. The space between the outer phalangeal cells and the cells of Hensen is known as the *outer tunnel*.

The *cells of Claudius* are cuboidal in shape and have a clear cytoplasm. They line the outermost portion of the basilar membrane.

The cuticular plates of the sustentacular cells collectively form a cuticular membrane which is termed the *lamina reticularis*. It covers the organ of Corti and in surface view appears as a mosaic pierced by regularly arranged rows of holes in which the heads of the hair cells are inserted (Fig. 22-41).

The tectorial membrane (*Corti's membrane*). This appears as a continuation of the cuticular covering of the columnar cells of the limbus spiralis. Toward the edge of the vestibular lip, this cuticular formation becomes thickened into a striated gelatinous structure which overhangs the internal spiral sulcus and extends outward as far as the cells of Hensen. The upper surface is more convex than the lower one.

The tectorial membrane is particularly susceptible to distortion from the action of fixing reagents. Therefore it is usually shrunken and separated from the processes of the hair cells in fixed preparations. In the living condition it is in contact with the processes of the hair cells and the processes of these cells are stimulated by movements of the tectorial membrane which are related to vibrations in the endolymph (see below).

Innervation of the organ of Corti. The cochlear division of the auditory nerve enters the axis of the modiolus from the internal auditory meatus and divides into a number of branches. From these, numerous

is relatively empty. The apical portion contains the cuticular plate into which the hairs are inserted. Note the extensive extracellular space between hair cells and the apical portions of the outer phalangeal (or Deiters') cells inserted between the hair cells to form the rigid reticular lamina. ×3500. (From C. Smith 1968 Advances Sci., vol. 24, p. 419.)

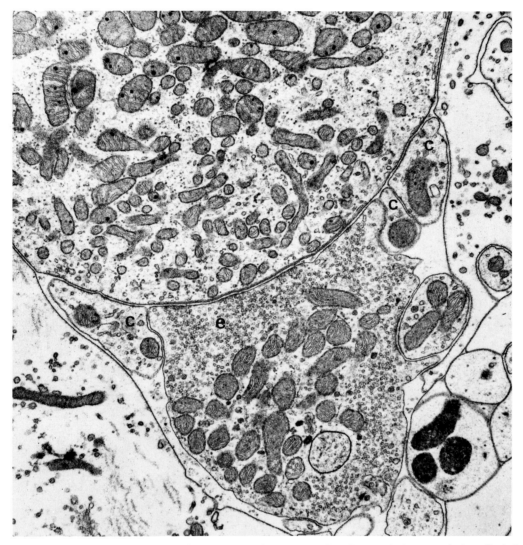

Fig. 22-40. Electron micrograph of the nerve endings on the basal part of the outer hair cell of the chinchilla organ of Corti. One large efferent (*e*) and three small afferent (cochlear) (*c*) nerve endings terminate on the hair cell. Note the large number of mitochondria in this portion of the hair cell. ×31,500. (From Smith, C., and Rasmussen, G. 1965 J. Cell Biol., vol. 26, p. 63.)

fibers radiate to the osseous spiral lamina, in the base of which they enter the *spiral ganglion* (Fig. 22-35).

The cells of the spiral ganglion are peculiar, in that while of the same general type as the spinal ganglion cell, they maintain their embryonic bipolar condition throughout life. Their central processes follow the already described course through the modio-lus and thence through the internal auditory meatus to their terminal nuclei in the medulla. Their peripheral processes also become myelinated and pass outward in bundles in the osseous spiral lamina. From these are given off branches which enter the tympanic lip of the limbus, where they lose their myelin and pass through the *foramina nervosa* (minute apertures in the tympanic

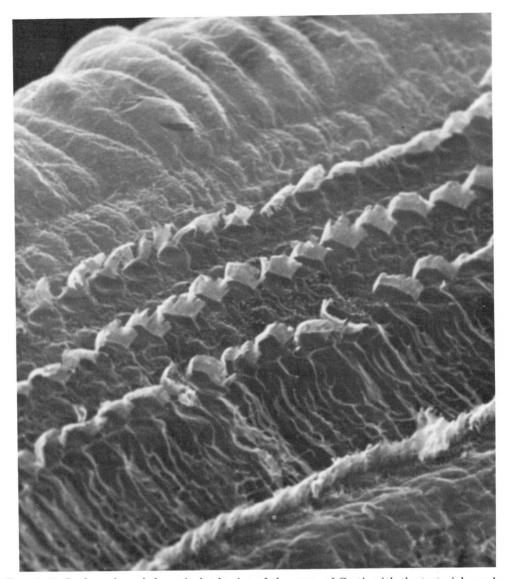

FIG. 22-41. Surface view of the reticular lamina of the organ of Corti, with the tectorial membrane removed, showing hairs projecting from the single row of inner hair cells and three rows of outer hair cells. Scanning electron micrograph after freeze drying. ×1000. (From Marovitz, W., et al. 1970 Proceedings of the Third Annual Scanning Electron Microscope Symposium. I.I.T. Research Institute, Chicago.)

lip) to their terminations in the organ of Corti. In the latter, the fibers run in three bundles parallel to the inner tunnel. One bundle lies just inside the inner pillar beneath the row of inner hair cells (Fig. 22-38). A second bundle runs in the tunnel to the outer side of the inner pillar. The third bundle crosses the inner tunnel (*tunnel fibers*) and turns at right angles to run between the outer phalangeal cells. In Figure 22-38, these fibers appear as small dots between the phalangeal cells. From all of these

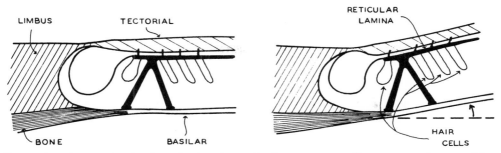

FIG. 22-42. Diagram showing how the shearing action between two stiff structures, the tectorial membrane and the reticular lamina, bends the hairs of the hair cells. (From Davis, H. 1957 *In* Physiological Triggers and Discontinuous Rate Processes, edited by T. Bullock. American Physiological Society, Washington, D.C.)

bundles of fibers, delicate terminal fibers are given off which end in branching telodendria around the bases of the hair cells.

PHYSIOLOGY OF THE AUDITORY MECHANISM

Sound vibrations which impinge upon the tympanic membrane will cause it to vibrate at the same frequency as the incident sound waves. The movement consequently imparted to the auditory ossicles will serve to move the base of the stapes in and out of the oval window at the same frequency as that of the stimulating sound. Since the fluid perilymph on the other side of the oval window lies in a chamber with rigid bony walls and is itself incompressible, it follows that the inward movement of the stapes will produce a pressure within the perilymph which can be relieved only by a compensating outward movement of the secondary tympanic membrane covering the round window.

Two avenues for the transfer of this change in pressure are available. It could travel the length of the scala vestibuli and pass by way of the slender helicotrema to the perilymph of the scala tympani, thence to be relieved by the outward bulging of the secondary tympanic membrane of the round window, or it could be transmitted across the vestibular membrane of Reissner to the fluid endolymph of the cochlear duct. This would cause a displacement of the basilar

membrane toward the scala tympani and consequently the pressure is transmitted to the perilymph of the scala tympani and released at the round window. Thus a sound vibration of a given frequency would cause movements of the basilar membrane of equal frequency.

Because the hair cells are held within a framework mounted on the basilar membrane, and their hairs are in contact with the overlying tectorial membrane, and because these membranes are "hinged" at different points, movements of the basilar membrane will cause the hairs to bend (Fig. 22-42). This bending constitutes the effective stimulus for the hair cells, with consequent activity which is translated into nerve impulses in the associated nerve fibers.

Although the above may represent a reasonable description of the chain of events initiated by sound vibrations and resulting in stimulation of the hair cells, it fails to account for the fact that the auditory mechanism is capable of differentiating between vibrations of different frequencies—in other words, pitch or tone. It is known that damage to structures at the base of the cochlea leads to a loss of hearing for high tones and that damage near the apex affects reception of lower tones. Because the length of the basilar membrane is shorter near the base of the cochlea and longer near the apex it seemed quite reasonable to assume that the

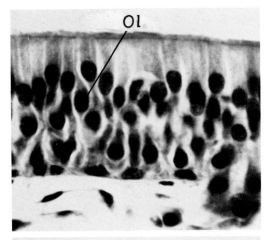

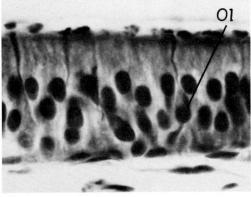

FIG. 22-43. Photomicrographs of the olfactory mucosa showing the olfactory receptor cells (*Ol*) between the sustentacular cells. The *upper figure*, stained with hematoxylin and eosin, also shows part of a gland of Bowman (*lower right*); the *lower figure* is a silver-stained preparation which demonstrates the bipolar nature of the olfactory neurons. ×1100. (From preparations by Dr. G. Hamlett.)

basilar membrane vibrated in a specific region for different sound frequencies.

It is now known, however, that large regions of the basilar membrane vibrate for all frequencies but that the waves of vibration that travel up the cochlear spiral produce maximum displacement of the membrane at different sites depending on the tone of the incident sound. The lower the frequency of the sound waves, the farther from the oval window the maximum displacement of the basilar membrane occurs.

Central nervous system mechanisms then sort out the input signals so that the site of maximum basilar membrane displacement (as well as vibratory patterns in adjacent regions) and thus the pitch and quality of a sound is discerned. The loudness of a tone is thought to be determined by the amount of basilar membrane set into maximum motion. It has also been suggested that the outer hair cells are particularly concerned with determining the intensity of sound and the inner hair cells with pitch discrimination. It should also be recalled that the nerve endings on hair cells are arranged not only for the reception of excitation but also for inhibition. This brings to the organ of Corti central nervous system mechanisms of inhibition for use in providing for pitch and loudness discrimination.

It is well to remember that the total number of hair cells in man is probably less than 20,000. These cells can be damaged or destroyed by sounds of exceptionally high intensity and are not replaced if lost. One cannot lose many cells from the extraordinarily delicate and sensitive organ of Corti without suffering significant hearing loss. The protection of the ear against excessive noise must be taken seriously.

THE ORGAN OF SMELL

The sense of smell is perceived in a restricted specialized portion of the mucosa in the upper part of each nasal cavity. This *olfactory mucosa* contains nerve cell bodies which provide the mechanism for olfactory reception on their exposed ends and send an axon from their basal end to the first olfactory way station in the brain—the *olfactory bulb*.

The olfactory mucosa. This can be distinguished with the naked eye by its brownish-yellow color which contrasts with the reddish tint of the surrounding respiratory mucosa. The epithelium is pseudostratified columnar, and is considerably thicker than that of the respiratory region. The surface cells are of two kinds: (1)

sustentacular cells, and (2) olfactory cells (Figs. 22-43 and 22-44).

(1) The *sustentacular cells* are the more numerous. Each cell consists of: (a) A superficial portion which is shaped like a stout cylinder and contains pigment and granules arranged in longitudinal rows, (b) A middle portion which contains an oval nucleus and (c) A thin filamentous process which extends from the nuclear portion down between the cells of the deeper layers. The luminal surface of the cell is covered with microvilli. Immediately subjacent to the surface, a series of desmosomes bind the apical portion of the cell to the adjacent olfactory cells.

(2) The *olfactory cells* lie between the sustentacular cells. Their nuclei are spherical, lie at different levels, and most of them are more deeply placed than those of the sustentacular cells. From the nuclear portion of each cell a delicate process extends to the surface, where it is expanded in a minute knob (sometimes called the olfactory vesicle). From this terminal knob several cilia arise, each from a typical basal body. Near their base these are typical cilia, but more distally their long, narrow extensions contain only two microtubules. The cilia do not project vertically but are flattened against the mucosal surface; they are thought to be the portion of the olfactory cell that reacts with odor-producing chemicals. The mucosal surface and the cilia are constantly bathed by the product of special tubular glands (the glands of Bowman) which underlie the olfactory mucosa and deliver their products to its surface.

From the opposite pole of the olfactory cell a longer process extends centrally which, as a centripetal nerve fiber of one of the olfactory nerves, passes through the cribriform plate of the ethmoid bone (Fig. 22-45) to terminate in the olfactory bulb. The olfactory cell is thus seen to be of the nature of a bipolar ganglion cell with a short peripheral and a longer central process. This is the only example in man of the peripherally placed

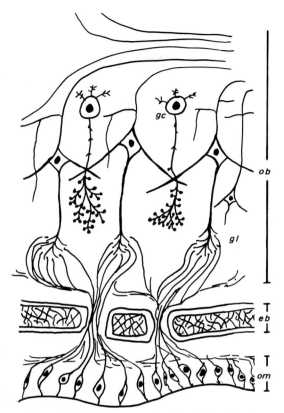

Fig. 22-44. Diagram showing the olfactory mucosa (*om*) and the olfactory bulb (*ob*) separated by parts of the ethmoid bone (*eb*). The nerve fibers arising from the bipolar cells in the olfactory mucosa synapse with mitral and tufted cells in the glomerular layer (*gl*) of the bulb. The axons of the mitral and tufted cells pass deeply, give off collaterals and then travel centrally. The granule cell (*gc*) has a large process which gives rise to arborizations among the dendrites of the mitral and tufted cells; this process both receives and provides synapses. Is it an axon or a dendrite? (Modified from J. Price and T. Powell 1970 J. Cell Sci., vol. 7, p. 91.)

sensory ganglion cells found in certain lower animals. Between the basal portions of the olfactory cells and the basal processes of the sustentacular cells are small irregular cells of unknown function termed *basal cells*.

The basement membrane supporting this epithelium is not well-developed. The underlying *stroma* consists of loosely arranged collagenous fibers, delicate elastic fibers and

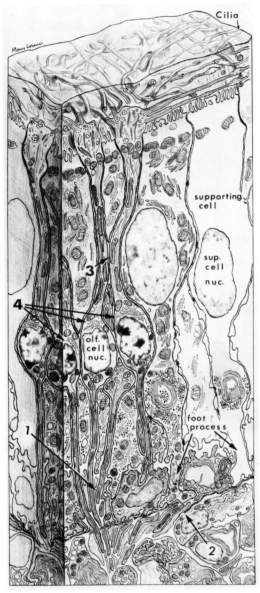

FIG. 22-45. Schematic drawing showing the olfactory mucosa with the sensory cells terminating in apical expansions from which many modified cilia arise and lie on the mucosal surface. The supporting cells are surmounted by microvilli. *1*, axons arising from olfactory neurons; *2*, basement membrane; *3*, apical portion of olfactory neuron; *4*, cell bodies of olfactory neurons. (Drawing by Mary Lorenc, from D. Frisch 1967 Am. J. Anat., vol. 121, p. 87.)

connective tissue cells. Embedded in the stroma are the numerous simple branched tubular glands (mentioned above). Each gland consists of a duct, a body and a fundus. The secreting cells are large and irregular and contain a yellowish pigment which, with that of the sustentacular cells, is responsible for the peculiar color of the olfactory mucosa.

The olfactory bulb. In man this is a small structure relative to the massive cerebral hemispheres; in some lower animals it constitutes a much more substantial portion of the brain. It consists of both gray matter and white matter arranged in six distinct concentric layers (Fig. 22-45). These are as follows (from superficial to deep): (1) The layer of olfactory fibers, (2) the layer of glomeruli, (3) the plexiform layer, (4) the layer of mitral cells, (5) the granule layer and (6) the layer of longitudinal fiber bundles. Through the center of the last named layer runs a band of neuroglia which represents the obliterated lumen of the embryonal lobe. The relations of these layers to the olfactory neuron system are as follows.

The layer of olfactory fibers (Fig. 22-45) consists of a dense plexiform arrangement of the axons of the above-described olfactory cells. From this layer the axons pass into a layer containing discrete fiber nests, the olfactory glomeruli. Here the olfactory cell axons make contact with the dendritic terminals of the main relay neurons of the bulb, the mitral cells and the tufted cells. These are large neurons; their axons leave the bulb to form the olfactory tract which carries signals to the central parts of the brain.

This direct relay path is influenced by the presence of several other neurons in the bulb, especially the prominent granule cells. These have cell bodies in the granule cell layer and dendrites extending into the plexiform layer. The granule cell is a form of anaxonic interneuron, distinguished by having no definitive axon and both providing and receiving synapses on adjacent regions of its dendritic surfaces (reciprocal synapses). The granule cells are thought to provide inhibitory activity for the initial processing of olfactory information that occurs in the olfactory bulb.

From the above discussion the student will realize that the olfactory cells of the nasal mucosa are very much akin to sensory ganglion cells as, for example, in the dorsal root ganglion. These cells have the responsibility to receive chemical stimuli, to provide for transduction to a nervous impulse and to conduct this signal to a region of the central nervous system. The mechanism by which chemicals stimulate the olfactory cells is not known but it is known that effective stimuli must be volatile and must be at least slightly soluble in both water and lipid. Olfactory cells have extraordinary sensitivity; certain substances can be detected at concentrations much lower than those measurable by any method of chemical analysis. The sense of smell is closely related to the sense of taste, discussed below, but of the two, olfaction is by far the more sensitive.

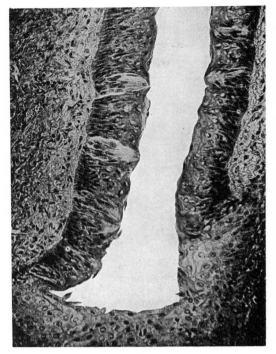

FIG. 22-46. Photomicrograph of a section through trench surrounding circumvallate papilla (human). Several taste buds are shown.

THE ORGAN OF TASTE

The organ of taste consists of specialized taste buds located mainly within the mucosa of the tongue but also within parts of the palate and the pharynx. Taste buds are concentrated in the tongue, especially in the side walls of the circumvallate papillae (Fig. 22-46), in some of the fungiform papillae, and in folds (foliate papillae) which occur along the posterolateral margin of the tongue.

The taste bud (Figs. 22-46 and 22-47) is an ovoid epithelial structure embedded in the epithelium and connected with the surface by means of a minute canal, called a taste pore. Packed within the concavity of the taste bud are two types of cells—a slender, dense, spindle-shaped cell generally called the neuroepithelial or taste cell, and a stouter, lighter cell called the sustentacular cell. The smaller, dark cell bears on its apical surface a bunch of long slender micro-

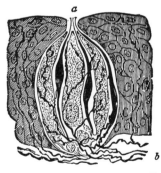

FIG. 22-47. Taste bud from side wall of circumvallate papilla. a, taste pore; b, nerve fibers, some of which enter the taste bud—intragemmal fibers—while others end freely in the surrounding epithelium—intergemmal fibers. (Merkel-Henle.)

villi. These contain densely packed microtubules which extend as long straight fascicles deep into the cell cytoplasm. The "taste hairs," as these microvilli are called, extend to the region of the pore at the apex of the taste bud. These dark cells contain a rich granular endoplasmic reticulum suggesting that they secrete the dense material commonly seen in the apical part of the taste bud.

The sustentacular cells form a shell several cells thick around the taste cells and are intermixed with them. The apical portion of these cells also contains numerous microvilli but these are shorter than those of the taste cell and do not project as far into the taste pore.

Sensory fibers of the 7th, 9th and 10th cranial nerves end within the taste buds. Because the nerve endings are found related to both cell types it is not altogether certain which cell (or if both) act(s) as the taste receptor and is able to excite the related nerve endings. It is known that different taste buds are specialized for the perception of salty, sweet, sour or bitter tastes, and that these tastes are better perceived on certain parts of the tongue than on others. Substances must be in solution to be tasted, and the amounts required to stimulate sensation are much greater than for the sense of smell. As with many of the other receptors discussed above the acuteness of the sense of taste declines with age.

REFERENCES

THE EYE

ASHTÜN, N., BRINI, A., AND SMITH, R. 1956 Anatomical studies of the trabecular meshwork of the normal human eye. Brit. J. Ophthal., vol. 40, pp. 257–282.

AURELL, G., AND HOLMGREN, H. 1946 Metachromatic substance in cornea with special reference to question of its transparency. Nord. Med., vol. 30, pp. 1277–1279.

COHEN, A. I. 1963 Vertebrate retinal cells and their organization. Biol. Rev., vol. 38, pp. 427–459.

DAVSON, H. (editor) 1962 The Eye, vols. 1–4. Academic Press, New York.

DEROBERTIS, E. 1956 Morphogenesis of the retinal rods; an electron microscope study. J. Biophys. Biochem. Cytol. (suppl.), vol. 2, pp. 209–218.

DETWILER, S. R. 1943 Vertebrate Photoreceptors. The Macmillan Company, New York.

DOWLING, J. E., AND BOYCOTT, B. B. 1966 Organization of the primate retina: Electron microscopy. Proc. Roy. Soc. London [Biol.], vol. 166, pp. 80–111.

DOWLING, J. E. 1967 The site of visual adaptation. Science, vol. 155, pp. 273–279.

DOWLING, J. E. 1970 Organization of vertebrate retinas. Invest. Ophthal., vol. 9, pp. 665–680.

DUKE-ELDER, S., AND WYBAR, K. C. 1961 The anatomy of the visual system. In System of Ophthalmology (Duke-Elder, S., editor), vol. 2. The C. V. Mosby Company, St. Louis.

DUKE-ELDER, S., AND GLOSTER, J. 1968 The physiology of the eye and vision. In System of Ophthalmology (Duke-Elder, S., edtior), vol. 4. The C. V. Mosby Company, St. Louis.

HAY, E. D., AND REVEL, J-P. 1969 Fine structure of the developing avian cornea. In Monographs in Developmental Biology, vol. 1. S. Karger, Basel, Switzerland.

HECHT, S. 1938 The nature of the visual process. Harvey Lect., Ser. 33, pp. 35–64.

JAKUS, M. A. 1956 Studies on the cornea. J. Biophys. Biochem. Cytol. (suppl.), vol. 2, pp. 243–252.

JAKUS, M. A. 1961 The fine structure of the human cornea. In The Eye (Smelser, G. K., editor), pp. 343–366. Academic Press, New York.

KRONFELD, P. C. 1962 The gross anatomy and embryology of the eye. In The Eye (Dawson, H., editor), vol. 1, pp. 1–62. Academic Press, New York.

MANN, I. 1950 The Development of the Human Eye. Grune & Stratton, Inc., New York.

NOBACK, C. R., AND LAEMLE, L. K. 1970 Structural and functional aspects of the visual pathway of primates. In The Primate Brain, Advances in Primatology, vol. 1, pp. 55–81.

PAPACONSTANTINOU, J. 1967 Molecular aspects of lens cell differentiation. Science, vol. 156, pp. 338–346.

PAPPAS, G. D., AND SMELSER, G. K. 1961 The fine structure of the ciliary epithelium in relation to aqueous humor secretion. In The Structure of the Eye (Smelser, G. K., editor), pp. 453–467. Academic Press, New York.

POLYAK, S. L. 1941 The Retina. University of Chicago Press, Chicago.

ROHEN, J. W. 1964 Das Auge und seine Hilfsorgane. Handb. mikr. Anat. Menschen. (v. Möllendorff, W., and Bargmann, W., editors), vol. 3, part 4. Springer-Verlag, Berlin.

SALZMANN, M. 1933 The Anatomy and Histology of the Human Eyeball in the Normal State. Trans. by E. V. L. Brown. J. B. Lippincott Company, Philadelphia.

SMELSER, G. K. (editor) 1961 The Structure of the Eye. Academic Press, New York.

TONOSAKI, A., AND KELLY, D. E. 1971 Fine structural study of the origin and development of the sphincter pupillae muscle in the West Coast newt (Taricha torosa). Anat. Rec., vol. 170, pp. 57–74.

WALD, G. 1960 The molecular organization of visual systems. In Light and Life (McElroy, W. D., and Glass, B., editors), p. 724. The Johns Hopkins Press, Baltimore.

WALD, G. 1964 The receptors of human color vision. Science, vol. 145, pp. 1007–1016.

WALLS, G. L. 1942 The Vertebrate Eye and Its Adaptive Radiation. Cranbrook Institute of Science, Bloomfield Hills, Mich.

WALSH, F. B., AND HOYT, W. F. 1969 Clinical Neuro-Ophthalmology, ed. 3, The Williams & Wilkins Company, Baltimore.

WOLFF, E. 1968 The Anatomy of the Eye and Orbit, ed. 6, Revised by R. J. Last. W. B. Saunders Company, Philadelphia.

YOUNG, R. W. 1967 The renewal of photoreceptor cell outer segments. J. Cell Biol., vol. 33, pp. 61–72.

YOUNG, R. W. 1970 Visual cells. Sci. Amer., vol. 223, pp. 80–91.

THE EAR

BAST, T. H., AND ANSON, B. J. 1949 The Temporal Bone and the Ear. Charles C Thomas, Publisher, Springfield, Ill.

DAVIS, H. 1959 Excitation of auditory receptors. In Handbook of Physiology, sect. 1, vol. 1, pp. 565–584. American Physiological Society, Washington, D.C.

DEREUCK, A., AND KNIGHT, J. (editors) 1968 Hearing Mechanisms in Vertebrates. Little, Brown and Company, Boston.

ENGSTROM, H. 1961 The innervation of the vestibular receptor cells. Acta Otolaryng. (suppl.), vol. 163, pp. 30–41.

FRIEDMANN, I. 1962 The cytology of the ear. Brit. Med. Bull., vol. 18, pp. 209–213.

HENTZER, H. 1970 Histologic studies of the normal mucosa in the middle ear, mastoid cavities and Eustachian tube. Ann. Otol. Rhin. Laryngol., vol. 79, pp. 825–833.

IURATO, S. (editor) 1967 Submicroscopic Structure of the Inner Ear. Pergamon Press, New York.

RASMUSSEN, G. L., AND WINDLE, W. F. 1960 Neural Mechanisms of the Auditory and Vestibular Systems. Charles C Thomas, Publisher, Springfield, Ill.

SHAMBAUGH, G. E. 1932 Cytology of the internal ear. In Special Cytology, ed. 2 (Cowdry, E. V., editor), vol. 3, pp. 1335–1367. Paul B. Hoeber, Inc., New York.

SMITH, C. A. 1968 Electron microscopy of the inner ear. Ann. Otol. Rhin. Laryngol., vol. 77, pp. 629–643.

V. ILBERG, C., AND VOSTEEN, K.-H. 1969 Permeability of the inner ear membranes. Acta Otolaryng., vol. 67, pp. 165–170.

VON BÉKÉSY, G. 1960 Experiments in Hearing. Edited and Translated by E. G. Wever. McGraw-Hill Book Company, New York.

WERSALL, J. 1956 Studies on the structure and innervation of the sensory epithelium of the cristae ampullares in the guinea pig. Acta Otolaryng. (suppl.), vol. 126, pp. 1–85.

WERSALL, J. 1961 Vestibular receptor cells in fish and mammals. Acta Otolaryng. (suppl.), vol. 163, pp. 25–29.

ORGANS OF SMELL AND TASTE

ARSTILA, A., AND WERSALL, J. 1967 The ultrastructure of the olfactory epithelium of the guinea pig. Acta Otolaryng., vol. 64, pp. 187–204.

FRISCH, D. 1967 Ultrastructure of the mouse olfactory mucosa. Am. J. Anat., vol. 121, pp. 87–119.

KARE, M. R., AND HALPERN, B. P. (editors) 1961 Physiological and Behavioral Aspects of Taste. University of Chicago Press, Chicago.

OAKLEY, B., AND BENJAMIN, R. M. 1966 Neural mechanism of taste. Physiol. Rev., vol. 46, pp. 173–211.

REESE, T. S. 1965 Olfactory cilia in the frog. J. Cell Biol., vol. 25, pp. 209–230.

ZOTTERMAN, Y. (editor) 1963 Olfaction and Taste. The Macmillan Company, New York.

INDEX

721